Invertebrate Zoology

PAUL A. MEGLITSCH
Drake University

New York

OXFORD UNIVERSITY PRESS

London Toronto   1967

The completion of this book was made possible by the hard work and good nature of the crew at 3701, and to them it is gratefully dedicated.

Preface

It is assumed that the reader is not a fully trained zoologist, and so in this book, in the first chapters especially, an attempt has been made to develop a background for the appreciation of the factors that have shaped animals and have produced lines of adaptive change. A comprehension of some of the reasons why the form and functions of animals are so suitable for the habitats they occupy may be gained by taking these factors into account. All animals have evolved under a very similar set of rules, and the many differences one sees among them have their origin in the complex interplay of their physiological capacities and limitations, and the levels of activity and size that these capacities and limitations permit, in addition to the effects that choice of habitat produces upon size and activity. It is hoped that attitudes and points discussed in the study of the lower invertebrates will be borne in mind through later chapters, even though not repeated in the text.

Comparative physiology has been given more emphasis in the discussions than has generally been the practice. This departure is based on a deep conviction that the basic conditions under which the physiological processes are carried out are best understood by observing them in organisms with simple, intermediate, and high levels of organization, and that the physiological processes become intelligible when discussed with appropriate regard for the conditions under which an animal lives. The primary discussion, however, is focused on the animals, and every effort has been made to keep the material on physiology at a level intelligible to the general student of zoology, who is not necessarily proficient in physiology.

In selecting illustrations a conscious attempt has been made to include some classical figures from the work of early investigators of invertebrates, some from intermediate periods, and some from modern works. For the most part, figures have been reproduced as originally drawn in order to help the student develop a capacity to interpret and appreciate the kinds of illustrations found in professional or review articles.

I am indebted to the hundreds of men who have devoted their lives to amassing the information on which invertebrate zoology is based. I should especially like to acknowledge the heavy debt I owe to the many persons who have written textbooks, monographic accounts, review articles, and series of books on the invertebrates. Without their efforts, it would be impossible to construct any reasonably comprehensive discussion. Their work has provided many ideas and has guided my choice of many illustrations used here. Student and teacher alike are encouraged to consult these sources. Three series of books in English cannot be too highly praised: the excellent, classical discussions given in *The Cambridge Natural History*, edited by S. F. Harmer and A. E. Shipley; *A Treatise on Zoology*, edited by Ray Lankester; and the modern series written by L. H. Hyman, *The Invertebrates*. For those who can read French, the fine series of volumes making up the *Traité de Zoologie*, edited by P.-P. Grassé, is an excellent account of many invertebrate groups and includes many excellent illustrations. For those who can read German two fine series of volumes are also available: Bronn's *Klassen und Ordnung des Thier-Reichs* is a series of monographs which are remarkable for their exhaustive treatment of the structure and natural history of the groups that are covered; *Handbuch der Zoologie*, edited by W. Kükenthal and T. Krumbach, has excellent accounts of invertebrate groups and a fine selection of illustrations. Other books which cover invertebrate groups or provide general information about invertebrate physiology, development, or ecology are listed in the general references following each chapter. In a book of this kind, references are not intended primarily to support the text but to provide convenient avenues for further study by especially interested students.

It has been my intention to write a book about invertebrates which will be useful for students taking courses in invertebrate zoology. These courses can vary enormously in the approach they take and in the material they cover. Some require only a single semester, others two quarters, and some last a whole year. The materials deemed most important by an instructor will vary with the biome in which the laboratory lies, its closeness to coastal or fresh-water habitats, and with the role the course is intended to play in the development of the departmental curriculum. Moreover, there is far too much to cover in any single course, no matter how much time is allotted, and every instructor must make choices of the material he wishes his students to cover intensively, that which he wishes them to study more casually, for the major ideas, and that material to be omitted.

To help the instructor make these choices, some material has been repeated in what seemed to be strategic places.

Figure legends have been expanded to include discussion of some of the major ideas, so that an examination of the illustrations and their captions in any given chapter will maintain continuity should the instructor choose not to assign the text in that chapter. A study of figures and legends should also prove useful as a method for review.

The major ideas on which a course will center have been worked into the chapter dealing with the Protozoa, with the thought that at the beginning of a course the over-all aspects of the life of an animal need some review. When a basic idea is encountered in later sections dealing with more highly organized phyla, the discussion is often based on what has been said in the earlier chapters on the Protozoa. The index will refer the reader to the original development of the idea and it is hoped that he will relate the information to other organisms as they are considered.

I wish to express my appreciation of the helpful discussions and manuscript reading by Drs. L. P. Johnson, P. R. Rogers, and H. Swanson. Dr. C. Cutress, of the Division of Marine Invertebrates in the Smithsonian Institution, has been particularly helpful in obtaining photographs of a number of subjects, and has my gratitude. Too much credit cannot be given to Alison

Meglitsch, who has worked so hard and effectively in illustrating the text and in co-ordinating the activities of the rest of the staff who were involved in preparing illustrations. Without her the task would have been impossible. Douglas Cummings, Mark Ross, Douglas Nicolet, Janice White, and Neil Meglitsch made many of the drawings, and Stephen Meglitsch prepared many of the labels on the figures for the publisher's copy. Rosalie Ransome helped enormously in making the work of the illustrating crew effective and pleasant. To all of them I want to express my thanks.

Finally, I am also deeply indebted to the many scientists who prepared the originals from which we worked, and to the journals and publishing companies who permitted us to use the material. One of the hardest tasks has been to get in touch with the many publishers of books and journals whose illustrations we borrowed. I sincerely trust and hope there have been no omissions. Pictures ever speak louder than words, and this would have been a silent book indeed had it not been for my collaborators in laboratories all over the world.

Des Moines   PAUL A. MEGLITSCH
November 1966

Acknowledgments

I am deeply indebted to the many zoologists whose work has produced so many of the figures included in this book. Without their labors, a book of this kind could not be completed. I am also grateful to the many publishers who have given permission to use figures from their books.

Alder and Hancock, 1855. *Monograph of the British nudibranchiate Mollusca.* Ray Society, London.
Allegre and Jahn, 1943. *Trans. Amer. Micr. Soc.* 62.
Allmann, 1856. *Monograph of the Fresh-Water Polyzoa.* Ray Society, London.
Anderson, 1962. *Jour. Protozool.* 9
Andersson, 1907. *Wiss. Ergebn. Schwed. Südpolar Exped.* 5.
Andres, 1884. *Fauna u. Flora Golf Neapel* 1.
Andrew, 1959. *Textbook of Comparative Histology.* Oxford Univ. Press, New York.
Andrews, 1890. *Studies Biol. Lab. Johns Hopkins Univ. Circ.* 9.
Apel, 1885. *Zeitschr. wiss. Zool.* 42.
Arndt, 1924. *Arch. Protistenk.* 49.
Ashworth, 1904. *Liverpool Mar. Biol. Comm. Mem.* 11.
Atkins, 1932. *Quat. Jour. Micr. Sci.* 75.
Atkins, 1933. *Jour. Mar. Biol. Assoc. U. K.* 19.
Avel in Grassé, *Traité de Zoologie*
Bahl, 1933. *Quat. Jour. Micr. Sci.* 76.
Baker and Wharton, 1952. *An Introduction to Acarology.* Macmillan, New York.
Ball, 1916. *Jour. Morphol.* 27.
Balss in Kükenthal and Krumbach, *Handbuch der Zoologie*
Barrois, 1877. *Trav. Inst. Zool. Wimereux* 1.
Barrows, 1918. *Univ. Calif. Publ. Zool.* 18.
Bateson, 1886. *Quat. Jour. Micr. Sci.* 25.
Bather, 1898. *Geol. Mag.* 5.
Bather, 1928. *Geol. Surv. Canada Bull.* 49.
Bauer, 1864. *Nova Acta Acad. Leopold Carol.* 31.

Baumann, 1919. *Zeitschr. wiss. Zool.* 118.

Becker, 1922. *Zool. Jahrb., Anat.* 43.

Bebard, 1934. *Ill. Nat. Hist. Surv. Bull.* 20.

Belding, 1965. *Textbook of Clinical Parasitology.* Appleton-Century-Crofts, New York.

Benham, 1889. *Quat. Jour. Micr. Sci.* 31.

Benham in Harmer and Shipley, *The Cambridge Natural History*

Berlase, 1909. *Redia* 5.

Berrill, 1961. *Growth, Development, and Pattern.* W. H. Freeman, San Francisco.

Berrill, 1962. *Can. Jour. Zool.* 40.

Biehler, 1913. *Zool. Jahrb., Anat.* 36.

Bigelow, 1909. *Harvard Mus. Comp. Zool.* 37.

Blochmann, 1912. *Handwörterbuch der Naturwissenschaften* 2.

Bodenstein, 1947. *Jour. Exp. Zool.* 104.

Borg, 1926. *Zool. Bidrag.* 10.

Bouchot-Boutin and Bobin 1954. *Arch Anat. Micr. Morph. Exp.* 43:137

Boulenger, 1935. *A Natural History of the Seas.* Duckworth, London.

Boutan, 1886. *Arch. Zool. Exp.* 3.

Bouvier, 1902. *Zool. Jahrb. Anat.* sup. 5:675

Boveri, 1899. *Festschrift für Kupffer.*

Boveri, 1901. *Zool. Jahrb., Anat.* 14.

Boycott and Young, 1961. *Biol. Rev.* 36.

Braem, 1951. *Zoologica* 37.

Bresslau, 1904. *Zeitschr. wiss. Zool.* 76.

Brien, 1936. *Arch. Biol.* 48.

Brien, 1953. *Ann. Soc. Roy. Zool. Belg.* 84.

Brien and Huysmans, 1937. *Ann. Roy. Soc. Zool. Belg.* 68.

Brien and Renier-Decoen, 1949. *Bull. Biol. France Belg.* 84.

Bristowe, 1958. *The World of Spiders*, Collins, London.

Bristowe and Millot, 1932. *Proc. Zool. Soc. London* 1932.

Broch in Kükenthal and Krumbach, *Handbuch der Zoologie*

Bronn, 1859–1948. *Klassen und Ordnungen des Thier-Reichs.* Winter'sche Verlagsh., Leipzig.

Brooks, 1893. *Johns Hopkins Univ. Biol. Lab. Mem.* 2.

Brown, ed., 1950. *Selected Invertebrate Types.* John Wiley and Sons, New York.

Bullock, 1944. *Jour. Comp. Neurol.* 80.

Bullough, 1958. *Practical Invertebrate Anatomy.* Macmillan, London.

Burdon-Jones, 1952. *Phil. Trans. Roy. Soc. London* 263B.

Burger, 1891. *Zool. Jahrb., Anat.* 4.

Burger, 1895. *Fauna u. Flora Golf Neapel* 22.

Bury, 1895. *Quat. Jour. Micr. Sci.* 38.

Buxton, 1913. *Zool. Jahrb. Anat.* 14, sup.

Calman in Lankester, *Treatise on Zoology*

Calvez, 1938. *Arch. Zool. Exp. Gen.* 80:1

Cameron, 1956. *Parasites and Parasitism.* Methuen, London.

Canu, 1892. *Trav. Zool. Inst. Lille* 6.

Cardell and Philpott, 1960. *Trans. Amer. Micr. Soc.* 79.

Carlisle and Knowles, 1959. *Endocrine Control in Crustacea.* Cambridge Univ. Press, Cambridge.

Carpenter, 1884. *Challenger Rep., Zool.* 26.

Caullery and Mesnil, 1901. *Arch. Anat. Micr.* 4.

Chadwick, 1907. *Liverpool Mar. Biol. Comm. Mem.* 15.

Chadwick, 1923. *Liverpool Mar. Biol. Comm. Mem.* 25.

Chandler and Read, 1961. *Introduction to Parasitology.* John Wiley and Sons, New York.

Child, 1900. *Arch. Entwicklungsmech.* 9.

Chitwood, 1931. *Zeitschr. Morph. u Ökol. Tiere* 23.
Chitwood and Chitwood, 1937. *Introduction to Nematology.* Baltimore.
Chuang, 1956. *Proc. Zool. Soc. London,* 127.
Clare and Tauber, 1940. *Iowa State Coll. Jour. Sci.* 14.
Clark, 1956. *Quat. Jour. Micr. Sci.* 97.
Clark, 1907. *Smithson. Misc. Collect.* 35, No. 1723.
Clark, 1915–50. *Bull. U. S. Natl. Mus.* 82.
Claus, 1872. *Zeitschr. wiss. Zool.* 22:331
Claus, 1888. *Arb. Zool. Inst. Wien.* 8:1
Cleveland, 1949. *Jour. Morphol.* 85.
Cleveland, 1956. *Jour. Protozool.* 3.
Cloudsley-Thompson, 1958. *Spiders, Scorpions, Centipedes, and Mites.* Pergamon, New York.
Coe, 1912. *Conn. Geol. Nat. Hist. Surv. Bull.* 19.
Coe, 1926. *Mem. Mus. Comp. Zool. Harvard* 47.
Coe, 1930. *Zool. Anz.* 102.
Comstock, 1924. *An Introduction to Entomology.* Cornell Univ. Press, Ithaca, N.Y.
Conklin, 1897. *Jour. Morphol.* 13.
Conklin, 1905. *Jour. Acad. Nat. Sci. Phila.* 13.
Cooke in Harmer and Shipley, *The Cambridge Natural History*
Cori, 1893. *Zeitschr. wiss. Zool.* 55.
Correa, 1948. *Zoologia,* Univ. Saõ Paulo 13.
Corliss, 1959. *Jour. Protozool.* 6.
Crofts, 1937. *Phil. Trans. Roy. Soc. London* 228.
Cuénot in Grassé, *Traité de Zoologie*
Cumings, 1912. *Bull. Geol. Soc. Amer.* 23.
Dahlgren and Kepner, 1908. *Principles of Animal Histology.* Macmillan. New York.
Davidson, 1886–88. *Trans. Linn. Soc. London, Zool.* 4.
Dawydoff, in Grassé, *Traité de Zoologie*
Dawydoff and Grassé in Grassé, *Traité de Zoologie*
de Beauchamp, 1907. *Arch. Zool. Exp. Gen.* 36.
de Beauchamp, 1909. *Arch. Zool. Exp. Gen.* 40.
de Beauchamp, 1930. *Bull. Soc. Zool. France* 54.
de Coninck, 1942. *Natuurw. Tidjschr.* 24.
Delage, Y. and E. Hèrouard, 1896–1903. *Traité de Zoologie Concrète.* Schleicher Frèrès, Paris
de Man, 1910. *Zool. Jahrb., Syst.* 20.
Dendy, 1893. *Quat. Jour. Micr. Sci.* 35.
Dohrn, 1881. *Fauna u. Flora Golf. Neapel* 3.
Drew, 1899. *Biol. Lab. Johns Hopkins Univ. Mem.* 4.
Drew, 1899. *Anat. Anz.* 15.
Duboscq, 1921. *C. R. Soc. Biol.* 84.
Duerden, 1899. *Jour. Linn. Soc. London, Zool.* 27.
Eales, 1961. *Littoral Fauna of Great Britain.* Cambridge Univ. Press, Cambridge.
Eason, 1964. *Centipedes of the British Isles.* Cambridge Univ. Press, Cambridge.
Edmondson (ed.), 1959. *Ward and Whipple's Freshwater Biology.* John Wiley and Sons, New York.
Elliott, 1934. *Arch. f. Protistenk.* 82.
Entz, 1921. *Arch. f. Protistenk.* 43.
Essig, 1942. *College Entomology.* Macmillan, New York.
Essig, 1958. *Insects and Mites of Western North America.* Macmillan, New York.
Evans, 1900. *Quat. Jour. Micr. Sci.* 44.
Faure-Fremiet, 1954. *Jour. Embryol. Exp. Morph.* 2.
Faure-Fremiet, 1958. *Quat. Jour. Micr. Sci.* 99.
Faust and Khaw, 1927. *Am. Jour. Hyg., Monogr. Ser.* 8.

Fauvel in Grassé, *Traité de Zoologie*
Ferguson, 1940. *Zool. Anz.* 129.
Fernau, 1914. *Zeitschr. wiss. Zool.* 110:253
Filipijev, 1931. *Proc. Zool. Soc. London,* 1931.
Fisher, 1919. *U. S. Natl. Mus.* 100.
Folsom and Wardle, 1934. *Entomology.* Blakiston and Co., Philadelphia.
Fraipont, 1897. *Fauna u. Flora Golf Neapel* 14.
Franc in Grassé, *Traité de Zoologie*
François, 1878. *Arch. Zool. Exp. Gen.* 9.
Frenzel, 1892. *Arch. Naturgesch.* 58.
Fretter, 1937. *Trans. Roy. Soc. Edinburg.* 59.
Fretter and Graham, 1962. *British Prosobranch Molluscs,* Ray Society, London.
Fuhrmann, 1895. *Zool. Jahrb., Anat.* 9.
Fulinski, 1916. *Zool, Anz.* 47.
Gabe, 1956. *Arch. Anat. Mikr. Morph. Exp.* 46.
Gardiner, 1895. *Jour. Morphol.* 11.
Gelei, 1927. *Zool. Anz.* 73.
Gelei, 1930. *Zeitschr. Morph. Ökol. Tiere* 18.
Gerhardt and Kästner in Kükenthal and Krumbach, *Handbuch der Zoologie*
Gerould, 1896. *Proc. Boston Soc. Nat. Hist.* 27.
Gerwerzhagen, 1913. *Sitzungsber. Heidelberg Akad. Wiss., Math. Naturwiss.* 4B.
Ghatia and Gulati, 1927. *Arch. f. Protistenk.* 57.
Giesbrecht, 1892. *Fauna u. Flora Golf Neapel.* 19.
Gislén, 1924. *Zool. Bidrag.* 9.
Goette, 1907. *Zeitschr. wiss. Zool.* 87.
Goodrich, 1945. *Quat. Jour. Micr. Sci.* 86.
Grassé, ed., (1948–   ) *Traité de Zoologie.* Masson et Cie, Paris.
Gravier and Fage, 1925. *Ann. Sci. Nat. Zool.* 10
Greef, 1880. *Zeitschr. wiss. Zool.* 42.
Green, J. 1961. *A Biology of Crustacea.* Quadrangle Books, Chicago.
Grell, 1956. *Protozoologie.* Springerverlag, Berlin.
Grobben, 1923. *Sitzungsber. Akad. Sci. Wien, Math. Naturwiss.* 132.
Grove, 1925. *Quat. Jour. Micr. Sci.* 69.
Guberlet, 1925. *Publ. Pug. Sound. Biol. Stat.* 5.
Gurney, 1931–33. *British Fresh-Water Copepods.* Ray Society, London.
Hadzi, 1909. *Univ. Wien Arb. Zool. Inst.* 17.
Haecker, 1938. *C. R. Acad. Sci. U.S.S.R.* 19.
Halkin, 1901. *Arch. Biol.* 18.
Hall, 1953. *Protozoology.* Prentice-Hall, Englewood Cliffs, N.J.
Hamann, 1889. *Jen. Zeitschr. Naturwiss.* 33.
Hamburger, 1907. *Zeitschr. wiss. Zool.* 86.
Hammer, 1908. *Arch. Biontol.* 2.
Hancock, 1859. *Philos. Trans. Roy. Soc. Lond.* 148.
Hanson and Lowy, 1959. *Jour. Physiol.* 149.
Hanström, 1926. *Acta Zoologica* 7.
Hanström, 1928. *Vergleichende Anatomie des Nervensystems der wirbelosen Tiere.* Springerverlag,
     Berlin.
Harant and Grassé in Grassé, *Traité de Zoologie.*
Hargitt, 1904. *Bull. U. S. Bur. Fish.* 24.
Harmer, 1885. *Quat. Jour. Micr. Sci.* 25.
Harmer and Shipley, 1895–1909. *The Cambridge Natural History.* Macmillan, London.
Hart, 1936. *Trans. Amer. Micr. Soc.* 55.
Haswell, 1893. *MacLeay Mem. Vol.,* Linn. Soc. N. S. Wales.

Haye, 1930. *Arch. f. Protistenk.* 70.

Hayes, 1938. *Trans. Amer. Micr. Soc.* 57.

Hegner, 1933. *Invertebrate Zoology.* Macmillan, New York.

Hegner, Root, and Augustine, 1938. *Parasitology.* Appleton-Century, New York.

Heider, 1909. *Zool. Anz.* 34.

Heider, 1912. *Verh. Deutsch. Zool. Gesellsch.* 22.

Hein, 1904. *Zeitschr. wiss. Zool.* 77.

Heinze, 1937. *Zeitschr. Parasitenk.* 9.

Heller, 1931. *Zeitschr. Morph. Ökol. Tiere* 24.

Herdmann in Harmer and Shipley, *The Cambridge Natural History*

Hertwig and Hertwig, 1878. *Die Nervensystem u. Sinnesorgane der Medusen.* Leipzig.

Hesse, 1897. *Zeitschr. wiss. Zool.* 62.

Hesse, 1899. *Zeitschr. wiss. Zool.* 65.

Hesse, 1902. *Zeitschr. wiss. Zool.* 72.

Hickernell, 1917. *Biol. Bull.* 32.

Hincks, 1878. *Quat. Jour. Micr. Sci.* 18.

Hofeneeder, 1930. *Arch. Protistenk.* 71:1

Hoff, 1942. *Ill. Biol. Monogr.* 19.

Hoff, 1949. *Ill. Nat. Hist. Surv. Bull.* 24.

Hofsten, 1918. *Zool. Bidrag* 7.

Hoogstraal, 1962. *Jour. Parasit.* 48.

Hörstadius, 1939. *Publ. Staz. Zool. Napoli* 17.

Huth, 1913. *Arch. f. Potistenk.* 30.

Hyman, 1940–59. *The Invertebrates.* McGraw-Hill Book Co., New York.

Hyman, 1941. *Poc. U. S. Natl. Mus.* 89.

Isgrove, 1909. *Liverpool Mar. Biol. Comm. Mem.* 18.

Ivanov, 1954. *System. Zool.* 31.

Ivanov in Grassé, *Traité de Zoologie*

Iwanoff, 1933. *Zool. Jahrb., Anat.* 56.

Jackson, 1912. *Boston Soc. Nat. Hist. Mem.* 7.

Jaeckel, 1918. *Zeitschr. Palaeontol.* 3.

Jahn, 1949. *How To Know the Protozoa.* Brown, Dubuque, Ia.

Jakus and Hall, 1946, *Biol. Bull.* 91.

Janet, 1922. *Le Volvox.* Mem. 2.

Janicki, 1917. *Zeitschr. wiss. Zool.* 87.

Johannsen and Butt, 1941. *Embryology of Insects and Myriapods.* McGraw-Hill Book Co., New York.

Johnson and Snook, 1927. *Seashore Animals of the Pacific Coast.* Macmillan, New York.

Kahl, 1932. *Die Tierwelt Deutschlands,* 30.

Kästner in Kükenthal and Krumbach, *Handbuch der Zoologie*

Kaston and Kaston, 1953. *How To Know the Spiders.* Brown, Dubuque, Ia.

Kaufmann, 1958. *Nauk,* 129.

Keister, 1948. *Jour. Morphol.* 83.

Kessel *et al.,* 1961. *Trans. Amer. Micr. Soc.* 80.

King, 1935. *Jour. Morphol.* 58.

Kirby, 1949. *Univ. Calif. Publ. Zool.* 45.

Kleinholz, 1950. *Biol. Bull.* 99.

Koch, 1863. *Die Myriapoden.*

Kofoid, 1898. *Ill. Nat. Hist. Surv. Bull.* 5

Kofoid and McLennan, 1933. *Univ. Calif. Publ. Zool.* 39:1

Kofoid and Swezy, 1921. *Calif. Univ. Mem.* 5.

Kofoid and Swezy, 1922. *Univ. Calif. Publ. Zool.* 20.

Komai, 1922. *Studies on Two Aberrant Ctenophores—Coeloplana and Gastrodes.* Kyoto.

Komai, 1934. *Kyoto Univ. Sci. Mem. B.*

Komiya and Tajima, 1940. *Jour. Schanghai Sci. Inst. Sect.* 4, 5.

Korscheldt, 1936. *Lehrbuch der vergleichenden Entwicklungsgeschichte der wirbellosen Tiere.* Fisher, Jena.

Kraeplin in Bronn, *Klassen und Ordnung des Their-Reichs*

Kreis, 1934. *Capita Zoologica* 4.

Krijgsman, 1925. *Arch. f. Protistenk.* 52.

Kudo, 1954. *Protozoology.* Thomas, Springfield, Ill.

Kudo and Daniels, 1963. *Jour. Protozool.* 10.

Kühn, 1910. *Zool. Jahrb. Anat.* 30.

Kükenthal and Krumbach (eds.), 1923– *Handbuch der Zoologie.* W. de Gruyter, Berlin.

Kuntz, 1951. *Trans. Am. Micr. Soc.* 70.

Lang, 1939. *Kungl. Fysiogr. Sallsk. Lund.* 9

Lang, 1948. *Ark. Zool.* 41A.

Lankester (ed.), 1900–1909. *A Treatise on Zoology.* A. and C. Black, London.

Lankester and Bourne, 1883. *Quat. Jour. Micr. Schi.* 23.

Lawrence, 1963. *Biology of the Cryptic Fauna of Forests,* Balkema, Amsterdam.

Lazier, 1924. *Univ. Calif. Publ. Zool.* 22.

Leger, 1906. *Arch. f. Protistenk,* 7.

Leidy, 1879. *Rep. U. S. Geol. Surv.* 12.

Lemche and Wingstrand, 1959. *Galathea Rep.* 3.

Lemmermann, 1914. *Die Süsswasser-Flora Deutschland, Osterreichs, und des Schweiz.* Fischer Verlag, Berlin.

Lilljeborg, 1883. *Mem. Acad. Sci. France* 42.

Lilljeborg, 1900. *Nov. Acta reg. Soc. Sci. Upsala* 3.

Linko, 1900. *Mem. Acad. Imp. Sci. St. Pétersbourg* 10.

Livanov, 1906. *Zool. Jahrb. Anat.* 19:29

Looss, 1894. *Bibliotheca Zool.* 6.

Looss, 1900. *Mem. Inst. Egypt.* 3.

Looss, 1905. *Rec. Egypt. Gov. School Med.* 3.

Lovén, 1874. *Kong. Svenska Vetensk. Akad. Hdl.* 11.

Ludwig, 1800. *Zeitschr. wiss. Zool.* 34.

Luther, 1904. *Zeitschr. wiss. Zool.* 77.

Lyman, 1882. *Challenger Rep. Zool.* 5.

Lynch, 1933. *Quat. Jour. Micr. Sci.* 76.

Lynch, 1945. *Jour. Parasit.* 31.

MacBride, 1907. *Quat. Jour. Micr. Sci.* 34.

MacBride in Harmer and Shipley, *The Cambridge Natural History.*

MacGinitie and MacGinitie, 1949. *Natural History of Marine Animals.* McGraw-Hill Book Co., New York.

MacKinnon and Ray, 1937. *Parasitol.* 29:457

Macy, 1934. *Univ. Minn. Agr. Ep. Stat. Bull.* 98.

Malaquin, 1901. *Arch. Zool. Exp. Gen.* 9.

Mann, 1953. *Biol. Rev.* 28.

Mann, 1962. *Leeches (Hirudinea), Their Structure, Physiology, Ecology, and Embryology.* Pergamon, New York.

Marcus, 1904. *Ril. Fac. Fil. Cién. Lutr. Univ. Sao Paulo* 43:5

Marcus, 1937. *Zoologia,* Univ. São Paulo, 1.

Marshall and Orr, 1955. *The Biology of a Copepod.* Oliver and Boyd, London.

Mast, 1927. *Arch. f. Protistenk.* 60.

Matthai, 1926. *Phil. Trans. Roy. Soc. London* 214.

May, 1919. *Ill. Biol. Monogr.* 5.

Mayer, 1910. *Medusae of the World.* Carnegie Inst., Washington.

Mayer, 1912. *Ctenophores of the Atlantic Coast of North America*. Carnegie Inst., Washington.

McClelland, 1959. *Jour. Protozool.* 6.

McDunnough, 1933. *Canad. Entom.* 65.

McLennan, 1939. *Jour. Morphol.* 65.

Mead, 1900. *Bull. U. S. Fish Comm.* 19.

Meeck, 1917. *Rep. Dove Mar. Lab. Cullercoats* 6.

Meglitsch, 1960. *Trans. Roy. Soc. N. Z.*, 88:265

Meisenheimer, 1900. *Zeitschr. wiss. Zool.* 69.

Metalnikoff, 1900. *Zeitschr. wiss. Zool.* 68.

Metcalf, 1923. *U. S. Natl. Mus. Bull.* 120.

Metschnikoff, 1886. *Embryological Studien an Medusen*. Vienna.

Michaelson in Kükenthal and Krumbach, *Handbuch der Zoologie*.

Micoletzky, 1907. *Zeitschr. wiss. Zool.* 87.

Minchin and Thomson, 1915. *Quat. Jour. Micr. Sci.* 60.

Montgomery, 1903. *Zool. Jahrb., Anat.* 18.

Montgomery, 1904. *Proc. Acad. Nat. Sci. Phila.* 56.

Monticelli, 1892. *Festschrift 70. Geburtstag R. Leuckart*.

Morgan, 1891. *Jour. Morphol.* 51.

Moroff and Stiasny, 1909. *Arch. f. Protistenk.* 16.

Morse, 1902. *Mem. Boston. Nat. Hist.* 5.

Mortensen, 1928–51. *A Monograph of the Echinoidea*. Oxford Univ. Press, London.

Mortensen, 1931. *Selsk. Skr. Natuurw. Kong. Danske Vidensk.* 4.

Mortensen, 1938. *Selsk. Skr. Natuurw. Kong. Danske Vidensk.* 7.

Morton and Holme, 1955. *Jour. Mar. Biol. Assoc. U. K.* 34.

Moulton, 1909. *Bur. Entom. U. S. Dept. Agr. Bull.* 80.

Mueller and Van Cleave, 1932. *Roosevelt Wild Life Annals* 3.

Mühldorf, 1914. *Zeitschr. wiss. Zool.* 111.

Myers, 1936. *Jour. Roy. Mich. Soc.* 56.

Naef, 1913. *Erg. Fortschr. Zool.* 3.

Narasimhurti, 1933. *Quat. Jour. Micr. Sci.* 76.

Näsmark, 1937. *Zool. Bidrag.* 16.

Nawitzki, 1931. *Zool. Jahrb., Anat.* 54.

Newell, 1937. *State Geol. Surv. Kansas* 10.

Nicol, 1948. *Quat. Rev. Biol.* 23.

Noble and Noble, 1962. *Animal Parasitology Laboratory Manual*. Lea and Febiger, Philadelphia.

Noble and Noble, 1961. *Parasitology*. Lea and Febiger, Philadelphia.

Nouvel, 1933. *Ann. Inst. Oceanogr. Monaco.* 13.

Nutting, 1901. *Proc. Wash. Acad. Sci.* 3.

Nutting, 1939. *Jour. Morphol.* 89.

Oka, 1891. *Jour. Coll. Sci. Univ. Tokyo* 4.

Okada, 1927. *Bull. Biol. Frances Belg.* 61.

Oudemans, 1885. *Quat. Jour. Micr. Sci.* 25.

Owen, 1953. *Jour. Mar. Biol. Assoc. U. K.* 35.

Pace, 1906. *Quat. Jour. Micr. Sci.* 50.

Parker, 1920. *Jour. Exp. Zool.* 31.

Paul, 1939. *Jour. Parasit.* 21.

Pawlowsky 1924. *Quat. Jour. Micr. Sci.* 69.

Pelseneer, in Lankester, *Treatise on Zoology*

Penard, 1902. *Faune Rhizopode que du bassin Liman*. Kündig, Geneva.

Pennak, 1953. *Fresh-Water Invertebrates of the United States*. Ronald Press, New York.

Peters, 1931. *Zeitschr. wiss. Zool.* 139.

Petrunkewitch, A. 1916. *Morphology of Invertebrate Types*. Macmillan, New York. .

Pflugpfelder, 1955. *Mikrokosmos* 44.

Pitelka, 1961. *Jour. Protozool.* 8.
Pixell, 1912. *Quat. Jour. Micr. Sci.* 58.
Plate, 1885. *Mitt. Zool. Stat. Neapel* 7.
Pockock, 1933. *South Africa. Mus. Ann.* 16.
Pratt, 1951. *Common Invertebrates of the United States*, Blakiston, New York
Prenant, 1925. *Trav. Stat. Zool. Wimereux* 9.
Prosser and Brown, 1061. *Comparative Animal Physiology.* Saunders, Philadelphia
Prouho, 1887. *Arch. Zool. Exp. Gen.* 5.
Prouvot, 1892. *C. R. Acad. Sci. Paris.* 114.
Pruvot, 1892. *C. R. Acad. Sci. Paris* 114:1211
Ramsay, 1949. *Jour. Exp. Biol.* 26.
Randall and Jackson, 1958. *Jour. Biophys. and Chem Cytol.* 4.
Rees, 1940. *Parasitol.* 32.
Rees, 1939. *Jour. Mar. Biol. Assoc. U. K.* 23.
Reichenow, 1921. *Arch. f. Protistenk.* 42:80
Remane, 1926. *Zeitschr. Morph. Ökol. Tiere* 5.
Richter in Kükenthal and Krumbach, *Handbuch der Zoologie*
Ricketts and Calvin, 1952. *Between Pacific Tides.* Stanford Univ. Press, Stanford
Riepen, 1922. *Arch. Morph. Gen. Exp.* 5.
Riessinger, 1925. *Zeitschr. Morph. Ökol. Tiere* 5.
Ritter-Zahoney in Bronn, *Klassen und Ordnung der Tier-Reichs.*
Robertson, 1908. *Univ. Calif. Publ. Zool.* 4.
Robertson, 1910. *Univ. Calif. Publ. Zool.* 6.
Roeder, 1953. *Insect Physiology*, John Wiley and Sons, N.Y.
Roger, 1945. *Bull. Soc. Geol. France.* 14.
Rogick, 1935. *Trans. Amer. Micr. Soc.* 54.
Rogick, 1940. *Trans. Amer. Micr. Soc.* 59.
Rosen, 1916. *Bull. Soc. Neuchâtel. Sci. Natur.* 43.
Ross, 1937–38. *Ill. Nat. Hist. Surv. Bull.* 21.
Ross, 1956. *A Textbook of Entomology.* John Wiley and Sons, New York.
Roth, 1960. *Jour. Protozool.* 7.
Rothman, 1963. *Trans. Am. Micr. Soc.* 82.
Ruebush, 1941. *Trans. Am. Micr. Soc.* 60.
Ruebush and Hayes, 1939. *Zool. Anz.* 128.
Rullier, 1954. *Arch. zool. Exp. Gen.* 91:195
Runnström, 1927. *Bergens. Mus. Aarb.* 1.
Salensky, 1912. *Mem. Acad. Imp. Sci. St. Pétersbourg* 30.
Salfi, 1933. *Arch. Zool. Ital.* 19:121
Sars, 1891. *Norwegian North Atlantic Expedition 1876–1878. Zoologie,* 20.
Sars, 1892–1921. *An Account of the Crustacea of Norway.* Cammermeyers, Copenhagen.
Sasser and Jenkins, 1960. *Nematology.* Univ. North Carolina Press, Chapel Hill.
Sato, 1936. *Zool. Anz.* 115.
Savory, T. H. 1936. *The Arachnida.* Edward Arnold, London.
Schaeffer, 1916. *Arch. f. Protistenk.* 37.
Schauinsland, 1886. *Jena. Zeitschr. Naturwiss.* 19.
Schechter, 1959. *Invertebrate Zoology.* Prentice-Hall, Englewood Cliffs, N.J.
Scheer, B., 1961. *Recent Advances in Insect Physiology.* Univ. of Wash. Press, Seattle
Schneider, 1960. *Jour. Protozool* 7.
Schultze, 1922. *Arch. Zellforsch.* 16.
Scriban and Autrum in Kükenthal and Krumbach, *Handbuch der Zoologie*
Selenka, 1867. *Zeitschr. wiss. Zool.* 17.
Selenka, 1883. *Studien über Entwicklungsgeschichte der Tiere.*
Selensky, 1908. *Zeitschr. wiss. Zool.* 90.

Sélys-Longchamps, 1907. *Fauna u. Flora Golf. Neapel.* 30.

Shearer, 1911. *Quart. Jour. Micr. Soc.* 57:329.

Shimer and Shrock, 1944. *Index Fossils of North America.* John Wiley and Sons, New York.

Shipley in Harmer and Shipley, *The Cambridge Natural History*

Shrock and Twenhofel, 1953. *Principles of Invertebrate Paleontology.* McGraw-Hill Book Co., New York.

Shuurmans-Stekhoven and Tenuissen, 1938. *Expl. Parc. Nat. Albert Mission de Witte* 22.

Silén, 1952. *Ark. Zool.* 4.

Silén, 1954. *Ark. Zool.* 6.

Smith and Weldon in Harmer and Shipley, *The Cambridge Natural History*

Snodgrass, 1935. *Principles of Insect Morphology.* McGraw-Hill Book Co., New York.

Snodgrass, 1952. *Textbook of Arthropod Anatomy.* Cornell Univ. Press, Ithaca, N.Y.

Sollas, 1888. *Challenger Reports,* 25.

Southward, 1962. *Can Jour. Zool.* 40.

Spengel, 1884. *Mitt. Zool. Stat. Neapel.* 5.

Spengel, 1932. *Sci. Res. M. Sars. N. Atlantic Deep Sea Exped.* 5.

Stein, 1867. *Die Organismus der Infusionsthiere.*

Steiner, 1921. *Zool. Jahrb., Anat.* 43.

Stephenson, 1930. *The Oligochaeta.* Oxford Univ. Press, London.

Stiasny, 1914. *Zeitschr. wiss. Zool.* 110.

Stokes, 1888. *Jour. Tenton Nat. Hist. Soc.* 1

Stossberg, 1932. *Zeitschr. wiss. Zool.* 142.

Strickland, 1913. *Jour. Morphol.* 24.

Stummer-Traunfels in Kükenthal and Krumbach, *Handbuch der Zoologie*

Stunkard, 1917. *Ill. Biol. Monogr.* 3.

Summers and Kidder, 1936. *Arch. f. Protistenk.* 86.

Surface, 1907. *Proc. Acad. Nat. Sci. Phil.* 59.

Suter, 1917. *Manual of New Zealand Mollusca.* Govt. Printing Office.

Tannreuther, 1920. *Jour. Morphol.* 33.

Tartar, 1961. *The Biology of Stentor.* Pergamon, New York.

Théel, 1875. *Kungl. Svenska Vet. Akad. Handl.* 14.

Théel, 1882. *Challenger Reports, Zool.* 4.

Théel, 1906. *Kungl. Svenska Vet. Akad. Handl.* 42.

Tiegs, 1947. *Quart. Jour. Micr. Sci.* 88.

Tower, 1900. *Zool. Jahrb., Anat.* 13.

Turner, 1930. *Univ. Calif. Publ. Zool.* 33.

Valkanov, 1928. *Arch. f. Protistenk.* 63.

Van Benedin and Julin, 1884. *Arch. Biol.* 5:111

Van Cleave, 1947. *Jour. Parasit.* 33.

van der Horst in Kükenthal and Krumbach, *Handbuch der Zoologie*

Van Name, 1936. *Bull. Am. Mus. Nat. Hist.* 71.

Van Name, 1945. *Bull. Am. Mus. Nat. Hist.* 84.

Verrill, 1892. *Trans. Conn. Acad. Arts Sci.* 8.

Von Graaf, 1882. *Monographie der Turbellarien.*

Von Graaf, 1904. *Zeitschr. wiss. Zool.* 78.

Von Graaf, 1911. *Zeitschr. wiss. Zool.* 99.

Warburton in Harmer and Shipley, *The Cambridge Natural History.*

Warren, 1906. *Natal Mus. Annals* 1.

Waterman (ed.), 1960. *The Physiology of Crustacea.* Academic Press, New York.

Watson, 1916. *Ill. Biol. Monogr.* 2.

Weill, 1934. *Trav. Staat. Zool. Wimereux* 10.

Weissman, 1915. *C. R. Soc. Biol.* 78

Wells, 1944. *Proc. Zool. Soc. London* 114.

Wenyon, 1910. *Parasitol.* 3:63

Wesenberg-Lund, 1923. *Kong. Danske Vid. Selsk. Skrift Natur. Math. Afdel Raekke* 8.

Wheeler, 1913. *Ants, Their Structure, Development and Behavior.* Columbia Univ. Press, New York.

Whitman, 1882. *Mitt. Zool. Stat. Neapel* 4.

Whittington, 1957. *Biol. Rev.* 32.

Wigglesworth, 1933. *Quart. Jour. Micr. Sci.* 76.

Wigglesworth, 1953. *The Principles of Insect Physiology.* Methuen, London.

Wilhelmi, 1906. *Zeitschr. wiss. Zool.* 80.

Willey, 1953. *Jour. Morphol.* 50.

Williams, 1956. *Biol. Rev.* 31.

Wilson, 1900. *Quart. Jour. Micr. Sci.* 43.

Wilson, 1881. *Quart. Jour. Micr. Sci.* 21.

Wilson, 1883. *Trans. Roy. Soc. London* 174.

Wilson, 1894. *Jour. Morphol.* 9.

Woodland, 1905. *Quat. Jour. Micr. Sci.* 49

Wulfert, 1902. *Zeitschr. wiss. Zool.* 71.

Yamaguti, 1935. *Jap. Jour. Zool.* 6.

Yatsu, 1902. *Jour. Coll. Sci. Univ. Tokyo* 17.

Yonge, 1926. *Jour. Mar. Biol. Assoc. U. K.* 14.

Yonge, 1939. *Phil. Trans. Roy. Soc. London* 230.

Zacher in Kükenthal and Krumbach, *Handbuch der Zoologie.*

Zelinka, 1928. *Monographie der Echinodera*

Zwilling, 1939. *Biol. Bull.* 76.

Contents

Invertebrate Zoology

1
Introduction

A course in invertebrate zoology may be considered an exploratory trip through a strange country, the animal kingdom. It is a huge kingdom, containing well over a million species as well as a good deal of unexplored territory. No man in his lifetime could study it all. If he were to examine a different species every hour of an eight-hour day, his task would remain unfinished three hundred years later. How, then, can one become a well-informed zoologist? One must accept the method of the traveler, who makes no pretense of visiting every farm, village, and city in a foreign land. The wise traveler selects an itinerary that will take him into the plains and the mountains, into farming country and manufacturing centers, into villages and metropolitan centers. At the same time he relies on a guidebook to explain much and call his attention to things that might pass unseen.

No matter how good, however, a guidebook can never replace the experience of the visit. So it is in science. A book may be an aid, but it remains ever subordinate to the experience gained in the laboratory and field. This book is a guide to a part of the animal kingdom. It includes a woefully small part of the available information, for it is intended to be a guide for a short trip by new travelers not already familiar with the terrain and the culture. Should some of you decide on a lifetime trip, there are other and more complete guides to the localities sketchily covered here.

The division of zoology into vertebrate and invertebrate branches reflects something of man's innate egoism and has had some strange results. The phylum Chordata is arbitrarily split into vertebrate and invertebrate components, and a person specializing in vertebrates runs the risk of missing most of the animal kingdom. To a biologist from an alien world, the vertebrates might seem to be an interesting, but relatively insignificant, part of the animal kingdom, for less than 3 per cent of living animal species have backbones. The invertebrates are ecologically important in all environments, and in agriculture are becoming more important constantly. The proper study of animal life demands a careful consideration of the great bulk of the animal kingdom—the invertebrates.

It is no accident that nearly all of the truly basic zoological discoveries have been based on studies of invertebrates. They come in such a variety of sizes and shapes,

3

ranging from the minute *Leishmania* that crowd by the dozen into a single host cell to the giant squid, capable of battling a whale. They range from the almost amorphous mass of a fresh-water sponge to the delicate, crystalline beauty of a radiolarian. They are found in every habitat open to living things and follow the most varied assortment of life patterns. They include producer, decomposer, and consumer; parasite and host; predator and prey; biological saint and sinner. The experimental scientist can nearly always find some invertebrate somewhere that has just the properties his studies demand. The short life span of many invertebrates is often a great advantage, permitting the establishment of culture techniques that are far less expensive and time-consuming than are required for the vertebrates. From the practical as well as the historical point of view, a knowledge of invertebrates is essential for the zoologist.

During the eighteenth century and much of the nineteenth, the study of the classification and anatomy of animals dominated zoology. With the appearance of the evolutionary concept, the emphasis changed, and comparative studies of adult and immature stages were undertaken to describe the course of evolution and to recognize relationships. As the main streams of evolutionary descent were traced, the new facts posed new kinds of problems. How could the form of larvae, so similar when very young, come to be so different from stage to stage, and in different species diverge to such a remarkable extent? What sorts of controls underlay these changes? How could an animal stock undergo evolutionary changes that would be incorporated in its germplasm? How did the various organs work, and how did the manner of their working produce the kinds of selective influences upon which evolutionary changes depend? In these and similar questions, the seeds of physiology, genetics, ecology, biochemistry, and biophysics first took root. New branches of a science always

develop from attempts to solve problems arising from the more classical studies which preceded them. One cannot really understand the goals of modern science if one lacks a knowledge of the fundamental questions and approaches of past scientists. However, since one cannot trace through every step of the development of zoology, about the best that one can do, as teacher or student, is to try always to preserve some sense of the animal itself. A molecular biologist or population biologist may make great contributions to zoology as long as he continues to be aware of the part the principles he seeks play in the life of the animals he studies. Without this, the biochemist becomes a chemist who happens to work with protoplasmic material and whose interests center entirely on chemical rather than biological phenomena. For the zoologist, the important biochemistry, the imporant genetics, the important physiology, the events which it is his particular part to unravel and explain, go on in nature and not in the laboratory. He may spend the greater part of his working life in the laboratory, but the focus of his work should be the world outside it. In a very real sense, until the principle or process learned in the laboratory can be understood as it applies in the life of creatures in the forest and field, it has not yet become a functional part of zoology. If this attitude can be maintained, the modern scientist can never truly lose touch with his predecessors, for if he happens to forget one of the old and unsolved problems, he will rediscover it sometime in the future.

The general features of each phylum are reviewed in the text, and the major outlines of evolutionary relationship are discussed. An attempt has been made, in an introductory manner, to call attention to some of the physiological information that is now available, and to relate the physiological processes to the problems of survival in the natural habitats in which animals live. Trying to avoid being either antiquated or so modern that the older problems are not recognized has made it necessary to leave out a great deal. The interested student should seek to amplify the information given here in the hope of shoring up deficiencies, particularly in the areas of high interest. The references included in the text will be helpful in pursuing some of the groups more thoroughly.

A large number of new terms will be encountered. Every specialist requires a far more extensive vocabulary than is used here. Those who are studying invertebrates as a background for future specialization in invertebrate zoology should try to learn as much of the terminology as possible, with the idea of adding new terms later. Those who are learning something about invertebrates as a background for specialization in other fields, however, should work with the vocabulary long enough to understand the main ideas, after which the excess terms can be forgotten. The study of new terms can be made easier by underlining them in the text as they are encountered. The underlined terms catch the eye and make review easier. Definitions of terms in the text may also be underlined. This will be found helpful for terms not included in the glossary at the end of the book. If a word is used without definition in the accompany-

Table 1.1. Estimated number of known species of recent animals (Mayr)

Protozoa	30,000	Linguatula	70
Mesozoa	50	Chelicerata	35,000
Porifera	4,500	Crustacea	25,000
Coelenterata	9,000	Other Arthropods (excl. insects)	13,000
Ctenophora	90	Insecta	850,000
Platyhelminthes	6,000	Mollusca	80,000
Acanthocephala	300	Pogonophora	1
Rotifera	1,500	Broyozoa	3,300
Gastrotricha	175	Brachiopoda	250
Kinorhyncha	100	Echinodermata	4,000
Nematomorpha	100	Phoronidea	4
Nematoda	10,000	Chaetognatha	30
Priapulideae	5	Hemichordata	80
Nemertina	750	Tunicata	1,600
Entoprocta	60	Fishes	20,000
Annelida	7,000	Reptiles and Amphibia	6,000
Echiuroidea	60	Birds	8,590
Sipunculoidea	250	Mammals	3,200
Tardigrada	180		
Onycnophora	65	Total	1,120,310

(Taken from E. Mayr, E. G. Linsley, and R. L. Usinger, *Methods and Principles of Systematic Zoology*, McGraw-Hill, 1953.)

This table shows something of the variety of major groups of animals, and the relative abundance of species in each group. It is, of course, based on estimates, except for the birds, which is by direct count. Many new species are still to be found, and it may be assumed that no more than half of the species in many groups have been described. In some cases the additions will be far more extensive. Since the table was composed, the number of species of Pogonophora has increased to about 25, for example. Hyman, basing her estimate on the known rates of parasitism in various plant and animal groups estimates that there may be as many as 500,000 species of Nematoda, although only 10,000 are shown here. In some instances, several names may have been applied to the same species, and so make the numbers unrealistically large. On the whole, it seems certain that there are more errors which underestimate the number of species than those that overestimate it. Notice that the vertebrates make up only about 38,000 of the known species, or about 3%.

ing discussion, it is assumed that the reader is familiar with it. If he is not, he may find the word in the glossary. If it is not there, consult the index, where a citation to an explanation or definition of the term may be found in bold face print.

A book is a tool that can be improved with use. Marginal notations and underlining, if carefully done, can make a book a great deal more useful. Time spent in constructing a written outline of a chapter can often be more usefully spent in preparing the book itself for review. Color coded underlining can be used very effectively. New terms and definitions may be underlined in red, for example, while important summary phrases may be underlined in black. Points that are unclear can be underlined in another color, and later clarified by a marginal notation, while points that have been particularly stressed by an instructor can be identified by a marginal note or underlining in another color. A system of this kind has another advantage, for it leads to a more active analysis of the subject matter of a chapter and favors a more critical consideration of the topics covered than simple outlining often does. If a consistent color code is used and a selective set of marginal notations has been made in each book, your library is a flexible instrument that can be used to locate important material or review forgotten topics quickly and efficiently.

Toward a Point of View

Every scientist approaches the materials with which he works with questions. The zoologist has a special point of view and questions that are his own unique domain. He sees a whole animal as a problem, and asks such questions as "What kind of animal is this? What does it do and where does it live? How does it happen to be the way it is?" Answers to his questions demand answers of the anatomist, the physiologist, the taxonomist, the geneticist, and the ecologist. Zoology is a large field, encompassing the whole gamut of animal biology. It seeks to explain animals as animals and so must look for answers both within and outside of the organism.

The zoologist is intimately concerned with the knowledge of animal form. Each different kind of creature has a characteristic form through which it can be recognized. Form, however, is not to be understood by the study of structure alone, for it is the result of a complex and closely controlled process of development, during which genes determine its major aspects. The genes cannot be taken for granted; they, too, must be explained, not only as molecular entities but from an evolutionary or adaptational point of view. The genes responsible for the major attributes of an animal species have not been assembled accidentally or at random. During preceding ages, the members of a species that were handicapped by their genetic equipment were less able to survive and to breed, so that these strains have tended to disappear. When new configurations of genes appeared, the successful ones survived. To explain form we must see it as the product of genes, themselves the product of past success determined by usefulness. Indirectly, then, the form of an animal is a picture of success—a diagram sketched in protoplasm, portraying one of the million and a half successful designs for living.

How does a particular design happen to be successful? The answer must be sought through an understanding of function, for life is an active business, involving several kinds of activities. Energy and raw materials needed for growth, maintenance, and repair are obtained through food. Energy is released, typically by oxidations requiring oxygen and producing carbon dioxide as an end product; other waste materials are formed and are excreted. The search for food, shelter, mates and the escape from enemies involve movements that are coordinated with the immediate needs of the organism and the nature of its environment. The ancestors of every organism alive today successfully accomplished these labors until they reproduced themselves, an almost unimaginable record of continuous victory.

Success is not to be measured by complexity alone. It is not surprising that among the species still alive, some have achieved success with a minimum of means, with very few specialized parts and whatever degree of physiological simplicity life permits. A more important prerequisite of success is efficiency. Whether an organism be simple or complicated, the work done and the manner of doing it are intimately related to the equipment available for the purpose. Each component part of a successful organism is suitable in conjunction with the other parts; form and function go hand in hand, as it were, each at the same time determined by the other and determining the other. The constantly reshuffling and recombining genes, throughout the past ages, have been sensitive to this appropriateness of the whole, and it is the particular province of the zoologist to seek to explain this appropriateness, both of the parts to the animal as a whole, and of the animal to its environment.

Every living system, cell and animal alike, is in the import-export trade, conducted across the boundary dividing it from its environment. The entrance and exit of materials are especially related to the acquisition of food, the intake of oxygen, and the release of respiratory and metabolic wastes. These are the surface-centered processes, and the physiological and structural properties of surfaces are important factors in their execution. Active surfaces tend to show the same kinds of adaptive modifications, whether they are used for digestion, respiration, or excretion. Just as a larger store can serve more customers, a greater surface can secrete more enzymes, absorb more food or oxygen, and release more carbon dioxide or urea. The amplification of surface is a recurrent theme in zoology. It is seen again and again in

organisms at all levels, and especially clearly in the digestive, respiratory, and excretory systems. The plasmalemma of an absorptive cell is thrown into tortuous convolutions, and the digestive gland of a clam is branched and rebranched to form a sac composed of sacs. The surface of a tube is also increased by lengthening and by dilations; other factors being equal, a coiled intestine can absorb more food than a straight one. Each dilation of the digestive tube is a point where food slows down and so is exposed longer to enzymes or absorptive cells. Yet, these amplifications of surface are costly in material and in the energy needed to construct them. They are not likely to appear where they are not useful, and in smaller organisms one encounters them less often. Growth in size, usually a real advantage in competing with other creatures, is accompanied by great stress on the surface-centered processes, for surface rises by squares and volume by cubes. The doubling of linear dimensions increases surface area four times, and increases volume by a factor of eight, if the same shape is retained.

Protoplasm requires oxygen in relation to its volume, but oxygen is taken in only at the surface. Thus although respiratory surfaces tend to become more highly folded as animals increase in bulk, in most cases the metabolic rate falls nevertheless. Where adaptational lines lead to a reduction in intake or output requirements, surfaces are generally reduced. Thus the digestive surface of a parasite tends to fall rather than rise as it becomes more proficient at its trade.

The stirring principle is also important in improving the effectiveness of surfaces. At the surface, released material piles up and material taken in disappears. When excreted material is moved away and obsorbed material is delivered continuously, surface efficiency is improved. Stirring is accomplished by surface ciliation and by muscular movements. The ciliary ventilation of surfaces is more primitive, to be replaced by muscular contractions in larger or more highly specialized organisms. The same principle applies at the inner surface of absorptive and the outer surface of excretory membranes. Where body fluids can deliver wastes continuously to an excretory surface, more wastes can be liberated per unit of time, and where absorbed oxygen or food can be carried away by body fluids, more can be absorbed.

These basic rules about surface can explain a great deal about how animals are constructed and how they operate. Surface change is one of the most important forms of adaptation, recurring in many different situations and applying to a number of different systems.

It is also helpful to remember that several alternatives always present themselves as organisms gradually evolve. A stock of animals may develop new physiological or structural mechanisms that permit them to become larger or more complex or to invade some new kind of habitat. They may, on the other hand, compensate for physiological or structural limitations by living in the few habitats where their requirements for living are met. Another alternative is to grow in size but reduce activity to levels permitted by their physiological and structural competence. Undoubtedly different responses of originally similar stocks to such alternatives have favored differentiation to pelagic or to benthic life, to larger or to smaller species, and to more or to less evolutionarily progressive types. Such changes have tended constantly to reduce the competition between similar stocks of organisms, as they gradually come to require different things of their environment or move into different environmental niches.

2
Some Remarks About Classification

Zoologists often make pointed remarks about "common names," names commonly used to designate a particular plant or animal. Why are they relatively useless as scientific tools? Imagine a biochemist who, having weighed his chemicals to the fraction of a milligram and specified all impurities, goes on to say that he worked with a snail. No one could ever confirm a study having only this information. Was it a fresh-water, a marine, or a terrestrial snail? Large or small, herbivorous or carnivorous, air-breathing or equipped with gills? In actuality, one needs to know much more, for two snails of the same size, living side by side in the same tide pool, may be extremely different in many respects. A biochemist cannot be expected to provide all of the necessary information about the structure, physiology, and habits of every animal he uses, but he can accomplish the same thing by providing an accurate scientific name for his experimental material. Names, good names, are an essential part of the zoologist's equipment. Without them he is tongue-tied, unable to explain his work to others, and deaf to theirs as well.

Scientific Names

Like other words in our everyday vocabulary, usage of common names differs in different regions of the same country and, of course, even more widely among different countries. An English "snail" is a German "Schnecke" and a French "escargot." Common names are especially inadequate when applied to specific animals in a specific way. I have no idea how many different species of beetles are known as "June bugs" in the United States, but I am sure the number is large. Serious scientific work would be invalidated by the inaccuracies inherent in such names. Within the limits resulting from the natural variability of living creatures, a scientific name for an organism should be no less dependable than the scientific name for a chemical. Every name should a) stand for one kind of animal everywhere; b) stand for a particular kind of animal, as distinct from all other kinds; and c) be the only valid name for that kind of animal.

The Species

The meaning of the word "species" has undergone considerable change since it was first used. When animals were first being given scientific names, the idea of evolution had not yet been clearly stated and there was no knowledge of genetic variability within populations. Species were thought to be changeless or "fixed," their form having been determined at the time of creation. If an animal did not show all of the characteristics of the species to which it belonged, it was understood to be the result of accident or a mistake on the part of the animal itself. The modern viewpoint is broader. We understand that there is room for considerable genetic diversity within a species, and we also understand that a species gradually changes, adapting itself to an environment as the more successful genetic strains outbreed the less successful ones.

The evolving species is difficult to describe. Zoologists long believed that the only way to describe a species was as an "arbitrary" group, that is, as an assemblage of organisms that in the judgment of a competent specialist should be placed together. However, even from the first, the specialist could not be too arbitrary. If he were to put the young of an animal in a different species from the adults, even though they might look and behave differently, other zoologists would not accept his judgment as valid. Male and female, even though different, were also understood as belonging in the same species. Modern biologists are fairly well convinced that the species is best understood as a population of organisms which can or do interbreed freely, although other characteristics are also important.

Why should the ability to interbreed be a sensible criterion for the recognition of a specific kind of animal? In an interbreeding population, genetic changes appearing in any part of the population can ultimately appear in the descendants of any other member of the species. The whole population thus tends to evolve as a unit, adapting to environmental influences as a whole. Should two different species interbreed freely, they would tend to follow a common evolutionary path, eventually merging into a single unit and no longer distinguishable from one another. It follows that species names should be applied in a manner that, in nature, corresponds to barriers against interbreeding.

The qualification that different species do not interbreed "freely" is important. It is not too uncommon for two kinds of animals to be able to interbreed, but the hybrids are usually partially or wholly sterile, and in other cases lack the vigor needed to compete with the pure, parental types. Partial or complete reproductive isolation is characteristic of species, and is thought by many taxonomists to be the most important single criterion for their recognition.

It is clear that an interbreeding population will tend to include organisms similar in appearance and behavior because of genetic similarities. Furthermore, if they are to be able to interbreed they must occupy a fairly definite geographical territory. Modern systematists tend to describe species as populations characterized by distinctive form and behavior within fairly definite limits; by reproductive isolation from other similar species; and by a definite, more or less continuous, geographical distribution area. Such a natural population cannot be defined arbitrarily by a zoologist; it exists as a natural phenomenon. Moreover, it may not be easy to learn to recognize such natural populations. Field observations must be added to studies of morphological traits. The practical problems are such that most species are described, as they were a century ago, on the basis of structural features believed to be distinctive. However, if it is found that these structural characteristics put two reproductively isolated strains in the same species or split a single interbreeding group into smaller parts, the purely structural basis of species recognition is usually abandoned, to be replaced by whatever other bases are required to bring the species group into conformity with modern notions of classification.

Subspecies and Varieties

As a result of local geographical features, local populations tend to develop. These may adapt to local conditions, and eventually become recognizably different from one another. Such differences are the basis for geographical variants of the species, called *subspecies*. Differences between subspecies are impermanent. If two subspecies are allowed to interbreed, distinguishing characteristics disappear rapidly. Once a local population has lost its innate ability to interbreed freely with the larger species population, it must be recognized as a separate species.

The subspecies name is written immediately after the species name, so the whole constitutes a trinomial. *Rana esculenta* marmorata is a subspecies of frogs belonging to the species *esculenta* of the genus *Rana*. Other varieties, not based on geographically distinctive populations, may be used to designate portions of species populations. In general, zoologists are inclined to feel that even where such names are justified they should not be incorporated into the official classification.

Practical Problems

Accurate naming of experimental material and accurate identification of animals taken from a habitat often raise serious practical problems. A chemist may order his materials from a company that uses excellent methods for preparing accurately defined compounds, but a zoologist can obtain only a few kinds of animals from pure culture sources. Specimens can sometimes be sent to a specialist for accurate diagnosis, but there are too few taxonomists to provide this service routinely to all zoologists. As a result, the zoologist must, like the modern chemist who works with unusual compounds and like all the early chemists, prepare and name most of his own material.

Species have been described in many languages, and the descriptions are published in periodicals all over the world. Keeping up with the names that have been used is an impossible task for one person. Taxonomists, who work with one or a few groups of animals, are the specialists in the field, but even with the aid of specialists many mistakes have been made. Several investigators may describe the same animal under different names, unaware of each other's work. Someone may unwittingly use a name that someone else has already used for another species. Again, a new species may be described adequately to distinguish it from all other species known at the time, but later work may uncover two or three different species, all having the traits used to characterize the first. Or an investigator may miss a distinguishing trait, giving two closely related species the same name. All sorts of such practical problems grow out of a system of names involving well over a million separate items and to aid in solving them a number of customs and rules are followed. Anyone professionally interested in zoology should be familiar with them.

The Binomial

When writing scientific names, the binomial consisting of genus and species names is used. Both words are italicized, and the genus name is capitalized. *Hydra oligactis* is the correct form of the name of one of the common species of *Hydra*. No other binomial can be correct for that particular species. We may write *Hydra* to refer to the whole genus, but this would never be combined with the name of its family. If one is referring to a subspecies, the whole trinomial is italicized; the species and subspecies names cannot be used as a binomial. Italicizing helps to make a name stand out in print, and also reminds the reader that the name is being used in a strict sense. The full species name should be written out the first time (*Hydra oligactis*), but in the same discussion, it may be abbreviated in subsequent sentences (*H. oligactis*). The author, of course, must be careful not to abbreviate several genera beginning with the same letter in the same discussion. An undertermined species of a Hydra would be termed *Hydra sp.* Referring to several such undetermined species, one would write *Hydra spp.*

Author References

Where such information is valuable to the reader, the first reference to a species should include a reference to the person who first described it. *Plasmodium ovale* Stevens is the correct form for such a reference. The reason for this is that it is almost impossible to be certain that Stevens is the only person who has given the name *ovale* to a species of *Plasmodium*. A later reader, knowing of another *Plasmodium ovale*, would not be sure which species you meant. Furthermore, the name of the author who originally describes a species aids in locating the original description. Occasionally you will see the author's name in parenthesis. *Plasmodium vivax* (Grassi and Faletti) means that the species *vivax* was assigned by the original authors to some other genus than *Plasmodium*, and has later been moved.

The International Rules

At the Fifth International Zoological Congress, which met in Berlin in 1901, the International Rules for Zoological Nomen-clature were adopted to establish policies leading to stable and dependable names for organisms. Although the original rules are nearly all in effect, some modifications have been made at subsequent meetings. The International Rules, sometimes called the International Code, consist of a series of rules and recommendations of such importance that all who plan to enter into the field professionally should be familiar with them, at least in broad outline. Those who describe species should be familiar with them in detail. The major objectives of the rules are to: a) ensure that no two different species shall have the same name, b) ensure that no one species shall have more than one "right" or "valid" name, and c) ensure that the one valid name will be permanently applied to the same species.

HOMONYMS

One of the rules is that no species name shall be considered valid if some other species belonging to the same genus bears that name. If someone should accidentally give a new species a name previously used within the genus, the two identical names are homonyms. The first species given the name retains it, and the second must be given a new name. Not all homonyms arise by inadequate literature search. Sometimes two genera, originally thought to be distinct, prove to be the same. When all or parts of two genera are combined, homonyms may be created.

THE RULE OF PRIORITY

To make sure that every species will have only one valid name where several have been used, the rule of priority applies. The first adequate description of a species takes preference and the name used in this description is the valid name. All more recently given names are synonyms. It sometimes turns out that very common animals, used in dozens or even in hundreds of studies, were described long ago by an obscure student in an obscure journal. The valid name, unknown to zoologists, would cause difficult adjustments if now used, and would increase confusion rather than reduce it. Methods of suspending the rules in such cases now exist.

TYPES

It is not easy to be certain that the same population of animals will always be associated with the same name. Where a species is abundant and is collected fairly regularly, there is litte difficulty. Rare species, however, especially in little-studied groups of animals, may not be seen again for decades. Many species have never been described after they were first collected, or at least have never been mentioned in a second publication. If one collects something resembling a rare species, how can he be sure that his material is really like the original? Differences in the interpretation of words used in descriptions, and even differences in how people draw their specimens, may make for uncertainty. This is partially solved by the designation of types. When a species is first described, one or several specimens should be deposited in a museum or other safe repository, so that it will be available for comparison later. The name is thus associated with the type specimens on deposit, and permanently belongs to whatever species the types represent. Several categories of types are defined. The locality from which the species is originally collected is the type locality, and if no types for a species exist, one may redescribe the species from specimens taken in the type locality. The first species to be assigned to a genus is the type species. If the genus is later divided into parts, the type species determines which part of the genus shall retain the original generic name.

OTHER RULES

Obviously, all must agree on the kind of notice a systematist must present if his names are to be recognized officially. Names used in a letter or newspaper article would never be seen by most students and are not valid. Adequate publication may be written in any of several languages, requires the use of reasonably permanent paper, and requires that the publication be offered for general sale.

Only a few major points have been mentioned here. It is worthwhile to study the rules in detail, for they are an invaluable guide to taxonomic practices. A reference to them is given at the end of the text.

Even with the rules, it is not easy to keep names and references straight. When a name has been changed, not everyone will be aware of it, and the older name will often be used. Field workers often report specimens under invalid names because they cannot be specialists in all of the groups occurring in the habitats they study. In other cases, honest differences of opinion develop, so that for a time no one is certain of the valid name for a species. But with all its problems, the taxonomist has in his system of nomenclature a remarkably flexible tool, capable of change where needed and yet with stability as its goal. Without it, scientific work on animals would be well nigh impossible.

The Higher Systematic Categories

Everyone is familiar with the order of the groups used in classification: Kingdom, Phylum, Class, Order, Family, Genus, and Species. Except for the species group, which modern systematists are trying to describe as a definite kind of natural population, all of the categories are fairly artificial, being merely a convenient system of pigeonholes. However, they are not entirely arbitrary, for it is convenient to use the hierarchy of groups to reflect our ideas about animal relationships. From this point of view, a genus should contain a group of species so similar that they appear to be closely related. Assigning a species to a genus is really the first step in organizing our information. It is useful in cataloguing, and also in systematizing. Since the exact course of evolution is not known in detail, the genus may or may not include species that are in fact closely related. The best that can be said is that in the judgment of competent students of classification, species placed in the same genus appear to be more closely related to each other or structurally more similar than they are to members of any other genus. It is reasonable to suppose that similarities in form are subtended by similarities in genes, and that these similar genes reflect blood relationship.

Families include similar genera, presumably closely related. Many of the families that zoologists recognize are also current in common speech: for example, the cat and dog families. Characteristics used to designate families are fairly detailed, and in many cases may be seen by persons who are not specialists. Family names are easily recognized in the literature, as all end in the suffix *idae*.

Orders include families of a similar nature. They are usually based on stable, relatively generalized characteristics. Many orders correspond to common names. Beetles all belong to the order Coleoptera; flies to the order Diptera; and termites to the order Isoptera. Differences between beetles and termites are so striking that one need not be a zoologist to recognize them.

Classes are still larger groups. The various orders put into the same class are recognizably similar, generally in a few important and highly generalized traits. All insects belong to the class Insecta, characterized by three pairs of thoracic legs, the absence of abdominal append-

ages, and other generalized traits. In most cases the untrained observer has difficulty in recognizing classes, although there are exceptions. Class Gastropoda includes the snails; few people would not know most of its members, though a few gastropods are not very snail-like in appearance. On the other hand, the similarities that put corals and sea anemones in the same class are not so obvious, and must be recognized through study of anatomical detail.

Phyla are the largest of the major subdivisions. Each phylum represents a main line of evolutionary development, more or less distinct from other main lines, and distinguished by similarities so basic that only the scientist is likely to notice them. Even the common name vertebrate does not include all of the phylum to which the vertebrates belong. Each phylum is characterized by an organizational plan specifying the broad aspects of its form, the level of organization and presence or absence of body cavities, the kinds of organ systems present, and the way in which these are structurally related. Typically, the phylum contains species with a reasonably uniform type of embryological development, upon which the similarities in basic organization, to a considerable extent, depend. In the classification used here, the subkingdom Protozoa contains but one phylum, the Protozoa. Although it would be possible to elevate the various major divisions of Protozoa to phylum rank, this is not done, as all of them show similarities in basic body form of the kind that members of the same phylum usually do. Probably they should be considered as a single, major evolutionary line within the animal kingdom, even though they may have had a diversified origin.

The prefixes *sub-* and *super-* are added to names to provide more categories, and indicate lines of relationship. A superclass contains several classes more coherent and uniform as a group than the other classes in the phylum. A subclass contains a coherent group of orders, set off from the other orders of the class. In very large phyla, it is sometimes useful to introduce other categories: tribes, legions, and the like. The same basic principles apply to their use.

The system of categories is remarkably efficient. If there were ten phyla, ten classes in each phylum, ten orders in each class, and so on, there would be room for a million species, and one could trace their major relationships with a set of seven names. Actually, some phyla are small and some very large, but the fact remains that the system of names used in classification provides a powerful tool, enabling the zoologist to collate information easily and efficiently.

An Animal Classification

The classification which follows is but one of many that might be used. It represents a particular stage in the development of our ideas about animal relationships. The student will probably want to refer to it a number of times during the course of his study. The arrangement shown is a modification of the classification proposed by Hyman (1940). The new features suggested by Hyman have tended to gain general acceptance. Some newer ideas have been developed, but they remain untested, and it seems wise in a book of this type to emphasize well-established, rather than controversial, schemes of classification.

Subkingdom Protozoa. Animals which are not multicellular.
> PHYLUM 1. PROTOZOA. With the characters of the subkingdom.

Subkingdom Metazoa. Multicellular animals.

Branch A. Mesozoa. Cellular animals with the organizational plan of a stereoblastula, composed of an outer layer of somatic cells and a group of enclosed, reproductive cells.
> PHYLUM 2. MESOZOA. With the characters of the branch.

Branch B. Parazoa. Cellular animals with incipient tissues, having several kinds of interior cells. There is no mouth or digestive tract, and no organ systems are present. The body is porous, containing one to many internal cavities lined with choanocytes.
> PHYLUM 3. PORIFERA. The sponges. With the characteristics of the branch.

Branch C. Eumetazoa. Cellular animals with tissues or organ systems, having a mouth and digestive cavity, unless secondarily lost. Interior cells of several kinds. Body not porous, and without cavities lined with choanocytes.

Grade I. Radiata. Eumetazoa with radial symmetry derived from the embryonic symmetry, or showing biradial or bilateral tendencies. Tissues are present and organ systems are incipient. Mesoderm, usually derived from the ectoderm, is present as an incipient tissue, without a high degree of cellular specialization. The only body space is the digestive cavity, which has a mouth, but no anus.
> PHYLUM 4. CNIDARIA. The coelenterates or cnidarians. Symmetry is radial, or modified radial approaching bilateral. The mouth is encircled by tentacles. Nematocysts are present and ctenes absent.
> PHYLUM 5. CTENOPHORA. The comb jellies. Symmetry is biradial. Tentacles, if present, do not encircle the mouth. Without nematocysts and with eight radially arranged rows of ctenes.

Grade II. Bilateria. Bilaterally symmetrical Eumetazoa, or those with embryonic bilateral symmetry later modified into radial symmetry. Organ systems are present, and the mesoderm is well developed, usually derived from the endoderm.

Division A. *Protostomia.* Bilateria in which the mouth arises from the blastopore or from the anterior margin of the blastopore.

Subdivision 1. *Acoelomates.* With the space between the epidermis and digestive tube occupied by a cellular parenchyma.

Superphylum Acoelomata. Bilateria without a coelom, with mesenchyme between the body wall and digestive tract; with an excretory system of protonephridia with flame bulbs; with body unsegmented or consisting of a strobila, with the youngest segments toward the head.

PHYLUM 6. PLATYHELMINTHES. The flatworms. Acoelomates without an anal opening; without a circulatory system.

PHYLUM 7. NEMERTINA. The nemertines. Acoelomates with an anus; with a proboscis in a hollow sheath above the digestive cavity; with a circulatory system.

Subdivision 2. *Pseudocoelomates.* With a space between the body wall and digestive tube, not lined with peritoneum and derived by dispersion of the mesenchyme.

PHYLUM 8. ACANTHOCEPHALA. Parasitic worms equipped with a spiny, protrusible proboscis, and lacking a digestive tract.

PHYLUM 9. ENTOPROCTA. Pseudocoelomates with a U-shaped digestive tube and mouth and anus close together, lying within a region surrounded by ciliated tentacles.

Superphylum Aschelminthes. A complex of pseudocoelomates, sometimes included in a single phylum and showing some evidences of relationship. All have an anterior mouth, posterior anus, and straight digestive tube.

PHYLUM 10. ROTIFERA. Microscopic aschelminths with a ciliated corona at the anterior end and a pharynx with internal jaws known as trophi; with a protonephridial system with terminal flame bulbs.

PHYLUM 11. GASTROTRICHA. Microscopic aschelminths without a corona but with regions of external cilia; with an unsegmented cuticle, usually equipped with spines, plates, or scales; with adhesive tubes; with a tubular pharynx lacking trophi.

PHYLUM 12. KINORHYNCHA. More or less spiny, marine aschelminths without superficial cilia and with body superficially segmented into 13 or 14 segments; with the anterior end an introvert, with a spiny covering; with a protonephridial system.

PHYLUM 13. PRIAPULIDA. Marine aschelminths with an anterior proboscis; with urogenital pores separate from the digestive tube in both sexes; with protonephridia terminating in solenocytes, joining the gonoducts.

PHYLUM 14. NEMATODA. Aschelminths without cilia and with the epidermis divided into four or more chords; with only longitudinal muscles in the body wall; with a long, muscular pharynx having a triradiate lumen; with an excretory system not composed of protonephridia; with the body covered by a continuous cuticle.

PHYLUM 15. NEMATOMORPHA. Horse-hair worms. Long, slender, cylindrical worms with dorsal and ventral epidermal chords; with gonoducts joining the intestine; with parasitic larval stages and free-living adults.

Subdivision 3. Coelomates. With a body cavity, the coelom, lined with peritoneum and appearing as a space in the mesoderm.

Superphylum Tentaculata. The lophophorates. With a circular, crescentic, or double spirally coiled ridge bearing ciliated tentacles and known as a lophophore; with mouth and anus near together, the intestine forming a loop; showing some deuterostome traits with protostome traits.

PHYLUM 16. PHORONIDA. Solitary, worm-like animals with a closed circulatory system; with one pair of metanephridia.

PHYLUM 17. ECTOPROCTA. The bryozoa or moss animals. Colonial animals with a lophophore, with the body encased in a gelatinous, chitinous, or calcareous covering; with the anus outside of the lophophore region.

PHYLUM 18. BRACHIOPODA. The brachiopods or lamp shells. Solitary animals with a lophophore, with the body enclosed in a bivalve shell secreted by a mantle; with one or two pairs of metanephridia.

Superphylum Inarticulata. Unsegmented, coelomate protostomes.

PHYLUM 19. SIPUNCULOIDEA. Naked, worm-like animals with a spacious coelom and without a mantle, without evidences of segmentation during development; with an eversible proboscis and a dorsal anus.

PHYLUM 20. MOLLUSCA. Protostome coelomates with a body fold, the mantle, covering the main mass of the body and secreting a shell; shell sometimes vestigial and sometimes in several pieces; with a coelom during development, reduced by encroachment of the haemocoel; without evidences of segmentation during development. One class shows evidences of segmentation in metameric arrangement of organs.

Superphylum Articulata. Segmented coelomate protostomes, characterized by segmentation of embryonic stages, even though the adult may have secondarily lost its metameric organization.

PHYLUM 21. ECHIUROIDEA. Naked, worm-like animals with a spacious coelom, lacking segmentation in adults but passing through segmented stages during development; with a ventral mouth and no eversible proboscis.

PHYLUM 22. ANNELIDA. The segmented round-worms. Worm-like animals with the body divided into a series of essentially similar metameres; with a spacious coelom, reduced in leeches, and typically divided into metameric compartments.

PHYLUM 23. TARDIGRADA. Water bears. Minute, segmented animals of uncertain affinities, showing many traits that are arthropod-like; with body segmented and equipped with four pairs of unsegmented legs terminating in claws shed with each molt; with a transitory coelom, possibly enterocoelous, replaced by a haemocoel; without appendages associated with the mouth.

PHYLUM 24. ONYCHOPHORA. Worm-like animals, with thin, unsegmented cuticle and pairs of unsegmented legs; heads with three pairs of appendages, two of which are associated with the mouth; with a tracheal system for respiration.

PHYLUM 25. PENTASTOMIDA. Worm-like, parasitic animals with arthropod-like traits, of uncertain affinities; with a cuticle shed during molting; with two pairs of claws or short appendages at the sides of the mouth; without a respiratory system.

PHYLUM 26. ARTHROPODA. Animals with jointed appendages, usually terminating in claws, pads, or spines; usually with the coelom greatly reduced and replaced by a haemocoel; with a segmented cuticle and segmented appendages; cuticle shed in molts.

Division B. Deuterostomia. Bilateria in which the mouth does not arise from the blastopore or near its anterior margin; with a coelom arising from the primitive gut.

PHYLUM 27. ECHINODERMATA. The echinoderms. Deuterostomes with secondary radial symmetry and a water vascular system.

PHYLUM 28. CHAETOGNATHA. Arrow-worms. Permanently bilateral deuterostomes, without an endoskeleton or gill slits, and with a digestive tube.

PHYLUM 29. POGONOPHORA. Permanently bilateral deuterostomes, without an endoskeleton or gill slits, and without a digestive tube.

PHYLUM 30. HEMICHORDATA. Permanently bilateral deuterostomes with gill slits, an endoskeleton, or both; and with an embryo lacking a typical notochord.

PHYLUM 31. CHORDATA. Permanently bilateral deuterostomes, with adults having gill slits, a vertebral column, or both, and with an embryo having a typical notochord.

References

Crombie, A. C. 1947. Interspecific competition. *J. An. Ecol.* 16: 44.

Dobzhansky, T. 1951. *Genetics and the Origin of Species.* Columbia Univ. Press, New York. (The classic statement of the genetic species concept.)

Elton, C. 1930. *Animal Ecology and Evolution.* Clarendon Press, Oxford.

Fisher, R. A. 1930. *The Genetical Theory of Natural Selection.* Clarendon Press, Oxford.

Hadzi, J. 1953. An attempt to reconstruct the system of animal classification. *System. Zool.* 2: 145.

Huxley, J., ed. 1940. *The New Systematics.* Clarendon Press, Oxford. (A symposium on problems of systematics.)

Kerkut, G. A. 1960. *Implications of Evolution.* Pergamon, London.

Mayr, E. 1942. *Systematics and the Origin of Species.* Columbia Univ. Press, New York.

———, E. G. Linsley, and R. L. Usinger. 1953. *Methods and Principles of Systematic Zoology.* McGraw-Hill, New York. (Includes a printing of the International Code.)

Meglitsch, P. 1954. On the nature of the species. *Syst. Zool.* 3: 49.

Preston, F. W. 1948. The commonness, and rarity, of species. *Ecol.* 29: 254.

Thorpe, W. H. The evolutionary significance of habitat selection. *J. An. Ecol.* 14: 67.

Wilson, E. O., and W. L. Brown, Jr. 1953. The subspecies concept and its taxonomic application. *Syst. Zool.* 2: 97.

3
Protozoa: Acellular Animals

Nearly three hundred years ago a protozoan was observed for the first time by Leeuwenhoek. In the years that followed, he wrote many enthusiastic letters describing the diminutive creatures he found in a drop of water. Since then, hundreds of zoologists, no less captivated, have concentrated on studies of protozoan form and behavior.

Anyone who has watched an amoeba move, feed, and reproduce can understand the suitability of the classical definition of Protozoa as "single-celled animals." An amoeba is certainly the structural equivalent of a cell, consisting of a single, undivided mass of protoplasm, covered by a plasmalemma, and containing a single nucleus as a genetic center. Also, an amoeba is evidently a tiny animal, carrying out all of the characteristic animal processes. Despite the fact that not all Protozoa are clearly animal, or single, or cells, the classical definition is retained because it emphasizes the most important characteristics of Protozoa in general.

Ordinarily we think of a cell as an undivided protoplasmic mass containing a single nucleus and surrounded by a plasmalemma. A *Paramecium* is a cell, except that it has a macronucleus and one or more

micronuclei. An *Arcella* contains two similar nuclei. Before segmentation, a malarial parasite has up to two dozen nuclei, and a large myxosporidian cyst may contain thousands of nuclei. Somewhere between the many uninucleate Protozoa and the large multinucleate forms, the resemblance to cells ends, but they remain cell-like in their continuous protoplasmic mass. In 1929, Dobell, an English protozoologist, pointed out that it is more accurate to think of Protozoa as very small organisms, not divided into cells. Today most prefer to think of them as acellular. It is unimportant whether we call them one-celled or acellular as long as we do not interpret "one-celled" naïvely, nor overlook the importance of Protozoa and algae in the development of cell stucture. Mitochondria, microsomes, Golgi material, endoplasmic reticulum, nucleus, and centrosomes are cellular components which appeared in organisms at the protozoan grade of organization.

Are Protozoa animals? A *Euglena* contains chlorophyll and carries on photosynthesis, but has many protozoan characteristics. Both botanists and zoologists claim *Euglena* and provide a place for it in their kingdoms. This is nonsensical, and many prefer to make Protozoa a part of a third kingdom, neither plant nor animal, called Protista. This method has the advantage of providing a single place for *Euglena* and others like it, but divides from the rest of the animal kingdom the obviously animal-like ciliates. Jahn (1949) has suggested that we recognize six kingdoms, in order to emphasize the great diversity in organizational plan among the simplest organisms. It is unimportant whether we call Protozoa animals or protists if we comprehend what is implied. Protozoa are not simply animals; they are the part of the animal kingdom which quite literally merges with the plant kingdom.

It is not uncommon for animals to develop social habits. Where Protozoa have become social organisms, another difficulty in precisely defining the phylum arises. Adaptation to social life tends to result in the formation of definite, structured social organizations. Division of labor and specialization within the social organization culminates in structurally and functionally differentiated animals, as is seen in social insects, where queens, drones, and one or more castes of workers are found. Each type has characteristic structural features, related to the special part it plays in the life of the whole society. A number of Protozoa form colonies consisting of a few to several thousand members. Differentiated vegetative and reproductive members are found in the more highly organized colonies. Through such adaptational lines, Protozoa approach the multicellular organization of Metazoa and Metaphyta, and the large, highly integrated colonies look and behave very much as though they were multicellular organisms. A line must be drawn, and an arbitrary one has been selected. A *Volvox* colony with several thousand members is a protozoan because it has only one kind of non-reproducing member, while a mesozoan with far fewer cells is a metazoan because there are

several kinds of cells which do not enter into the reproductive process. The large colonial Protozoa most clearly fit the designation "single-celled," for many believe that multicellular animals developed from such colonial forms and that the individual protozoan is the direct ancestor of cells.

On the whole, it is difficult to improve on Jahn's brief characterization of Protozoa (1949): "Protozoa are acellular, complex organisms of the Kingdom Protista. They are usually microscopic, and show similarities in most cases to the basic structure of a single cell, but also have many collective and individual morphological and physiological characteristics of their own which are not found generally in cells of Metazoa and Metaphyta. During the course of their ontogenetic development, which may be complex, they do not pass through a two-layered gastrula stage, and do not develop tissues specialized for carrying on part of the life processes of the organism."

Despite its simplicity, protozoan organization has proved extremely successful, adapting to permit invasion of many different habitats. Protozoa occur in soil, in all kinds of fresh-water and marine habitats, and in all climatic regions, wherever temperatures rise above the freezing point. They contribute to all trophic levels of the communities they inhabit. Some are photosynthetic producers, adding organic compounds to the local economy. Some absorb food through the body surface, contributing to the reduction of plant and animal remains. Some feed on microscopic producers or decomposers, acting as primary consumers and aiding in the prevention of overgrowth by these populations. Others feed on primary consumers, or fit higher into the food chain. The exploitation of the adaptive potentialities of a successful organizational plan fits organisms to differing habitats and patterns of living. Adaptive radiation is a characteristic evolutionary phenomenon. It is of great importance, as it reduces competition between originally very similar organisms. As organisms retire from intense competition, the abundance as well as the diversity of life increases.

The analysis of the results of adaptive radiation and some of the factors involved in it will make explicit some of the important concerns of other animal groups, as well. It is necessary to understand the nature of protozoan diversity, and how it is reflected in classification. One needs to observe how different kinds of organisms use different kinds of equipment to perform similar processes, and the extent to which convergence results. One needs to comprehend something of the evolution of function within the group as a whole as well as in particular subgroups, and how this line of adaptation is suitable for protozoan organizational levels. One needs, finally, to become aware of the persistent problems, and where they are now stabilized, awaiting new ideas and new techniques. To the extent that these objectives are achieved, one learns to recognize that more work in a particular area would be very useful at the present; that some group of organisms might be excellent material for a specific kind of experimental analysis; that some new technique would contribute materially to the solution of a specific problem at the present. For these reasons and for others, a knowledge of invertebrate zoology is essential for the scientist who expects to deal with animal material, whether his interests are morphological or physiological, and descriptive or comparative.

Fundamentals of Form and Function

The best approach to the Protozoa is to get a basic knowledge of how they are built and how they work, and enough vocabulary to understand the fundamentals of classification. Subsequently one can examine functional and morphological problems in greater detail, and perhaps gain an understanding of their phylogenetic relationships.

FOOD RELATIONSHIPS

Protozoa use three major methods of obtaining food. Some Protozoa are autotrophic, synthesizing organic compounds from inorganic substances obtained from the environment. Others are heterotrophic, requiring organic food from the environment in order to nourish themselves. Heterotropic organisms may be saprobic, absorbing what is needed through the body surface, or holozoic, eating solid food.

The most effective protozoan autotrophs are green flagellates, which carry on photosynthesis. They are abundant only where sufficient light, carbon dioxide, and mineral salts or other sources of nitrogen and phosphorus occur. All contain chlorophyll in a characteristic organelle, the chromoplast. A chromoplast is a chloroplast if only chlorophyll is present, but in most photosynthetic protozoans accessory yellow, reddish, or brown pigments are also found. They are not constantly illuminated, and photosynthetic organisms produce more carbohydrates during daylight hours than is needed, storing reserve food for use during the dark hours. A viscous mass of protein, the pyrenoid, serves as a center for transforming sugars into starch. Pyrenoids are found in or near the chromoplasts, often enclosed in a starchy envelope. They are self-reproducing, dividing when the chromoplast divides, in some species synchronously with the nucleus (Fig. 3.1B). Not all photosynthetic Protozoa store their excess food as starch. Leucosin and paramylon are two carbohydrate storage products which do not give a starch test. Some groups store foods as oils or fatty compounds. Each group of autotrophs is characterized by the nature of its reserve products.

Saprobic Protozoa are colorless forms which can live without ingesting solid food. No special organelles are required for saprobic life, but the absence of a mouth and chromoplasts cannot be taken as evidence of a saprobic habit. Many free-living and parasitic Protozoa ingest food by pseudopodial action, and saprobic organisms may have a mouth and gullet. Nevertheless, the simplest body organization occurs among some of the forms nourished by food absorption at the body surface.

Holozoic Protozoa require mechanisms for food capture, digestion, and egestion. Methods of food capture and ingestion are extremely variable and are discussed in sub-sequent sections. The characteristic organelle is the food vacuole, an intracellular digestive cavity surrounded by a vacuolar membrane derived from the plasmalemma (Fig. 3.1C). Recent studies indicate that the classical view of the vacuolar membrane and its activity may be somewhat erroneous. Roth (1960) found that the vacuolar membrane of *Pelomyxa* changes in appearance during the functional cycle of the vacuole. Immediately after ingestion of a particle, the vacuolar membrane becomes

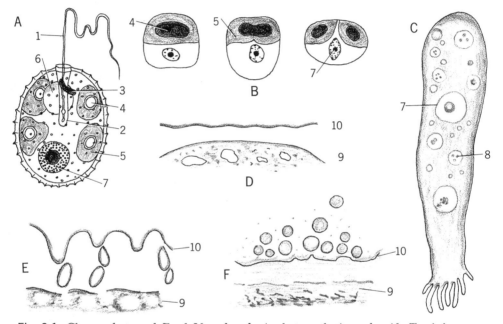

Fig. 3.1. Chromoplasts and Food Vacuoles. **A.** A photosynthetic euglenoid, *Trachelomonas hispida*, showing the structures typical of holophytic flagellates. **B.** Division of the pyrenoid and chromatoplast of the terminal zooids of *Hydrurus foetidus*, a colonial chrysomonad. **C.** A holozoic, marine amoeba, *Trichamoeba pallida*. It has food vacuoles, typical of holozoic Protozoa, and a posterior, tail-like uroid; like most marine Protozoa, it has no contractile vacuole. **D-F.** Diagrams of the vacuolar membrane of an amoeba, *Pelomyxa*, at three stages of digestion and absorption, as seen in electron micrographs. Soon after food is ingested, while it is still unchanged, the vacuolar membrane is simple (**D**). Projections of the membrane extend inward during active digestion (**E**) and vesicles appear to enter the vacuole. During active absorption, homogeneous material appears near the membrane (**F**), and extensions of the membrane containing this material extend into the cytoplasm. Pinocytic vesicles containing the material appear to enter the cytoplasm. (**A**, after Doflein; **B**, after Geitler, from Kudo. **C**, after Schaeffer. **D-F**, based on electron micrographs in Roth.) 1, flagellum; 2, reservoir; 3, stigma; 4, pyrenoid; 5, chromoplast; 6, contractile vacuole; 7, nucleus; 8, food vacuole; 9, food mass; 10, vacuolar membrane.

smoother than the plasmalemma. At first the vacuole swells, presumably as materials are secreted into it, and the vacular membrane develops many finger-like microvilli which project into the cavity (Fig. 3.1 D–F). The vacuolar fluid becomes acid at this time and then shifts gradually to an alkaline reaction. During this period of digestion, the membrane takes on an entirely different appearance. A layer of material resembling the homogeneous, and presumably digested, substance on the inner surface of the membrane appears in the cytoplasm immediately around the vacuole, and the vacuolar membrane forms small vesicles on its outer surface, which break away and move off into the cytoplasm. The vesicle formation resembles pinocytosis at the plasmalemma, and may not only hasten the absorption of materials by increasing surface, but may also provide a mechanism permitting the entrance into the cytoplasm of materials that cannot diffuse through the membrane. The exhausted food vacuole makes contact with the plasmalemma, and food residues are discharged. Where a pellicle or heavy cellulose cell wall is present, an interruption of the surface sheathing is needed to permit elimination.

Only free-living Protozoa have been mentioned. Many live in or on the bodies of plants or animals. Epizoic forms inhabit the body surface of other organisms and are usually independent of the host for food. Endozoic Protozoa live within the host body and derive nourishment from the host. They may be coelozoic, living in hollow organs; histozoic, living in tissues; or cytozoic, living in host cells. Endozoic species may ingest cells or other solid foods, living as holozoic forms, or may absorb what they need through the body surface like saprobic organisms. Some appear to cause the host no hardship and so are commensals; others cause mild to severe disturbance and are parasitic in the strict sense. A few have developed a relationship with their host resulting in mutual benefit,

referred to as mutualism or symbiosis. In recent years the term symbiosis has tended to evolve into a term designating any close relationship between two organisms, and mutualism replaces it as a term indicating mutual benefit. Many small photosynthetic flagellates live within other Protozoa or Metazoa. The extent of their contribution to the host is not known in many cases. Actually, any of the relationships between producers and consumers may serve as the basis for mutual benefit. The photosynthetic form may obtain carbon dioxide or nitrogenous wastes from its heterotrophic host, benefiting both. Or it may aid the host by liberating oxygen or providing organic food. A special mutualistic relationship exists between certain flagellates which can digest wood, and wood-eating roaches and termites. Without their protozoan inhabitants the insects starve, even when provided adequate food. The Protozoa are protected by their insect host and provided with a supply of masticated wood.

RESPIRATION

The small size of Protozoa makes the respiratory problem one of no great moment. Respiratory exchange occurs at the body surface, no doubt facilitated by currents created by cilia and flagella.

EXCRETION AND OSMOREGULATION

The disposal of excretory wastes occurs at the body surface. On the basis of our present information, Protozoa appear to be ammonotelic; that is, they excrete most of their nitrogen as ammonia.

In many organisms, excretion and osmoregulation are closely related, and it is probable that some excreted material leaves with fluid discharged by the contractile vacuole. However, the primary function of the contractile vacuole system is to expel water taken in from a hypotonic environment. Contractile vacuoles are usually missing in animals living in marine or parasitic environments, but are well developed in Protozoa from fresh-water habitats. The contractile vacuole system may be simple or quite complex. In simple contractile vacuoles, two or more small accessory vacuoles unite or empty into a larger vacuole, which discharges after full diastole has occurred. In ciliates, a system of canals discharges into the contractile vacuole (Fig. 3.2A–D). In full diastole these canals are inconspicuous. As the main vacuole discharges, the outer regions of the canals dilate with incoming fluid; these

are the ampullae. The ampullar contents are injected into the forming contractile vacuole through injection canals during middle diastole. Many observers have described osmiophilic materials around the radiating canal system, and some have thought they might represent Golgi material. In electron microscopy, electron-dense granules which are not Golgi-like are sometimes seen, but Schneider has recently described many small tubules, apparently associated with the endoplasmic reticulum, which surround the ampullae and may be the sometimes reticulate osmiophilic material described in some ciliates (Fig. 3.2E).

INTERNAL TRANSPORT

Even the largest Protozoa find internal transport no problem. Cytoplasmic streaming distributes materials throughout the continuous protoplasmic mass of the organism. This cyclosis follows no set pattern in most Protozoa, but in ciliates tends to become established as a definite cyclical movement of the endoplasm. The mechanics of cyclosis have not yet been satisfactorily explained.

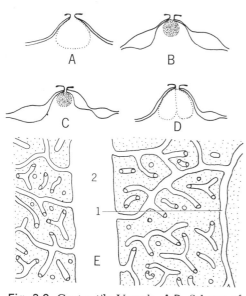

Fig. 3.2. Contractile Vacuole. A-D. Scheme of successive stages of the *Paramecium* contractile vacuole cycle, seen from the side. As systole begins (A) the radial canals are empty and the vacuole full. As systole ends (B) the radial canals are filling. During diastole (C-D), water enters the injection canals and is forced as vesicles into the vacuolar region. A contractile vacuole forms as the vesicles merge. E. Scheme of a small region of a radial canal of *Paramecium*, from electron micrographs, showing the many microtubules arising from the endoplasmic reticulum (1) and emptying into the radial canal (2). (A-D, modified from King. E after Schneider.)

Mechanisms of Response

The typical animal moves restlessly in a search for food, for mates, for shelter, and for living room. If its movements are to yield the greatest probability of survival, they must be suitably related to environmental factors. Responses involve a receptor system, the sense organs of higher animals; a conducting system, the nervous system of higher animals; and an effector system, the parts which lead to movement, secretion, or other responses.

RECEPTION OF STIMULI

Protozoa are sensitive to many kinds of stimuli, including touch, temperature changes, light, and many chemicals. How stimuli are received is not clear. Amoebae, with no visible organelles, are constantly changing and have no fixed reference points. Their response indicates that the general protoplasmic mass can receive stimuli as well as conduct them. Cilia and flagella appear to be highly sensitive, especially to touch. Many ciliates have motionless bristles which appear to act as receptors. In *Euplotes*, the dorsal bristles are surrounded by delicate fibrils that may be used in sensory conduction.

The only special sensory organelle is the stigma or eye-spot. The stigma is a reddish body, commonly found in photosynthetic flagellates and usually located near the flagellar root system (Fig. 3.1A). The fine structure of the stigma resembles that of a chromoplast, but with eye-spot chambers adjacent to the flagellum (Fig. 3.3). The stigma is often cupped, shading the light-sensitive material from one side, and in a few dinoflagellates has developed into an ocellus with a starchy lens (Fig. 3.11C). Shading and lens development add a direction sense to a general sensitivity to light levels.

LOCOMOTOR ORGANELLES AND CO-ORDINATION

Three major types of locomotor organelles occur among Protozoa. A considerable part of classification depends on the kinds and distribution of these locomotor parts. Pseudopodia are characteristic of Sarcodina, although they occur in flagellates as well. They are semipermanent to transitory extensions of protoplasm from the body surface. Flagella are permanent or semi-permanent locomotor organelles characteristic of the Mastigophora, although they occur in Sporozoa and Sarcodina as parts of swarmers or microgametes. They usually persist throughout the adult life of flagellates, although some species resorb the flagellum and become temporarily inca-

pable of movement. Flagella are usually larger than cilia, and occur singly or in small numbers. Cilia and flagella differ especially in the nature of their root systems and associated parts. Cilia, found only in the ciliates, are built like flagella but have a complex system of kinetosomes and fibers composing a characteristic infraciliature. They typically occur in rows on the body surface, or as parts of compound organelles formed by the union of many cilia.

Pseudopodia. Five kinds of pseudopodia can be distinguished among Sarcodina. In some cases the amoeba flows along without forming definite extensions of the body.

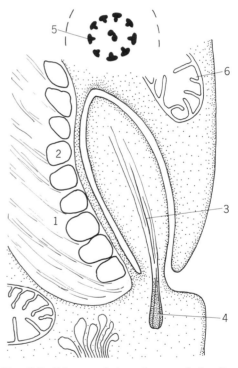

Fig. 3.3. Scheme of the stigma and flagellar base of *Chromulina*, a chrysomonad (after Fauré-Fremiet). 1, chromoplast; 2, eyespot chamber; 3, fibrillar core of flagellum; 4, kinetosome; 5, diagram of the arrangement of fibrils in the flagellum, as seen in cross section; 6, mitochondrium.

Such amoebae are said to be limax forms, because of their slug-like shape (Fig. 3.4B). The broad, advancing margins at the tip of the body are protoplasmic waves. Most of the large amoebae and many smaller ones move by lobopodia, which are finger-shaped, round-tipped pseudopodia ordinarily containing both ectoplasm and endoplasm (Fig. 3.4A). Filopodia are slender, ectoplasmic pseudopodia, pointed at the tips, and sometimes branching. They never anastomose to form networks (Fig.

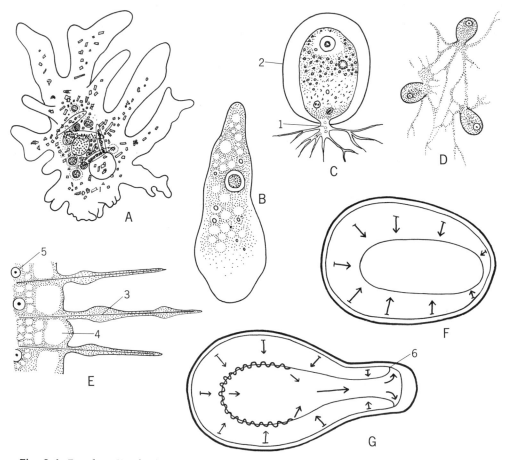

Fig. 3.4. Pseudopodia. A. *Amoeba dubia*, with lobopodia. B. *Vahlkampfia limax*, moving by protoplasmic waves. C. *Chlamydophorus stercorea*, a testacean moving by filopodia that extend through the pylome (1), an opening in the test (2). D. *Microgromia socialis*, a testacean with rhizopodia that anastomose to form a reticulum used in food capture. E. Axopodia in a small part of the surface of *Actinosphaerium eichhorni*, showing the axial filaments (3) of the pseudopodia, a contractile vacuole (4), and several of many nuclei (5). F-G. Two diagrams showing pseudopodial formation. The arrows with square tails show the pressure of the plasmagel on the plasmasol, and the straight arrows the flow of protoplasm. The wavy line in G indicates the site of conversion of plasmagel to plasmasol. In the region of reverse conversion (6) macromolecular folding reduces protoplasmic volume, facilitating its flow forward. (A, after Schaeffer. B, after Kudo. C, after Wenyon. D, after Cash, from Kudo. E-G, after Jahn.)

3.4C). Rhizopodia are much like filopodia, but branch extensively and fuse together to form meshworks which act as food traps; in some cases the rhizopodia of several organisms unite to form a multicellular reticulum (Fig. 3.4D). Axopodia are also slender and composed of ectoplasm. They contain a slender axial filament (Fig. 3.4E), composed of many fibers laid parallel to each other when seen in the electron microscope. Anderson and Beams find the fibrils reminiscent of contractile fibrils, and suggest that the axial filament may cause axopodial movement. It was once believed that the axial filaments of axopodia might be derived from the axial filaments of flagella, and so indicate close relationship to flagellates. Fine structural details do not support this point of view; the axopodial filament does not terminate in a kinetosome-like structure nor resemble the derivatives of flagella in structure.

Although amoeboid movement has been studied over a long period of time, it has not yet been satisfactorily explained. There can be no doubt that pseudopodia are produced in different ways in different organisms, and that the mechanics of lobopodia differ from the mechanics of filopodia. Lobopodial movements are complex, involving several activities: a) change of plasmagel into plasmasol at the "posterior" end, and of plasmasol to plasmagel at the "anterior" end; b) contraction of the gelated protoplasm; and c) streaming of the plasmasol.

A delicate membrane covers the surface of an amoeba. Beneath it is a clear zone of ectoplasm, differentiated from the inner, more granular endoplasm. The ectoplasm and the outermost part of the endoplasm is in the gel state, and makes up the plasmagel. The more fluid, inner endoplasm is the plasmasol.

The plasmagel exercises a constant, slight pressure on the plasmasol, and can contract to increase this pressure. If for any reason the restraining influence of the plasmagel is locally insufficient, the plasmasol erupts, flowing into an extending pseudopodium (Fig. 3.4F, G). As the plasmasol reaches the advancing tip, it spreads, fountain-like, turning backward to be converted into plasmagel and extend the plasmagel tube of the pseudopod. If plasmagel forms too rapidly at the tip, a continuous retaining layer forms and stops further movement. If this does not happen and if new plasmasol is continuously formed at the "posterior" end of the organism, movement can continue indefinitely. The change of plasmasol to plasmagel involves a loss of volume, so that the protoplasm may stream forward to occupy the space made available in this way.

This explanation leaves many important questions unanswered. The initial direction of movement depends on the presence of a weak area in the plasmagel. What causes this weak point, and how does it happen to form on the surface opposite the point where an amoeba is touched? How does the presence of food organisms evoke pseudopodial formation? We lack sufficient evidence to offer adequate answers to these questions. Recent movies recording endoplasmic streaming do not substantiate the idea that the whole endoplasmic interior is in the plasmasol state during movement. Evidently there is need for further study.

Flagella. Flagella are delicate, whip-like structures, which beat to propel flagellates through the water. Their finer details can be seen only with the electron microscope. It is interesting to find that the detailed structure of flagella is approximately the same, no matter what kind of cell or organism they are attached to. The outer covering is continuous with the plasmalemma of the body surface, and contains a matrix in which a ring of nine filaments surround two central filaments (Fig. 3.5A). The 11 fibrils are enclosed in an inner sheath. The two central fibers confer bilaterality, and the plane of flagellar beat is associated with the orientation of the central filaments. The whorl of nine outer and two inner fibrils is seen in cilia, also, and in other parts of cells derived from or growing like cilia and flagella.

The flagellum is a versatile tool, able to make a variety of movements. Movements may be rapid or slow, and forward, backward, or lateral. The effective stroke brings the rigid, slightly cupped flagellum downward. The recovery stroke consists of a wave passing along the flagellum to position it for a second effective stroke (Fig. 3.5B–D). Undulating movements can be used to produce forward or backward movement, as well as movement to the side. It is not clear how controls for such varied movements are associated with the rather simple basal structure.

Flagellar movements cease if the flagellum is detached from the flagellar root system. Flagellar roots are extremely diverse and much more work is needed to establish homologies. This is clearly indicated in the very simple flagellar substructure of trypanosomes, where a small, dark-staining body occurs at the base of the flagellum, and a larger, DNA-containing body lies near it. The small body has been called a basal body, kinetosome, and blepharoplast; the large body has been termed a parabasal body and a blepharoplast as

well as a kinetoplast. For the sake of simplicity, the term kinetosome will be applied to the body resembling the ciliate kinetosome and containing extensions of the flagellar fibrils.

The axoneme of the flagellum terminates in the kinetosome; the two central fibers sometimes terminate in a small electron-dense body, termed by some a basal body, and sometimes continue into the cytoplasm. In some forms a plate of electron-dense material separates the axoneme and kinetosome. The kinetoplast of the trypanosomes lies nearby. When the organism divides, the kinetosome divides first, then the kinetoplast, and later the nucleus. A plate-like structure lies nearby; it resembles Golgi material and the parabasal body of other flagellates but is not attached to the kinetosome or kinetoplast. However, according to Meyer and Quieroga (1960), it migrates with them when the trypanosome changes its structure to assume a *Leishmania* form. The importance of the flagellar substructure in initiating division is widespread, indicating its relationship to the centriole.

Chilomonas has a more complex flagellar root system (Fig. 3.8H). A parabasal body,

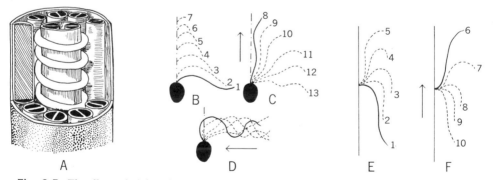

Fig. 3.5. Flagella and Cilia. A. Diagram of a flagellum, showing the inner structure from electron micrographs. The two central and nine peripheral fibers are characteristic. B-D. Flagellar movements of *Monas*, a protomonad. B, preparatory stroke; C, effective stroke; D, lateral movement. E-F. Ciliary action. E, preparatory stroke; F, effective stroke. The arrows in B-F show direction of movement and the numbers show successive positions of the cilium or flagellum. (A, after Manton and Clarke, from Berrill. B-D, after Krijgsman. E-F, after Verworn, from Kudo.)

which has a lamellate form and resembles the Golgi material, is associated with it. The function of parabasal bodies remains unknown. A slender, striated fiber passes back from the flagellar roots, often touching the nucleus. Seen in electron micrographs, it is built like a ciliary root, which is not thought to be conductive. Many flagella have such threads connecting various elements of the flagellar root system; these are thought to contribute to flagellar control. All have been called rhizoplasts and it remains to be seen how many kinds of threads are present.

Some of the most complex flagellar root systems are found in endozoic Protozoa. In *Trichomonas* (Fig. 3.6A), three flagella extend forward and one trailing flagellum is attached to the body by a delicate undulating membrane. The body is supported by an axostyle, often closely associated with the flagellar roots or nucleus. Details of a somewhat similar root system are shown in Fig. 3.6B. The centriole stands at the heart of the whole root system, connected by rhizoplasts to all of the associated structures.

In termite flagellates, both centriolar and flagellar root systems become extremely complex. According to Kirby, the structure

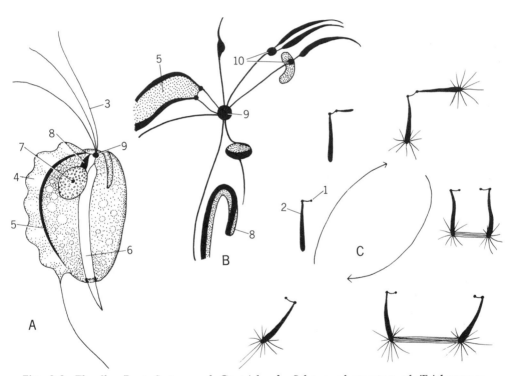

Fig. 3.6. Flagellar Root System and Centriole. A. Scheme of structure of *Trichomonas*, showing relation of body parts. B. The centriole and flagellar root system of *Macrotrichomonas hirsuta*. C. Changes in form of *Trichonympha* centriole through a division cycle. Between divisions the centriolar apparatus consists of a long centriole to which a short centriole is attached. As division begins, the short centriole grows, coming to match the long centriole as astral rays develop. The two centrioles separate as the spindle forms; each develops a new short centriole that is retained after division. (A, after Grell. B, after Grassé. C, after Cleveland.) **1,** short centriole; **2,** long centriole; **3,** flagellum; **4,** undulating membrane; **5,** costa; **6,** axostyle; **7,** nucleus; **8,** parabasal body; **9,** centriole; **10,** kinetosome.

of *Devescovina* is very complex, and includes a prominent costa, lying at the base of the undulating membrane and also connected to the root system by a rhizoplast. The centriolar apparatus becomes elongated and otherwise modified in many termite flagellates. Cleveland has done much to describe its structure and activities. In *Trichonympha*, for example, a long and short centriole are attached together. At the onset of division, the short centriole elongates, and both develop astral rays (Fig. 3.6C). As they separate above,

a spindle develops below. The two old centrioles, now both long, each form a new short centriole during the last parts of division.

Flagella form rows, superficially like rows of cilia. These have a substructure consisting of associated kinetosomes, which form a spiral band around the body. When the organism is ready to divide, it untwists so the bands become longitudinal. Gametes are formed, which unite, and subsequently the zygote undergoes torsion to produce the normal, spiral bands of the adult.

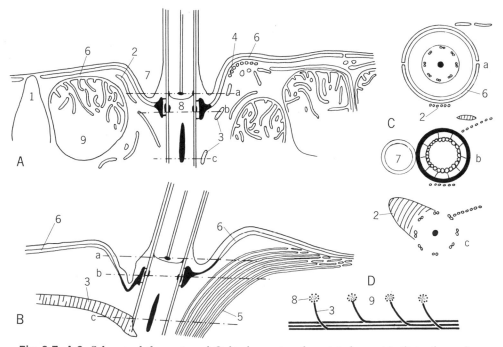

Fig. 3.7. A-C. Scheme of the cortex of *Colpoda campanula*, a tetrahymenid ciliate, from electron micrographs. **A**, transverse section with the left side of the body at the left. **B**, longitudinal section, with the anterior end at the left. **C**, cross sections of the cilium, with the left side at the bottom, at levels marked **a**, **b**, and **c** in preceding figures. **D**. Diagram of the kinetosome and kinetodesmose system, with the right side of the body above. Only the kinetosome and kinetodesmose system is shown at **D**. A thread from each cilium passes to the kinetodesmose. This basal apparatus constitutes a kinety, extending the length of a ciliary row. A-C show the relationship of the cilia and kinetosome to other cortical structures. A parasomal sac lies in front of each cilium. Flattened sacs (ciliary corpuscles) curve down from the surface to connect with the kinetosomes. Longitudinal and transverse fibers form a network, distinct from the kinetodesmose systems, associated with the ciliary base. (A-C, after Pitelka. D, after Metz, from Grimstone.) **1**, protrichocyst; **2**, transverse fibril; **3**, kinetodesmal fiber; **4**, longitudinal band; **5**, postciliary fibrils connecting with the longitudinal fibers; **6**, ciliary corpuscle; **7**, parasomal sac; **8**, kinetosome; **9**, mitochondrium.

Some other termite flagellates become multi-flagellated by becoming multinucleated, with each nucleus associated with a parabasal body, and a basal structure for the one or several flagella involved. This organization is termed a karyomastigont and may be represented twice or many times within the body of a single flagellate.

Where flagella occur in rows or in other patterns, division of the body occurs between the rows rather than across them. It is thus a longitudinal division insofar as the flagellar substructure is concerned. Ciliates characteristically divide across their rows of cilia, providing an important criterion for distinguishing between flagellates with numerous flagella and ciliates.

Cilia. Like flagella, cilia are composed of nine peripheral and two central filaments enclosed in a sheath continuous with the plasmalemma. Each cilium terminates in a kinetosome placed in a satellite corpuscle, and, typically, in two striated rootlets (Fig. 3.7A–C). A fiber arises from the kinetosome. It passes to the left and joins other fibers from cilia of the same row. The compound fiber is the kinetodesmose. The row of kinetosomes and their kinetodesmose is a kinety (Fig. 3.7D). These bodies and fibers make up the infraciliature, the details of which are extremely useful in determining ciliate relationships.

The infraciliature presumably provides co-ordination and control as well as playing a decisive role during the differentiation of organisms in reproduction. A wave of effective beat passes along adjacent kinetics in unison, causing a spiral movement of the organism as a whole. The details of co-ordination, however, remain uncertain in forms with uniform body ciliature.

Ciliary adaptation has followed several different lines. The somatic cilia occur at the body surface and have an infraciliature distinctively separated from the buccal or oral cilia located in or near the oral region. In some ciliates, somatic cilia have been greatly reduced. In many cases cilia unite to form compound ciliary organelles. The most important somatic organelles of this kind are cirri, tuft-like brushes of fused cilia. Their kinetosomes are united into a fiber plate at the base, which is attached to a neuromotor fibril. It has been shown experimentally that the separation of a cirrus from its fibril leads to unco-ordinated movements.

The oral ciliature is variously modified, depending on the nature of the oral apparatus (see p. 62). The most important compound ciliary organelles in the oral region are undulating membranes, formed of a united row of cilia, and an adoral zone of membranelles (Figs. 3.8, 3.27C). Each membranelle is a flat plate of fused cilia, with a compound fiber plate at its base, formed of the united roots of the component cilia. They are arranged in a linear series and beat in a co-ordinated fashion, presumably because of a longitudinal conducting fibril passing along the fiber plates.

In the dividing ciliate, the plane of fission cuts across the kineties. The kinetosomes of each kinety can divide to provide more kinetosomes, thus providing for kinety growth. In some forms, new kinetosomes appear near the division plane, while in others the kineties grow terminally. The infraciliature of the oral region is distinctive. In some ciliates, a particular kinety, termed kinety one, gives rise to kinetosomes which form an anarchic field and give rise to the new oral infraciliature. In other ciliates, the oral apparatus enters directly into the division process and is itself responsible for the formation of the new oral infraciliature (Fig. 3.8). Evidently the infraciliature is either itself responsible for initiating much of morphogenesis in ciliates, or it reflects cortical factors faithfully.

The Nuclear Apparatus

Protozoan nuclei are extremely interesting because of their diversity in structure and methods of division. Two basic types are recognized: vesicular, containing considerable nuclear sap; and compact, containing little nuclear sap. The distribution of the DNA material within the nucleus varies considerably. It often occurs as small, discrete particles associated with the nuclear membrane, with or without an endosome, a large mass of DNA or RNA material characteristic of most vesicular nuclei. Chromosomes may form from either the peripheral chromatin or the chromatin of the endosome.

When more than one nucleus is present, all are usually alike. Exceptions occur in ciliates, where a massive, compact micronucleus and one or more small, vesicular micronuclei are found, and in many Sporozoa, where nuclei for vegetative and generative functions may occur.

When Protozoa are cut into parts, pieces with an intact nuclear apparatus soon recover, while those without nuclei

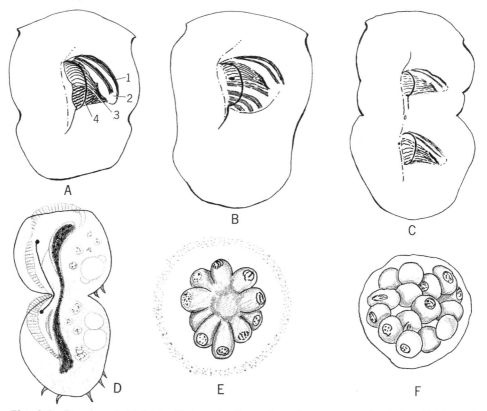

Fig. 3.8. Binary and Multiple Fission. **A.** Formation of a new mouth during division of *Urocentrum*. The single buccal opening is on the left at the start of division and the special buccal ciliature is in four fields, an anterior oral polykinety (1), posterior oral polykinety (2), composite oral kinety (3), and ciliary field (4). During division the ciliary field divides to form a new ciliary field for the anterior mouth and the four ciliated fields of the posterior mouth. Such phenomena show that fission is a highly organized process in more complexly formed Protozoa. **D.** Division of *Euplotes patella*, showing simultaneous division of the micronucleus and macronucleus. **E-F.** Multiple fission during sporoblast formation in a sporozoan, *Ovivora thalassemae*. The cytoplasm divides to form a number of daughters, leaving a small mass of residual protoplasm behind. (**A-C**, after Fauré-Fremiet. **D**, after Turner. **E-F**, after MacKinnon and Ray, from Hall.)

soon deteriorate and die. Dying pieces without nuclei show evidences of inability to produce shells and digestive enzymes; apparently the nucleus functions in metabolism through controlling enzyme production and determining the synthetic capacities of the organism. We have learned to think of nuclei, and especially of chromosomes, as the carriers of a genetic code, inscribed in the molecular architecture of DNA. Information is transmitted to daughter nuclei during nuclear division, and is reorganized and assembled in new combinations during sexual reproduction.

A nucleus contains at least one full set of genes and so comprises a complete genetic code. It is improbable that a highly integrated system like a nucleus or such involved processes as mitosis and meiosis could have arisen in a single evolutionary step. It is to such primitive organisms as Protozoa that we must look for evidence of this development, although it is to be inferred more from the form of the dividing nucleus than from the form of the interphase nucleus (see p. 81).

Methods of Reproduction

Both sexual and asexual reproduction occur among Protozoa. Some reproduce asexually only. As this is true of groups which are apparently primitive for other reasons, it seems probable that sexual reproduction appeared while organisms were at the protozoan grade of organization.

Asexual reproduction involves the division of the parent body, either equally or unequally, to produce one or more young individuals which develop into mature organisms. It always involves a single parent and neither meiosis nor fertilization occurs.

Binary fission is the most common form of asexual reproduction. The parent body divides equally to produce two daughters, which regain adult size and form. Where there is a definite body axis, fission may be transverse, as in ciliates, or longitudinal, as in flagellates. Fission involves karyokinesis, or nuclear division, and cytokinesis, or cytoplasmic division. Preparation for division may be simple or involve complex reorganization. Extensive macronuclear reorganization accompanies fission of ciliates in many cases, and the infraciliature and compound ciliary organelles may also participate in pre-division reorganization. Many Protozoa undergo fission in the encysted state. In this case extensive dedifferentiation may precede fission. After or during the latter part of karyokinesis, cytoplasmic constriction begins. The two daughters require differing degrees of redifferentiation, depending on the extent of reorganization prior to division. In all cases, however, a growth and differentiation process follows cytokinesis.

Multiple fission. Multiple fission is common in some groups of Protozoa, especially the sporozoan parasites, Foraminifera and Radiolaria. Preparation for division involves repeated nuclear division without cytokinesis to form a multinucleate organism. The cytoplasm then cleaves to form many uninucleated individuals. Although there are exceptions, the products of multiple fission often enter into a new phase of the life cycle of the organism, serving as swarmers or infective stages for new host cells. It is not uncommon for multiple fission to leave a mass of residual protoplasm, which dies.

Plasmotomy. Multinucleated Protozoa sometimes divide into two or more multinucleated daughters. This is plasmotomy. The daughters may continue to undergo asexual reproduction, or may enter into another phase of the life cycle.

Budding. Budding is a type of asexual reproduction in which one or more small daughters are produced by the parent. It may be considered an unequal form of fission, and like fission involves preparatory phases before budding and a later period of growth and differentiation. Budding may occur at the body surface or in an internal cavity; the former is termed endogenous, the latter, exogenous.

SEXUAL REPRODUCTION

No phylum produces more diversified material for the study of modes of sexual reproduction, for both simple and complex types occur. Sexual reproduction involves specialized nuclear divisions during meiosis, resulting in a change from diplophase to haplophase, and the union of gametes to restore diploidy. It may be amphimictic, involving the union of gametes from different parents, or automictic, in which the gametes arise from the same parent. In either case, the uniting gametes may be whole organisms, or nuclei only. Where whole organisms unite, the union is termed syngamy. Where only nuclei unite, the process is conjugation. Conjugation occurs only among ciliates, while syngamy occurs in all other groups where sexual reproduction occurs.

Meiosis evidently occurs among sexually reproducing protozoans, but the details are not well known in most cases. Genetic evidence of an incontrovertible nature shows that meiosis occurs in *Paramecium aurelia*, and chromosome counts showing haploid and diploid numbers have been reported from all major groups of Protozoa. Among ciliates, the second division of the micronucleus during conjugation is reductional insofar as chromosome number is concerned, although the matter is somewhat complicated by the absence of a definite tetrad stage. The absence of distinctive tetrads suggests that the definitive meiotic process has not reached the metazoan level in all Protozoa, but there remains a strong tendency for meiosis to require two divisions, as in Metazoa. Among some of the photosynthetic flagellates, meiosis immediately follows zygote formation, as often happens in algae.

Syngamy. The gametes may be morphologically similar (isogametes) or dissimilar (anisogametes). Isogamy is most common among more primitive members of some groups, and is undoubtedly more primitive than anisogamy. In at least some isogamous species, the gametes are chemically differentiated. In this case a gamete belongs to a mating type, and can unite only with a gamete from a different type, thus ensuring outbreeding. Gametes vary widely in form. They may be flagellate or amoeboid, and in some cases are highly differentiated, especially in the case of motile microgametes. The zygote commonly enters into a quiescent phase. Thus in colonial flagellates the zygote secretes a heavy cyst membrane and completes its development after winter or when conditions have become more favorable, resembling algal zygospores. In many of the sporozoans, the zygote becomes an oöcyst, in which the spores, quiescent until they reach a new host, are formed.

Conjugation is characteristic of ciliates. Although it is essentially comparable in all, it is best followed in a species with a single macronucleus and a single micronucleus. Two ciliates, ready for conjugation, partially unite, the pellicle and body surface undergoing extensive local changes during union. Porter (1960) has recently described the cortical differentiation of *Paramecium aurelia* during conjugation. As conjugation continues, the macronucleus has, or will soon, disintegrate. The micronucleus divides, usually twice, to produce four haploid micronuclei (or pronuclei), all but one of which disintegrate. The persisting nucleus divides once again, to form a stationary pronucleus and a wandering pronucleus (Fig. 3.9), the former remaining within the original parent, and the other passing to the other conjugant. The two organisms now separate, and the pronuclei unite to form a zygote nucleus, which divides repeatedly, giving rise to micronuclei and to macronuclear primordia which grow into macronuclei. Several postconjugation fissions, differing somewhat with the species, restore the normal nuclear complement to each daughter organism. Among some ciliates, especially stalked or sessile forms, conjugation has evolved in the same direction as syngamy, with the appearance of macroconjugants and microconjugants.

Autogamy is a modification of conjugation permitting the same outcome, but requiring a single organism. The macronucleus breaks down, the micronucleus undergoes meiosis, and two pronuclei from the same organism unite to form a zygote nucleus.

The Classes of Protozoa

It would be convenient if animal classification were all finished and one had only to learn it, but we are far from this goal. As new facts are discovered and new ideas grow out of them, the details of classification are constantly changing. A great number of new ideas about protozoan classification have been expressed. Some are quite revolutionary, and have not yet been sufficiently tested. The classification used here is relatively conservative, especially in the case of flagellates and the Sarcodina, but has the virtue of preserving most of the familiar names that have been used for most of the twentieth century.

Fig. 3.9. Scheme of Conjugation, as in *Paramecium caudatum*. A. Joining of two animals. B. First meiotic division of the micronucleus and degeneration of the macronucleus. Macronuclear degeneration is hastened in the diagrams; in reality, macronuclear fragments are still present when the conjugants first separate. C. Second meiotic division of micronuclei. One haploid nucleus (pronucleus) remains viable in each organism; the rest degenerate. D. Degeneration of three nuclei and division of the viable pronucleus into migratory and stationary pronuclei in preparation for nuclear fusion. E. Fusion of the pronuclei in each conjugant and separation of the two animals. At this time a single, diploid zygote nucleus (synkaryon) is present. F. First division of the zygote nucleus. G. Second nuclear division in the postconjugant. H. Third nuclear division in the postconjugant. I. Differentiation of the micronuclear and macronuclear primordia. J. After the first postconjugation fission. K. After the second postconjugation fission, with the normal nuclear complement restored. The eventual outcome is the recombination of genes through meiosis and synkaryon formation, and the replacement of the old macronucleus with a new one derived from the zygote nucleus.

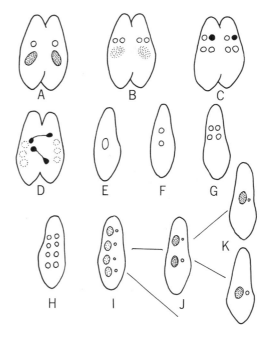

Classification

Subkingdom Protozoa. Acellular animals or colonies of acellular animals.

    Phylum Protozoa. With the characters of the subkingdom.

        Subphylum Mastigophora. The flagellates. Protozoa with flagella in the adult stage. It should be noted that many can resorb the flagellum temporarily, or pass through definite stages of the life cycle when no flagellum is present.

            Class I. Phytomastigophorea. The plant-like flagellates. Typically flagellates with chromoplasts, capable of photosynthesis, but including many colorless forms with detailed similarities to members of the various orders of photosynthetic flagellates.

            Class II. Zoomastigophorea. The zooflagellates. Colorless flagellates, saprobic or holozoic, without the characteristic organelles or reserve food bodies of the phytoflagellates.

        Subphylum Sarcodina. Protozoa characterized by pseudopodia, without flagella in the adult stage, and generally moving by means of protoplasmic streaming. Some pass through short stages of the life cycle which are flagellated, and a few develop flagella under appropriate environmental conditions.

            Class I. Rhizopodea. Sarcodina without axial filaments in their pseudopodia, and generally not universally symmetrical. If radiating filopodia are present they are algal feeders, often parasitic on algae.

            Class II. Actinopodea. Universally symmetrical, in most cases, with radiating axopodia, or filopodia. If radiating filopodia are present, they do not branch and the organisms are not parasitic on algae.

        Subphylum Eusporozoa. Parasitic Protozoa with a complex life cycle, involving spore formation immediately after sexual reproduction. The spores are simple, and always lack polar filaments.

            Class I. Telosporidea. With the characters of the subphylum.

        Subphylum Cnidosporidea. Parasitic Protozoa with a complex life cycle involving both sexual and asexual phases. The spores are complex in form, containing one or more polar filaments.

            Class I. Myxosporidea. Spores contain one or more polar filaments, each enclosed in a polar capsule. The spore membrane is formed of two or more valves, which are formed by valvular cells and meet at sutures.

            Class II. Actinomyxidea. Spores contain three polar filaments, each enclosed in a polar capsule. The spore membrane is made of three valves or one, and contains from one to many sporozoites.

            Class III. Microsporidea. Spores contain a polar filament which may or may not be enclosed in a polar capsule. The spore membrane is simple, not composed of separate valves.

        Subphylum Acnidosporidea. Parasitic Protozoa with simple spores lacking polar filaments, and with a life cycle that does not involve sexual reproduction immediately before spore formation.

Class I. Haplosporidia. An incompletely known group, which is characterized by simple spores, and appears to have a life cycle which does not include a sexual phase.

Subphylum Ciliophora. Protozoa with cilia for locomotion at some stage of the life cycle, and with macronuclei and micronuclei. Sexual reproduction involves conjugation or allied processes rather than syngamy.

Class I. Ciliata. With the characters of the subphylum.

Subclass Holotrichia. Ciliates which are primitively characterized by uniform body ciliation and lack highly specialized, compound ciliary organelles associated with the mouth, or which pass through stages in development showing these characteristics. If an adoral zone of membranelles is present, it is unlike that characteristic of the Spirotrichia.

Subclass Spirotrichia. Ciliates with strong tendencies toward reduction of somatic ciliation, and with an adoral zone of membranelles forming the left border of the buccal region, winding clockwise toward the cytostome.

The Mastigophora

A study of flagellate diversity emphasizes their affinities with other groups. The phytoflagellates are classified as algae by botanists. Some zooflagellates become almost indistinguishable from Sarcodina, and others with Ciliophora. Evidently the stem flagellates were an extremely plastic group and contributed heavily to the early evolutionary development of both plant and animal kingdoms.

PHYTOMASTIGOPHOREA— THE PHYTOFLAGELLATES

Flagellates are common in fresh-water and marine collections throughout the year. When a collection is examined, some of the flagellates prove to be green or greenish, yellow or brown. These are phytoflagellates. Unfortunately a number of colorless ones are also phytoflagellates, which complicates the matter of identification.

The first problem in identification is to determine which order a given form belongs to, and in the majority of cases this is not difficult. The main problem is to mobilize the necessary information and use it in an orderly fashion. A good plan is to look first for the characteristic furrows and flagella of the dinoflagellates. If they are present, one's task is over, for no other flagellates have these traits. If they are not there, what color is it? If it is green, it must be either a phytomonad or a euglenoid. If yellowish or brownish, it must be a chrysomonad or cryptomonad. In either case, one need only look for the critical differences between the two orders left.

The easiest way to organize such critical and useful information is in the form of a key which orders the necessary observations so as to lead to the proper diagnosis. The following key will help to distinguish between the orders of phytoflagellates and is constructed in a double forking pattern. Two co-ordinate choices are offered in each step through the key. It is necessary to select the more fitting of these, and then follow the subsequent descriptions and number designations until the name of the order under consideration is reached. Since in the future ordinal characters will not be presented in key form, the student who is examining several orders may find it useful to construct one from the information in the text.

1. Body with a transverse furrow containing a transverse flagellum and a longitudinal furrow containing a posterior, trailing flagellum:..............*Order Dinoflagellida*
1. Without such furrows and flagella.
   2. Color yellowish or brownish:
      3. With a gullet (more properly a vestibule) from which two anterior or lateral flagella arise; body usually rigid and flattened and with an oblique or transverse, shallow groove; reserve food stored as starches............*Cryptomonadida*
      3. Without a vestibule; often plastic; reserve food stored as fat and leucosin . . .
      Chrysomonadida
   2. Color green:
      3. Small, usually rigid, flagellates with two or more flagella; without a vestibule, the flagella passing through pores in the cellulose covering; reserve food stored as fats and starches.................................*Phytomonadida*
      3. Medium to large, usually plastic; with one or two flagella; often with a vestibule; reserve food stored as paramylon............................*Euglenida*
         4. Small, usually rigid, flagellates with two or more flagella; without a vestibule, the flagella passing through pores in the cellulose covering; reserve food stored as fats and starches.................................*Phytomonadida*
         4. Medium to large, usually plastic; with one or two flagella; often with a vestibule; reserve food stored as paramylon......................*Euglenida*

A key of this kind is always imperfect. A few of the dinoflagellates lack the characteristic furrows but show their relationship by other, more detailed similarities, or by having a typical dinoflagellate stage in their life cycle. Some of the phytomonads and euglenoids have red haematochrome which masks the chlorophyll green. But for the majority of common forms, it will suffice. The colorless flagellates present a special problem. In general, if a colorless flagellate has a conspicuous vestibule, it is a phytoflagellate, and one looks for the firm body, and somewhat flattened form of the cryptomonads in combination with two flagella, in contrast to the usually plastic form and one or two flagella of the euglenoids. It must be admitted, however, that nothing can take the place of considerable experience in recognizing the colorless phytoflagellates.

A great deal of work has recently been devoted to characterizing the compounds which are required by phytoflagellates when cultured under various conditions. Out of the mass of detail, a few basic points are emerging. It appears that very few of the chlorophyll-bearing forms can subsist on a completely inorganic medium. Many require acetates or fatty acids, and some are greatly stimulated by vitamin B_{12} or other B fractions. It has also become clear that many of the green phytoflagellates do very well in the dark, if provided with appropriate carbon and nitrogen sources, eventually becoming bleached. Evidently the line between the saprobic and photosynthetic forms is less sharp than was once believed. Another interesting discovery is that some of the colorless phytoflagellates have very considerable ability to synthesize organic compounds, presumably by chemosynthesis rather than by photosynthesis. Although a great deal more work will be required before accurate categories can be devised, it seems evident that there are many transitional steps between the complete autotroph and saprobic forms with relatively low synthetic capacities.

A number of the phytoflagellates ingest solid food. Food ingestion may occur in the vestibule, or by pseudopodia formed at the body surface. Apparently the digestion and absorption of food from the food vacuole follows the typical protozoan pattern.

THE CHRYSOMONADIDA

Something of the nature of chrysomonad diversity is reflected by the representatives shown in Fig. 3.10. A consideration of the

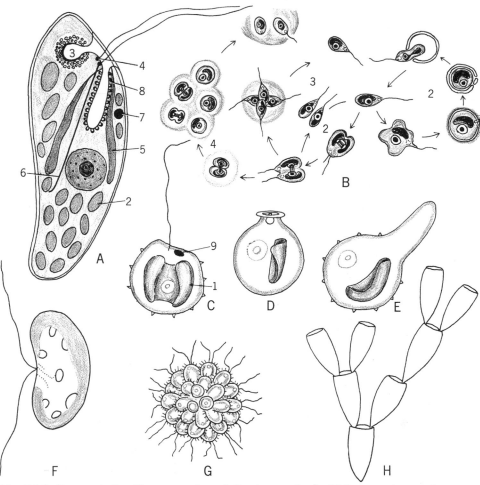

Fig. 3.10. Representative Chrysomonads and Cryptomonads. A. *Chilomonas paramecium*, a colorless cryptomonad with anterior flagella. B. The life cycle of *Chromulina*, showing encystment in arc 1, fission in arc 2, colony formation in arc 3, and palmella formation in arc 4. C-E. *Chromulina*, a typical chrysomonad. C, flagellated form; D, encysted form; E, amoeboid form. F. *Nephroselmis olivacea*, a photosynthetic cryptomonad with laterally placed flagella. G. Colony of a chrysomonad, *Synura uvella*. H. Scheme of arboreal colony formation in a loricate chrysomonad, *Codonodendron ocellatum*. (A, after Anderson. B, after Kühn, from Kudo. C-E, after Hofeneeder, from Jahn. F-G, after Stein. H, after Pascher, from Hall.) 1, chromoplast; 2, paramylon body; 3, contractile vacuole; 4, basal body of flagellum; 5, parabasal body; 6, rhizoplast; 7, amphosome, a body of uncertain function, possibly a vestigial stigma; 8, trichocyst or ejectisome; 9, stigma.

kinds of adaptations found among them helps to understand what one should look for when trying to identify phytoflagellates. Some are colonial; others live as isolated individuals. Some are sessile; others are free-swimming. Some are amoeboid; others have a definite body form. Some secrete a flask-shaped case called a lorica. Beneath all of this diversity, however, is a certain uniformity. All have one or two yellow to brown chromoplasts and store foods as oils and leucosin.

The life cycle of *Chromulina* (Fig. 3.10B) shows some of the common capacities of phytoflagellates, and emphasizes some of the important evolutionary trends among chrysomonads. The common free-swimming form, equipped with one or two chromoplasts and a stigma, has a single flagellum. It may undergo repeated longitudinal binary fissions, each involving division of flagellum, flagellar root system, nucleus, chromoplast, and eventually the cytoplasm. It may also become precystic, lose its flagellum, and secrete a cyst membrane, becoming resistant to certain environmental factors. Chrysomonad cysts are unusual in having a siliceous membrane and an opening containing a plug, through which they eventually emerge. They may also secrete a gelatinous matrix in which daughters remain embedded to form small colonies of motile forms, the individual members of which reproduce by fission (arc 3). Under some conditions they lose their flagellum and become embedded in a gelatinous matrix, living as alga-like non-motile cells. This is the palmella stage, not uncommonly seen in phytoflagellates. The palmella is transitional between the motile, more animal-like photosynthetic flagellates and the non-motile algae. In spite of this variety of methods of reproduction and life forms, sexual reproduction is unknown in chrysomonads.

THE CRYPTOMONADIDA

Cryptomonads are yellowish, brownish, or olive-green forms with accessory pigments like those of dinoflagellates. In several ways they show similarities to dinoflagellates and may have arisen from the same stem forms. There are three major groups. The Phaeocapsina live permanently as a palmella, assuming the cryptomonad form only briefly for dissemination. The free-swimming cryptomonads belong to a different suborder, and are placed in two families, Cryptomonadidae, with two anterior flagella and the anterior end more or less truncated; and Nephroselmidae, kidney-shaped, with a transverse furrow and two lateral flagella (Fig. 3.10A, F).

The reproductive capacities of the cryptomonads parallel those of the chrysomonads. Sexual reproduction is unknown, and palmella stages are less prominent, except for the Phaeocapsina. Encysted forms, however, have a continuous sheath of cellulose, thus differing from the chrysomonads.

THE PHYTOMONADIDA

Phytomonads are small, green flagellates without a vestibule and with a definite cellulose membrane. It is a large group, and includes a number of common genera. The majority have two flagella; if three or more are present, the flagellar number is used to determine the family to which species are assigned. One or two large, cup-shaped chromoplasts or many small ones may be present. Two families are determined on characters other than the number of flagella; the Phacotidae have a bivalve shell (Fig. 3.11D) and the Volvicidae includes colonial species. Because of their interest in connection with the colonial theory of metazoan origin, the colonial phytomonads are discussed in Chapter 5 (see p. 90).

It is among phytomonads that isogamy and anisogamy can be most easily com-

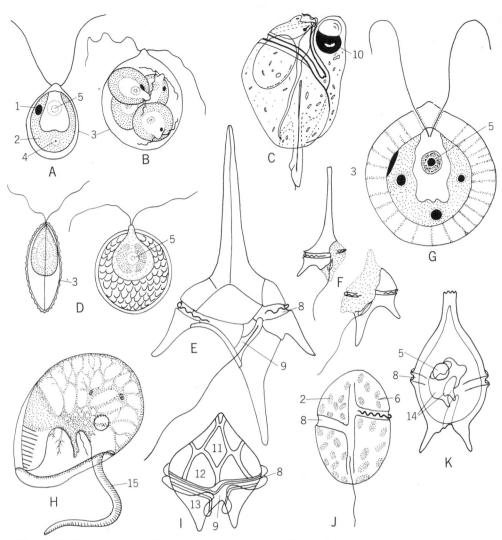

Fig. 3.11. Representative Phytomonads and Dinoflagellates. A-B. *Chlamydomonas angulosa*, a typical phytomonad, with heavy cell wall and no stigma or vestibule. A, trophic individual; B, division within the old cell wall. C. *Erythropsis cornuta*, a dinoflagellate having an oblique furrow and a huge ocellus with a starchy lens. D. *Phacotus lenticularis* in front and side views, showing the bivalve test. E-F. *Ceratium hirudinella*, a dinoflagellate with a cellulose test composed of discrete plates and a body drawn out into processes. E, trophic individual; F, daughters, immediately after division, each with half of parent test, as they appear before regenerating the missing test plates. G, *Haematococcus pluvialis*, a phytomonad with red pigment (haematochrome). H. *Noctiluca scintillans*, an aberrant, luminescent dinoflagellate with a tentacle. I. A *Peridinium* test, showing the component plates. J. *Gymnodinium racemosus*, a naked dinoflagellate. K. The pusule system of *Peridinum*. (A-B, after Dill, D. after Oltmanns, from Jahn. E, after Entz; C and J, after Kofoid and Swezy, from Hall. F, after Lauterborn. K, after Haye. G, after Elliott. H, after Robin, from Kudo.) 1, stigma; 2, chloroplast; 3, cell wall; 4, pyrenoid; 5, nucleus; 6, epicone; 7 hypocone; 8 cingulum or girdle; 9, sulcus; 10, ocellus; 11, apical plate; 12, precingular plate; 13, postcingular plate; 14, pusule; 15, tentacle.

41

pared. Within the same genus both isogamy and anisogamy are sometimes seen, suggesting that the differentiation of gametes is repetitively occurring within the members of the order. Among colonial species, however, the smaller, apparently more primitive species are isogamous and the more highly specialized forms are exclusively anisogamous.

All of the methods of asexual reproduction outlined for chrysomonads occur in phytomonads, although not all types occur in all species. Palmella formation and encystment is common. Colony formation is restricted to the Volvicidae and reaches a high stage of development. An interesting feature of phytomonad fission is that the daughters often remain for a time within the parent cell wall. In some cases, two or three sequential fissions produce four or eight small daughters still held within the parental membrane (Fig. 3.11B).

THE DINOFLAGELLIDA

Dinoflagellida is a large group and contains many biologically interesting species. The dinoflagellates are distinctive, nearly all showing some modification of the basic form shown in Fig. 3.11I, at least at some time during the life cycle. A number of them, however, are highly modified as adults, especially those which have taken up a parasitic life on copepods or fish. A most unusual form, Noctiluca, reaches a maximal size of over 2 mm. and is highly phosphorescent. It sometimes appears in huge numbers, making the oceans phosphorescent at night and giving the waters a reddish tinge by day. A small suborder contains a few species with a bivalve shell and anterior flagella, without traces of the typical grooves.

In many dinoflagellates the sulcus is spiralled, resulting in a highly modified body form (Fig. 3.11C). Among these are some with complex light-sensitive ocelli, equipped with a starchy lens. Most of the

dinoflagellates are marine although there are a number of fresh-water forms. Among them are some with a heavy armor composed of definite plates cemented together (Fig. 3.11E). Some are highly sensitive to environmental factors, their appearance changing with the season, and with the depth of the ponds or lakes in which they grow. The heavy shell is a problem during fission; it ruptures along predetermined sutures between plates, and each daughter reforms the missing part of the shell.

The majority reproduce asexually by binary fission, although some, especially the parasitic forms, reproduce by budding. Multiple fission to produce small flagellated swarmers is common, and a number of forms encyst, releasing swarmers when the cyst germinates. The most common form for swarmers resembles Gymnodinium or Glenodinium, two genera with simple form. Sexual reproduction has been reported for Noctiluca, which forms small isogametes, but is not very fully described.

THE EUGLENIDA

Euglenoid flagellates are medium-sized to large, green or colorless forms, usually with a conspicuous vestibule. They are more common in fresh-water than marine habitats, and include many familiar species. Euglena (Fig. 3.12A) is widely studied and reasonably typical of the family Euglenidae, which includes all of the photosynthetic euglenoids. Reserve foods are laid down as paramylon, a carbohydrate that does not give a starch test. There are two families of colorless euglenoids, Astasiidae, with one flagellum, and Anisonemidae, with two. Colorless species may be saprobic or holozoic; some of the forms which are normally holozoic can live under saprobic conditions.

There is considerable uncertainty about the relationship of the vestibule to the cytostome in holozoic species. At least Peranema ingests food, not through the vestibule, but by a separate cytostome. On the other hand, observers have reported the ingestion of small food organisms by pseudopodial action of the vestibule wall.

Euglenoids reproduce by fission, either as free-swimming individuals or in a palmella stage. Some species are known to form division cysts, within which fission occurs. Colonial euglenoids are unknown, except for the sessile *Coalacium*, which forms branching colonies. Sexual reproduction by isogamy has been described for a few species, but is certainly not common in the order.

Zoomastigophorea—the Zooflagellates

The colorless zooflagellates are extremely varied and are best characterized by the absence of chlorophyll or the other structures characteristic of the phytoflagellates. There are five orders, whose characteristics are summarized below. Some recommend the establishment of a sixth order, the Trichomonadida for *Trichomonas*-like forms, here assigned to Polymastigida.

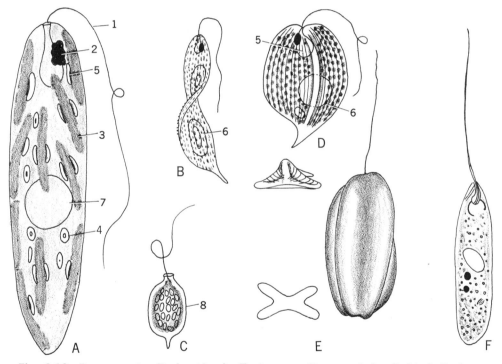

Fig. 3.12. Representative Euglenoids. A. *Euglena gracilis*, a typical cylindrical *Euglena*. B. *E. spirogyra*, a large, flattened *Euglena* with two oval paramylon bodies. C. *Trachelomonas urceolata*, a euglenoid living in a test. D. *Phacus pleuronectes* in end and top views. E. *Petalomonas alata*, a colorless euglenoid with a firm test, in top and end views. F. *Peranema trichophorum*, a plastic, colorless euglenoid. (A, B, after Johnson. D, after Allegre and Jahn. E, after Shawhan and Jahn, from Jahn. C, after Stokes, from Kudo. F, after Hyman.) 1, flagellum; 2, stigma; 3, chromoplast; 4, pyrenoid; 5, vestibule; 6, paramylon; 7, nucleus; 8, cellulose test.

Order Rhizomastigida. An undoubtedly polyphyletic group of Protozoa that have both flagella and pseudopodia in adult stages. There may be from one to many flagella, and pseudopodia also vary in number and form.

Order Protomastigida. Small zooflagellates with one or two flagella; body usually naked, and with or without a protoplasmic collar or an undulating membrane. Reproduction is asexual, although sexual reproduction has been reported in a few cases.

Order Polymastigida. Zooflagellates with three to eight flagella, naked or with a flexible pellicle, and typically with a complex flagellar root system.

Order Hypermastigida. Zooflagellates living in the gut of wood-eating insects with a complex organization and a high degree of protoplasmic specialization; with many flagella arranged in rows or tufts, and a single nucleus.

Order Opalinida. Zooflagellates living in the colon of amphibians, with many flagella arranged in rows and two or many nuclei, all similar in form. These flagellates are flattened and ciliate-like, and are sometimes classified as ciliates.

THE RHIZOMASTIGIDA

Rhizomastigids have both pseudopodia and flagella. This is very nearly their only common trait. It is an order used to assemble all of the borderline species between the Sarcodina and Mastigophora. Some have axopodia, resembling the Heliozoa (Fig. 3.13A), while others have lobopodia and resemble the Amoebida. They emphasize the close relationship of Sarcodina and Mastigophora, and show that a number of distinctive flagellate stocks probably have crossed the borderline to establish diverse sarcodine stocks.

THE PROTOMASTIGIDA

The protomonads are small, saprobic, holozoic, or parasitic zooflagellates. They are an interesting group, for several distinctive adaptational lines have appeared among them, and the parasitic species include pathogens causing serious disease in man and his domestic animals.

The choanoflagellates (Fig. 3.13C) are one of the distinctive protomonad lines. They are characterized by a delicate protoplasmic collar, which surrounds the base of the flagellum. Food particles, swept against the collar by currents set up by the flagellum, adhere and are passed to the main body mass, where digestion occurs

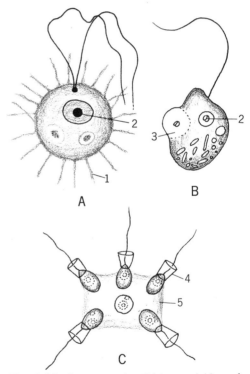

Fig. 3.13. Representative Rhizomastigids and Protomonads. **A.** *Heliobodo radians,* a rhizomastigid with flagella and radiating filopodia. Both flagella and pseudopodia of some kind occur in rhizomastigids. **B.** *Oikomonas termo,* a minute protomonad. **C.** *Protospongia haeckelii,* a choanoflagellate forming colonies. (A, after Valkanov. B, C, after Lemmermann.) **1**, filopodium; **2**, nucleus; **3**, food vacuole; **4**, collar; **5**, gelatinous matrix of colony.

in food vacuoles. All are small; nearly all are sessile. Some live within a lorica, and a number are colonial. The choanoflagellates are similar to the characteristic choanocytes of sponges; this similarity was once thought to demonstrate that they gave rise to the sponges. It seems more probable, today, that the similarity is an interesting case of convergence, or, perhaps, that the choano-flagellates are descendants of sponge cho-anocytes which took up an independent existence. The fact that nearly all of the sponges are marine and choanoflagellates are fresh-water forms argues for the idea of convergence.

Many holozoic and saprobic protomon-ads without collars are common in stag-nant water. They may have one or two flagella; when two are present, one may be trailing or both may extend anteriorly. They show about the same range of diversity as the choanoflagellates in most respects (Fig.

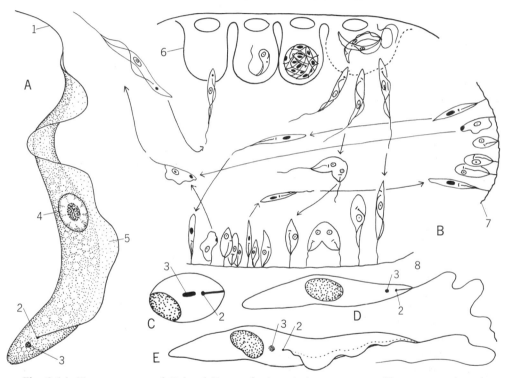

Fig. 3.14. Trypanosoma and Related Forms. A. A typical trypanosome, *Trypanosoma brucei*. B. Life cycle of *Trypanosoma lewisi*, living in rats and fleas, showing the transformations accompanying the life cycle. At the top, trypanosomes enter the flea stomach with rat blood, where they infect stomach cells and reproduce. The resulting offspring may continue the fission cycle in the stomach, or may enter the rectum, where they become leptomonads and approach leishmania forms. Leptomonads from the rectum may infect the pyloric part of the hindgut. Crithidia may be formed in the rectum or in the pylorus, and can infect the rectal wall or pass out with feces and infect the host rat. C-E. Forms assumed by trypanosomes during their life cycles. C, leishmania form; D, leptomonad form; E, crithidia form. (A, after Grell. B, based on Minchin and Thomson. C-E, from Med. Protozoa and Helminth., U. S. *Navy Medical School Bull.*) 1, flagellum; 2, basal granule of flagellum; 3, blepharoplast; 4, nucleus; 5, undulating membrane; 6, stomach wall; 7, inner lining of pylorus; 8, inner lining of rectum.

3.13B). They are solitary or colonial, loricate or naked, and free-swimming or attached. A few of the species belonging to this general adaptational type live as intestinal commensals.

The most important protomonads are parasitic forms belonging to the family Trypanosomatidae. The kinetosome and kinetoplast may be found at the anterior end of the body, near the middle of the body, or at the posterior end. As a result there may be no undulating membrane, a short undulating membrane, or a long one (Fig. 3.14C-E). In some, the free flagellum is lacking. In the same species, the body form changes during the developmental cycle.

Trypanosoma occurs as a blood parasite in warm-blooded and cold-blooded vertebrates, and has a life cycle involving a blood-sucking, invertebrate host, within which intracellular multiple fission, similar to that seen in Sporozoa, occurs in the stomach epithelium. In *T. lewisi*, transmitted by a flea, trypanosomes from the stomach change into crithidial and leptomonad forms as they pass through the hind-gut, and eventually change into small, infective trypanosomes which are voided with the feces and infect a rat if it eats the fresh feces (Fig. 3.14B). In *T. gambiense*, which is transmitted by the bite of a tse-tse fly, the trypanosomes from the stomach become elongated as they migrate to the salivary glands after the schizogony cycle. Here they attach as crithidia, and metamorphose into small infective trypanosomes, injected with saliva into the wound caused by the fly bite. *T. gambiense* causes African sleeping sickness, and *T. cruzi* causes Chagas' disease, an important problem in South America. *Leishmania* are closely related forms which live within host cells and are carried by sand flies. *Leishmania* cause kala azar, oriental sore, and Espundia, important tropical diseases of the Mediterranean, near East, oriental, and South American regions.

THE POLYMASTIGIDA

Polymastigids are almost exclusively endozoic, some living as commensals or mild parasites, usually in the digestive tract, and many as mutualistic inhabitants of the gut of wood-eating insects. The body is much more complex than in protomonads. Each nucleus is associated with a cluster of three to eight flagella, a more or less complex flagellar root system, and a parabasal body. This complex is a karyomastigont. The majority of polymastigids have but one karyomastigont, but others have two, and a small suborder of mutualistic species have many (Fig. 3.15A-C.)

Trichomonas (Fig. 3.6A) is an important genus, including several species infecting man. *T. vaginalis* causes vaginitis, but the other species appear to be commensals. Spontaneous abortion in cattle is caused by *Tritrichomonas foetus*, transmitted during mating. *Giardia intestinalis* (Fig. 3.15B), sometimes called "the old man of the gut," is a curious dikaryomastigont living in the human duodenum, where it causes some intestinal disturbance.

HYPERMASTIGIDA

Hypermastigids occur as commensals or mutualistic inhabitants of roaches and termites. They are easily recognized by their many flagella, arranged more or less uniformly over the upper part of the body surface, or in spiral rows, or tufts (Fig. 3.15D). They include some of the most highly differentiated Protozoa; certainly the most highly differentiated flagellates. Wherever termites or wood roaches are available, the interesting polymastigid and hypermastigid forms can be obtained in quantity.

Molting hormones of the host wood roach induce sexual activity in its flagellate fauna. By injecting ecdysone into mature insects, it has been possible to induce changes that never occur in normal adult insects. Cleveland, Burke and Karlson (1960) described abnormal mitoses and other aberrations caused by ecdysone, and discusses the interesting possibility that hormones and other internal factors may be instrumental in the development of some of the diversities in form and life cycle so characteristic of parasitic organisms.

OPALINIDA

Opalinids occur in the colon of frogs and toads. They were originally classified as protociliates, because they had no differentiated macronuclei and micronuclei, and their sexual reproduction involves syngamy of anisogametes instead of conjugation. When it was found that they divide between rather than across the rows of locomotor organelles, it became apparent that they are at least as closely related to flagel-lates as ciliates, and, perhaps, share rather more basic traits with flagellates. It seems improbable that the commensal opalinids stand in direct ancestry to primitive ciliates, but they demonstrate some of the kinds of adaptations that may have produced ciliates from flagellate ancestors: the elaboration of flagella in rows; the development of a met-achronal co-ordination of adjacent rows; and, perhaps, a degree of multinuclearity. Some opalinids have many nuclei; others have only two (Fig. 3.16). In no case is there evidence of macronuclear and micronuclear differentiation.

RHIZOPODEA

Most of us think of rhizopods first when we think of Sarcodina. Except for a very few species, all Sarcodina without axopodia are rhizopods; the exceptions are a few

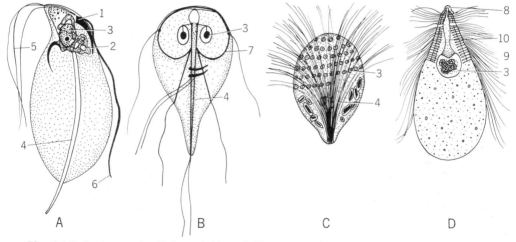

Fig. 3.15. Representative Polymastigids and Hypermastigids. A. *Foaina inflata*, an intestinal polymastigid from a termite, *Neotermes*. This is a typical monokaryomastigont, with a single nucleus and flagellar root system. B. Dikaryomastigont with two nuclei and flagellar root systems, *Giardia intestinalis*, from the human intestine. C. *Stephanonympha nelumbium*, a polykaryomastigont, with many nuclei and flagellar root systems, also a termite symbiont. D. *Trichonympha*, a typical hypermastigid living in termites and wood roaches. Note the many flagella and the single nucleus. (A, after Kirby. B, after Kofoid and Swezy. C, after Kirby, from Jahn. D, after Cleveland.) 1, cresta; 2, parabasal body; 3, nucleus; 4, axostyle; 5, anterior flagellum; 6, trailing flagellum; 7, margin of sucker; 8 anterior nipple; 9, bell; 10, axial core.

Helizoa which have radiating filopodia. They are holozoic organisms catching food with pseudopodia. The large amoebae using lobopodia often take sizable food organisms; *Pelomyxa*, for example, feeds on *Paramecium* when given the opportunity. Forms with long, slender filopodia, and especially those with branching and anastomosing rhizopodia, are trappers, engulfing small particles or organisms that come in contact with the widely spread pseudopodia. Their structure is generally simple insofar as the living parts of the organism are concerned, but the shelled forms sometimes produce highly organized tests. There are four orders of Rhizopodea, with the characteristics summarized below. Many recognize a fifth order in the slime molds, Mycetozoida. Because of the peculiar nature of their life cycle, most now assign them to the plant kingdom, although they produce small amoeboid swarmers and large, multinucleate, amoeboid plasmodia.

Order Proteomyxida. Rhizopods with radiating or irregularly arranged filopodia or rhizopodia, floating or parasitic on algae; often disseminating by means of flagellated swarmers.

Order Amoebida. Rhizopods of simple form, with lobopodia; body naked or with a delicate pellicle; reproduction asexual, with a few reports of sexual reproduction.

Order Testacida. Rhizopods with a test, formed of sand grains or other particles, of secreted plates or prisms; test with a single aperture, the pylome, through which lobopodia or filopodia extend.

Order Foraminiferida. Multinucleate rhizopods with a typically calcareous shell formed of a series of chambers and opening through a pylome; shell pierced by many small pores through which protoplasm extends to form long filopodia or, more commonly, rhizopodia; with a complex life cycle.

PROTEOMYXIDA

Proteomyxids are floating or parasitic forms which feed on algal cells or filaments and are often stained reddish by products of the ingested chlorophyll. Some superficially resemble the Heliozoa, with radiating filopodia, but their reddish color and life in, among, and upon algae helps to recognize them. An interesting adaptation is seen in *Labyrinthomyxa*, which has flagellated swarmers that penetrate the host cells, and which develops into amoeboid stages with anastomosing pseudopodia within the parasitized cell (Fig. 3.17A).

AMOEBIDA

Amoebae are common in fresh-water and marine habitats, and parasitize many kinds of invertebrates and vertebrates. Some are minute; most are medium-sized to large, and a few are very large. *Pelomyxa carolinensis*, also known as *Chaos*, may reach 5 mm. in diameter and has up to a thousand nuclei. Taxonomy and classification

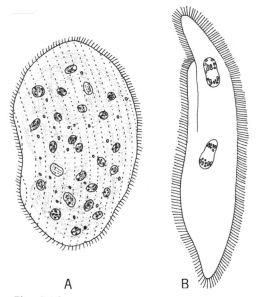

Fig. 3.16. Representative Opalinids. A. *Opalina ranarum*, a typical, flattened, multinucleated opalinid. B. *Protoopalina mitotica*, a cylindrical, binucleate opalinid. (A, after Ghatia and Gulati. B, after Metcalf.)

are difficult, partly because amoebae are difficult to describe, and partly because minute details of form must be observed to make some of the necessary distinctions. The major traits to look for, other than the habitat and number of nuclei, include: a) the length, form, and number of pseudopodia; b) whether the pseudopodia contribute directly to movement or are used for other purposes; c) whether the pseudopodia are ridged or smooth and the outer surface is wrinkled by a definite pellicle as they move; and d) what kinds of inclusions and crystals are present.

Parasitic amoebae occur in coelenterates, man, and most kinds of animals between. The most important human amoeba is *Entamoeba histolytica*, which causes amoebic dysentery. A serious medical problem in tropical and subtropical regions, it sometimes causes severe outbreaks in temperate climates as well. It is transmitted when cysts (Fig. 3.17G) are eaten with contaminated food or water. The cysts germinate in the intestine; a quadrinucleated amoeba emerges which undergoes special divisions to reduce the nuclear number to the normal single nucleus. The amoebae (Fig. 3.17C) grow, attacking the intestinal mucosa by secreting a histolytic enzyme. Active division occurs and large areas of the intestinal lining may be destroyed, causing severe diarrhoea and dysentery. The amoebae migrate by way of the blood stream from the intestinal wall to other organs where they produce amoebic abscesses. These are especially common in the liver, but have also been reported from lungs, brain, skin, and

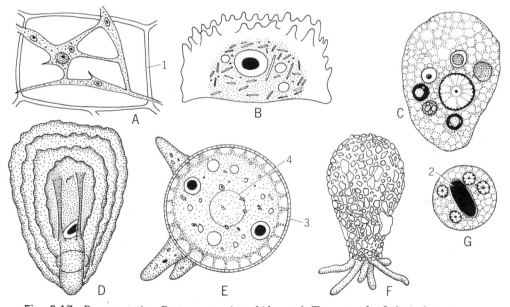

Fig. 3.17. Representative Proteomyxa, Amoebida, and Testacea. **A.** *Labyrinthomyxa sauvageaui*, a protomyxid living in algal cells. **B.** *Hartmanella klitzkei*, with a conspicuous ectoplasmic zone. C and G. Trophic and encysted stages of *Entamoeba histolytica*, an amoeba parasitizing the human intestine and causing amoebic dysentery. **D.** *Thecamoeba verrucosa*, an amoeba with a heavy pellicle, as it appears when moving slowly. **E.** *Arcella*, a testacean with a transparent, secreted test. **F.** *Difflugia pyriformis*, a testacean with a test formed of foreign particles. (A, after Duboscq. B, after Arndt. F, after Pénard, from Hall. C and G, after Kudo. D, after Jahn.) 1, wall of parasitized cell; 2, chromatoid body; 3, test wall; 4, pylome.

other body parts. Under some conditions, not yet completely characterized, the active amoebae become sluggish, lose their food vacuoles, and eventually begin the secretion of a cyst membrane. The precystic amoeba become rounded as the cyst wall develops, and the nucleus divides twice, so four are present in the mature cyst. This life cycle, in its general nature, is characteristic of most amoeboid intestinal parasites.

TESTACIDA

Testaceans are shelled amoebae, usually with lobopodia, but occasionally with filopodia or rhizopodia. The shells are extremely variable; some are chitinous, some siliceous, and some are formed of foreign particles cemented together (Fig. 3.17E-F). With the exception of one family, the Gromiidae, all are similar in having a single chamber within the shell, opening to the exterior by a single aperture, the pylome. In the Gromiidae several openings occur. The Gromiidae are often included in the Foraminiferida and actually do not fit comfortably in either Amoebida or the Foraminiferida. They are of interest because they may retain some characteristics of ancestral stocks that may have provided the link between the two orders.

Testaceans with soft shells undergo binary fission, but other methods are required where the shell is heavy. A form of budding is common; the daughter individual protrudes through the pylome and remains attached to the parent until a new shell has formed. In *Arcella*, the parent shells are often dark brown, while the daughters have clear, transparent shells. Multiple fission also occurs in a few species. Sexual reproduction has been reported for some species; gametes may be amoeboid or flagellate.

FORAMINIFERIDA

Foraminifera are large, shelled rhizopods, almost exclusively marine. Their shells sink to the bottom, collecting as foraminiferan ooze. The shells contribute heavily to the substance of sedimentary rocks, and as a result the identification of foraminifera aids in the recognition of strata in a region. Their importance in locating the domes in which oil may be found has stimulated a great deal of work on fossil foraminifera. Some 300 genera, classified in about 50 families are now known, the majority occurring only as fossils.

Foraminiferan shells (Fig. 3.18) are usually composed of a series of chambers, often of increasing size, the last open to the exterior. Most of the shells are perforate, containing many small pores through which protoplasm emerges. A continuous layer of protoplasm covers the shell surface, and gives rise to an extensive meshwork of rhizopodia. Although some shells are formed of foreign particles cemented together and a few are siliceous, the majority are calcareous. The first chamber is the proloculum, to which succeeding chambers are added. Some members of a species have shells with a large proloculum and are called megalospheric; others have a small proloculum and are called microspheric.

Modern foraminifera have a complex life cycle with alternating sexual and asexual generations. According to Myers, microspheric shells are generally much less common, probably because they arise from zygotes and fertilization is relatively uncommon, at least in pelagic species. The microspheric organisms are larger and multinucleate, although the proloculum of the shell is small. When mature the microspheric organisms undergo multiple fission, giving rise to small organisms that initiate the megalospheric generation (Fig. 3.18B). The megalospheric forms have a large proloculum but remain uninucleate and are smaller than microspheric organisms. In some species, two megalospheric organisms become associated in fertilization cysts, where they produce gametocytes that undergo meiosis and give rise to gametes. After fertilization, the zygotes secrete a microspheric proloculum, and eventually escape from the cyst, growing into the large, microspheric adults. Not all foraminifera form fertilization cysts. Some liberate thousands of flagellated, free-swimming gametes.

Actinopodea

The characteristic organelle of actinopods is the axopodium, although a few have apparently lost the axial filament from their pseudopodia and have filopodia. Two distinctive adaptational lines occur, each recognized as an order. The Radiolarida are marine, and have a perforated, membranous central capsule which separates differentiated outer extracapsular and inner intracapsular layers of cytoplasm. A complex and often beautiful skeleton of radiating siliceous or strontium sulfate rods is usually present, often consolidated into intricate forms. The Heliozoida lack a skele-

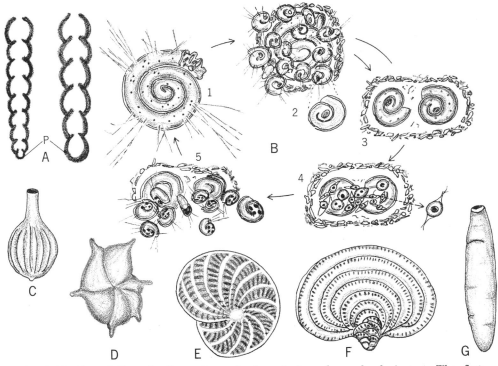

Fig. 3.18. Foraminifera. A. Comparison of microspheric and megalospheric test. The first chamber or proloculum (p) is small in the microspheric test and large in the megalospheric test. Successive chambers are added according to the growth pattern characteristic of the species. B. Life cycle of *Spirillina vivipara*. A large, multinucleate organism is shown at 1. It reproduces asexually to form many uninucleate megalospheric forms (2), which escape, encyst in pairs (3), and develop into gametes (4). After syngamy, the zygotes develop into small microspheric organisms (5) which in turn develop into mature multinucleate, microspheric forms. C-G. Some examples of foraminiferan tests, to illustrate a part of the range of shapes. C, *Lagena striata*; D, *Hantkenia alabamensis*; E, *Elphidium crispa*; F, *Pavonina flabelliformis*; G, *Bathysiphon humilis*. (B, modified from Myers. C, after Rhumbler. D, after Cushman, from Kudo. F, after Parr; G, after Calvez, from Hall.)

ton of radiating spicules and a central capsule, and are predominantly fresh-water species.

RADIOLARIDA

The skeletons of radiolarians, like those of foraminiferans, sink to the bottom of the sea, forming extensive deposits of radiolarian ooze, eventually incorporated in sedimentary rocks. As the skeletons are usually siliceous, it is easy to clean them off with acid, and an enormous number of fossil species, some pre-Cambrian, are known. Classification is largely based on the nature of the central capsule and the skeleton.

Radiolaria, alive or as skeletons, are among the most beautiful of animal forms. Despite their skeleton, they are beautifully adapted for a floating existence. Their universal symmetry, with radiating parts, provides surface and extends pseudopodia as traps against which planktonic organisms brush and lose their lives. The outer cytoplasm is without nuclei and forms the frothy calymma, filled with large vacuoles containing a fluid of low specific gravity (Fig. 3.19E). Food ingested by the pseudopodia is passed to the inner part of the calymma, where it is digested in food vacuoles. The calymmar alveoli burst during rough water conditions, and the organisms descend to deeper water, where new alveoli form to bring them to the surface again. In some forms, a thin, assimilative layer, the phaeodium, covers the central capsule. The phaeodium is often packed with brownish granules, believed to be waste products. The capsular membrane separates the cortical protoplasm from the intracapsular protoplasm, within which one or many nuclei are found. The intracapsular protoplasm is usually dotted with fatty droplets, crystals, and pigment granules, red, yellow, and sometimes blue in color. The central capsule is perforated, sometimes uniformly and sometimes in one or three pore fields, permitting contact between the extracapsular and intracapsular protoplasm.

Details of the life cycle are uncertain. According to Kuhn, many flagellated swarmers, presumably gametes, are liberated, which develop into adults after fertilization. Adults undergo binary fission or budding to reproduce asexually. Dividing forms usually divide the skeleton, unless it is strongly consolidated, each daughter regenerating the missing skeletal elements.

HELIOZOIDA

Heliozoans, like radiolarians, are adapted for a floating existence, and the pseudopodia are more important as extensions of the body to make contact with food than for locomotion. They are holozoic, feeding on algae or small animals that touch their pseudopodia. There is evidence that some species secrete a toxic substance which stuns or kills the prey. When large particles of food are ingested, many pseudopodia co-operate; the axial filaments are resorbed and the pseudopodia merge and enlarge. In *Actinophrys* and *Actinosphaerium*, two of the common genera, the outer protoplasm is highly vacuolated, reminiscent of the radiolarian calymma (Fig. 3.19A, C). Many Heliozoida have a gelatinous envelope, and some have chitinous or siliceous plates or spicules embedded in the gelatinous covering. A few have become sessile, the stalk attaching to a perforated capsule through which the axopodia emerge (Fig. 3.19B). They show many tendencies which resemble radiolarian adaptations, but are evidently a distinctive adaptational line.

Eusporozoa

Many Protozoa make their living as parasites, developing special characteristics in adapting to their peculiar environment. In general, a parasitic habit favors: a) the reduction of digestive structures; b) the development of attachment organs if the parasite lives in a peristaltic, hollow organ; and c) a great increase in reproductive potential. A number of distinctive protozoan lines have responded to parasitism by developing a habit of sporulation, producing numerous, small, infective, and usually highly protected spores. Sporulation sets them apart from the parasitic flagellates, sarcodines, or ciliates. All sporulating forms were once collected under the general term Sporozoa, but they are proving so diverse in the details of their life cycles and spore form that it seems advisable today to separate them into several subphyla. The largest

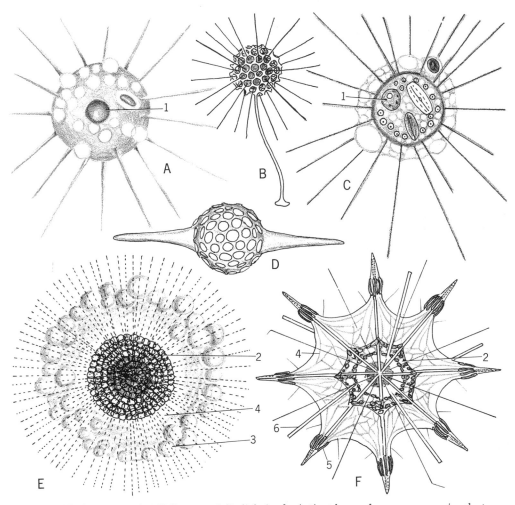

Fig. 3.19. Representative Heliozoa and Radiolaria. A. *Actinophrys sol*, a common uninucleate heliozoan. B. *Clathrulina elegans*, a stalked heliozoan with a perforate test, through which the axopodia protrude. C. *Actinosphaerium eichorni*, a common multinucleate heliozoan. D. Central capsule of *Sphaerostylus ostracion*. E. *Thalassicola nucleata*, a radiolarian that reaches up to 5 mm. in diameter. F. *Acanthometra*, another radiolarian, with heavy, muscular fibrils (myofrisks) that increase its volume when contracted, causing it to float upwards. (B, after Leidy. C, after Kudo. D, after Jahn. E, after Huth. F, after Moroff and Stiasny.) 1, nucleus; 2, central capsule; 3, calymma; 4, extracapsular cytoplasm; 5, myofrisk; 6, skeletal spine.

and best known of these is the Eusporozoa, characterized by simple spores and a life cycle in which sexual reproduction immediately precedes sporulation. It is a relatively homogeneous group, requiring but a single class, the Telosporidia.

The generalized telosporidian life cycle begins with the infection of a host by a spore, either taken with food or water, or transmitted by bites of blood-sucking invertebrates. The spores germinate to give rise to schizonts, which reproduce asexually in any of several ways during the period of schizogony. Eventually gamonts are formed, which undergo meiosis and form one or many gametes or gamete nuclei. The zygote typically forms an oöcyst, contained in a resistant membrane, and produces one or many sporonts, which give rise to spores.

Sporozoan classification is by no means stable, for electron microscope studies are revealing structural details suggesting unsuspected relationships. The Telosporidia are usually divided into three orders: Gre-

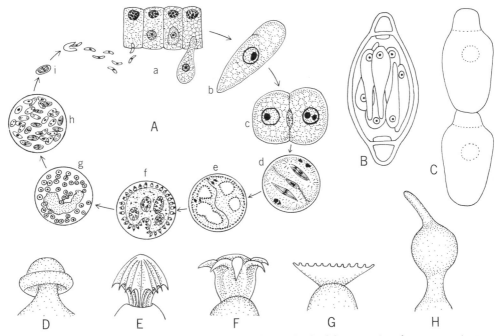

Fig. 3.20. Gregarines. A. Life cycle of *Lankestrella culicis*. At (a) sporozoites from a germinating spore are entering epithelial cells for a period of intracellular growth and development, emerging at least to develop into mature trophic forms (sporadins) (b) in the gut lumen. Two sporadins come together (c) and secrete a common cyst membrane (d). Repeated nuclear divisions and multiple cleavage (e, f) produce gametes that undergo syngamy to form zygotes (g). Each zygote develops into a spore (h) containing 8 sporozoites. The sporozoites escape when the spore is eaten by an appropriate host. B. Spore of *Rhynchocystis porrecta*, showing the enclosed sporozoites. C. Two sporadins of *Gregarina blattarum* in syzygy. D-H. The epimerites of several cephaline gregarines, illustrating the diversity of form and variety of attachment organs. D, *Discorhynchus truncatus*; E, *Sciadiophora phalangii*; F, *Corycella armata*; G, *Dactylophorus robusta*; H, *Bulbocephalus elongatus*. (A, after Wenyon. B, after Hesse. C, after Kudo, from Kudo. D-G, after Léger. H, after Watson.)

garinida, Coccidia, and Haemosporidia. Levine (1961) has suggested that the Haemosporidia should be considered a subdivision of the Coccidia. The orders are based on characteristics that will become more meaningful as life cycles are examined. Gregarines are unique in having the mature parasite extracellular, whereas in Coccidia and Haemosporidia it is intracellular. Haemosporidia have a motile zygote, and produce spores without a spore membrane, while Coccidia have an immobile zygote and form spores protected by a resistant membrane.

GREGARINIDIA

Gregarines show several traits which are unique among the Telosporidia. They may be less intensively adapted to the parasitic habit than the other subclasses, but too little is known about host-parasite relationships to make such conclusions final. As gregarines live in hollow organs rather than within cells, they are the only Telosporidia in which attachment organs have appeared. Adaptation to life in an organ cavity is generally thought to require less specialization than to life in a host cell; it should be noted, however, that gregarines pass through an intracellular stage in their life cycle. One order of gregarines has no schizogony cycle in the life cycle, in this being unique and sacrificing some of the reproductive potential of most Telosporidia.

Infection begins when the host ingests a spore. The spores typically contain eight sporozoites, each of which enters a host epithelial cell (Fig. 3.20A). The sporozoites grow for a time, eventually emerging into the lumen of the host organ and developing into large, more or less vermiform, sporadins. When the sporadins mature, they become associated in a union known as syzygy, and a cyst membrane forms around them, ordinarily in pairs. The encysted sporadins act as gamonts, each undergoing many nuclear divisions, followed by cytoplasmic cleavage, to form numerous gametes. In some forms isogametes are produced; in others anisogametes. In either case, the zygote serves as a sporont, secreting a spore membrane and dividing to form eight sporozoites. This life cycle is typical of the Eugregarinida. The Schizogregarinida differ primarily in having a period of schizogony, during which the sporadins increase by budding, multiple fission, or plasmotomy.

The sporadins are the most commonly observed stage of the life cycle. Schizogregarine and acephaline eugregarine sporadins are undivided, while the cephaline eugregarines are divided by a partition into an anterior, smaller protomerite and a larger deuteromerite (Fig. 3.20C). Many of the cephaline gregarines have an attachment organelle, the epimerite, at the anterior tip of the protomerite. Epimerites are sometimes fantastically formed, and are useful in taxonomic separation of many genera (Fig. 3.20D-H).

COCCIDIA

Coccidia are parasites of higher invertebrates and vertebrates, some causing serious loss to poultry raisers and affecting other domestic animals. When spores germinate in the digestive tract, the sporozoites are freed and penetrate epithelial cells, growing into schizonts (Fig. 3.21). Unlike the similar stages of gregarines, they remain within the host cells, undergoing multiple fission to produce many merozoites. These leave the destroyed host cell and infect other cells to repeat the schizogony cycle. Eventually, merozoites develop into gamonts instead of schizonts. Gamonts develop into macrogametes or microgametes, the zygote secretes a resistant cyst membrane and becomes an oöcyst (Fig. 3.21A). The zygote divides a characteristic number of times, depending on its genus, to form sporonts, which secrete a spore membrane and divide to form a number of sporozoites characteristic of the genus (Fig. 3.21B). Oöcysts, containing the spores, are liberated from the host and are infective for other animals. In one family, the Aggregatidae, the life cycle has become more complex and two host species are parasitized. *Aggregata eberthi*, for example, undergoes schizogony in a crab, and sexual reproduction and sporogony in a cuttlefish which feeds on the crabs. Another group, the haemogregarines (Fig. 3.21C-E), carry out their schizogony within blood cells or reticuloendothelial cells, and are transmitted by blood-sucking invertebrates in which sexual reproduction and sporulation occur.

HAEMOSPORIDIA

Haemosporidia are blood parasites transmitted by blood-sucking invertebrates. Schizogony occurs in the vertebrate host; sporogony in the invertebrate. The most important genus is *Plasmodium*, responsible for malaria.

The malaria sporozoite is introduced by the mosquito when a blood meal is taken (Fig. 3.22 q-a). In some *Plasmodium* species, the sporozoites enter cells of the reticuloendothelial system, undergoing schizogony to produce cryptozoites, infective for other reticuloendothelial cells or, under appropriate conditions, for erythrocytes. This is the exoerythrocytic schizogony cycle. When cryptozoites enter erythrocytes a young schizont is formed, which passes through characteristic stages. The young schizont is ring-shaped, with a central vacuole. It becomes band-form or amoeboid, eventually growing to fill or nearly fill the host cell. The nucleus divides repeatedly until 12 to 24 nuclei are present; the mature schizont cleaves in multiple fission to produce merozoites, infective for other host cells. Some merozoites become gamonts instead of schizonts, differentiating into macrogametocytes or microgametocytes, which remain quiescent in the host cell until they are taken with blood by a mosquito. In the mosquito stomach, the gametocytes mature, the microgametocyte

forming numerous slender, motile sperm. The zygote, characteristic of the Haemosporidia, is motile and is called an oökinete. It penetrates the wall of the mosquito stomach, and rounds up to form an oöcyst, within which sporulation occurs. Many naked sporozoites are formed, which migrate to the salivary glands of the mosquito, ready to infect a new vertebrate host.

The malaria paroxysm is correlated with the erythrocytic schizogony cycle. The number of infected erythrocytes increases geometrically, and as toxic materials are released with the merozoites, it is not long before symptoms occur at the end of each schizogony cycle. The onset of the paroxysm is a severe chill, followed by a febrile period with temperatures of 104°

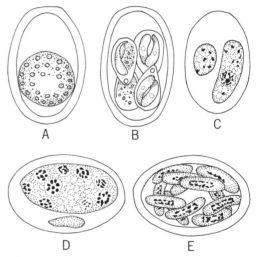

Fig. 3.21. Coccidia and Haemogregarinida. A-B. Young and mature oocysts of *Eimeria steidae*, a coccidian from the intestine of rabbits, showing the zygote and the four spores, each with two sporozoites arising from it. C-E. Stages in the development of haemogregarine, *Haemogregarina stepanowi*, a blood parasite of turtles and leeches. C, a macrogametocyte in a turtle erythrocyte; D, a schizont; E, a group of merozoites in an infected erythrocyte. (A-B, after Wasilewski, from Kudo. C-E, after Reichenow, from Hall.)

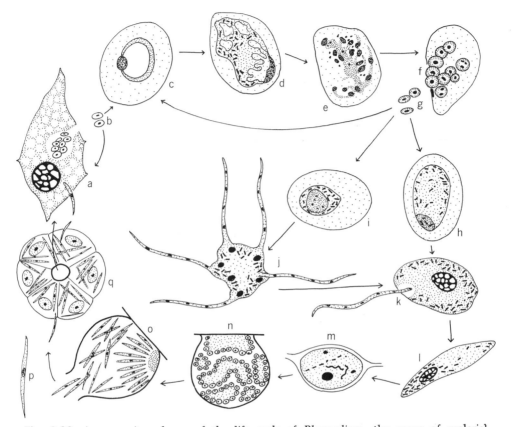

Fig. 3.22. A composite scheme of the life cycle of *Plasmodium*, the genus of malarial parasites. The bite of an infected mosquito introduces naked sporozoites into the body of the vertebrate host. In at least some species of *Plasmodium*, the sporozoites enter reticuloendothelial cells (a), setting up an exoerythrocytic schizogony cycle. The sporozoite develops into a schizont that undergoes multiple fission to produce many minute cryptozoites (b), which emerge from the host cell and infect other reticuloendothelial cells or, under appropriate conditions, enter the blood and infect erythrocytes (c). Here they produce characteristic ring forms, enlarged in the diagram, which grow into schizonts and establish an erythrocytic schizogony cycle. They grow, undergo repeated nuclear divisions, and eventually multiple fission (d-f), producing merozoites (g) infective for other erythrocytes. The schizogony cycle may be repeated indefinitely, with a malarial paroxysm associated with each cycle if the infection is heavy. Some merozoites, however, develop into macrogametocytes (h) or microgametocytes (i). When blood is taken by a mosquito, the erythrocytes containing gametocytes are digested in the mosquito stomach. The freed gametocytes mature into gametes (j-k), and fertilization results in a motile zygote or oökinete (l), characteristic of Haemosporidia. The oökinete penetrates the stomach wall and forms an oöcyst on its outer surface (m-n). Many naked sporozoites are formed in the oöcyst (o). These escape and migrate through the haemocoel to the salivary glands (p-q), where they accumulate and are injected when the mosquito takes its next blood meal.

57

F. or more. The fever terminates in profuse sweating, the defervescent stage. The three principal human species are *Plasmodium vivax*, in which schizogony requires 48 hours and a paroxysm occurs every third day (benign tertian malaria); *P. falciparum*, requiring 36 to 48 hours for schizogony and a paroxysm about every third day (malignant tertiary malaria); and *P. malariae*, with a 72-hour schizogony cycle and a paroxysm every fourth day (quartan malaria).

The Cnidosporidea

The characteristic cnidosporidian organelle is a spirally wound polar filament, occurring in the spore, and often contained within a polar capsule. The polar capsule is remarkably similar to cnidarian nematocysts, but this is probably a matter of convergence rather than an indication of relationship. Its function remains something of a mystery. It may anchor the spore to the intestinal epithelium when it enters a new host, preventing its elimination from the digestive tube before spore germination is complete. There are three classes, Myxosporidea, Actinomyxidea, and Microsporidea.

MYXOSPORIDEA

The vast majority of myxosporidia parasitize fishes, although a few species live in other cold-blooded vertebrates. The spores are easily recognized, for the spore wall is composed of two or more valves meeting in sutures, and one or more polar capsules can be seen in fresh material (Fig. 3.23B). One or two sporozoites are found in the spore; if one is present, it is binucleate. The sporozoites are gametes, the two sporoplasmic nuclei uniting to form a zygote nucleus before or at the time of spore germination. The amoeboid zygote migrates to the host organ, and grows into a schizont, amoeboid in coelozoic species

(Fig. 3.23A) but forming a large multinucleate cyst or tumor in tissue-inhabiting forms. Schizogony consists of many nuclear divisions, accompanied by budding or multiple fission in amoeboid schizonts. During schizogony, two kinds of nuclei appear, vegetative nuclei, apparently trophic in function, and generative nuclei, which enter into spore formation. Sporonts form as distinct cells containing generative nuclei, and undergo repeated karyokinesis to develop a set of nuclei necessary to constitute one or two spores, depending on the species. In each sporont, one or two sporoblasts appear, containing definite cells which differentiate into the spore parts. Capsulogenous cells secrete the polar capsules, and valvular cells form the valves of the spore. A binucleate sporoplasmic cell may divide into two uninucleate sporozoites, or remain as a binucleate sporozoite. Mature spores escape from the host, before or after its death depending on their site within the host. Taxonomy depends largely on the arrangement of valves and polar capsules in the spore, and over-all spore form.

ACTINOMYXIDEA

Actinomyxidea are a small and poorly known group of parasites found in annelids. They are characterized by triradiate symmetry, three polar capsules, and, in some species, many sporozoites (Fig. 3.23F). The life cycle differs markedly from that of the myxosporidians, insofar as it has been described. The whole adult parasite serves as a sporont, and spore formation takes a somewhat different course.

MICROSPORIDEA

Microsporidea are intracellular cnidosporidians found in a variety of invertebrates and cold-blooded vertebrates. *Nosema* is an important genus, causing disease in silkworms and honey bees. The microsporidian spore (Fig. 3.23E) is simpler than the spore of Myxosporidea, with a simple spore membrane, and in many cases, no polar capsule surrounding the polar filament. Recent electron microscope observations by Kudo and Daniels show that the filament is a hollow thread.

The life cycle differs from the myxo-

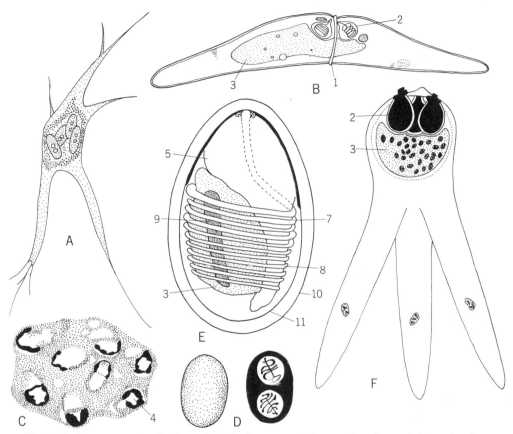

Fig. 3.23. Representative Cnidosporidia. A. A myxosporidian trophozoite containing developing spores. B. A spore of *Ceratomyxa inversa*, showing the bivalved spore membrane, and polar capsules containing polar filaments, typical of Myxosporidia. C. A mature sporont of a miscrosporidian, *Thelohania legeri*. D. Fresh and stained spore of a microsporidian, *Telomyxa glugeiformis*, showing the absence of spore valves and the polar filaments without a polar capsule, typical of Microsporidia. E. Structure of a microsporidian spore, as revealed by electron micrographs. F. The spore of an actinomyxidian, *Guyenoti sphaerulosa*, with three polar capsules and triradiate symmetry, typical of Actinomyxidia. (A-B, after Meglitsch. C, after Kudo. D, after Léger and Hesse. E, after Kudo and Daniels. F, after Naville, from Kudo.) 1, suture, where the two shell valves meet; 2, polar capsule, containing the coiled polar filament; 3, sporoplasm or sporozoite; 4, developing spores; 5, polaroplast, a laminated structure that may swell to cause extrusion of the polar filament; 6, polar mass and polaroplast membrane; 7, anterior polar filament; 8, posterior polar filament, hollow like the anterior filament, but narrower; 9, sporoplasm nucleus; 10, outer membrane of spore wall; 11, inner membrane of spore wall.

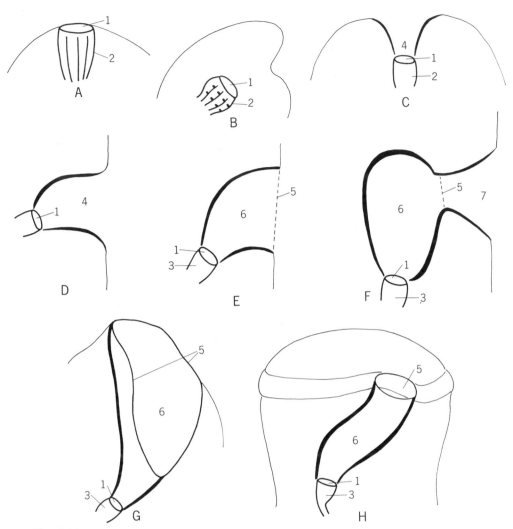

Fig. 3.24. Ciliate Cytostomal Evolution. Several distinctive evolutionary trends can be seen in ciliate mouth structure. The primitive position of the mouth is at the anterior end of the body; it tends to move to a lateral or ventral position. The primitive mouth is without cilia or has cilia continuous with the body ciliature, behaving like body cilia during division. The mouth of more highly specialized ciliates is preceded by a buccal cavity, containing buccal cilia that are often fused to form compound ciliary organelles and behave unlike the somatic ciliature during division. The most primitive mouth structure is seen in rhabdophorine gymnostomes (A), with the mouth in the primitive position and without cilia. It opens into a cytopharynx supported by a loose basket of rod-like trichites. The migration of the mouth to a ventral or lateral position and the consolidation of the trichites to form a solid pharyngeal basket leads to the condition seen in cyrtophorine gymnostomes (B). Trichostomes have a mouth opening into a preoral vestibule, whose cilia are continuous with the somatic ciliature and behave like body cilia during division. The vestibular cilia are never fused to form compound ciliary organelles. The mouth is in the primitive position in the most primitive trichostomes (C), but is ventral or lateral in the more highly specialized trichostomes (D). Hymeno-

sporidian life cycle. The intracellular schizonts undergo many divisions, while the host cell hypertrophies enormously. Eventually the schizonts form binucleate cells, within which syngamy occurs. The zygote serves as a sporont (Fig. 3.23C), undergoing nuclear divisions to give rise to a number of sporoblasts characteristic of its genus.

Acnidosporidea

Acnidosporidea are characterized by simple spores, and a life cycle unlike the telosporidean life cycle. Very little detailed work has been directed toward them, and relationships within the group are uncertain. One group, the Haplosporidia, occurring in lower vertebrates and invertebrates, apparently undergoes only schizogony, lacking sexual stages. A perplexing group of muscle parasites, the Sarcosporidia, are often included with the Acnidosporidea, but their affinities are now being questioned. An easy example to obtain is *Coelosporidium periplanetae* from the malpighian tubules of cockroaches.

Ciliophora

The subphylum of ciliated Protozoa is a large and diversified group of organisms, adapted for a variety of habitats and so superficially dissimilar, but exceedingly homogeneous insofar as basic structural elements are concerned. Their nuclei are differentiated into macronuclei, predominantly vegetative in function, and micronuclei, from which the macronuclei are derived and which are especially important during sexual reproduction. The ciliary apparatus differs in complexity and distribution, but the fine details of its structure remain consistent, and distinctive somatic and oral ciliatures are characteristically present. Sexual reproduction involves the union of nuclei but not cells.

The outer surface is covered with a pellicle, through which the cilia extend. Details of ciliary structure have already been described. Trichocysts are saccular pellicular organelles, which are of two kinds. Some paralyze or stun prey organisms, and are sometimes called toxicysts. Others form needle-like rods when extruded (Fig. 3.25B), with a differentiated cap at the tip. They are often localized near the cytostome, but in some species are uniformly distributed over the whole body surface, alternating with the cilia. The outer layer of protoplasm is firm, forming a cortex in which the trichocysts are embedded. Myonemes are sometimes present, lying in the outer layer of the cortex. These contractile fibers permit the animal to extend or contract parts of the body. Pores

stomes have a preoral buccal cavity differing from a vestibule in having specialized buccal cilia that behave unlike somatic cilia during division, and which are usually fused to form undulating membranes, a peniculus as in *Paramecium*, or other compound organelles. The more primitive hymenostomes have a buccal overture at the body surface which leads into the buccal cavity, at the bottom of which the cytostome and cytopharynx are located (E). The more complex hymenostomes have a vestibule with vestibular cilia, leading into the buccal overture of the buccal cavity (F), as in the peniculines. Spirotrichs and hypotrichs are characterized by an adoral zone of membranelles which borders much of the buccal overture (G). The huge buccal cavity (usually called the peristome) contains the special ciliature typical of a buccal cavity and leads to the cytostome. Peritrichs also have a buccal overture leading to a buccal cavity with specialized cilia. The narrow, funnel-shaped buccal cavity, often called the infundibulum, leads to the cytostome (H). (After Corliss.) 1, cytostome; 2, pharyngeal basket of trichites supporting the cytopharynx; 3, cytopharynx; 4, primitive vestibule leading to the cytopharynx; 5, buccal overture; 6, buccal cavity; 7, secondary vestibule leading to the buccal overture.

for the contractile vacuoles and egestion of food vacuole contents are present, usually in a characteristic position.

The two subclasses of Ciliata are based primarily on the adoral zone of membranelles, which in the spirotrichs forms a clockwise spiral leading into the oral region. The holotrichs are more variable, but do not have the kind of adoral zone characteristic of spirotrichs. A formidable vocabulary has grown up about the elements of the ciliate oral apparatus. Corliss, who has contributed greatly to our understanding of ciliate infraciliature, has offered a series of definitions which may simplify some of the taxonomic problems. Schematic representations of the relationships of mouth parts are shown and discussed in Fig. 3.24, and should be examined carefully before attempting to understand the classification of ciliates. Nine orders of Holotricha, and six orders of Spirotricha are recognized; their characteristics of the more important ones are summarized below.

Subclass Holotrichia. Ciliates without an adoral zone of membranelles leading to the cytosome.

Order Gymnostomatida. With the cytopharynx strengthened by rods known as trichites; body relatively simple. It is divided into two suborders, Rhabdophorina and Cyrtophorina. *Rhabdophorina* have a simple body form and ciliation and a simple method of mouth formation during fission; they are typically carnivorous with an expansible cytopharynx. *Cyrtophorina* are often flattened, with only ventral cilia, and may have a complex method of mouth formation during fission; the cytostome is ventral and with a basket of fused trichites; typically herbivorous.

Order Trichostomatida. Cytostome with a vestibule and vestibular ciliation, sometimes fairly complex and body with uniform ciliation in most cases.

Order Chonotrichida. Cytostome with a vestibule and vestibular ciliation, drawn out into a funnel; body rigid, without somatic cilia, and attached as adults.

Order Suctorida. Profoundly modified holotrichs, ciliated only as larvae and without a mouth, feeding by tentacles.

Order Apostomatida. Ciliates with a small rosette surrounding the mouth and typically living in marine crustaceans.

Order Astomatida. Saprobic ciliates without a mouth or tentacles, with uniform body ciliation, generally living as parasites in oligochaete annelids.

Order Hymenostomatida. Cytosome with a buccal cavity containing specialized buccal ciliature and sometimes with a vestibule between the buccal cavity and cytostome; buccal cavity ventral and body ciliation diverse, generally free living. There are three suborders, Tetrahymenina, Peniculina, and Pleuronematina. *Tetrahymenina* are characterized by a buccal ciliature with an undulating membrane at the right of the cytostome and three membranelles on the left; typically there is no vestibule and body ciliation is uniform. *Peniculina* are characterized by a buccal ciliature with one or several compound organelles known as peniculi with cilia fused or separate. Generally a vestibule is present. *Pleuronematina* have the buccal ciliature dominated by the right-hand undulating membrane, often very large, with membranelles on the left reduced or united with right-hand membrane; mouth usually near middle of body; usually with a prominent caudal cilium.

Order Thigmotrichida. Cytostome with a buccal cavity and specialized buccal ciliature near the middle, on the ventral, or at the posterior surface; with prominent thigmotactic cilia and reduced body ciliation elsewhere.

Order Peritrichida. Oral apparatus at apex of body, with membranelles and membrane in circular whorls around body, entering through a deep buccal cavity, the infundibulum.

Subclass Spirotrichia. Cilates with an

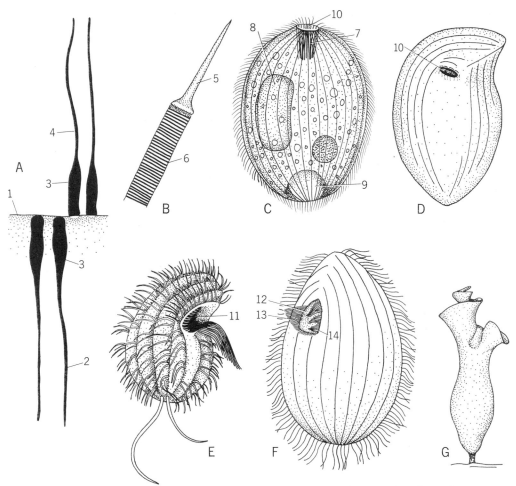

Fig. 3.25. Trichocysts and Some Representative Ciliates. **A.** Trichocysts of a ciliate, *Dileptus*, before and after discharge, suggesting that they invert during discharge. **B.** Diagram of a discharged trichocyst of *Paramecium*, as seen in electron micrographs, showing the solid barb and striated shaft. **C.** *Prorodon discolor*, a typical rhabdophorine gymnostome. **D.** *Chilodonella labiata*, a typical cyrtophorine gymnostome, without specialized oral ciliature but with a rather complex oral structure. **E.** *Colpoda steinii*, a fairly complex trichostome with a vestibule containing modified cilia, laterally placed. **F.** *Tetrahymena pyriformis*, a hymenostome with a buccal cavity containing specialized ciliature, including an undulating membrane on the left and three membranelle-like membranes on the right. **G.** *Spirochona gemmipara*, a chonotrich, showing the absence of somatic cilia and the extension of the vestibular region to form a complex funnel, characteristic of the group. (**A**, after Hayes. **B**, based on Jakus and Hall. **C-G**, after Corliss.) **1**, pellicle surface; **2**, trichocyst root; **3**, trichocyst bulb; **4**, trichocyst thread; **5**, barb; **6**, shaft; **7**, basket of trichites in cytopharynx; **8**, macronucleus; **9**, contractile vacuole; **10**, opening of cytostome; **11**, opening of vestibule; **12**, buccal overture opening into the buccal cavity; **13**, undulating membrane on the left side of the buccal cavity; **14**, the three undulating membranes on the right of the tetrahymenine buccal overture, resembling the adoral zone membranelles of spirotrichs.

adoral zone of membranelles winding clockwise to the cytostome.

Order Heterotrichida. With the body cilia usually uniform and simple body shape; often very large.

Order Oligotrichida. With little or no body ciliation, and a conspicuous adoral zone, often extending on the body apex; generally small.

Order Tintinnida. With reduced body ciliation and an apical adoral zone with interspersed tentacular bristles; with a lorica made of foreign particles.

Order Entodiniomorpha. With reduced body ciliation and often with a dorsal zone of membranelles in addition to the adoral zone; with a firm pellicle, but never with a lorica; living in the gut of ruminants and other herbivorous mammals.

Order Odontosomatida. Without cirri and with flattened, complex body form; adoral zone much reduced, with eight mebranelles; with definite pellicle, often pulled out in spines.

Order Hypotrichida. With cirri or cilia on the ventral surface and bristles, presumably sensory, on the dorsal surface; body flattened and pellicle rigid, and with a conspicuous adoral zone surrounding a very large buccal cavity, known as the peristome.

GYMNOSTOMATIDA

The gymnostomes are the simplest and most primitive of the ciliates in a number of ways. The oral apparatus is less complex than in other orders, for there is no special oral ciliature, and the cytostome is not separated from the body surface by a vestibule. Many of the most common ciliates belong to this order; nearly every culture has at least a few gymnostomes in it. The gymnostomes are divided into two suborders, the Rhabdophorina, with anterior or lateral mouth, and the Cyrtophorina, with a ventral mouth. The rhabdophorines are the more primitive, as evidenced by the oral position and loose basket of trichites, as well as by simple methods of fission and mouth formation. The rhabdophorines are predominantly carnivorous, and include the prostomes, with an anterior mouth (Fig. 3.25C), and pleurostomes, with the mouth laterally placed. The herbivorous cyrtophorines have a consolidated pharyngeal basket. The body is often flattened with unciliated regions (Fig. 3.25D).

ORDER TRICHOSTOMATIDA

Trichostomes are highly varied, and probably include a number of unrelated organisms derived from different ancestral types. The outstanding features include the often highly asymmetrical form, and the presence of a vestibule, a depressed region of the body containing somewhat modified somatic ciliature, but without the complex buccal ciliature found in a true buccal cavity. A number of the more complicated trichostomes form division cysts, within which they dedifferentiate and divide once or twice. The young organisms have simple gymnostome characteristics, but undergo complex morphogenetic changes involving torsion, and differential growth of different kineties to assume the modified trichostome form of the adult. Trichostomes occur in fresh and salt water, and some are endoparasitic. *Colpoda* (Fig. 3.25E) is a typical form. Some interesting members occur in the intestine of sea urchins. Because the full morphological details of the group have not been worked out as yet, it is probable that the classification of the trichostomes will undergo some important modifications.

An interesting recent modification has moved *Paramecium*, long considered the best known of the trichostomes, to the Hymenostomatida, and moved *Balantidium*, a well-known genus of intestinal parasites, into the trichostomes. *Balantidium coli* is a human parasite, responsible for balantidial dysentery.

CHONOTRICHIDA

The chonotrichs are sessile organisms, usually found attached to marine crustaceans. *Spirochona* (Fig. 3.25G), however, is attached to fresh-water gammarids and is a good representative of the group. The adult forms are completely without body cilia, and give rise to young by budding. The buds develop into migratory larvae, which are similar to cyrtophorine gymnostomes, and undergo a very extensive metamorphosis to develop into the highly specialized adult. During this process, the vestibule becomes greatly enlarged to form an apical funnel.

SUCTORIDA

The suctorians were long considered so unlike other ciliates that they were put into a separate subclass. Recent studies, however, indicate that they have close affinities with the holotrichs, although the adult stages show no obvious relationship. The adults are completely devoid of cilia, and are sessile, often attached by a non-contractile stalk (Fig. 3.26A-C). The body is sometimes branched, and irregular, and sometimes nearly spherical. Many inhabit a lorica. Tentacles are characteristic organelles. These hollow, tubular organelles may be suctorial, terminating in knobs, or raptorial, terminating in sharp points. Suctorial tentacles are used in feeding, and raptorial tentacles, when present, for capture of prey. Suctoria reproduce asexually by budding, producing larvae reminiscent of gymnostomes. They attach and undergo extensive metamorphosis to become an adult after passing through a migratory phase.

APOSTOMATIDA

The apostomes are a very interesting, small group of ciliates living in or on marine Crustacea. They are highly modified, and often have two hosts. A characteristic, although not quite universal organelle, is a peculiar rosette, which surrounds the tiny cytostome. The ciliature is characteristically arranged in spiral rows (Fig. 3.26F). Lwoff (1950) has summarized the very interesting and complex morphogenetic changes associated with the life cycle.

ASTOMATIDA

The astomes are parasitic ciliates which completely lack a mouth. At one time the lack of a mouth was considered the only criterion for the astomes, but in recent years study of the infraciliature has resulted in assigning some astomous ciliates to other orders. Most of them live in oligochaete hosts, although some occur in Crustacea. They generally have a very uniform somatic ciliature, and inasmuch as no oral apparatus is present, fission follows a simple pattern. Their affinities with other ciliates remain uncertain. *Anoplophrya* (Fig. 3.26E) is a good representative genus, occurring in marine crustacea and terrestrial annelids.

HYMENOSTOMATIDA

In hymenostomes, the depression leading to the mouth is equipped with specialized buccal ciliature, thus becoming a true buccal cavity. A fairly large group of ciliates are assigned to the hymenostomes, and three distinctive adaptational lines, based primarily on oral structure and the details of stomatogenesis during fission, can be recognized. These are recognized by Corliss (1959) as distinctive suborders, the Tetrahymenina, the Peniculina, and the Pleuronematina. The Tetrahymenina is a large group of relatively simple species, with a buccal cavity and without a vestibule, and typically with three membranes, comprising a short adoral zone, on the left side of the buccal cavity. The right side of the buccal cavity has a single undulating membrane. While these parts are somewhat differently placed in different genera, they are similar in character. *Tetra-hymena* (Fig. 3.25F) is a typical example. In the Peniculina, the buccal ciliature is considerably more complex. The characteristic organelle is the peniculus, believed to be comparable to the single membra-nelles of *Tetrahymena*, and always represented by two or more organelles in the buccal region. In many species, the buccal cavity has withdrawn from the body surface, and a vestibule, with somewhat modified somatic ciliature, is present. *Paramecium* is a typical member, although it

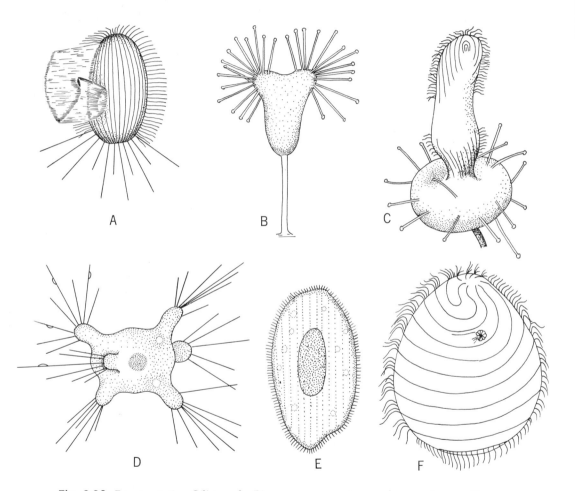

Fig. 3.26. Representative Ciliates. A. *Pleuronema coronatum,* a hymenostome with a conspicuous undulating membrane on the right side of the buccal overture. B. *Acineta tuberosa,* a suctorian with two clusters of capitate tentacles. C. *Podophrya collina,* a suctorian, reproducing by budding. Note the holotrich-like ciliation of the bud. D. *Staurophrya elegans,* an asymmetrical suctorian with raptorial tentacles. E. *Anoplophrya orchestii,* an astome ciliate. F. *Foettingeria actinarium,* an apostome ciliate, showing the rosette-shaped mouth. (A-C, F, after Corliss. D, after Zacharias, from Kudo. E, after Summers and Kidder.)

possesses a quadrulus not present in other peniculine ciliates, and an endoral membrane which probably is homologous with the undulating membrane of the tetrahymenine hymenostomes. Where new mouth formation involves one or several kineties in the tetrahymenine group, the posterior part of parent mouth contributes the primordia of the daughter mouth, so that somatic and oral ciliature remain autonomous in the peniculine and also the pleuronematine group. The Pleuronematina oral region is equipped with a conspicuous undulating membrane on the right, and the adoral zone is often very inconspicuous. The cytostome is near the middle of the body. Long caudal bristles, apparently sensory in function, or one or more long caudal cilia, are often present, and the somatic ciliature is often reduced. Stomatogenesis is autonomous, as in peniculines. *Pleuronema* (Fig. 3.26A) and *Cyclidium* are representative genera.

THIGMOTRICHIDA

Thigmotrichs live in or on clams and mussels. The most characteristic feature is a special field of thigmotactic cilia, which attach them to the host; other somatic cilia may be reduced. It is a small group which includes some highly modified and most interesting ciliates. *Boveria* is an example with a poorly developed thigmotactic region; *Hemispeira* (Fig. 3.27I), exceptional in living on the surface of starfish, is an example of a highly modified species.

PERITRICHIDA

The Peritrichida are among the most common and distinctive ciliates. They have been very successful; about 1000 species have been described. It is probable that *Vorticella*, the most commonly observed genus, was the first protozoan seen by Leeuwenhoek. The body is highly modified, no doubt in response to the predominantly sessile habit. Stalked forms are more or less bell-shaped, with a flattened apical surface. A conspicuous adoral zone winds counterclockwise toward the mouth, composed of one or two inner and one outer wreath of semi-membranes (Fig. 3.27F). According to Corliss (1959), the outer, more delicate wreath corresponds to the undulating membrane of tetrahymenine hymenostomes, and the heavier wreath to the adoral zone. In peritrichs, the buccal cavity has become a deep, funnel-shaped depression, often called the infundibulum, from which the buccal ciliature emerges to circumscribe the apical region.

In stalked forms, like *Vorticella*, the body ciliature is absent in the adult, but the motile larva has a posterior circlet of cilia. In mobile species, a similar circlet occurs in the adult.

The stalks are often contractile, and in some genera branch to form arboroid colonies. Contractile stalks consist of an outer sheath enclosing a spasmoneme, which consists of an outer whorl of elongated fibers and an inner mass of kinoplasm. The kinoplasm is thought to contract, and the outer fibrils to serve as antagonists. In some colonial forms, the spasmonemes branch with the stalk, so that the whole colony contracts as a unit, while in others each member contracts individually. When the stalk contracts, the bell is withdrawn somewhat and the lip beside the oral ciliature folded over it. This is made possible by myonemes in the cortex.

The mobile forms characteristically have a prominent adhesive disk at the aboral end, often provided with elaborate skeletal parts, and surrounded by a circlet of thigmotactic cilia (Fig. 3.27G). *Trichodina* is a common example, living on the surface of *Hydra*, amphibian larvae, and on the gills of fishes.

HETEROTRICHIDA

The heterotrichs are the simplest of the subclass Spirotricha. The order is divided

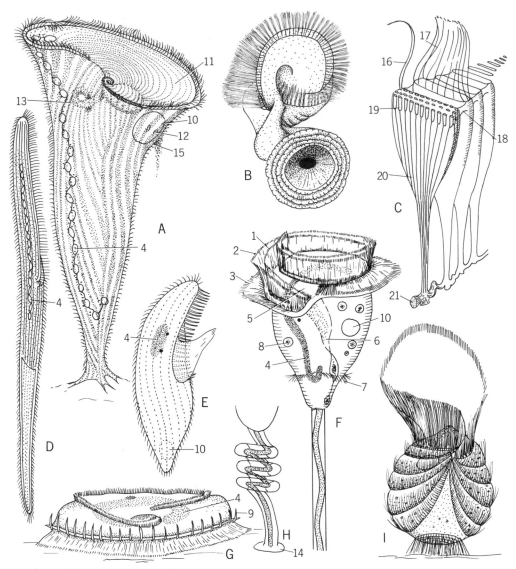

Fig. 3.27. Representative Ciliates. **A.** *Stentor coeruleus*, a large heterotrichine heterotrich, often seen in cultures. **B.** *Lichnophora macfarlandi*, a lichnophorine heterotrich, with reduced body ciliature and a basal disc encircled by concentric cycles of thigmotactic cilia, used to maintain contact with the wall of the sea cucumber respiratory tree, in which the ciliate lives. **C.** Details of the structure of adoral zone membranelles, as seen in electron micrographs. **D.** *Spirostomum minus*, an elongated heterotrichine heterotrich with the spiral of the adoral zone partly masked by elongation. *Spirostomum* is a common genus of large ciliates. **E.** *Blepharisma hyalinum*, a heterotrichine heterotrich, with uniform body ciliation and an adoral zone leading into the mouth. **F.** *Vorticella*, a sessiline peritrich. Notice the right-handed spiral of specialized cilia leading to the buccal overture. **G.** *Cyclochaeta domerguei*, a mobiline peritrich, seen from the side. In top view it is circular. **H.** Stalk of *Vorticella*,

68

into two suborders, the large Heterotrichina, containing typical heterotrichs, and the small Lichnophorina, with a highly modified body and a thigmotactic field.

The typical heterotrichs are among the most commonly observed ciliates, and are widely used as experimental material for various types of physiological studies. They are characterized by a uniform body ciliature, resembling that of primitive holotrichs, and by the conspicuous adoral zone of membranelles of the typical spirotrich type (Fig. 3.27C). The adoral zone lies to the left of a depressed region, corresponding to the buccal cavity of the holotrichs, but termed the peristome. The adoral zone frequently begins on the body surface and winds to the peristome margin, forming a clockwise spiral toward the mouth. One or more undulating membranes on the right side of the cytostome, within the peristome, are often present. A number of common, large ciliates might be taken as representatives. *Stentor, Condylostoma, Blepharisma,* and *Spirostomum* (Fig. 3.27A, D, E) are often seen. *Lichnophora* (Fig. 3.27B), a free-living or commensal ciliate with the body divided into a thigmotactic disk surrounded by wreaths of cilia, a neck region, and a flattened oral region with large peristome, is typical of the lichnophorine type.

OLIGOTRICHIDA

The oligotrichs have a reduced body ciliation, and swim as well as feed with the use of the adoral zone. They are not numerous; only about 100 species are known. *Halteria* (Fig. 3.27F), a very common fresh-water genus, has a circlet of bristles which, when contracted, causes a sudden springing movement. *Strombidium,* occurring in both fresh and salt water, is another representative species.

TINTINNIDA

The tintinnids are almost exclusively marine, and although enclosed in a lorica composed of gelatinous material usually holding foreign bodies, are almost exclusively pelagic. The body ciliature is reduced or absent, and the prominent adoral zone is interspersed with filamentous tentaculoids. There are many species. *Tintinnopsis* is a typical example (Fig. 3.28C).

ENTODINIOMORPHA

The Entodiniomorpha, a highly specialized group of ciliates, are characteristic commensals found in the digestive tract of hoofed herbivores. Sharp (1914) made an extensive study of *Epidinium,* demonstrating a very complex cortex, and the presence of skeletal plates, unique to this order. The body ciliature is sparse or lacking, and in a number of ways relationship to the oligotrichs is indicated. The characteristic dorsal zone of membranelles found in many of them appears to have been derived from the adoral zone of membranelles. The body form is extremely variable, often drawn

contracted. I. *Hemispeira asteriasi,* a thigmotrich with a conspicuous thigmotactic field encircled by cilia. (A, after Tartar. B, after Balamuth, from Corliss. C, after Randall and Jackson. D, after Kahl. E, after Wang and Nie, from Hall. F, based primarily on drawings of *Vorticella* by Noland. G, after MacLennan. I, after Wallengren, from Kudo.) 1-3, the three rows of semimembranes leading to the *Vorticella* mouth; 4, macronucleus; 5, buccal overture; 6, infundibulum, the peritrich buccal cavity; 7, telotroch, a posterior band of cilia providing mobility in a detached bell, and usually not present in stalked forms; 8, food vacuole; 9, part of the basal skeleton of the thigmotactic region; 10, contractile vacuole; 11, frontal field, the part of the body surrounded by the adoral zone; 12, pore for contractile vacuole; 13, cytopharynx; 14, holdfast; 15, cytopyge, where food vacuole contents are expelled; 16, cilium; 17, membranelle; 18, intermembranellar connective; 19, kinetosome; 20, ciliary root; 21, basal fiber.

into processes. *Entodinium* may be taken as a reasonably typical representative (Fig. 3.28A).

ODONTOSTOMATIDA

The odontostomes, a very small and relatively poorly known group of curious ciliates, occur in water containing high concentrations of organic matter. The body is flattened, often ridged and drawn out into processes, and the adoral zone contains eight membranelles. The body ciliation is reduced to a few ciliated bands. *Saprodinium* is typical of the group (Fig. 3.28D).

HYPOTRICHIDA

The hypotrichs are familiar to all who have examined many samples of marine or fresh water for Protozoa. They are flattened forms, with the body ciliature reduced to a set of cirri, composed of many cilia fused together. The more primitive forms, like *Oxytricha* (Fig. 3.28E), have rows of marginal and ventral cirri, while the more highly derived forms, like *Euplotes* (Fig. 3.28F), have the cirri greatly reduced. The number and placement of the cirri are the most significant taxonomic characteristics. One small family, of which *Aspidisca* is representative, has greatly reduced adoral zones.

The dorsal surface contains a number of sensory bristles, which, according to Roth, are essentially very short cilia, with a fine structure identical to that of other cilia.

Several unusual features of hypotrichs have raised the curiosity of many investigators, although full explanations have not been obtained. The macronucleus, which is elongated in many hypotrichs, undergoes a peculiar reorganization prior to fission (see p. 84). The hypotrichs are most interesting in their response to injury, for the complement of cirri is resorbed and a new set is formed, in much the same manner as in dividing organisms. This strange activity suggests that a complex and precisely controlled morphogenetic pattern is involved.

Functional Adaptation

Even in the simplest of animals, the complexities of living require division of labor among specialized parts; if life is to go on successfully the specialized parts must mesh to form a harmonious system serving all the necessary functions. The nature and function of one part, therefore, tend to influence the course of adaptation of other parts, just as the interplay between form and function in the organism help to determine its course of evolution as well as its ecological relationships. For example, food acquisition determines an organism's occupation and defines much of its relationship to its environment, regardless of the techniques used in processing food or disposing of residues.

Feeding and Digestion

To obtain food, Protozoa engage in a variety of occupations. The most popular are manufacturing, thieving, browsing, hunting, and trapping. A few Protozoa must be considered as miners, and some are hired as special technicians. Each vocation leads to one or several distinctive adaptational lines, from which one can learn something about the animal's problems.

FOOD SYNTHESIS—THE MANUFACTURERS

Phytoflagellates are predominantly manufacturers, producing much of what they need themselves, as well as products that are passed along the aquatic food chains. In pelagic communities, they are often the predominant producers, all other organisms depending primarily on their products.

The synthetic organisms import simple raw materials, and use energy to power their synthetic activities. Photosynthesis, depending on light energy, is best known of these activities, but it is increasingly clear that many colorless phytoflagellates are capable of extensive chemosynthesis.

The machinery by which syntheses are accomplished is molecular, composed of enzymes and energy transfer systems, and so goes beyond the limits of our discussion. Although the essentials are invisible, photosynthetic forms reveal themselves by their chromoplasts, containing chlorophyll, lam-

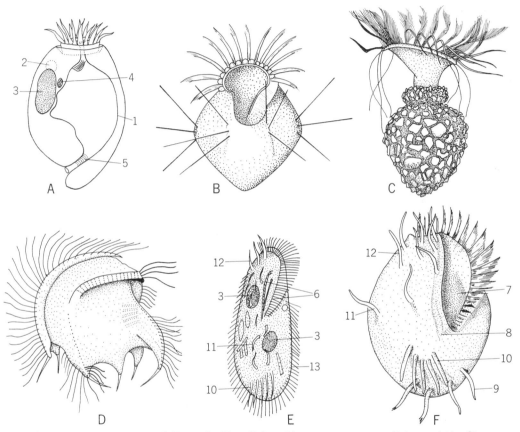

Fig. 3.28. Representative Ciliates. **A.** *Entodinium biconcavum,* an entodiniomorphid ciliate. Note the absence of body cilia and the sharply defined cortical ectoplasmic zone. **B.** *Halteria grandinella,* an oligotrich, with body ciliation reduced to springing bristles, and with an adoral zone. **C.** *Tintinnopsis ventricosa,* a tintinnid with reduced body ciliation and a test formed of foregn particles. **D.** *Saprodinium dentatum,* an odontostome, with highly specialized body ciliation and a reduced adoral zone. **E.** *Oxytricha fallax,* a hypotrich with ventral cirri used in locomotion. **F.** *Euplotes patella,* a common hypotrich, without marginal cirri. (**A,** after Kofoid and MacLennan. **B,D,** after Kahl. **C,** after Corliss. **F,** after Pierson, from Corliss. **E,** after Stein.) 1, boundary between endoplasm and ectoplasm; 2, contractile vacuole; 3, macronucleus; 4, micronucleus; 5, rectal tube; 6, buccal overture; 7, peristome or buccal cavity; 8, site of cytostome; 9 caudal cirrus; 10, anal cirrus; 11 ventral cirrus; 12, frontal cirrus; 13, marginal cirrus.

ellate under the electron microscope, and presenting an enormous surface for activity. Pyrenoids and characteristic food deposits are also visible evidences of synthetic activity. Differences in food reserves, while depending on biochemical adaptations involving enzyme systems, remain as morphological markers; as a result, species with similar biochemical habits are often assembled in the same taxa.

Recent specification of the requirements of green and colorless phytoflagellates have revealed some interesting facts. The results are far too complex for an analysis here, but a few major lines may be mentioned. It is clear that many of the green flagellates require organic carbon, in the form of acetate or fatty acid. They usually thrive with nitrates as a nitrogen source, although some require ammonium salts. Some of the colorless forms can also use acetate as fatty acid. However, colorless organisms cannot use nitrates, but need ammonium salts, amino acids, or peptones. Green flagellates apparently can live as saprobic forms if deprived of light, but under these conditions require more complex nitrogen sources, usually peptones.

With our newer concept of planetary evolution, which visualizes organic compound formation as beginning when a reducing atmosphere was present, our ideas of early evolution of organisms have altered. Heterotrophs no doubt preceded autotrophs, and under these assumptions, one may speculate on whether the first flagellate stems may not have been saprobic, developing chemosynthetic mechanisms which, through the consolidation of a photosynthetic enzyme system, became more efficient and permitted a higher degree of complete autotrophism. Certainly, it is no longer possible to think of a single great stride from autotrophic to saprobic nutrition.

FOOD ABSORPTION—THIEVES AND BEGGARS

Many Protozoa depend on food absorbed through the body surface. Some of these saprobic forms require relatively simple substances, combining absorption with synthesis. Others live only in water rich in organic material, where bacterial decay processes provide them with required organic carbon and nitrogen sources. These appear to be true beggars, contributing little to the community digestion, but absorbing what they need. The beggar needs little but his cup, and so it is with saprobes. The digestive and feeding apparatus tend to deteriorate. However, many organisms combine saprobic and holozoic habits, depending on which method the environment favors at a given moment. In these, of course, the mechanisms for food capture and digestion are retained.

It is a short step from begging to thieving, and a short step from a saprobic life to parasitism. Some of the protozoan beggars are opportunists, living as saprobic forms or as parasites when the opportunity arises. Parasitism, however, is not an easy way of life. It requires a delicate adjustment between parasite and host, and often demands profound adaptations of reproductive or other activities, adaptations which will be discussed elsewhere. From the standpoint of nutrition, however, the parasite remains simple, unless it takes host cells into food vacuoles and lives as a holozoic animal.

FOOD CAPTURE—BROWSERS, HUNTERS, AND TRAPPERS

Mammal herbivores are quite unlike carnivores, but the differences are far less marked in Protozoa. The three-dimensional pastures and forests of a pond present about the same problems to the blind protozoan herbivores as to the carnivores, and browsers adapt along the same lines as hunters and trappers. Occasionally consistent differences can be noted. The predominantly carnivorous rhabdophorine gymnostomes have large, anterior or lateral mouths with extensible baskets of free trichites, while the predominantly herbivorous cyrtophorines have small, ventral mouths, with consolidated pharyngeal trichites, for example.

Yonge (1954), in his excellent discussion of the adaptation and evolution of the digestive system, recognizes five functional regions, for: a) food reception, b) conduction and storage, c) digestion and food fragmentation, d) absorption, and e) conduction and feces formation. It is interesting to observe that, even in Protozoa, evidences of most of these regional adaptations can be found.

Food capture and ingestion are closely related in most Protozoa. The region for food reception adapts along lines suitable for the feeding habits. One can distinguish between two general kinds of feeding— hunting, involving seeking and capturing prey, and trapping or filtering, often by sessile organisms. The two are not sharply separated, but at the extremes of each adaptational line marked differences are observed.

It is difficult to generalize about the protozoan hunter, for it may move by flagella, cilia, or pseudopodia, and may have a definite mouth or engulf food at any point. An amoeba can capture a *Paramecium* that moves much more rapidly, not by pursuit, but by protoplasmic engulfment of its unwary prey. A few hungry *Pelomyxa* in a culture containing *Paramecium* are surprisingly successful. On the other hand, *Didinium*, a rhabdophorine gymnostome, actively pursues and captures *Paramecium*, providing a spectacular display of hunting prowess. The best one can say is that the hunter is actively motile, moving to sample its environment, and that it is either equipped with a large, often distensible cytostome or can form engulfing pseudopodia.

Filter-feeding and hunting become indistinguishable in motile ciliates possessing extensive buccal ciliature that sweep particles into the mouth. Motile flagellates can also depend on currents for feeding. Holozoic phytoflagellates, for example, sweep food particles into the vestibule, where they are ingested by pseudopodial action. The best examples of filter-feeding are provided by sessile ciliates, such as peritrichs, whose buccal ciliature is adapted to create effective vortices, bringing food into the buccal cavity. The sessile choanoflagellates also show an interesting adaptation to this type of feeding. Their flagella sweep food organisms against the collar, which ingests them.

Some of the sessile, floating, and slow-moving protozoans have become adapted to trapping. The trapper increases his catch by covering a greater area; the suctorian tentacles, and radiating axopodia of heliozoans and radiolarians, as well as the long, branching, and sometimes anastomosing filopodia and rhizopodia of foraminiferans and some testaceans, accomplish this purpose. Once contact with the prey is made, the trapper must subdue and ingest it. Toxic substances to stun or kill prey occur in Suctoria and have been reported in Heliozoa and Radiolaria. The ephelote suctorians have sharp, raptorial tentacles which can pierce prey, and suctorial tentacles for its ingestion. When large prey organisms are caught, several tentacles or pseudopodia may co-operate in their ingestion and digestion occurs in the endoplasm; but where prey organisms are small they may be digested within the pseudopodia. The most prominent adaptations of some Sarcodina are the protoplasmic nets formed co-operatively by the anastomosing rhizopodia and used very effectively as seines for trapping small organisms.

DIGESTION AND ABSORPTION

Once food is ingested, all holozoic Protozoa seem to process and absorb it in approximately the same manner. All use food vacuoles, the characteristic organelle for intracellular digestion. In most organisms, digestion is a sequential process, involving the serial use of enzymes that act best at different pH values. There is evidence of a sequential change in food vacuoles, although the details of digestion remain largely unknown. The cycle of activity in the vacuolar membrane has been mentioned (p. 22). It is related to a pH cycle, reported by numerous investigators working with a variety of organisms. At first the vacuolar pH is neutral to slightly alkaline; within the first ten minutes or so, the pH begins to fall. Maximal acidity reported by most investigators ranges between pH 3.0 and 4.5. From this point, pH rises from neutral to slightly alkaline, and often falls again by the time of egestion. Howland (1928), however, found entirely different pH changes in *Actinosphaerium* vacuoles, which are neutral at first. The pH gradually falls to about 4.3 during the mid-point of digestion, and rises to near neutrality at the time of egestion. The range of foods that can be utilized is, of course, determined by the suit of enzymes produced. There is far too little information about this phase of digestion. Evidently the ability to utilize protein is widespread, and pepsin-like and trypsin-like enzymes have been reported in a variety of forms. The ability to use carbohydrates varies, and appears, on the whole, to be less widespread. Several amoebae and ciliates produce diastase-like enzymes, and cellulase and cellobiase have been demonstrated in flagellates from the gut of wood roaches. Fat digestion is of secondary importance in most Protozoa. Several kinds of amoebae contain lipases. Most enzymes reported from protozoans are most effective in an alkaline environment, strengthening the evidence that digestion usually occurs after the early fall in pH. The changes in the vacuolar membrane of *Pelomyxa* and *Paramecium*, for example, suggest that digestion and absorption are at least partly sequential, with early changes favoring movement of materials into the vacuole, and later changes favoring absorption and pinocytosis.

Egestion

Egestion is a simple matter in naked Protozoa. Amoebae generally accumulate exhausted food vacuoles in the tail-like uroid, and eventually leave the contents behind. Where there is a definite body covering, some point for egestion is required. This is variously called the anal spot and cytoproct. In a few ciliates, a definite canal leads to a permanent opening, the cytopyge (Fig. 3.28A). In these adaptations, we see the first evidences of Yonge's regions of conduction and feces formation (Yonge, 1954).

Respiration

Foods, whether synthesized or obtained from the environment, are used for synthesis of compounds needed in growth, maintenance, and repair. The synthesis of protoplasmic compounds and the physical activity of the organism require energy. In most Protozoa, energy release is aerobic, involving the use of free oxygen as the final hydrogen acceptor. In some, however, anaerobic energy release, not dependent on environmental oxygen, occurs. No special organelles for respiration are found in Protozoa. The study of respiration is largely a matter of following respiratory exchange, the uptake of oxygen and release of carbon dioxide, and of the biochemical description of the mechanisms involved in aerobic and anaerobic energy release.

The details of the stepwise degradation of foods cannot be covered here. While some work has been centered on protozoan material, detailed differences between species are poorly understood; only general patterns are known. On the whole, energy release is remarkably like that of higher Metazoa. The tricarboxylic cycle characteristic of higher plants and animals appears less commonly than a possibly more primitive dicarboxylic cycle. A description of anaerobic metabolism in trypanosomes and related genera provides considerable information. Von Brand (1946) has attempted to correlate physiological and biochemical evolution in this group.

Rates of respiratory exchange have been determined in a number of species, but the results are difficult to evaluate because of differences in experimental conditions and uncertainty about the physiological state of the organisms used. There is clear evidence that the physiological condition of the organisms has a great effect on oxygen consumption. Respiration rises with food intake and changes with age. *Chilomonas* from 72-hour cultures use only one third as much oxygen as animals from 24-hour cultures, for example. Pigon (1959) found that *Colpoda* oxygen uptake falls to about a tenth of its normal rate during encystment, and believes that it results from a change in terminal oxidase. Cyanide resistance in ciliates provides an interesting tool for recognizing changes in respiratory physiology. In *Colpoda* cysts, cyanide resistance is like that of active animals, but in *Paramecium*, cyanide resistance rises in older, or starved individuals.

Excretion

Protein degradation produces nitrogenous wastes which must be expelled from the body. The detailed patterns of nitrogen metabolism, beyond the scope of this discussion, ultimately determine what kinds of waste products are eliminated. Most aquatic invertebrates are ammonotelic, excreting ammonia as the primary nitrogenous waste. While much more diversified studies are needed before generalizations can be made with any confidence, the evidence today strongly supports the view that Protozoa, in general, are ammonotelic. Soldo and von Wagtedonk (1961) report that *Paremecium aurelia* liberates ammonia, presumably as a result of amino acid deamination, but not from purine metabolism. Purines they believe to be excreted as hypoxanthine, with some guanine and adenine. On the whole, *Tetrahymena* appears to be like *Paramecium*. Early investigators often indicated some excretion of

urea and uric acid; these results seem questionable in the light of recent work. Certainly, if they are formed they are not a very important part of protozoan excretion. It should be noted that brownish inclusions in some radiolarians and foraminiferans, and various crystals seen in amoebae and other Protozoa, may be wastes undergoing storage excretion. This involves conversion of wastes to non-toxic substances and storage for a time. They may be eventually expelled, either through the anal spot or by methods used for food vacuoles.

Soluble waste materials are simply released from the body surface without the intervention of special excretory organelles. Undoubtedly some soluble wastes leave with the water expelled by the contractile vacuole system, but there is no evidence that the contractile vacuoles have a special excretory function.

Transport

Little can be said of internal transport in Protozoa. Transport occurs at the cellular level through molecular movement, and by protoplasmic circulation, either involving definite protoplasmic flow or resulting from deformations of the body.

Endoplasmic streaming, cyclosis, is important in moving food vacuoles through organisms. It takes a definite route in many ciliates, so the state of digestion can be estimated by the position which a food vacuole occupies.

Protective Devices

Life is hazardous, even for small animals. Every animal faces so many threats that strong selective pressures favor the development and improvement of special protective devices. It is evident that much of protozoan behavior results in avoidance of toxic environmental conditions, and special protective structures are common. Most of these are useful in preventing mechanical injury, or providing protection against predators, drying, and excessive water intake.

SURFACE ENVELOPES

Surface envelopes provide protection against mechanical injury and drying, as well as against some toxic chemicals. In a sense, the plasmalemma is the universal protective envelope, maintaining the integrity of the protoplasmic mass. It is repaired rapidly when broken. A pellicle is a heavier sheathing, which usually adheres closely to the plasmalemma. Some of the Sarcodina, many flagellates, and all ciliates have a pellicle. Where pellicles are thin, considerable flexibility remains; where they become thick the body form remains constant. A pellicle is usually pierced by openings for ingestion, egestion, and contractile vacuole expulsion.

Unfortunately, there has been no consistent terminology for coverings. Many sessile and some free-swimming Protozoa inhabit a loose-fitting, vase-shaped container, called a lorica. Some Protozoa, like *Difflugia* (Fig. 3.17F), build a test of sand grains or other foreign particles cemented together, and still others, like foraminifera, secrete a heavy shell of silica or calcium carbonate. The terms "shell," "test," and "case" are often used synonymously.

Resistant coverings are sometimes formed for brief parts of a life cycle. This is especially true of parasites, which usually pass from one host to another as cysts or as spores, covered by a resistant membrane which protects them while out of the host. Many free-living Protozoa also encyst, surviving unfavorable environmental conditions and aiding in dissemination.

Protozoan Responsiveness

According to Hitchcock (1961), an amoeba, when struck by a beam of light reacts by the suppression of plasmasol flow. The suppression varies with the wavelength. Yet an amoeba has no known light-sensitive organelle, no specialized part for the conduction of stimuli, and no permanent organelles for movement. Its responsiveness rests on the generalized sensitivity of its protoplasm and consists of various kinds of modifications of metabolic patterns induced by external factors.

Animals are complex protoplasmic systems, constantly adjusting to internal and external factors. The resulting activity constitutes behavior. An external stimulus can conceivably disturb any of a sequential series of biochemical reactions, so altering metabolism and changing activity. Such direct effects of the environment on metabolism, generalized or specialized, are sometimes overlooked as a part of the organism's response mechanism, yet if the organism did not selectively adapt these responses to environmental conditions, survival would become largely a matter of chance.

Every protozoan has an optimal temperature for growth; above or below this temperature growth decreases until at the minimal and maximal temperatures it ceases altogether. The minimum-optimum-maximum pattern is effective for many environmental factors and for many functions, such as movement, respiration, or specific biochemical reactions. Generally an environmental factor has a minimal or maximal level at which it becomes toxic, depending on the kind of function it affects, and thus operates as a critical limiting factor in distribution. It is not surprising that special sensitivities and behavior tend to develop in relation to the factors most frequently encountered and most likely to become toxic. Protozoan sensitivity is usually based on generalized protoplasmic reception rather than definite organelles, so there is often no sharp line between physiological, ecological, and specific behavioral reactions. Protozoans generally respond to physical, chemical, and biotic factors by changes in growth rates, physiological adjustments, selection of suitable habitats, and specific behavior patterns.

Most specific behavior involving movements of the body and orientation or habitat selection are based on the avoiding reaction. This is a reversal of movement, usually accompanied by turning, because of the mechanics of locomotion. Avoidance is the basis of trial-and-error behavior, for when the organism moves forward once more, it again reverses itself if it comes in contact with the stimulating agent. Reversal may be evoked by decreasing or increasing strength of stimuli, so that the organism is led toward or away from the stimulating agent. If its over-all movement leads toward the stimulus, its response is positive; if away, negative. The reactions described above are phobotactic, as they do not require a definite orientation to the stimulus. Topotactic behavior involves definite orientation and is considerably less common. Some Protozoa orient to light and many to electrical stimuli; some chemically induced responses of Protozoa also appear to be topotactic. The prefix added to the stem-word "tactic" designates the type of stimulus involved (see Table 3.1).

Table 3.1. Types of tactic behavior

STIMULUS	TYPE OF TAXES
Temperature	Thermotaxis
Light	Phototaxis
Electric	Galvanotaxis
Pressure	Barotaxis
Gravity	Geotaxis
Contact	Thigmotaxis
Currents	Rheotaxis
Chemicals	Chemotaxis
Moisture	Hydrotaxis

CHEMICAL SENSITIVITY

Chemical sensitivity is probably universal among Protozoa, although not all are sensitive to the same chemicals. The widespread occurrence of chemosensitivity is to be expected, for all organisms are affected by the chemical nature of their environment. Adaptations in the form of tactic responses or metabolic modifications are necessary for survival. Either the presence of toxic substances or the absence of essential material may prove critical; both positive and negative responses occur. The mechanics of chemoreception are poorly understood for all animals and remain essentially unknown in Protozoa. However, chemoreceptor cells in Metazoa are usually equipped with hair-like processes, and it is not improbable that cilia and flagella act as chemoreceptors for at least some substances.

Protozoa are often repelled by substances, and through trial-and-error behavior eventually select regions with low concentrations of the compound. In this manner they select environments with a suitable pH, avoid dangerously high concentrations of CO_2, or avoid some toxic compounds. In most of these reactions there is no orientation to the substance; however, some Protozoa appear to orient to certain food materials and to secretions liberated during sexual reproduction. The migration of some parasitic Protozoa within the host may reflect orientation to chemical stimuli.

Sensitivity to the chemical environment is also shown in habitat selection, undoubtedly reflecting metabolic patterns that are specifically responsive to the limiting factors in distribution. Hydrogen ion concentration is an important factor in distribution and growth. While the optimal pH is near 7.0 for many species, *Carteria obtusa* is said to have an optimal pH between 3.5 and 4.5, and the optimal pH for a number of ciliates and flagellates is near 8.0. Minimal and maximal pH vary also, but tend to be symmetrically arranged about the optimum, with the whole range extending between about 1.5 and 2.0 pH units. Some species, however, can tolerate very wide pH ranges. *Euglena gracilis*, for example, can tolerate pH as low as 3.0 to 3.5 and as high as 9.0 to 9.5.

Salinity is also an important factor in distribution; most Protozoa are fresh-water or marine species. Many fresh-water Protozoa are killed by sea water diluted from 10 to 50 per cent. A gradual elevation of salinity can acclimatize some to life in full-strength sea water, often with accompanying changes in form. Marine Protozoa, lacking contractile vacuole systems, are very sensitive to low salinities and cannot be acclimatized by gradual changes. Brackish-water species are often very tolerant of salinity changes; some can live in fresh water or sea water.

Oxygen, organic material, and mineral content are important limiting factors in distribution. Springs and mountain streams are often rich in oxygen and contain little organic material. When low in mineral content as well, they provide a habitat for katharobic species; when high in minerals, for oligosaprobic forms. Most of the common species seen in laboratory cultures prefer water containing enough organic material to support some bacterial decomposition, and therefore with a somewhat reduced oxygen content; they are mesosaprobic. Polysaprobic species live in bottom slime or water heavily contaminated with sewage, where rapid bacterial decomposition produces much CO_2 and little or no free oxygen is present.

SENSITIVITY TO CONTACT

Protozoa may be positively or negatively thigmotactic. If an amoeba is touched, pseudopodia are formed at the opposite side and it moves away; if it is floating, however, it responds positively when a pseudopodium makes contact with something solid. Evidently no definite organelles are required for reception of stimuli of this kind. The mechanics of reception of tactile stimuli in Protozoa are not understood. Presumably, the deformation of the body of an amoeba sets up changes in local potentials which provide a stimulus. Cilia and flagella are highly sensitive to touch,

and many hypotrichs have short bristles on the dorsal surface which appear to be mechano-receptors. Tactile stimuli are important in sorting out particles for ingestion in feeding ciliates, as well as in evoking avoiding reactions. Positively thigmotactic Protozoa tend to gather or withdraw singly into narrow spaces or under objects, thus affecting their choice of habitat.

SENSITIVITY TO TEMPERATURE

Sensitivity to temperature is widespread, if not universal. Protozoa in some cases select temperatures at or near the optimum when exposed to a temperature gradient. There is no direct information about thermoreception, but responses are of the phobotactic type. Other kinds of radiant energy also evoke responses. At least some species react negatively to ultraviolet light and to X ray. It is interesting to find Protozoa avoiding toxic factors that man cannot sense without special instruments.

Minimal, maximal, and optimal temperatures vary with species. Minimal temperatures for many are near 0° C., and maximal temperatures tend to lie between about 32° and 40° C., but there are many exceptions resulting in habitat choice. A few species survive in thermal springs at temperatures between 50° and 60° C. Dallinger (1887) carried out a classical experiment in temperature acclimatization, in which, over a period of seven years, he acclimatized three species of colorless flagellates to life at about 70° C. It is not yet clear whether such acclimatization depends primarily on modifications in the cytoplasmic components or on selection of temperature-tolerant genetic types.

SENSITIVITY TO LIGHT

Light sensitivity varies widely. Most Protozoa avoid strong light and tend to avoid complete darkness, although the responses appear to depend on the amount of light to which they have been previously conditioned. Light responses are generally of the phobotactic type, but green flagellates with a stigma orient to light. The stigma is one of the first special sense-organelles to appear, and it shows in its adaptations something of the major problems in photoreception. Generalized light sensitivity, as seen in Protozoa without a stigma, is not well suited to distinguish the direction from which light comes, except insofar as differences occur at the illuminated or shaded sides of the body. Shading is required for an eye-spot to be effective in recognizing the direction of the stimulus. Shading is provided by pigments arranged around the light-sensitive material. A cup-shaped stigma permits light to enter only through the open side, thus providing direction sense. Sensitivity is increased by a lens, present in Protozoa only in a few dinoflagellates. The fact that simple metazoan eye-spots show similar adaptational trends clearly demonstrates the importance of evolutionary convergence.

Topotactic response has been analyzed extensively in *Euglena*. When the orientation of the stigma to light is changed, resulting in its being shaded, a stimulus reaches the flagellum, changing its beat to bring the axis of the body in line with the light source. As a result, the animal tends to make a narrow spiral as it moves toward the light source (Fig. 3.29).

Orientation to light stimuli encourages the green flagellates to remain in the parts of a pond where light penetration supports photosynthesis. Light of different wavelengths is differentially effective for photosynthesis, and differentially effective in producing phototactic responses. It can be shown that high light intensities evoke some specialized responses in the photosynthetic flagellates. In some species, protective pigment migrates to the body surface, providing shading when light concentrations are excessively high.

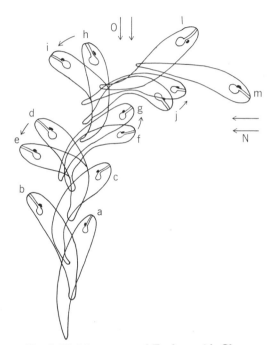

Fig. 3.29. Movements of *Euglena* with Change in the Light Source. The tailed arrows at top and right indicate the direction of light rays, the straight arrows the direction of movement of *Euglena*. The *Euglena* was moving as shown at a-c when the light came from direction O; at this time light O was turned off and light N was turned on. The animal turned at d-e, f-g, and h-i, and then moved off toward the new light source. This is trial and error performance, involving acceptance or rejection of the consequences of a random turning. (After Mast, from Hegner.)

CONDUCTION OF STIMULI

It is evident that stimuli are conducted from the point of reception to another point, at which activity changes. How conduction occurs remains uncertain. In amoeboid organisms, generalized protoplasmic conduction is apparently used. In organisms with specialized, permanent locomotor organelles, it is not unreasonable to expect that some kind of permanent conduction organelles should evolve. In a few Protozoa, evidence of conducting fibrils appears to be incontestable. Sharp (1914), for example, demonstrated a series of fibrils used in co-ordination of the complex loco-motor organelles of *Entodinium*; in *Euplotes*, a hypotrich, severing the fibrils which pass forward from the cirri results in a loss of co-ordination. The fibrillar elements of the infraciliature provides a system which could be, and perhaps is, used for co-ordination. In some cases, discontinuities in the fibrillar system have been detected with the electron microscope. Such discontinuities would not necessarily rule out conductive functions, however, for synaptic gaps are characteristic of the nervous systems of most animals. The rhizoplasts of the flagellar root system may also serve for conduction, and there is some evidence to show that the flagellum depends on the root system for initiation of beat. At the present, one can only say that for the more generalized ciliates a fibrillar system which would serve admirably for co-ordination is present, but that more refined experimental techniques are required to demonstrate how, and to what extent, it plays a co-ordinating role.

Nuclear Adaptation

Recent decades have emphasized the importance of the nuclear apparatus as the bearer of a genetic code. It is the center of metabolic control, exercised by regulation of enzyme formation. While there is some diversity of nuclear form among Metazoa, the nuclei of a sponge and a whale are remarkably alike. Nuclei vary far more widely among Protozoa, and it is possible that something of the evolution of nuclear form and function may be learned from them.

Many Protozoa are multinucleate. All Sporozoa are multinucleate at some stage of the life cycle, and multinucleate forms occur in Sarcodina and Mastigophora as well. In most cases the multinucleate condition is merely a preparation for multiple fission or spore formation, but some Protozoa are permanently multinucleate. *Opalina* (Fig. 3.16A) and *Pelomyxa* are such multinucleate forms.

Among some multinucleated Protozoa, two or more kinds of nuclei may be distinguished. Many Myxosporidia have two kinds of nuclei. One kind, the generative nucleus, divides by amitotic or nearly amitotic methods; it is thought to be important only in metabolism and to be unable to participate in reproduction (Fig. 3.30A-C). The other kind, the generative nucleus, forms definite chromsomes when dividing and is active in reproduction. In sporoblasts, nuclei serve as centers for the formation of cells that will give rise to polar capsules, shell valves, and sporozoites, thus showing further evidence of differentiation. It is not yet clear how nuclei arising from a common nuclear ancestor can become structurally or functionally different in either Protozoa or Metazoa. The most familiar example of nuclear differentiation is seen in the ciliates, which have a massive and primarily vegetative macronucleus and a small, vesicular, and primarily reproductive micronucleus. While both macronuclei and micronuclei divide when the ciliate divides, the macronucleus degenerates during sexual reproduction and the micronuclei give rise to new macronuclei (p. 35). As in the myxosporidia, the primarily reproductive nucleus divides by some form of mitosis, while the macronuclei divide by amitosis.

Macronuclear amitosis is well exemplified in *Paramecium*. The macronucleus elongates, constricts, and divides into two parts, one for each daughter animal. Meanwhile, chromosomes appear in the micronucleus, which also divides. There is no visible mechanism for ensuring genetic equivalence in the daughter macronuclei. There is evidence that the macronucleus of *Paramecium* is compound, containing many subnuclei, each apparently equivalent to one micronucleus. If these subnuclei are divided by methods ensuring genetic equivalence of the daughter subnuclei, a macronuclear fragment containing a single subnucleus would be equipped with a full set of genes, and the apparent anomaly would be explained.

NUCLEAR EVOLUTION

DNA is a constituent of all kinds of life. It is closely associated with genes in dissimilar organisms. It must have emerged as the primary carrier of genetic information at a very early stage in the history of life. Although bacteria and blue-green algae do not have a nucleus in quite the same sense as other organisms, the great majority of acellular and multicellular plants and animals retain DNA in a unified nucleus. The unified nuclear system, containing a full genetic code, no doubt developed from previously existing, more diffuse systems. All modern Protozoa have one or more definite nuclei, so it may be supposed that the first true Protozoa had a primitive, unified nucleus.

What kind of nucleus did the first Protozoa have? The problem is a difficult one, for the answer must be sought through indirect evidence. Primitive organisms still survive, competing successfully with more modern animal types, and sometimes primitive parts may be found which yield clues to the course of evolutionary development. Nuclear functions are no doubt associated with chemical constitution and structural organization, as are the functions of other parts, but nuclear physiology remains an obscure and difficult field. It is not surprising that when so little is really known of the different functions of structurally different nuclei within the same organism, even more uncertainty exists about the nature and function of the parts and compounds found within nuclei. Our only definite information about nuclear function centers about the nucleic acids and their genetic role. Probably much of nuclear evolution centers about the way that hereditary factors are borne and transmitted to daughter nuclei.

Compact nuclei, like the ciliate macronuclei, appear to be highly specialized and not likely to resemble the primitive nucleus, even though they divide amitotically. Vesicular nuclei differ widely in form, both in interphase and division. Some undergo divisions essentially like the mitosis seen in Metazoa, while others divide in a simple manner resembling amitosis. There are many intermediate types between these extremes, suggesting that something of the evolutionary development of mitosis may still be learned from Protozoa.

The simple type of division seen in vegetative nuclei of some Myxosporidia (Fig. 3.30A-C) provides a good example. It is amitotic since no chromosomes can be seen. A small, central endosome divides and the nucleus constricts so that one daughter endosome comes to lie in each daughter nucleus. When generative nuclei of the same species divide, chromosomes are formed. Perhaps, as many have believed, it is not so important for vegetative nuclei to produce exactly equivalent daughter nuclei. In any case, the existence of mitotic division in the same organism suggests that the simple division of generative nuclei is degenerate rather than primitive. A third point should also be made. The division has a definite, although uncomplicated, organization. In the dividing endosome there may be the remnants of a spindle apparatus, and, perhaps, room for some mechanism to control the distribution of genetic factors to the daughter nuclei.

Nuclear divisions in which chromosomes cannot be seen occur in many other Protozoa and in nuclei which are not vegetative. In some Protozoa, the single nucleus divides much like the myxosporidian vegetative nucleus. The endosome divides, and as the daughter endosomes move apart, a desmose appears between them. The desmose is a spindle element, and it is sometimes seen in the center of a spindle where chromosomes are formed during division. As a desmose occurs without chromosomes in some species which appear primitive, it seems probable that it is a primitive forerunner of the spindle and includes the centriolar homologue.

The centriole cannot be seen as a definite granule in some protozoan endosomes,

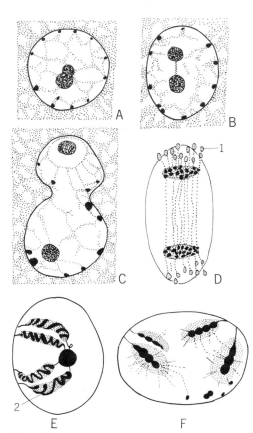

Fig. 3.30. Nuclear Division in Protozoa. A-C, Amitotic division of a vegetative nucleus of a myxosporidian. *Myxosoma catostomi*. Note the connection between the endosomes. They divide first and appear to govern the division process. D. Dividing nucleus of *Pelomyxa illinoisensis*. Note the small blocks of chromatin, which behave like chromosomes, and the polar granules, in which the individual spindle fibers terminate. E,F. Two stages in the nuclear division of *Spirotrichonympha polygyra*. Note the spirally wound chromonemata in the chromosomal matrix, and the chromomere attaching the chromosome to the nuclear membrane. The nucleus is elongating at F, but there is nothing comparable to the usual spindle apparatus. (A-C, after Kudo. F-G, after Cleveland, from Kudo. E, after McClelland.) 1, polar granule; 2, chromonema.

but a series can be constructed demonstrating the probable migration of the centriole to the outside of the nuclear membrane. Once outside the nucleus it assumes a special role in flagellates, becoming associated with the flagellar root system. In Heliozoa the axial filaments of the axopodia sometimes converge on the centriole, which is surrounded by a mass of specialized protoplasm, apparently comparable to the metazoan centrosphere. Protozoan spindles vary from little more than a desmose to fully developed spindles, comparable to those seen in Metazoa.

Chromatin elements of the nucleus vary in a manner suggesting a gradual evolution and development of mitotic processes. In the dividing *Amoeba proteus*, many small masses of chromatin line up in the center of a somewhat indistinct spindle and move toward opposite poles like chromosomes; a similar division occurs in the nuclei of *Pelomyxa* (Fig. 3.30D). In their small size and lack of definite centromeres these chromatin masses are more like chromomeres than chromosomes. On the other hand, some of the flagellates have well-developed chromosomes with a spirally wound chromonema (Fig. 3.30E, F). To discuss the full range of diversity is impossible here; those who wish to follow it further may refer to the excellent work of Bêlár (1926).

To summarize, we may conclude that protozoan nuclei are diverse in form as well as function, and that the dividing nucleus shows evidence of division patterns of increasing complexity. Until genetic work has been carried out on species with differing kinds of nuclear division, it will be impossible to completely evaluate the significance of the visible phenomena.

A curious feature of protozoan nuclear division is that in very few cases is the nuclear membrane absorbed during division. A number of terms have been suggested for the differing types of mitoses, but as there has not yet been sufficient comparative work it is doubtful if the terms can be applied meaningfully in all cases (see Table 3.2).

Table 3.2. Types of nuclear division

Amitosis.	Nuclear divisions with no evidence of chromosomes.
Cryptomitosis.	Nuclear divisions with a simple or complex spindle but no lining up of chromosomes or chromomeres on an equatorial plate.
Paramitosis.	Nuclear divisions with definite chromosome-like bodies on the spindle, if it is present, but with no shortening of the chromosomes during prophase.
Promitosis.	Nuclear divisions with a spindle and chromosomes, differing from mitosis in the persistence of the nuclear membrane throughout division.
Eumitosis.	Nuclear divisions with a spindle and chromosomes which shorten during prophase, and in which the nuclear membrane disintegrates during division.

Reproductive Cycles

A life cycle describes the reproductive potentialities of a species, following the young through whatever alternatives there may be to reach the adult stage once again. Life cycles may be simple or complex; in complex cycles several kinds of asexual reproduction may be used in addition to sexual reproduction.

The simplest life cycle may be thought of as repeated asexual reproduction by fission. A number of more primitive flagellates and amoebae have never been observed in the encysted state nor in any stage of sexual reproduction, and may have this simplest type of life cycle. It should be noted, however, that further studies may reveal the occasional use of modified methods of asexual reproduction or some kind of sexual process.

THE FISSION CYCLE

Fission is not a simple matter of co-ordinated nuclear and cytoplasmic division. It involves profound changes of the body organization, and usually involves the obvious replacement of some of the organelles of highly differentiated forms. The replacement of the highly specialized parts may be essential for continued survival; it occurs as a common phenomenon in sexual reproduction and is frequently a conspicuous part of the fission process and of encystment. Fission cycles include periods of a) maturity, b) preparatory pre-fission changes, c) active fission, and d) post-fission growth and differentiation. These periods often overlap to a considerable extent.

The mature organism has a characteristic form and varies within a size range typical of the species. What determines that fission shall begin? Evidently the growth rate is involved, for the period between fissions increases when the environment is poor. Tartar has reported some exciting grafting experiments with *Stentor*. When small organisms not ready for fission are grafted to large ones about ready to divide, both small and large organisms divide. Perhaps some modification of the macromolecular configuration of the endoplasm initiates fission. On the other hand, in most ciliates the initial visible changes occur in the cortex.

Whatever the initial stimulus may be, the fission of a highly specialized protozoan is a complex process. The division of *Euplotes* provides a good example. Chatton and Seguéla (1940), and later Bonner (1954), have carefully described the fission process. About eight hours before the cytoplasm cleaves, morphogenetic fields appear on the ventral surface. These fields are reticulate and contain the bases of the future cirri. As the net expands, the cirri are brought into position and a new oral apparatus forms. Cytoplasmic division does not divide a parent organism; it merely separates two daughter organisms already highly differentiated. The parental set of organelles is largely replaced; the daughter animals have an entirely fresh set of cirri and have extensively reformed oral parts. The period of growth and differentiation has extended well into the pre-fission period, and the old organelles are still present when cytoplasmic constriction occurs. In many ciliates the pre-fission and post-fission changes are not so extensively intermingled.

The micronucleus divides mitotically, and the macronucleus undergoes extensive reorganization prior to division. Conspicuous reorganization bands appear at the tips of the C-shaped macronuclei, passing along its whole length and meeting in the middle. Radioactive tagging shows the bands to be centers of active DNA synthesis. Eventually the macronucleus softens and becomes an irregular mass, which is divided amitotically (Fig. 3.8D). Cytoplasmic cleavage follows nuclear division, separating two partially differentiated daughters, which grow to normal adult size and regain their characteristic form.

In such organisms, fission appears to include a reorganization of nuclear and cytoplasmic parts; presumably most differentiated parts become senile and must be replaced as a part of the normal life cycle even in asexually reproducing forms. The nuclear reorganization is far less striking in most Protozoa, but many species are said to liberate material from the nucleus as a part of fission, either occasionally or routinely. Some flagellates also partly dedifferentiate during fission. The parabasal body and parts of the kinetic system are often replaced with each fission. Little is known of pre-fission changes or post-fission differentiation in Sarcodina and Sporozoa. Undoubtedly, in the less differentiated forms these phases of fission are less spectacular.

Fission cycles are amplified by use of other methods of reproduction. The most common addition is encystment. Encystment occurs in parasitic forms as a means of increasing their resistance during trans-

fer from host to host, and in free-living forms for weathering unfavorable environmental conditions. Some Protozoa encyst to prepare for fission; such fission cysts may be little more resistant than the free-living adults. Encystment, like fission, involves extensive dedifferentiation of the organism, the reorganization of the protoplasm, and the reformation of organelles at the time of encystment. Multinucleate cysts, which produce a number of young when encystment occurs, are not uncommon among parasitic species.

Palmella stages are common among many phytoflagellates. The organisms entering the palmella phase resorb their locomotor organelles, but retain the ability to carry on photosynthesis, and reproduce by fission while in the palmella form. Temporary colony formation may also occur. The life cycle of *Chromulina* (Fig. 3.10B) provides a good example of a complex asexual life cycle.

FISSION-SEXUAL LIFE CYCLES

The appearance of sexual reproduction as an alternative to asexual reproduction was an evolutionary step of profound importance, and had great consequences on the development of life cycles. The origin of sexual reproduction remains a mystery. It is difficult to see how such a complex system as meiosis and fertilization might have arisen at a single step. It is scarcely less difficult to see how parts of the process could have been useful enough to be fixed in populations. It seems probable that meromixis, the occurrence of gene recombinations in the absence of gamete formation and fertilization, preceded ordinary sexual reproduction. Meromixis is best known in organisms without the highly developed nuclear apparatus typical of Protozoa, as, for example, blue-green algae. It is possible that the primitive protozoan nucleus retained something of ancestral meromictic potentialities. In this case, nuclear evolution may have entailed the formalization of gene distribution during asexual reproduction by the development of mitosis, and more or less concurrent development of organized gene recombinations leading to meiotic divisions and fertilization. Until more is known of the genetic properties of Protozoa undergoing amitotic and simple mitosis-like karyokinesis, this important question will remain unanswered.

Sexual reproduction has the obvious advantage of permitting gene recombinations, therefore stimulating evolutionary change. It has another advantage in ciliates, where it has been most extensively studied. Most strains of ciliates, when prevented from undergoing sexual reproduction, lose vigor and develop characteristics resembling senility. Conjugation or autogamy restores vitality to the stock. While this function of sexual reproduction is widespread among ciliates, it is evident that many flagellate stocks do not require sexual reproduction for this purpose.

Fission is the common method of reproduction in most groups of Protozoa. After sometimes prolonged periods of repeated fission, sexual reproduction occurs. In ciliates, the physiological state of the organism gradually changes during the fission period. For a time after conjugation, the organisms are not capable of mating even when placed under conditions favorable to it. The onset of sexual reproduction in such stocks is largely determined by internal physiological conditions. Even when capable of conjugation, however, ciliates retain the ability to reproduce by fission for considerable periods before becoming severely handicapped by physiological deficiencies. Environmental stimuli induce sexual activity in many Protozoa. Seasonal changes or a deteriorating environment generally stimulate sexual reproduction, and in some parasitic species physiological changes of the host organism start the sexual cycle.

In ciliates, the sexual part of the life cycle involves conjugation or autogamy (p. 34). In conjugation the mating organisms unite temporarily for nuclear exchange, and in ciliate autogamy, nuclei serve as gametes.

In other Protozoa, sexual reproduction involves the permanent union of gametes, or syngamy. In many groups gametes are differentiated into motile microgametes and non-motile macrogametes, containing reserve food material. It has been shown in a number of cases that substances stimulating syngamy or conjugation are liberated by gametes or by organisms ready for conjugation. These substances may play a role in favoring the meeting of the gametes or conjugants, or in establishing mating types. The appearance of mating types is important, for it tends to prevent inbreeding. In some mating-type systems, a gamete or conjugant can unite with individuals belonging to any mating type but its own. In others, especially well represented by *Paramecium aurelia*, the species is divided into a group of mating types, each consisting of two strains. Mating occurs only between the two strains of each type.

METAGENETIC LIFE CYCLES

In a few groups of Protozoa, an alternation of sexually reproducing and asexually reproducing generations occurs, each with a characteristic form. This is best seen in the Foraminifera (Fig. 3.18B). The alternation of asexual and sexual reproduction has become formalized into a system in which the offspring of a sexually reproducing generation are obliged to reproduce asexually. The introduction of obligatory steps evidently results in a more highly specialized form of life cycle.

SCHIZOGONY-SPOROGONY LIFE CYCLES

Among the Telosporidia, an alternation of sexual and asexual generations is almost universal. The general features of this kind of life cycle are not always apparent because of the differences in the appearance of the various stages in different groups. Schizogony is a period of asexual reproduction, usually occurring by multiple fission, producing infective merozoites. These grow into schizonts which again undergo schizogony. The process continues until a gamont appears, which develops into gametes from which a zygote is produced. After many divisions, the zygote either directly or indirectly produces sporonts, which differentiate into spores. Each spore contains one or more sporozoites, which reach a new host and here become schizonts.

Modifications of this type of cycle are numerous. In some cases two kinds of hosts are used, one for the schizogony part of the cycle, and another for the sporogony part of the cycle, as in *Plasmodium* (Fig. 3.22). In other cases, again as in *Plasmodium*, there may be two kinds of schizogony cycles in different host cells.

The relationship of schizogony to sporogony differs in Telosporidia and Cnidosporidia. Although Cnidosporidia undergo many nuclear divisions, or may undergo plasmotomy to increase the number of schizonts, schizonts do not give rise to gamonts as in Telosporidia. Sporonts arise from schizonts, and fertilization occurs at another point in the life cycle. It has been generally believed that the basic form of the life cycle is such a fundamental attribute of a group of organisms that it must indicate relationship of groups. This assumption is somewhat weakened by the Cnidosporidia, where fertilization occurs at different points in the life cycle of Myxosporidia and Microsporidia, and one must conclude either that the unusual polar filaments have arisen in unrelated groups by convergence or that the details of the life cycle have undergone remarkable changes since Microsporidia and Myxosporidia diverged from a common ancestral stock.

Protozoan Phylogeny

Where did Protozoa come from? What groups originated from Protozoa? The answers to such questions are not easy to come by. Phylogenetic relationships are always perplexing, and where the fossil record cannot be used, changes that occured in the remote past must be inferred from similarities and differences that can be seen today. Some evolutionary changes are convergent, increasing similarities in analogous parts as these parts adapt to carry out particular functions more effectively, and eventually increasing the similarity of originally dissimilar stocks. Other evolutionary changes are divergent, resulting in increasing the differences observed in stocks with similar origins. In many cases it is extremely difficult to determine whether similar parts have resulted from convergence or whether they reflect relationship. Difficulties are increased by the fact that classification not uncommonly brings together organisms similar today but with diverse origins. Groups containing such combinations of organisms are said to be polyphyletic.

It is generally agreed that the flagellates include the most primitive Protozoa. If current ideas of early planetary evolution are correct, the original reducing atmosphere, under the influence of electrical energy in storms, gave rise to organic compounds, and the first living creatures had a reservoir of organic materials to draw from. We know little about the nature of the first heterotrophic life, but it is quite possible that the earliest Protozoa appeared as saprobic forms while heterotrophic life was still the easiest to pursue. In this case the first flagellates were probably colorless forms, and the direction of evolution may have been toward chemosynthetic forms, perhaps not unlike some of the simpler colorless phytoflagellates, in which photosynthetic mechanisms appeared. It is probable, however, that most if not all of the modern colorless phytoflagellates have originated from photosynthetic forms by bleaching and loss of the chromoplasts. Differences in the pigments present in the chromoplasts appear to be very stable within groups, on the whole, and probably are of ancient origin. The highly diversified chrysomonads, through palmella stages, lead off toward the brown algae, and through amoeboid forms may lead toward the Sarcodina. The lack of a heavy cellulose membrane in most chrysomonads makes them a potential ancestral stock for many Sarcodina. The lack of sexual reproduction in chrysomonads emphasizes their primitive nature. The euglenoid flagellates, through such forms as *Peranema*, may have been ancestral to some of the zooflagellates, but remain closely allied to the plant kingdom as a more or less independent group. The highly plastic dinoflagellates may have been ancestral to other stocks, perhaps through parasitic forms to some of the sporozoan groups. The occurrence of multiple fission in dinoflagellates makes them a potential source of organisms with schizogony cycles. The phytomonads lead off toward the green algae as chrysomonads lead to the brown algae, and through the colonial habit, may lead toward blastula-like colonial ancestors that could have given rise to the Metazoa, assuming that some colonial forms became heterotrophic. The zooflagellates are undoubtedly polyphyletic, having arisen from various kinds of phytoflagellates which lost autotrophic capacities in favor of holozoic life. It is in the zooflagellate group that flagellar systems become complex, and on the basis of modern forms would provide the most likely ancestral stocks for ciliates. However, the most complex of the zooflagellates, the ones that seem most like what a ciliate ancestor should be, are all endozoic. It seems probable that ciliates arose originally from free-living ancestral strains. While it is not wholly impossible that the first ciliates were parasitic or commensal, most would prefer the idea that the ancestral zooflagellate stocks have not been seen or are completely extinct.

Few would doubt that Sarcodina, as now constituted, is a polyphyletic group. Axopodia are seen in some flagellates, as are lobopodia. It is quite probable that the traits which distinguish at least some of the modern groups of Sarcodina are adaptations which first appeared within the flagellate groups. Chrysomonads, dinoflagellates, and amoeboid zooflagellates probably include the most prolific source of Sarcodina.

Evidence provided by the infraciliature of ciliates suggests that the holotrichs are the probable ancestral stocks for all of the more complex ciliates. The detailed evidence cannot be discussed here; the reader is referred to the excellent discussion given by Corliss (1959), whose ideas are incorporated in the classification of ciliates.

Sporozoa are evidently polyphyletic. Telosporidian life cycles are so stable in their general nature that it is tempting to think of them as a homogeneous group. The Gregarina appear to be most primitive, as they are not cytotrophic and have the simplest life cycles. However, if one were to choose the most probable ancestors of Gregarines and Coccidia, one would probably elect different stocks. Most have chosen flagellates or Sarcodina as the most probable ancestral forms for the Telosporidia. The occurrence of nematocyst-like structures in some Dinoflagellida and multiple fission in others, coupled with a parasitic habit in still others, has lead to the idea that the Cnidosporidia may have arisen from them. It cannot be maintained with great conviction, however, and the Sarcodina-like nature of the more primitive myxosporidians is very striking.

The phylogenetic relationships that we can now describe are almost wholly hypothetical; even the most widely accepted relationships are often based on what is a rather superficial resemblance. This is not surprising when one considers that such highly specialized groups as the Foraminiferida and Radiolaria were in existence in the lower Cambrian period. Radiolaria living today belong to the same genera and show the same characteristics as some of the earliest fossil forms. It is probable that the major evolutionary developments occurred long ago, and that many minor convergences and divergences have obscured major relationships to such an extent that no firm conclusions will be possible in the foreseeable future.

References

Allen, R. D. 1962. Amoeboid Movement. *Scient. Amer.* 206: 112.

Beale, G. H. 1954. *The Genetics of "Paramecium aurelid."* Cambridge Univ. Press, Cambridge, Eng.

Bélár, K. 1926. Der Formwechsel der Protistenkerne. *Ergebn. u. Fortschr. Zool.* 6: 1.

Bonner, J. T. 1954. The development of cirri and bristles during binary fission in the ciliate *Euplotes eurystomus. Jour. Morph.* 95: 95.

von Brand, T. 1946. Anaerobiosis in invertebrates. *Biodynamica,* p. 137.

Calkins, G. N., and F. M. Summers, eds. 1941. *Protozoa in Biological Research.* Columbia Univ. Press, New York.

Chatton, E., and J. Seguéla. 1940. La continuité génétique des formations ciliares chez les Ciliés hypotriches. Le cinétome et l'argyrome au cours de la division. *Bull. biol. France-Belgique* 74: 349.

Cleveland, L. R., A. W. Burke, Jr., and P. Karlson. 1960. Ecdysone-induced modifications in the sexual cycles of the protozoa of *Cryptocercus. Jour. Protozool.* 7: 229.

———, S. R. Hall, E. P. Sanders, and J. Collier. 1934. The wood-feeding roach *Cryptocercus,* its protozoa, and the symbiosis between the protozoa and the roach. *Amer. Acad. Sci. Mem.* 17: 185.

Corliss, J. L. 1955. The opalinid infusorians, flagellates or ciliates? *Jour. Protozool.* 2: 107.

———. 1956. Evolution and systematics of the ciliates. *System. Zool.* 5: 68, 121.

———. 1959. An illustrated key to the higher groups of ciliated protozoa, with definitions of terms. *Jour. Protozool.* 6: 265. (B)

———. 1961. *The Ciliated Protozoa.* Pergamon, New York.

Dallinger, W. H. 1887. The president's address. *Jour. Roy. Micr. Soc.,* p. 185.

DeBruyn, P. 1947. Theories of amoeboid locomotion. *Quart. Rev. Biol.* 22: 1.

Ehret, C. F., and E. L. Powers. 1959. The cell surface of *Paramecium. Int. Rev. Cytol.* 8: 97.

Elliott, A. M. 1959. Biology of *Tetrahymena. Ann. Rev. Microbiol.* 13: 79.

Epstein, S. S., and G. M. Timmis. 1963. Simple antimetabolites of vitamin B_{12}. *Jour. Protozool.* 10: 63.

Fritsch, F. E. 1929. Evolutionary sequence and affinities among the protophyta. *Biol. Rev.* 4: 103. (B)

Greider, M. H., W. J. Kostir, and W. J. Frajola. 1958. Electron microscopy of *Amoeba proteus. Jour. Protozool.* 5: 139.

Grell, K. G. 1956. Protozoa and algae. *Ann. Rev. Microbiol.* 10: 307.

Grimstone, A. V. 1961. Fine structure and morphogenesis in protozoa. *Biol. Rev.* 36: 97. (B)

Hall, R. P. 1953. *Protozoology.* Prentice-Hall, Englewood Cliffs, N. J.

Hastings, J. W. 1959. Unicellular clocks. *Ann. Rev. Microbiol.* 13: 297.

Hitchcock, L., Jr. 1961. Color sensitivity of the amoeba revisited. *Jour. Protozool.* 8: 322.

Honigberg, B. M. 1963. Evolutionary and systematic relationships in the flagellate order Trichomonadida Kirby. *Jour. Protozool.* 10: 20.

Howland, R. B. 1928. The *p*H of gastric vacuoles. *Protoplasma* 5: 127.

Huff, C. G. 1947. Life-cycle of malarial parasites. *Ann. Rev. Microbiol.* 1: 43.

Jahn, T. 1946. The euglenoid flagellates. *Quart. Rev. Biol.* 21: 246.

———. 1949. *How To Know the Protozoa.* Brown, Dubuque, Ia.

Kirby, H. 1950. *Materials and Methods in the Study of Protozoa.* Univ. of Calif. Press, Berkeley.

Kitching, J. A., and J. E. Padfield. 1960. The physiology of contractile vacuoles. *Jour. Exp. Biol.* 37: 73.

Kudo, R. R. *Protozoology.* 1954. Thomas, Springfield, Ill. (!)

Lackey, J. B. 1938. A study of some ecological factors affecting the distribution of protozoa. *Ecol. Monogr.* 8: 503.

Levine, N. D. 1961. Problems in the systematics of the 'sporozoa.' *Jour. Protozool.* 8: 442.

Lorch, I. J., and J. F. Danielli. 1954. Nuclear transplantation in amoeba. *Quart. Jour. Micr. Sci.* 94: 445.

Lund, E. E. 1941. The feeding mechanisms of various ciliated protozoa. *Jour. Morph.* 69: 563.

Lwoff, A. 1950. *Problems of Morphogenesis in the Ciliates.* Wiley, New York.

———. 1951–5. *The Biochemistry and Physiology of Protozoa, I, II.* Academic Press, New York. (!)

Manwell, R. D. 1961. *Introduction to Protozoology.* St. Martin's Press, New York. (!)

McLellan, J. F. 1959. Nuclear division in *Pelomyxa illinoisensis* Kudo. *Jour. Protozool.* 6: 322.

Meyer, H., and L. T. Quieroga. 1960. Submicroscopical aspects of *Schizotrypanum cruzi* in thin sections of tissue culture forms. *Jour. Protozool.* 7: 124.

Noble, E. R. 1955. The morphology and life cycles of trypanosomes. *Quart. Rev. Biol.* 30: 1.

Noland, L. 1957. Protoplasmic streaming. *Jour. Protozool.* 4: 1.

Pigon, A. 1959. Respiration of *Colpoda cucullus* during active life and encystment. *Jour. Protozool.* 6: 303.

———, and J. E. Edström. 1961. Excystment ability, respiratory metabolism, and ribonucleic acid content in two types of resting cysts of *Colpoda cucullus*, O. F. Müller. *Jour. Protozool.* 8: 257.

Pitelka, D. 1962. *The Electron Microscopic Structure of Protozoa.* Pergamon, New York. (!)

Porter, E. D. 1960. The buccal organelles in *Paramecium aurelia* during fission and conjugation, with special reference to kinetosomes. *Jour. Protozool.* 7: 211.

Preer, J. R. 1959. Nuclear and cytoplasmic differentiation in protozoa. *Growth Symp.* 16: 3.

Pringsheim, E. G. 1941. The interrelationship of pigmented and colourless protozoa. *Biol. Rev.* 16: 191.

Roth, L. E. 1960. Electron microscopy of pinocytosis and food vacuoles in *Pelomyxa*. *Jour. Protozool.* 7: 176.

Sassuchin, D. 1934. Hypertension in protozoa. *Quart. Rev. Biol.* 9: 215.

Schneider, L. 1960. Elektronenmikroskopische Untersuchungen über das Nephridialsystem von *Paramecium*. *Jour. Protozool.* 7: 75.

Sleigh, M. A. 1960. The form of beat of cilia of *Stentor* and *Opalina*. *Jour. Exp. Biol.* 37: 1.

Soldo, A. T., and W. J. van Wagtedonk. 1961. Nitrogen metabolism of *Paramecium aurelia*. *Jour. Protozool.* 8: 41.

Sonnenborn, T. M. 1947. Recent advances in the genetics of *Paramecium* and *Euplotes*. *Adv. Genet.* 1: 264. (B)

Tartar, V. 1961. *The Biology of Stentor.* Pergamon, New York. (G)

Turner, J. P. 1933. The external fibrillar system of *Euplotes* with notes on the neuromotor apparatus. *Biol. Bull.* 64: 22.

Watson, J. M. 1946. The bionomics of coprophilid protozoa. *Biol. Rev.* 21: 121.

Weiss, P. B. 1954. Morphogenesis in the protozoa. *Quart. Rev. Biol.* 29: 207.

Wellerson, R., Jr., and A. B. Kupferberg. 1962. On glycolysis in *Trichomonas vaginalis*. *Jour. Protozool.* 9: 418.

Wichterman, R. 1955. *The Biology of Paramecium.* Blakiston, Philadelphia. (B)

Yusa, A. 1957. The morphology and morphogenesis of the buccal organelles in *Paramecium* with particular reference to their systematic significance. *Jour. Protozool.* 4: 128.

Zahl, P. A. and J. J. A. McLaughlin, 1959. Studies in marine zoology, IV. On the role of algal cells in the tissues of invertebrates. *Jour. Protozool.* 6: 344.

Zeledon, R. 1960. Comparative physiological studies on four species of hemoflagellates in culture, I. Endogenous respiration and respiration in the presence of glucose. *Jour. Protozool.* 7: 146.

4
Introduction to Metazoa

The highly plastic and successful protozoan organizational plan imposed but one serious limitation—that of size. An undivided mass of protoplasm becomes physiologically and structurally ineffective if too large. It suffers from lack of mechanical strength if flattened or elongated, and from lack of surface area if it approaches a spherical shape. Large animals are of necessity multicellular.

Metazoa have escaped being limited to cellular size through multicellularity, but some are smaller than the largest Protozoa. Protozoa form colonies, some of which have thousands of members, while some of the smallest Metazoa consist of less than a hundred cells. Where such overlapping occurs, how can one distinguish between Protozoa and Metazoa?

Colonial Protozoa

Protozoa form linear, branching, plate-like, or spheroid colonies. In linear and branching colonies, each member lives as an individual with little or no compromise required by its colonial habit. In a few instances, the whole colony has come to exhibit integrated behavior. In *Zoothamnion*, a colonial vorticellid, the contractile elements branch with the stalk, and the whole colony retracts as a unit when any member is touched. In linear and branching colonies, however, the integration of the colony is usually minimal. Most of the plate-like and spheroid colonies are not attached, and so swim about freely. Members use their flagella together to propel the whole colony, and other concessions must be made if the members are to live together effectively. A significant loss of the individuality of members occurs, with a corresponding integration of the group as a whole.

A series of phytomonad colonies demonstrates this adaptational trend clearly (Fig. 4.1). In the transition from the small colonies of *Gonium* to the large ones of *Volvox*, several distinct tendencies can be recognized. Sexual reproduction in *Gonium* is by isogamy; in *Volvox*, by anisogamy. This supports the idea that the smaller colonies are more primitive. All of the members of the smaller colonies have the same appearance and potentiality. In *Pleodorina*, however, a few non-producing members occur, and in *Volvox* only a few members can give rise to gametes or agametes. The non-reproducing members have a distinctive form and limited potentialities. The same consequences of social life appear in other phyla. The differentiation of morphologically distinctive reproductive and non-reproductive members occurs in colonial coelenterates and social insects, for example. The highly integrated social unit comes to function as a superorganism, and the members (zooids) come to be its organs. Evolutionary factors lead to the adaptation of zooids composing a superorganism as to the adaptation of parts of

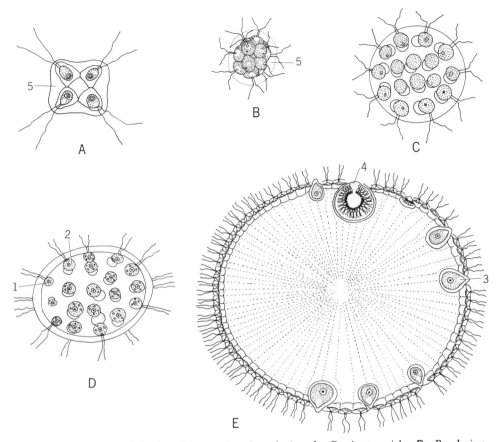

Fig. 4.1. Protozoan Colonies of Increasing Complexity. A. *Gonium sociale.* B. *Pandorina morum.* C. *Eudorina elegans.* D. *Pleodorina illinoisensis.* E. *Volvox globator,* as seen in section. This series illustrates how protozoan colonies of increasing size and complexity may lead toward metazoan organization. The few members of simple colonies are equivalent, able to divide to form a new colony, to develop into gametes, and to carry on photosynthesis or other aspects of normal vegetative life. *Pleodorina,* however, has small non-reproducing members and large reproducing members, different in potentiality and in appearance. Hundreds or thousands of small non-reproducing zooids of *Volvox* colonies are differentiated, while a few larger reproductive zooids are able to become ova, sperm, or agametes that develop directly into daughter colonies. These colonies could become coeloblastula-like metazoans by the differentiation of several kinds of non-reproducing zooids. Solid rather than hollow colonies might become stereoblastula-like metazoans in the same manner. (A, after Chlordat. B, after Smith. C, after Goebel. D, after Kofoid. E, after Janet, from Kudo.) 1, non-reproducing zooid; 2, reproductive zooid; 3, developing ovum; 4, developing sperm packet; 5, matrix.

an organism, eventually producing several kinds of non-reproducing zooids which serve as the organs of the superorganism.

Some colonial Protozoa have characteristics ordinarily associated with Metazoa in a rudimentary form. Polarity appears in the more complex colonies. *Pleodorina* zooids differ at the two poles, and some *Volvox* colonies spiral through the water with one pole functioning as an anterior end. At this pole the non-reproductive members have larger stigma and more powerful flagella. The differentiation of somatic cells characteristic of Metazoa is thus foreshadowed in *Volvox*. In *Gonium*, as in *Volvox*, a controlled series of cell divisions transforms the zygote or agamete into a colony of predetermined form with, in many instances, a predetermined number of individuals. These divisions closely resemble cleavage divisions of metazoan embryos.

It has been convenient to draw the line separating Protozoa and Metazoa at the point where non-reproductive members become differentiated into several types. Some mature *Volvox* colonies thrust slightly beyond this boundary. A few other Protozoa do also. Myxosporidian spores are structurally equivalent to a colony consisting of members differentiated into polar capsules, shell valves, and sporozoites. The degree of specialization seen in these forms is very slight compared to the many cell types found in multicellular animals, and they appear to be much more closely allied with the Protozoa than with any other metazoan group. Exceptional cases serve to emphasize the arbitrariness of our definitions. The evolutionary process is a continuous phenomenon; organisms can be expected to sometimes exceed the limits of their phyla.

The Major Types of Metazoa

The typical metazoan body is composed of, or derived from, layers of cells. The simplest arrangement is found in Mesozoa. The outer covering of these small, parasitic animals is formed of a single layer of cells, but no inner layer corresponding to an endoderm is present. In this they resemble a blastula and also a *Volvox*. One or more reproductive cells occur within the covering layer; in this, also, they resemble *Volvox*. Their organizational level is above that of *Volvox*, however, in the differentiation of the somatic cells of the covering layer (Fig. 4.2).

Sponges belong to Parazoa. A single layer of cells forms the outer covering. Sponges have an internal cavity or system of cavities lined by a layer of cells, all or part of which are choanocytes, resembling choanoflagellates (Figs. 3.13C; 5.6A). They ingest food and propel water through the cavity system. Between the inner and outer layers is a mesogloea, containing a number of different cell types. Parazoa are separated from other Metazoa because the system of cavities is not like a digestive tract, and the other organ systems found in Metazoa are lacking.

All of the remaining multicellular organisms are Eumetazoa. The body is covered by cells derived from the embryonic ectoderm. Typically, they have a digestive cavity, lined by cells derived from the embryonic endoderm, and a third layer of cells, the mesoderm, between the inner and outer layers. This layer is missing only in the hydrozoan coelenterates. The mesoderm is ultimately derived from either the outer or inner layer of cells during embryonic development, but establishes itself as a third embryonic layer.

The Mysterious Mesozoa

The Mesozoa once included a large number of peculiar organisms, simple in form and not obviously members of other phyla. Some are now known to be larvae and others have proved to be highly modified Protozoa. The phylum Mesozoa is now composed of two orders of animals, the Dicyemida and Orthonectida, which show evidences of relationship.

DICYEMIDA

Dicyemids are common parasites of the kidneys of squids and octopi. The nematogen stage is most often seen (Fig. 4.2). Nematogens are small, ciliated, worm-like animals with a constant number of cells. The outer layer of cells, the somatoderm, surrounds an elongated axial cell. The head is composed of eight or nine polar cells forming a polar cap or calotte, and two parapolar cells immediately behind. The trunk somatoderm contains from 10 to 15 cells, depending on the species. As nematogens mature the nucleus of the axial cell divides to form germ-cell nuclei, about which agametes form. These undergo

cleavage-like divisions within the parent, producing daughter nematogens. They escape and reproduce in the same manner.

When the host becomes sexually mature, the nematogens are transformed into rhombogens. Some of the cells become charged with inclusions, forming verruciform cells. Rhombogen germ cells give rise to infusoriform larvae (Fig. 4.2B). Two unciliated apical cells and several large, ciliated cells cover the surface of the short, oval larva. The interior of the larva is the urn. It is made up of four central cells, covered behind and laterally by two large, flat capsule cells. Just anterior to the central cells is a small urn cavity, bounded anteriorly by two small, ciliated cells located just behind the apical cells, and a quartet of

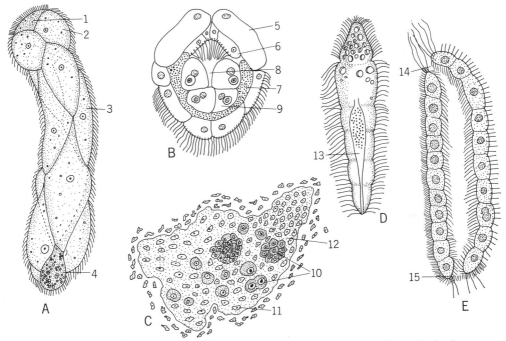

Fig. 4.2. Mesozoa. A. Nematogen of *Pseudicyema truncatum*, a typical dicyemid. B. Section of dicyemid infusoriform larva. C. Male plasmodium of *Rhopalura ophiocomae*, an orthonectid mesozoan. D. Male *Rhopalura*. E. Longitudinal section of *Salinella*. (A, after Whitman. B, after Neuvel. C, after Caullery and Mesnil. D, after Atkins. E, after Frenzel.) 1, polar cap; 2, parapolar cell; 3, trunk cell; 4, verruciform cell; 5, apical cell; 6, ciliated cover cell of urn; 7, capsule cell of urn; 8, cavity of urn; 9, central cell of urn; 10, agametes and embryos; 11, vegetative nucleus; 12, plasmodium; 13, testis; 14, mouth; 15, anus.

small cover cells. The infusoriform larvae escape from the host, and the remainder of the life cycle is unknown. They may enter some other host to undergo sexual phases of the life cycle.

Heterocyemids are rare parasites of cephalopods, rather like the dicyemids but with a significantly different although little-known life cycle. They appear to be enough like the dicyemids to be placed in the same order.

ORTHONECTIDS

Orthonectida is an order of rare parasites found in a variety of invertebrate hosts. The asexual stages are completely unlike dicyemids. They form a multinucleated, amoeboid plasmodium, reproducing by plasmotomy (Fig. 4.2C). The plasmodium ultimately gives rise to males and females, which resemble dicyemid nematogens (Fig. 4.2D). An outer somatoderm surrounds an inner cell mass made up of many germ cells. The germ cells give rise to eggs and sperm. When sexually mature, the parent organisms leave their hosts and mate as free-swimming organisms. Zygotes develop within the female parent, becoming larvae like the infusoriform larvae of dicyemids. They escape from the parent, and after a migratory period become infective for new hosts.

SALINELLA

A minute, unique animal was obtained in cultures made from salt-bed material taken in Argentina, and named *Salinella* by Frenzel. *Salinella* (Fig. 4.2E) is made of a single layer of cells, surrounding a central digestive cavity ending in a mouth and an anus. The ventral body surface is ciliated, and bristles occur on the dorsal surface around mouth and anus. The surfaces of the digestive cavity are ciliated. It reproduces by transverse fission, and may reproduce sexually when two organisms form a common cyst. Young, unicellular organisms

like hypotrichs may arise from encysted individuals. It is evident that *Salinella* is not closely related to the Dicyemida or the Orthonectida, nor can it be classified with any other phylum. It remains unclassifiable at present, and would require the erection of a new phylum within the Mesozoa to be assigned a reasonable taxonomic position.

WHAT ARE MESOZOA?

It may, at first, seem obvious that Mesozoa are a link between Protozoa and Metazoa. It is tempting to think of them as essentially blastula-like animals with external somatic cells, well-developed polarity, and internal reproductive cells, as seen in some of the spherical colonial Protozoa. They could have arisen from a colonial protozoan stock. Since flagellates have demonstrated a great evolutionary plasticity and appear to have been ancestral to ciliates, the ciliated outer layer need not rule out the possibility of flagellate ancestry. The complex life cycle is not more complex than some seen in parasitic Protozoa.

But an organism may be simple for two quite different reasons. Its simplicity may be primitive or may be secondary, resulting from a degeneration of parts that were once more complicated. Both views of Mesozoa have been expressed, and at the present no one can state with certainty that mesozoan simplicity is the result of degeneration or primitiveness. Inasmuch as most parasitic stocks show some degeneration, at least some mesozoan traits are likely to reflect degeneration.

Some zoologists have pointed out similarities between Mesozoa and trematode flatworms. Stunkard emphasizes the complex life cycle in both, involving a free-swimming larva, larval stages able to reproduce, and the parasitic habit. Yet complex life cycles have arisen independently in many parasitic groups, and the similarities of trematode miracidia and ciliated mesozoan larvae may be superficial. Certainly convergence could produce two forms with the amount of similarity actually seen.

Because an embryo tends toward conservatism and the retention of primitive characteristics, developmental stages are especially valuable in tracing relationships. Mesozoa are puzzling from this aspect as well. Are they comparable to a blastula with internal reproductive cells, or a gastrula with an inner layer that is reproductive rather than nutritive in function? If comparable to a gastrula, they might be likened to the planula larva of certain coelenterates, which are also externally ciliated and contain a solid mass of internal cells. The development of the mesozoan larva, in which the outer layer of cells gradually covers the axial cell, resembles gastrulation by epiboly (see p. 98), but it develops from an agamete rather than a zygote. The urn cavity might be interpreted as a remnant of either blastocoel or gastrocoel.

The Mesozoa are puzzling because of certain limitations of the comparative method in zoology. If one understands something of these limitations, he may avoid jumping to hasty conclusions. Homologous parts are recognized by similarities in embryonic origin, and are evidence of ancestral relationships. Unfortunately, an embryo is a living, adapting organism. It may be so profoundly changed that recognition of homologies becomes difficult or impossible. Similarities of development may result from the convergent effect of the adaptation of originally unlike embryos to cope with similar problems of survival and development. The Mesozoa will continue to be puzzling until more evidence can be obtained.

General Characteristics of Metazoa

The general characteristics of multicellular animals have been mentioned, in part, in preceding pages. The critical characteristic is the presence of several types of somatic cells. Histogenesis, the embryonic differentiation of specialized cell and tissue types, is therefore a characteristic process. Although a commonwealth of cells, each metazoan functions as an integrated organism and the masses of cells are neither random nor chaotic. Polarity and the appearance of body axes are characteristic of Metazoa, but occur in a rudimentary sense in complex protozoan colonies.

The metazoan begins as a unicellular zygote, structurally equivalent to a protozoan. It passes through a series of developmental stages in becoming a multicellular animal. Developmental changes occur in Protozoa also, but protozoan embryology is fundamentally unlike metazoan embryology. Cytoplasmic differentiation leads to organelle formation in Protozoa; this is approximately equivalent to the changes taking place in the histogenetic development of each specialized metazoan cell. Metazoan embryology involves an early period of cleavage, dominated by a series of cell divisions. Cleavage is followed by periods of morphogenetic movements, involving changes in the form of masses or layers of cells as they are transformed into the various structures of the adult. The first morphogenetic movements result in the formation of embryonic cell layers, called germ layers. The layered origin of the adult may be almost completely hidden by profound changes in the germ layers during later development, or may be clearly visible in the adult, with the layers retaining something of their original embryonic relationships. The way germ layers form and the course of their development are of great importance in understanding invertebrate relationships. Histogenesis may start during early development, but the more detailed changes usually occur during later organogeny, after the organ rudiments have been shaped by morphogenetic movements. The morphogenetic movements produce certain body cavities during development. These cavities, and their relationship to the germ layers, are also important factors in recognizing relationships.

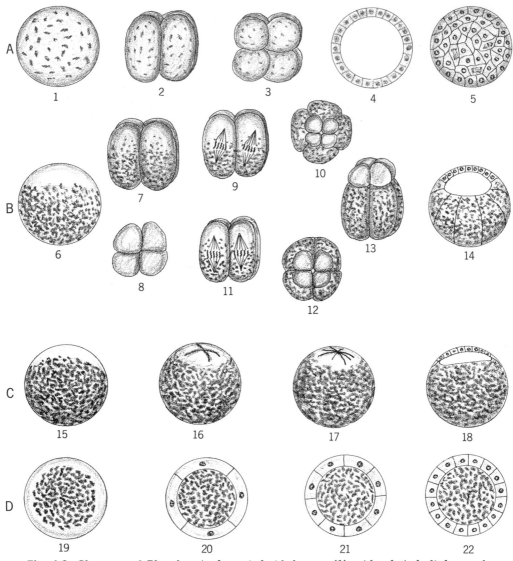

Fig. 4.3. Cleavage and Blastulae. At **A**, an isolecithal ovum (**1**), with relatively little, evenly distributed yolk, is shown undergoing total (holoblastic) equal cleavage. A four-celled embryo (**2**), divides to form equal quartets of cells (**3**). Further equal divisions may produce a coelo-blastula with a central blastocoel (**4**) or a stereoblastula (**5**) without a blastocoel. At **B**, a moderately telolecithal ovum (**6**), with yolk concentrated in the vegetal hemisphere, is shown undergoing total, unequal cleavage. The four-celled embryo (**7, 8**) is shown in polar and side views. Protostomes typically undergo spiral cleavage (**9, 10**); slanting of the spindles results in the formation of a quartet of micromeres which lie over the furrows between the four macro-meres. Deuterostomes typically undergo radial cleavage (**11-13**); as the spindles parallal the primary axis, the quartet of micromeres lies immediately over the quartet of macromeres. Either spiral or radial cleavage of this kind may lead to a coeloblastula (**14**) with an excentric blastocoel, or to a stereoblastula with unequal blastomeres. Increased yolk content is associated

96

CLEAVAGE—EMBRYONIC ORIGIN
OF MULTICELLULARITY

Cleavage is a period of embryonic development during which the zygote is divided into a number of cleavage cells or blastomeres. Cleavage terminates with the formation of a blastula, which continues its development by special morphogenetic movements called gastrulation. The form of the blastula is a direct outgrowth of zygote structure and the pattern of cell divisions occurring during cleavage.

Cleavage divisions follow a definite pattern, characteristic of the organism. They are associated with the form of the zygote and the distribution of yolk material in it. Three basic types of ova may be recognized, isolecithal, telolecithal, and centrolecithal (Fig. 4.3). Isolecithal ova have little yolk, about equally distributed through the cytoplasm. In telolecithal ova, the yolk is concentrated at the vegetal pole. Ova may be moderately or strongly telolecithal, depending on the quantity of yolk present. The yolk of centrolecithal ova forms a central mass.

Isolecithal ova usually cleave in a characteristic manner. The first cleavage follows the primary axis of the ovum, passing from animal to vegetal pole, producing a two-celled embryo. The whole ovum divides, so cleavage is said to be total, or holoblastic. The second division is at right angles to the first, and also passes from the animal to the vegetal poles, producing a four-celled embryo. The third cleavage is at right angles to the first two, so cutting across the primary axis. This is a transverse cleavage, and produces an embryo consisting of a quartet of blastomeres in the animal half, and a similar quartet in the vegetal half. If the two quartets are approximately equal in size, cleavage is said to be equal; if they are markedly dissimilar in size, it is termed unequal. Moderately telolecithal ova usually develop like isolecithal ova, undergoing holoblastic cleavage (Fig. 4.3). However, most isolecithal ova undergo equal cleavage, while telolecithal ova usually undergo unequal cleavage. The difference in size of the two quartets of cells increases with increasing yolk concentration at the vegetal pole.

Whether cleavage is equal or unequal, the third cleavage spindles may parallel the primary axis or be at an angle to it. If the spindles parallel the main axis, the upper quartet of cells lies directly above the lower ones and cleavage is radial. If the spindles are slanted, the cells of the upper quartet lie over the furrows between the cells of the lower quartet and cleavage is said to be spiral. A clockwise rotation of the upper quartet of cells is caused by dextrotropic cleavage; a counterclockwise rotation by levotropic cleavage. Generally, the members of a phylum have a characteristic type of cleavage, so this trait is useful in tracing relationships.

The cytoplasm of strongly telolecithal ova is concentrated in a small area at the animal pole. Only the cytoplasm divides; the large mass of yolk remains undivided. Such cleavage is termed partial or mero-

with increased inequality of cleavage, leading to the type of development shown at C. Here a strongly telolecithal ovum (15), with yolk heavily concentrated in the vegetal hemisphere, is shown undergoing partial (meroblastic) cleavage. The cleavage furrows do not wholly divide the zygote (16, 17), and the blastula (18) consists of a field of cells resting on an undivided mass of yolk. The space between the yolk and the cells is comparable to the blastocoel. At D, a centrolecithal ovum, with yolk concentrated in a central mass (19) is shown undergoing superficial cleavage. Cleavage divisions divide the surface protoplasm but not the mass of yolk (20, 21). The resulting blastula (22) is solid, with an undivided mass of yolk at the site of the blastocoel.

blastic. Centrolecithal ova have cytoplasm concentrated at the periphery of the ovum, and generally the only part of the ovum to divide is the peripheral layer. Cleavage of this type is superficial.

In echinoderms, chordates, and some other kinds of animals, cleavage is indeterminate. When cleavage is indeterminate, the blastomeres are equally potent and the ovum has sufficient plasticity to regulate its development when injured. If the first two or four blastomeres are separated, each continues its cleavage to form a diminutive blastula, which in some cases continues its development to form diminutive larvae. Twins, triplets, or quadruplets can be obtained from a single zygote. In many phyla cleavage is determinate, and the exact destiny of the early blastomeres is determined when they are formed. When a two-celled embryo is separated into isolated cells, each produces only half of a larva. Indeterminate and determinate cleavage is also useful in recognizing relationships between phyla.

BLASTULA

The blastula varies considerably in different kinds of animals. Many blastulae have a blastocoel, located centrally if the ovum was isolecithal or displaced toward the animal pole if the ovum was telolecithal (Fig. 4.3). Such hollow blastulae are called coeloblastulae. Others are solid, without a blastocoel, and are termed stereoblastulae. Stereoblastulae arise from both isolecithal and moderately telolecithal ova. Where cleavage is meroblastic, only the upper part of the zygote is divided, so that the blastula consists of a disc of cells lying on top of an undivided yolk mass. The blastocoel is reduced to the separation of cells from the yolk mass. These are known as discoblastulae. Centrolecithal ova, undergoing superficial cleavage, produce periblastulae, consisting of a continuous layer of cells surrounding a central, undivided yolk mass.

GASTRULATION—THE BEGINNING OF GERM-LAYER FORMATION

Until the blastula is fully formed, embryonic development is dominated by cleavage divisions. The blastula is transformed into a gastrula by cell movements known as gastrulation. Gastrulation is accomplished in a variety of ways, but in all cases starts the formation of the germ layers. The most important methods are invagination, epiboly, involution, delamination, and ingression.

Gastrulation by invagination occurs in many coeloblastulae and is the type most commonly emphasized in introductory texts. The vegetal hemisphere of the blastula pushes inward to form a saccate space, the gastrocoel, also known as the archenteron and the primitive gut. The gastrocoel opens to the exterior through the blastopore. As invagination proceeds, the gastrocoel grows at the expense of the blastocoel. The blastocoel may be completely obliterated or may persist as a fairly large cavity. Although fairly important as a method of gastrulation, it is less common than some of the other methods.

Gastrulation by epiboly and involution are probably modifications of gastrulation by invagination (Fig. 4.4). They occur in animals with telolecithal ova, where the large amount of yolk in the vegetal hemisphere makes invagination of blastomeres difficult or impossible. Where unequal cleavage has produced large macromeres at the vegetal pole and micromeres at the animal pole, the smaller, more active cells may move down over the larger, more inert, yolk-filled cells. This movement is epiboly. It results in a gastrula with a blastopore at the vegetal pole and with at least a vestige of a gastrocoel. Gastrulation by involution is most commonly seen in discoblastulae produced by meroblastic cleavage. At some point, usually related to the future symmetry of the organism, cells turn inward and move back under the surface cells and over the yolk mass. This produces a doubled surface layer separated from the yolk by a small space, the rudiment of the gastrocoel. Evidently this type of gastrula is highly modified and lacks a typical blastopore or gastrocoel. As it develops from a discoblastula, it is called a discogastrula.

Gastrulation by invagination, epiboly, or involution produces a gastrula with a central cavity or some vestige of it, usually opening to the outside by a blastopore.

This type of gastrula is called a coelogastrula.

When gastrulation occurs by delamination or ingression, however, there is nothing comparable to a blastopore and there may be no evidence of a gastrocoel. This type of gastrula is a stereogastrula. Gastrulation by delamination may occur in either of two ways. A coeloblastula may produce a two-layered gastrula by tangential cell divisions, cutting off the inner portions of the blastomeres as an inner mass of cells.

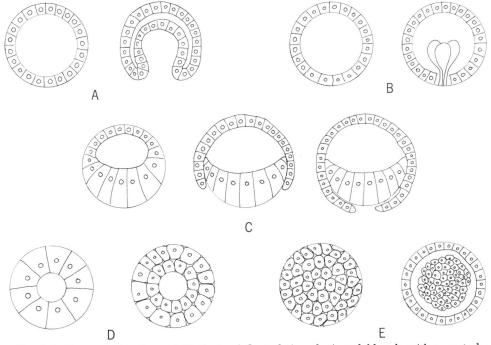

Fig. 4.4. Types of Blastulae and Methods of Gastrulation. A. A coeloblastula with a central blastocoel, as might result from the total, equal cleavage of an isolecithal ovum, undergoing gastrulation by invagination. The gastrula has a primitive gut (archenteron), which opens to the outside by way of a blastopore. B. A similar blastula undergoing gastrulation by polar ingression. In this case, no blastopore is formed, and the endoderm cells within may come to be a solid mass or be hollowed out to form a primitive gut. C. A coeloblastula with the blastocoel displaced toward the animal pore, as commonly results from total, unequal cleavage of moderately telolecithal ova, undergoing gastrulation by epiboly, the downward movement of micromeres over the macromeres. This may result in a gastrula without a primitive gut, although a blastopore is formed at the vegetal pole. D. A blastula with large cells undergoing gastrulation by tangential cell division. In this case no blastopore is formed, and the endoderm may be solid or hollowed out to form a primitive gut. E. A stereoblastula gastrulating by delamination. This results in a stereogastrula without a primitive gut or blastopore, although the endoderm may later hollow out to form a primitive gut.

This obscures the central cavity, or produces a gastrula without an opening to the interior cavity. Stereoblastulae can gastrulate by delamination through the separation of the outer cells from an inner cell mass. This usually involves a sorting out process, accompanied by flattening of the outer cells; it produces a solid gastrula without gastrocoel or blastopore. Gastrulation by ingression occurs when surface cells migrate to the interior. Ingression may be unipolar, occurring only at one pole, or multipolar, occurring at various points on the blastula surface. Ingression forms a gastrula without gastrocoel or blastopore. Unipolar ingression may be a modification of invagination.

Gastrulation produces a two-layered embryo, composed of the primary germ layers. The outer layer is the ectoderm and the inner layer, the endoderm. If present, the gastrocoel is the primordium of the digestive cavity, and the blastopore may be thought of as the primitive, embryonic mouth. For reasons that will become evident later, the gastrula is of considerable interest in speculation about evolutionary relationships. The blastopore is sometimes retained as the adult mouth; sometimes it is closed off and a secondary mouth is formed some distance away. Some have divided the animal kingdom into two main branches, the *Prostomata*, which retain the blastopore as a mouth, and the *Deuterostomata*, which form a new mouth some distance away from the closed blastopore.

MESODERM—THE THIRD GERM LAYER

Despite dissimilarities in the form of gastrulae and in the methods of gastrulation, gastrulae have some remarkably constant features. That a two-layered embryo should have inner and outer layers is scarcely surprising, but it is remarkable that these layers should tend to form the same body parts, even in dissimilar animals with dissimilar gastrulae arising by diverse methods of gastrulation. The ectoderm of most animals gives rise to the outer, epithelial covering of the body and its derivatives, to the lining of the most anterior and posterior parts of the digestive tract, and to the nervous system and sense organs. The endoderm gives rise to the epithelial lining of the remainder of the digestive tract, and the glands and other derivatives arising from it. Since all of the cells of a typical gastrula are a part of either the inner or outer layers, it is evident that all other tissues must also arise from them. However, this occurs by way of forming a third germ layer, the mesoderm. Mesoderm formation occurs in a variety of ways and at varied times during development. As it is derived from endoderm or ectoderm, it is considered the secondary germ layer, and the other layers are the primary germ layers. Ectoderm and endoderm are more or less homologous throughout the animal kingdom, except, possibly, in the sponges. Mesoderm, on the other hand, is more variable. There is evidence of two kinds of mesoderm, which may or may not be considered similar enough to be homologous.

Mesoderm arises either as a loose connective tissue or as an epithelial layer. The loose type of mesoderm is called mesenchyme. Mesoderm is mesenchymal in sponges, coelenterates, and ctenophores. In these phyla, all of the mesoderm is derived from the ectoderm and so may be called ectomesoderm. In all other metazoans, the bulk of the mesoderm arises from the endoderm and is called endomesoderm. While ectomesoderm is invariably mesenchymal, endomesoderm may be epithelial or mesenchymal. It arises at such different times and in such varied ways that there is real doubt that all endomesoderm can be considered homologous. Nevertheless, extensive correlation of the endomesodermal derivatives among diverse animals gives support to the germ-layer concept.

Ectomesoderm arises by simple ingression of cells from the ectoderm. The space between the ectoderm and endoderm is occupied by a jelly-like matrix, the mesogloea, which comes to have a greater or lesser population of cells depending on the extent of cellular ingression. This type of mesoderm formation was not recognized at first, and the phyla with ectomesoderm were once called diploblastic, or two-layered.

Endomesoderm formation is too diverse to discuss in detail here. In some animals, all of the mesoderm arises from a special blastomere, formed during early cleavage. In others it arises as a mesenchymal mass, and in still others it appears as an epithelial tissue stemming from the endoderm.

BODY CAVITIES

Metazoan architecture is best understood by considering the relationship of the germ layers and their derivatives to the important body cavities. The blastocoel is the first cavity to appear and parts of it may persist in adults. The gastrocoel is generally permanent, forming the digestive cavity. Sponges are exceptional, in that the system of cavities is entirely unlike those found in other animals, indicating an independent line of descent. In the most primitive Eumetazoa, the gastrocoel is the only embryonic cavity and the digestive cavity is the only body cavity of the adult. This is true of the Cnidaria and Ctenophora, and of the acoelomate Bilateria.

In Aschelminthes and higher invertebrates, the mesoderm does not completely fill the space between the digestive tube and body wall. A "body cavity" is present, separating the body wall from the digestive tube. There are two kinds of body cavities, the pseudocoelom and coelom. In animals with a pseudocoelom, the mesoderm adjacent to the digestive tube is mesenchymal, and eventually disappears as the spongy spaces unite to form a large space. In these animals the body wall is lined with mesodermal tissue, but separated from the digestive tube by the pseudocoelom (Fig. 4.5). In animals with a true coelom, the coelomic space appears within the meso-

derm and both body wall and digestive tube are lined with mesoderm.

A true coelom may be formed in either of two ways. If the mesoderm arises as mesenchyme, it is at first a solid mass filling the space between ectoderm and endoderm. Delamination occurs, resulting in the separation of an outer somatic layer and an inner splanchnic layer. The somatic layer adheres to the body wall and the splanchnic layer to the digestive tube. The coelomic space is thus completely surrounded by mesodermal tissue. When the coelom develops in this way, development is schizocoelous. Where the mesoderm arises as a pouch or double epithelial layer arising from the endoderm, somatic and splanchnic layers are foreshadowed from the start, and the coelom is, in a sense, a derivative of the digestive cavity. This type of development is termed enterocoelous.

The Origin of Metazoa

Zoologists have been disagreeing about the origin of Metazoa since the evolutionary concept was developed. Inasmuch as fossil evidence cannot be obtained, our conclusions must be based on other kinds of evidence.

Comparative studies of early embryonic development drew attention to the fact that dissimilar animals may have embryos with striking similarities. The recapitulation principle states that "ontogeny recapitulates phylogeny," or that embryonic development is a shortened form of the evolutionary history of the species, so similarity of early embryonic stages reflects common ancestry. It was once thought to apply in greater detail than is believed today. An embryo has all the problems of survival that an adult must meet, and adapts to fit its environment. Serious modifications of the basic embryonic features may result. Furthermore, the course of embryonic development is very short, while evolutionary history has been long; it is obvious that some steps must be abbre-

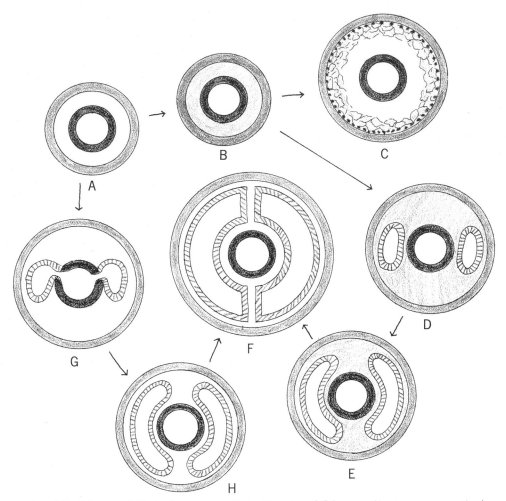

Fig. 4.5. Scheme of Body Layers and Body Cavities of Metazoa (in transverse section). The endoderm is shown as a dark layer, the ectoderm an intermediate shade, and the mesoderm the lightest shade. Peritoneal mesoderm is shaded with diagonal lines. The cnidarian level of organization is shown at **A**, with an "informal" mesoderm of mesogloea between the ectoderm and endoderm. The development of a "true" mesoderm, typically of endodermal origin, converts this organization into that of an acoelomate (**B**). Acoelomates may become pseudocoelomates; the mesoderm separates from the endoderm, leaving a space between the endoderm and body wall, the pseudocoelom (**C**). This cavity has no peritoneal lining. The typical coelomate construction is shown at **F**, with only the peritoneal mesoderm included. The coelom, a cavity lined with peritoneum, lies between the body wall and the gut. It is divided into lateral compartments by a dorsal and a ventral mesentery, both composed of two layers of peritoneum. Most protostomes are schizocoels, in which spaces appear in the mesoderm on each side of the body (**D**), and grow (**E**), eventually achieving the form shown at **F**. A coelom first appearing as spaces in the mesoderm is called a schizocoel. Deuterostomes are typically enterocoelous; the mesoderm arises as lateral outpocketings of the primitive gut (**G**), which grow and detach (**H**) eventually meeting above and below the gut to form the dorsal and ventral mesenteries. A coelom formed in this manner is called an enterocoel.

viated or omitted. Nevertheless, it cannot be seriously doubted that embryonic forms preserve traces of ancestral history, and so provide important clues to relationship.

The first really comprehensive theory of metazoan origin was put together by Haeckel (1874), a German zoologist of the nineteenth century. His theory was simple, neat, and persuasive. It had a great vogue, but is now thought to be erroneous in its details. It was so long predominant, however, that it has had a great influence on the interpretations seen in most introductory texts. Haeckel's theory was neat and persuasive, partly because it ignored a part of the evidence, and partly because, whatever its deficiencies, it was brilliantly assembled.

Starting with the recapitulation principle, Haeckel deduced that the course of evolutionary development should involve a stage comparable to a zygote, and subsequently pass through stages comparable to blastula, gastrula, and eventually to modern types of Metazoa. He pointed out that the zygote is essentially comparable to a protozoan, and that in flagellated colonies such as Volvox, a modern form resembling a blastula could be demonstrated. He postulated an animal, the blastaea, which resembled a blastula but had a definite antero-posterior axis and nutritive cells at the posterior end. He believed the next phase of development to have been a gastraea, an ancestral, gastrula-like form, with the nutritive cells invaginated to form a primitive digestive tract. He considered the coelenterates to be modern animals at the gastraea level, for he understood them to be diploblastic, without traces of mesoderm.

Unfortunately, Haeckel's theory is probably too simple to be correct. If embryonic development closely parallels evolution, the coelenterate embryo does not substantiate the gastraea theory. In most cases it is a stereogastrula, lacking a digestive cavity; it more closely resembles a mesozoan than Haeckel's gastraea. The kind of evidence that Haeckel depended on most heavily does not support his theory in the phylum generally thought to be the most primitive of the true Metazoa.

Lankester (1877), with others, thought the first ancestral forms beyond the blastula stage were probably solid, resembling the planula larva of coelenterates (Fig. 6.2A), and thus somewhat like Mesozoa. Metschnikoff (1882), too, thought the most probable ancestor was planuloid; it was his term for a hypothetical ancestral form which was conferred to the coelenterate larval form. Metschnikoff pointed out that coelenterates depend largely on intracellular digestion, taking food into food vacuoles instead of using their coelenteron. He, too, thought that the cells of the blastula-like ancestor most probably became amoeboid and moved into the interior as a more or less solid mass.

Today there are several theories, and a great deal of discussion about them. One group prefers the colonial theory, which conceives of colonial protozoans as the most probable source of early metazoan stocks. Others prefer the syncytial theory, which derives metazoans from a multinucleate protozoan stock which cleaved to become cellular after it had become quite specialized.

The colonial theory resembles the ideas expressed by Haeckel in supposing that blastula-like colonies were in the line of development. Most would follow Metschnikoff's idea that the inner layer was originally solid rather than arranged about a central cavity, and might derive metazoans from colonies shaped like Synura rather than Volvox. The older theories stated that the gastrae-like stage gave rise to hydroid coelenterates; today it is more popular to think of the medusoids as primitive. Hyman (1940) suggests a stage like Naef's metagastraea, a small, bottom-feeding organism with cilia, a mouth, a gastrocoel, and an aboral sense organ, which developed into a jellyfish of the trachyline type (p. 127). Others prefer the theory that a more planuloid ancestral strain developed into a medusoid form.

The syncytial theory has its chief modern proponents in Hadzi and Hanson. They would derive Metazoa from multinucleated ciliate stock, in which cell membranes appeared to give it a multicellular form, producing organisms like primitive flatworms. According to this view, bilateral symmetry is primitive and all radially symmetrical organisms have become radial secondarily. The most primitive of the coelenterates would be the sea anemones, from which the remaining coelenterate groups would be derived.

There are serious difficulties to both ideas. Greenberg and Hand have recently discussed some of these. No modern phytoflagellates provide a very good model for the kind of colony that might have given rise to metazoans. They are essentially plant-like, and have many traits that contrast with the probable nature of the first multicellular animals. Autotrophic nutrition is easily lost, but most colorless phytoflagellates retain cellulose and many retain plastids unlike those found in animal stocks. Meiosis typically occurs after fertilization in the phytomonad stocks, requiring profound changes in the relation of haplophase and diplophase portions of the life cycle if they are to be considered ancestral to animals. Chrysomonad colonies like *Synura* might provide a better model, but many of these have siliceous membranes, and modern species are photosynthetic. Their lack of sexual reproduction may be considered favorable or unfavorable; if sexual reproduction appeared in the group, meiotic divisions may have occurred before fertilization, for example. Some would prefer to postulate an extinct zooflagellate group of colonial organisms as possible ancestors of the Metazoa. Perhaps the strongest argument in favor of a colonial theory is that the kind of differentiation that could have transformed a colonial protozoan into a multicellular organism occurs in colonial animals, metazoan as well as protozoan, whereas no known organism carries on its early differentiation without cleavage divisions. Where organisms become syncytial as adults, or have syncytial tissues, the cells which make up the syncytium are initially discrete. Local differentiation of cells is far more easily visualized than local differentiation of organelles and adjacent nuclei within the same cytoplasmic mass.

There are no final answers. There can be no final answers until far more critical evidence has been gathered than is now available. Perhaps, with Greenberg, we will want to emphasize that the origin of multicellularity is not likely to have happened only once, and so much water has passed over the dam in the perhaps billion years since it all happened that we can place little dependence on comparative techniques. We know that many groups of vertebrates and invertebrates have become extinct, and it may well be that the key forms that might have given us clues are irretrievably gone.

References

Bather, F. A. 1893. Recapitulation Theory in Palaeontology. *Nat. Sci.* 2: 275.

Haeckel, E. 1874. Die Gasträa Theorie. *Jena Ztschr. Naturw.* 8, 9, 10.

Hadzi, J. 1953. A reconstruction of animal classification. *Syst. Zool.* 2: 145.

Hand, C. 1959. On the origin and phylogeny of the coelenterates. *Syst. Zool.* 8: 163.

Hanson, E. 1958. On the origin of the eumetazoa. *System Zool.* 7: 16.

Hatschek, B. 1893. Keimblattertheorie. *Verh. Deuts. Zool. Gesell.* 3: 11.

Heider, K. 1914. Phylogenie der Wirbellosen. In *Die Kultur der Gegenwart.* T. 3, Abt. 4, Bd. 4.

Hertwig, O., and R. Hertwig. 1882. Die ·Coelomtheorie. *Jena Ztschr. Naturw.* 15.

Jägersten, G. 1950. On the early phylogeny of the metazoa. *Zool. Bidrag.* 30: 321.

Lankester, E. R. 1877. Embryology and classification. *Quat. Jour. Micr. Sci.* 17: 399.

McConnaughey, B. 1954. The life cycle of the dicyemid mesozoa. *Univ. Calif. Publ. Zool.* 55:

Metschnikoff, E. 1886. *Embryologische Studien an Medusen.* Holder. Wein.

Stunkard, H. W. 1954. The life-history and systematic relations of the mesozoa. *Quart. Rev. Biol.* 29: 230.

5
The Parazoa

Sponges are among the most unusual animals. They occur most abundantly in shallow water along the coastline, attached to the bottom or to submerged objects. They occur in deep water as well, and a few species have adapted to life in fresh water. Their way of life is so unlike that of other animals that they were long believed to be plants, and were not finally recognized as animals until 1825. Adult sponges are always attached and are motionless. Even when touched they do not draw away, although some round up or contract the surface openings when handled.

Sponges have many unusual features. An obvious peculiarity is the porous nature of the body, from which the name Porifera stems. On close inspection, two kinds of pores are found: many small ones and a few large ones. Particles suspended in the water near a living sponge enter the many small incurrent pores, or ostia, and emerge from the large excurrent pores, or oscula. A system of passageways and cavities, differing in complexity with the species, connects the ostia and oscula. As water passes along these channels, food particles are ingested and respiratory exchange occurs. Choanocytes, each with a delicate protoplasmic collar around the base of its flagellum, propel water through the passageways to aerate and nourish the body and are primarily responsible for food ingestion. A unique skeleton of many needle-like spicules, sometimes in association with a meshwork of organic fibers composed of spongin, prevents the collapse of the body and the closure of its passageways and openings.

Sessile life is associated with several important evolutionary trends, beautifully exhibited by sponges. Active animals benefit from streamlining and bilateral symmetry, while sessile animals tend to be radially symmetrical or asymmetrical. Selective pressures favoring improvements of sensory, muscular, and nervous systems also benefit active animals. As sessile animals make few body movements, selective pressures favoring the development or maintenance of nervous, sensory, and locomotor parts are lacking. These parts tend to degenerate in complex animals that assume a sessile habit. Sponges are primitive, and have apparently lived as sessile organisms from their earliest appearance. They have failed ever to acquire a nervous system or sense organs, and have very simple contractile elements.

Sessile creatures cannot pursue prey and adaptations for trapping or filtering food from the water are associated with a sessile life. The pores and canals of sponges make an admirable filtering system, and the major evolutionary trends have centered about modifications in the complexity and arrangement of the canal system and of the chambers containing the choanocytes.

Absence of a nervous system and poor development of contractile elements make for a low level of integration in behavior. This is associated with a very limited degree of individuality in colonial sponges. Most sponges are formless masses, consisting of a number of ill-defined individuals with obscure body limits and little evidence of physiological isolation.

Their many unusual features emphasize their distinctiveness and justify recognizing sponges as a special branch of the Metazoa, the Parazoa. That they have specialized along lines entirely unlike those followed by other animals does not mean that they are unsuccessful. At least 3000 species of sponges have been described, and in their quiet way they are exceedingly effective. It is quite probable that in some distant future, when many animal groups now thought to be highly successful have become extinct, sponges will still be living along the coastlines and in the ocean depths, filtering what they need from currents of water streaming through their bodies.

Classification of Sponges

Sponge classification is unusual in being of little value except to the specialist. It is based almost entirely on skeletal structures, and while body organization is to some extent correlated with the skeletal parts; the body form of sponges classified in different orders is often quite similar.

Class Calcarea. The calcareous sponges. Skeleton composed of discrete calcareous spicules, not differentiated into small flesh spicules and large skeletal spicules.

Order Homocoela. The ascon sponges. Sponges of simple asconoid form. Example: *Leucoselenia* (Fig. 5.1).

Order Heterocoela. Sponges of syconoid or leuconoid form. Example: *Scypha* (Fig. 5.2).

Class Hexactinellida. The glass sponges. Skeleton composed of six-rayed, siliceous spicules or triaxon spicules, often united to form networks; without a surface epithelium. Example: *Euplectella* (Fig. 5.5).

Class Demospongia. Skeleton composed of siliceous spicules, spongin fibers, or both; generally with small flesh spicules and large skeletal spicules; of leuconoid form.

Subclass Tetractinellida. Without spongin and with tetraxon spicules.

Subclass Monaxonida. With or without spongin and with large skeletal spicules of the monaxon type. Example: *Spongilla* (Fig. 5.4).

Subclass Keratosa. With a skeleton of spongin only.

Asconoids—The Flagellated Spongocoel

The most simply organized sponges are known as asconoids because of their sac-like form. Asconoids provide the best introduction to sponge morphology. The simplicity of their organization is no doubt primitive, for the more complex sponges can be derived from the asconoid form and the olynthus embryo is asconoid in character.

Leucoselenia is most commonly studied as an example of an asconoid sponge. It grows as groups of slender, tubular individuals attached by a common stolon to objects in shallow, wave-washed water. Water enters through microscopic incurrent openings and is expelled through a single, large osculum (Fig. 5.1). Tubular buds without excurrent openings arise from the wall of the parent ascon.

The structure of the ascon wall is characteristic. An epidermis of close-fitting pinacocytes covers the surface. Among the pinacocytes are tubular cells, the porocytes, through which the ostia pass. Collared choanocytes line the internal cavity or spongocoel. Their flagella force water from the osculum and draw it into the spongocoel through the ostia. A jelly-like matrix, the mesogloea, fills the space between the epidermis and choanocytes. Wandering amoebocytes occur in the mesogloea. Special amoebocytes called calcoblasts secrete the spicules, which give skeletal support to the ascon tube. Most of the spicules are simple, elongated monaxons or triradiate triaxons. A few tetraradiate tetraxons may occur.

Syconoids—Choanocyte Canals

The next level of complexity in sponge structure is termed the syconoid type for *Sycon*, a well-known example. The syconoid form is derived from the asconoid form, and syconoids look like somewhat larger editions of asconoids. They retain a tubular shape and each individual ends in a single osculum. The syconoid body wall, however, is thicker and more complex, and the spongocoel is lined with pinacocytes. The choanocytes have come to lie in a series of radially arranged choanocyte canals.

Scypha is usually studied as an example of syconoid structure. Each sponge is vase-shaped, with a terminal osculum protected by a fringe of monaxon spicules forming an oscular collar (Fig. 5.2). Syconoids are

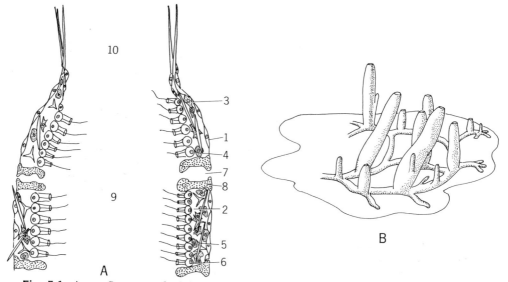

Fig. 5.1. Ascon Structure. **A.** Scheme of structure of the upper part of an ascon sponge. **B.** Colony of *Leucoselenia*, a typical ascon sponge. (A, after Hyman.) The vase-shaped body is covered with flattened pinacocytes (1). The middle layer is the mesogloea (2), which contains mesenchyme cells (3) and amoebocytes (4) and is supported by skeletal spicules (5). A layer of choanocytes (6) lines the body wall. Water enters through the ostia (7), intracellular canals, through special tubular cells, the porocytes (8). It passes into the spongocoel (9) and leaves by way of the osculum (10).

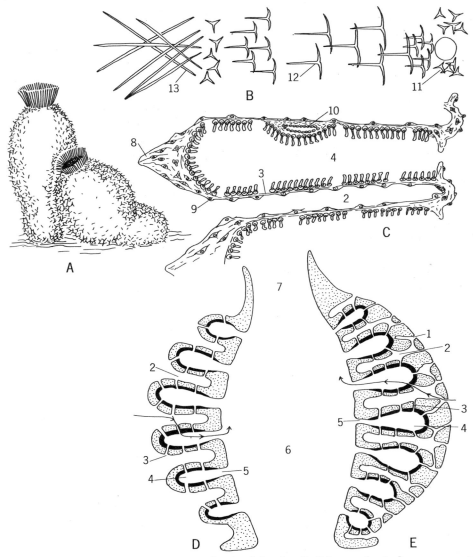

Fig. 5.2. Syconoid Structure. A. Habit sketch of *Scypha*. **B.** Scheme of spicule arrangement in the wall of a choanocyte canal of *Sycon*, arranged as if it were in the canal immediately below. **C.** Scheme of an incurrent and choanocyte canal in a syconoid sponge. **D.** Scheme of the wall of a syconoid sponge without a cortex, with the choanocyte layer shown dark. **E.** Scheme of the wall of a syconoid sponge with a cortex. (A, after Brown. B-E, after Hyman.) *General form, in order of water flow:* 1, dermal pore; 2, incurrent canal; 3, prosopyle; 4, choanocyte canal; 5, internal ostium; 6, spongocoel; 7, osculum. *Microscopic anatomy:* 8, mesenchyme at the end of choanocyte canal; 9, epidermis composed of pinacocytes; 10, amphiblastula in wall of choanocyte canal. *Spicules:* 11, triradiate spicules around internal ostium; 12, sagittal triradiates on radial canal; 13, monaxons at end of radial canal.

never found in highly branched colonies, although one or more buds may be found on the side of the body.

Body organization is best seen in sections. The spongocoel has evaginated to form the choanocyte-lined radial canals, or choanocyte canals. The spaces between them are filled with incurrent canals. Tiny openings, the prosopyles, connect the choanocyte and incurrent canals. Water flows through the external ostia, into the incurrent canals, through the prosopyles, and so into the choanocyte canals (Fig. 5.2C). Here food is ingested by the choanocytes. The choanocyte flagella force the water through the internal ostia into the spongocoel and out through the osculum.

Flattened pinacocytes cover the outer surface of the body and line the incurrent canals. The spongocoel is lined with similar endopinacocytes. Syconoid mesogloea resembles asconoid mesogloea. It contains amoebocytes of various kinds and spicules. The spicules are arranged in a definite pattern, characteristic of the genus or species. Giant monaxons form the oscular collar. Smaller monaxons project through the cortex. Triaxons lie along the walls of the canals, with the longest ramus directed toward the distal end. Small tetraxons or triaxons support the spongocoel wall.

Sycetta is a simpler asconoid, with choanocyte canals only. Each choanocyte canal is a simple outpocketing of the spongocoel and is exposed directly to the surrounding water. However, the outer margins of the choanocyte canals of nearly all syconoids are attached, forming incurrent canals, as in *Scypha*. The most complicated syconoids, like *Grantia*, have a more highly developed cortex, pierced by external pores. Narrow, branching and anastomosing canals lead from the pores to the incurrent canals (Fig. 5.2E).

Syconoid sponges pass through an asconoid stage during embryonic development. The choanocyte canals form by the simple evagination of the body wall, pro-

viding evidence of the derivation of syconoids from asconoid ancestral stocks.

Leuconoids—Choanocyte Chambers

Leuconoids are the most complexly organized sponges. Most leuconoids form large masses, containing many oscula. Each osculum marks one member of the large, colonial mass, but the limits of the members are so ill defined that it is impossible to distinguish them clearly.

Leuconoid organization is an elaboration of the syconoid form, for calcareous leuconoids may pass through embryonic syconoid stages. Leuconoids can be derived from syconoids by the further folding and outpocketing of the choanocyte canals to form clusters of round or oval choanocyte chambers. The choanocyte chambers surround an excurrent canal, into which they discharge water. Smaller excurrent canals merge to form larger ones, all eventually uniting in a major excurrent canal, through which water reaches the osculum. The cortex contains a system of branching canals, delivering water to the choanocyte chambers by way of small pores, the prosopyles. Water leaves the choanocyte chambers through similar pores, the apopyles.

There are three major types of leuconoids (Fig. 5.3). Eurypylous structure has just been described. Sponges with the choanocyte chambers joined to the excurrent canal by a narrow tube, the aphodus, are said to have an aphodal structure. Sponges with the incurrent canal joined to the choanocyte chamber by similar narrow tube, the prosodus, have a diplodal structure. The flow of water through sponges of various types is summarized in Table 5.1.

Spongilla, a fresh-water sponge, may be used as an example of leuconoid structure. Spongilla forms small masses attached to submerged objects, and is often greenish because of symbiotic flagellates, or zoochlorella.

A thin cortex forms the sponge surface (Fig. 5.4). It is pierced by many small dermal pores and propped up by columns of spicules extending to the lower mesenchymal mass, and covers the extensive subdermal cavity. Water flows from the subdermal cavity into short incurrent canals, which open through wide prosopyles into the choanocyte chambers. Wide apopyles deliver the water into excurrent

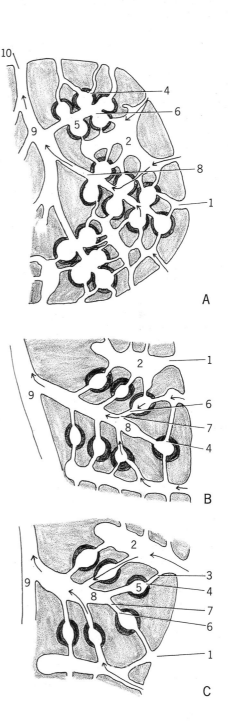

A

B

C

Table 5.1. Flow of water through sponges

Asconoid
Ostia (in porocytes)—spongocoel—osculum

Syconoid I.
Prosopyles—choanocyte canals—internal ostia —spongocoel—osculum

Syconoid II.
Dermal ostia—incurrent canals—prosopyles— choanocyte canals—internal ostia—spongocoel —osculum

Eurypylous leuconoid
Dermal ostia—(subdermal spaces)—incurrent canals—prosopyles—choanocyte chambers— apopyles—excurrent canals—osculum

Aphodal leuconoid
Dermal ostia—(subdermal spaces)—incurrent canals—prosopyles—choanocyte chamber—apopyles—aphodus—excurrent canals—osculum

Diplodal leuconoid
Dermal ostia—(subdermal spaces)—incurrent canals — prosodus — prosopyle — choanocyte chamber—apopyle—aphodus—excurrent canal —osculum

Fig. 5.3. Scheme of Leuconoid Form. **A.** Euryplous leuconoid form, with choanocyte layer shown in black. **B.** Aphodal leuconoid form. **C.** Diplodal leuconoid form. The adaptive line leads from chambers open to the incurrent and excurrent canals toward chambers with definite canals bringing water into and taking water from the choanocyte chambers. The canal system increases the efficiency of water flow (after Hyman, 1940). *In the order of water flow:* **1**, dermal pore; **2**, incurrent canal; **3**, prosodus; **4**, prosopyle; **5**, choanocyte chamber; **6**, apopyle; **7**, aphodus; **8**, excurrent canal; **9**, main excurrent channel; **10**, osculum.

canals, which eventually discharge into a small spongocoel terminating in an osculum. Unless very small, each *Spongilla* has many oscula.

Most sponges are leuconoids. Leuconoid structure occurs in Calcarea and Demospongia. Many minor variations in structure are known.

Hexactinellids—The Glass Sponges

Hexactinellida have the most beautiful sponge skeletons. Hexactinellids are well-defined, vase- to funnel-shaped individuals, attached to the substrate by a tuft of root spicules. They are deep-water forms, and usually only the skeleton is recovered.

The skeletal framework is composed of six-rayed, or hexactine, spicules, from which the group gets its name. Small crossbars of silica may attach the large spicules together, forming a continuous lyssacine network. Others have a solid dioctynine skeleton, formed of spicules fused at their tips. The skeleton is pierced by many,

rather regularly arranged parietal spaces and looks like a glass basket (Fig. 5.5). In life, the solid framework of fused spicules is accompanied by smaller spicules, generally missing in museum preparations.

Hexactinellid soft parts are syconoid-like, but have some unique features. A delicate syncytium, the trabecular net, covers the surface. A similar trabecular net lines the spongocoel. Pinacocytes are wholly missing. Variously shaped choanocyte chambers occur in the meshes of the trabecular nets, tending to form a middle layer. The spongocoel and osculum are large. A porous cap, the oscular sieve, guards the osculum of many species.

The Cellular Components of Sponges

Each sponge cell is a surprisingly independent functional unit. Sponge cells do not differentiate into the many distinctive types generally found in Metazoa, and each cell is left with quite broad functional capacities. Sponges are best considered to

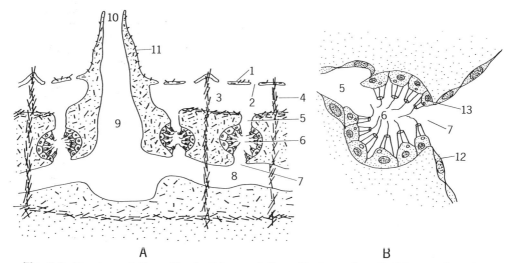

A   B

Fig. 5.4. Structure of *Spongilla*. **A.** Scheme of *Spongilla* in section. **B.** Scheme of section through a choanocyte chamber. (A, composite; B, adapted from Brien.) **1,** dermal surface of colony; **2,** dermal pore; **3,** subdermal cavity; **4,** column of spicules supporting the dermal membrane; **5,** prosopyle; **6,** choanocyte chamber; **7,** apopyle; **8,** excurrent canal; **9,** spongocoel; **10,** osculum; **11,** oscular chimney; **12,** endopinacocyte; **13,** choanocyte.

A

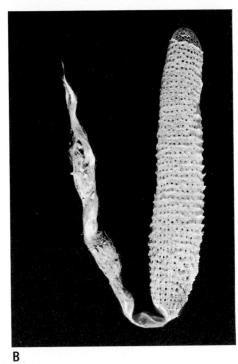

B

Fig. 5.5. A. *Microciona,* a member of the Demospongia. B. Skeleton of a hexactinellid, *Euplectella,* also known as Venus's flower basket. The lacy, siliceous skeleton surrounds a central spongocoel, and the animal is anchored by root spicules which extend into the bottom material. (Courtesy of General Biological Supply Co.)

be animals composed of cells rather than of tissues, or, in other words, animals at the cellular level of organization.

Highly flattened pinacocytes cover the surface and line all internal canals or spaces not lined with choanocytes. They are sometimes united to form a syncytial epithelioid membrane. Internal pinacocytes are called endopinacocytes. Some pinacocytes are contractile, although they contain no contractile fibers. They contract by rounding up, thus reducing the surface area they can cover. As they are tightly attached to one another, they squeeze the body, and if the skeleton is not too rigid can cause the body to round up.

Asconoids have porocytes scattered among the pinacocytes (Fig. 5.6A). These large, tubular cells contain the microscopic ostia. A cytoplasmic flange, the pore diaphragm, can close the ostium. Porocytes are able to ingest and digest food, and may sometimes metamorphose into amoebocytes. Adult syconoids and leuconoids have no porocytes; the ostia are simple openings in the pinacocyte layer. However, in *Spongilla* the dermal pores are said to begin as porocytes during embryonic development. It is not known how extensively this method of producing pores may be used in complex sponges.

Nothing in a sponge is comparable to the gastrodermis, which lines the digestive cavity of other Metazoa. Choanocytes line the spongocoel of asconoids and certain canals and chambers of syconoids and leuconoids. They ingest food and have flagella, but here the similarity to gastrodermal cells appears to end. Their functional competency does not parallel that of gastrodermis cells, and their embryonic origin is different. Furthermore, other sponge cells can ingest food and except in the Calcarea, which have very large choanocytes, it is doubtful if digestion is an important function of choanocytes. Food particles are passed on to amoebocytes, where most, if not all, of digestion occurs.

Choanocyte flagella create water cur-

rents in the canal and chamber system. The cellular anarchy characteristic of sponges is exemplified by the lack of co-ordination of the flagellar beat of adjacent cells. Nevertheless, choanocytes cause ample water currents. *Leucandria*, a small leuconoid sponge, has been studied in this respect. A specimen 10 cm. high and 1 cm. in diameter has about 2,250,000 choanocyte chambers, and can pass 22.5 liters of water through its body in a day. Apopyles are somewhat larger than prosopyles, increasing the efficiency of the choanocyte chambers. A large spongocoel makes ejection of water from the osculum more difficult. The spongocoel is reduced or absent in larger, more complex sponges. As the excurrent canals join, the total cross-sectional area of the canal system decreases, and water flows

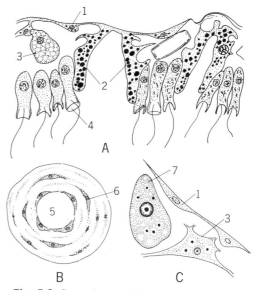

Fig. 5.6. Some Sponge Histology. A. Part of a cross section through the wall of an asconoid sponge. B. A prosopyle of a calcareous sponge, showing concentric myocytes. C. Epidermis and amoebocytes of *Spongilla*. (A, after Prenant. B, after Dendy. C, after Hyman.) 1, epidermis of pinacocytes; 2, porocyte containing incurrent pore; 3, amoebocyte; 4, choanocyte; 5, prosopyle; 6, myocyte; 7, archeocyte.

at an ever increasing rate as it approaches the osculum.

Other sponge cells are imbedded in the mesogloeal matrix. Nearly all are amoeboid. The amoebocytes carry out all of the processes not accounted for by pinacocytes and choanocytes in most sponges. This demands a greater functional plasticity than is customary in metazoan cells. It is not yet clear whether there are many kinds of amoebocytes or one or a few kinds that change appearance as they undertake different functions. They remain histological mysteries, for although several kinds can usually be recognized in any given sponge, it has not been possible to show that the kinds correspond in different species.

Some amoebocytes develop slender, branching pseudopodia and often unite to form syncytial units; these are collenocytes. Chromocytes contain pigments, and thesocytes are filled with reserve food. Archeocytes (Fig. 5.6C) are particularly important. They are undifferentiated, embryonic cells and are usually the only cells capable of forming sperm or ova. Sponges are made even more difficult histological subjects because other cells may assume an amoeboid shape and wander off into the mesogloea. Porocytes and choanocytes are said to transform into amoebocytes in some sponges.

An important function of amoebocytes is the secretion of spicules and spongin fibers of the skeleton. When an amoebocyte becomes active in skeleton formation it is called a scleroblast. Scleroblasts are named for the kind of skeleton they form. Calcoblasts form calcareous spicules and silicoblasts form siliceous spicules. Spongioblasts form spongin fibers.

Calcareous spicule formation had best be described. The spicule begins within the cytoplasm of a binucleate scleroblast. As it grows, the binucleate cell divides into a founder cell and a thickener. Each axis of a spicule begins within a separate scleroblast; a triradiate spicule begins in three scleroblasts and eventually has three

founders and three thickeners (Fig. 5.7A). The founder cell moves along the surface, apparently determining the length of the ray. It is followed by the thickener, which deposits additional material on the surface. When the spicule is fully formed, the founder and thickener move away and are lost in the mesogloea.

Siliceous spicules are formed within a single silicoblast unless they are very large, when several cells may work together or form a syncytial mass within which the spicule is laid down. Spongin fibers are formed in an entirely different manner. Each spongioblast develops a vacuole, within which spongin material collects. They line up, so that the short sections

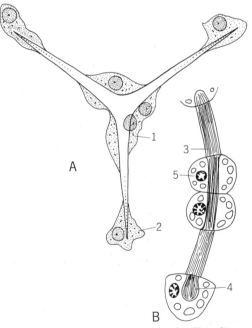

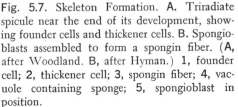

Fig. 5.7. Skeleton Formation. A. Triradiate spicule near the end of its development, showing founder cells and thickener cells. B. Spongioblasts assembled to form a spongin fiber. (A, after Woodland. B, after Hyman.) 1, founder cell; 2, thickener cell; 3, spongin fiber; 4, vacuole containing sponge; 5, spongioblast in position.

are united into a single, long fiber (Fig. 5.7B).

Sponges are so poorly co-ordinated in most matters that the complex cellular co-operation observed in skeleton formation is amazing. Little is known of the factors that make it possible for a group of scleroblasts to lay down a spicule of complex form, with rays meeting in precisely determined angles. The factors resulting in the formation of different kinds of spicules in different body regions are also unknown. Intriguing questions are suggested, for example, by *Scypha* scleroblasts, which form giant monaxons in the oscular region and in the walls of the choanocyte canals lay down triradiate spicules with the long axis of each parallel to the canal. Evidently the scleroblasts receive some kind of information, genetic or otherwise, that results in spicule constancy in a given species. The details remain obscure, but may provide information about unique methods of cellular co-operation when revealed.

A few other kinds of cells are found in some sponges. Slime-secreting gland cells occur in some. Two kinds of elongated cells also occur, desmacytes and myocytes (Fig. 5.6B). Desmacytes are found in the cortex, providing fibrous strength as well as aiding in cortex contraction. Myocytes are rather like smooth muscle cells, and are arranged in sphincter-like bands around the pores of some sponges.

Sponge Skeletons

Sponge classification and identification depend largely on skeletal details. Spicules are so varied that a large specialist vocabulary has been developed to permit their description. Only a few of the more basic terms can be mentioned here. The terms are introduced to describe something of skeletal diversity, and also to exemplify the kind of specialized vocabulary that develops in the detailed study of any animal group. This kind of vocabulary is one of the reasons for specialization; one cannot be fluent in the vocabulary of all groups.

Some spicules make up the major skeletal elements and others are more or less randomly scattered in the soft parts. Larger skeletal spicules are called megascleres and smaller flesh spicules are microscleres. Some sponges lack flesh spicules, and in Calcarea there is no sharp distinction between megascleres and microscleres.

Spicules are named according to their form. A monaxon is a straight or curved spicule without branches, consisting of one or two rays. If all growth has occurred in one direction the two ends differ and the spicule is monactinal, or one-rayed. A diactinal spicule grows in both directions and has similar ends; they are called rhabds (Fig. 5.8). The prefix "micro-" is used to designate a microsclere; thus a microscleric rhabd is simply a microrhabd.

Tetraxons are spicules with four rays, although some are simplified by the loss of one or more rays. If the rays are all of equal length the spicule is a calthrops. Usually one arm, the rhabdome, is much longer than the others. The shorter rays are clads, and the three clads together are the cladome. Cladome and rhabdome never meet at right angles, so tetraxon spicules are easily recognized, even when simplified by the loss of some rays. The cladome of some spicules is a simple or ornamented disc; birotular spicules have a disc at both ends of the rhabdome. The commonest spicule of calcareous sponges is the triaene, formed of three rays not meeting at right angles. It is thought to be a tetraxon with the rhabdome missing.

Triaxon spicules have three axes, meeting at right angles, and so have six rays. These hexactinal spicules are found only in Hexactinellida, and are diversely modified. Some rays branch, and sometimes some rays are reduced or lost.

Polyaxon spicules, called asters, are also found. These have many rays meeting at a central point.

Layers of silica may be deposited irregularly on the spicule suface, transforming them into desmas. Desmas are often cemented together to form a solid meshwork, or lithistid skeleton. Desmas are named for the kind of spicule on which the new material is deposited. A monocrepid desma began as a monaxon, a tetracrepid desma as a tetraxon.

Something of the long evolutionary history of sponges is reflected in the great variety of spicule types. Evolutionary convergence has often produced a similar body form in sponges which have quite different kinds of skeletons. The result is that the relationships of modern sponges are almost impossible to determine. Taxonomic work based on skeletal detail reflects diversity as well or better than anything that might be used, and is almost as likely to reflect relationships.

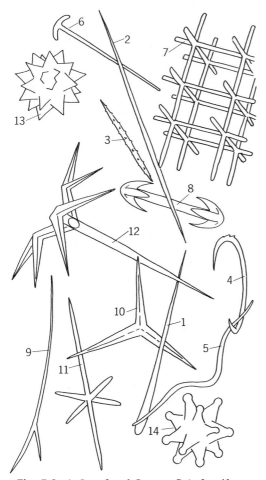

Fig. 5.8. A Sample of Sponge Spicules (from various sources). **1,** style (monactinic monaxon); **2,** rhabd (diactinic monaxon); **3,** micro-acanthorhabd (small, thorny rhabd); **4,** sigma (curved monaxon); **5,** toxa (bow-shaped monaxon); **6,** root spicule from a hexactinellid; **7,** part of the dictyonine skeleton of a hexactinellid; **8,** amphidisc; **9,** diaene; **10,** triradiate spicule; **11,** hexactinine spicule; **12,** tetractine spicule with a long rhabdome and a cladome of three bifurcated clads; **13,** oxyaster; **14,** sphaeraster.

The Functions of Sponges

No doubt physiology at the molecular level is as complex in sponges as in other animals, but very little is known of it. Details of some of the most unusual sponge abilities remain unexplained. We have no real information, for example, about the details of skeletal formation. What cellular mechanisms permit sponges to produce siliceous spicules when they grow in water containing so little dissolved silica? How are the form and placement of spicules determined? These examples could be multiplied many times. Until a great deal of work had been completed, only generalized accounts of the way body parts function can be given.

FOOD CAPTURE AND DIGESTION

It is only in obtaining food and other materials from the environment that sponges have capitalized on their multicellular organization. Lashing choanocyte flagella force water through the porous body, enabling the sponge to process a large amount of fluid. Important dissolved materials, such as oxygen, silica, and calcium salts, are extracted and food particles are ingested as they come in contact with the cells.

Food ingestion is entirely protozoan in its character. Small particles are engulfed, food vacuoles are formed, and digestion is entirely intracellular. Choanocytes ingest by far the greater part of the food particles, but amoebocytes, porocytes, and even epidermal cells can ingest food.

The amount of food ingested depends on the surface exposed and the amount of water filtered. Folding of the spongocoel to form choanocyte canals, and further folding to form choanocyte chambers, increases the surface available for food ingestion and also improves water circulation.

Digestion occurs in food vacuoles and food is absorbed across the vacuolar membrane, as in Protozoa. However, in most sponges the cells that ingest food do not digest it. The small Demospongia choanocytes take food in but pass it on immediately to amoebocytes for digestion. The ability to pass food from cell to cell is not unique in sponges, but is unusually important in their physiology. Wandering amoebocytes transport food as newsboys distribute papers. They may be transformed into storage cells or nurse cells (trophocytes) to build up food reserves for young oöcytes or amoebocytes preparing to form gemmules. Embryos develop for a time in the parent body, lying adjacent to a trophic membrane formed by the choanocytes, from which they receive food (Fig. 5.10D).

One important point stands out. The choanocyte-lined chambers are not comparable to the digestive cavities of other animals. In sponges the ingestion, digestion, and absorption of food are far more diffuse cellular processes than in other Metazoa.

RESPIRATION AND EXCRETION

So little is known of the details of energy release and energy transfer in sponges that they cannot be discussed profitably. The metabolic wastes of sponges are also incompletely characterized. At least some sponges are ammonotelic, producing appreciable quantities of ammonia and little or no urea, uric acid, or other complex nitrogenous wastes. Crystals resembling wastes are said to accumulate in amoebocytes, but have not been characterized chemically. They are freed in the excurrent canals. Ammonotelic excretion is to be expected in sponges, as it is generally characteristic of aquatic animals.

No special respiratory organs can be designated, but it is obvious that the stream of water moving through the body provides excellent conditions for respiratory exchange. A large surface is exposed, and a new supply of water is constantly provided. The percentage of oxygen removed from the water entering an organism is known as oxygen withdrawal. Hazelhoff found that oxygen withdrawal varies considerably with the species; *Aplysina aerophoba* absorbs 57 per cent of the dissolved oxygen passing through its body, comparing favorably with many of the higher Metazoa, while some sponges absorb a very small percentage of available oxygen. Considering the quantity of water they process, this seems relatively unimportant. Where water flows rapidly over an extensive surface, low withdrawal rates may provide adequate oxygen.

Sponges are generally aerobic and sensitive to low oxygen availability. Closure of the osculum for a time results in an above-normal oxygen uptake during recovery. Evidently some kind of oxygen debt system operates in sponges. When metabolism is carried out under conditions of oxygen shortage, complex organic end products are formed. If these accumulate in the body, they are oxidized when oxygen becomes available, and oxygen use rises. Closure of the oscula prevents the washing out of these compounds by water flowing through the sponge, and it is not surprising that they consume more oxygen afterwards.

Respiratory exchange and excretion appear to be predominantly functions of individual cells. It is easy, however, to overlook the importance of sponge organization in permitting the cellular independence characteristic of the phylum. Without such a porous body and the volume of water passing through it, internal cells could neither respire nor excrete independently. In this sense, the choanocytes and canal system make a real contribution to respiratory and excretory functions.

INTERNAL TRANSPORT

It is evident that while the flow of water through the body is important in transport, it is by no means comparable to the circulatory system of higher metazoans. Diffusion and active transport of materials through cell membranes account for most of the movement of materials in the body.

Cell-to-cell internal transport cannot be ignored, however, for food is passed from choanocyte to amoebocyte, and the motile tissue cell plays an important role in distribution of substances. Food reserves in masses of amoebocytes are mobilized for use. Amoebocytes are the work-horses of sponge economy, functioning as instruments for internal transport and for a variety of other metabolic functions.

Protective Devices

Sponges lack special sense organs and the ability to escape, and it may seem that they are helplessly exposed to damage. The facts are otherwise. Fishes tend to avoid sponges, and anyone who has handled them without protection understands. The sharp bristles penetrate any soft tissue exposed to them, and sponges also appear to have a disagreeable taste and smell. They produce irritating substances; the sap of freshwater sponges is fatal when injected into mice. Oddly enough, many small animals apparently take up residence in the sessile and apparently harmless sponges for protection. Some crabs decorate themselves with sponges, perhaps for camouflage or perhaps because so many animals avoid sponges. *Dromia* holds a piece of live sponge over its back, and some hermit crabs occupy snail shells with attached sponges. The shell disappears as the sponges grow. Eventually only the sponge is left, and the crab, apparently protected by the disagreeable nature of the sponge, carries its partner about. This has become an intimate relationship, for some sponges are found almost exclusively in association with hermit crabs.

Mechanisms of Response

Sensory stimuli, transmitted by nerves, evoke a response in almost all animals. Sponges are an exception, for there is no nervous system. Any contractile parts of a sponge act as independent effectors, receiving stimuli and acting upon them.

Response to environmental stimuli is limited and centers about the direct response of individual cells. Myocytes, desmacytes, and pinacocytes can contract slowly, closing ostia and oscula and reducing body surface. A sharp stimulus given at a definite point slowly spreads and evokes responses in nearby cells. A needle prick near an osculum results in its closure, but a similar prick some distance away leaves it unaffected. Transmission of such a stimulus is slow, about 1 cm./min. This kind of conduction, requiring no nervous system, is termed neuroid conduction.

Growth and Reproduction

Porifera are primitively organized Metazoa, with many cells retaining protozoan characteristics. Their growth, reproduction, and morphogenesis pose tantalizing problems and contribute to our understanding of the nature of the earliest multicellular animal stocks.

ASEXUAL REPRODUCTION

Asexual reproduction occurs as the result of accidental fragmentation of the body, of exposure to unfavorable environmental conditions, or as a part of the normal life cycle. Budding, essentially the differentiation of a small primordium on the parent body into a young individual, is the most common type of asexual reproduction. Small buds appear on the sides of the body and grow and differentiate into young sponges, detaching to take up an independent life or remaining as a new member of a colony. Fresh-water and some marine sponges produce special buds, called gemmules. Gemmules of fresh-water sponges

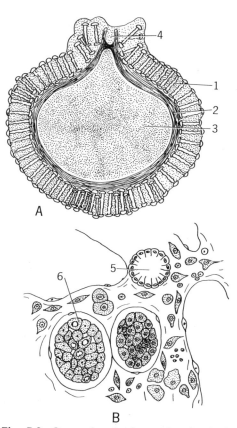

A

B

Fig. 5.9. Gemmules. A. Gemmule of a fresh-water sponge. B. Early stages in the formation of gemmules in a marine sponge. (A, after Evans. B, after Wilson.) 1, outer membrane containing supporting amphidiscs; 2, inner membrane; 3, mass of archeocytes which will give rise to new sponge; 4, micropyle, through which the archeocytes will escape; 5, young gemmule, with surface epithelium; 6, older gemmule.

have a complex, hard shell; they are produced most abundantly in the fall and germinate the next spring (Fig. 5.9A). Gemmules of marine Demospongia are formed more or less continuously and undergo prompt development, giving rise to juveniles that pass through stages resembling the embryos produced during sexual reproduction.

Fresh-water gemmules begin as masses of amoebocytes, filled with food from special nurse cells. Other amoebocytes form a covering around the central mass, and differentiate into a layer of columnar cells that secrete a hard, inner membrane. Scleroblasts from the parent mesogloea form special gemmule spicules, depositing them into the cylindrical layer formed by the columnar cells. The gemmule wall is broken at the micropyle, a pore through which the cells emerge during germination.

Marine gemmules also begin as a mass of amoebocytes, surrounded by other cells. The outer layer develops into a flagellated surface epithelium. Mature gemmules have a flagellated and non-flagellated pole. After a free-swimming period, they settle and attach at the naked end, developing into young sponges.

Sponges have a fabulous ability to regenerate. Tips of the branches of some sponges regularly break off and produce masses of cells that become young sponges. Many sponges form reduction bodies during unfavorable periods. The main mass of the body deteriorates, leaving a residual mass that develops into young sponges under favorable conditions. Gemmules and reduction bodies are ideal stages for dissemination. Motile or long quiescent, they may reach points at some distance from the parent colony, an important capacity in the young of sessile animals.

Sexual Reproduction

Gametes generally arise from amoebocytes, but there are conflicting reports of sperm development. Growth and food storage at the expense of nearby nurse cells transform an archeocyte into an ovum. Meiosis occurs at the end of the growth period.

Sperm development is rarely seen and there is uncertainty about details. Amoebocytes and choanocytes have been observed in sperm formation. Gatenby (1919) convincingly described the transformation of choanocytes into spermatogonia. However they may arise, spermatogonia form masses surrounded by layers of flattened cells, known as spermatocysts. Spermatocysts disappear as spermatids form. Mature sperm find their way to the excurrent canal system and eventually reach the incurrent canal system of other sponges. While most sponges are hermaphroditic, cross-breeding is insured by differing times of sperm and ovum maturation.

According to Gatenby (1919), sperm are ingested by the choanocytes, which fuse with the ovum and set the engulfed sperm free. Others have reported similar observations, but in some cases amoebocytes take the place of choanocytes. It seems probable that this unusual method of fertilization is not uncommon.

Embryonic Development

The puzzling embryonic development of sponges involves stages bewilderingly like and unlike similar stages of other animals. The embryo remains in the mesenchyme of the parent, during early stages deriving nourishment from parent cells. It emerges as a blastula or gastrula, and swims about for a time. Ultimately, it attaches and develops into an olynthus in Calcarea, and a rhagon in Demospongia.

Calcarean zygotes undergo holoblastic cleavage. The young embryo lies near the choanocytes, imbedded in the mesenchyme. In the 16-cell stage, eight blastomeres are macromeres and eight are micromeres. Macromeres lie against the parent choanocytes. The micromeres appear to be in the animal hemisphere where the polocytes are liberated. The macromeres cease dividing, and

the micromeres continue to divide, developing flagella which project into the blastocoel. Meanwhile, a functional mouth develops in the center of the macromeres, and parent cells are ingested.

At this time inversion occurs. Inversion is an unusual process, during which the cells pass through the mouth, turning the embryo inside out and bringing the flagella to the outer surface. *Volvox* undergoes a similar inversion during development (Fig. 5.10A-C), supporting the idea that flagellated colonies were ancestral to sponges.

At this time, the choanocytes form a nutritive trophic membrane around the blastula. Both macromeres and micromeres divide, forming approximately equal masses when the amphiblastula escapes from the parent. The free-swimming amphiblastula swims with its flagellated micromeres forward.

Except for the inversion of cells, development has been typical of most animals up to this point. The small cells at the animal pole are like the micromeres of other animals, and the large cells at the vegetal pole, with a history of being associated with the nourishment of the embryo, are not unlike the macromeres of most animals. From this point on, however, the sponge embryo does everything wrong.

The amphiblastula usually attaches before gastrulation. Gastrulation may occur by invagination or by epiboly, but it is the micromeres which invaginate and the macromeres that grow over the micromeres in epiboly. What would have become the ectoderm of other metazoans is now inside, and what should have been the endoderm forms the outer covering. As development proceeds, the inner layer of cells produce choanocytes, archeocytes, and some amoebocytes, while the outer layer forms pinacocytes, porocytes, and scleroblasts.

The larva attaches at the blastopore and the central cavity is the beginning of the spongocoel (Fig. 5.10E). As the osculum breaks through at the free end, the embryo becomes a simple asconoid sponge, known as an olynthus. The spongocoel evaginates to form choanocyte canals in syconoids. *Leucoselenia* achieves the same result in a different manner. A solid gastrula is formed, with flagellated cells at the surface and non-flagellated cells within. When the larva attaches, the interior cells migrate to the surface to form the epidermis.

The embryo of primitive tetractinellid Demospongia escapes from the parent as a coeloblastula, composed entirely of small flagellated cells, and so lacks macromeres. It attaches at its anterior end. Anterior cells invaginate and become the inner choanocytes, and posterior cells change into covering epithelium. The resulting rhagon

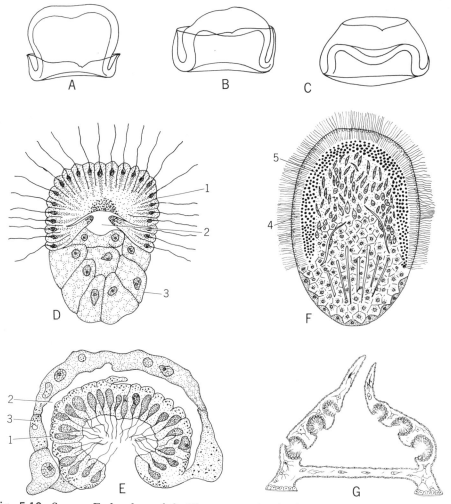

Fig. 5.10. Sponge Embryology. A-C. Three stages in the inversion of a *Volvox* blastula. D. Amphiblastula of *Sycon*, showing the flagellated micromeres and macromeres. E. *Sycon* embryo after gastrulation and attachment, with choanocytes developing from micromeres and outer wall from macromeres. F. Swimming demospongian larva, essentially a differentiating stereoblastula. G. A rhagon larva of a tetractinellid sponge (A-C, after Pocock, from Berrill. D-E, after Hammer. F, after Wilson. G, after Sollas.) 1, micromere; 2, blastocoel; 3, macromere; 4, flagellated layer; 5, inner cell mass.

(Fig. 5.10G) larva is somewhat conical. The rhagon choanocytes evaginate to lay down the primary choanocyte chambers, assuming a syconoid form. Further out-pocketings of the choanocyte layer produce the typical choanocyte chambers of leuconoid sponges. An osculum eventually breaks through at the top.

The solid blastula of other Demospongia gastrulates by delamination while still within the parent. The outer cells develop flagella and the inner cells become amoebocytes. A small area of non-flagellated cells occurs at the posterior pole of the larva. The stereogastrula emerges from the parent, and after swimming about for a time, attaches at the anterior end. Inversion occurs, bringing the internal cells to the surface, where they form pinacocytes and mesenchyme.

Regeneration

Animals that reproduce asexually usually have high regenerative powers, and sponges are no exception. Small pieces of sponge detached from the parent organism can regenerate new sponges. Pieces grow slowly, often requiring months to reach adult size. Sponges have the remarkable power of reconstitution. A sponge squeezed through silk bolting cloth is dissociated into isolated cells and small clusters of cells. The cells become amoeboid and reaggregate, at first into delicate meshworks and later into small spherules. They coalesce to form syncytial masses as they come together, with the more granular internal part of each cell retaining its individuality. The clear hyaloplasm of the whole mass thus becomes available for making large pseudopodia, hastening coalescence. Each spherule is made of a covering layer of pinacocytes and a central mass of mesenchymal cells and choanocytes. The excurrent canal system is formed as internal cells die and are engulfed by amoebocytes, clearing away lacunar spaces. The incurrent canal system

is formed by collencytes just under the covering layer. Choanocytes remain active and form choanocyte chambers. The reconstitution process, first described by Wilson, has been studied more recently by Fauré-Fremiet, Brien, and Spiegel (see bibliography).

Phylogenetic Relationships

Sponges have obviously gone their own way along a developmental line foreign to other Metazoa. They have arisen from Protozoa, undoubtedly from some flagellate stock. If any more detailed statement is undertaken, difficulties arise.

From what group of flagellates did sponges arise? The choanocytes resemble choanoflagellates. A genus of choanoflagellates forming irregular masses of jelly containing scattered zooids (Fig. 3.13) was named *Protospongia*, as it seemed a possible design for a sponge ancestor. Choanoflagellate colonies have no embryonic stages like sponges, however, and the striking inversion of sponge embryos, so like inversion of *Volvox*, seems to imply relationship. On this basis, sponge ancestors might be described as somewhat spherical, blastula-like colonial flagellates with a habit of embryonic inversion. Unfortunately, all of these are photosynthetic, and must certainly have lost their photosynthetic powers before becoming sponge-like.

The unique use of macromeres and micromeres during embryonic development emphasizes the distinctiveness of sponges. It is clear that by the time early sponges had developed these embryonic habits, they had already embarked on a completely independent line of evolutionary development.

Relationships within the phylum are uncertain. Adult Calcarea include the simplest species, apparently arising from a simple, asconoid stem. Some Calcarea have reached leuconoid organization, and in all probability by several different avenues. Hexactinellids are so unlike other sponges that they cannot be definitely related to other groups. Available evidence points to the tetractinellids as the most primitive Demo- spongia, probably arising from ancestral stocks resembling the rhagon embryos, and to the Keratosa as the most advanced sponge form.

References

Bidder, G. P. 1923. The relation of the form of a sponge to its currents. *Quart. Jour. Micro. Sci.* 67: 293.

―――― and G. S. Vosmaer-Roell. 1928. *Bibliography of Sponges, 1751–1913.* Cambridge Univ. Press, Cambridge, Eng.

Brien, P. 1936. La Réorganisation de l'éponge après dissociation par filtration et phénomènes d'involution chez *Ephydatia fluviatilis. Arch. Biol.* 48: 145.

Dendy, A. 1926. On the origin, growth, and arrangement of sponge spicules. *Quart. Jour. Micr. Sci.* 70: 1.

Fauré-Fremiet, E. 1932. Morphogénèse expérimentale (reconstitution) chez *Ficulina ficus* L. *Arch. d'Anat. Micro. Morph. Exp.* 28: 1.

Galtsoff, P. 1925. Regeneration after dissociation. *Jour. Exp. Zool.* 48: 183, 223.

Gatenby, J. B. 1919. Germ cells, fertilization, and early development of *Grantia compressa* (*Sycon*). *Linn. Soc. London, Jour. Zool.* 34: 261.

Jewell, M. E. 1935. An ecological study of the fresh-water sponges of northern Wisconsin. *Ecol. Monogr.* 5: 461.

Jones, W. D. 1959. Spicule growth rates in *Leucoselenia variabilis. Quart. Jour. Micr. Sci.* 100: 557.

Laubenfels, M. W. de. 1932. Marine and fresh-water sponges of California. *Proc. U.S. Natl. Mus.* 81. (F)

Leveaux, M. 1939. La Formation des gemmules chez les Spongillidae. *Ann. Soc. Roy. Zool. Belg.* 70: 53.

Parker, G. H. 1914. On the strength of water currents produced by sponges. *Jour. Exp. Zool.* 16: 443.

Rasmont, R., *et al.* 1958. Ultrastructure of choanocyte collar cells in fresh water sponges. *Nature* 181: 58.

Smith, F. 1921. Distribution of fresh-water sponges of North America. *Bull. Ill. Nat. Hist. Surv.* 14: 9. (F)

Spiegel, M. 1954. The role of specific surface antigens in cell adhesion, I. The reaggregation of sponge cells. *Biol. Bull.* 107: 130.

Wilson, H. V. 1907. On some phenomena of coalescence and regeneration in sponges. *Jour. Exp. Zool.* 5: 245.

―――― . 1925. Silicious and horny sponges collected by the Albatross. *U.S. Nat. Mus. Bull.* 1930. 100, Vol. 2. pt. 4. 273.

―――― , and J. T. Penney. 1930. The regeneration of sponges (*Microciona*) from dissociated cells. *Jour. Exp. Zool.* 56: 73.

6
The Radiata

Radiata are the most primitive Eumetazoa. Unlike Parazoa, they have some rudimentary organs of the kind seen in higher animals. Unlike other Eumetazoa, they are primarily radially symmetrical. Mesozoa and Parazoa stand at the cellular level of organization, while Radiata are primarily composed of tissues and incipient tissues. Cells retain considerable independence in incipient tissues, but the progressive subordination of cells to masses or layers of cells as independent functional units is evident in Radiata.

The name "Radiata" is suitable because of the primary radial symmetry characteristic of its members. The point symmetry of a perfect cylinder is converted into radial symmetry by the appearance of polarity between two different, opposing surfaces. Thus the point symmetry of a spherical blastula is converted into radial symmetry by polarity and the differentiation of an animal hemisphere with micromeres and a vegetal hemisphere with macromeres. The radial symmetry of the blastula becomes manifest with gastrulation and the appearance of a blastopore-animal pole axis, retained in Radiata as the oral-aboral axis. Point or universal symmetry is suitable for

floaters without a constant orientation to their environment like many Heliozoida. Radial or line symmetry is especially suitable for sessile or floating animals with definite upper and lower surfaces. Thus a jellyfish floats with its mouth down, and a *Hydra* attaches with its mouth up. Radial symmetry is characteristic of the Radiata. Sea anemones and corals have a strong tendency toward bilaterality, but live like radially symmetrical animals. Ctenophores, too, are biradial, and have acquired habits of movement resembling bilateral animals.

An important contribution of Radiata to animal development is the coelenteron, or gastrovascular cavity. The traffic in energy and materials between an organism and its environment is central to its way of life. The appearance of a digestive cavity serving the whole commonwealth of cells has favored other changes in a metazoan direction. The coelenteron is the only body cavity in Radiata, and in level of organization they stand between the sponges, also radially symmetrical in primitive species but without a coelenteron, and the higher metazoa. In a sense, the study of Radiata is a study of the consequences of having a coelenteron.

The coelenteron is derived from the primitive gut of the embryo, and the mouth from the blastopore. No proctodaeum appears, and an anus is never formed. Only the preliminary phases of digestion take place in the coelenteron; the final phases of digestion occur intracellularly in its lining cells. The coelenteron is a gastrovascular cavity, for it serves in transport as well as digestion and some of its modifications are related to its use in distributing substances.

Phylum Cnidaria

Hatschek (1888) was the first to properly sort out sponges, cnidarians, and ctenophores, and his name Cnidaria is most appropriate for the phylum. For many years it was called Coelenterata; coelenterate is a useful synonym of cnidarian and is still widely used.

Cnidaria include jellyfish, sea anemones, corals, and various *Hydra*-like polyps. It is a very successful phylum, with about 9000 modern species, and includes some of the most important, most interesting, and most beautiful animals. Cnidaria occur in oceans everywhere, but prefer shallower, warmer waters. Only a few species have succeeded in fresh water. Sea anemones, often beautifully tinted creatures with petal-like tentacles, have been called flowers of the sea, and many jellyfish are no less attractive. Under a microscope, many small hydroids and corals reveal a delicacy and precision of form that is no less impressive. The largest jellyfish, *Cyanea arctica*, weighs nearly a ton and may have tentacles up to a hundred feet long. Huge aggregations of coral polyps have formed reefs and atolls, increasing the surface available for life.

The outstanding features of the Cnidaria include:

1. Primary radial symmetry about an oral-aboral axis derived from the primary axis of the gastrula, or biradial symmetry with the development of a sagittal plane and the retention of external radial features.

2. Body formed of three layers: an outer epidermis derived from the ectoderm; an inner gastrodermis, derived from the endoderm; and a cellular or non-cellular mesogloea, at least largely derived from ectoderm.

3. A single body cavity, the coelenteron, derived from the primitive gut, and a single opening, the mouth, derived from the blastopore.

4. Special offensive and defensive organoids called nematocysts, formed by interstitial cells.

5. One or more whorls or fields of tentacles around the mouth almost universally present.

6. No excretory or respiratory systems, but with a neurosensory apparatus composed of a nerve net, formed of non-polarized protoneurons and various types of sensory cells, sometimes assembled in special sense organs.

7. A strong tendency toward polymorphism, with hydroid and jellyfish forms and often with a variety of specialized zooids growing together in a colony.

THE CLASSES OF CNIDARIA

Three well-defined classes are recognized, each with distinctive features in its polypoid (or hydroid) or its jellyfish (or medusoid) phases.

Class Hydrozoa. The hydroids and craspedote medusae. Solitary or colonial cnidarians, with a non-cellular mesogloea and a coelenteron without gastric tentacles or septa and without a stomodaeum. The life cycle may be exclusively polypoid, exclusively medusoid, or with both polypoid and medusoid phases, but the polypoid phase is usually predominant.

Class Scyphozoa. The acraspedote medusae. Medusae without a velum, usually free swimming but rarely attached by an aboral stalk. The mesogloea is cellular, and the coelenteron has no stomodaeum, has filamentous gastric tentacles, and is often divided by septa into four compartments. The life cycle lacks a polypoid stage or includes a larval polyp that may develop into the medusa or give rise to medusae by transverse fission.

Class Anthozoa. Sea anemones and corals. Exclusively polypoid Cnidaria with a richly cellular mesogloea, in some forms approaching a fibrous connective tissue. The body wall turns in at the mouth to form a stomodaeum lined with ectoderm, which opens into the coelenteron. The coelenteron is divided into compartments by septa with nematocysts along their border. Zygotes develop directly into polyps.

Class Hydrozoa

A few Hydrozoa live in fresh water, notably *Hydra*, widely studied in introductory courses, and *Craspedacusta*, the freshwater jellyfish, but nearly all are marine. Some Hydrozoa are solitary and others form colonies of thousands of zooids. A single polyp is usually small, but *Branchiocerianthus*, living nearly two miles below the surface, may reach six feet in height. They prefer shallow water, their colonies contributing heavily to surface growth on submerged objects. Differing classifications have been proposed; Hyman recognizes the five orders listed below.

Order Hydroida. The hydroids. Solitary or colonial polyps that bud off free medusae or produce sessile, degenerate medusae; medusae have eye-spots, or ocelli, and ectodermal balance organs called statocysts. There are two suborders, the *Gymnoblastea* (Anthomedusae) and the *Calyptoblastea* (Leptomedusae). Gymnoblastea are the tubularian hydroids, without a skeletal cup or theca and producing tall, bell-like medusae with ocelli and no statocysts. Calyptoblastea are the campanularian hydroids, with a theca, and producing flat medusae with statocysts.

Order Milleporina. The millepores. Colonial hydroids forming a massive, porous exoskeleton; with two kinds of polyps, feeding gastrozooids, and tactile dactylozooids of elongate form; producing degenerate but free medusae.

Order Stylasterina. Similar to millepores, but with small dactylozooids, usually arranged in systems, and with permanently sessile, degenerate medusae.

Order Trachylina. The trachyline medusae. Medusae with balance organs having endodermal statoliths, and with the tentacles usually set above the margin of the bell; with or without a reduced polypoid phase in the life cycle.

Order Siphonophora. The siphonophores. Free-swimming or floating colonies composed of several kinds of highly specialized zooids; with reduced medusae, rarely freed.

Trachylines

According to one view of cnidarian phylogeny, the trachyline medusae are the most primitive modern cnidarians. *Gonionemus* and *Craspedacusta* are often studied as representative trachylines and make a good introduction to the form and life cycle of Cnidaria.

The conspicuous phase of the *Gonionemus* life cycle is the medusa (Fig. 6.1). It is a small jellyfish, about 25 cm. in diameter, which swims about or clings to seaweed by adhesive pads on its tentacles. When sexually mature it produces gametes. After fertilization, a solid blastula and gastrula are formed, and the embryo develops into a planula larva (Fig. 6.2A). The planula attaches after swimming about for a time, developing into a minute polyp (Fig. 6.2B). The polyp can reproduce asexually by budding off small, unciliated, planula-like frustules, which creep about for a time, attach, and develop into new polyps. Eventually the mature polyps bud off medusae that detach and swim away. In the *Gonionemus* life cycle, it is clear that the polyp is little more than a larval form, although it can reproduce. The polyp

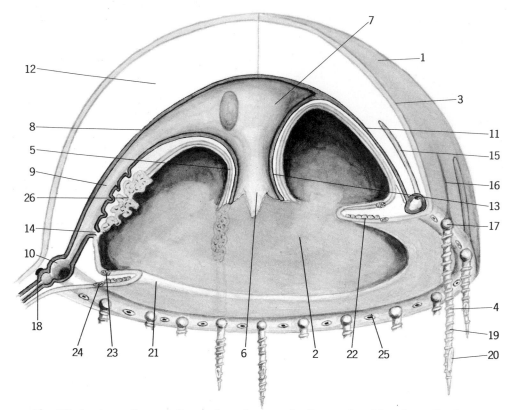

Fig. 6.1. Anatomy of a trachyline medusa. A composite diagram, based largely on *Gonionemus*, showing the left side cut through a radial canal, and the right side cut between radial canals. The bell or umbrella of the medusa has a convex upper surface, the exumbrella (1), and a concave lower surface, the subumbrella (2), covered with epidermis (3). Tentacles (4) hang from the bell margin, and a manubrium (5) hangs in the center of the subumbrellar surface. It ends in a quadrangular mouth (6) and opens into the gastric cavity (7), lined with gastrodermis (8). Four gastrodermal radial canals (9) connect the gastric cavity and the ring canal (10). A single layer of gastrodermis, the gastrodermal lamella (11), extends between the radial canals. A thick layer of mesogloea (12) separates the exumbrellar epidermis and the gastrodermis, and a very thin layer of mesogloea, the mesolamella (13), separates the subumbrellar epidermis and gastrodermis. In some species each radial canal opens into the subumbrellar space by pores (14), probably used for excretion. Blind centripetal canals (15) arise from the ring canal of some species. Tentacles may be solid or hollow, but have an epidermal covering and a gastrodermal core, which sometimes extends into the mesogloea as tentacular roots (16). Tentacular bulbs (17), open to the ring canal, are located at the tentacle bases; they sometimes have ocelli (18). Rings or other prominences filled with nematocysts (19) are found on the tentacles. *Gonionemus* has adhesive pads (20) which are used to cling to seaweed. The conspicuous velum (21) is composed of two layers of epidermis and contains a band of circular muscle (22). An upper nerve ring (23) lies above the attachment of the velum to the bell, and a lower nerve ring (24) below it. The two nerve rings are separated by the mesolamella. Statocysts (25) are balance organs imbedded in the bell margin. Gonads (26) lie on the radial canals of mature specimens.

128

is even further reduced in some trachylines and is sometimes omitted from the life cycle. Among hydroids the polyp is far more important, and the medusa phase may be little more than a gadget for making eggs and sperm. The medusa stage is completely omitted in *Hydra*. Scyphozoan jellyfish have reduced hydroids, and the sea anemones and corals have no medusa phase. Cnidaria are unique in having a larval phase, being stable morphologically and able to reproduce, which is as successful a life form as the adult medusa. In the competition between the medusoid and polypoid form, the medusa has sometimes emerged victorious and at other times the polyp has become the dominant form of the life cycle.

MEDUSA FORM AND FUNCTION

Morphological details of trachyline medusae are shown in Fig. 6.1. They are carnivorous, stunning, paralyzing, or killing small animals with the nettle cells or nematocysts in their tentacles. Other nematocysts are adapted to attach the prey to the tentacles. Movements of the tentacles and the manubrium deliver food to the mouth. The food enters the gastric cavity where it is rapidly attacked by enzymes and reduced to a mush during preliminary digestion. The gastrodermal cells are flagellated and set up currents in the coelenteron, distributing the partly digested material throughout the radial and ring canal system. Digestion is completed in food vacuoles in the gastrodermal cells. Food residues are ejected from the mouth, although very small particles may escape through pores located near the junction of the radial and ring canals. It is evident that the coelenteron and its branches are a true gastrovascular cavity, combining digestive and transport functions.

Respiration occurs at the external surface and the lining of the gastrovascular cavity. Liberation of dissolved nitrogenous wastes into the surrounding water or into

the coelenteron requires no special structures. There is evidence that solid nitrogenous wastes may accumulate in gastrodermal cells near the pores on the radial canals.

Contractile fibers are imbedded in the bases of the epidermal cells. The fibers are aggregated to form longitudinal muscles in the manubrium and tentacles and weak radial muscles in the subumbrella. The tentacular and manubrial musculature brings about movements used in food capture and ingestion. The subumbrellar epidermis is two-layered. The inner epidermis is associated with the radial muscles; the outer epidermis with the heavier circular muscles. A band of circular muscle lies between the epidermal layers of the

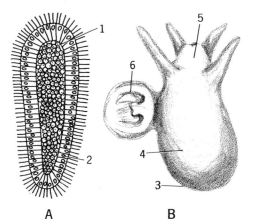

A   B

Fig. 6.2. A. A planula larva. B. A polyp of a trachyline medusa, with a medusa bud attached. The trachyline zygote grows into a planula larva, with a solid mass of endoderm cells (1) within, and a covering of ciliated ectoderm (2). It metamorphoses into a hydra-like polyp after attaching at its anterior end. The point of attachment becomes the base or pedal disc (3) of the polyp. A more or less cylindrical column (4) bears tentacles at its upper end. Within the whorl of tentacles a hypostome or manubrium (5) lies, with the mouth at the center. When mature, the polyp reproduces asexually by budding, forming medusa buds (6) that detach and develop into free-swimming medusae. The mature medusae reproduce sexually.

velum. Swimming movements are produced by the subumbrellar and velar musculature. Sudden contractions of the subumbrellar and velar muscles forces a jet of water from the subumbrellar space, narrowed at its aperture by the velum, and this thrusts the animal forward. The muscles relax and the subumbrellar space fills again. Swimming movements are repeated rhythmically, the rate of pulsation changing with light concentration, temperature, and the presence of food.

Information about the environment is provided by sensory cells, some scattered in the epidermis and others forming patches of sensory epithelium at strategic points. Concentrations of sensory cells occur in tentacles and manubrium, and a ring of sensory epithelium circles the body just above the nerve rings. Patches of sensory epithelium also occur on the tentacular bulbs and other marginal protuberances. Special sense organs occur on the bell margin. Many medusae have eye-spots or ocelli, located in the wall of the tentacular bulbs or at the base of the tentacles. Balance organs of one kind or another also lie on the bell margin, permitting the animal to right itself when tilted (p. 178).

The nervous system consists of multipolar or bipolar nerve cells that conduct stimuli in either direction. These protoneurones form a nerve net or plexus immediately below the epidermis. The plexus is usually denser along the radial canals, forming radial nerves. Heavy concentrations of bipolar protoneurones form two nerve rings, a larger upper ring just above the velar attachment, and a smaller lower ring just below the velar attachment. The two rings are separated by the thin mesogloeal layer of the velum, the mesolamella, but are connected by fibers passing through it. The lower ring innervates the balance organs and the velar and subumbrellar musculature. The upper ring innervates the tentacles, ocelli, tentacular bulbs, and tracts and patches of sensory epithelium at the bell margin.

Two suborders of trachylines are recognized, Trachymedusae and Narcomedusae. Trachymedusae are of the type just described. They are characterized by a smooth bell margin, gonads on the radial canal, and a manubrium. Narcomedusae have a scalloped bell margin, gonads on the floor of the gastric cavity, and have no manubrium. The mouth opens directly into the gastric cavity. *Gonionemus* (Fig. 6.1) and *Craspedacusta* are good examples of trachymedusae, showing tetramerous radial symmetry in the four radial canals and quadrangular mouth. *Aglantha* (Fig. 6.3A) is another trachymedusa with a very tall bell

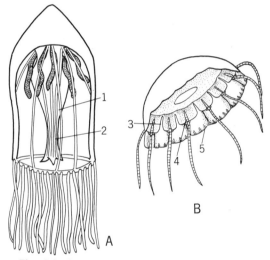

Fig. 6.3. A. *Aglantha*, a trachymedusa. B. *Cunina*, a narcomedusa. (A, after Hargitt, from Pratt. B, after Bigelow.) *Aglantha* is unusual in having a part of the subumbrella containing the radial canals pendant as a pseudomanubrium (1). It ends in the manubrium (2). Eight large gonads hang down in the subumbrellar spaces from the eight radial canals. *Cunina*, a typical narcomedusa, has no manubrium and has a scalloped bell margin, with tentacles arising from the exumbrella. The large, central gastric cavity forms gastric pouches (3); there is no ring canal. Sensory tracts, peronia (4), connect the bases of the tentacles to indented points on the bell margin. Small sensory tracts, the otoporpae (5), run over the bell margin at the balance organs (lithostyles).

and a long pseudomanubrium containing radial canals, ending in a true manubrium without radial canals. As in some other trachymedusae, there are more than four radial canals. *Cunina* (Fig. 6.3B) is a typical narcomedusa. Note the absence of a manubrium, the flattened form and scalloped bell margin, the scalloping of the gastric cavity, and the prominent sensory tracts, common distinguishing features of the narcomedusae. In general, Narcomedusae have lithostyles for balance organs,

while trachymedusae have statocysts (p. 178).

Most trachylines have no polyp stage. Development proceeds from a zygote, through indeterminate cleavage, blastula, gastrula, and planula larva stages. The planula does not attach but develops a mouth and transforms into an actinula larva (Fig. 6.4). The actinula broadens, invaginates at the oral end to form a subumbrella, and grows tentacles to become a diminutive medusa. Some trachylines, like *Gonionemus*, have small polyp stages. *Craspedacusta* has small polyps without tentacles, which form small colonies. If the trachylines are the most primitive Cnidaria, the polyp is a sessile actinula which developed the ability to bud and eventually established itself as a successful animal in its own right.

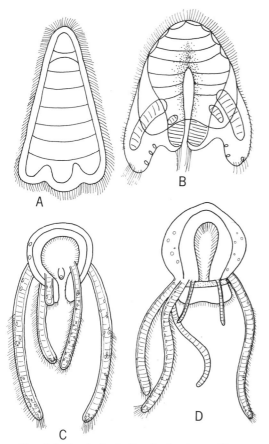

Fig. 6.4. An Actinula Developing into a Young Medusa. (After Metschnikoff.) The planula develops into an actinula as the mouth region invaginates, establishing a subumbrellar space. As tentacles form at the future bell margin, the medusa form emerges.

Hydroida

As a group, Hydroida have the best balance between medusae and polyps, although the polyp is dominant in most species. Polyps are sessile, while medusae float or swim feebly, at the mercy of ocean currents and tides. The inactive polyp merely extends its tentacles to catch prey and retracts, often into a protective exoskeleton, to avoid enemies. Medusae orient themselves in daily cycles or with weather changes, alternately rising to the surface or swimming deep. Polyps typically reproduce asexually and medusae sexually, although exceptions occur. Polyps often form large colonies, while medusae are typically solitary. The adaptation of these two forms, each in directions suitable for its activities, has profoundly influenced cnidarian evolution.

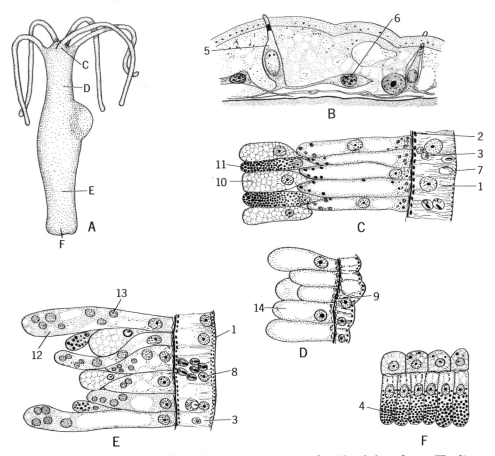

Fig. 6.5. Histology of *Hydra*. **A.** A *Hydra*, with a testis on the side of the column. The lines c-f indicate the levels at which the corresponding sections have been cut. **B.** The epidermis of the hypostome of *Hydra*. **C-F.** Sections through the *Hydra* hypostome (**C**), the upper part of the column in the region of active digestion (**D**), the stalk region where digestion does not occur (**E**), and the pedal disc (**F**). Note highly developed glandular cells in the gastrodermis of the hypostome, used to lubricate the mouth area. In the gastric region many enzymatic gland cells occur and food vacuoles are seen in the nutritive-muscular cells. In the stalk region enzymatic gland cells are absent and the gastrodermis is vacuolated. The epidermis is composed of low, cuboidal cells. The gastrodermis of the pedal disc is inactive and the epidermis consists of glandular cells. Cellular specializations thus define oral, gastric, stalk, and basal regions in *Hydra*, although these may not be obvious externally. (B, after Hadzi. C-E, after Hyman.) *Epidermis:* **1**, epidermal cell; **2**, myonemes at the base of the epitheliomuscular cells; **3**, interstitial cell; **4**, epidermal gland cell; **5**, neurosensory cell; **6**, protoneuron; **7**, nematocyst; **8**, nucleus of epitheliomuscular cell. *Mesogloea:* **9**, mesolamella. *Gastrodermis:* **10**, granular type of gland cell in the hypostome; **11**, mucous type of gland cell in the hypostome; **12**, nutritive muscular cell; **13**, food vacuole; **14**, enzymatic gland cell.

HYDRA

Hydra is the most intensively studied cnidarian, in introductory courses and in the research laboratory. Common in ponds and clear streams, *Hydra* feeds voraciously on microcrustaceans, annelids, insects, and occasionally on newly hatched fish. Usually it moves only to contract or expand the body or tentacles, but it can glide on the pedal disc or move by somersaulting or looping movements. Occasionally it secretes a gas bubble and floats for a time. *Hydra* is a typical solitary polyp, its body consisting of a base, modified as a pedal disc; a stem, often invisible externally; a column, containing the active gastrodermis; and a hypostome, a conical region between the tentacles at the top of the column and the mouth (Fig. 6.5A).

Hydra is an excellent histological subject, and has been described in great detail. The findings apply in principle to other hydroid polyps. Epidermis and gastrodermis are separated by a thin mesogloeal plate, the mesolamella. Epidermis and gastrodermis are incipient tissues in *Hydra*, consisting predominantly of one cell type, but containing a number of other cells and having broad functions rather than the narrow functions typical of true tissues.

Histological structure of several regions of the body are shown in Fig. 6.5. Large, vacuolated epithelio-muscular cells, with expanded bases containing two longitudinally oriented muscle threads, predominate in the epidermis. The muscle threads or myonemes attach to the mesolamella and shorten the body when contracted. Narrow, elongated sensory cells, ending in fine processes or tiny bulbs, are scattered among the epithelio-muscular cells. Their basal fibers make contact with the nerve plexus. Adhesive secretions are formed by epidermal gland cells with basal myonemes, situated on the pedal disc. Small interstitial cells are packed in at the bases of the epi-thelio-muscular cells. They are unspecialized, and can replace any of the other cell types. They are especially prominent in the growth zone at the upper end of the column and at points where buds or sex organs are developing. Many interstitial cells become cnidoblasts, forming nematocysts of various kinds.

Multipolar neurones form a plexus in gastrodermal and epidermal layers. Their several neurites make connections with the neurites of adjacent protoneurones to form a nerve net.

Large nutritive-muscular cells predominate in the gastrodermis. Their transverse myonemes constrict and lengthen the body when contracted, acting as antagonists to the epidermal myonemes. Mucous gland cells are abundant near the mouth and enzymatic gland cells secrete enzymes for the preliminary extracellular digestion of food. Nutritive-muscular cells have two flagella, and most gland cells have one. Their beating causes currents that aid in food distribution. Interstitial and sensory cells also occur in the gastrodermis, but less abundantly than in the epidermis. The gastrodermis is regionally specialized, as shown by changes in nutritive-muscular cell form and by differing frequencies of gland cells. The oral region secretes slime for lubricating food, aiding in swallowing. The column contains gastrodermis where most digestion and absorption occurs. The stem region has a low, inactive gastrodermis.

Cnidoblasts and nematocysts. When an interstitial cell begins to secrete a nematocyst it is termed a cnidoblast. As the nematocyst matures, the cnidoblast attaches to the mesogloea and extends its distal tip to the epidermis surface. A bristle-like cnidocil develops which serves as a trigger when properly stimulated (Fig. 6.6A). Fibrils develop in the cytoplasm. Some are supportive, but others are thought to be contractile and aid in nematocyst discharge, at least in some Cnidaria. The nematocysts of *Physalia*, the Portuguese man-of-war, do

not discharge when the animal is anesthetized, supporting the view that cnidoblast myonemes aid in discharge; and some
fibers in *Hydra* cnidoblasts stain differentially like muscle fibers.

Each nematocyst consists of a capsule,
its amorphous contents, a cap, and an inverted tube, sometimes expanded basally
as a butt (Fig. 6.6E,G). The tube everts
and the capsular contents are discharged
when the nematocyst discharges. The tube
and butt are often covered with bristles.
At least 18 types of nematocysts have been
described from Cnidaria, and differences
of form occur in each type. Nematocysts
stun, paralyze, or kill prey or enemies, entangle food and attach it to tentacles, and
perform other, sometimes unknown, functions. Desmonemes (volvents) have a tube
closed at the end and coil like a corkscrew
around bristles on prey, attaching them to
the tentacles. Haplonemes have an open
tube, but no butt. There are several kinds
of haplonemes. Anisorhizas have the tube
dilated somewhat at the base, and isorhizas (glutinants) have a tube of the same
diameter throughout. They contain an
adhesive substance, sticking the prey to
the tentacles. Heteronemes have the tube
dilated at the base as a butt. There are a
number of kinds of heteronemes. Rhabdoids have a cylindrical butt, euryteles have
the butt dilated at its summit, and stenoteles (penetrants) have the butt dilated at
its base. Heteronemes are offensive and
defensive weapons. Stenoteles penetrate the
prey surface and inject toxic material, causing severe pain when large enough to
penetrate the human skin. Desmonemes,
two kinds of isorhizas, and stenoteles occur
in the hydras.

Nematocyst discharge is not well understood. According to Iwanzoff (1896), water
passes through the capsule wall, increasing
internal pressure and everting the tube.
This mechanism appears to fit the evidence
in nematocysts of the sea anemone, *Metridium*, but *Physalia* nematocysts appear to
require muscle contraction.

Nematocysts are true independent effectors, and do not require nerve stimuli for
activation. If they are to be of use they
must act at suitable times and in suitable
ways. Every animal undergoes cyclical
changes, from hunger to satiation, from
youth to old age, and in response to cyclical
changes in their environment. If an inde-

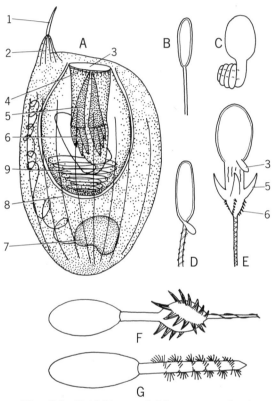

Fig. 6.6. Cnidoblast and Nematocysts. A. A
schematized cnidoblast containing an undis-
charged nematocyst. B-G. Discharged nematocysts. C, *Hydra* desmoneme (volent); D, *Hydra*
atrichous isorhiza (streptoline glutinant); D,
Hydra holotrichous isorhiza (stereoline glutinant); E, *Hydra* stenotele (penetrant);
F, eurytele; G, amastigophore. (A, after
Schultze. B-D, E, after Hyman; F-G, after
Weill.) 1, cnidocil; 2, supporting rods of
cnidocil; 3, operculum; 4, rods supporting operculum; 5, stylet; 6, spine; 7, nucleus; 8, fibers
supporting cnidoblast; 9, filament of cnidoblast.

Table 6.1. Types of nematocysts

TYPE	CHARACTERISTICS	FUNCTION	OCCURRENCE
Rhopaloneme	Tube an elongated, closed sac	Entangling prey	Siphonophora
Desmoneme (or volvent)	Tube a closed thread, coiling on discharge	Entangling prey	Hydroida and Siphonophora
Isorhiza (or glutinant)	Open tube of even diameter; without a butt	Uncertain	All classes
Anisorhiza	Open tube, dilated at base; without a butt	Uncertain	Siphonophora
Mastigophore	Open tube with a cylindrical butt; tube extends beyond the butt.	Penetration, anchorage, toxic?	Anemones; Corals; Zoanthids
Amastigophore	Butt cylindrical; no tube beyond butt.	Penetration, anchorage, toxic?	Anemones
Eurytele	Butt dilated at summit; tube long, open.	Penetration, anchorage, toxic	Hydroida; trachymedusae Scyphozoa.
Stenotele (or penetrant)	Butt dilated at base; tube long, open.	Penetration, anchorage, toxic	Hydrozoa

pendent effector is to fit into the life of the organism, its threshold of response must be modifiable. There is much evidence for such changing thresholds. Few nematocysts discharge when they are stimulated with a glass rod, but more discharge if objects with different textures are used. Well-fed animals do not discharge nematocysts when they come in contact with food. Meat juices lower the threshold of activation, and some lipoid-like materials are effective in lowering the threshold of some cnidarian nematocysts. As the threshold is lowered, a weaker mechanical stimulus evokes discharge.

Discharged nematocysts with open tubes expel the capsule contents. Heteronemes generally release a toxic substance. Various toxins have been named and described by their effects, but they are not biochemically characterized. Rapid anesthetization or death of the prey follows a nematocyst attack. Some scyphomedusae and siphonophores can inflict severe pain, serious illness, or even death on man. Most cnidarians, however, cannot irritate the human skin.

Cnidaria lack the muscular and nervous equipment to grasp prey with their tentacles. Only by using an immoblizing agent and something to attach prey to the tentacles could the slow-moving Cnidaria become sucessful carnivores. The effectiveness of nematocysts is shown by the fact that Cnidaria are almost exclusively carnivorous.

HYDROID POLYPS

Hydrozoan polyps are usually more conspicuous than the medusae. While all hydrozoan polyps conform to the basic pattern seen in *Hydra*, there is great diversity in structural detail.

Typical hydroid polyps are composed of three parts, a base, stem, and hydranth. Adaptations of the base center about attachment, with some provision for the protection of the living, basal tissues. Colonial forms usually arise from a hydrorhiza, a tangled mass of branching and anastomosing stolons. Each stolon is essentially like the column, with a central coelenteron enclosed in a wall composed of epidermis, mesogloea, and gastrodermis. They are covered by a protecting sheath of chitinous periderm, secreted by epidermal cells. Solitary polyps usually attach by unbranched, solid holdfasts which die away to leave hollow peridermal tubes behind. *Hydractinia* commonly attaches to snail shells containing hermit crabs. Its stolons fuse into a network, from which continuous upper and lower sheets of periderm extend (Fig. 6.7A). The lower epidermis secretes layer after layer of periderm, attaching the colony firmly. The upper periderm disappears, although scattered peridermal spines extend upward through the surface. *Hydra* is exceptional in showing no stolonic branching and in having an adhesive pedal disc. Such species are somewhat motile, gliding on the pedal disc or creeping about with the aid of the tentacles.

The hollow stem and living basal parts make up the coenosarc of colonial hydroids. The coenosarc houses a continuous coelenteron, distributing food throughout the colony. As a plant stem lifts leaves to the sun, the cnidarian stem lifts the hydranths above the surface, increasing the number of animals that can occupy the available surface. The stem provides support as well as food transport, and often buds off new hydranths or medusae. The upright main stem of colonial hydroids is the hydrocaulus; of solitary forms, the caulome. Sometimes the hydrorhiza extends upward as many parallel stolons, to form a hydrocaulome that superficially resembles a stem (Fig. 6.7B). The stem and its periderm provide adequate support for most polyps, but if the hydranth is very large, as in *Tubularia* and *Corymorpha*, the stem is filled with vacuolated gastrodermal cells which provide support by turgor. In such stems, multiple gastrodermal canals extend to the base (Fig. 6.7C).

The form of basal and stem regions is affected by colony growth patterns. In

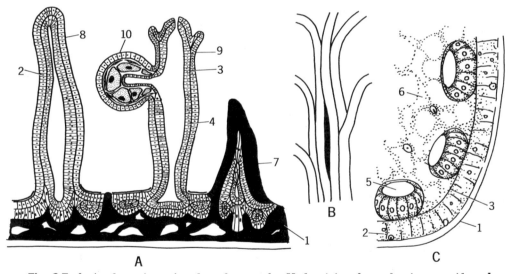

A

C

Fig. 6.7. A. A schematic section through part of a *Hydractinia* colony, showing a peridermal spine, a dactylozooid, and a gonozooid, the latter with a sessile gonophore attached. The thin upper periderm is interrupted, and gastrodermal canals pass through the heavy basal periderm, forming a mat-like coenosarc. This type of colony results from hydrorhizal growth. B. Part of the hydrocaulus of *Eudendrium*, consisting of parallel stolons. C. Cross section of *Tubularia* stem, showing vacuolated gastrodermis cells and gastrodermal canals. (A, composite. B, after Hyman. C, after Warren.) 1, periderm; 2, epidermis; 3, mesolamella; 4, gastrodermis; 5, gastrodermal canal; 6, vacuolated gastrodermis; 7, epidermal spine; 8, dactylozooid; 9, gonozooid; 10, gonophore.

colonies with hydrorhizal growth, single polyps bud irregularly from the basal coenosarc (Fig. 6.7A). Generally colonies have a hydrocaulus, giving rise to branches (hydrocladi) from which hydranths arise. Such colonies may exhibit monopodial growth or sympodial growth. The form of growth helps to distinguish between the Gymnoblastea and Calyptoblastea. Each stem or branch of gymnoblast hydroids with monopodial growth ends in a hydranth. New hydranths bud from a growth zone just below the terminal hydranth (Fig. 6.8A). Sympodial growth occurs in more primitive calyptoblasts. A budding zone at the base of the last hydranth produces a lateral bud that overtops its parent. The hydrocaulus is thus formed of the bases of successive hydranths (Fig. 6.8B). A second type of monopodial growth occurs in less primitive calyptoblasts (Fig. 6.8C). Each stem ends in a growing point that projects beyond the terminal hydranth, and new hydranths form at the base of the growing point. The budding pattern modifies the position of elder and younger hydranths, and has much to do with determining over-all colony form. Some colonies are bushy, others are feathery or flattened. Some branch alternately and some dichotomously. Colony form is an important taxonomic character.

Every hydroid colony has at least two kinds of zooids: gastrozooids and gonophores. Gastrozooids are ordinary feeding polyps, and gonophores are the buds from which medusae arise. Most calyptoblasts have special reproductive polyps, gonozooids, which produce gonophores and have reduced tentacles, mouth, and coelenteron. Colonial animals tend to become polymorphic, that is, they tend to specialize zooids for various purposes. This tendency was noted in protozoan colonies, where the first specialized members were reproductive organisms. Cnidaria present a parallel picture of colonial specialization.

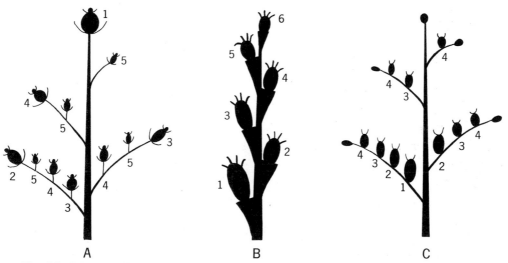

A   B   C

Fig. 6.8. Schematic Representation of Types of Colony Growth. A. Monopodial growth with terminal hydranths. B. Sympodial growth. C. Monopodial growth with terminal growth points. The numbers indicate the hydranth generations, with the original hydranth numbered 1. Monopodial growth with terminal hydranths results in colonies with the eldest hydranth of the stem or branch at the tip. With other types of growth, the eldest hydranth is basal, and age decreases regularly toward the tip of each branch.

Table 6.2. Types of Zooids

TYPE	FUNCTION	CHARACTERISTICS	OCCURRENCE
Gastrozooid (or trophozooid)	Feeding polyps	Typical polyp form	Universal in hydroids
Gonophore	Immature or sessile medusae	Buds, often plate-like or bell-shaped	Universal in hydroids
Gonozooid	Gonophore Production	Usually a polyp with reduced tentacles, and often without mouth	Common
Dactylozooid	Protection, food capture	Modified polyp with reduced mouth, coelenteron and tentacles	Common in Hydrozoa
Tentaculozooid	Same as dactylozooid	Tentacle-like	Common in some hydrozoan groups
Nematophore (or sarcostyle)	Food capture	Blunt ends, with nematocysts or adhesive cells	Plumularidae
Pneumatophore	Float	Hydroid?, modified to form a gas-filled chamber	Siphonophores
Nectophore	Swimming	Modified medusoid, with a velum and four radial canals, but without a mouth	Siphonophores
Phyllozooid (or bract)	Protective cover	Modified medusa, forming thick, leaf-like, helmet-shaped or prismatic covers	Siphonophores

Other kinds of specialized zooids with varied specialized functions occur among Hydrozoa and other Cnidaria (see Table 6.2).

The hydranths are the "animals" supported by the stem and coenosarc. They catch prey and carry out the preliminary digestion of food, in addition to other functions. The partly digested food is circulated through the colony, to be digested in the gastrodermis of the coenosarc and hydranths. Hydranths may also bud off new hydranths or medusae. Adaptation of the hydranth has centered about its major activities. Tentacles vary in form and arrangement, and specializations for gonophore production are common.

Gymnoblast hydranths are athecate; that is, the periderm ends at the base of the hydranth, leaving it naked. Several adaptational lines have appeared in gymnoblasts. According to Kühn (1913), *Syncoryne* (Fig. 6.9A) retains the primitive characteristics of one line in its scattered, capitate tentacles ending in nematocyst-filled knobs. *Pennaria* (Fig. 6.9B), with a basal whorl of finger-like filiform, and scattered capitate tentacles, has tended toward more definite placement of ten-

tacles, and is intermediate. *Tubularia* (Fig. 6.9C), with distinct basal and oral whorls of filiform tentacles would represent an end-point of this adaptational line. A second line, starting with *Clava*-like forms with scattered filiform tentacles, ends in forms like *Eudendrium*, with a single whorl of filiform tentacles (Fig. 6.9D). Some hydranths are highly specialized. *Hydractinia* colonies have spiral dactylozoids, with the tentacles reduced or missing, interspersed among the gastrozooids and gonozooids (Fig. 6.7A).

Calyptoblast hydranths are thecate, sitting in a peridermal cup into which they can withdraw. Calyptoblast hydranths usually have a single whorl of filiform tentacles, and are thought to have diverged from the gymnoblast line very early. Adaptation has especially centered on skeletal modifications, colony growth, and specialization of gonozooids. Forms like *Campanularia* and *Obelia*, with sympodial growth, are thought to be primitive because of the loose colony form and bell-shaped theca (Fig. 6.10B). In these forms, gonozooids generally form in the axils of the branches and are surrounded by flask-shaped gonothecae. Sessile thecae and monopodial growth are characteristic of the more highly specialized calyptoblasts, as seen in *Sertularia* and *Plumularia* (Fig. 6.10C,D). Some calyptoblasts have a theca with a closing lid, the operculum, formed of one or several pieces of periderm.

The typical gonozooid takes the form of a blastostyle, a club-shaped zooid with-

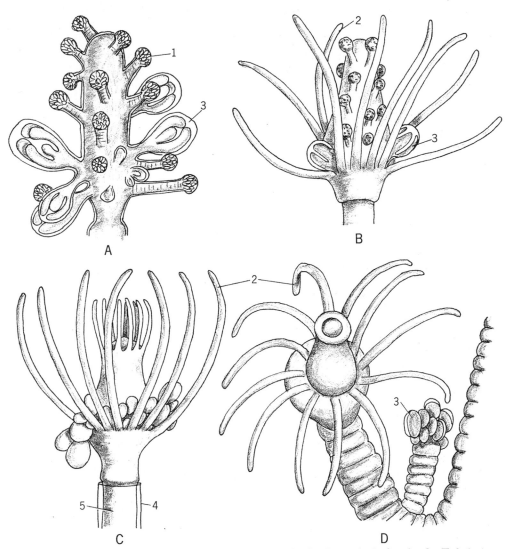

Fig. 6.9. Some Gymnoblastea. A. *Syncoryne* hydranth. B. *Pennaria* hydranth. C. *Tubularia* hydranth. D. *Eudendrium* hydranth. The hydranths may have filiform or capitate tentacles, the latter having clusters of nematocysts at the tip. *Syncoryne*, with scattered tentacles, is considered primitive. Tentacle position tends to become more definite, with the formation of a basal whorl, as in *Eudendrium*, or a basal whorl and oral whorl, as in *Tubularia*. The gonophores of most gymnoblasts arise from the gastrozooids, often appearing above the basal whorl of tentacles. (A, after Hyman. D, after Nutting.) 1, capitate tentacle; 2, filiform tentacle; 3, gonophore; 4, periderm; 5, coenosarc.

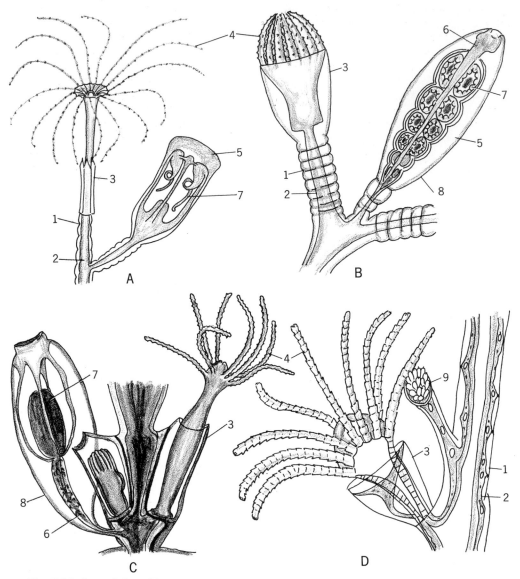

Fig. 6.10. Some Calyptoblast Hydranths. A. *Campanularia*. B. *Obelia*, with tentacles retracted. C. *Sertularia*. D. *Plumularia*. *Campanularia* and *Obelia* have simple sympodial growth patterns, and colony form is relatively simple. With monopodial growth, colony form becomes complex; hydrothecae are sessile, and gonangia are often very large, as in *Sertularia*. Calyptoblasts are especially characterized by their exoskeleton. The periderm (1) covers the coenosarc (2) that continues beyond the base of the hydranth as a hydrotheca (3), a protective cup. The hydranths have a single whorl of filiform tentacles (4). The gonozooids (5) consist of a blastostyle (6) surrounded by the gonophores (7). They sit in a gonotheca (8). The gonangium includes the gonotheca and gonozooid. *Plumularia* colonies include specialized zooids containing many nematocysts, the nematophores (9). (A, after Rees. D, after Hyman.)

out mouth or tentacles. On its surface many medusae buds or gonophores develop (Fig. 6.10 B). Plumularian colonies have an additional type of specialized polyp, the nematophore, whose clubshaped body is filled with adhesive glands and nematocysts.

HYDROID MEDUSAE

Gymnoblasts produce anthomedusae and calyptoblasts leptomedusae. The principal differences between them can be seen in Fig. 6.11. Anthomedusae are taller, retain the tetraradiate form in all cases, and have gonads on the radial canals. They usually have ocelli. Leptomedusae are flatter, may have lost their tetraradiate appearance by branching of the radial canals, and have statocysts on the bell margin. Gonads are borne on the manubrium rather than the radial canals. Only a few of the hydrozoan medusae are large. *Aequora* is an exception, and may reach several inches in diameter. Smaller medusae, like *Obelia* and *Pennaria*, show signs of reduction, but *Obelia* retain

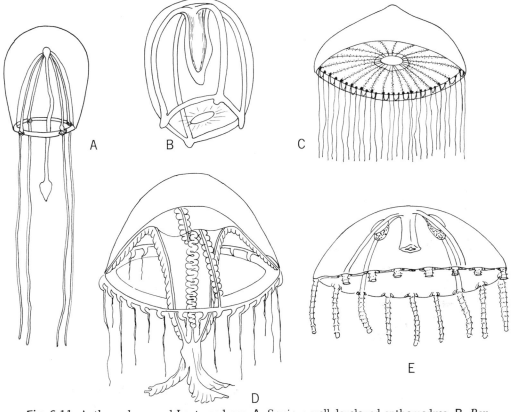

Fig. 6.11. Anthomedusae and Leptomedusae. A. *Sarsia*, a well-developed anthomedusa. B. *Pennaria*, a somewhat degenerate anthomedusa. C. *Aequora*, a large leptomedusa. D. *Tima*, another well-differentiated leptomedusa. E. *Obelia*, a small, but complete, leptomedusa without a velum. (A, C, after Hyman. B, D, after Mayer.) The tall, bell-shaped body and tetramerous symmetry, with four radial canals and four tentacles or clusters of tentacles are characteristic of anthomedusae. Leptomedusae are flattened, often have more than four radial canals, and usually have numerous tentacles at the bell margin. Anthomedusae are characterized by ocelli, and leptomedusae by statocysts.

the basic traits of their group and survive for some time as free-swimming organisms. *Pennaria* is much further reduced. Its tentacles are mere vestiges, and it survives for only a brief time after its release. Many hydromedusae remain permanently sessile on the parent hydranth, functioning as the reproductive organs of their colonies. Adaptation to a permanently sessile existence is accompanied by a striking reduction of the typical medusa form (p. 146).

MILLEPORINA AND STYLASTERINA

Millepores and stylasters are found among coral reefs in warm seas. They form a heavy, calcareous exoskeleton, the coenosteum, in place of a periderm. The porous millepore coenosteum is permeated in its upper levels by living coenosarc tubes in deep canals, and has cups in which the polyps set. As new coenosteum forms, the deeper coenosarc dies away, and cross partitions, the tabulae, form across the polyp cups. Millepores are usually massive and whitish or yellowish. Stylasters form more open, branched colonies and are often colorful, running to red and violet hues. Both have two types of zooids, gastrozooids and dactylozooids. Millepore gastrozooids are short, with tentacles reduced to nematocyst-filled knobs. Stylaster gastrozooids are more elongate and have stumpy tentacles. Millepore dactylozooids are elongated and have scattered capitate tentacles. Stylaster dactylozooids have no tentacles and are slender. Both form much-reduced medusae within the coenosteum.

SIPHONOPHORES

Siphonophores are striking creatures, of great interest because they are really highly polymorphic colonies, pelagic rather than attached, and made up of many highly modified medusae and polyps. They are most common in warm seas, but ocean currents and storms sometimes bring large numbers into cooler waters. Many are beautifully colored, but dangerous because of their powerful nematocysts.

Various combinations of zooids bud from a common coenosarc. Three kinds of modified zooids occur: gastrozooids, dactylozooids, and gonozooids. Gastrozooids are feeding polyps, with a mouth and usually with a single, branching tentacle. Dactylozooids are long, tubular, tentacle-like zooids without a mouth, or shorter zooids with a long, unbranched tentacle. Gonozooids resemble gastrozooids, but may not have a mouth. Their branches, the gonodendra, resemble calyptoblast blastostyles. Medusoid zooids are swimming bells, bracts, gonophores, and floats. Swimming bells (nectophores) lack mouth, tentacles, and sense organs, but are muscular and propel the colony. Bracts (hydrophylla) are protective, leaf-like zooids, without resemblance to ordinary medusae. Gonophores vary from buds that live briefly after being freed, to sac-like, permanently sessile forms. Floats (pneumatophores) have been thought to be highly modified, inverted medusae, transformed into an air sac, but according to some recent studies may be modified polyps.

Siphonophores are extremely varied. *Muggiaea* is a typical calycophoran, with an apical swimming bell and a linear series of trailing zooids. The swimming bell is drawn out to form a protective sheath for the base of the coenosarc. The coenosarc trails as a long stem, to which a series of cormidia are attached. Each cormidium consists of a definite number and variety of individuals (Fig. 6.12A,B). New cormidia form at the coenosarc base, and increase in age and size distally. They eventually break off and take up a separate existence for a time.

With the appearance of a float, placed above the swimming bells, the linear stem becomes shorter, the members crowd together, and cormidia lose their individuality. This adaptive line ends with all of the zooids crowded around a short, often massive, coenosarc. The primary swimming

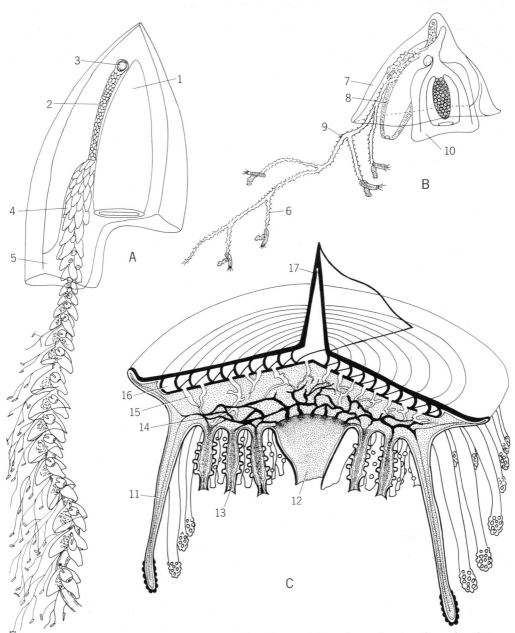

Fig. 6.12. Siphonophora. **A.** *Muggiaea*, a calycophoran siphonophore, showing the swimming bell and the upper part of the stem, with cormidia attached. **B.** *Muggiaea* cormidium. **C.** *Velella*, the purple sail, a chondrophoran siphonophore, cut away to show inner structure. (A-B, after Hyman. C, composite.) **1**, swimming bell; **2**, the upper end of the gastrovascular cavity (somatocyst); **3**, oil droplet; **4**, growth region of stem; **5**, hydroecium; **6**, tentillum, a branch of the stem containing nematocysts; **7**, bract; **8**, gastrozooid; **9**, tentacle; **10**, gonophore, serving as the swimming bell of the cormidium; **11**, dactylozooid; **12**, central gastrozooid; **13**, gonozooid with buds; **14**, coenosarc tubules; **15**, tracheal tube; **16**, air chamber; **17**, pneumatophore.

A

B

Fig. 6.13. A. *Physalia*, the Portuguese man-of-war, a well-known siphonophore. The large pneumatophore floats on the surface. The short, inconspicuous coenosarc, hidden by the specialized zooids, gives rise to the members of the colony. Gastrozooids, gonozooids, and long dactylozooids (fishing tentacles) with powerful nematocysts can be seen. B. A swimming *Cyanea*, one of the Scyphozoa. Note the marginal tentacles and the greatly folded oral lobes. (Courtesy of General Biological Supply Co.)

bell disappears with float development, although some, like *Nectalia*, retain some swimming bells with the float. Others, like *Physalia* (Fig. 6.13) lose them and are completely at the mercy of currents or winds carrying them onto a lee shore. *Velella*, the purple sail, carries a huge pneumatophore, probably a greatly expanded polyp, strengthened by chitin and with an upright sail (Fig. 6.12C). A large gastrozooid is surrounded by a whorl of gonozooids and an outer whorl of dactylozooids. *Physalia*, the most commonly studied siphonophore, has a large float, also said to be a modified polyp, with the aboral surface invaginated to form an inner air sac. Larger and smaller dactylozooids, gastrozooids, and gonozooids hang from the short coenosarc below the float.

Food capture is the function of dactylozooids, armed with powerful nematocysts. They carry the prey upward and the gastrozooids fasten to it, accomplishing preliminary digestion. Partly digested food is distributed by way of the coenosarc.

Siphonophores have carried polymorphism far further than the hydroids; the colony is a true superorganism. Their colonial nature was not recognized until relatively recent times. The highly specialized zooids are modified animals, serving as organs of the superorganism. The evident tendency of colonial animals to specialize non-reproductive members to form "organs" is one of the most persuasive arguments in favor of the colonial theory of metazoan origin, for if protozoan colonies did develop along these lines, the resulting highly specialized colony would be defined as a metazoan animal.

Hydrozoan Life Cycles

Hydrozoa are characterized by life cycles with alternating asexual polypoid, and sexual medusoid phases. Some, like *Obelia*, have about equally developed polyps and medusae. Others have large medusae and reduced polyps, or the reverse. At the extremes are forms like *Hydra*, wholly lacking a medusa, and *Liriope*, without a polyp stage.

Except for hydras, the mature polyp or colony produces gonophores. The parent polyp may be a normal gastrozooid, as in most gymnoblasts, or may be a gonozooid, specialized for medusa formation. Gonophores are sometimes produced on stems

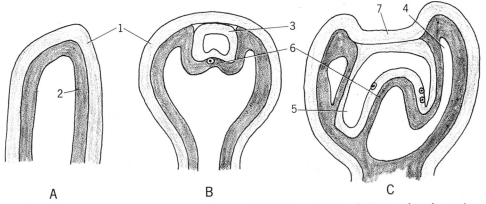

Fig. 6.14. Development of a Medusa from a Bud (schematized). A. Entocodon formation B. Radial canal formation and start of the manubrium. C. Velar plate formation, showing part of the gastrodermal lamella. (Based on Goette.) 1, epidermis; 2, gastrodermis; 3, entocodon; 4, radial canal; 5, future subumbrellar space; 6, manubrium; 7, velar plate.

or stolons. In any event, the young medusa bud is an evagination of the body wall, involving epidermis and gastrodermis. The tip epidermis develops into an entocodon, the primordium of the subumbrella (Fig. 6.14A-C). The gastrodermis below forms five growing tips, four marginal ones, which push over the entocodon to form the four radial canals, and a medial one, growing downward to form the manubrium. A single layer of gastroderm grows out from the radial canals to form the gastrodermal lamella. Lateral fusion of the radial canal tips forms the ring canal. Meanwhile, an entocodal space has appeared, and a velar plate has formed at the apex of the bud. Rupture of the velar plate and growth of the tentacles and other marginal organs complete the medusa.

As hydroids become predominant, the medusae become permanently sessile and degenerate. *Pennaria* medusae are partly degenerate, although freed for a brief free-swimming life (Fig. 6.11B). The next step in reduction is permanent attachment. In permanently sessile medusae, the marginal organs are the first to go. Tentacles and marginal sense organs, and eventually the mouth, disappear. Medusae of this type are permanently attached to the parent colony or polyp by an aboral connection and are called eumedusoids (Fig. 6.15A). The radial canals and velum are next to disappear; medusae reduced to this extent are termed cryptomeduosoids (Fig. 6.15B). The gastrodermis scarcely develops in heteromedusoids, and remains entirely inactive in styloid medusae (Fig. 6.15C). Permanently sessile medusae without radial canals, or more extensively reduced, are often called sporosacs. Sessile medusae occur singly or in clusters; in calyptoblasts with blastostlyes, they cluster in large numbers on the gonozooid surface. Medusa reduction has not occurred at the same rate as the development of other parts, for some primitive cnidarians produce sporosacs and some progressive polyps release free medusae.

Medusa reduction is undoubtedly an outcome of polyp success. Many polyps remain active most of the year and have a

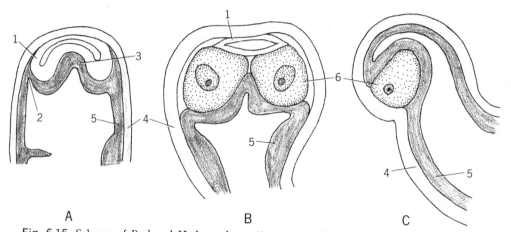

A   B   C

Fig. 6.15. Scheme of Reduced Hydromedusae (in section). The permanently sessile medusae tend to be reduced, eventually losing all similarity to normal medusae. A. Eumedusoid of *Tubularia*, with vestiges of radial canals and manubrium, and with a well-developed entocodon (compare with Fig. 6.14). B. Cryptomedusoid of *Clava*, considerably more reduced, but with entocodon and some gastrodermal elements. C. Styloid medusoid of *Eudendrium*, with all resemblance to a medusa lost. (A, based on Goette. B, based on Kühn. C, based on Wiessmann.) 1, entocodon; 2, radial canal; 3, manubrium; 4, epidermis; 5, gastrodermis; 6, ovum.

long life span, while medusae are often released at certain seasons and live for a short time. Such medusae tend to be little more than an agency for dissemination, and the zygotes and planula larvae are often carried about by tidal currents as effectively as the weak-swimming medusae. Under such circumstances, sessile medusae are just as effective and better protected than free medusae, and selective pressures to retain the complex medusan form disappear.

Hydrozoan gametes arise from interstitial cells or, more rarely, from normal epidermis or gastrodermis cells. They aggregate at a characteristic site to form a gonad. Spermatogenesis follows standard patterns. Many oöcytes form but few mature, the others becoming nurse cells or fusing with the eventual ovum.

Ova are released or undergo early development in the medusa, sometimes in special brood chambers. Holoblastic cleavage produces a coeloblastula, sometimes freed as a ciliated larva. Hydrozoan blastula never gastrulate by invagination. Endoderm forms by polar ingression accompanied by delamination (Fig. 6.16A). The stereogastrula is usually freed as a ciliated, planula larva.

After a migratory period, the planula attaches at the anterior pole. The endoderm cells form a primitive gut by rearrangement. A mouth breaks through and the larva grows into a polyp or a growing stem from which polyps arise. The planula of some tubularian hydroids remains in the gonophore, becoming a tentacled larva, the actinula. The actinula is released, and after creeping about for a time, attaches and grows into a polyp. In some cases the actinula develops into a medusa or buds off a medusa and dies (Fig. 6.16B,C).

Class Scyphozoa

The common jellyfishes, so often seen in coastal waters and usually feared by local swimmers, are Scyphozoa. Although there are only about 200 species of Scyphozoa, they become so abundant that they play an important ecological role and are found everywhere in oceans, extending to depths of 3000 meters or more. Five orders are recognized, each with one or more outstanding features which make them easy to recognize.

Order Stauromedusae. Adults developing directly from the scyphistoma larva and attached by an aboral stalk; coelenteron

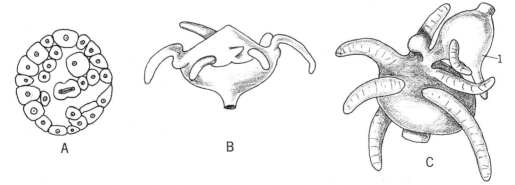

A   B   C

Fig. 6.16. Hydrozoan Development. A. Endoderm formation by multiple ingression in *Gonothyraea.* B-C. Stages in development of *Pegantha.* B, a young actinula; C, an older actinula in the process of forming other actinulae (1) by budding. The appearance of budding in developing actinulae larvae may have been the first step toward the formation of colonies in the hydroid generation. (A, after Wulfert. B, C, after Bigelow.)

divided by septa; without marginal sense organs other than modified tentacles. Example: *Haliclystus* (Fig.6.17).

Order Cubomedusae. Cubical medusae with four tentacles or groups of tentacles on the perradii; with four compound sense organs, the rhopalia, on the interradii; with the margin of the bell bent inward as a velarium; coelenteron divided by septa. Example: *Carybdea* (Fig. 6.19A).

Order Coronatae. Jellyfish with a scalloped margin separated by a furrow from the bell margin; tentacles borne on flattened blades known as pedalia; coelenteron divided by septa. Example: *Nausithoë* (Fig. 6.19B).

Order Semaeostomeae. Jellyfish with the corners of the mouth prolonged into long, frilly oral tentacles; without a furrow on the exumbrella or pedalia; with 8 to 16 rhopalia and a scalloped bell margin; without septa dividing the gastric cavity. Example: *Aurelia* (Fig. 6.18).

Order Rhizostomeae. With the oral tentacles fused and containing many canals and small mouths; with eight or more rhopalia and a scalloped margin; without septa in the coelenteron. Example: *Cassiopeia* (Fig. 6.19C).

Stauromedusae

Stauromedusae are the most unusual scyphozoans. They are jellyfish, but attach to seaweeds and other objects by an aboral stalk. They are probably best understood as permanently juvenile animals that never quite complete medusa formation. In any event, they retain many primitive characteristics and may provide some idea of what scyphozoan stem animals were like when they diverged from the hydrozoan line.

Lucernaria and *Haliclystus* are the most commonly observed stauromedusae. They are more common in cool waters than warm, and are from about 3 to 5 cm. across. The aboral stalk expands sharply to form the umbrella (Fig. 6.17). The mouth

is centrally located, at the end of a short manubrium. It leads into a coelenteron divided by four large septa into four gastric pockets. The septa are not simple partitions, but are hollow, containing deep subumbrellar funnels that extend well into the stalk, and open on the oral surface. The septa do not meet centrally; the coelenteron has a median open region. The oral surface is drawn out into lobes on which the tentacles are placed. Four gastric septa are characteristic of scyphozoans, although they are lost during embryonic development in some groups.

Semaeostomeae

Aurelia, a semaeostome, is the most common laboratory specimen for a study of scyphozoan form. Its morphological features are summarized in Fig. 6.18 and should be examined closely. The gastrovascular system is complex, with extensively branched radial canals and a coronal stomach composed of four gastric pouches. The gastric pouches superficially resemble those of stauromedusae, but develop differently. The symmetrical axes are easily determined. The margin of the bell is slightly lobulated, with a complex sense organ, the rhopalium, at each indentation. The eight rhopalia mark the four perradii and interradii. The four perradii are the major body axes; the four oral arms lie in the perradii, and the interradii are halfway between. Eight adradii lie between the perradii and interradii. In scyphomedusae, septa grow inward along the interradii to form four perradial gastric pouches, as in Stauromedusae. Gastric tentacles develop on the septa, and subumbrellar funnels, probably respiratory in function, push into the septa from the subumbrellar surface. In semaeostomes and rhizostomes, the septa and funnels disappear during development. The gastric cavity of *Aurelia* expands as the septa disappear, and the center of the adult gastric cavities lies where the

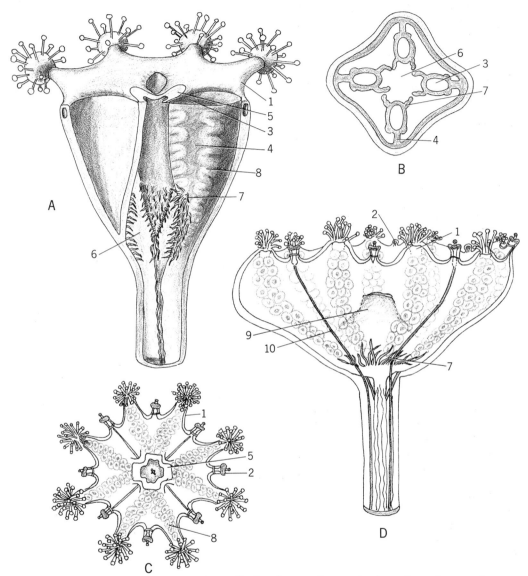

Fig. 6-17. Stauromedusae. **A.** Generalized scheme of organization of a stauromedusa. **B.** Schematic cross section of a stauromedusa. **C-D.** *Haliclystus salpinx* in side and oral view. (C-D, after Berrill.) 1, arm of oral disc, bearing tentacles; 2, rhopaloid or anchor, an adhesive organ; 3, subumbrellar funnel; 4, septum between the gastric pouches; 5, oral lobe; 6, stomach area; 7, gastric filament attached to the septa; 8, gonad; 9, manubrium; 10, muscle band used for retraction.

gastric septa once were. Here, gastric tentacles cluster on the coelenteron floor. As the septa disappear, new depressions, the peristomial pits, appear at the site of the old subumbrellar funnels.

Digestion follows the basic cnidarian plan. Food is attacked rapidly by extracellular enzymes in the gastric cavity and gastric pouches, and is reduced by pre-liminary digestion to small particles that can be distributed in the radial canal system. The particles are engulfed and digested intracellularly by the gastrodermal cells. Scyphozoan nematocysts are relatively powerful, and many feed on fish or other rather large prey. *Aurelia*, however, is a flagellary mucus feeder. Small particles and plankton are caught in slime secreted on

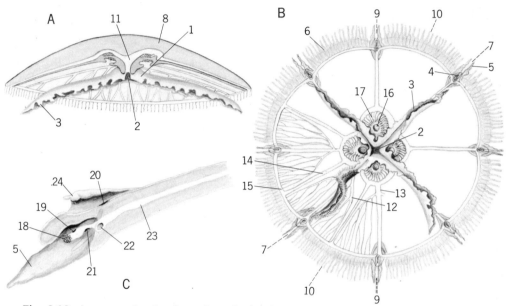

Fig. 6.18. Anatomy of a Scyphomedusa. **A.** *Aurelia* in section, from the side. **B.** Oral view of *Aurelia*. **C.** Section through a rhopalium. (A, modified from Schechter.) The manubrium (1) hangs down, ending in a quadrangular mouth (2), whose corners project as long oral arms (3), frilled as is typical of semaeostomes. Shallow marginal indentations contain the rhopalia (4), complex sense organs, each flanked by rhopalial lappets (5). The bell margin is scalloped to form lappets (6) between the rhopalia. Short tentacles hang down from the bell margin. The principal body axes are the perradii (7), determined by the oral arms and the indentations between the gastric pouches (8). The interradii (9) are midway between, and the adradii (10) terminate in the middle of each marginal lappet. The gastric cavity (11) is indented at the perradii to form the gastric pouches. Branched perradial canals (12) arise between the gastric pouches, and branched interradial canals (13) arise at their centers. Eight unbranched adradial canals (14) fall on the adradial axes. All join the ring canal (15) near the margin. Depressions, the subgenital pits (16), lie at the center of the horseshoe-shaped gonads (17), which shed their gametes into the gastrovascular cavity. The rhopalium is flanked on each side by rhopalial lappets (5). The statocyst (18) lies at the tip of the rhopalium; its weight causes it to sag downward when the bell margin is tilted upward. A small ocellus (19) lies on top of the rhopalium, and outer and inner sensory pits (20-21) lie at the back of the hood and on the lower surface of the rhopalium. The ring canal (22) lies at the base of the rhopalium, and an extension of the radial canal (23) continues into the base of the rhopalium. Small sensory lappets (24), characteristic of *Aurelia*, lie on each side of the hood.

the exumbrella. These are licked off the lappets by the oral arms, and currents produced by flagella in grooves on the oral arms carry them into the stomach. Scyphozoa feeding on larger prey use the gastric tentacles to pull it into the gastric cavity and to subdue it with nematocysts, if necessary. In addition, the filaments contain many gland cells and secrete enzymes for preliminary digestion.

Muscle cells lie at the base of the epidermis. Longitudinal fibers are found in tentacles and manubrium, and form radial muscles on the subumbrella. Swimming movements are produced by a striated coronal muscle encircling the subumbrella.

A subepidermal nerve plexus extends through tentacles, oral arms, and manubrium. It is concentrated near the rhopalia to form the rhopalial ganglia. Protoneurons

also aggregate to form radial strands along the main radii. Little is known of the subgastrodermal plexus, but it has been demonstrated in some scyphomedusae. Presumably it exercises control over the gastric tentacles.

Rhopalia are the characteristic sense organs (Fig. 6.18C). In *Aurelia*, they occur in indentations between marginal lappets. Each rhopalium is a hollow club, growing at the base of the larval tentacles. One or more ocelli are usually present, as well as one or two sensory pits lined with sensory epithelium. Endodermal lithocytes, containing heavy, calcareous particles, weight the rhopalial tip. When the margin of the bell is lifted, the weighted rhopalium sinks, stimulating the sensory epithelium and initiating righting movements.

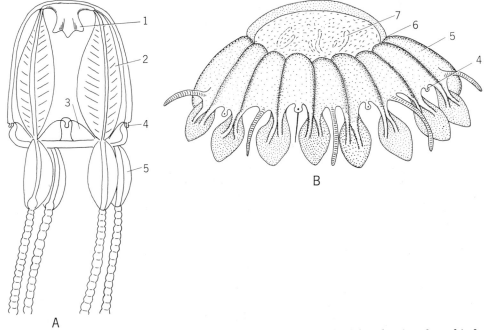

Fig. 6.19. Some Representative Scyphozoa. A. A cubomedusa, *Carybdea*, showing the cubical shape and the four tentacles with pedalia. B. A coronate medusa, *Nausithoë*, showing the characteristic coronal groove on the exumbrella. (A, after Hyman. B, after Mayer.) 1, manubrium; 2, gonad; 3, nerve ring; 4, rhopalium; 5, pedalium; 6, coronal groove; 7, gastric filament.

Other Scyphozoa

Cubomedusae are easily recognized by their cuboid shape, and the four interradial tentacles or clusters of tentacles at the corners. Each tentacle is flattened at its base into a blade-like pedalium. Septa divide the gastric cavity into perradial gastric pouches, each with a deep subumbrellar funnel (Fig. 6.19A). Most cubomedusae are small, 4 to 5 cm. across, and strong swimmers. They are most common in littoral regions of warm seas. The bell of a Coronatae medusa is divided into upper and lower parts by a coronal groove (Fig. 6.19B). They are more common in deep waters, are from about 5 to 15 cm. across, and are often brightly colored. Their septa contain subumbrellar funnels. Rhizostomes are like modified semaeostomes, as their oral arms have united to close off the original mouth opening and many suctorial mouths have appeared. They have no tentacles and often have a firm bell with dense mesogloea. The oral arms have nematocyst-filled appendages which replace the tentacles. As in semaeostomes, the subumbrellar funnels are lost and replaced by subgenital pits. Rhizostomes are tropical forms, some becoming fairly large. Diameters of 35 cm. or more are not uncommon.

SCYPHOZOAN LIFE CYCLES

Gametes form from gastrodermal interstitial cells. They gather as gonads, either on each side of the gastric septa or on the floor of the gastric pouches. Gametes are freed into the coelenteron and emerge through the mouth.

The semaeostome life cycle is best known. Early development occurs in the folds of the oral arms. Cleavage is indeterminate, and a hollow blastula is formed. Endoderm is first formed by multipolar ingression, but this is abortive, and invagina-tion later forms the functional endoderm (Fig. 6.20A). The blastopore closes, and a typical, motile planula escapes from the parent. It attaches and develops into a scyphistoma, a polypoid larva with four interradial gastric septa projecting into the coelenteron. Epidermal invaginations into the septa develop into subumbrellar funnels. Some scyphistomae live for long periods, reproducing by stolonic budding. When mature, transverse fission or strobilization produces larvae known as ephyrae (Fig. 6.20B-D). Some scyphistomae release one ephyra at a time; others produce a number simultaneously.

The saucer-shaped ephyra has a central gastric cavity and gastric tentacles at the site of the scyphistoma gastric septa. Canals extend to the base of the marginal rhopalia (Fig. 6.20E), marking the perradial and interradial axes. Rhopalial lappets flank each rhopalium. Rapid interrhopalial growth is accompanied by the appearance of adradial canals and the disappearance of subumbrellar funnels. The ends of the *Aurelia* radial canals anastomose to form a ring canal, and further growth of interrhopalial regions establish them as the major lappets of the bell margin.

Stauromedusa planulae lack cilia, and functional endoderm is formed by multipolar ingression. The planula attaches and becomes a polypoid larva, expanded orally and with eight perradial and interradial tentacles. The tentacles deteriorate to form adhesive knobs, and the eight adradial lobes, on which the adult tentacles develop, grow out between them. The four interradial septa grow inward, and the epidermis invaginates into them to form the subumbrellar funnels.

Class Anthozoa

Anthozoa, literally the flower animals, include sea anemones and corals. The anthozoan polyp has won out; medusae are never formed. The polyps have become

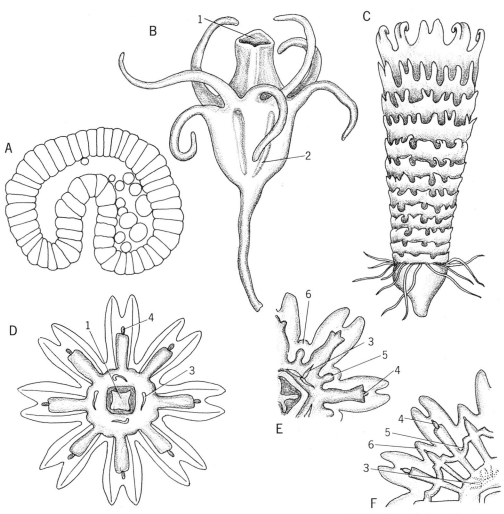

Fig. 6.20. Scyphozoan Development. **A.** *Cyanea* embryo, showing the double endoderm formation. Endoderm derived by ingression is in the blastocoel, and the second endoderm is being
formed by invagination. **B-F.** *Aurelia* development, schematized. The *Aurelia* zygote develops
into a planula that attaches and becomes a scyphistoma (B). The scyphistoma is a small
polyp with rudiments of the four interradial septa characteristic of Scyphozoa. Scyphistomae
live for several years, budding off new scyphistomae during warm seasons and producing larval
medusae known as ephyrae by transverse fission (C) during winter and spring. When they are
released the ephyrae have eight rhopalia and rhopalial lappets, but the interradial areas are
undeveloped. The young ephyrae grow rapidly in this region (F-F) to establish the marginal
lappets, while the ring canal and additional radial canals develop. (A, after Okada. B-F, after
Schechter.) **1,** mouth; **2,** interradial septa; **3,** gastric filament; **4,** rhopalium; **5,** ring canal;
6, interradial region.

153

large and complex. *Stoichactis*, from the Australian barrier reef, may reach a meter across. Septa partially divide the coelenteron, amplifying its surface. The epidermis invaginates at the oral end as a stomodaeum, forming a pharynx leading from the mouth to the coelenteron. One or two flagellated grooves, the siphonoglyphs, are located at the corners of the more or less slit-like pharynx. The lateral compression of mouth and pharynx and the siphonoglyphs convert the basic radial to a biradial symmetry. No anterior and posterior ends develop, and anthozoans live as becomes a radially symmetrical animal. The mesogloea is richly cellular, actually a dense mesenchyme or fibrous connective tissue.

Anthozoa are divided into two subclasses, the Alcyonaria and the Zoantharia, and 11 orders are recognized. The characteristics of the more important orders are summarized below.

Subclass Alcyonaria. Polyps with eight feathery tentacles and a coelenteron divided by eight single, complete septa; with a single siphonoglyph; colonial forms with an endoskeleton.

Order Stolonifera. Polyps connected by basal stolons or mats and not fused; skeleton of spicules, sometimes consolidated to form tubes. Example: *Clavularia* (Fig. 6.22A).

Order Alcyonacea. With the lower ends of the polyps fused and only oral ends protruding; skeleton of separate spicules; often consolidated, but with no axial core. (Fig. 6.21).

Order Gorgonacea. The horny corals. With an axial skeleton of horny or calcareous material; polyps rarely dimorphic and short, not reaching the base.

Order Pennatulacea. The sea pens and sea pansies. With small lateral polyps attached to sides of a long axial polyp; polyps always dimorphic; with a skeleton of separate calcareous spicules. Example: *Renilla* (Fig. 6.23).

Subclass Zoantharia. With simple, usually unbranched tentacles; with coelenteron divided by septa never of the alcyonarian pattern; solitary or colonial forms which never have a skeleton of separate calcareous spicules.

Order Actinaria. The sea anemones. With paired, complete and incomplete septa, often in multiples of six, polyps solitary, often with a pedal disc, and with one or more siphonoglyphs (Fig. 6.24).

Order Madreporaria. The stony corals. Solitary or more commonly colonial, *Actinaria*-like polyps without a siphonoglyph and forming a compact, calcareous exoskeleton (Fig. 6.26).

Order Antipatharia. The thorny corals. Deep-water, tropical and subtropical corals with polyps having 6, 10, or 12 single, complete septa, six simple or eight branched tentacles, and two siphonoglyphs; skeleton with a thorny, organic axial core of slender, branching form.

Order Zoanthidea. Usually colonial polyps, usually found growing on sponges, corals, shells, or other animals, without a skeleton, and with septal pairs consisting of one complete and one incomplete septum; with one siphonoglyph.

Order Ceriantharia. Long solitary polyps with a basal region adapted for burrowing and a slender column, usually buried in sand; with oral and marginal whorls of tentacles and many single, complete septa; with a single siphonoglyph. Example: *Cerianthus* (Fig 6.27).

Alcyonaria

Alcyonaria are consistent in form and make a good introduction to anthozoan form. All are colonial, the polyps projecting from stolons, fleshy mats, or vertical extensions of coenenchyme, the anthozoan equivalent of the coenosarc. The essentials of alcyonarian form are shown and described in Fig. 6.21. Skeletal elements differ widely, but the polyp form is essentially stable. The eight tentacles are branched, and surround a mouth with the body wall turned

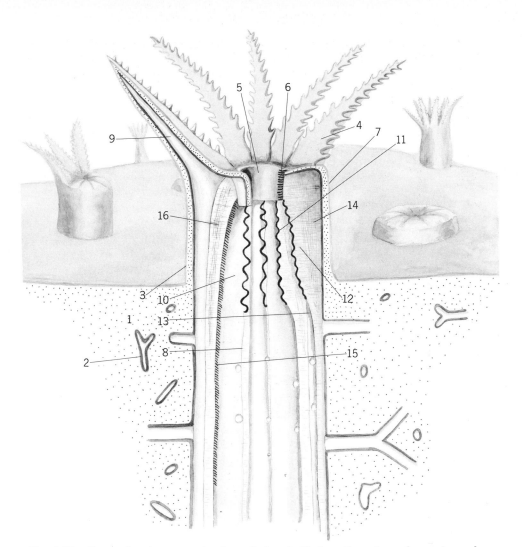

Fig. 6.21. Alcyonarian Anatomy. A schematic longitudinal section of an alcyonarian polyp, passing through a septum on the right and between septa on the left (based primarily on Hyman.) The common basal coenenchyme contains mesogloea (1) and branching gastrodermal tubes, the solenia (2), continuous with the coelenteron of the polyps. The exposed, distal part of the polyp is the anthocodium (3). It bears eight pinnate tentacles (4), characteristic of Alcyonaria. The mouth at the center of the oral disc opens into the pharynx (5), which is lined with ectodermal tissue and is derived from a stomodaeum. A furrow containing strong flagella, the siphonoglyph (6), defines the sulcal face (7) of the polyp. The eight septa (8) contain mesogloea and are covered with gastrodermis. They widen orally and attach to the pharynx, dividing the coelenteron into compartments (10) continuous with the cavity of the tentacles (9). The margins of the septa (12) are thickened to form septal filaments (11) below the pharynx. Longitudinal fibers form a strong retractor muscle (13) on the sulcal side of each septum; transverse muscles (14) cross each septa. The sulcal septa (15) are those on each side of the siphonoglyph and have retractor muscles facing each other. The asulcal septa (16) are opposite, and bear strong flagella. The siphonoglyph flagella draw water into the polyp and the asulcal flagella drive water out, creating a circulation through the coelenteron and solenia.

155

in as a pharynx. A flagellated groove, the siphonoglyph (Fig. 6.22C) pulls water into the coelenteron. Eight partitions, the septa, composed of gastrodermis and mesogloea, extend inward from the body wall, uniting with the pharynx and ending in free thickened margins, the septal filaments. The two septa opposite the siphonoglyph, the asulcal septa, differ from the others. They have strong flagella which force water out of the pharynx and extend far deeper than the other septa. The polyp extends far below the surface, embedded in a common mesogloeal mass in which the skeletal spicules develop. It is covered by a common sheet of epidermis. Endodermal canals, the solenia, branch throughout the living coenenchymal tissues.

The voracious polyps kill any food organisms of suitable size. Food reaching the oral disc is rapidly swallowed, lubricated by slime secreted in the pharynx. Septal filaments on all but the asulcal septa play the same role as scyphozoan gastric tentacles, grasping, immobilizing, and aiding in preliminary digestion of prey. When preliminary digestion is completed, food particles are engulfed and digested intracellularly by cells of the general gastrodermis as well as by septal filament cells. Egestion is by way of the mouth.

Water circulation in the coelenteron is maintained by the powerful flagella of the siphonoglyph and asulcal septa. Food and oxygen are thus distributed through the solenial tubes to the coenenchyme cells, and wastes are removed.

Muscles are poorly developed. The longitudinal, epidermal muscles of the tentacles continue into the oral disc, and epidermal fibers of the disc sometimes follow the pharynx wall. A weak ring of circular muscle circumscribes the mouth. Gastrodermal fibers are antagonistic to epidermal fibers. They are weakly developed over most of the body and form transverse muscles on the asulcal face of each septum. More powerful longitudinal gastrodermal fibers on the sulcal face of the septa serve as retractors, drawing the polyps into their cup. The coenenchyme usually has no muscle fibers.

The nervous system is sketchy. An epidermal plexus, somewhat concentrated near the mouth and tentacle bases, forms

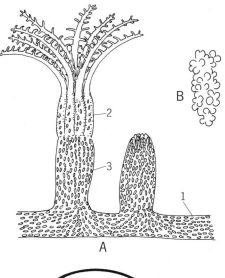

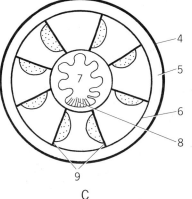

Fig. 6.22. Alcyonaria. **A.** Part of a stolon, an expanded polyp and a contracted polyp of *Clavularia*, an alcyonarian that forms simple colonies. **B.** A spicule from the surface of a *Clavularia* colony, enlarged. **C.** Scheme of an alcyonarian polyp in cross section, through the region of the pharynx. (A-B, after Hyman.) **1**, stolon; **2**, anthocodium; **3**, anthostele, a non-retractile part of the polyp, into which the anthocodium is withdrawn; **4**, epidermis; **5**, mesogloea; **6**, endoderm; **7**, pharynx; **8**, siphonoglyph; **9**, sulcal septa.

strands along the attachments of septa and oral disc. A gastrodermal nerve plexus lies in the septa and perhaps elsewhere. Stimulating one polyp causes contractions of others; it may be inferred that a nerve plexus extends through the coenenchyme. Sensory cells are sparse; some species do not respond to touch. There are no special sense organs.

The elongated mouth and flattened pharynx with a single siphonoglyph confer a bilateral symmetry on the polyp, and determine a sagittal plane, bisecting the siphonoglyph and passing between the two asulcal septa. Beneath the apparent bilateral symmetry is an octomerous radial symmetry. It is topologically correct and biologically wrong to think of an alcyo-narian as bilaterally symmetrical, for its relationship to its environment is that of a simple, octomerous, radially symmetrical animal. The siphonoglyph surface is often called the ventral surface. Inclined polyps are oriented with the siphonoglyph below, taking water in below and discharging it above, but it cannot be too strongly emphasized that dorsal and ventral do not mean to alcyonarians what they mean to ordinary bilateral animals. It is preferable to refer to the sulcal and asulcal surfaces, as these terms reflect functional relationships.

Some polymorphism occurs in Alcyonaria. Some species have typical, feeding autozooids, and siphonozooids, specialized by powerful siphonoglyphs to circulate

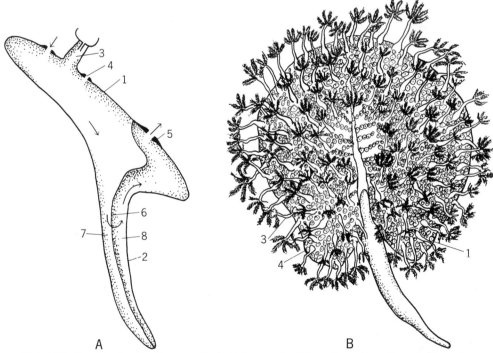

Fig. 6.23. *Renilla*, the Sea Pansy, a Pennatulacean. **A.** Schematic section through the colony, showing the circulation of water in the gastrovascular cavity. **B.** Colony of *Renilla*, showing the broad rachis containing many polyps and siphonozooids and the naked penduncle, which is thrust into the soft bottom. (A, after Parker, from Brown. B, after Hyman.) **1**, rachis; **2**, penduncle; **3**, anthocodia (autozooid); **4**, siphonozooid; **5**, exhalant siphonozooid; **6**, porous septum of peduncle; **7**, inferior canal of peduncle; **8**, superior canal of peduncle.

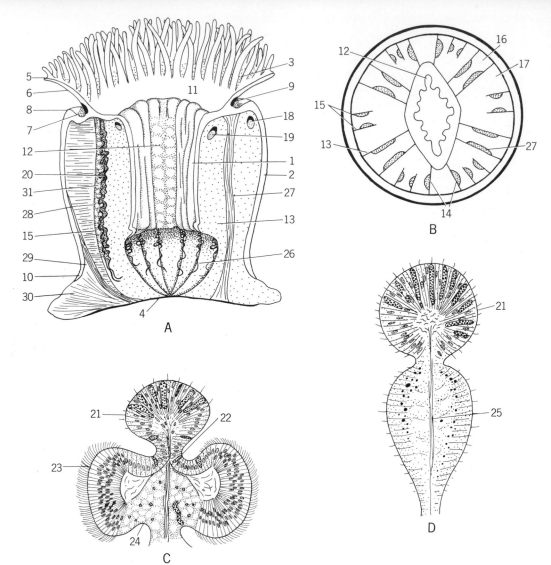

Fig. 6.24. Sea Anemone Anatomy. **A.** Schematic hemisection of a sea anemone, showing the endocoelic surface of a primary septum and the exocoelic surface of a secondary septum. **B.** Schematic cross section of a hexamerous sea anemone in the pharynx region. **C.** Cross section of a septal filament above the end of the pharynx. **D.** Cross section of a septal filament below the end of the pharynx. (A, composite. C-D, after Hyman.) The body wall is composed of an outer epidermis, mesogloea, and an inner gastrodermis. The same layers are found in the pharynx (1), but are inverted. The body is made of an upright column (2), topped by the oral disc (3) and attached by a pedal disc (4). The oral disc and column meet at the margin (5). A thin-walled, upper part of the column, the capitulum (6), is divided from the main part of the column by the fosse (7), a ring-shaped groove, and the collar (8). A sphincter muscle (9) encircles the body at this point. A groove, the limbus (10), separates the base of the column from the pedal disc. A peristome (11) separates the mouth from the tentacles on the oral disc. At opposite corners of the mouth, siphonoglyphs (12) occur; they extend to the bottom of the pharynx. Paired septa partially divide the enteron into compartments. Primary septa (13) attach to both body wall and pharynx. The primary septa attaching on each side of the siphonoglyphs are the directive septa (14). Secondary septa (15) are shorter than

158

water through large, fleshy colonies. Some have inhalant and exhalant siphonozooids.

Differences in colony form and skeletal structure introduce considerable diversity into Alycyonaria. The orders Stolonifera, Telestacea, and Coenothecalia are sometimes combined with Alcyonacea. They include the soft corals, the blue corals, and the organ-pipe corals (Fig. 6.22A; 6. 26A). Gorgonacea are the horny corals, with a skeleton containing gorgonin, a proteinaceous, horny material, sometimes infiltrated with calcareous substance. They include the bright-colored, bizarre sea fans, sea feathers, and sea whips which give a weird beauty to the ocean floor in shallow tropical waters. Pennatulacea are the sea pens. They form colonies with a large axial polyp, from which secondary polyps arise. *Renilla*, the sea pansy, is a well-known example (Fig. 6.23A,B). The axial polyp is usually divided into a peduncle, thrust into the soft bottom, and a rachis, from which the secondary polyps arise. The peduncle contains a double channel, connected by solenia in the rachis. Strong currents of water are taken in by inhalant siphonozooids, circulated through the colony, and expelled through exhalent siphonozooids, with sufficient force to support the colony and keep it inflated.

Zoantharia

Most Anthozoa belong to the Zoantharia; about 1000 species of sea anemones and 2500 species of stony corals are known. Sea anemones are abundant along sea coasts, and corals form huge reefs in warmer waters. However, Zoantharia also occur in deep waters, and some species are polar. It is a diversified group of animals, and because the method of asexual reproduction favors anomalies, members of the same species differ in septal numbers and arrangement. They are best characterized as anthozoans that never have eight single septa or eight branched tentacles like Alcyonaria. Most species are hexamerous, with pairs of septa occurring in multiples of six, but there are many exceptions to this rule.

ACTINARIA

The delicate coloring and radial form of sea anemones give them a beauty rarely matched in the animal kingdom. They differ markedly from Alcyonaria, for their symmetry is usually hexamerous rather

primary septa and do not attach to the pharynx. Still shorter tertiary septa may be found between the secondaries. The space between the two members of a septal pair is an endocoel (16), and the space between pairs is an exocoel (17). Septa are penetrated by marginal stoma (18) and oral stoma (19), which connect the endocoels and exocoels in the region of the pharynx. Septal filaments (20) occur at free margin of the septa. Above the end of the pharynx the septal filaments are trilobed. The medial lobe is the cnidoglandular tract (21), which connects to the other lobes by the intermediate tract (22). The two lateral lobes are the flagellated tracts (23), which end basally in the reticulated tracts (24). A mesogloeal core (25) extends into the filaments from the septa. The lateral lobes extend only to the end of the pharynx; beyond this point the filament is made up of the cnidoglandular tracts. Near the basal end of the septa, the septal filaments are detached from the septa, continuing on as thread-like acontia (26). Longitudinal muscles form retractor muscles (27) on the septal faces. The retractor muscles face the exocoel in directive septa; in all others they face the endocoel. Gastrodermal circular muscles extend into the septa as transverse muscles (28). Parietal muscles (29) extend from the base of the septa into the pedal disc, where they continue as basilar muscles (30). Gonads (31) may be located near the base of the septal filaments.

than octomerous and biradial rather than bilateral, as most have two siphonoglyphs. The important features of sea anemone form are summarized in Fig. 6.24 and should be studied carefully before reading about the way sea anemones carry out their functions.

Sea anemones are quite diverse. The oral disc varies considerably in size and may bear one or more whorls of tentacles, or tentacles crowded over the whole surface. Many sea anemones feed on small particles. These have cilia on the body surface, causing upward currents that waft bits of food to the tentacles. The oral disc and tentacles are also ciliated. When a particle touches a tentacle the tentacle bends and blows it toward the mouth. The tentacles have many nematocysts and adhesive glands, and, when larger food organisms are eaten, food is pushed into the mouth.

Mouth and pharynx structure is much the same as in Alcyonaria, but most anemones have two siphonoglyphs; a few have one or none. Slime glands in the pharynx aid in swallowing. Digestion follows the usual cnidarian plan. Preliminary digestion is rapid, depending on enzymes from gland

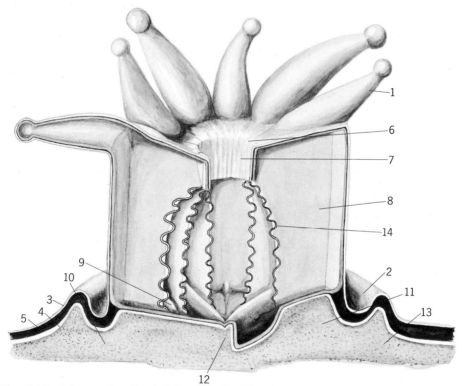

Fig. 6.25. Scheme of a Coral Polyp. Corals differ from sea anemones in their generally colonial habits and in having a skeleton. 1, tentacle; 2, the rim of the cup or theca in which the polyp rests, covered by the coenenchyme extending to other polyps; 3, the upper layer of coenenchyme; 4, the lower, calcoblastic layer of the coenenchyme, which secretes the skeleton; 5, the gastrovascular cavity; 6, peristome; 7, pharynx; 8, a primary septum of the polyp; 9, a secondary septum of the polyp; 10, a primary scleroseptum or skeletal septum, extending upward from the floor of the theca; 11, a secondary scleroseptum (note that the sclerosepta alternate wtih the polyp septa); 12, the columella, a central column where the primary sclerosepta meet; 13, the basal plate of the skeleton; 14, a septal filament.

cells in the septal filaments. The final, intracellular phase of digestion occurs in the general gastrodermis, greatly amplified by septa. Sea anemones have characteristic septa, typically occurring in pairs, placed in corresponding positions on either side of the sagittal plane. Primary septa are complete, uniting with the pharynx and the oral disc. Secondary septa are narrower; as they do not reach the pharynx they are incomplete. Third and fourth cycles of septa, decreasing in breadth, are often present. Septa attaching at the siphonoglyphs are directives, and have the septal muscles differently placed (Fig. 6.24B). Septal filaments are trilobed, with tracts of nematocysts, gland cells, and flagella. In many anemones the filaments continue at the base as thread-like acontia, lacking the flagellated tracts found in septal filaments (Fig. 6.24D). Acontia are extruded from the mouth and from pores in the body wall, the cinclides, when anemones are disturbed, and are probably protective as well as digestive. Food residues are eventually expelled from the mouth.

Siphonoglyphs and flagellated tracts of the septal filaments cause a continual intake and circulation of water. The currents transport food particles and ventilate the internal surfaces, permitting more effective respiratory exchange.

Epidermal muscles form longitudinal fibers in the tentacles and radial fibers in the oral disc. The latter fold in the disc when the animal contracts. The column and pharynx usually have no epidermal muscle. Circular muscle in all parts of the body is gastrodermal. Special circular muscle fibers form a sphincter beneath the oral disc, permitting it to be concealed when the animal contracts. The strong septal retractor muscles are gastrodermal. When the animal contracts, water escapes through the cinclides. Creeping movements of the pedal disc are largely made by the parietal and basilar muscles.

The body wall has an extensive epidermal nerve plexus and the septa have a gastrodermal plexus. Fibers through the mesogloea connect the plexi. There is little or no centralized control, although stimuli spread from one tentacle to another and repeated simuli fail to evoke responses. There are no special sense organs. Neurosensory cells are scattered through the epidermis and are concentrated in tentacles, oral disc, and pedal disc.

MADREPORARIA

Madreporaria are the most abundant Zoantharia and the most important, ecologically. In shallow, warm waters they form fringing reefs, atolls, and barrier reefs. At night and on dull days, the polyps expand, feeding on the abundant ocean plankton.

Coral polyps are essentially colonial anemones, connected by flat extensions of the body wall, the coenenchyme. A hard, calcareous exoskeleton is secreted by the lower surface of the coenenchyme. Each polyp sits in a depression, the theca. Ridges, the sclerosepta, project upward from the thecal base and the body wall follows their contours, folding inward, usually between the two septa of a pair (Fig. 6.25). Septa, coelenteron and pharynx are as in anemones, but the septal filaments lack flagellated tracts.

Corals do much to create a unique environment in shallow tropical seas. Many invertebrates and the bright reef fishes are found only in the special world created by corals. Reefs are limestone formations, formed of coral exoskeletons and heavily charged with organic material, especially in upper strata, where growing corals occur. Calcareous algae, millepores, and other calcareous Alcyonaria contribute to reefs, and in the Caribbean, gorgonians add touches of color and ornamentation.

Reef corals grow best at depths of 100 feet or less and at 22° C. or above. They contain zooxanthellae (actually dinoflagellates) as do many other Cnidaria. If corals and zooxanthellae are in a mutualistic relationship and corals cannot live or are handicapped without them, the restrictions on coral distribution could be explained. Edmondson (1928) found that corals died after 18 days in total darkness, but Yonge and Nichols (1931) found them completely carnivorous and maintain that they expel zooxanthellae when starved. Zahl and McLaughlin (1959) find that zooxanthellae probably seek corals because of their nitrate and phosphorous requirements, but although they produce oxygen it is not clear how important this is to corals. It might permit an increased metabolic rate and so favor a more rapid growth. It has been suggested that corals live in warmer waters because of the lower solubility of carbon dioxide. Evidently the critical limiting factors have not yet been determined.

The mechanics of atoll and reef formation are not yet certain. Probably several methods work simultaneously. Darwin (1842) believed that barrier reefs develop with the subsidence of land on which fringing reefs occur. Others have suggested that any platform of the right depth will provide a foothold for reefs, whether a fringing reef was present or not. Daly (1915) suggests that varying ocean levels resulting from changing ice-cap dimensions create substrates on which corals grow. On the whole, borings have indicated that Darwin may have been right about the Australian barrier reef and that the Daly hypothesis may best account for atolls.

Astrangia is the common coral of our cooler waters, but in Florida and the West Indies many types occur. Coral skeletons are often beautifully marked, with skeletal septa arranged in regular or irregular systems, depending on the growth patterns exhibited by the polyps. The many fossil corals can be recognized by these patterns and are of some importance in dating deposits.

OTHER ANTHOZOANS

The Antipatharia are thorny corals, and are found in deep tropical and subtropical waters. Their axial skeleton has many thorny outgrowths, and is covered by a coenenchyme containing the polyps. The Zoanthidea are usually colonial and are epizoic on various marine animals. The Ceriantharia are remarkable, elongated polyps which bury themselves in the sand, extending the oral disc and tentacles (Fig. 6.27). Some become quite large, reaching a length of 35 cm.

Anthozoan Reproduction

Gametes form from gastrodermal interstitial cells and gather as gonads in the septa. Anthozoa may be monoecious or dioecious. Fertilization may be external or internal, and some brood the young in special brood sacs.

Considering the similarity of zoantharian and alcyonarian adults, surprising differences occur during development. Alcyonaria form a stereoblastula; endoderm arises by delamination and a mouthless planula is formed. The planula attaches at the anterior end, and a mass of ectoderm grows inward to form the stomodaeum (Fig. 6.28A). Endodermal folds grow in from the body wall to form the septa. It becomes the first or primary polyp in Pennatulacea and Telestacea. In other groups it puts out stolons and soon loses its identity among other members of the colony. Zoantharia form a coeloblastula, which usually invaginates but may undergo multipolar ingression during gastrulation. The planula retains a blastopore, and stomodaeum formation occurs at this point. Septa develop as in Alcyonaria. The differences in development substantiate the idea that the two subclasses are separate anthozoan lines. Curiously, zoantharian development is consistent with Haeckel's gastreae theory, while alcyonarian development is consistent with Metschnikoff's views. That they go back as independent lines to Protozoa seems too improbable to be seriously entertained. One can only conclude that the early development of Cnidaria is not alone

A

B

Fig. 6.26. Some Colonial Anthozoa. A. *Plexaurella grisea,* one of the horny corals, or Gorgonacea. B. A part of the skeleton of *Tubipora,* an organ pipe coral. These belong to the Stolonifera. The stolon is plate-like, and each polyp is protected by an erect tube. At intervals, new stolonic plates develop. (Continued on pages 164–5)

163

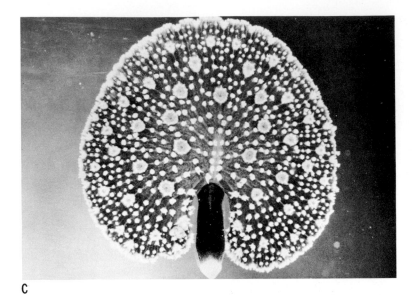

C

D

C. *Renilla reniformis*, a sea pansy, one of the Pennatulacea. Note the large axial polyp and the rachis containing many zooids, some of which are larger siphonozooids. D. *Mancina areolata*, one of the Madreporaria with confluent polyps occupying a channel in the skeletal mass. Several open mouths can be seen.

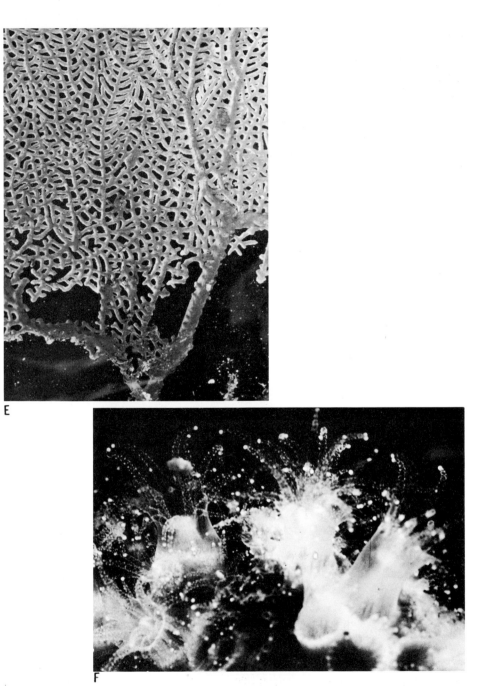

E

F

E. The skeleton of *Gorgonia*, a sea fan, perhaps the best known of the Gorgonacea. F. A part of a colony of *Astrangia*, a madreporarian coral with separate polyps in distinct thecae. (A, C-E, courtesy of the Smithsonian Institution. F, courtesy of General Biological Supply Co.)

sufficient to permit firm conclusions about their origin.

The zoantharian planula does not attach; it becomes a motile, anemone-like larva. The first larval stage resembles a primitive anemone, *Edwardsia,* and is called the Edwardsia larva (Fig. 6.28E). It has eight septa, four directives, and four unpaired lateral septa. Its symmetry is octomerous, like Alcyonaria. The lateral septal pairs are completed as four new septa grow out, and the larva enters the Halocampoides stage. Tentacles develop after attachment to complete the polyp form. Coral polyps begin to form a skeleton immediately and start a coenenchyme.

Asexual reproduction is important in Anthozoa. Polyps are added to colonies by buds from the coenenchyme or from older polyps. Some anemones reproduce asexually by longitudinal fission. *Metridium* reproduces asexually by fragmentation of the pedal disc, producing young with irregularities in septal and siphonoglyph arrange-

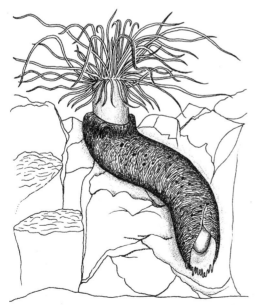

Fig. 6.27. *Cerianthus,* a member of the order Ceriantharia. The epidermis secretes a mucous tube, within which the body remains. (After Andres, from Hickson.)

ment. New mouths and whorls of tentacles appear in the coral coenenchyme. They develop septa continuous with the septa of adjacent polyps (Fig. 6.28B). Some corals form new mouths in the oral disc of a parent polyp. They may separate completely from the parent or remain attached to form a compound polyp of irregular form. Evidently there is a variety of control mechanisms affecting asexual reproduction in Anthozoa.

Growth and Regeneration in Cnidaria

Like most animals with a high capacity for asexual reproduction, Cnidaria have good regenerative powers. Classical experiments showed that cutting a *Hydra* into cylindrical pieces is only temporarily embarrassing; each piece develops new tentacles and a pedal disc to become a tiny animal. Further studies defined the size of the piece needed to form a new animal and showed that tentacles form at the oral end of the piece. The original polarity persists in the regenerating piece. Yet the same kind of piece grafted into place in the column of an intact animal becomes a part of the new body, gradually moving toward the base and successively acting as gastric region, budding zone, stem, and base of the polyp (Fig. 6.29). Evidently the whole organism impresses its metabolic pattern on the tissues that compose it, holding the potentiality for growth and differentiation in check. *Tubularia* stems show the same factors in operation (Fig. 6.29). A cut stem with a hydranth at one end develops no new hydranth; one without a hydranth develops a new hydranth on the hydranth end. A ligature around the stem changes the results; a new hydranth develops at both ends of the stem. A capillary tube at the ligature, however, prevents the formation of the second hydranth. Evidently some substance from the hydranth moves along the body, preventing hydranth formation. For an excellent discussion of the factors acting during growth and differentiation of Cnidaria, Berrill (1961) can be highly recommended.

The grafting experiment mentioned above shows that the *Hydra* body is not static. *Hydra* has a growth zone, high in the column, where new interstitial cells constantly form. They spread down the column and upward through oral regions and tentacles, accompanying the epidermis

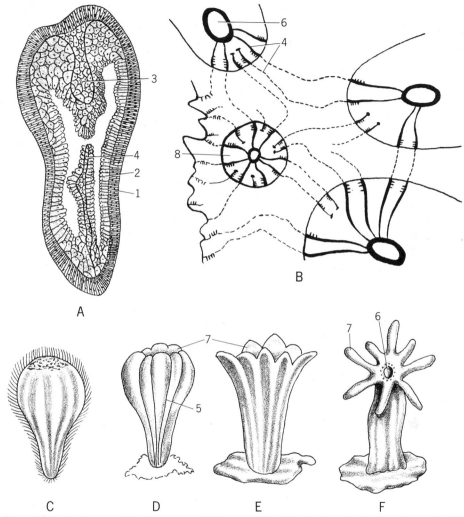

Fig. 6.28. Anthozoan Development. **A.** Larva of *Renilla* in longitudinal section, showing stomodaeum formation. **B.** Budding of a coral, *Orbicella*, showing a forming bud and three adjacent polyps. Note that the forming sclerosepta are continuations of the sclerosepta of pre-existing polyps. **C-F.** Stages in the development of a sea anemone, *Lebrunia*. The planula loses its apical tuft when ready to settle (**C**). After attachment, tenacles begin to form, a mouth breaks through, and the pedal disc develops (**D-F**). (**A**, after Wilson. **B**, after Matthai. **C-F**, after Duerden.) 1, ectoderm; 2, endoderm; 3, the solid stomodaeum before the rupture of the mouth opening; 4, septum; 5, lines of septal attachment; 6, mouth; 7, tentacles; 8, developing bud.

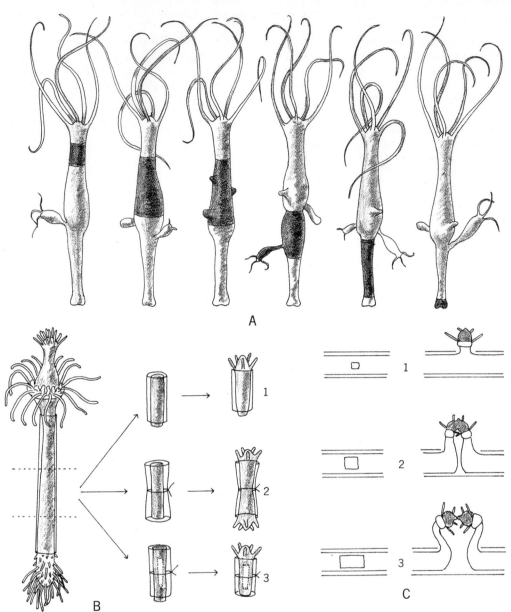

Fig. 6.29. A. A stained piece of a *Hydra* column is grafted into place in an unstained individual. The series of diagrams shows the movement of the grafted tissue toward the base. It becomes, successively, part of the gastric region, the budding zone, the stalk, and the basal disc. **B.** Summary of experiment showing the movement of a substance along the stalk of *Tubularia*, within the periderm. Transection of the stalk results in the formation of a hydranth at the original oral end of the stalk (1), but a ligature around the periderm (2) results in the formation of a hydranth at each end of the stalk. Insertion of a capillary tube (3) in the ligated region prevents the formation of an aboral hydranth. **C.** Summary of experiment involving the removal of pieces of periderm of different sizes. A single hydranth forms at a small opening (1), but if the opening is large (2-3) two complete hydranths form. (A, after Brien and Renier-Decoen. C, modified from Zwilling.)

and gastrodermis, and differentiating into new cells as required. Eventually all of the cells are replaced; in a matter of three weeks, a *Hydra* has become, in all reality, a new animal.

Buds and gonads arise far from the growth zone of Hydra. Is growth of the interstitial cells important in the regulation of Hydra form? Brien and Renier-Decoen (1925) find that *Hydra* with interstitial cells inactivated by irradiation will regenerate their form, but later die because they cannot replace cells. Grafting small bits of normal tissue containing interstitial cells into the irradiated animal prevents death.

The plasticity of Cnidaria may have much to do with determining the nature of life cycles. *Aurelia* produces small eggs that gastrulate by unipolar ingression and larger ones that gastrulate by invagination. Scyphozoa that produce small eggs generally gastrulate by ingression, and species that produce large eggs by invagination. During development of small eggs, the gastrula endoderm is brought into contact with the ectoderm, favoring linear growth and polyp formation. Very large eggs produce gastrulae with the invaginated endoderm not in contact with the ectoderm. Linear growth is not stimulated; the embryo widens and grows directly into a medusa. The results of such studies warn against construing modifications of life cycles as definite evidence of relationship. Many may turn out to be reactions of organisms with similar but extensive plasticity to a balance of such external factors as temperature and the chemical environment, and internal factors such as egg size and the dimensions of bud fields.

Phylum Ctenophora

Ctenophora are common in marine plankton. They are most abundant near the surface, but also occur at great depths. About 80 species have been described, but some are abundant enough to be ecologically important. They feed on small plankton organisms and are voracious. Nelson (1925) found up to 125 oyster larvae in a single *Mnemiopsis*, and as digestion is rapid, this represents the take in a short feeding period. *Mnemiopsis* can evidently have a significant effect on the oyster population when abundant.

Features distinguishing ctenophores from Cnidaria include:

1. radially arranged rows of ciliated plates (ctenes) for swimming;

2. tentacles absent or not in whorls around the mouth;

3. adhesive cells (colloblasts) for food capture and the almost complete absence of nematocysts;

4. determinate rather than indeterminate cleavage;

5. a distinct larval type, the cydippid, and the almost complete absence of a planula;

6. complete absence of polymorphism and alternation of polypoid and medusoid stages;

7. an aboral sense organ; and

8. muscle cells arising from the mesogloea rather than epidermis or gastrodermis.

On the other hand, ctenophores resemble Cnidaria in:

1. having a strong biradial symmetry and an oral-aboral axis;

2. a medusa-like body with a gelatinous mesenchymal mesogloea;

3. a similar, but more advanced gastrovascular cavity; and

4. the absence of any body cavity other than the coelenteron.

Classification

The ctenophores are classified in two classes and five orders, largely on the basis of comb rows, tentacles, and body shape.

Class Tentaculata. Ctenophores with tentacles.

Order Cydippida. Simple spherical or ovoid forms with two retractile tentacles arising in sheaths; with gastrovascular branches ending blindly (Fig. 6.30).

Order Lobata. Body with two large oral lobes, and four folds, known as auricles, defining auricular grooves; auricular grooves containing tentacles and used in feeding; tentacles variously arranged, without sheaths; with the oral ends of the gastrovascular canals joined by a ring canal. Example: *Mnemiopsis* (Fig. 6.31D).

Order Cestida. Body compressed and ribbon-like, with four rudimentary comb rows; with tentacular sheaths and reduced main tentacles and secondary tentacles along the oral margin of the body. Example: *Velamen* (Fig. 6.32A).

Order Platyctenea. Strongly flattened, with very short oral-aboral axis; creeping animals with two tentacles in sheaths; comb rows often missing in adult. Example: *Ctenoplana* (Fig. 6.32C).

Class Nuda. Ctenophores without tentacles.

Order Beroidea. Conical, with a wide mouth and pharynx, and with meredional, ramified gastrovascular canals. Example: *Beroë* (Fig. 6.32B).

The Cydippida

Cydippids are the least modified ctenophores, and are usually studied as an introduction to ctenophore form. The basic structure is summarized in Fig. 6.30. The often syncytial epidermis contains many gland cells, sensory cells, and pigment granules. The pharynx forms from an embryonic stomodaeum and is lined with epidermis, and the stomach and gastrovascular canals are lined with gastrodermis. Between these layers a gelatinous mesogloea, derived from the ectoderm, is found. It contains amoebocytes, connective tissue fibers, muscle fibers, and, presumably, some nerve cells.

Food is caught by the sticky colloblasts on the tentacles. Colloblasts are such highly modified cells that the normal cell structures cannot be seen. Spherules of sticky material cover the surface (Fig.

6.31A). It is tethered by a straight filament and when pulled out by a trapped animal is withdrawn by a spiral, contractile filament. The long, trailing tentacles are effective food traps; they are contracted and food is wiped off on the mouth. Food is digested rapidly in the flattened pharynx. The partly digested food enters the stomach and is circulated through the gastrovascular canals, where it is digested intracellularly. Food residues are ejected through the mouth or out of the small anal pores at the aboral end. The branches of the gastrovascular system reach the most important parts of the body; tentacular canals lie at the tentacle bases, and meredional canals lie beneath the eight comb rows.

The comb rows are composed of a series of short ciliary plates (ctenes), set in a series. The cilia are strong, and propel the animal slowly through the water. Smooth muscles develop from amoeboid mesogloeal cells. Longitudinal, circular, and radial fibers pass through the mesogloea, and circular fibers encircle the mouth to form a sphincter. Longitudinal fibers in the tentacle core retract it into the sheath and manipulate it when covered with food.

There are no respiratory structures. Cell rosettes (Fig. 6.31B), consisting of a double circlet of ciliated gastrodermal cells, surround openings leading from the gastrovascular canals to the mesogloea. Their function is unknown. They may be excretory, may help regulate body fluids, or may help to distribute food to the mesogloea. In any case, most nitrogen is excreted as ammonia, presumably from body and coelenteron surface.

The epidermal nerve plexus is concentrated as a ring around the mouth and at the base of the comb rows, where it forms the radial nerves. The nerves are not true nerves, but condensations of the nerve net.

Epidermal neurosensory cells are scattred about, with some concentration in the mouth region. The aboral sense organ is a statocyst, or balance organ, useful in maintaining normal orientation.

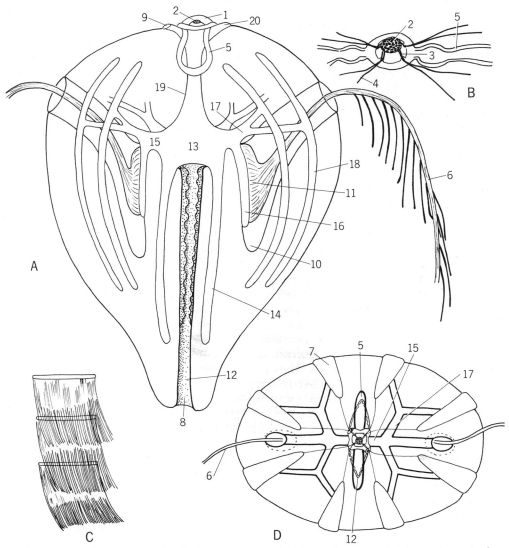

Fig. 6.30. Cydippid Anatomy. A. Scheme of a cydippid seen from the side along the sagittal plane. B. Aboral sense organ with the dome removed. C. Several ctenes, highly magnified. D. Scheme of a cydippid seen from the aboral pole. (A, after Hyman. B-D, composite.) *External features:* 1, dome of aboral sense organ; 2, statoliths; 3, balancer; 4, ciliated furrow; 5, polar field; 6, tentacle; 7, comb row; 8, mouth; 9, anal pore. *Internal parts:* 10, tentacle sheath; 11, tentacle base; 12, flattened pharynx, with a ruffled glandular wall; 13, flattened stomach; 14, pharyngeal canal; 15, transverse canal; 16, tentacular canal; 17, interradial canal; 18, meredional canal; 19, aboral canal; 20, anal canal.

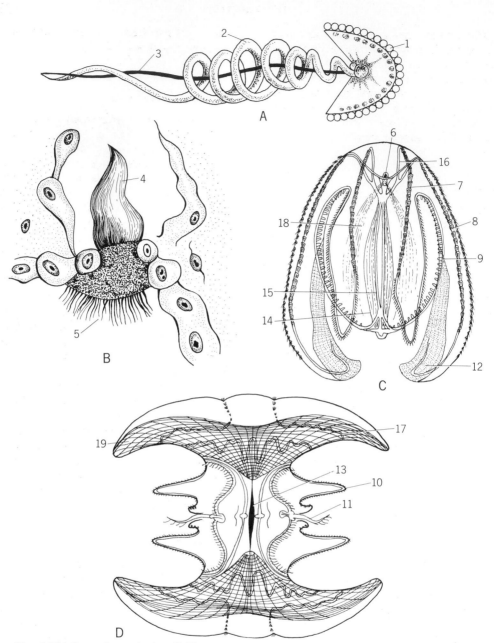

Fig. 6.31. Ctenophora. A. A colloblast, the characteristic adhesive cell of ctenophores. B. A rosette organ. C. Sagittal view of a young *Mnemiopsis*. D. Oral view of a *Mnemiopsis*. (A-B, after Komai, from Andrew. C, after Hyman. D, after Mayer.) *Colloblast:* 1, adhesive bodies; 2, spiral filament; 3, straight filament. *Rosette:* 4, ciliary tuft; 5, cilia extending into the gastrovascular cavity. *Mnemiopsis:* 6, aboral sense organ; 7, subtentacular comb row; 8, subsagittal comb row; 9, tentacles in the auricular groove; 10, auricle; 11, principal tentacles; 12, oral lobe; 13, mouth. *Digestive system:* 14, pharynx; 15, pharyngeal canal; 16, meredional canal; 17, loop from meredional canal. *Muscles:* 18, muscle bands; 19, muscles of oral lobe.

The nervous system controls muscular movements and determines the activity of the cilia on the comb rows. The radial nerves extend to the statocyst; if the statocyst is removed, the comb rows act independently. Cutting across a comb row leaves the upper and lower parts coordinated but independent.

Other Ctenophores

Mnemiopsis is a common member of Lobata. It reaches four inches or so in length, and is brightly luminescent, flashing like a light bulb when disturbed. The body is narrow in the tentacular plane, and the large sagittal faces extend down as oral lobes (Fig. 6.31C,D). *Bolinopsus*, found on both coasts, has shorter comb rows that do not reach the oral lobes.

The sagittal faces have been greatly drawn out in Venus's girdle, *Velamen* (Fig. 6.32A), making it ribbon-shaped. The four sagittal comb rows are very long and the tentacular ones very short. Rudimentary tentacles are retained in a sheath. Their graceful, transparent bodies, reaching a length (or breadth, to be precise) of a meter or more, shimmer blue and green as they swim. Unlike most ctenophores, *Velamen* undulates as it swims and has a well-developed muscle system.

Platyctenea are aberrant, creeping ctenophores found in Oriental seas. The pharynx is expanded to form the oral surface and the oral-aboral axis is flattened, giving them a worm-like shape (Fig. 6.32C). They were once thought to be a link between flatworms and ctenophores, but for various reasons are now considered as the ends of a distinctive ctenophore line leading nowhere.

Beroë (Fig. 6.32B) is a common beroid, occurring on both east and west coasts. Some *Beroë* reach 20 cm. or more in length. They are flattened in the tentacular plane, and have a very large mouth and pharynx. Many diverticula arise from the meredional canals. *Beroë* feeds on large organisms, which are swallowed whole.

Radiata Functions

A number of the invertebrate phyla were already established by the end of the Proterozoic era, some 600 million years ago. Judging from their level of organization, Radiata must have been among the first animal stocks to become metazoan. For perhaps a billion years they have adapted continuously to varied and changing environments. Yet today their simple bodies are built of two epithelial layers separated by a gelatinous mesogloea. All retain traces of a primary radial symmetry and have only a coelenteron as an internal cavity.

The adaptive lines that have fitted Radiata for life over the vast periods of time involved and yet left them with such simple structure provide an insight into the plasticity and potentialities of simple animals, and help us to understand what early evolutionary development may have been. Observing the modern consequences of evolutionary trends in simple living systems provides information about the nature of the most basic life processes, and also about the kinds of adaptational avenues that lead to greater efficiency, or suit an animal to a type of habitat.

FOOD CAPTURE

Radiata are sessile, floating, or weakly swimming forms, suitable to their symmetry. They are carnivores that cannot pursue prey, and have other methods of food capture. The methods they use are early developments of techniques employed by many other animal groups.

Most of the Radiata are trappers, capturing food that comes in contact with the body surface. Trappers need tools for their trade. More advanced animals may build snares, but primitive animals use parts of their body as tools, and the Radiata have acquired projections of the body surface for food capture. The extensions are simple tentacles, generally, although some Scyphozoa use oral arms instead. While development of nervous and muscle systems makes tentacles more effective, no more effective tool was developed until body organization became far more complex, and animals acquired appendages. As neither oral arms nor tentacles of Radiata can lash

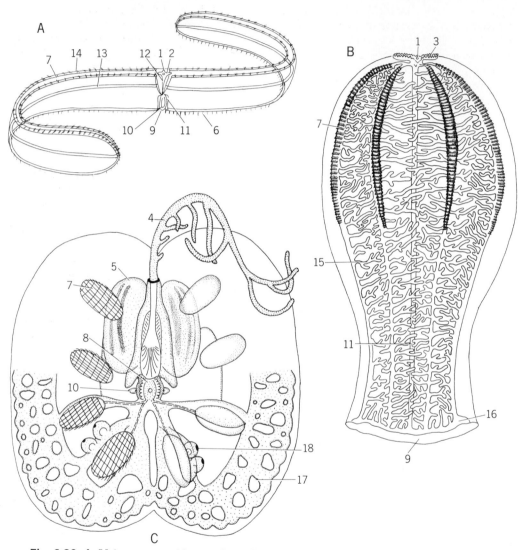

Fig. 6.32. A. *Velamen*, a cestid ctenophore. B. *Beroë*, one of the Nuda. C. Scheme of *Ctenoplana*, a platyctene ctenophore. (A, after Mayer. B, after Hyman; C, after Komai.) *External features:* 1, aboral sense organ; 2, polar field; 3, papillae on polar field; 4, principal tentacle; 5, tentacle sheath; 6, marginal tentacle; 7, comb row; 8, anal pore; 9, mouth. *Gastrovascular system:* 10, pharynx; 11, pharyngeal canal; 12, aboral canal; 13, subtentacular meredional canal; 14, subsagittal meredional canal; 15, branches from meredional canal; 16, canal along the mouth rim; 17, peripheral meshwork of gastrovascular canals. *Other parts:* 18, gonad.

out and wrap around prey, further improvements are needed to make them effective. Parts to immobilize and attach prey to the tentacles are universal among Radiata that feed with tentacles: nematocysts in Cnidaria and colloblasts in Ctenophora. An extended tentacle with nematocysts is a simple tool, but it enables a *Hydra* to capture a *Daphnia* as large as itself and a great deal faster, and enables a floating siphonophore to capture fishes as powerful and fast as mackerels. Food is brought to the mouth by the tentacles, or the mouth is set on a movable extension of the body, the manubrium, and is brought partway to the food.

Flagellary and ciliary mucus feeding are very popular techniques among animals. Food is caught in mucus, and food and mucus are swept into the mouth. The feeding of *Aurelia* has been described (p. 150), and is a typical case. Mucus and food particles are conveyed to the mouth by flagellated grooves in the oral arms. Primitive anemones use ciliary currents in much the same manner, sweeping particles up along the sides of the body, and onto the sticky tentacles or oral disc. Cilia on the tentacles propel food particles to the mouth. *Mnemiopsis* exemplifies ciliary feeding in ctenophores. The auricular ridges on the tentacular surface enclose ciliated grooves, which swirl food particles about and bring them in contact with small tentacles. The tentacles trap the prey, and draw it toward the mouth.

DIGESTION

Radiata stand intermediate between the higher metazoans, with a digestive tube opening at mouth and anus, and the Protozoa and Parazoa that have no cavity for extracellular digestion. Food reception occurs at the mouth and mouth cavity, provided with lubricating slime glands, and large organisms are ordinarily swallowed promptly. However, other methods may be used. The original mouth is gone

in rhizostomes, and many tiny mouths have appeared in the oral arms. Large fish may be caught and held against the suctorial mouths. Enzymes are ejected on the prey; preliminary digestion takes place outside of the body, and tiny, partially digested food particles are swept into the suctorial mouths by ciliary action.

Most Cnidaria lack a special swallowing region, or, as Yonge (1954) terms it, a region for conduction and storage of food. However, Anthozoa and Ctenophora have a stomodaeum which turns in at the mouth. It brings muscles with it, and is important in swallowing. There is no storage organ or crop in the stomodaeum of Radiata, although the pharynx of ctenophores is divided into a swallowing region and a dilated part with folded surface where much of preliminary digestion occurs.

The general features of digestion and absorption are the same in all Radiata. Food is rapidly attacked by extracellular enzymes to effect a preliminary digestion. The small particles that result are ingested by gastrodermal cells, and final digestion and absorption occurs intracellularly. What is digested depends on the battery of enzymes available to hydrolyze foods. Cnidaria have little or no ability to digest carbohydrates, and a very limited ability to digest fats. Proteases, usually most effective in neutral to alkaline media, are responsible for preliminary digestion.

Digestion tends to be a sequential process. The first phases of preliminary digestion produce intermediate products from proteins, and the pH of the coelenteron tends to shift toward the alkaline side. In final, intracellular digestion, peptidases complete the process. There is some tendency to differentiate the coelenteron into regions for preliminary digestion and for final, intracellular digestion. Even in *Hydra*, the upper part of the body contains far more enzymatic gland cells than the lower part. In colonial polyps, preliminary digestion takes place in the hydranths, and much of final digestion occurs in the coenosarc or coenenchyme. In medusae, the system of radial and ring canals distributes the products of preliminary digestion to other parts, where final digestion occurs. The upper part of the ctenophore pharynx serves as the site of preliminary digestion, and the canal system distributes particles for ingestion by the gastrodermis elsewhere.

Digestion is limited by the surface available to bear enzymatic cells and nutritive cells. The consequences of surface-amplifying adaptations are seen in the larger Cnidaria and ctenophores, in the canal system of medusae and ctenophores and the septa of Anthozoa. The unicellular glands of small polyps like *Hydra* tend to be replaced by patches of gland cells, and in the gastric filaments of Scyphozoa and the septal filaments of Anthozoa, surface amplification is accompanied by a concentration of cells with a particular functional competency to form histologically differentiated parts.

INTERNAL TRANSPORT

The gastrovascular cavity combines circulatory and digestive functions. The circulatory function is minimal in small animals like *Hydra,* for the surrounding water provides oxygen and a place to dump organic wastes, and no cell is far removed from the coelenteron or external medium. The transport function becomes important in large solitary individuals or in colonies with a large coenenchyme. There is nothing comparable to blood. The gastrovascular contents contain dissolved or particulate food, mucus, enzymes, and possibly co-ordinating substances. In many instances it is not very sharply separated from the sea outside, for the siphonoglyphs and septal flagella of Anthozoa draw water in and discharge it, and the mouth is generally open in most ciliary feeders.

Body movements and the gastrodermal flagella move the gastrovascular fluid

through the coelenteron and its branches. Few muscular adaptations to move the fluid are found, but *Sertularia* polyps may have a muscular gastric pouch which contracts to force food into the coenosarc, and *Tubularia* polyps use the basal part of the hydranth to pump food into the stem and roots.

Transport is a more severe problem in the bulkier medusae and ctenophores. The challenge is met by canalization of the coelenteron and a greater organization of flagellar propulsion of the coelenteric fluid. Canal systems tend to become truly circulatory in function, particularly in species with digestion restricted to a gastric cavity or gastric pouches with gastric filaments. In *Cyanea*, currents in the radial canals pass outward near the roof and inward below. The flow is outward in the unbranched and inward in the branched radial canals of *Aurelia*. In the ctenophore, *Pleurobrachia*, gastrodermal cilia occur on the medial face of the canals and large, nutritive cells on the distal face.

The most effective circulatory devices are found in the Anthozoa, where siphonoglyph and septal flagella circulate the coelenteric fluid. That fluid circulation is a critical problem is shown by the differentiation of zooids as special circulatory individuals. The siphonozooids produce strong currents, adequate to keep fluid moving in a complex system of solenial tubes.

RESPIRATION

Radiata have very low oxygen requirements. Red coral oxygen use is only 0.03 cc/gm/hr, and *Aurelia* oxygen consumption is 0.02 cc/gm/hr. Similar low figures are given for other coelenterates and ctenophores. The large mass of mesogloea, containing few cells, and the sessile or floating habit are undoubtedly important in keeping oxygen requirements low. Activity changes the rate of oxygen consumption. Corals and anemone consume more oxygen when expanded, and *Aurelia* oxygen use varies with the oxygen content of the water.

The respiratory picture of many Cnidaria is complicated by the presence of zooxanthellae or zoochlorellae. Whether they provide something necessary for their hosts or not, the photosynthetic cells liberate oxygen while carrying out photosynthesis, and may elevate activity in this way.

EXCRETION

As is generally true of aquatic invertebrates, Cnidaria appear to be ammonotelic, releasing most of their nitrogenous wastes as ammonia. Small quantities of uric acid, creatinine, xanthine, and guanidine have been recovered from cnidarian tissues, but their importance and the biochemistry related to them have not been described. Inclusions resembling more complex nitrogen compounds have been described in cells located at various points, but no firm conclusions can be drawn. A dark region, sometimes called the "liver," is found below the float of some siphonophores. It contains guanine crystals, and may be an excretory organ.

OSMOREGULATION

Most Radiata have a very limited ability to control the tissue water concentration. This has been a factor in restricting most of them to marine habitats. They are usually osmoconformers, taking up water or giving off salts to match their environments. *Cyanea*, for example, reaches equilibrium with its environment within 36 hours, and corals respond similarly. Even in fresh-water *Hydra*, exposure to distilled water soon leads to osmotic swelling and disintegration. Presumably some substance present in pond water permits *Hydra* to exclude water. The mechanism, however, has not been described.

Most cnidarians that have been tested show a limited ability to control some specific ions. Medusae tend to have more potassium and less sulphate than the water in which they live, and the calcium content of anemones is below the surrounding medium.

If an animal cannot control its salt and water concentration, it can occur only in regions within the limits of its tolerance. The total salt concentration and the concentration of specific ions thus become specific critical limiting factors in distribution. *Aurelia* survives well in brackish water because it has a high tolerance for low salt concentration rather than because it has developed control mechanisms. The majority of the Radiata have a narrow tolerance, and are restricted to habitats approaching full ocean salinity. Thus corals are killed by a few hours' to a few days' exposure to sea water diluted by rains.

MECHANISMS OF RESPONSE

Sense organs, nerves, and muscles are poorly developed in Radiata, partly in association with their primitive level of organization, and partly with their sessile or floating habit.

Generalized neurosensory cells are found in the epidermis and, more sparsely, in the gastrodermis. Several morphological types are recognized in some Cnidaria, but the functions of the different types are not known. Sensory cells are usually elongated, with basal processes that make contact with nerve cells and with distal ends having bristles or bulbs. Radiata in which no other kinds of sensory receptors have been found are sensitive to touch, chemicals, and light.

Generalized or dermoptic light sensitivity is common among Cnidaria. Coral polyps expand in diffuse and contract in bright light. *Gonionemus* and some other medusae without eye-spots change their swimming rates with changed light intensity. Hydras choose blue-green over red environments; some sea anemones are color blind, while others respond differently to blue-green and red-yellow light. Dermoptic light sensitivity tends to disappear with the development of ocelli. *Aurelia* and *Sarsia* become photo-insensitive when their ocelli are removed.

Regions of high activity or parts more exposed to the environment tend to be better equipped with sensory cells. Concentration of sensory cells in Radiata, as in other animals, tends to occur near the mouth. Tentacles and pedal disc are also regions of sensory cell aggregation. The next logical step is the development of sensory epithelia, composed wholly or predominantly of sensory cells. Patches of sensory epithelia with long sensory hairs occur at the base and sides of scyphozoan rhopalia and in tracts associated with the nerve ring. A somewhat different sensory epithelium lines the sensory pits at the upper and lower surfaces of rhopalia in semaeostomes and rhizostomes. Little is known of the functional significance of morphologically different sensory epithelia; in some cases, as in the polar field of ctenophores, it is not certain that they are sensory. The radiate animals, however, clearly show that one of the first steps in sensory differentiation is the development of multicellular patches of sensory epithelium.

Special light-sensitive organs occur in or near the tentacular bulbs of many hydromedusae, and as a part of the rhopalia of some scyphomedusae. Scattered light-sensitive cells can provide information about the intensity and quality of light, but are not well suited to indicate the direction from which it comes. The advantage of ocelli is that the combination of pigment cells and light-sensitive cells permits collecting information necessary for direction sense. Some ocelli of different complexity are shown in Fig. 6.33A,B. The simplest is a pigment spot ocellus, with pigment cells between the light-sensitive cells. Shading becomes more effective if the ocellus is invaginated as a cup, especially if a lens is added, and in Cnidaria, simple pigment cup ocelli and ocelli with a definite lens occur.

No clear line of ocellus evolution can be shown among Cnidaria. Ocelli may or may not be present in hydromedusae and scyphomedusae, and the complexity of ocelli varies independently of the level of organization. *Sarsia* ocelli are far more advanced than the other parts of its body, and closely related medusae may have simple ocelli or none at all. This kind of distribution is typical of parts that are developing independently. The mechanics of light reception determine the nature of an effective organ to a very considerable extent, and evolutionary convergence is the rule rather than the exception in light-receptive organs.

Medusae usually orient with the oral surface down and the aboral surface up. This posture is favored by the weight distribution of the body, and many species tend to assume their normal position without balance organs. Many medusae, however, have balance organs. All anthomedusae have statocysts, but in most groups they occur sporadically, present in some and absent in others. Statocysts are variable in form. They contain heavy cells (lithocytes) weighted by inclusions (statoliths) contained in a cavity of the lithocyte. Leptomedusae lithocytes are specialized epidermal cells, lying in pits or vesicles formed by the closure of pits (Fig. 6.33C). Generally, open statocysts have many lithocytes and closed statocysts have few. Narcomedusae have gastrodermal lithocytes, contained in club-shaped lithostyles surrounded by long, sensory hairs. Trachymedusae have closed statocysts, each containing a lithostyle-like club in a cavity lined by sensory epithelium. Each rhopalium of *Aurelia* contains a cavity continuous with the ring canal and ends in many lithocytes of gastrodermal origin, with sensory pits above and below its base. This type of balance organ, like the ocelli, tends to be held within rather narrow limits of design by the nature of the environmental factor it is intended to reflect. Gravity pulls a weighted body down, and as vesicles or pits are overturned, the heavy object within stimulates different parts of the sensory epithelium. The weighted object may be a spheroid in a cavity or a weighted club. In any case, the weighted part sags against a sensory epithelium and so provides information about the direction of gravitational pull.

The ctenophore aboral sense organ (Fig. 6.30B) is a statocyst, but designed somewhat differently than the statocysts of Cnidaria. The heavy body, also called a statolith, is compound, formed of concretions from many disintegrated epidermal cells. It is suspended on four sigmoid tufts of fused cilia (balancers), which communicate with the ciliated furrows leading to the comb rows. A dome of fused cilia covers it. Body orientation determines which of the balancer tufts it sags upon, and direct stimulation of appropriate comb rows results.

Balance organs set up corrective reflexes which restore normal body orientation, known as "righting reflexes." If the bell of *Aurelia* is tilted, unequally strong swimming movements of the lower and raised side of the bell tend to return the animal to a normal position. If the rhopalia are removed, the ability to right is lost. Removal of the ctenophore aboral sense organ destroys the animal's ability to maintain a resting posture with the aboral end up, and prevents co-ordination of the ciliary beat of the comb rows.

The cnidarian nervous system is made of unpolarized protoneurones, able to conduct impulses in either direction. The primitive nervous system appears to be formed of an epidermal plexus of multi-

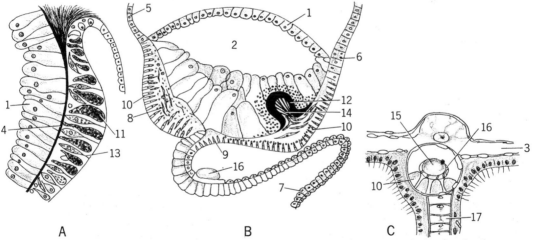

Fig. 6.33. Sense Organs. **A.** A pigment spot ocellus from *Turris*, in section. This is the simplest type of ocellus, consisting of alternating pigment and neurosensory cells. **B.** The ocellus and adjacent region of *Tiaropsis*. This is an ocellus of an advanced type, with a definite pigment cup, admitting light only through the cup opening, and with the neurosensory cells inverted, having the sensory tips at the bottom of the cup. This is the inverse type of ocellus. *Tiaropsis* also has a statocyst of the open type at the base of the velum. **C.** A statocyst of the closed type from *Obelia*. (A-B, after Linko. C, after the Hertwigs.) 1, endoderm; 2, radial canal; 3, ring canal; 4, mesolamella; 5, exumbrellar epidermis; 6, subumbrellar epidermis; 7, velum; 8, upper nerve ring; 9, lower nerve ring; 10, sensory epithelium; 11 pigment cell; 12, pigment cup; 13, neurosensory cells with sensory tip directed outward; 14, inverted neurosensory cells with sensory tip directed inward; 15, statolith; 16, statocyst; 17, tentacle base.

polar cells, making connections with neurosensory cells and with muscle fibers, and a similar, but more sparse, gastrodermal plexus. Fibers through the mesogloea connect the two plexi. Considerable difference of opinion has existed about whether the neurites of adjacent protoneurones are separated by synaptic spaces or are structurally united. It appears that both schools of thought were correct, and Cnidaria have both kinds of nerve nets. In the siphonophore *Velella,* a nerve net of large, syncytial fibers serves for rapid transmission of stimuli and another, smaller, discontinuous net conducts slower, spreading stimuli. In net-like nerve plexi, stimuli spread in all directions, and the strength of the stimulus is correlated with the distance it travels. A stretched net conducts stimuli more rapidly, perhaps because it tends to modify the multipolar cells into bipolar cells. Generally, and perhaps for the same physiological reasons, impulses channeled along a constant pathway often follow condensations of the nerve net composed of predominantly bipolar neurones.

Cnidaria are best understood as animals without a central nervous system. There is never a structure comparable to a brain; the most progressive cnidarians have, at the most, a nerve ring encircling the medusa bell or a series of independent rhopalial ganglia. The absence of definite nerve centers may be interpreted as primitive or may be considered an outcome of radial symmetry. Certainly, radial symmetry has a devastating effect upon nervous centralization, as will be noted when the radially symmetrical echinoderms are studied. Two kinds of evidence may be used to recognize more primitive nervous arrangements. One is centralization and the other is its depth. Generally, the more complex animals have insunk nervous systems, derived from the epidermis but located in deeper body regions. The nervous system of the radiate animals is simple from both points of view, and

remains an argument against the derivation of Cnidaria from the flatworms.

Phylogenetic Relationships

Few aspects of zoology are as fascinating and difficult to agree about as phylogenetic relationships. Some mention of cnidarian origin was necessary in dealing with the origin of Metazoa (p. 103). Basically there are two points of view. One is that the radiate organisms are the most primitive true Metazoa, and the other is that they stem from aberrant, deteriorated flatworms that assumed a sessile habit and became secondarily radial in form. Despite the efforts of its proponents, the latter view is not as persuasive as the former. Histological evidence favors the conception both of a gradually differentiating mesoderm, rather than a mesoderm continuously deteriorating to form a mesogloea, and of a progressively developing nerve cell, rather than a deteriorating neuron that becomes a protoneuron.

The alternative is to consider Radiata as primitive, and this demands a choice between the polyp form and the medusa form as the original stock. Earlier zoologists considered the polyp as the primitive coelenterate form. More recently, the view that the shortest life cycle, as represented by some trachylines, is primitive has been popular. The polyp forms are thus seen as elaborations of the actinula larva. Presumably, the earliest ancestral stocks were planula-like and eventually evolved into a creeping form with tentacles, rather like actinulae. This developed into a medusa and the actinula was retained as a larval form. Budding habits may have developed in actinulae to establish a polypoid form, and so have led to the alternating polypoid and medusoid phases of the cnidarian life cycle. The most probable ancestral stocks, if this view is maintained, would lead directly to the trachylines, with a simple, and presumably primitive, life cycle. Hydrozoan stocks may be supposed to have given rise to the siphonophores very early, and to the Hydroida by further development of colonial polyps.

Early trachyline ancestral stocks are thought to have given rise to scyphozoan and anthozoan stems independently, and to have given rise to a completely independent stem that evolved into modern ctenophores. Among Scyphozoa, the stem forms are probably either Cubomedusae or Stauromedusae. If Stauromedusae look primitive because they are permanently

juvenile, as some think, it is probable that the first cubomedusan forms were not greatly unlike them.

Anthozoan origins remain obscure. The hexamerous antipatharian polyps appear most primitive, and it may be that octomerous symmetry appeared to the addition of a siphonoglyph and an associated pair of directives, leading to Zoantharia.

Whatever patterns may have led to the Radiata are lost in the haze of distant epochs. Our clues are far too slender to permit any strong advocacy of any specific evolutionary line.

References

Barth, L. G. 1940. The determination of the regenerating hydranth in *Tubularia*. *Phys. Zool.* 17: 335.

Batham, E. J., *et al.* 1960. The nerve net of the sea anemone, *Metridium senile*, the mesenteries and collum. *Quart. Jour. Micr. Sci.* 101: 487.

Bryden, R. B. 1952. Ecology of *Pelmatohydra oligactis* in Kirkpatrick's Lake, Tennessee. *Ecol. Monogr.* 22: 45.

Carlgren, O. 1934. Revision der Actinarien. *Ark. Zool.* 26: 1.

————. 1949. A survey of the Ptychodactiaria, Corallimorpharia, and Acinaria. *Kungl. Svensk. Vetensk. Handl.* Ser. 4, 1: 1.

Chapman, G. 1953. Studies on the mesogloea of coelenterates. *Quart. Jour. Micr. Sci.* 94: 155.

Cuttress, C. E. 1955. Systematic study of anthozoan nematocysts. *System Zool.* 4: 120.

Darwin, C. 1896. *The Structure and Distribution of Coral Reefs.* Murray, London.

Dawydoff, C. 1933. Morphologie et biologie des Ctenoplana. *Arch. Zool. Exp. Gen.* 75: 103.

Fraser, C. 1944. *Hydroids of the Atlantic Coast of North America.* Univ. of Toronto Press, Toronto. (F)

Fewkes, J. W. 1881. Jellyfishes of Narragansett Bay. *Bull. Mus. Comp. Anat. Harvard* 8: 141. (F)

Garstang, W. 1946. The morphology and relations of the Siphonophora. *Quart. Jour. Micr. Sci.* 87: 107.

Hand, C. 1959. On the origin and phylogeny of the coelenterates. *System Zool.* 8: 163.

Heider, K. 1927. Von Nervensystem der Ctenophoren. *Ztschr. Morph. Ökol. Tiere* 9: 638.

Hess, A., *et al.* 1957. Observations on the structure of *Hydra* as seen with the electron and light microscope. *Quart. Jour. Micr. Sci.* 98: 315.

Hickson, S. J. 1924. *An Introduction to the Study of Recent Corals.* Univ. of Manchester Press, Manchester, Eng.

Hoyle, G. 1960. Neuromuscular activity in the swimming sea anemone, *Stomphia coccinea. Jour. Exp. Biol.* 37: 671.

Hyman, L. H. 1931. Studies on hydras, IV. *Trans. Am. Micr. Soc.* 48: 242.

————. 1940. Observations and experiments on the physiology of medusae. *Biol. Bull.* 79: 282.

————. 1940. *The Invertebrates*, Vol. 1. McGraw-Hill, New York.

Jones, C. S. 1949. The control and discharge of nematocysts in *Hydra. Jour. Exp. Zool.* 105: 25.

Komai, T. 1934. On the structure of *Ctenoplana. Kyoto Univ. Col. Sci. Mem.*, Ser. B. 9: 245.

Kramp, P. L. 1961. Synopsis of the medusae of the world. *Jour. Mar. Biol. Soc.* 40: 1.

Laubenfels, M. W. de. 1955. Are the coelenterates degenerate or primitive? *System. Zool.* 4: 43.

Mackie, G. O. 1960. Structure of the nervous system in *Velella*. *Quart. Jour. Micr. Sci.* 101: 119.

Mayer, A. G. 1910. *Medusae of the World.* Carnegie Inst., Washington, D.C.

———. 1912. *Ctenophores of the Atlantic Coast of North America.* Carnegie Inst., Washington, D.C.

Pantin, C. F. A. 1950. Behavior patterns in lower invertebrates. *Soc. Exp. Biol. Symp.* 4: 175.

Nutting, C. C. 1900, 1904, 1915. American hydroids. *Bull. U.S. Mus. Spec. Bulls.* (F).

Rees, W. J. 1957. Evolutionary trends in the classification of capitate hydroids and medusae. *Bull. Brit. Mus. Nat. Hist. Zool.* 4: 453.

Rose, S. M. 1957. Cellular interaction during differentiation. *Biol. Rev.* 32: 351.

Russell, F. S. 1955. *Medusae of the British Isles.* Cambridge Univ. Press, Cambridge, Eng.

Schulze, P. 1917. Neue Beiträge zu einer Monographie der Gattung *Hydra. Arch. Biontol.* 4: 33.

Stephenson, T. A. 1928, 1935. *British Sea Anemones.* Ray Society, London.

Torrey, H. B. 1902. Hydroida of the Pacific Coast. *Univ. Calif. Publ. Zool.* 1: 1. (F)

Wilson, D. P. 1947. The Portuguese man-of-war, *Physalia physalis*, in British and adjacent seas. *Jour. Mar. Biol. Assoc.* 27: 139.

Yanagita, T. M. 1959. Physiological mechanisms of nematocyst response in sea anemones. *Jour. Exp. Biol.* 36: 568.

7
The Acoelomate Bilateria

Bilateria includes all Eumetazoa not belonging to the Radiata. All share a primary bilateral symmetry, sometimes lost in sessile or slow-moving adults but evident during embryonic development.

Bilateral symmetry is especially suitable for active movement, and Bilateria generally show the evolutionary consequences of selective pressures associated with an active life. The bodies of even sessile or slow-moving animals often show the imprint of past activity. The complex of adaptive trends initiated by active movement is best observed in simpler animals. Locomotor organs are augmented, and for the most part this implies development of muscles. The muscles of Bilateria are almost wholly mesodermal in origin, and their improvement gives impetus to mesodermal growth and differentiation. As muscles develop, new demands are placed on the sense organs and nervous system, which adapt by further specialization. On the principle that it is better to see where one is going than where one has been, sense organs tend to aggregate at the anterior end, with a nerve center or brain nearby. Thus active animals tend to develop a head, and cephalization is a consequence of bilateral symmetry and the activity associated with it.

As locomotor, sensory, and nervous systems develop, additional metabolic requirements arise. Nutritive, respiratory, and excretory functions are amplified, and complex systems associated with these functions develop in more highly organized animals. Greater size and complexity encourage the development of mechanisms for internal transport. In short, the establishment and development of the typical animal organ systems are encouraged by the activity associated with bilateral symmetry, and bilaterality was a critical factor in determining the course of animal evolution.

The most primitive Bilateria are acoelomate, for the coelenteron is the only body cavity. The organization of acoelomate Bilateria is not greatly advanced over that of Radiata, but the effects of the new symmetry are evident. The acoelomates are worms, elongated along the primary body axis. Small species move by the primitive ciliary method, but larger ones wriggle and squirm, revealing the growing importance of muscles in locomotion. Sense organs are only moderately developed. The nervous system may seem unimpressive, but cephalization has begun and there is a definite central nervous system. Platyhelminthes differ from Radiata in the details but not the basic form of the digestive cavity, but nemertines have a tubular gut with mouth and anal openings. They have no respiratory system, but a protonephridial system foreshadows the more efficient excretory organs of higher phyla. A circulatory system first appears in nemertines, and it may be said that the organization of animals in the higher invertebrate phyla must have been greatly influenced by the acoelomate phase through which their ancestors passed.

A mass of mesenchymal cells occupying the space between the epidermis and gastrodermis characterizes the acoelomates. The mesenchyme occupies the same position as the mesogloea, but is not the same. Mesogloeal cells are scarce, and wander into the matrix from the epidermis. Mesogloeal formation has not become a formal embryonic process. In flatworms and higher phyla, the bulk of the mesoderm arises from endoderm by processes fixed as a definite part of embryonic development. The ectoderm and endoderm gain definiteness and are relieved of many functions as the mesoderm emerges as a "true" germ layer. The mass of mesodermal tissue in which the organs are embedded is not an unmixed blessing, for it interferes with internal transport. New spaces or body cavities which hasten internal transport appear in pseudocoelomate and coelomate animals, but the acoelomates are handicapped. Nevertheless, the solid, acoelomate construction is a logical step in the history of animal form.

Phylum Platyhelminthes

Flatworms suffer severe physiological handicaps. The mesodermal parenchyma contains more cells than mesogloea and has higher metabolic requirements. Planaria

have an oxygen consumption about ten times that of the average cnidarian on a per gram per hour basis, yet they are scarcely better equipped than Radiata to provide oxygen or to discharge carbon dioxide. The digestive system is essentially like the Radiata digestive system and works in the same way. Little is known of excretory physiology, but it appears to be relatively primitive. Probably only the small size and flattened form brings the internal cells close enough to the external surface and gastrodermis to compensate for the higher metabolic requirements and the weakness of the transport system. Two of the three classes are wholly parasitic, and the third includes a number of epizoic and endozoic species. The high incidence of parasitism may reflect a tendency of flatworms to retire from competition with physiologically better-endowed organisms into a less competitive environment.

Among the outstanding differences between the Radiata and the Platyhelminthes, the following flatworm traits may be listed as especially important:

1. Bilateral symmetry replaces radial symmetry.

2. They are slightly cephalized, typically with anterior eye-spots and chemoreceptive organs and a brain.

3. The third germ layer, mesoderm, is fully established and produces a mesenchymal parenchyma that fills the space between the epidermis and gastrodermis.

4. They have a synaptic nerve net of unipolar, bipolar, and multipolar neurons, tending to condense as longitudinal nerve trunks and a bilobed, anterior brain. While there is no morphological distinction between dendritic and axonic neuron endings, neurons are sometimes arranged to serve as definite sensory, associative, and motor neurons.

5. A system of protonephridial tubules with terminal flame bulbs is present.

6. A complex, typically hermaphroditic reproductive system appears in the members of the phylum.

7. Ova of primitive free-living forms undergo determinate, spiral cleavage. A special cell, the mesendoblast, is formed, from which both mesoderm and endoderm arises. This type of cleavage is characteristic of a number of the higher phyla.

The phylum is divided into three classes, with dissimilar features and habits. Although there are no definitely identified fossil flatworms, it may be assumed that the main classes diverged in the remote past.

Class Turbellaria. The free-living flatworms. Unsegmented flatworms, usually free living and aquatic, but including some epizoic, endozoic, and terrestrial species; adults with an epidermis, at least partially ciliated, and usually with inclusions known as rhabdoids; enteron present in all but the Acoela; life cycle simple.

Class Trematoda. The flukes. Epizoic or endozoic, unsegmented flatworms; adults without epidermis, rhabdoids, or external cilia; body covered by a cuticle; with one or more suckers for attachment to the host; with an enteron; life cycle simple or complex.

Class Cestoda. The tapeworms. Endozoic flatworms, usually composed of a number of segments known as proglottids; adults without an epidermis, rhabdoids, or external cilia; body covered with a cuticle; with attachment organs, typically at the anterior end; without a mouth or enteron; with hermaphroditic reproductive organs in each proglottid; life cycle complex.

Each class contains a bewildering array of species, often differing profoundly in adult form and larval or embryonic development. Flatworms are undoubtedly the most primitive Bilateria, and their diversity reflects the extensive evolutionary experimentation to be expected in primitive creatures suffering from metabolic limitations. It is by no means easy to create some order from the resulting chaos. Classification has been considerably modified in recent years, and not all agree on the best system to use.

Turbellaria—Free-Living Flatworms

All free-living flatworms are Turbellaria, but some Turbellaria live in or on aquatic hosts. Turbellaria are predominantly marine, although there is a considerable freshwater fauna, and a few live in moist, terrestrial habitats. They are about 0.5 mm. to 60 cm. long, with most less than 5 cm. Many are broad and leaf-shaped, and while some are nearly cylindrical, even these tend to be ventrally flattened. Freshwater species are white or uniformly dark-colored in most cases, but marine species have characteristic pigmentation, often bright in warm seas. *Dugesia tigrina* is the most common American species, and the larger *D. dorotocephala* is usually found in spring-fed waters. They are the most commonly studied species in student laboratories. The anatomy of *Dugesia* is summarized in Fig. 7.1, and should be examined carefully before undertaking a consideration of Turbellaria as a whole.

TURBELLARIAN CLASSIFICATION

Five types of Turbellaria can be recognized; they are usually considered as orders. In recent years a tendency to elevate suborders to orders has appeared, but for our purposes this can be ignored. Those interested should consult Hyman's discussion of classification in *Fresh-Water Biology* (1959). Some common examples are mentioned with the classification below; an examination of figures representing them will help to elucidate the classification.

Order Acoela. Small, marine worms with a mouth but no enteron, sometimes with a simple pharynx; without protonephridia; with a submuscular nerve plexus, concentrated anteriorly near a statocyst, and with a tendency to form longitudinal trunks; usually without eyes; without definite ovaries or testes, gametes being produced in the parenchyma; usually free

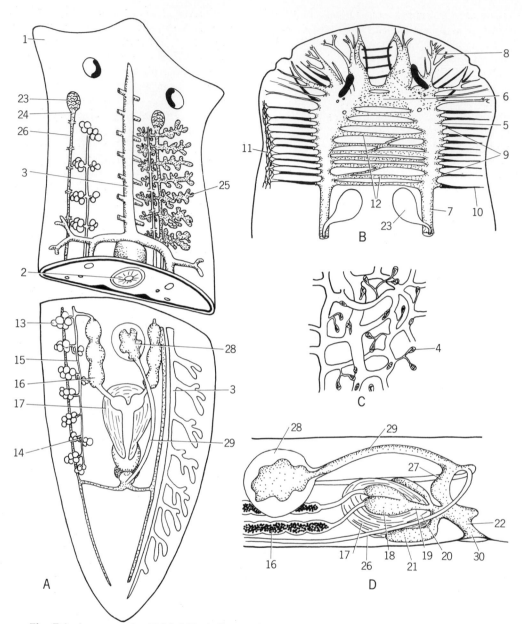

Fig. 7.1. Anatomy of a Triclad Turbellarian. **A.** Scheme of organ systems, based on *Dugesia*.
B. Brain and anterior part of the nervous system of *Dugesia*, with the ventral peripheral nerves
and commissures shown in black. **C.** A part of a protonephridial reticulum, produced by branching and anastomosing of primary and secondary longitudinal excretory canals. **D.** Copulatory
apparatus of *Dugesia tigrina*. (B, after Micoletzky. C, after Benham, from Hegner. D, after
Hyman, from Brown.) *Dugesia* is moderately cephalized, and has prominent eyespots as well
as sensory auricles (1) at the sides of the head. A cylindrical pharynx (2) lies in a pharyngeal
cavity, and can be protruded through the mouth (not shown). Food passes into the intestinal

186

swimming, occurring among algae and about rocks or in mud of the littoral zone; a few endozoic in echinoderms. Examples: *Childia* (Fig. 7.2A), *Convoluta* (Fig. 7.2B), *Polychoerus* (Fig. 7.2C).

Order Rhabdocoela. Small, fresh-water, and marine worms, with a saccate enteron lacking diverticula; a simple or bulbous pharynx and one or two protonephridial tubules; nervous system with bilobed brain and eight or ten longitudinal nerve trunks; oviducts present; usually with a complex, armed penis. There are four suborders. *Catenulida* have a simple pharynx, a ciliated gastrodermis, a single protonephridium, four pairs of longitudinal nerve trunks, and a dorsal male pore and unarmed penis. They are usually sexually immature and reproduce asexually. Examples: *Stenostumum* (Fig. 7.2D), *Catenula* (Fig. 7.2E). *Macrostomida* are marine and freshwater species, with simple pharynx, ciliated gastrodermis, one pair of longitudinal nerve trunks, paired protonephridia, and complete male and female systems with separate gonopores and no yolk glands.

Examples: *Macrostomum* (Fig. 7.2F), *Microstomum* (Fig. 7.2G). *Neorhabdocoela* are marine, fresh-water, or terrestrial, sometimes epizoic or endozoic rhabdocoels with a bulbous pharynx, two pairs of longitudinal nerve trunks, paired protonephridia, a germovitellarium producing ova and yolk cells or separate yolk glands; they do not reproduce asexually. A varied group. Examples: *Dalyellia* (Fig. 7.3B); *Paravortex*, parasitic on marine molluscs (Fig. 7.3A); *Typhloplana* (Fig. 7.3E); *Mesostoma*, (Fig. 7.3C); *Gyratrix* (Fig. 7.3D). *Temnocephalida* are small, flattened, epizoic worms with a posterior adhesive disc and usually with 5, 6, or 12 tentacles; they are tropical or subtropical. Example: *Temnocephala* (Fig. 7.4A).

Order Alloeocoela. Moderately sized worms, predominantly marine, with a simple, bulbous, or plicate pharynx and straight enteron, usually with some evidences of lateral diverticula; paired protonephridia often branched and with accessory nephridiopores; three to four pairs of longitudinal nerve trunks; often with ciliated pits,

trunks (3), of which there are three in triclads, one anterior trunk and paired posterior trunks (the left omitted for clarity). Each of the intestinal trunks opens into many lateral diverticula, shown only at the lower right. On each side of the body a protonephridial reticulum (C) occurs. It consists of several longitudinal trunks that branch and anastomose, opening to the exterior through a series of nephridiopores. The terminal branches end in flame bulbs (4) containing a tuft of cilia. The brain lies in the head region; it is composed of two cerebral ganglia (5) connected by a broad commissure (6). The ganglia are expansions of the paired ventral nerve trunks (7). Paired sensory nerves to the head (8) arise from the brain, and dorsal sensory nerves (9) arise from the nerve trunks. A series of ventral commissures (10) connect the nerve trunks with a delicate marginal nerve plexus (11). Dorsal commissures (12) connect the two nerve trunks. The many testes (13) are connected by delicate sperm ductules (14) to the main lateral sperm ducts (15) on each side of the body. The sperm ducts are dilated to form spermiducal vesicles (16), where sperm are stored prior to mating, and enter the penis bulb (17). Here they expand as bulbar cavities (18) and unite to form the ejaculatory duct (19), which opens at the tip of the muscular penis papilla (20). The penis papilla projects into the male antrum (21), which opens into the common genital antrum (22). The paired ovaries (23) empty into oviducts, expanded slightly near the ovary to form seminal receptacles (24), where sperm received during mating are eventually stored. Many yolk glands (25) are connected by yolk ductules to the oviduct, which is therefore termed the ovovitelline duct (26). The two ovovitelline ducts converge behind the female antrum (27), into which they open. The female antrum communicates with the common genital antrum. A saccate copulatory bursa (28) receives sperm at the time of mating. It is connected with the female antrum by a bursal canal (29), which functions as a vagina during mating. A common gonopore (30) serves both male and female systems.

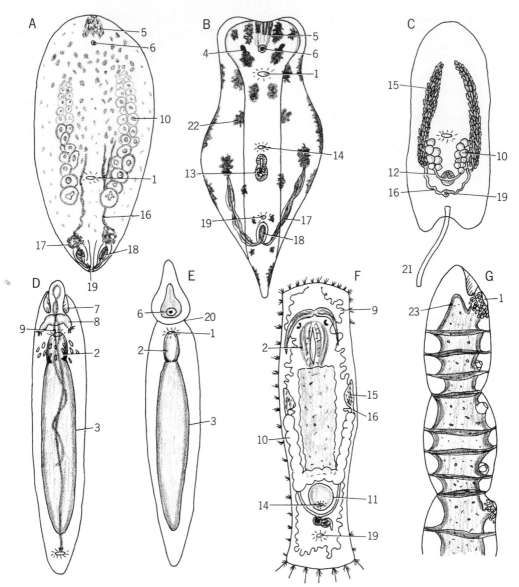

Fig. 7.2. Representative Acoels and Rhabdocoels. **A.** *Childia spinosa,* an acoel belonging to the family Proporidae, characterized by the absence of female gonoducts. **B.** *Convoluta,* an acoel belonging to the family Convolutidae, with at least one seminal bursa, a vagina, and a gonopore. **C.** *Polychoerus,* another convolutid acoel, with a caudal filament and pigment spots. **D.** *Stenostomum,* a rhabdocoel belonging to the suborder Catenulida, characterized by a simple pharynx, a single, median protonephridium, and no female gonoducts. Members of the family Stenostomidae have no circular groove in front of the mouth. **E.** *Catenula,* another catenulidan rhabdocoel. Members of the family Catenulidae have a circular groove around the body in front of the mouth. **F.** *Macrostomum appendiculatum,* a rhabdocoel belonging to the suborder Macrostomida, with a simple pharynx and complete male and female reproductive systems with separate gonopores. Members of the family Macrostomidae have no

188

cilated grooves, and caudal adhesive regions; usually with many testes and a penis papilla. There are three main suborders. *Lecithoepitheliata* usually have an armed penis and have no yolk glands. Example: *Prorhynchus* (Fig. 7.4F). *Holocoela* have a slightly lobulate enteron, an unarmed penis, and yolk glands more or less distinct from ovaries. Examples: *Pseudostomum* (Fig. 7.4B), *Plagiostomum* (Fig. 7.4D). *Seriata* have a plicate pharynx, and a distinctly lobulated enteron. They have many yolk glands and are found in marine and fresh-water habitats. Examples: *Monocelis* (Fig. 7.4C); *Otomesostoma* (Fig. 7.4E); *Bothrioplana* (Fig. 7.4G).

Order Tricladida. Moderate to large Turbellaria with a central to posterior mouth and plicate pharynx; enteron with one anterior and two posterior trunks and lateral diverticula; reticulate protonephridia and numerous nephridiopores; one pair of ovaries and separate yolk glands; many testes or one pair; a penis papilla and a single gonopore. There are three main suborders, associated with habitat. *Maricola* are marine triclads with enteric trunks having few diverticula and a bursa in variable positions. They attach ova to objects by narrow pedicels and do not reproduce asexually. They live in temperate to subpolar seas and prefer gravelly littoral or brackish habitats; some are epizoic. Examples: *Bdelloura*, which lives on the gills of horseshoe crabs (Fig. 7.5A); *Procerodes* (Fig. 7.5B). *Paludicola* are fresh-water triclads with a central mouth, a bursa anterior to the penis papilla, and a common gonopore; they often have anterior adhesive organs, and produce eggs in cocoons. They often reproduce asexually. Examples: *Dugesia* (Fig. 7.1); *Kenkia* (Fig. 7.5D); *Procotyla* (Fig. 7.5E). *Terricola* are terrestrial triclads, found in tropical to subtropical lands, with an elongate form, two to many eyes, without a bursa or with bursa behind penis; usually with separate male and female antra. Example: *Bipalium* (Fig. 7.5C).

Order Polycladida. Thin, often large, leaf-like, marine Turbellaria, with a many-branched enteron and plicate pharynx; many radiating nerve cords and usually with many eyes; many testes and ovaries and no yolk glands; usually dull but with some bright-colored species; some epizoic or associated with hermit crabs or molluscs. There are two suborders. *Acotylea* have no sucker behind the female gonopore and the eyes not in paired clusters; tentacles are marginal rather than nuchal if present. Example: *Stylochus* (Fig. 7.6A). *Cotylea* have a posterior glandulo-muscular disc, and tentacles are marginal when present; eyes are across the front end or in pairs of clusters in the tentacles or where tentacles would occur; pharynx ruffled or tubular; without a terminal bursa. They are characteristic of warmer waters. Examples: *Notoplana* (Fig. 7.6B); *Euryleptus* (Fig. 7.6C).

It will not be possible to introduce so many examples for all phyla. The examples shown are largely representative of dif-

preoral extension of the enteron. G. *Microstomum lineare*, a macrostomidan rhabdocoel belonging to the family Microstomidae, which have a preoral extension of the gut. Members of the Microstomidae often reproduce asexually to form chains of zooids. Several members of a chain are shown. Note the differentiating mouths, indicating the position of future zooids in the chain. (A-C, G, after von Graaf. F, after Ferguson.) *Digestive system:* 1, mouth; 2, pharynx; 3, enteron or intestine. *Sense organs:* 4, eyespot; 5, frontal organ; 6, statocyst; 7, ciliated pit. *Nervous system:* 8, brain. *Protonephridial system:* 9, protonephridial tubule. *Female reproductive system:* 10, ovary; 11, ovum; 12, oviduct; 13, bursa; 14, female gonopore. *Male reproductive system:* 15, testis; 16, sperm duct; 17, spermiducal vesicle; 18, penis; 19, male gonopore. *Other features:* 20, preoral groove; 21, caudal filament; 22, pigment spot; 23, preoral extension of coelenteron.

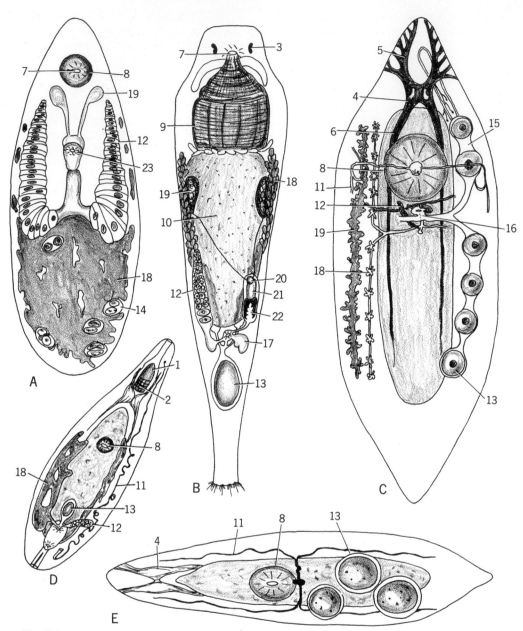

Fig. 7.3. Representative Rhabdocoels. A. *Paravortex gemellipara*, another dalyelloid rhabdocoel belonging to the family Graffidae, which lives in the mantle cavity and viscera of the salt-water clam, *Modiolus*. The family is characterized by the gonopore set well forward and the unarmed penis. B. *Dalyellia*, a rhabdocoel belonging to the Lecithophora, characterized by having one or two yolk glands that form yolk deposited in the capsule rather than in the ovum. Ova of the ectolecithal type are formed. The Lecithophora are divided into a number of groups. The dalyelloids include the Lecithophora with a doliiform pharynx. *Dalyellia* is the principal genus of the family Dalyellidae, which occur predominantly in fresh water and have

ferent families of the various orders and suborders, and have been assembled so that the nature of familial and ordinal traits can be seen. There is evidently room, even within the rather narrow specifications of orders and suborders, for considerable diversity of form.

Turbellarian Structure and Physiology

ANCESTRAL STOCKS

What kind of animals gave rise to the first flatworms? There have been several suggestions. The platyctene ctenophores (Fig. 6.30B) resemble polyclads in many ways. The idea that such creeping ctenophores gave rise to flatworms of the polyclad type was once very popular. The platyctene ctenophores are aberrant and highly specialized, and modern zoologists are inclined to look for plastic, generalized stocks, as they seem more likely to have the adaptive potential needed to establish new organizational patterns. The similarities between platyctene ctenophores and flatworms may be merely superficial, the result of convergence in animals exposed to somewhat similar selective pressures. The most persuasive idea is that flatworms developed from a planuloid ancestral stock, somewhat resembling the planula larvae of many Cni-

daria. This stock may have had flagellated or ciliated ancestors; in any case it came to have a ciliated epidermis and a mass of internal cells. The hypothetical ancestor probably had an apical sense organ like some Cnidaria, and according to Hyman (1951), had a subepidermal nerve net resembling the nerve net of Radiata, with some concentration near the sense organ. The mouth is thought to have developed from the blastopore, opposite the apical sense organ, so the oral-aboral axis corresponds to the functional anteroposterior axis of the planuloid. But the mouth is ventral in flatworms, and in this case must have migrated anteriorly, with a shift in the body axes. As a matter of fact, during embryonic development, just such a shift of axes can sometimes be demonstrated (Fig. 7.15G,H).

If this view of flatworm ancestry is correct, the planuloid ancestral stock probably diverged along two major lines, one leading to the Radiata and the other toward flatworms. It is not clear when the enteron first appeared. It may have developed independently in the cnidarian and flatworm lines; in this case the ancestral flatworm stocks may have been very like some of the modern Acoela. It may have appeared before the divergence of the two lines, in which case the lack of an enteron in Acoela may be the result of degeneration. What-

a penis with a complex armature. C. *Mesostoma*, representing a large genus of common freshwater rhabdocoels belonging to the subfamily Mesostominae, characterized by dorsal or lateral testes and protonephridia that open into the pharyngeal cavity. D. *Gyratrix hermaphroditicus*, a representative kalyptorhynchid lecithophoran. The kalyptorhynchids have a conspicuous glandulomuscular adhesive organ at the anterior end. E. *Typhloplana viridata*, a typhloplanoid lecithophoran. Typhloplanoids have a mouth more posteriorly located than the dalyelloids, a rosulate pharynx, and a common gonopore. Typhloplanidae is the largest family; it includes many fresh-water and terrestrial forms, and is divided into several subfamilies. *Typhloplana* belongs to the subfamily Typhloplaninae. (A, after Ball. B, after Ruebush and Hayes. C, after Ruebush, from Pennak. D, after von Graaf, from Edmondson. E, after Hyman.) *External features:* 1, end cone of proboscis; 2, muscular part of proboscis; 3, eyespot. *Nervous system:* 4, brain; 5, anterior sensory nerve; 6, ventral nerve trunk. *Gastrovascular system:* 7, mouth; 8, rosulate pharynx; 9, doliiform pharynx; 10, intestine. *Protonephridial system:* 11, protonephridium. *Female reproductive system:* 12, ovary; 13, ovum; 14, two ova in capsule; 15, uterus; 16, copulatory bursa; 17, seminal receptacle; 18, yolk gland. *Male reproductive system:* 19, testis; 20, seminal vesicle; 21, penis; 22, penis stylet; 23, common gonopore.

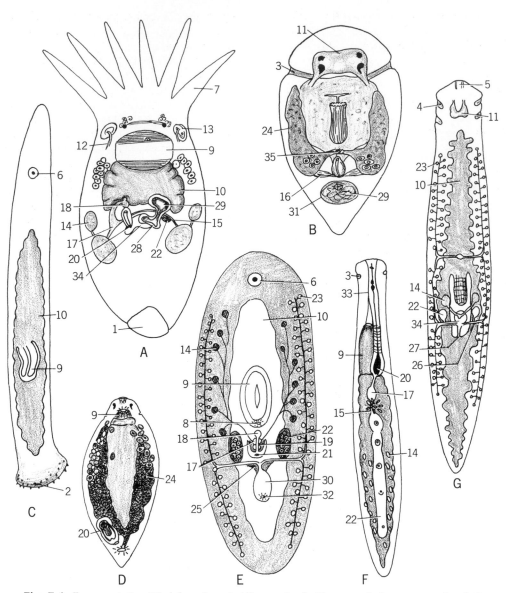

Fig. 7.4. Representative Rhabdocoels and Alloeocoels. **A.** *Temnocephala*, an example of the rhabdocoel suborder Temnocephalida. They are somewhat trematode-like, and live as ectocommensals on various fresh-water animals in tropical and subtropical habitats. The posterior adhesive disc and two to twelve tentacles are characteristic. **B.** *Pseudostomum*, an alloeocoel belonging to the suborder Holocoela, with yolk glands partially distinct, a simple or slightly lobulated intestine, and usually with an unarmed penis. **C.** *Monocelis*, an alloeocoel belonging to the suborder Seriata, characterized by an at least slightly lobulated intestine, yolk glands opening into yolk ducts, and a plicate pharynx. The family Monocelididae is characterized by statocysts and lateral or posterior adhesive papillae. **D.** *Plagiostomum wilsoni*, another member of the Holocoela, belonging to the family Plagiostomidae, with anterior mouth, bulbous pharynx, and posterior gonopore. It is a common marine and fresh-water genus.

ever happened in the ancient past, there çan be no doubt that the Acoela includes forms that are remarkably like what an ancestral planuloid stock should have been. They have a number of traits that appear to be primitive: 1) lack of protonephridia; 2) lack of definite gonads; 3) lack of gonoducts; and 4) a very simple nervous system of the plexus type.

ACQUISITION AND DIGESTION OF FOOD

Many Turbellaria contain zoochlorella, and some are said to subsist entirely by digesting their symbiotic partners if necessary, but feeding is a major problem in most Turbellaria. A few take in some plant material, but the majority are strict carnivores. Feeding habits have undoubtedly influenced sense organ development. Efficient chemoreceptors are sensitive to meat juices, and rheoreceptors enable some to detect nearby prey by water disturbances.

Food capture is not a simple matter. Organs are needed to grasp the prey. Whorls of tentacles are suitable for sessile or floating animals, but not for actively moving forms. The flatworms can be said to have invented the first tools suited to active, predaceous animals. Capturing organs are built of gland cells, sometimes with the aid of muscle fibers. Two kinds of

glands are available: cyanophilous glands, which secrete slime, and eosinophilous glands, which secrete adhesive substances. Frontal glands, formed of slime cells and sensory cells, are found in acoels and some alloeocoels and may be seen in representatives shown in Figs. 7.2 and 7.4. Glandulo-epidermal adhesive organs are formed only of adhesive glands and modified epidermis, without muscles. The marginal adhesive zone of triclads is an organ of this kind. Caudal adhesive areas are often found, consisting primarily of eosinophilous glands; they project individually or form adhesive papillae. These parts, not used directly in food handling, enable the animal to cling to the substrate, often an important act during food capture but more important in movement. Glandulo-muscular adhesive organs include special musculature in addition to adhesive glands. The muscles are often arranged in a sucker-like pattern (Fig. 7.7A), but true suckers, sharply set off from the parenchyma, are very uncommon in Turbellaria. In a few Turbellaria, the glandulo-muscular organ is developed into a grasping proboscis, as in *Kenkia* (Fig. 7.5D).

Prey is grasped by the pharynx and adhesive organs, and a quiet but desperate battle begins. The worm clings to the substrate with whatever equipment it may

E. *Otomesostoma auditivum*, another member of the Seriata, but belonging to the family Otomesostomidae, characterized by the presence of a statocyst and the absence of adhesive papillae. F. *Prorhynchus stagnalis*, an alloeocoel of the suborder Lecithoepitheliata, characterized by the simple oviduct and the absence of yolk glands. *Prorhynchus* is a member of the Prorhynchidae, which have the male reproductive system opening into the buccal cavity. G. *Bothrioplana semperi*, also belonging to Seriata but to the family Bothrioplanidae, which have two ciliated pits, adhesive papillae, but no statocyst. The intestine of *Bothrioplana* approaches the triclad condition. (A, after Haswell. B,D,F, after von Graaf. C, after Hyman. E, after Bresslau.) *External features:* 1, adhesive disc; 2, adhesive papilla; 3, ciliated groove; 4, ciliated pit; 5, frontal organ; 6, statocyst; 7, tentacle. *Gastrovascular system:* 8, mouth; 9, pharynx; 10, intestine. *Nervous system:* 11, brain. *Protonephridial system:* 12, protonephridium; 13, excretory ampulla. *Male reproductive system:* 14, testis; 15, sperm duct; 16, spermiducal vesicle; 17, seminal vesicle; 18, prostatic vesicle; 19, penis; 20, penis stylet; 21, male gonopore. *Female reproductive system:* 22, ovary; 23, yolk gland; 24, germovitellarium; 25, shell gland; 26, oviduct; 27, genitointestinal canal; 28, uterus; 29, bursa; 30, female antrum; 31, bursal pore; 32, female gonopore; 33, buccogenital canal; 34, common genital antrum; 35, common gonopore.

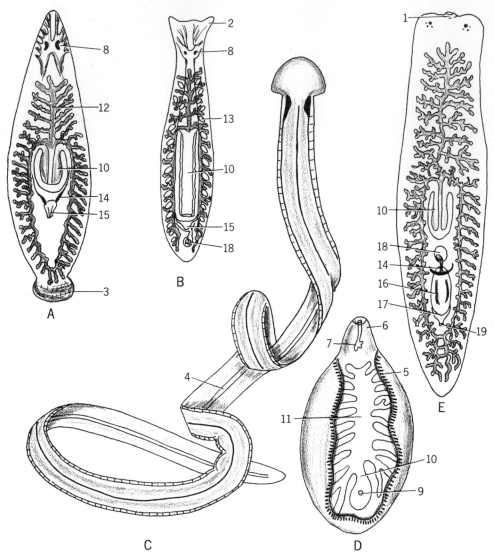

Fig. 7.5. Representative Triclads. Triclads are divided into three suborders, Maricola, Paludicola, and Terricola. Maricola have no bursa or have one or two bursae behind the penis or have a separate bursal pore; they are marine. Paludicola live in fresh water, can reproduce asexually, and have a bursa in front of the penis, connected to the female antrum by a long copulatory canal, as in *Dugesia* (Fig. 7.1). Terricola are terrestrial triclads, of elongate form, and have no bursa, or if a bursa is present, have it located behind the penis. A. *Bdelloura candida* is a maricolan that lives on the surface of *Xiphosura*, the horseshoe crab, and has a posterior adhesive disc for attachment to its host. B. *Procerodes littoralis*, a free-living maricolan triclad. C. *Bipalium kewense*, a terricolan triclad of elongated shape and with many eyes. D. *Kenkia rhynchida*, a paludicolan triclad of the family Kenkiidae, which includes cave-dwelling forms with a snout-like anterior glandulo-adhesive organ. E. *Procotyla fluviatilis*, a paludicolan belonging to the family Dendrocoelidae, which are usually white and have a cen-

have and secretes mucus and an adhesive substance to entangle and immobilize the prey. The prey tries to pull away. It is an all-out struggle, with no holds barred; even the penis armature is sometimes used to injure the prey. The prey is usually swallowed whole, but species with a tubular pharynx sometimes thrust the pharynx into the tissue and secrete proteolytic enzymes, softening the tissue for ingestion, and some species with a bulbous pharynx also ingest small tissue fragments. *Stylochus* avoids the struggle, nipping off small bits of oyster tissue as it moves about within the shell.

Some Acoela have only a mouth. Food goes directly into the parenchyma, where it is phagocytized by parenchymal cells and digested. This is probably the primitive method of ingestion and digestion.

Generally, however, an embryonic stomodaeum produces a pharynx, lined with cells derived from ectoderm, and a pharyngeal cavity between the mouth and the pharynx. The round or slit-shaped mouth appears at the site of the blastopore. It may occur anywhere on the midventral surface but is usually in the middle three-quarters of the body. Modified subepidermal muscles open and close the mouth.

Flatworms have developed three types of pharynx construction: simple, bulbous, and plicate. A simple pharynx is merely a short length of invaginated epidermis, without specialized musculature (Fig. 7.7C). It is found in acoels and in some rhabdocoels and alloeocoels. A bulbous pharynx contains special muscles, and a thin-walled pharyngeal cavity lies between the mouth and pharynx. A bulbous pharynx may be rosulate, doliiform, or variable. The spherical rosulate pharynx is set at right angles to the main body axis and is richly supplied with gland cells (Fig. 7.7D). The doliiform pharynx is cask-shaped, and lies parallel to the body axis (Fig. 7.3B). The circular and longitudinal muscles form a lattice which is often conspicuous. A variable pharynx is a modification of the doliiform, with modified muscle layers and a variable shape. Many rhabdocoels and some alloeocoels have a bulbous pharynx. A plicate pharynx is a fold of the body wall, projecting into the pharyngeal cavity. In its simplest form, it is a tubular part, as in *Dugesia* (Fig. 7.1). The plicate pharynx lies in a pharyngeal cavity lined with epidermis and is itself covered with epidermis (Fig. 7.7E,F). The plicate pharynx of many polyclads is a ruffled curtain, hanging from the roof of the pharyngeal cavity. The plicate pharynx, and sometimes the bulbous, is thrust through the mouth opening during feeding, and food enters through the pharyngeal opening. The histological construction of a plicate pharynx is complex (Fig. 7.7B). It is richly supplied with nerves, and its control is largely intrinsic. A detached pharynx can move about and will sometimes ingest food. A curious multiplication of the pharynx is seen in some planarians. More than one pharynx (polypharyngy) may be present in the pharyngeal cavity, and sometimes there are several mouths. The pharynx always opens directly into the main gut.

The main enteric cavity, usually termed the intestine, is the site of digestion and absorption. Turbellaria are partly subdivided on the basis of intestinal form. Acoels have no intestine. Rhabdocoels have a saccate or tubular intestine without diverticula. Alloeocoels have lateral diverticula, which vary in distinctness. Triclads have three main intestinal trunks, and polyclads have many. The main trunks of

tral adhesive organ. (All after Hyman.) *External features:* **1,** adhesive organ; **2,** auricle; **3,** caudal adhesive disc; **4,** creeping sole; **5,** rhabdite margin; **6,** snout; **7,** snout glands. *Internal organs:* **8,** brain; **9,** mouth; **10,** pharynx; **11,** prepharyngeal intestine; **12,** intestine. *Reproductive system:* **13,** testis; **14,** sperm duct; **15,** penis; **16,** penis bulb; **17,** penis papilla; **18,** copulatory bursa; **19,** gonopore.

triclads and polyclads usually branch extensively.

Tall gastrodermal cells, ciliated in some rhabdocoels and polyclads, line the intestine. Digestion occurs as in Radiata. Preliminary digestion occurs in the intestinal lumen, and precedes the final, intracellular phase of digestion. The relative importance of extracellular and intracellular phases probably differs, with flatworms having a ciliated gastrodermis more dependent on extracellular digestion. *Dugesia* fed beef liver after a period of starvation ingests small bits of tissue rapidly. About

an hour is needed to fill the intestinal diverticula. Food vacuole formation begins promptly, with little evidence of preliminary digestion. Gastrodermal cells imbibe water and swell, becoming syncytial. Food vacuoles become dense masses of protein material during the first eight hours and disappear slowly during the next five days, presumably as the result of proteolytic digestion. A different pattern is seen in *Leptoplana*, a polyclad with a ruffled, plicate pharynx. The pharynx clings tightly to prey, and pharyngeal secretions induce preliminary digestion outside of the body.

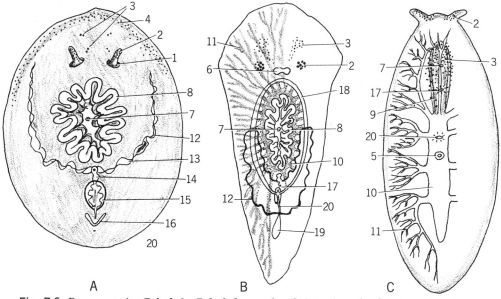

Fig. 7.6. Representative Polyclads. Polyclads are classified in the suborder Acotylea, without an adhesive organ behind the female gonopore and with tentacles in the nuchal region when present, and in the suborder Cotylea, with an adhesive organ behind the female gonopore and with marginal tentacles containing eyes or clusters of eyes in their place. A. *Stylochus ellipticus*, a common acotylean polyclad belonging to the section Craspedommata, which have a band of marginal eyes in addition to cerebral and tentacular clusters of eyes. B. *Notoplana atomata*, a common acotylean polyclad belonging to the section Schematommata, which lack marginal eyes and have four clusters of eyes near the brain. C. A euryleptid polyclad belonging to the suborder Cotylea, with a sucker-like glandulomuscular adhesive organ behind the female gonopore and marginal tentacles with eyes. (After Hyman.) *External features:* 1, tentacle; 2, tentacular eyes; 3, cerebral eyes; 4, marginal eyes; 5, adhesive disc. *Internal features:* 6, brain; 7, mouth; 8, ruffled plicate pharynx; 9, tubular plicate pharynx; 10, intestine; 11, intestinal diverticula. *Male reproductive system:* 12, sperm duct; 13, spermiducal vesicle; 14, seminal vesicle; 15, prostatic vesicle; 16, penis papilla; 17, male gonopore. *Female reproductive system:* 18, oviduct; 19, seminal bursa; 20, female gonopore.

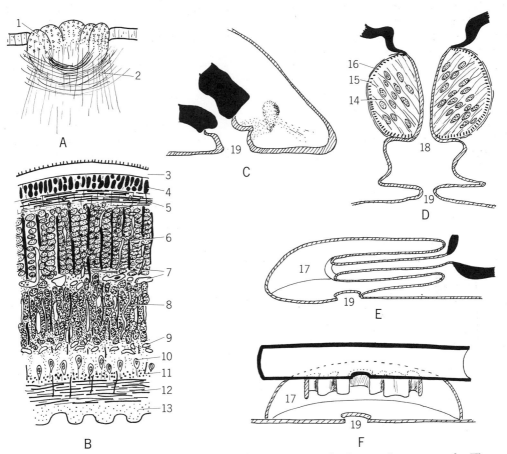

Fig. 7.7. Turbellarian glandulomuscular adhesive organ and pharyngeal structure. **A.** The glandulomuscular organ of *Procotyla*, in ventral view. The muscles are not cut off from the body by a septum as in a true sucker. **B.** Segment of a cross section through the pharynx of *Dugesia*, showing the component layers of tissue. **C-F.** Scheme of the structure of the various types of pharynx seen in Turbellaria. **C**, simple pharynx; **D**, rosulate pharynx; **E**, cylindrical plicate pharynx; **F**, ruffled plicate pharynx. The gastrodermis, shown in black, does not enter into pharynx formation. A simple pharynx is a non-muscular chamber. A rosulate pharynx is muscular, and is preceded by a pharyngeal cavity that opens at the mouth. A plicate pharynx is an extension of the body wall, containing muscle and other elements. It is extensible, and is thrust through the mouth opening during feeding. (**A-D**, after Hyman.) **1**, adhesive gland; **2**, muscle fibers of glandulomuscular organ; **3**, outer epidermis, composed of the tips of insunk cells; **4**, outer longitudinal muscle layer; **5**, outer circular muscle layer; **6**, cyanophilous glands; **7**, main nerve plexus; **8**, eosinophilous glands; **9**, inner nerve plexus; **10**, nuclei of insunk epithelium; **11**, inner layer of longitudinal muscles; **12**, inner layer of circular muscles; **13**, inner insunk epithelium; **14**, radial muscle; **15**, longitudinal muscle of rosulate pharynx; **16**, circular muscle of rosulate pharynx; **17**, pharyngeal cavity; **18**, protonephridium joining the pharyngeal cavity at the excretory beaker; **19**, mouth.

197

Softened tissues are ingested and appear to be completely reduced in the intestine, the gastrodermal cells absorbing the end products. Parenchymal muscles force the intestinal contents out to the tips of the diverticula and back to the main intestinal trunk repeatedly, presumably hastening food fragmentation and absorption. Proteases and lipases have been recovered from several Turbellaria. Until recently there has been no evidence of carbohydrate digestion, but Jennings (1957) reports that triclads can digest starch.

RESPIRATION

Turbellarian energy release appears to be predominantly aerobic, with few peculiarities. It is largely cyanide-sensitive. This indicates that a Warburg-Keilin system is involved in which, after dehydrogenation, hydrogen is transferred by a cytochrome-oxidase system to the final hydrogen acceptor, oxygen. A small cyanide-resistant fraction is probably maintained by iron-free oxidases.

No special organs for respiratory exchange or transport occur. The epidermal cilia ventilate the body surface, and undoubtedly improve the rate of absorption. Haemoglobin has been reported from a few rhabdocoels, but is not widely distributed. Available evidence, on the whole, supports the idea that for lack of a more effective system of respiratory exchange and transport, the respiratory requirements of internal cells are a critical limiting factor, favoring small size and a flattened shape.

EXCRETION

All but the acoels have a protonephridial system, consisting of protonepridial tubules and terminal flame bulbs. Each tubule is lined with flattened to cuboid epithelium. Capillary branches with terminal flame bulbs (Fig. 7.8A) are attached to the tubules, so that the tubule is closed off at the end. Each flame bulb lies in a cell known as a flame cell, but in some cases a single cell contains several flames. Systems with few flame bulbs may have lateral flames (Fig. 7.8B) on the walls of the protonephridia. The contents of the tubule are discharged through a nephridiopore. The protonephridial system tends to vary in complexity among the orders. Acoels lack protonephridia. Rhabdocoels have one or two recurved protonephridia. Larger alloeocoels often have two or three protonephridia on each side, with accessory nephridiopores. Triclads have the most complex system. As many as four protonephridia on each side branch and anastomose to form a protonephridial reticulum, with numerous nephridiopores (Fig. 7.1C).

The protonephridial system is poorly developed in marine species and highly developed in fresh-water forms. Accumulation of water in *Stenostomum* tissues evokes formation of new flame bulbs, and in blood flukes, flame bulbs inactive when the animal is in urine become active with dilution of the urine. Protonephridia evidently serve to discharge excess water. Little is known of their importance in excretion. Acoels, which have no protonephridia, take up vital dyes in mesenchymal cells and discharge them through the mouth. Vital dyes have given inconsistent results when applied to Turbellaria with protonephridia. Dye sometimes accumulates along the tubule walls, but does not enter through the flame bulbs. Some species have large cells (athrocytes) wrapped around the protonephridial tubules, which take up dyes (Fig. 7.8C). The evidence suggests that protonephridia may serve to discharge wastes, but that tubule walls and athrocytes are the primary sites of excretion. It is reasonable to suppose that flatworms, like other aquatic invertebrates, are ammonotelic. Proteins can be stored as fats, indicating that deamination takes place. Ammonia formation would be a probable result.

The mechanics of the flame-cell system are not understood. Flame-bulb cilia circulate the fluid in the tubules, perhaps influencing the rate of entry of substances through the wall. They do not evacuate the fluid; the tubules are emptied by peristaltic movements resulting from muscles adjacent to the wall.

PARENCHYMA AND INTERNAL TRANSPORT

The mesodermal parenchyma around the internal organs is characteristic of acoelomates. The parenchyma is composed of closely packed, discrete cells in some small Turbellaria, but is usually a spongy, syncytial network, with many fluid-filled spaces (Fig. 7.9A). Discrete cells are scattered about in the syncytium. These free parenchymal cells are amoeboid; they gather at a wound and contribute heavily to regenerative processes and also play an important part in the formation of reproductive organs. They are probably somewhat equivalent to the interstitial cells of Radiata.

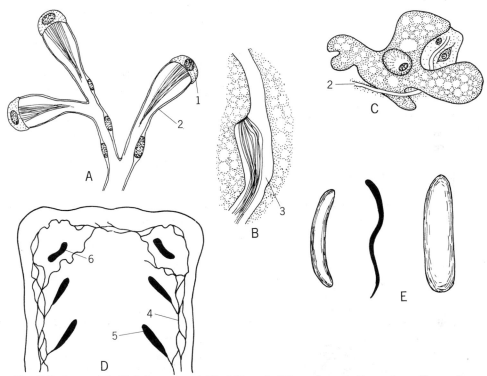

Fig. 7.8. Protonephridial System and Rhabdites. A. Three flame bulbs and capillary tubes. Note that the upper end of each tubule is completely closed off by the flame bulbs, characteristic of protonephridia. B. A lateral flame of *Mesostoma* located in a main protonephridial tubule. Lateral flames agitate the fluid in the tubule where relatively few flame bulbs occur in the system. C. An athrocyte of *Rhynchomesostoma* around a protonephridial capillary. These cells probably pick up wastes and deposit them in the tubule. D. Part of the protonephridial reticulum of *Dendrocoelum*, somewhat magnified in relation to body size, showing a part of the protonephridial reticulum in the head region, and several lateral branches to accessory nephridiopores. E. Shapes of rhabdites. An ordinary rhabdite is shown at the left, a rhammite in the center, and a chondrocyst on the right. (A, after Pennak. B-C, after Luther. D, after Wilhelmi. E, after Hyman.) 1, flame bulb; 2, capillary tubule; 3, main protonephridial tubule; 4, protonephridial reticulum; 5, accessory nephridiopore; 6, eye.

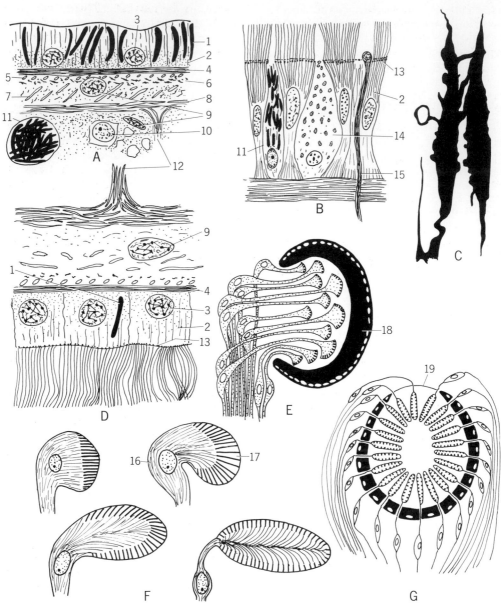

Fig. 7.9. Turbellarian Histology. **A.** Longitudinal section through the dorsal epidermis and subepidermal musculature of a fresh-water planarian. **B.** Longitudinal section through the epidermis of a polyclad. **C.** Part of the subepidermal longitudinal muscle fibers of a planarian. Note the bulge containing a nucleus on the fiber on the left. **D.** Longitudinal section through the ventral surface of a fresh-water planarian. **E.** Scheme of an inverse pigment cup ocellus as seen in a planarian. In an ocellus of this type the sensory cells enter through the open side of the cup, and the sensory tips extend toward the floor of the cup. **F.** Four stages in the evolution of the retinal club, showing the rod border spreading over the tip of the retinal cell and the migration of the nucleus away from the sensory tip. **G.** Scheme of a converse pigment cup

Parenchymal tissue fluid is circulated as muscular body movements squeeze the parenchyma, and it aids in internal transport. Protoplasmic continuity of the parenchymal syncytium may help to distribute substances held in the cytoplasm. The transport of materials is poorly provided for, however, and internal transport remains a major physiological weakness.

LOCOMOTION AND MOVEMENT

Small Turbellaria, a half a millimeter or so long, flash across a microscope field like large ciliates, leaving an entirely different impression than large worms like *Dugesia*. Muscles contribute little to the movement of small species. Moving a large animal with cilia is rather like rowing an ocean liner. Wriggling movements become more important, and such large forms as the land planarians look superficially like earthworms as they move. Yet ciliary movement is never abandoned by Turbellaria, and muscles are never fully exploited. The most effective muscular locomotor organ in the phylum is the cercarial tail, occurring in larval trematodes devoid of epidermis and external cilia (see p. 223).

Small or primitive species have uniform ciliation. Larger species, and especially terrestrial species, have strong ventral cilia and weak or no dorsal cilia. Large Turbellaria have many cyanophilous glands on the ventral surface. Slime secretions lubricate the surface, increase water viscosity, and provide resistance against which the cilia can thrust. Many species cannot move without leaving a slime trail. *Dugesia* uses its marginal adhesive zone to keep in contact with the substrate. When slime accumulates ventrally it can move effectively. Epidermal and subepidermal glands also form rhabdoids (Figs. 7.8E; 7.9A,B). Rhabdoids differ in form in different species, but appear in all cases to be firm secretions that dissolve rapidly when extruded. They probably do not contribute to movement, but serve to protect against irritating chemicals.

Some acoels have muscle fibers at the base of epidermal cells, as in Cnidaria. Otherwise, flatworm muscle arises from mesoderm. In this sense, it is the "new" muscle, used so effectively in higher invertebrates and vertebrates. It has a relatively simple structure in most flatworms. The elongated muscle cells have a persistent myoblast which clings to the surface and encloses the nucleus (Fig. 7.9C). Muscle fibers are usually unstriated, and patterns of striae are simple when present. Medusae depend more on muscles for movement than most flatworms, and many have more highly developed muscle tissue than flatworms.

Muscle fibers form layers below the epidermis and pass through the parenchyma. Subepidermal muscle usually consists of outer circular and inner longitudinal layers, separated by a few to many diagonal fibers (Fig. 7.9A,D). Small species have delicate muscles; larger species have conspicuous muscles, sometimes with additional layers. Land planarians have conspicuous bundles of longitudinal muscles. Pharynx muscles are modified subepidermal muscle. Parenchymal muscles are extremely variable. Large species may have interlacing patterns of transverse, longitudinal, dorsoventral,

ocellus, as seen in land planarians. In an ocellus of this type the retinal cells pierce the wall of the pigment cup and extend toward the opening. (A and D, after Hyman. B, after Pock. C, after Gelei. E, after Bresslau, in Kükenthal and Krumbach. F, after Hofsten. G, after Hesse.) 1, rhabdite; 2, epidermis; 3, epidermal nuclei; 4, basement membrane; 5, circular muscle; 6, pigment; 7, diagonal muscle; 8, longitudinal muscle; 9, fixed mesenchymal nucleus; 10, free mesenchymal cell; 11, gland cell forming rhabdites; 12, parenchymal muscle; 13, basal bodies of cilia; 14, mucous gland cells; 15, neck of mesenchymal gland cell; 16, main cell body of retinal cell; 17, retinal club; 18, pigment cup; 19, cornea.

and diagonal fibers passing through the parenchyma.

SENSE ORGANS

Flatworm organization is not suitable for a dramatic development of sense organs, but active locomotion and an anterior-posterior axis have favored some progressive changes. Some cephalization is apparent, and the widespread occurrence of light-sensitive organs indicates their greater importance in flatworms than in cnidarians. Receptors sensitive to chemicals, currents, and touch are somewhat more highly organized than in Radiata.

Photoreception. A simple pigment-spot ocellus is the primitive light-sensitive organ in flatworms, but occurs only in a few acoels and rhabdocoels. Most flatworm eyes are pigment cup ocelli. Animals may have inverse eyes, with the retina turned away from the light, or converse eyes, with the retina turned toward the light. Both types of eyes are found among flatworms (Fig. 7.9E,G). The most common type of eyes is the inverse pigment cup, like the *Dugesia* eye, with retinal cells entering the open side of the pigment cup, and ending in a light-sensitive, striated border at the bottom of the cup. Land planarians have complex eyes of the converse type, with the retinal cells passing through the pigment cup wall. These eyes have an epidermal cornea, and might be capable of forming a vague image.

Flatworm photoreceptors are neurosensory cells. They contain a light-sensitive striated border and a process extending to the nervous system or a ganglion. A tendency to increase the area of the light-sensitive striated part of the cell, and to separate it from the nucleus can be seen in flatworms (Fig. 7.9F). When the nucleus lies outside of the light-sensitive region, the striated border tends to be differentiated as a retinal club, as in the eye of land planarians.

Many Turbellaria are negatively topotactic to light. The pigment cup provides unilateral shading, and so confers a direction sense. However, in *Dugesia* the retinal cells must be parallel to light rays to be stimulated, providing a mechanism for precise orientation to light. If all eye-spots are removed, planarians select a dark background and eventually find the least highly illuminated region available. The choice of backgrounds is phobotactic, depending on random movement rather than oriented response. Evidently a dermotropic light sense is also operating.

Chemoreception. Chemoreceptors are important in food recognition. Several kinds of chemoreceptive organs are found in Turbellaria. The frontal organs of acoels and some rhabdocoels are formed of slime cells and chemoreceptive cells. Most chemoreceptors are ciliated pits or grooves containing glandular and chemoreceptive cells. Chemoreceptors of this type are common among flatworms; the ciliated auricular grooves at the base of planarian auricles are examples. Cilia circulate water over the chemoreceptive cells, presumably helping to give a directional sense. Each chemoreceptor has one or several bristles. Near the brain, chemoreceptors are elongated to form a sensory nerve (Fig. 7.10). Marginal chemoreceptors form a sensory epithelium with a ganglion at the base; the sensory nerve arises from the ganglion.

Planaria give highly positive, oriented responses to meat juices and snail blood, and can be led about with blood in capillary tubes. The animal lifts its head and swings it to face directly toward the stimulus and moves directly toward it. Orientation is dependent on equal stimulation of the auricular sense organs, for if one auricle is removed, the animal turns continuously toward the intact auricle when in the presence of meat juices.

Touch Reception. Tactile cells are abundant throughout the body surface. They are somewhat concentrated anteriorly and sometimes cluster together to form definite tactile organs, as in the auricles of planarians. Touch receptors are neurosensory cells with one or more bristles protruding through or between epidermal cells, and with processes extending to the nerve trunks or brain (Fig. 7.10).

Turbellaria usually respond negatively to strong and positively to weak mechanical stimuli. The positive response of some species is destroyed with the brain. Planarians have a negatively thigmotactic dorsal surface and a positively thigmotactic ventral surface. When turned over, they right themselves by twisting the body. When the ventral tactile cells of the head touch the substrate, the worm moves off. This reaction is not dependent on gravity but on loss of contact at the ventral surface. It occurs, more slowly, in planarian pieces without a brain. It is an adaptive response, as contact with the substrate is important in locomotion.

Rheoreception. Rheoreceptive cells have been identified in some rhabdocoels. They are large cells, with sensory bristles projecting beyond the epidermis. In *Mesostoma*, they occur along the sides of the body (Fig. 7.10).

Rheoreceptors are probably widespread in Turbellaria, and may aid in food capture. Oriented responses to water currents are common in animals from lotic (running water) environments but usually lacking in animals from still water. Lotic flatworms usually move upstream in weak currents and grasp the substrate in strong currents. Acclimatization in a current develops definite responses in some species that are normally indifferent to currents.

Reactions to Gravity. Many acoels, some rhabdocoels, and a few alloeocoels have statocysts. Their distribution suggests that they are primitive structures. When present, a single, median statocyst lies near the brain. Hyman (1951) suggests that the accumulation of nerve tissue near the statocyst may have initiated brain formation in primitive flatworms. Flatworm statocysts are built like cnidarian statocysts. Each contains a large cavity, within which a lithocyte containing one or several statoliths is found.

Orientation to gravity is not important to many flatworms, for they right themselves by thigmotactic responses. Flatworms with statocysts respond positively when oxygen is abundant, collecting at the bottom of a container. As oxygen levels fall they react negatively, swimming to the surface. Apparently orientation to gravity is used to bring the animal to oxygen when oxygen supplies are limited.

NERVOUS SYSTEM

Evolutionary trends first seen in flatworms establish a general pattern retained in the nervous systems of the higher invertebrates on the annelid-arthropod stem. Factors associated with the development of the nervous system are 1) cephalization; 2) more abundant and more highly specialized sensory cells; 3) a more varied and more complex muscle system; and 4) demands associated with higher integration in actively moving animals.

Of all the Turbellarians acoels have the most primitive nervous system, consisting of a nerve plexus between the epidermis and the subepidermal muscle. It is located as in Cnidaria, perhaps reflecting relation-

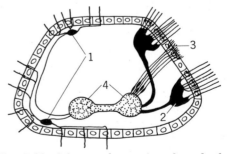

Fig. 7.10. Scheme of a section through the head of *Mesostoma*, showing the relationship of the neurosensory cells and brain (after Gelei.) Tangoreceptors (1) are shown on the left and rheoreceptors (2) and chemoreceptors (3) on the right, with the connections to the brain (4).

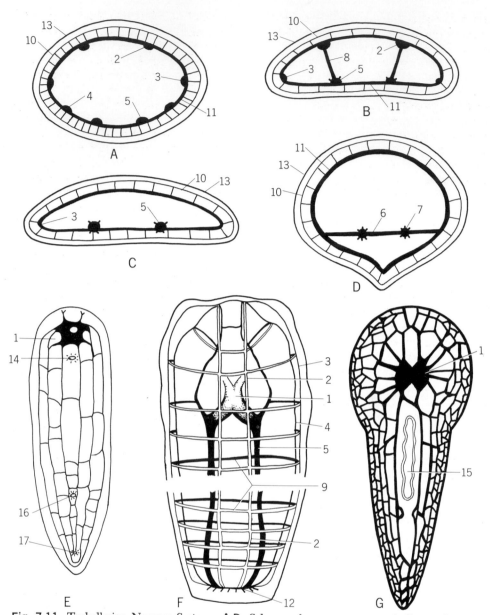

Fig. 7.11. Turbellarian Nervous Systems. A-D. Scheme of nervous system of alloeocoels and triclads, showing the relationship of nerve trunks and plexi. A, alloeocoel; B, marine triclad; C, fresh-water triclad; D, land triclad. E. The nervous system of an acoel, *Convoluta*, showing the anterior concentration of the nerve plexus (brain) around the statocyst, and the tendency toward the formation of longitudinal trunks. F. Anterior and posterior ends of the nervous system of *Bothrioplana*, an alloeocoel, with the ventral elements darkened and the dorsal elements unshaded. G. The ventral, submuscular nerve plexus of a polyclad, *Gnesioceros*, showing the tendencies toward a radial arrangement of trunks. (A-D, G, after Hyman. E, after Bresslau, in Kükenthal and Krumbach. F, based on Reissinger.) **1,** brain; **2,** dorsal nerve cord;

ships with ancestral planuloids. The plexus is concentrated anteriorly near the statocyst, and thins out posteriorly to form a diffuse nerve net with vaguely defined longitudinal trunks (Fig. 7.11A). It differs from the cnidarian pattern in the ill-defined longitudinal trunks and in the nerve center around the statocyst.

The main nervous layer of other flatworms is the submuscular plexus beneath the subepidermal muscle, although a delicate subepidermal plexus may be present. The brain is a typically bilobed ganglionic mass, sometimes associated with a statocyst but more often associated with a pair of ventral longitudinal nerve trunks. The plexus tends to be concentrated to form serially arranged ring commissures between the longitudinal trunks. More highly specialized flatworms tend to have a simplified system with fewer longitudinal trunks.

Most acoels have a submuscular nerve plexus, consisting of a fine and coarse net. Five pairs of longitudinal strands can be recognized, the dorsal, dorsolateral, marginal, ventrolateral, and ventral trunks (Fig. 7.11A,E). Meshes of the plexus connect the trunks, and a brain surrounds the statocyst. The marginal trunk is sometimes missing, leaving a total of eight longitudinal trunks, creating what is probably a superficial resemblance to the eight strands associated with the ctenophore comb rows.

The bilobed polyclad brain is enclosed in a capsule, and bilateral but somewhat radially arranged nerve trunks arise from it (Fig. 7.11G). Two nerve trunks paralleling the pharynx may be homologous with the ventral nerve trunks of other Turbellaria. All nerve trunks lie in the submuscular plexus. A delicate subepidermal plexus is also present. The somewhat

biradial nerve trunks have been cited as evidence that polyclads are primitive. According to this view, acoels are degenerate and the first flatworms developed from radiate ancestral stocks. This view has been less popular in recent times. Certainly the arrangement of the polyclad nerve and intestinal trunks may be associated with the broad, leaf-like body shape, having no phylogenetic importance.

In all other Turbellaria, the nervous system is strongly bilateral and has little resemblance to nervous systems of Radiata. Primitive alloeocoels have four pairs of longitudinal nerve trunks, the dorsal, lateral, ventrolateral, and ventral, connected by commissures that tend to form rings around the body (Fig. 7.11C,D). Connections between the main tracts occur in the general submuscular plexus. Rhabdocoels show evidences of retrogressive changes. Some have the four pairs of longitudinal trunks found in primitive alloeocoels, but most have only two ventral nerve trunks, with few lateral branches or commissures.

The plexus, commissure, and longitudinal trunk system are simplified in more highly developed alloeocoels. Most alloeocoels, like marine triclads, have only three longitudinal trunks, the ventrolaterals having disappeared (Fig. 7.11E). Only a few fresh-water triclads have dorsal nerve trunks, and the marginal trunks are reduced to little more than the sharply bent edges of the submuscular plexus. As a result, only two nerve trunks remain. The commissural rings found in other Turbellaria become a ladder-like set of medial commissures and peripheral connections with the margin, where the lateral trunks were originally located (Figs. 7.1B; 7.11F). A more or less delicate subepidermal plexus is also present.

3, marginal nerve cord; 4, ventrolateral nerve cord; 5, ventral nerve cord; 6, ventral nerve plate; 7, nerve trunks; 8, commissure between dorsal and ventral nerve cords; 9, ring commissure; 10, subepidermal nerve plexus; 11, submuscular nerve plexus; 12, terminal fusion; 13, epidermis; 14, mouth; 15, pharynx; 16, bursal pore; 17, male gonopore.

The most complex brain is found in triclads. The *Dugesia* brain is formed by thickenings of the ventral trunks and a connecting commissure (Fig. 7.1B). In some other triclads, the brain is composed of dorsal ganglia arising from the surface of the ventral trunks (Fig. 7.12A). Land planarians have developed along an entirely different line, perhaps because of the elongated body form. A nerve plate connects the two ventral margins of the submuscular plexus, and the longitudinal nerve trunks lie in the nerve plate (Fig. 7.11D). The nerve plate probably assumes the brain functions.

Unipolar, bipolar, and multipolar neurons occur in flatworms. The neuron arrangement is diffuse in primitive acoels, but becomes organized in more complex forms. Hänstrom (1926) found that the marginal nerve of *Bdelloura* consists of a series of cells with tips ramifying into the epidermis and of fibers extending into the lateral nerves (Fig. 7.12B), evidently functioning as sensory neurons. Highly branched unipolar neurons in the nerve trunks innervate parenchymal muscles and serve as motor neurons. Other neurons lie entirely within the nerve trunks or commissures and act as associational fibers. Although there is no evidence of the cytological differentiation of axons, functional differentiation of neurons into sensory, motor, and associational types is an important progressive step in nervous evolution.

Flatworms are by no means brilliant, but studies show that behavior is modified on the basis of past experience. The learning process is laborious, requiring long conditioning, and retention is brief. *Dugesia* can be taught to make avoiding

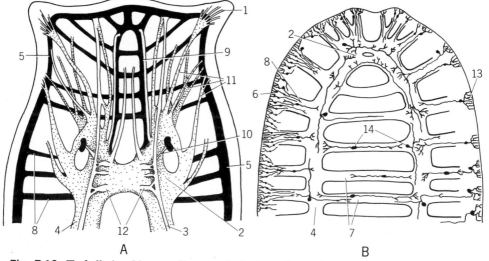

Fig. 7.12. Turbellarian Nervous Systems. A. Brain and anterior nerves of *Crenobia alpina*, a fresh-water triclad. Dorsal nerves are shown in white; ventral in black. It is interesting to compare with the *Dugesia* brain region (Fig. 7.1). *Crenobia*, unlike *Dugesia*, has a full complement of longitudinal nerve trunks for paludicolans. B. Anterior end of *Bdelloura candida*, a marine triclad, showing the position of some associational and sensory neurons. (A, after Micoletzky. B, after Hanström.) 1, auricle; 2, brain; 3, dorsal nerve cord; 4, ventral nerve cord; 5, marginal nerve cord; 6, marginal nerve plexus; 7, commissures between ventral nerve cords; 8, commissures between ventral and marginal nerve cords; 9, anterior extension of ventral nerve cord; 10, optic nerve; 11, sensory nerves from brain; 12, roots of dorsal nerve; 13, sensory neurons in marginal plexus; 14, associational neuron.

movements under conditions not ordinarily evoking them, but cannot be taught to turn toward conditions it normally avoids. Apparently flatworms have no ability, or a very limited one, to inhibit normal responses. Hovey (1929) taught a polyclad to remain more quiescent when exposed to light by touching its anterior margin whenever it began to move, but even the most gifted never learned to remain wholly quiescent. Removal of the brain prevented the learning response, indicating its importance in associative learning.

REPRODUCTIVE SYSTEM

The reproductive systems of Radiata consist only of gonads, often ill defined, and in primitive flatworms they are only slightly more highly organized. In higher Turbellaria, and especially in the parasitic classes, the reproductive system has become exceedingly complex. A tremendous development of this system has occurred within the phylum. Evolutionary experimentation with a new system often results in remarkable diversity. It has produced a bewildering array of variations in the form and composition of both male and female flatworm systems, and often organs dissimilar in origin are used for similar purposes. The system of names, on the whole, is based on function. Much specialized information is needed to discuss homologies or relationships profitably, and even to identify species. Serial sections are usually needed to identify Turbellaria.

Flatworms are almost exclusively hermaphroditic. The male and female systems are distinct, but may join terminally in a common chamber, the genital antrum, and may open through a common gonopore.

The Male System. The acoel testis is ill defined. Free parenchymal cells aggregate in a region characteristic of the species and enter into spermatogenesis.

In other Turbellaria the testis is enclosed in a membrane and is sharply delimited from the parenchyma.

Sperm ducts are incomplete in some acoels, but are the most stable elements of the male system. There may be one, a pair, or many testes. Each testis, when many are present, is served by a small sperm ductule, which joins the main sperm duct on each side (Fig. 7.1A). The two sperm ducts unite to form a medial common sperm duct, usually near the copulatory complex. The end of the common sperm duct is modified to form an ejaculatory duct, which passes through the copulatory complex.

Sperm accumulate before mating in muscular, dilated regions of the sperm ducts or ejaculatory duct. Storage organs in the sperm ducts are spermiducal vesicles. The first part of the ejaculatory duct is often expanded as a storage organ, the seminal vesicle. Species rarely have storage organs of both types.

The ejaculatory duct is the modified end of the common sperm duct, ending in a chamber, the male antrum, and serving as the center about which the copulatory complex is assembled. In addition to a seminal vesicle, the copulatory complex usually includes prostatic glands and an intromittent organ for mating. The most common intromittent organ is a penis, a muscular part protruded through the gonopore and inserted into the copulatory complex of the mate. Some have a cirrus, a muscular part of the tube that is everted during mating. Some Turbellaria have no intromittent organ.

The prostatic apparatus may consist of unicellular glands opening into the seminal vesicle, the ejaculatory duct or, more rarely, the sperm ducts. Many Turbellaria have a muscular prostatic vesicle, a sac into which the prostatic glands empty. Interpolated prostatic vesicles are sac-like dilations of the ejaculatory duct. Free prostatic vesicles are diverticula, connected to the ejaculatory duct by a prostatic duct.

The function of the prostatic secretion is uncertain. It contributes to the vehicle for sperm suspension and appears to be important for normal viability and activity of the sperm. Muscular contractions of the prostatic vesicle force secretion out during mating. Some Turbellaria have prostatoids. These are pyriform, often cuticularized structures, sometimes present in large numbers (Fig. 7.13C). Their exact function is unknown. Reference to representative species in Figs. 7.2 to 7.6 will permit comparison of the form of male systems of a number of diverse Turbellaria.

The muscular penis lies beyond the prostatic apparatus. It is sometimes divided into a penis bulb, which may enclose the seminal vesicle and prostatic vesicle, and a penis papilla, which projects into the male antrum (Fig. 7.1D). The penis papilla may be muscular or cuticularized. The cuticular region is highly specialized, sometimes forming a system of hooks, bars, spines, or a cuticular tube known as the penis stylet (Figs. 7.13A,B). Sometimes the stylet completely replaces the muscular part of the penis papilla. Stylet form, often fantastic, is important in identification of species. Some Turbellaria have no female copulatory organs, and the stylet is used to inject sperm through the body surface into the parenchyma. Generally, however, it enters into the female copulatory duct.

The Female System. Acoel ovaries, like the testes, are ill defined, without a covering membrane and consist of clusters of free parenchymal cells undergoing oögenesis. In all other Turbellaria, the ovaries have definite boundary membranes. Two kinds of ova and two kinds of ovaries must be distinguished in Turbellaria. Acoels, polyclads, and some primitive rhabdocoels have ordinary ovaries, producing endolecithal ova, with yolk reserves stored in the egg cytoplasm. All other flatworms form ectolecithal ova, free of yolk but encapsulated with special yolk cells

containing the needed food reserves. Some of these have a germovitellarium, producing both ova and yolk cells, while others have a separate ovary and yolk gland (Fig. 7.14). Primitive rhabdocoel stocks had an ovary with four arms meeting medially at the female antrum and gonopore. Each branch probably produced endolecithal ova. No modern rhabdocoels have such an ovary, but *Gnosonesima*, a primitive alloeocoel, has a germovitellarium with four arms, each forming ova enclosed in a follicle of yolk cells. This may reflect the way the primitive ovary became a germovitellarium, but if so, most Turbellaria have secondarily acquired a different method of yolk-cell formation, with one part of the germovitellarium converted into a yolk gland and another part into a region forming ectolecithal ova. Generally there are two yolk-producing arms and one ova-producing arm, with the remaining arm lost, although other patterns occur. Evolutionary adaptation has transformed a primitive ovary, producing endolecithal ova, through a germovitellarium, producing ectolecithal ova and yolk cells, to definitive secondary ovaries, producing ectolecithal ova, and to separate yolk glands.

Ovaries are served by oviducts and yolk glands by yolk ducts. Generally the junction of oviducts and yolk ducts converts the oviduct into an ovovitelline duct, carrying eggs and yolk cells. The disposition of oviducts, yolk ducts, and ovovitelline ducts varies with the position and number of ovaries and yolk glands. If the ovaries are paired, the two oviducts unite to form a common oviduct or open separately into the female antrum. The ovaries of some Turbellaria are broken into small, discrete follicles, each served by an oviductule which unites with the main oviduct on each side. Yolk glands, too, may be compact or follicular; yolk ductules unite to form a main yolk duct on each side of the body. The yolk ducts usually unite to form a common yolk duct, sometimes expanded into a storage sac, the yolk reservoir. In *Dugesia*, the yolk ductules open into the oviducts, which are then termed ovovitelline ducts (Fig. 7.1A).

The oviduct or ovovitelline duct usually connects to a chamber, the female antrum, and a female copulatory complex. The duct is often dilated, usually near the ovary, as a seminal receptacle, where sperm received during mating are stored.

In its simplest form, the female copulatory complex consists of a female pore and vagina, as in *Stylochus* (Fig. 7.14D). More often the vagina is replaced by a female antrum, which opens through a female gonopore or joins a common genital antrum to open through a common gonopore, as in *Dugesia* (Fig. 7.1D). In this case an organ for receiving the male organ and into which sperm are injected is often present. This is the saccate copulatory bursa, connected to the antrum by a bursal canal. The bursal canal serves as a vagina during mating, and the sperm

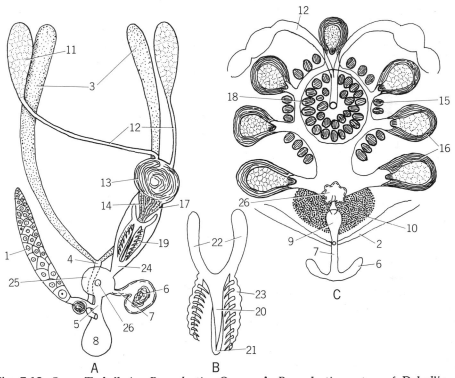

Fig. 7.13. Some Turbellarian Reproductive Organs. A. Reproductive system of *Dalyellia*, a rhabdocoel. B. Penis stylet of *Dalyellia rossi*. C. Copulatory complex of *Coronadena*, a polyclad with replicated male parts. (A-B, after von Graaf. C, after Hyman.) 1, ovary; 2, oviduct; 3, yolk gland; 4, common yolk duct; 5, ovovitelline duct; 6, seminal bursa; 7, bursal canal; 8, uterus; 9, vagina; 10, cement gland. *Male reproductive system:* 11, testis; 12, sperm duct; 13, seminal vesicle; 14, prostatic vesicle; 15, small prostatoid; 16, large prostatoid; 17, penis bulb; 18, penis papilla; 19, penis stylet; 20, median dorsal piece of stylet; 21, median ventral piece of stylet; 22, main stem of stylet; 23, distal stem of stylet, with spines; 24, male antrum; 25, common genital antrum; 26, common gonopore.

are injected into the bursa. They remain here for a short time, later migrating through the antrum and oviducts to reach the seminal receptacle for longer storage. Many variations will be seen among the

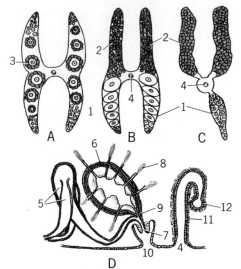

Fig. 7.14. Turbellarian Reproductive Systems. A-C. Stages in the evolution of the female reproductive system of rhabdocoels and alloeocoels. As a definite ovary develops from the indistinct clusters of cells undergoing oogenesis found in the most primitive turbellarians, a germovitellarium appears. This was originally tetrapartite, as in *Gnosonesima* (A). Further development of the germovitellarium has led to the separation of the function of yolk elaboration from gamete formation. In *Gnosonesima*, follicles of nurse cells surround the developing ovum. More commonly, the germovitellarium is divided into two yolk-forming regions and two gamete-producing regions (B). As these regions become more discrete, often with the disappearance of one of the ovumproducing arms, a system with separate yolk glands and one or two ovaries develop (C), as is commonly seen in rhabdocoels and alloeocoels. D. Reproductive system of *Euplana gracilis*, a common leptoplanid polyclad. (After Hyman.) 1, ovary; 2, yolk gland; 3, follicle; 4, female gonopore; 5, seminal vesicle; 6, prostatic vesicle; 7, penis papilla; 8, prostatic gland; 9, prostatic duct; 10, male gonopore; 11, vagina; 12, junction of vagina and oviduct.

representative species shown in Figs. 7.2 to 7.6. *Dalyellia*, like many other species, has a diverticulum, the uterus, arising from the genital antrum, into which ova pass. Ova are not stored here, but enter for encapsulation. Few Turbellaria have an organ for egg storage, for most release ova one or a few at a time. The distal part of each polyclad oviduct, however, is expanded as a true uterus, where ova are stored prior to encapsulation.

The capsule is secreted around the ova at various points. It is usually formed in the male or female antrum, but sometimes in the uterus, when present. The acoels, which lack a full system of ducts, secrete capsule walls at the body surface.

The female system is remarkably variable, and only a few of the major variations have been mentioned. With such great diversity among parts, homologies are not easily recognized, and the adaptive lines leading to our modern species are difficult to understand. A curious feature of the female system of some Turbellaria, also seen in some monogenetic trematodes, is the genito-intestinal canal (Fig. 7.23D). This connects the oviduct or vagina with the intestine, and has led some zoologists to believe that ova originally left the body this way. There are difficulties with this idea, but it may reflect a primitive association of gut and reproductive system. In this case, it seeems more probable that the bursa, which has secretory epithelium and digests excess sperm and prostatic secretions, is derived from the gut cavity.

Embryonic Development

Endolecithal and ectolecithal ova develop in entirely different ways, the presence of external yolk cells leading to aberrant forms of development. The development of endolecithal ova is far more important for understanding relationships.

ENDOLECITHAL DEVELOPMENT

Endolecithal polyclad ova undergo holo-blastic, unequal cleavage and produce a cellular embryo with micromeres and macromeres. The spindles are set obliquely in dividing blastomeres, so the blasto-meres do not lie directly above each other but over the furrows between blastomeres in the tier below (Fig. 7.15A); this type of cleavage is known as spiral. The fate

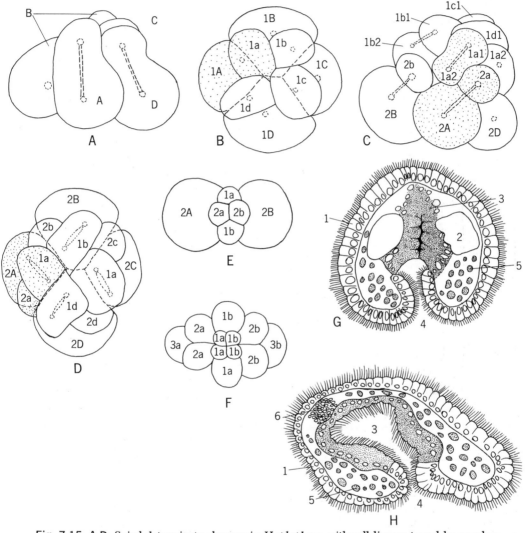

Fig. 7.15. A-D. Spiral determinate cleavage in *Hoploplana*, with cell lineage traced by number-ing, as described in the text. E-F. Spiral cleavage in an acoel, *Polychoerus*, resulting from the transverse cleavages of the two-celled rather than the four-celled stage. G-H. Later stages in the development of *Hoploplana*, showing the shift in the axis of the embryo. (A-D, G-H, after Surface. E-F, after Gardiner.) **1**, ectoderm; **2**, yolk mass; **3**, intestine; **4**, stomodaeum; **5**, mesenchyne; **6**, cerebral ganglion.

of each cell is determined at the time of its formation, so cleavage is determinate.

The first two divisions produce four equal blastomeres. Cell lineage studies, determining the destiny of these cells and their daughters, have been carried out. A system to designate the ancestry of each cell in the embryo is needed. Wilson, an American embryologist, worked out the one used. The first four blastomeres are termed A, B, C, and D. The system used to designate their descendants is outlined in Table 7.1 and should be consulted while considering the course of development as described below.

The third cleavage division is unequal and oblique, producing a quartet of micromeres (1a, 1b, 1c, 1d) and a quartet of macromeres (1A, 1B, 1C, 1D) (Fig.

Table 7.1. Designation of blastomeres in spiral determinate cleavage

```
                                              ┌ 1a¹¹¹
                                     ┌ 1a¹¹ ┤
                            ┌ 1a¹ ┤         └ 1a¹¹²
                            │      │         ┌ 1a¹²¹
                            │      └ 1a¹² ┤
                   ┌ 1a ┤                  └ 1a¹²²
                   │     │         ┌ 1a²¹ ┌ 1a²¹¹
            ┌ A ┤   │    └ 1a² ┤         └ 1a²¹²
            │    │   └ 1A       │         ┌ 1a²²¹
            │    │              └ 1a²² ┤
      ┌ AB ┤     │   ┌ 1b                └ 1a²²²
      │    │     └ B ┤
      │    │         └ 1B
Ovum ┤
      │         ┌ C ┌ 1c
      │         │   └ 1C
      └ CD ┤
                │   ┌ 1d
                └ D ┤       ┌ 2d
                    └ 1D ┤       ┌ 3d
                         └ 2D ┤       ┌ 4d
                              └ 3D ┤
                                   └ 4D
```

Scheme of divisions, with letter and number designations of blastomeres, is shown fully up to the formation of the first quartet of micromeres (1a, 1b, 1c, 1d). Beyond this point, only the divisions of micromere 1a and of macromere 1D are shown. The other micromeres and macromeres are, of course, dividing in the same manner.

7.15A,B). The micromeres continue to divide, 1a dividing into cells $1a^1$ and $1a^2$, with $1a^1$ being the daughter closer to the animal pole. When $1a^1$ divides, it produces $1a^{11}$ and $1a^{12}$. This system of designation continues and can be expanded indefinitely.

The next division of the macromeres produces a second quartet of micromeres (2a, 2b, 2c, 2d) and a quartet of macromeres (2A, 2B, 2C, 2D) (Fig. 7.15C-D). The macromeres divide again to form micromeres 3a, 3b, 3c, 3d, and macromeres 3A, 3B, 3C, and 3D. The next division of macromeres forms the last quartet of micromeres, 4a, 4b, 4c, and 4d, and macromeres 4A, 4B, 4C, and 4D. After this division, macromeres 4A-D and micromeres 4a-c, which are filled with yolk material, move into the interior and are exhausted as food supplies.

In polyclads, the first quartet of micromeres (1a-d) forms the anterior, dorsal, surface ectoderm, the pigment cells of the eyes, the brain and nervous system, the frontal glands when they are present, and in some cases an apical tuft of sensory hairs in the larva. This tuft may correspond to the apical sense organ of some cnidarian larvae, and to a similar apical tuft in the trochophore larvae of annelids and molluscs. The second quartet of micromeres (2a-d) contributes to the surface ectoderm and forms most of the ectomesoderm of the pharyngeal musculature and parenchyma. The third quartet of micromeres (3a-d) contributes to the surface ectoderm and somewhat to the pharyngeal ectomesoderm. Cells 4a-c and 4A-D eventually deteriorate as their food content is exhausted. Cell 4d is the mesendoblast, giving rise to all of the endoderm and endomesoderm. It moves into the interior and at the first division forms cells $4d^1$, from which all endoderm is derived, and $4d^2$, which gives rise to the endomesoderm, eventually forming the parenchyma, the parenchymal and subepidermal muscle, and the reproductive organs.

Gastrulation is by epiboly, and the blastopore soon closes. The ectoderm cells that will form the nervous system, the mesoderm from $4d^2$, and the endoderm from $4d^1$ are interior. Yolk material coalesces to form oil droplets. The ectoderm becomes ciliated and invaginates to form a stomodaeum at the site of the blastopore, developing into a simple pharynx as it contacts the endodermal cells. Endodermal cells rearrange themselves to form an enteron (Fig. 7.15G). The embryonic axis shifts, bringing the brain primordium forward and changing the enteron position (Fig. 7.15H). It is this shift that strengthens the argument that a change in the body axes of a planuloid ancestral stock produced ancestral flatworms.

Usually the embryo flattens and develops into a tiny worm. Some pass through a free-swimming larval stage, known as Müller's larva, with eight ciliated ectodermal lobes. A few species produce Gotte's larva, with four ciliated lobes.

Early development of acoels is similar, but spiral cleavages begin at the two-cell stage, producing pairs instead of quartets of cells (Fig. 7.15E,F). The stereogastrula has no trace of an enteron, and develops without the intervention of larval stages.

ECTOLECITHAL DEVELOPMENT

Ectolecithal development is so aberrant that cleavage stages cannot be homologized with endolecithal cleavage, although traces of spiral cleavage have been reported. No definite germ layers can be distinguished, and organogeny involves the differentiation of cell masses into larval or adult parts. Yolk cells do not contribute directly to embryo formation. They are surrounded during development, gradually disappearing as their contents are used.

Rhabdocoel and alloeocoel development is similar. The ovum divides into a mass of blastomeres, which come to lie on the future ventral side of a syncytial mass of yolk cells. The blastomeres develop into an epithelium, which gradually surrounds the yolk mass, and three inner cell masses (Fig. 7.16A). The anterior mass becomes the brain, nervous system, and pigmented and sensory cells of the eyes. The middle mass becomes the parenchyma and musculature of the pharynx. the posterior mass forms the reproductive system and posterior end of the body. The

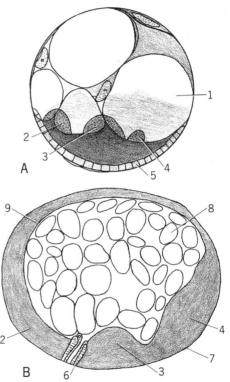

Fig. 7.16. A. A stage in the development of a rhabdocoel with an ectolecithal ovum, showing the three embryonic regions. B. A stage of triclad development, with yolk material already ingested through the embryonic pharynx, and with the three embryonic regions visible. (A, after Bresslau. B, after Fulinski.) 1, vacuole; 2, anterior region, which will form the brain; 3, middle region, which will form pharynx; 4, posterior region, which will form posterior end of body; 5, developing epidermis; 6, embryonic pharynx; 7, outer limiting membrane; 8, ingested yolk; 9, inner limiting membrane.

blastomeres adjacent to the yolk digest it and eventually become the enteron, at first solid but later becoming hollow.

Several triclad ova are often in the same capsule. Each divides to form a group of blastomeres, some of which surround the fluid part of the yolk and the remaining blastomeres, thus becoming the covering membrane of the embryonic sphere. Some internal blastomeres migrate to the surface and differentiate into a temporary embryonic pharynx and intestine. Yolk is drawn into the intestine through the embryonic pharynx, pushing the undifferentiated blastomeres against the surface membrane where they form the embryonic wall from which the body develops (Fig. 7.16B). Three masses, similar in position and destiny to those formed in rhabdocoels, are formed, and the innermost blastomeres become the enteron.

The amount and distribution of yolk have a tremendous effect on early embryonic development of all kinds of animals. It is common to find eggs rich in yolk undergoing modified development in all phyla. It will not be possible to describe development for all of these forms. They generally demonstrate the principles seen in flatworms. Cleavage patterns are greatly disturbed, and larvae are omitted. Yet, beneath the aberrancy, patterns more or less comparable to the development of small, yolk-poor eggs can be seen. In flatworms, the three cell masses formed in ectolecithal ova correspond, to some extent, to the quartets of micromeres produced in endolecithal development. The anterior mass is somewhat like blastomeres 1a-d, and the middle mass like cells 2a-d.

The development of the ectolecithal ova of cestodes and trematodes (p. 225, 234) is more highly modified and adds to the evidence of the profound influence of yolk on development. Yolk cells are a new and unique feature in flatworms; it is not surprising to find diverse methods of using them. However, one important point

should be noted. The modifications of development resulting from yolk cells illustrate, again, the adaptability of the embryo, and the danger of relying too heavily upon embryonic evidence in establishing relationships. The recapitulation principle must be applied with care.

Asexual Reproduction

The high regenerative capacities of fresh-water planarians have conferred upon the Turbellaria an undeserved reputation for great regenerative abilities and for common asexual reproduction. Some Turbellaria cannot reproduce asexually, and the ability to regenerate is relatively low in these groups.

Land planarians reproduce asexually by fragmentation and regeneration. Asexual reproduction occurs in some rhabdocoels and fresh-water planarians by transverse fission. The site of the fission plane is predetermined; in planarians the regenerative pattern is modified at the site of the future head. Generally fission precedes any visible differentiation of the daughter animal, but the eyes and pharynx of daughter *Dugesia paramensis* are visible before active fission occurs. Rhabdocoels are constricted at the site of future fissions, and considerable differentiation occurs before the daughters separate (Fig. 7.2G). Chains of zooids are sometimes formed, each in a different stage of differentiation.

Regeneration

The ability to regenerate is limited except in forms that reproduce asexually, but in these species is very high. The results of experiments repeatedly demonstate the importance of the anterior-posterior axis. Reasonably large pieces with anterior and posterior cut edges regenerate a head and tail but retain the polarity of the animal from which the piece was cut. Very short pieces produce two-headed or other abnormal forms, indicating a polarity insufficient to evoke normal development. Anterior pieces regenerate more successfully than posterior pieces. The same principle applies in Turbellaria with lesser regenerative capacities. The anterior pieces of a polyclad regenerate perfectly, but only parts anterior to the cerebral ganglia have this ability. Posterior pieces regenerate lost posterior parts, but not lost anterior parts.

The head region or the cut surface nearest the head has some kind of dominance growing out of its position on the axis, presumably associated with axial, physiological gradients. This view is supported by results in organisms with fission planes. Pieces containing the tail of the anterior zooid and the head of the posterior zooid show reversals of symmetry or other abnormalities. Factors responsible for axial organization are not yet clear, nor is it known how they influence free parenchymal cells, largely responsible for regeneration. More work is needed in this area, for considerable theoretical interest centers about the analysis of the anterior-posterior axis as a functional factor in development.

Class Trematoda—The Flukes

Class Trematoda includes the leaf-like, unsegmented, parasitic flatworms with an enteron, commonly known as flukes. Flukes are successful animals; nearly 6000 species have been described. Adults parasitize all vertebrate classes, with fishes the most common hosts. Some are external parasites, clinging to the body surface, while others are semi-external, living in the mouth cavity, gills, or cloaca. Still others are internal parasites, most commonly situated in the gut. Some have a direct life cycle, with larvae that do not reproduce and metamorphose into adults. Others have a more or less complex, indirect life cycle, with a succession of larval stages, some of which reproduce and most of which die instead of becoming adults. Only the last larval stage is able to become adult. Trematodes with a direct life cycle usually pass all developmental stages in a single host species. Those with an indirect life cycle live as larvae in an intermediate host, and may live as larvae in a second intermediate host. Adults live in a final host. First intermediate hosts are usually molluscs. Second intermediate hosts, when present, are often fish or other cold-blooded vertebrates. The final hosts are vertebrates.

Flukes are extremely varied; it must be left to parasitologists to discuss diversity of form, function, and details of life cycles fully. They are far too important to ignore, and some features are of particular concern to the invertebrate zoologist. For those interested in greater detail, excellent texts on parasitology are available. Before considering the classification and characteristics of the organs, Fig. 7.17 should be examined, and the general structure of the Chinese liver fluke worked out.

Classification of Trematodes

Trematode classification has been considerably modified in recent years. There is some difference of opinion concerning the best system to use. The following was proposed by La Rue.

Subclass Monogenea. External or semi-external parasites of aquatic animals, especially of fishes and amphibia; with a mouth lacking an oral sucker or with a weak oral sucker, a pharynx, and usually bifurcate enteron; two anterior nephridiopores; a large posterior attachment organ, the opisthaptor, usually equipped with hooks and typically with two glandulo-muscular attachment organs at the anterior end forming a prohaptor; rather short uterus containing few ova; life cycle direct, without alternation of hosts.

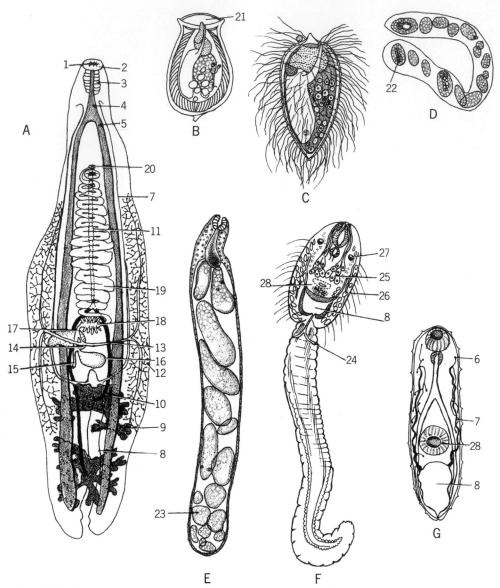

Fig. 7.17. *Opisthorchus sinensis*, the Chinese liver fluke, a well-known trematode which parasitizes man. **A.** Scheme of structure of the adult animal. **B.** Capsule, containing a miracidium. **C.** The miracidium, the first larval stage, which emerges from the capsule after it is eaten by a snail and penetrates into the haemocoelic lacunae, where it develops into a sporocyst. **D.** Mature sporocyst from a snail, containing daughter larvae known as rediae. **E.** Redia from snail, containing developing cercariae. **F.** Cercaria, which emerges from the host snail and swims about for 1 to 2 days in search of an acceptable fish to serve as a second intermediate host. **G.** Metacercaria as it appears after excystment. Excystment normally occurs when the metacercaria is eaten by the final host. (**A**, after Belding. **C**, after Hsü and Khaw, from Belding. **B-E**, after Faust and Khaw. **F**, after Komiya and Tajima, from Chandler and Read.) *Digestive system:* **1**, mouth; **2**, oral sucker; **3**, pharynx; **4**, esophagus; **5**, intestinal crura.

Order Monopisthocotylea. Monogenetic trematodes without a genitointestinal canal; opisthaptor a single disc, usually with one to three pairs of large hooks and many marginal hooklets. Example: *Gyrodactylus* (Fig. 7.18A).

Order Polyopisthocotylea. Monogenetic trematodes with a genitointestinal canal; opisthaptor with discrete suckers or clamps, on a single disc or free. Example: *Polystoma* (Fig. 7.18C).

Subclass Aspidobothrea. Internal parasites of molluscs and cold-blooded vertebrates with a mouth lacking an oral sucker, and, usually, a small pharynx and saccate enteron; a single posterior nephridiopore; a huge ventral sucker divided into compartments or a ventral row of suckers without hooks; life cycle direct, usually without an alternation of hosts. Example: *Aspidogaster* (Fig. 7.19A).

Subclass Digenea. Adults are internal parasites of vertebrates, with a mouth usually surrounded by an oral sucker, a bulbous pharynx, and a bifurcate enteron; a single, posterior excretory pore; a ventral sucker or acetabulum lacking hooks; a long uterus, usually filled with ova; complex life cycle involving larval hosts, typically molluscs.

Order Strigeatoidea. With a fork-tailed cercaria, usually developing in sporocysts; miracidia primitively with two flame cells. Example: *Schistosoma* (Fig. 7.19B).

Order Echinostomida. Cercaria with a strong, unforked tail; miracidia with one pair of flame cells. Example: *Fasciola* (Fig. 7.18B).

Order Opisthorchida. Cercaria with excretory ducts in the tail and without a stylet. Example: *Opisthorchis* (Fig. 7.17).

Order Plagiorchiida. Cercaria without excretory ducts in the tail and usually with a stylet. Example: *Prosthogonimus* (Fig. 7.18D).

Some Effects of Parasitism

Parasites live in environments as variable as aquatic animals; each host species and host organ differs, and each presents peculiar problems. Many parasitic adaptations are invisible modifications of metabolic patterns, suitable for the specific oxygen levels, body defenses, and chemical peculiarities of the host organ. Others affect the visible form of the organ systems. Although the specific environments occupied by parasites are diverse, all must cope with some of the same problems, and there is a resulting tendency toward convergent changes in unrelated parasitic groups.

Young aquatic animals can grow up in the home lake; if they had to find a new lake each generation, most species would die. Some parasites live for several generations in the host body, but the host life span is limited and all parasites must often seek a new host—the equivalent of finding another lake. This discontinuity of the habitat a parasite calls home sparks several adaptive trends, including the following, both of which are found in almost all parasites.

1. Parasites have a high reproductive potential. Sessile animals often have migratory young or shelled eggs used as disseminules to spread the species. Parasites also depend primarily on young stages to locate new hosts. The chance that any one larva or egg will reach a suitable host may be very small, but the improbable

Protonephridial system: 6, flame cell; 7, protonephridial tubule; 8, bladder. *Male reproductive system:* 9, testis; 10, sperm duct; 11, common sperm duct. *Female reproductive system:* 12, yolk gland; 13, yolk duct; 14, oviduct; 15, Lauer's canal; 16, seminal receptacle; 17, ovovitelline duct; 18, ootype, surrounded by Mehlis's gland; 19, uterus; 20, common gonopore. *Larval structures:* 21, operculum of capsule; 22, young redia; 23, germ balls; 24, nephridiopore; 25, penetration glands; 26, cystogenous glands, used to secrete the metacercarial cyst membrane; 27, ocellus; 28, ventral sucker.

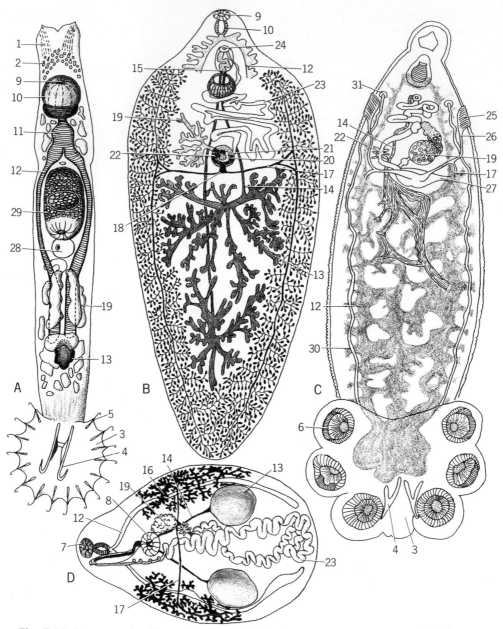

Fig. 7.18. Representative Trematodes. **A.** *Gyrodactylus*, a monogenetic trematode belonging to the suborder Monopisthocotylea, characterized by a weak or no oral sucker, and a simple posterior attachment organ or opisthaptor. There is no genitointestinal canal. **B.** *Fasciola hepatica*, the sheep liver fluke, a digenetic trematode of the echinostome type, somewhat schematized. The digestive tract is shown only at the anterior end. **C.** *Polystoma integerrinum*, a monogenetic trematode of the suborder Polyopisthocotylea, which have an oral sucker, an opisthaptor with several suckers and anchors, and a genitointestinal canal. **D.** *Prosthogonimus macrorchis*, a plagiorchid digenetic trematode. (**A,** after Mueller and Van Cleave. **B,** after

becomes probable if tried often enough. A parasite producing a million ova, each with one chance in a hundred thousand to be eaten by a suitable host, is reasonably certain to have some successful young. The two most common consequences are nicely exemplified by trematodes: reproductive organs tend to become large and complex, and larval stages often develop the ability to reproduce.

2. Larval parasites tend to adapt, ecologically, to the habits of the host. As a good hunter knows the habits of the game he seeks, a good parasite adapts its behavior to conform to the habits of suitable host animals. This is most commonly achieved by a larva's fitting itself into the food chain of the final host. A larva which lives in a copepod, often eaten by fish, has partly solved the problem of finding its way to a fish-eating bird or mammal. Other systems are used. Larval parasites may live in blood-sucking animals that feed on the final host, fitting themselves into the food habits of the larval host. These adaptations are important for the maintenance of many parasitic life cycles.

Important parts of animals cannot be deficient without reducing the chances of survival, so selective pressures for the maintenance of normal form constantly operate. However, if parts are unimportant or functionless, these selective pressures become very weak and the parts tend to disappear. Parasites have little use for some parts important in free-living animals. Internal parasites, like cave animals, rarely have eyes and usually have few sense organs of other kinds. Locomotor organs are poorly developed, and

the digestive tract may become useless if the parasite can absorb what is needed through the body surface. Degenerative changes of this kind are almost universal consequences of a parasitic life. On the other hand, organs of attachment, which may not be important in free-living animals, are often important in parasites, and so tend to develop. Both progressive and retrogressive changes are associated with adaptation to parasitism.

Trematode Organ Systems

Most adult trematodes are small, between a few millimeters and 5 cm. long. A few are elongated; the Nobles refer to one from the sunfish, *Mola mola*, that reaches 20 feet in length, but most are flattened and leaf-like. The larval hosts are usually molluscs, and adult hosts are usually vertebrates. They are like Turbellaria in many ways, and have similar organ systems.

An outstanding peculiarity is the absence of an epidermis. The surface layer is lost during development, and thereafter the protective cuticle rests directly on the parenchyma (Fig. 7.20). Insunk gland cells and some subcuticular cells may be of epidermal origin, however.

ATTACHMENT ORGANS

Attachment organs are the most conspicuous and characteristic external features. External parasites are most likely to be detached, and monogenetic trematodes adapt to their precarious position by re-

Chandler and Read. C, after Paul. D, after Macy.) *External features:* 1, anterior adhesive organ; 2, adhesive glands; 3, opisthaptor; 4, anchor; 5, marginal hook; 6, sucker; 7, oral sucker; 8, ventral sucker or acetabulum. *Digestive system:* 9, mouth; 10, pharynx; 11, esophagus; 12, intestine. *Male reproductive system:* 13, testis; 14, sperm duct; 15, seminal vesicle. *Female reproductive system:* 16, yolk gland; 17, yolk duct; 18, common yolk duct; 19, ovary; 20, oviduct; 21, oötype; 22, Mehlis's gland; 23, uterus; 24, common gonopore; 25, copulatory pore; 26, copulatory duct; 27, genitointestinal canal; 28, ovum; 29, embryo. *Protonephridial system:* 30, protonephridium; 31, nephridiopore.

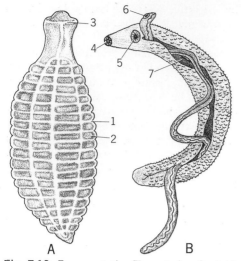

Fig. 7.19. Representative Trematodes. A. *Aspidogaster conchicola*, a typical aspidobothrian, characterized by the huge ventral sucker. B. *Schistosoma mansoni*, a strigeid blood fluke that parasitizes man. The sexes are separate and the smaller female is carried in the gynecophoric canal of the male. (A, after Monticelli. B, after Looss, from Chandler and Read.) 1, sucker; 2, alveolus of sucker; 3, mouth; 4, oral sucker of male; 5, acetabulum of male; 6, acetabulum of female; 7, gynecophoric canal.

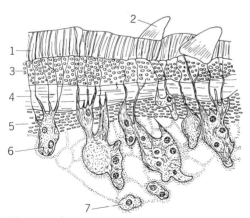

Fig. 7.20. Longitudinal section through the surface of *Fasciola hepatica* (after Hein). 1, cuticle; 2, cuticular scale; 3, circular muscle; 4, longitudinal muscle; 5, diagonal muscle; 6, cells secreting the cuticle; 7, mesenchymal cell.

markable attachment organs. A prohaptor, usually consisting of a pair of glandulo-muscular organs, is often present at the anterior end (Fig. 7.18A). The posterior attachment organ or opisthaptor is larger and more conspicuous, consisting of a large disc with suckers, large hooks, and smaller hooklets (Fig. 7.18A,C). The Aspidobothrea have a no less remarkable attachment organ, the whole ventral surface being modified as a huge, compartmented sucker or a series of discrete suckers (Fig. 7.19A). Digenetic trematodes usually have a small oral sucker surrounding the mouth and a larger ventral sucker (acetabulum) somewhere on the ventral midline.

DIGESTIVE SYSTEM

The stomodaeal region consists of a mouth, pharynx and generally an oral sucker. The short buccal cavity is followed by a pharynx of the bulbous type, rosulate in the majority of trematodes but doliiform in some monogenetic trematodes. Most trematodes ingest detached cells, blood cells, mucus, or tissue exudates. Tissues are injured by the oral sucker and pharynx, sometimes with the aid of cuticular spines. Some trematodes secrete enzymes that soften host tissues and prepare them for digestion.

Food usually passes through a gastrodermal esophagus on its way to the main enteron. In Aspidobothrea and some Monogenea, the enteron is saccate as in rhabdocoels, but most have two intestinal caeca (crura), sometimes with intestinal diverticula. Probably some food is absorbed through the body surface. This may be related to the generally simple form of the intestine. Digestion is predominantly extracellular and food is stored primarily as glycogen. Some fat is also stored.

RESPIRATION

Internal parasites are predominantly anaerobic, but use oxygen when available. Anaerobic glycolysis, producing carbon dioxide and various organic acids, is the chief method of energy release.

EXCRETION

Trematodes have a protonephridial system like Turbellaria. Capillary tubules with terminal flame cells connect with paired protonephridial tubules. The system first appears in the larvae, and the details of its development have been followed through the life cycles of several species. Tubules and their branches have a constant arrangement, characteristic of various trematode groups. The number and arrangement of flame cells are also constant features, and are of considerable value in taxonomy, helping to relate unknown larvae to adults. During the development of cercariae, the two protonephridial tubules unite medially to form a bladder (Fig. 7.21). The tubules continue to the tail, where they open through separate nephridiopores. When the tail is shed, the posterior excretory pore, characteristic of Digenea, is formed. The bladder is thin walled at first, but may come to have a heavy epithelial lining. This trait is used to divide the Digenea into two superorders.

Much work remains to characterize excretory physiology. Various organic acids are released, presumably as end products of anaerobic respiration, and some are undoubtedly discharged partly by the protonephridial system. The activity of the system rises in a diluted medium, so it may be concluded that in trematodes as in Turbellaria, the protonephridial system is concerned with water expulsion.

PARENCHYMA AND INTERNAL TRANSPORT

Trematode and turbellarian parenchyma are essentially the same, but some Digenea have a lymphatic system, the only special system for internal transport in the phylum. Canals, lined with flattened cells derived from the parenchyma, ramify extensively through the parenchyma and the muscular organs (Fig. 7.22B). Free cells, resembling vertebrate haemocytoblasts, float in the enclosed fluid. They are formed in a center at the junction of the two intestinal crura. This primitive circulatory system is one of several instances in which progressive adaptations, absent or poorly developed in free-living flatworms, reach their highest development among parasitic members of the phylum.

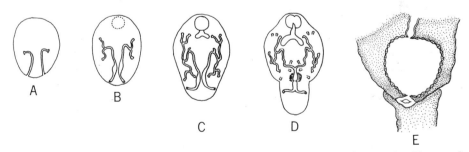

Fig. 7.21. Development of the protonephridial system in a trematode cercaria, *Notocotylus urbanensis*, showing the formation of the bladder from the union of the two protonephridial tubules, the early branching of the tubules, and the formation of excretory pores in the cercarial tail. With the loss of the tail, the original nephridiopores are lost and an excretory pore from the bladder serves to discharge urine. (After Kuntz.)

LOCOMOTION AND SUPPORT

With the development of a cuticle and the loss of epidermis and external cilia, movement is relegated entirely to muscles. Muscles reach their highest development among the parasitic members of Platyhelminthes, an unusual situation. Primitive monogenetic trematodes have muscle

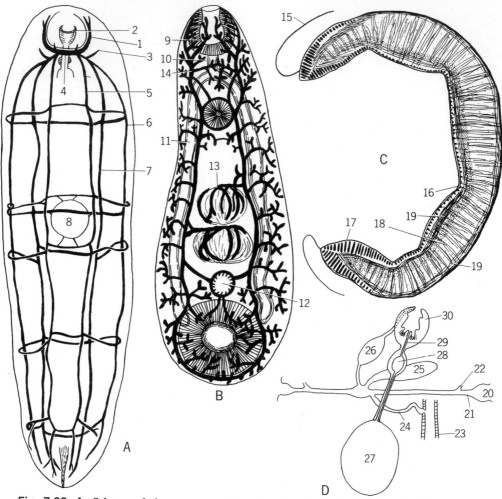

Fig. 7.22. A. Scheme of the nervous system of a trematode. **B.** The lymphatic system of *Cotylophoron cotylophorum*, a digenetic trematode. **C.** Section through the acetabulum of a digenetic trematode. **D.** Scheme of the reproductive system of a polystomoid monogenetic trematode. (A, after Looss. B, after Wiley. C, after Näsmark, D, after Stunkard.) 1, oral sucker; 2, mouth; 3, anterior nerve; 4, cerebral ganglion; 5, ventral nerve trunk; 6, lateral nerve trunk; 7, dorsal nerve trunk; 8, acetabulum; 9, pharynx; 10, esophagus; 11, intestine; 12, bladder; 13, testis; 14, lymphatic vessel; 15, body surface; 16, cuticle; 17, circular muscle; 18, radial muscle; 19, longitudinal muscle; 20, copulatory pore; 21, copulatory canal; 22, yolk duct; 23, intestinal crura; 24, genitointestinal canal; 25, ovary; 26, uterus; 27, testis; 28, spermiducal vesicle; 29, penis papilla; 30, penis bulb.

layers like turbellarians. Other flukes have a diagonal muscle layer within the longitudinal layer (Fig. 7.20). Parenchymal muscles are poorly developed, but are specialized to form muscles for operating the hooks and anchors used for attachment. Suckers are formed of specialized subcuticular muscle, with modifications of the primitive layers of the body wall (Fig. 7.22C).

The cercarial tail is a secondary adaptation for movement and is undoubtedly the most effective muscular locomotor organ in the phylum. Tail ultrastructure has been described by Cardell and Philpott. A layer of smooth muscle lies just beneath the cuticle (Fig. 7.23). Within the smooth muscle, a diagonal layer of striated muscle is found. A dense layer of mitochondria surrounds the parenchyma. The striated fibrils, as in most rapidly contracting muscles, have wide anisotropic bands and narrow isotropic bands. Presumably the mitochondrial layer serves the high oxidative requirements of the tail muscles.

SENSE ORGANS

Trematode sense organs are poorly developed. Some Monogenea have eyes, but otherwise they occur only in free-living, larval stages of some Digenea. Eyes may occur in miracidia and cercariae. Eye structure is simple; sometimes only a single retinal cell occurs. Touch receptors are especially abundant in the attachment organs.

NERVOUS SYSTEM

The trematode nervous system is built on the plan seen in Turbellaria. There is no subepidermal plexus, as the epidermis is missing. The submuscular plexus consists of a mesh, in which three pairs of longitudinal nerve trunks, the dorsal, lateral, and ventral, are found. The trunks are connected by commissures, tending to form rings (Fig. 7.22A). Monogenetic

trematodes lack dorsal trunks and may lack lateral trunks, resembling some of the simpler rhabdocoels. Two dorsal cerebral ganglia lie between the oral sucker and pharynx, and are connected by a broad, ganglionic commissure. Attachment organs, pharynx, and parts of the reproductive system are innervated by peripheral nerves.

In many phyla, the parasitic species have a degenerate nervous system, but flukes (and cestodes, also) have a nervous system as complex as the free-living Turbellaria. Flatworms are simply organized in any case, and the loss of sense organs in parasites is balanced by the development of muscles for attachment and the greater use of muscles for movement, correlated with the absence of cilia. The compensatory changes result in the maintenance of the nervous system at about the same level in parasitic as in free-living species.

REPRODUCTIVE SYSTEM

The reproductive system is greatly developed. Its parts are like the parts of turbellarian systems, but the arrangement is somewhat different and the parts much larger.

Male System. Monogenetic trematodes have from one to many testes and a rhabdocoel-like sperm duct system. Spermiducal vesicles sometimes occur near the copulatory complex, which is also rhabdocoel-like, and has a muscular or armed

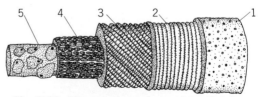

Fig. 7.23. Ultrastructure of cercarial tail (after Cardell and Philpott). 1, cuticle; 2, smooth muscle; 3, diagonal strands of striated muscle; 4, mitochondrial layer; 5, parenchyma.

penis. Aspidobothrea also have a turbellarian-like system, with one or two testes, but with a cirrus as an intromittent organ.

Two compact, but sometimes greatly branched, testes are almost universal among digenetic trematodes. The two

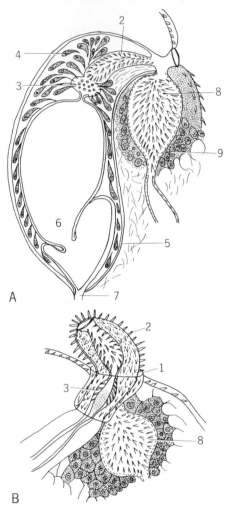

A

B

Fig. 7.24. The region of the cirrus sac and metraterm of a digenetic trematode, with the cirrus withdrawn at A and everted at B (after Looss). 1, gonopore; 2, cirrus; 3, prostatic vesicle; 4, prostatic gland; 5, cirrus sac; 6, seminal vesicle; 7, sperm duct; 8, metraterm, the modified end of the uterus serving as a vagina; 9, gland cells.

sperm ducts unite as a common sperm duct, and enter the copulatory complex. Spermiducal vesicles may be found. The copulatory complex may include only an unspecialized ejaculatory duct, but in most Digenea it is contained in a large, muscular cirrus sac, and includes a seminal vesicle, prostatic glands, and sometimes a prostatic vesicle. The muscular cirrus is the terminal, often armed, section of the ejaculatory duct that is everted during mating (Fig. 7.24). A small genital antrum opens through a common gonopore. Schistosomes are exceptional in having separate sexes. The slender female is often found in a ventral groove on the body of the much larger male (Fig. 7.19B).

Female System. The female system is more diverse than the male system, but is also turbellarian-like. As in Turbellaria, detailed differences are important in taxonomy. Only essentials can be mentioned here; a text on parasitology should be consulted for details.

Monogenetic trematodes usually have one or two copulatory canals with independent copulatory pores (Fig. 7.22D). The inner end of the copulatory canal opens into the oviduct or yolk duct system. There is no bursa, but a part of the copulatory canal may be modified as a seminal receptacle. Beyond the union of oviduct and yolk duct systems, the ovovitelline duct is slightly dilated as an oötype, surrounded by Mehlis's gland, also known as the shell gland. Here the ovum is encapsulated. The ovovitelline duct continues as a very short uterus; ova are released singly or a few at a time. An interesting feature is the genitointestinal canal, characteristic of one of the two monogenetic orders. When present, it connects the vagina and right intestinal caecum, and is apparently identical with the genitointestinal canal of some Turbellaria.

The basic pattern of the digenetic female system is simple enough, but is subject to myriad modifications. The following description should be compared to the representative flukes shown in Figs. 7.17A and 7.18. The single ovary opens into an oviduct, down which ova pass. Scattered, follicular yolk glands empty into yolk ductules, which unite to form the main yolk ducts on each side. The yolk ducts unite near the oviduct, and may expand as a yolk reservoir at the base of the common yolk duct. Ova are fertilized in the upper part of the ovovitelline duct, formed by union of common yolk duct and oviduct.

Laurer's canal connects the oviduct of some flukes with a dorsal pore (Fig. 7.17A). This is a copulatory canal, usually connected with a seminal receptacle, where sperm received during mating are stored. Laurer's canal ends blindly in the parenchyma of most flukes or is missing, and the terminal part of the ovovitelline duct serves as a vagina. This region is often armed with hooks or has a special musculature; in this case it is a metraterm.

In any case, ova are fertilized soon after entering the ovovitelline duct and pass into the oötype, a small chamber in which the capsule wall begins to form, and which is surrounded by the loosely arranged cells of Mehlis's gland. According to Smyth and Clegg, inclusions in yolk cells which form the capsule wall, the shell globules, are released immediately after the ova and yolk cells have passed Mehlis's gland, and harden to form the capsule wall. The wall is thickened as additional material gathers on the inner surface. They describe the hardening of the capsule wall as a quinone tanning process, producing a scleroprotein. The exact function of Mehlis's gland remains obscure, but it probably secretes a material that promotes the hardening of the wall, and perhaps stimulates the coalescence of the shell globules. The encapsulated ova move into a dilated part of the ovovitelline duct, the uterus. Here the capsule hardens and darkens, and ova usually undergo the first part of development.

The uterus is remarkably large in most trematodes, looping back and forth and sometimes making several circuits of the body. Thousands of ova may accumulate in such uteri. The uterus narrows sharply at the end, and with or without a specialized metraterm, opens into the genital antrum. The ova leave through the common gonopore.

Trematode Life Cycles

Embryonic development provides evidence of turbellarian relationships, as some of the same aberrancies associated with ectolecithal development occur in both groups. In Monogenea, a mass of blastomeres forms and the outer cells become an epithelial membrane. Some internal cells deteriorate, forming an enteric cavity. This begins posteriorly, and for a time the enteron is open through an embryonic "anal pore" which pierces the epithelial covering (Fig. 7.25B). No explanation of the anal pore is available; it eventually closes. Two cell masses form and one develops into the pharynx, while the other, always in contact with the pharynx, becomes the brain. The cell masses are reminiscent of similar masses seen in rhabdocoel development.

Yolk cells of digenetic trematode embryos remain discrete and external to the embryo. The first division of the ovum produces one somatic and one propagative cell. Each subsequent division of the propagative cell produces a somatic and a propagative daughter (Fig. 7.25C), so the embryo becomes a mass of somatic blastomeres and one propagative cell. An outer epithelial membrane eventually forms, enclosing the remaining blastomeres and the propagative cell. The propagative cell gives rise to the germ balls and propagative cells of the miracidium, and the remaining internal cells form masses that differentiate into the miracidial parts (Fig. 7.25A). The development of the propaga-

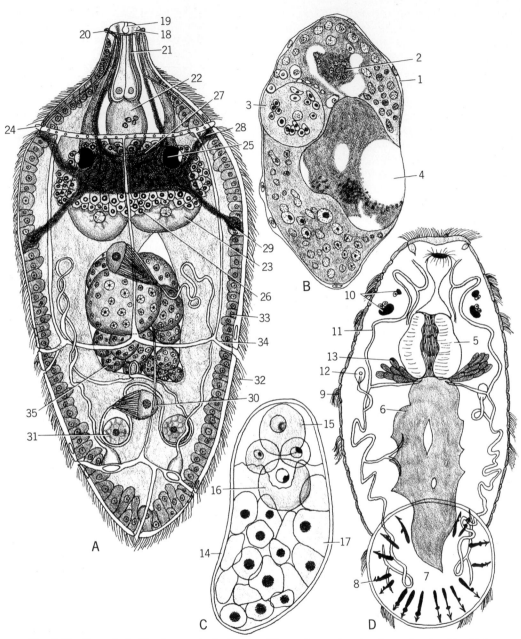

Fig. 7.25. Trematode Development. A. A miracidium of complex structure, showing the high stage of differentiation that this larval stage may attain. B. Embryo of a monogenetic trematode, *Polystoma*, showing organs arising from cell masses reminiscent of those seen in ectolecithal turbellarians. C. The four-cell stage of a digenetic trematode, *Parorchis*. The four blastomeres lie at the upper side of the capsule, and the mass of yolk cells below them. The propagatory cell is distinguishable from the other blastomeres. D. A *Polystoma* larva, with several bands of locomotor cilia. Note the resemblance of the opisthaptor to *Gyrodactylus*,

tive cell is apparently a modification of cleavage associated with larval reproduction, for the germinal tissue of the miracidium is the stem tissue for all larval reproductive bodies.

Monogenea. Monogenetic trematodes produce capsules in which development has already begun, and which hatch a few days to a few weeks after being freed. A free-swimming larva (Fig. 7.25D), with eyes and usually with three or four transverse bands of cilia, emerges. The larval opisthaptor resembles the opisthaptor of *Gyrodactylus.* The larva dies in a day or two if it has not found a suitable host. It attaches to the host and metamorphoses into an adult. Metamorphosis often involves a profound change of the opisthaptor, accomplished by shedding the larval attachment organ or by gradual metamorphosis. During metamorphosis, the ciliated epidermis is shed and the eyes are usually lost.

A curious feature of the *Polystoma* life cycle may show how a complex life cycle involving several host species might have developed. *Polystoma* lives in frog urinary bladders. Larvae attach to tadpoles, and become sexually mature but retain the larval form if the tadpoles are young. On older tadpoles they remain immature until the tadpole metamorphoses, when they move into the urinary bladder, lose the larval traits, and become sexually mature

Digenea. Digenetic trematodes always have a complex life cycle, involving several free-living and parasitic larval stages. The progression of larval stages is from miracidium to sporocyst to redia to cer-

caria (Fig. 7.17B-G). The cercaria becomes a metacercaria by encysting and develops into the adult in the final host. Life cycles may be lengthened or shortened by the addition of a generation of daughter sporocysts or rediae, or by the omission of sporocysts or rediae.

MIRACIDIUM. The miracidium is highly differentiated although minute (Fig. 7.25A). Four or five tiers of ciliated, epidermal cells cover the surface. Nerves to eyes, sensory papillae, and muscles rise from the brain. Each sinuous protonephridial tubule has one or two flame bulbs. An anterior apical papilla contains openings of the large, central apical glands and lateral penetration glands. Propagative cells and germ balls, derived from the embryonic propagative cell, fill the body space. Miracidia swim continuously, as if aware of their need to find a host in a few hours. Some miracidia have a chemotactic mechanism to aid in host recognition, but others seem to find the host accidentally. The miracidium sheds its ciliated epidermal cells as it enters the host. Histolytic secretions of the penetration glands aid in entry. Most species have miracidia that can successfully enter and develop in several species of snails or clams.

SPOROCYST. The miracidium metamorphoses into a sporocyst in the host. Contact with the host induces metamorphosis, which continues *in vitro* if the parasites are removed from the host after the initial contact. Metamorphosis involves extensive simplification, for the sporocyst is little more than a brood sac containing germ balls, propagative cells, and immature, de-

although the adult worm will have several suckers on the opisthaptor. (A, after Lynch. B and D, after Halkin. C, after Rees.) 1, epidermis; 2, brain primordium; 3, pharynx primordium; 4, intestinal primordium; 5, pharynx; 6, intestine; 7, opisthaptor; 8, marginal hook; 9, ciliary band; 10, ocelli; 11, nephridium; 12, nephridiopore; 13, pharyngeal gland; 14, capsule wall; 15, propagatory cell; 16, somatic cell; 17, yolk cell; 18, apical papilla; 19, pore for apical gland; 20, pore for penetration gland; 21, gland cell; 22, apical gland; 23, penetration gland; 24, lateral sensory papillae; 25, eye; 26, nerve cell; 27, brain; 28, lateral nerve; 29, posterior nerve; 30, flame bulb; 31, athrocyte; 32, ciliated epidermis; 33, subepithelium; 34, line between epidermal cells; 35, germ ball.

veloping larvae (Fig. 7.17D). Some trematode sporocysts give rise to a second generation of sporocysts, which then produce cercariae. Most fluke sporocysts produce rediae. Thus, depending on the species, sporocysts may contain daughter sporocysts, rediae, or cercariae.

REDIAE. The vermiform redia is considerably more differentiated than a sporocyst. The body wall is often pierced by a birth pore, and the body may have lateral or ventral appendages. Primordia of the digestive, nervous, and protonephridial systems are present (Fig. 7.17E). The central cavity is packed with propagative cells, germ balls, and immature larvae. Some rediae produce a second generation of rediae, but generally they produce cercariae.

CERCARIAE. The cercaria is a more advanced larva, with primordia of most of the adult organs and larval organs that disappear during metamorphosis. The broad fluke-like body ends in a muscular tail, variable in form and distinctive in the principal trematode groups. Digestive, nervous, and protonephridial systems are well developed (Fig. 7.17F). Propagative cells assemble to form the primordia of the reproductive organs. Many large, unicellular penetration glands are usually present, and some cercaria have an anterior stylet that aids in host penetration. Many cercariae have eye-spots. Cercariae emerge from the intermediate host and take up a short, free-swimming existence. Some encyst on vegetation likely to be eaten by herbivorous final hosts. Others penetrate a second intermediate host, encysting in its muscles or other organs, developing into adults when the second intermediate host is eaten by the carnivorous final host. A few cercariae actively penetrate the skin of the final host, migrating to the appropriate host organ. Schistosomes (blood flukes) follow the last course, taking up final residence in mesenterial blood vessels. The encysted cercariae are known as metacercariae.

METACERCARIAE. Most flukes have tailless metacercariae, the tail being shed as cercariae enter the final host or as the cyst membrane is laid down. Metacercariae undergo a partial metamorphosis, the larval cercarial organs degenerating during and after encystment. The reproductive organs remain immature, and the final steps of metamorphosis occur in the final host.

IMPORTANCE OF LIFE CYCLES. Knowledge of parasitic life cycles is of great importance, for relationships can often be determined more easily in immature than in mature forms, and the best methods of controlling human or domestic animal parasites are often dependent on knowledge of the life cycle. The incidence of infection in a region can be reduced greatly by reducing the number of intermediate hosts or the chances of intermediate hosts to become infected. Some wild or domestic animals serve as reservoir hosts, keeping an infection going even when sewage disposal or case treatment has reduced the likelihood of ova reaching the intermediate hosts from human patients. Knowledge of the intermediate hosts and of the kinds of animals that feed upon them is often useful in locating the reservoir hosts in an area.

The complex trematode life cycle was not easily discovered. The first to be worked out was for the sheep liver fluke, described by Thomas in 1883. Since then, many have been described in detail.

The ability of larval forms to multiply asexually is of great importance in increasing the probability of successful completion of a life cycle. As many as 200,000 cercariae may be released by a single infected snail. Larval reproduction is not a true alternation of generations, however. It is more correct to think of it as a highly specialized form of polyembryony, fixed through embryonic development by the differentiation of propagative cells. Polyembryony, the formation of several embryos from a single ovum, occurs in several other animal phyla.

The Cestoda—The Tapeworms

Cestodes are usually divided into a number of segments known as proglottids, with one or two complete, hermaphroditic reproductive systems in each segment. Some are important human parasites, and others are economically significant parasites of domestic animals. The morphology of adult and larvae of *Taenia* is summarized in Fig. 7.26, and should be examined carefully before continuing.

Classification of Cestodes

Cestodes have been known since ancient times; they are probably among the parasitic worms mentioned in an Egyptian papyrus of about 1550 B.C. Cestode classification has been somewhat less controversial than trematode classification, with relatively few recent changes. There are many orders; only a few more prominent ones are mentioned here. The classification and figures of representatives should be examined carefully before considering the group as a whole.

Subclass Cestodaria. Embryos with ten hooks; body unsegmented and without a scolex; a single reproductive system as in trematodes. Example: *Gyrocotyle* (Fig. 7.27E).

Subclass Eucestoda. Embryos with six hooks; body usually segmented, composed of scolex and a strobila of proglottids; a complete reproductive system in each proglottid.

Order Tetraphyllidea. Scolex with four lappet-like attachment organs known as bothridia and often with hooks; proglottids in various stages of development; yolk glands in lateral bands in the proglottids; genital pores lateral; in elasmobranch

fishes. Example: *Phyllobothrium* (Fig. 7.27C,D).

Order Trypanorhyncha. Scolex with two or four bothridia and four protrusible, spiny proboscides in sheaths; yolk glands in cortical layer around the proglottid; genital pores lateral; in elasmobranchs and some fishes. Example: *Tentacularia* (Fig. 7.27A,B).

Order Pseudophyllidea. Usually segmented, with one terminal or two lateral, groove-shaped attachment organs known as bothria; most proglottids in a strobila at the same stage of development; yolk glands in dorsal and ventral layers across proglottids; uterus opening at a uterine pore; genital pores usually midventral; in bony fishes or terrestrial vertebrates. Example: *Diphyllobothrium* (Fig. 7.28C,D).

Order Proteocephaloidea. Scolex with four cup-shaped suckers and with an apical sucker or glandular organ; yolk glands in lateral bands in each proglottid; uterus ruptures to form midventral uterine pores; genital pores lateral; in cold-blooded vertebrates. Example: *Ophiotaenia* (Fig. 7.28A,B).

Order Cyclophyllidea. Scolex with four cup-shaped suckers and usually with an apical rostellum; proglottids in various stages of development; yolk gland compact and posterior; uterus without a uterine pore; genital pores usually lateral; typically in warm-blooded vertebrates. Example: *Taenia* (Fig. 7.26).

Cestode Organ Systems

Cestode organ systems are modified by the segmented nature of the body and by the parasitic habit, but follow the general organization of other flatworms. The most outstanding peculiarity is the complete absence of mouth and enteron.

Food Acquisition. All cestodes are internal parasites and absorb food through the body surface. It is possible that where the head or scolex works itself deeply into

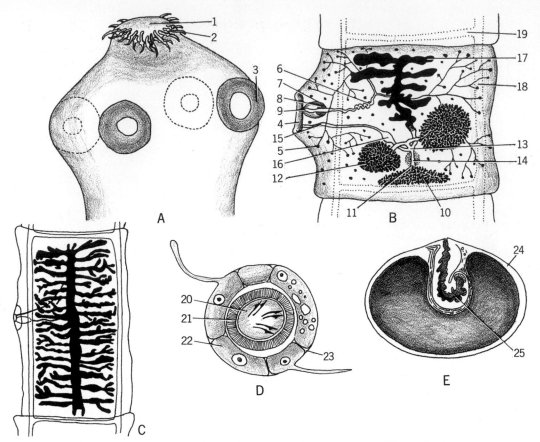

Fig. 7.26. Cestode Structure. **A.** The scolex or head of *Taenia solium*. The scolex forms in the larva, which is encysted in the muscle tissue of the intermediate host. When the muscle is eaten by the final host the scolex attaches to the intestinal wall and buds off a series of segments or proglottids that remain attached to the scolex. The scolex and attached proglottids form a ribbon-shaped strobila. The youngest proglottids occur at the budding zone, while the older ones come to lie further down in the chain. As they age, the proglottids differentiate, and eventually become mature. **B.** A mature proglottid of *T. solium* with the reproductive organs fully differentiated. Such mature proglottids produce a great number of ova. Ova are encapsulated and stored in the uterus, which branches repeatedly as the ova accumulate. **C.** A gravid proglottid of *T. solium*, with degenerating reproductive systems and a uterus filled with encapsulated ova. Such proglottids detach and emerge from the final host with the feces. Capsules are liberated when the proglottids break down. **D.** A capsule of *T. saginata*, containing the developing hexacanth embryo. The capsules are generally termed ova but are actually encapsulated larvae, infective for the herbivorous intermediate host. When eaten by an intermediate host a cysticercus develops from the hexacanth embryo. **E.** A cysticercus, with an inverted scolex. These bladder-worms are infective for the final host. (**A**, after Chandler and Read. **B-C**, after the Nobles. **C**, after Roudabush, from the Nobles. **D**, after Belding. **E**, after Leuckart, from Belding.) *External features:* 1, rostellum; 2, rostellar hooks; 3, acetabulum or sucker; 4, gonopore. *Male reproductive system:* 5, testis; 6, sperm duct; 7, cirrus sac; 8, seminal vesicle; 9, cirrus. *Female reproductive system:* 10, yolk gland; 11, yolk duct; 12, ovary; 13, oviduct; 14, oötype, surrounded by Mehlis's gland; 15, vagina; 16, seminal receptacle; 17, uterus. *Protonephridial system:* 18, longitudinal excretory canal; 19, transverse excretory canal. *Capsule:* 20, hexacanth embryo; 21, striated embryophore; 22, granular layer; 23, capsule wall. *Cysticercus:* 24, bladder wall; 25, inverted scolex.

230

the intestinal mucosa, it may absorb material not available to the segments. The cuticle must be permeable to foods despite its heavy appearance. As there is no epidermis, the cuticle rests directly on the parenchyma. Cestode cuticle consists of a thick homogeneous layer, covered by a thin comidial layer. Rothman found the comidial

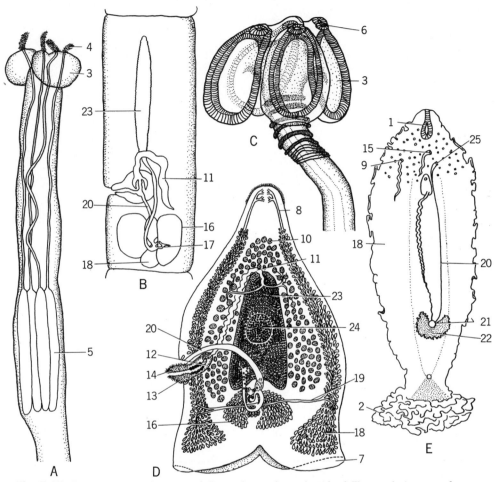

Fig. 7.27. Representative Cestodes. **A-B.** Scolex and proglottid of *Tentacularia musculara*, a trypanorhynchid cestode. Trypanorhynchids are especially characterized by the four spiny, retractable proboscides on the scolex. **C-D.** Scolex and proglottid of a tetraphyllidean cestode. Tetraphyllideans are characterized by the four large bothridia on the scolex and by proglottids with lateral bands of yolk glands and lateral gonopores. **E.** *Gyrocotyle urna*, a typical cestodarian. These cestodes have no scolex, and the body is not segmented. (A-B, after Hart. C-D, after Goodchild, from Brown. E, after Lynch.) *External features:* 1, sucker; 2, rosette; 3, bothridia; 4, proboscis; 5, proboscis receptacle; 6, terminal sucker; 7, marginal lobe. *Protonephridial system:* 8, excretory canal; 9, excretory pore. *Male reproductive system:* 10, testis; 11, sperm duct; 12, seminal vesicle; 13, cirrus pouch; 14, cirrus; 15, male gonopore. *Female reproductive system:* 16, ovary; 17, oviduct; 18, yolk gland; 19, yolk duct; 20, vagina; 21, seminal receptacle; 22, Mehlis's gland; 23, uterus; 24, uterine pore; 25, copulatory pore.

layer a dense covering of delicate micro-
trichs in electron micrographs; each has a
dense outer layer and a core continuous
with the homogeneous layer. The cuticle
is unique in containing mitochondria, and
many tiny vesicles that could be interpreted
as pinocytic vesicles concerned with food
absorption (Fig. 7.29A). Cuticle formation has not been explained. A number of
insunk cells, epidermal or parenchymal in
nature, penetrate the basement membrane
and would be well suited for cuticle secretion, but it is difficult to see how mitochondria come to be in a secreted cuticle.

Respiration. Respiration is anaerobic, involving glycogen degradation and the formation of carbon dioxide and various
organic acids. Different species release different combinations of acids, indicating
diversity among the respiratory enzymes.
Available oxygen is taken up and used. Cytochrome C has been found, and presumably a typical cytochrome-oxidase system

exists. Under natural conditions, however,
oxygen is rarely available in appreciable
amounts.

Excretion. The protonephridial system
of cestodes consists of a dorsal and ventral
excretory duct on each side of the body,
from which typical secondary canals ending in flame bulbs arise. The ventral ducts
are usually connected by a transverse excretory duct at the posterior end of each
proglottid; rarely, the dorsals are also connected by a transverse duct. Other longitudinal canals may be present; some
Cyclophyllidea have as many as twenty.
The main longitudinal ducts continue into
the strobila and are connected by a plexus
of tiny tubules, possibly indicating that
ancestral cestodes had a recurved protonephridial tubule.

The nephridia are probably osmoregula-
tory and discharge the organic acids formed
during energy release as well as some of the
nitrogenous wastes. Vital dyes accumulate
in granules in some proglottids; this may

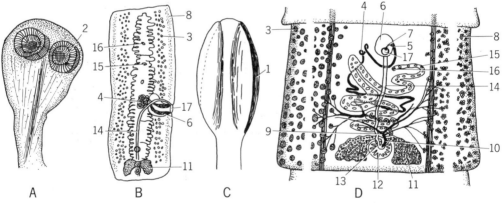

Fig. 7.28. Representative Cestodes. **A-B.** Scolex and proglottids of *Ophiotaenia*, a proteoceph-
alid cestode. The scolex with four suckers and proglottids with lateral bands of yolk glands and
uterine pores formed by the rupture of the body wall are characteristic. **C-D.** Scolex and
proglottid of *Diphyllobothrium*, a typical pseudophyllidean cestode. The one or two sucking
grooves or bothria on the scolex and proglottids with a discrete uterine pore are characteristic.
Testes are shown only on the left and yolk glands only on the right of the proglottid.
(**A-B**, after Van Cleave and Mueller. **C**, after Hyman. **D**, after Goodchild, in Brown.) *External
features:* 1, bothrium; 2, acetabulum. *Male reproductive system:* 3, testis; 4, sperm duct;
5, seminal vesicle; 6, cirrus sac; 7, cirrus. *Female reproductive system:* 8, yolk gland; 9, yolk
duct; 10, common yolk duct; 11, ovary; 12, oötype and Mehlis's gland; 13, common oviduct;
14, vagina; 15, uterus; 16, uterine pore; 17, common gonopore.

mean that some storage excretion normally occurs.

Parenchyma and Internal Transport. Cestode parenchyma is syncytial, with fluid-filled spaces as in other flatworms. It undoubtedly functions in the same manner.

Locomotion and Movement. Adult tapeworms have no external cilia, and movement depends entirely on muscular contraction. A thin layer of circular and one or two layers of longitudinal muscles are present. The parenchymal muscles form one or two heavy layers of longitudinal fibers and dorsal or ventral sheets of transverse fibers (Fig. 7.29C). The transverse and longitudinal fibers may form a muscular septum enclosing the inner part of the parenchymal tissue. A few dorsoventral muscles are usually present. Parenchymal muscles are especially prominent in the scolex, where they are arranged to manipulate the scolex attachment organs (Fig. 7.29B).

Sense Organs. Many free nerve endings are probably sensory, but little is known of sensory reception in cestodes. There are no special sense organs. Certain club-shaped neurosensory endings are known to be tactile.

Nervous System. Progressive changes in the cestode musculature have apparently

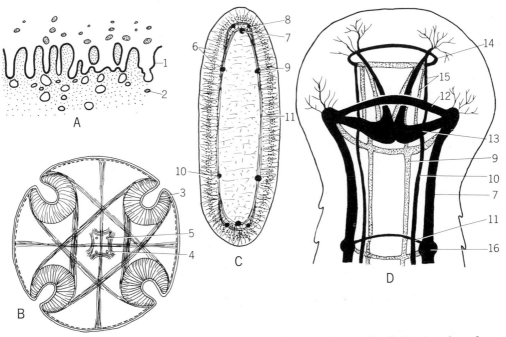

Fig. 7.29. A. Scheme of cestode cuticle, as seen in electron micrograph. B. Section through the scolex of a taenioid tapeworm, showing the arrangement of muscle fibers. C. Scheme of section through the proglottid of a taenioid tapeworm, showing the distribution of nerve cords. D. Central nervous system of *Moniezia*, a taenioid. (A, based on photographs in Rothman. B, after Fuhrmann. C, after Becker. D, after Tower.) 1, microtriche at margin of cuticle; 2, pore canals, possibly pinocytic vesicles containing surrounding medium; 3, sucker; 4, brain; 5, excretory vesicles; 6, mesenchymal longitudinal muscle layer; 7, lateral nerve cord; 8, accessory lateral nerve cord; 9, dorsal nerve cord; 10, ventral nerve cord; 11, commissural nerve ring; 12, nerve ring; 13, transverse commissural ganglion; 14, rostellar nerve ring; 15, anterior nerve; 16, ganglion on commissural nerve ring.

balanced the reduction of sense organs, for the nervous system is about as complex as in free-living flatworms. Two main longitudinal nerve trunks parallel the excretory ducts, and accessory longitudinal trunks are usually present (Fig. 7.29C). Each proglottid contains at least one ring commissure. The brain lies between the two lateral trunks, and is surrounded by a ring commissure, with large ganglia at its junctions with the lateral trunks and smaller ones at junctions with the other longitudinal trunks (Fig. 7.29D). A rostellar ring commissure in front of the brain connects the anterior projections of the longitudinal trunks.

Reproductive System. Tapeworms leave no doubt that their major business is the formation of ova. The few unsegmented cestodes have a single hermaphroditic reproductive system, but other cestodes have at least one full set of reproductive organs in each proglottid—and little else.

MALE SYSTEM. Details of the male system are essentially as in other flatworms. Detailed differences are useful in taxonomy, but contribute little to a further understanding of the reproductive process. Testes are numerous, and are strewn at random in the proglottid or lie in lateral fields. Arrangement of the testes, and other reproductive organs, tends to be characteristic of cestode orders, and an examination of the details in representatives shown in Figs. 7.27 and 7.28 will be helpful. Sperm ductules unite to form a sperm duct, usually much coiled, which enters the copulatory complex. Cestodes have an armed or unarmed cirrus, enclosed in a muscular cirrus sac. Sometimes a muscular dilation of the ejaculatory duct or sperm duct forms a propulsion vesicle. Prostatic glands usually open into the sperm duct or ejaculatory duct, but prostatic vesicles are rare.

FEMALE SYSTEM. A single, bilobed ovary, sometimes dorsoventrally forked to form four arms, lies in each proglottid. Yolk glands are almost universally follicular, but form a compact organ in taenioids. A

yolk-duct system empties into a single yolk duct and joins the oviduct shortly after its emergence from the ovary (Fig. 7.26B). Except in cyclophyllideans, an ovicapt pulls ova into the oviduct by strong peristaltic contractions. Near the ovicapt, a vagina branches off from the oviduct; it runs to the genital antrum and often contains a dilated seminal receptacle, where sperm received during mating are stored. Beyond the entrance of the vagina, the ovovitelline duct continues as a uterus, small in mature proglottids, but becoming coiled or branched in gravid proglottids filled with ova. Ova are retained until the proglottid is shed or leave by a uterine pore. A Mehlis's gland encloses the oviduct where the eggs are encapsulated, as in flukes.

The cestode and trematode female systems would correspond very well if the cestode vagina were the uterus, and if the uterus were Laurer's canal. There must have been a shifting of external pores, or else the part known as Laurer's canal in trematodes must correspond to the cestode uterus. Both views have been held, but it would be difficult to choose between them on the basis of present information. As cestodes and trematodes have probably arisen independently of rhabdocoel ancestral stocks, the similarities may be somewhat accidental.

CESTODE LIFE CYCLES

All cestodes have a complex life cycle, but some life cycles have been secondarily simplified by the omission of some stages. Larval reproduction occurs in some cestodes, but is less common than in trematodes. Larval stages differ somewhat in different groups, so no simple list can be given.

Embryonic Development. Development begins while the ova are in the uterus. Each ovum is encapsulated with one or several yolk cells. The capsule wall is usually retained, but in *Taenia* the thin capsule is eventually shed, the final shell being formed during development. Regardless of the destiny of the capsule wall, two membranes form around the embryo during development of pseudophyllids and cyclophyllids. The outer membrane forms first; it is built from one or several blastomeres appearing during early cleavage. The pseudophyllid outer membrane encloses the yolk, and the inner mass of cells produces a second, delicate inner membrane, apparently the embryonic ectoderm (Fig. 7.30A). The remaining cells develop into an onchosphere, an oval, hooked embryo (Fig. 7.30B). The capsules are liberated from the host, and when they enter the water, a ciliated larva known as a coracidium emerges. The outer membrane is left behind, but the inner ectodermal membrane bears cilia (Fig. 7.31B).

In the cyclophyllid, *Taenia*, the ovum forms micromeres, mesomeres, and macromeres during cleavage. The two or three macromeres absorb yolk from the yolk cells and form a syncytial nutritive membrane; the single yolk cell remains outside (Fig. 7.30C). Later, several mesomeres form an inner membrane around the remaining blastomeres. This hardens into a heavy shell, known as the embryophore. The inner cell mass forms the onchosphere. The capsule, and often the outer membrane, is lost, and the embryo is surrounded only by the embryophore when it leaves the host. Not all *Taenia* shed the capsule; a few retain it and have a thinner embryophore.

Life cycles are not known for all cestode orders. Pseudophyllids and cyclophyllids are best known. Pseudophyllids usually have two intermediate hosts, the first a crustacean and the second a fish or some other vertebrate. Cyclophyllids have a single intermediate host, usually an arthropod, but sometimes a vertebrate or other

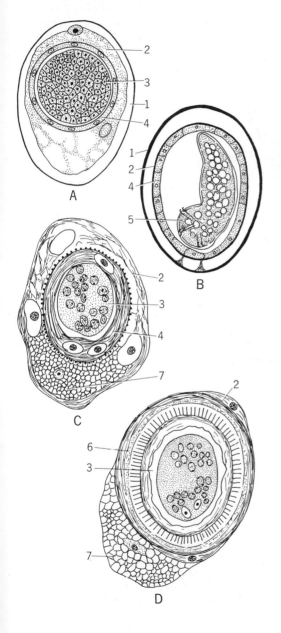

A

B

C

D

Fig. 7.30. Cestode Development. A-B. Two stages in the development of a pseudophyllidean, *Eubothrium*, showing the inner and outer membrane laid down and the mature hexacanth. C-D. Two stages in the development of *Taenia*, showing the formation of the inner membrane, and the outer membrane disappearing while the inner membrane forms a striated shell. (A-B, after Schauinsland. C-D, after Janicki.) 1, capsule; 2, outer membrane; 3, embryo; 4, inner membrane; 5, hexacanth embryo; 6, shell; 7, yolk cell.

invertebrate. A few have no intermediate host, the final host being infected directly by the shelled larvae.

The larva emerging from the capsule is always hooked, but Cestodaria larvae (decacanths) have ten hooks, and Eucestoda larvae (hexacanths) have six hooks. The external ciliated layer of decacanths and some hexacanths is shed after the larva is eaten by a suitable host. The correspond-

ing embryophore of cyclophyllid capsules is digested when the capsule is eaten.

PROCERCOID. In both Cestodaria and pseudophyllids, the embryo uses its hooks to work into the host tissues and develops into a procercoid, an elongated larva covered by a thick cuticle and with a tail containing the hooks (Fig. 7.31A). Large frontal glands open at the anterior end. It remains quiescent until its host is eaten by

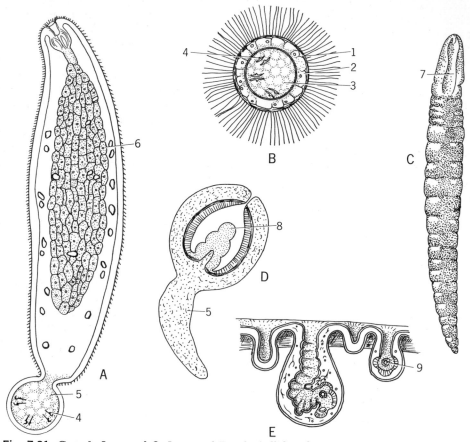

Fig. 7.31. Cestode Larvae. A–C. Larvae of Pseudophyllidea. **A,** a mature procercoid, showing the hooks and large frontal gland. **B,** a ciliated coracidium, adapted to be eaten by an aquatic arthropod. **C,** a plerocercoid, which develops when a fish eats the arthropod containing the procercoid. D–E. Larvae of taenioid cestodes. **D,** a cysticercoid, differing from a cysticercus in its solid construction. **E,** a coenurus, a cyst-like larva containing a number of scolices. (A–B, after Rosen. D, after Hamann. C, after Belding. E, after Fantham, Stephens, and Theobald, from Belding.) **1,** outer membrane; **2,** inner membrane; **3,** hexacanth embryo; **4,** hook; **5,** tail; **6,** frontal gland; **7,** bothria; **8,** rostellum; **9,** inverted scolex.

a second intermediate host, usually a fish.

PLEROCERCOID. The procercoid penetrates the gut wall of the second intermediate host, apparently with the aid of frontal gland secretions. It becomes a plerocercoid (Fig. 7.31C) by elongating and forming the attachment organs of the scolex at the anterior end. Primordia of most of the organ systems are present except for the reproductive organs, which do not appear until proglottids are formed. Cestodaria, however, have only one intermediate host, and the procercoid develops into the adult. The adult does not strobilate, and is plerocercoid-like. Cestodaria may be cestodes in which the plerocercoid has become sexually mature instead of primitive cestodes, as was once believed.

When eaten by a suitable host, plerocercoids develop into adults. Little metamorphosis is required, for the scolex and major organs are already formed. Proglottids begin to develop and gradually mature.

CYSTICERCOID. The cyclophyllid onchosphere develops into a cysticercoid larva (Fig. 7.31D). The middle of the body grows up around the anterior end to form a cavity containing the scolex, while the tail, containing the hooks, remains free. The scolex is not turned inside out. When the host containing the cysticercoid is eaten, the body is digested away from the scolex, which develops proglottids and becomes mature.

CYSTICERCUS. Some cyclophyllids form a cysticercus instead of a cysticercoid. The scolex of a cysticercus is turned inside out (Fig. 7.26E) and hangs in a large cavity formed by the rest of the body. This larva, often known as a bladderworm, develops into an adult by eversion of the scolex and strobilization.

Cysticercoids and cysticerci may reproduce by budding. The most noteworthy examples are the hydatid cysts of *Echinococcus granulosus*, a tiny tapeworm living in dogs. The eggs are eaten by herbivores, especially sheep, and the onchospheres are carried by portal blood to the liver, where hydatids are most commonly found. They grow into a cyst, with an inner, germinative layer that forms daughter cysts. Many inverted scolices form within the daughter cysts (Fig. 7.32D). The cysts may become very large and interfere with the normal functioning of infected organs. Many infections with hydatids prove fatal.

Phylum Nemertinea

Nemertine worms are abundant in the littoral zone of temperate oceans, where they live among rocks and algae or in mucous tubes embedded in mud or sand. A few have invaded fresh water, and some live in humid tropical and subtropical land habitats. The smallest are only a few millimeters long, and the longest, *Lineus longissimus*, is said to reach 30 m. Most species are pallid or dull, but some are brightly colored. They are a relatively successful group, with about 500 to 600 known species.

They resemble Turbellaria in several ways:

1. They have a ciliated epidermis, and some species have rhabdites.

2. They are usually flattened and vermiform.

3. Parenchyma fills the space between the body wall and enteron.

4. They usually have a protonephridial system with terminal flame bulbs.

They differ from Platyhelminthes in a number of important and progressive ways:

1. They have a closed circulatory system, sometimes containing a respiratory pigment, haemoglobin.

2. They have a complete digestive system, with mouth and anus.

3. They have a unique proboscis, carried in a special chamber, the rhynchcoel, technically comparable to a coelom and so a progressive step in body organization.

4. Organs are assembled into more or less definite organ systems, as in higher invertebrates.

5. The muscular and nervous system are more highly developed.

The many progressive features of nemertines make it advisable to recognize them as distinct from the Platyhelminthes. Some zoologists, however, prefer to classify them as a separate subphylum of the Platyhelminthes.

The principal organ systems of a nemertine worm are shown in Fig. 7.32A. It will be helpful to examine them closely before considering the classification and body organization characteristic of the phylum.

CLASSIFICATION

The nemertines are a relatively homogeneous group, far less variable than any phylum so far discussed. The phylum is divided into two subclasses, as the degree of uniformity is approximately that of classes of other phyla.

Subclass Anopla. With the mouth behind the brain and the central nervous system below the epidermis or among the body wall muscles; proboscis without stylets, consisting of a simple tube, which may be narrower anteriorly but is not divided into distinct regions.

Order Palaeonemertini. With an outer circular and inner longitudinal layer of body wall muscles, and sometimes with a second, innermost circular layer; a dermis of hyaline, gelatinous connective tissue. Example *Cephalothrix.*

Order Heteronemertini. Body wall musculature of outer longitudinal, middle circular, and inner longitudinal layers; a dermis of fibrous material. Examples: *Cerebratulus* (Fig. 7.33A); *Lineus* (Fig. 7.32E).

Subclass Enopla. With the mouth in front of the brain and the central nervous system inside the body wall muscles; sometimes with a piercing organ, the stylet, associated with the proboscis; proboscis divided into anterior, middle, and posterior regions.

Order Hoplonemertini. With proboscis armed with one or more stylets; a straight intestine with paired, lateral pouches. Ex-

amples: *Nectonemertes* (Fig. 7.32C); *Amphiporus* (Fig. 7.32A).

Order Bdellonemertini. Proboscis without a stylet; intestine without diverticula and winding; with a posterior adhesive disc; endocommensals in molluscs. Example: *Malacobdella* (Fig. 7.32B).

BODY ORGANIZATION AND HISTOLOGY

Body organization and histological development are best seen in cross sections. The epidermis is far more complex than in Turbellaria. Interstitial cells, sometimes forming a syncytium, are crowded in between the narrowed bases of the ciliated cells (Fig. 7.33B,C). Nemertines, like Turbellaria, have many uses for mucus and leave slime trails behind them. Several kinds of unicellular glands and small clusters of gland cells opening through a single duct (packet glands) open through the epidermis. In heteronemertines, packet glands are insunk, lying in the dermis.

A dermis lies below the epidermis. It is a thin, hyaline, gelatinous connective tissue in palaeonemertines and hoplonemertines (Fig. 7.33B). In heteronemertines, it is differentiated into an outer hyaline layer and an inner fibrous region, characteristic of the order (Fig. 7.33C), and often containing some muscle fibers.

Muscle layers differ markedly in the nemertine groups. Palaeonemertines and hoplonemertines have an outer layer of circular and an inner layer of longitudinal muscles (Fig. 7.34A,C), and some have a second circular layer inside the longitudinal layer. The order is reversed in heteronemertines, with outer longitudinal, middle circular, and inner longitudinal layers (Fig. 7.34B). The muscle layers of the everted proboscis correspond to those of the body wall, and are reversed in the inverted proboscis.

The parenchyma is considerably more highly specialized. It is represented by the dermis, and by a gelatinous matrix containing vesicular cells that surrounds the blood vessels, nerves, and proboscis sheath.

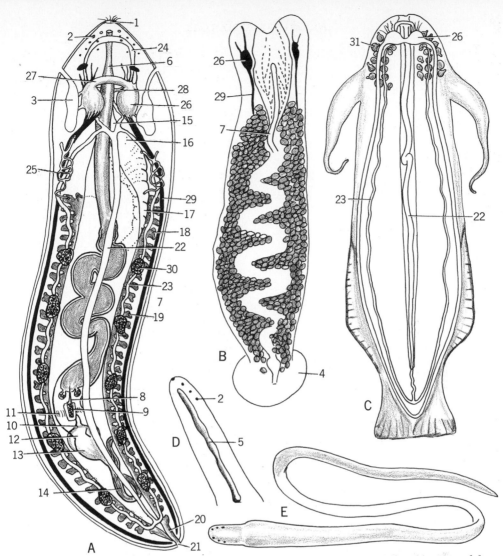

Fig. 7.32. Some Nemertinea. **A.** Scheme of a female hoplonemertine, *Amphiporus pulcher*, in dorsal view. Hoplonemertines have a mouth in front of the brain and a proboscis armed with stylets. **B.** A bdellonemertine, *Malacobdella*. Bdellonemertines have the brain behind the mouth and an unarmed proboscis, and also have a posterior adhesive disc. **C.** A pelagic hoplonemertine, *Nectonemertes mirabilis*, with lateral and caudal fins used in swimming. **D, E.** A heteronemertine, *Lineus ruber*, showing the whole worm and the head from side view. Heteronemertines have the mouth behind the brain and an unarmed proboscis. (A, after Bürger, from Goodchild, in Brown. B, after Guberlet. E, after Hyman. C, after Coe, from Pratt.) *External form:* 1, frontal organ; 2, ocelli; 3, cerebral organ; 4, adhesive disc; 5, cephalic slit. *Proboscis:* 6, rhynchodaeum; 7, anterior proboscis sheath; 8, stylet; 9, base of stylet; 10, diaphragm canal; 11, partition; 12, middle proboscis chamber; 13, posterior proboscis chamber; 14, proboscis retractor. *Digestive system:* 15, esophagus; 16, stomach; 17, pylorus; 18, caecal diverticula; 19, intestinal diverticula; 20, rectum; 21, anus. *Circulatory system:* 22, dorsal blood vessel; 23, lateral blood vessel; 24, cephalic lacuna. *Nephridial system:* 25, excretory canal. *Nervous system:* 26, cerebral ganglion; 27, dorsal cerebral commissure; 28, ventral cerebral commissure; 29, lateral nerve trunk. *Reproductive system:* 30, ovary; 31, testis.

The body-wall musculature increases at the expense of the parenchyma. When it is very thick, little parenchyma is present.

The position of the nerve trunks is also characteristic of the orders. Some palaeonemertines have epidermal nerve trunks, but they are generally just below the epidermis (Fig. 7.34A). In a few palaeonemertines and in heteronemertines the nerve trunks are among the muscles layers (Fig. 7.34B). In hoplonemertines and bdellonemertines, the trunks are in the parenchyma, completely within the muscle layers (Fig. 7.34C). In nemertines, as in flatworms, the nervous system is under the epidermis or is a part of the epidermis in primitive species, but withdraws to the interior in more highly specialized forms.

THE ORGAN SYSTEMS

Except for the very simple reproductive system, the organ systems of nemertines are better developed than in Turbellaria. They show the avenues of adaptive improvements which have, on the whole, been followed by the main invertebrate phyla of the annelid-anthropod stem.

Proboscis. The proboscis was once considered a part of the digestive system, but

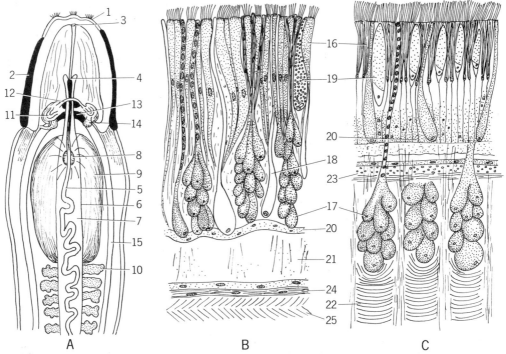

A   B   C

Fig. 7.33. A. Dorsal view of the front end of *Cerebratulus*. **B.** Epidermis of *Tubulanus*, a palaeonemertine. Palaeonemertines have a gelatinous dermis. **C.** Epidermis of *Baseodiscus*, a heteronemertine. Heteronemertines have a fibrous dermis. (All after Bürger.) *External form:* 1, sensory papilla; 2, cephalic slit. *Proboscis:* 3, proboscis pore; 4, attachment of proboscis to rhynchodaeum; 5, proboscis; 6, proboscis sheath; 7, rhynchocoel. *Digestive system:* 8, mouth; 9, foregut; 10, intestinal diverticulum. *Nervous system:* 11, brain; 12, dorsal commissure; 13, ventral commissure; 14, cerebral organ; 15, lateral nerve cord. *Histology:* 16, epidermal cell; 17, packet gland; 18, serous gland cell; 19, mucous goblet cell; 20, intestinal epithelium; 21, hyaline dermis; 22, fibrous dermis; 23, muscular layer in dermis; 24, circular muscle; 25, diagonal muscle.

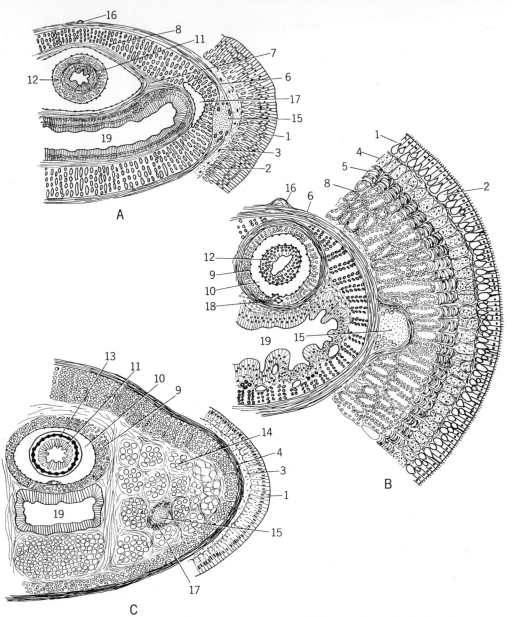

Fig. 7.34. Comparison of Cross Sections of Nemertines of Different Types. **A.** Section through a palaeonemertine, *Tubulanus*. Palaeonemertines have two or three layers of body-wall musculature, with circular fibers forming the inner layer. **B.** Section through a heteronemertine, *Lineus*. Heteronemertines have three layers of body-wall muscles, with the internal layer of longitudinal fibers. **C.** Section through a hoplonemertine. Hoplonemertines have nerve cords within the internal layer of muscles. (All after Hyman.) **1**, epidermis; **2**, gland cells; **3**, dermis; **4**, non-fibrous dermis; **5**, fibrous dermis; **6**, circular muscle; **7**, inner circular muscle layer; **8**, longitudinal muscle layer; **9**, proboscis sheath; **10**, rhynchocoel; **11**, proboscis lining; **12**, longitudinal muscle layer of proboscis; **13**, proboscis nerve ring; **14**, vesicular mesenchyme; **15**, lateral nerve cord; **16**, middorsal nerve cord; **17**, lateral blood vessel; **18**, middorsal blood vessel; **19**, digestive tube.

it arises separately and although important in food capture is no more a part of the digestive system than eyes or other sense organs that also aid in capturing food. The proboscis apparatus consists of a rhynchodaeum, proboscis, retractor muscle, and rhynchocoel. The rhynchodaeum is a tubular cavity, open at the proboscis pore and continuous posteriorly with the proboscis. The proboscis is a narrow, blind tube with muscular walls and a glandular lining (Fig. 7.32A). It is often much longer than the body and forms coils in the rhynchocoel, the cavity of the proboscis sheath. A retractor muscle attaches to the posterior end of the proboscis and the proboscis sheath, hauling in the everted proboscis when contracted. Strong contractions of the muscular proboscis sheath evert it explosively, turning it inside out and bringing its sticky, glandular surface in contact with prey. The stylet of the armed type of proboscis wounds the prey and pours a toxic secretion over it. The proboscis then wraps around the prey and pulls it to the mouth. Prey is generally swallowed whole, but some nemertines can suck out the tissues of animals too large to swallow.

Anopla have a simple, unarmed proboscis with rhabdites, and sometimes with nematocysts, in its lining. Hoplonemertines have an armed proboscis, with one or more stylets. A stylet is a spine, sitting on a prominence, the stylet base. The armed proboscis is divided into a long, anterior region, a bulbous middle region, and a posterior region containing the toxic secretion (Fig. 7.32A). The stylet sits on a glandular partition (diaphragm), which contains a pore permitting the escape of venom from the posterior region. Only the anterior part of the armed proboscis everts, bringing the stylet to the tip.

The rhynchocoel is lined with an epithelium derived from the mesoderm, and thus corresponds morphologically to a coelom. It is in no way a functional coelom, and

the correspondence is purely anatomical.

Digestive System. The outstanding development in the digestive system is the appearance of an anus, converting the enteron into a one-way street along which food can pass in an orderly manner. Each bit of food must pass each section of the gut. This is not the case in a gastrovascular cavity, in which an orderly, sequential system of food processing is not feasible. Nemertines have not fully exploited the possibilities of the new arrangement, but in many species regional specialization of the digestive tube is evident.

Thick, glandular lips lubricate the elastic mouth, and large organisms can be swallowed. The esophagus of many hoplonemertines opens into the rhynchodaeum, the mouth having been lost.

More highly specialized nemertines have a foregut, composed of a buccal cavity, esophagus and stomach, a midgut, composed of the intestine, and a hindgut, composed of a short rectum. The regions can sometimes be distinguished only by the histology of the lining cells, but are externally visible in hoplonemertines. The stomach is variable; in some forms it is drawn out into a pyloric tube lying on top of the anterior part of the intestine. The intestine is often simple, but usually has lateral diverticula, sometimes alternating regularly with the gonads (Fig. 7.32A). If the stomach opens into the intestine from above, an anterior caecum extends forward below the stomach. Diverticula disappear near the posterior end of the body, and the intestine continues to the anus as a rectum.

Accounts of nemertine digestion vary markedly, probably reflecting diversity in the way in which the gut is divided into regions. Extracellular digestion has become more important than in Turbellaria, but intracellular digestion still occurs. Extracellular digestion occurs in the stomach of some nemertines and the intestine of others. Proteins, fats, and carbohydrates are all used. Food is stored primarily as fat. Protein reserves and glycogen have also been reported.

Although the gut is tubular, its walls are embedded in solid tissue and are not free to move. Peristalsis cannot occur, and food is moved along the digestive tube by ciliary action. Cilia and flagella are the primitive mechanisms for moving materials within internal organs as well as for locomotion, and they are only gradually replaced in both situations.

Circulatory System. The first definite circulatory system is found in nemertines. It is a closed system, the fluid remaining in vessels or in spaces with endothelial linings, whereas in open systems blood emerges into the tissue spaces. Any distinction between open and closed systems is a delicate one, however, for probably no circulatory system is wholly closed. Nemertine blood circulates in blood vessels with at least a double wall, and in lacunae, which are lined by a single layer of endothelial cells. Contractile blood vessels have a complex wall (Fig. 7.36C), with an inner endothelium, a layer of hyaline connective tissue, a layer of circular muscles, and an enucleated surface layer.

The simplest system consists of two lateral blood vessels, connected by a cephalic lacuna and an anal lacuna (Fig. 7.35A). Smaller, irregular branches arise from the main trunks. Subdivision of the primitive vessels and addition of new trunks result in more complex systems (Fig. 7.35B,C). A common development is a ventral connective passing between the two lateral vessels below the rhynchodaeum. A middorsal vessel from the ventral connective runs beneath the rhynchocoel to the caudal lacuna. The system is made considerably more complex by vessels to the rhynchocoel and gut.

Corpuscles are found containing yellow, green, or orange pigments and also sometimes containing haemoglobin. Several kinds of amoeboid cells also occur in the blood of some nemertines.

The nemertine circulatory system is an important progressive development, but it is a primitive system. Blood-flow is not highly organized; blood may ebb and flow in a vessel, and transport is less efficient than in a system with one-way traffic following a definite circuit. The lack of valves makes effective blood routing impossible.

Respiration. Nemertines generally lack respiratory organs, but some pump water in and out of the foregut, which is richly supplied with lacunae. In this arrangement, the components of a respiratory system are seen: provisions for ventilating a respiratory surface, and vascularization of the surface to facilitate pick-up and delivery of respiratory gases. It is not known how effectively this adds to respiratory exchange at the body surface.

Excretory System. Nearly all nemertines have a protonephridial system. Protonephridial tubules of primitive nemertines are usually ciliated and end in multinucleate flame bulbs (Fig. 7.36D). Two important adaptive lines can be seen: first, the development of a close association of protonephridia and the circulatory system, and second, the tendency to break the protonephridial system into transverse segments. Some primitive nemertines have a pair of branched protonephridial tubules, with flame bulbs scattered in the tissues and with many accessory nephridiopores. The highly branched systems tend to break into separate nephridia, each associated with one nephridiopore. Each subdivision usually consists of a small cluster of capillaries, ending in flame bulbs, and connected with the nephridiopore by a regionally specialized tubule, having a thicker-walled, convoluted part and thinner-walled straight parts. In *Cephalothrix,* the flame bulb has become highly modified, consisting of a thin-walled capsule opening into the tubule by a pore passing through a ciliated section (Fig. 7.36E).

Some highly branched protonephridial systems have capillary branches closely applied to the walls of the lateral blood vessels (Fig. 7.36F). A more intimate association of flame bulbs and blood vessels is seen in palaeonemertines, where the flame bulbs push into the wall of the blood vessel. The blood-vessel wall may disappear, leaving the flame bulbs hanging in the blood. In some species, the capillary tubules extend into the blood vessel and the flame bulbs are missing (Fig. 7.36A). This arrangement is known as a nephridial gland.

Little is known of excretory physiology. Vital dyes collect in the tubule walls, but not in flame bulbs.

Locomotion. Nemertines depend heavily on cilia for locomotion, and many cannot move unless in contact with the substrate. However, muscles have undergone a dramatic development in nemertines, and in larger species cause muscular waves which help to propel the animal. Pelagic species have a caudal fin, and sometimes lateral fins as well (Fig. 7.32C). These species swim with undulatory movements of the body.

Sense Organs. Nemertine sense organs are like those of Turbellaria. Many have pigment cup ocelli in the head region.

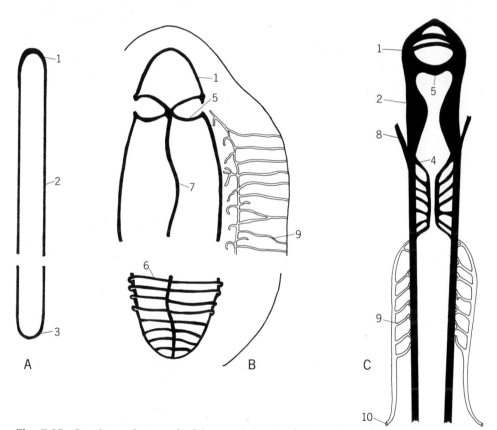

Fig. 7.35. Circulatory System. **A.** Scheme of the circulatory system of *Cephalothrix*, representing the primitive condition. **B.** Somewhat more complex circulatory system of *Amphiporus*, with some association of the nephridial and circulatory systems. **C.** More advanced circulatory system of *Tubulanus*, with a close association of nephridia and circulatory system. (A-B, after Audemans. C, after Bürger.) **1,** cephalic lacuna; **2,** lateral blood vessel; **3,** anal lacuna; **4,** rhynchocoel vessel; **5,** ventral connective; **6,** connectives; **7,** middorsal vessel; **8,** esophageal branch; **9,** nephridium; **10,** nephridiopore.

Statocysts occur in one genus. Ciliated grooves on the head are thought to act as chemoreceptors. The most characteristic sense organs are the cerebral organs, deep ectodermal pits which open into the ciliated grooves on the head. They occur in nearly all nemertines, and are closely associated with the cerebral ganglia and the vascular system. Their function is unknown; they may be chemoreceptors. The close association of gland tissue, nervous tissue, and blood vessels, however, may mean that they have an endocrine function.

Nervous System. The nervous system is built on the flatworm plan, but is more highly centralized, has a larger brain, and shows greater development of a single pair of longitudinal nerve cords. The brain is usually composed of four ganglia, a dorsal

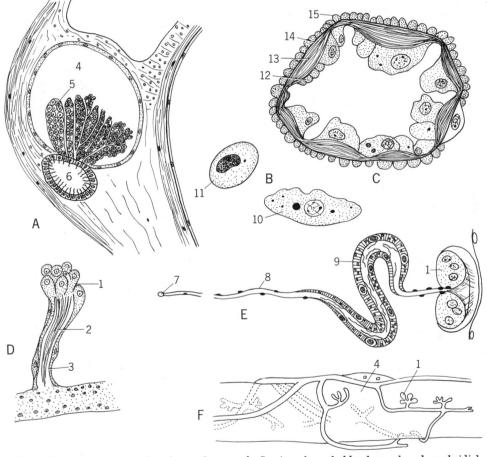

Fig. 7.36. Excretory and Circulatory System. **A.** Section through blood vessel and nephridial gland of *Procaranina*. **B.** Blood cells. **C.** Section of a contractile blood vessel. **D.** A multicellular flame bulb of *Drephanoporus*. **E.** A single nephridium of *Cephalothrix*. **F.** Nephridial tubules on the surface of a blood vessel, from *Amphiporous*. (**A**, after Nawitzki. **B**, in part after Prenant. **B**, in part, and **C**, after Riepen. **D-F**, after Bürger. **E**, after Coe.) 1, flame bulb; 2, ciliary flame; 3, capillary; 4, lateral blood vessel; 5, nephridial gland; 6, main nephridial tube; 7, nephridiopore; 8, straight tubule; 9, convoluted tubule; 10, lymphocyte; 11, red cell; 12, endothelium; 13, gelatinous layer; 14, circular muscle layer; 15, outer non-nucleated layer.

pair connected by a commissure above the rhynchodaeum, and a ventral pair connected by a commissure under the rhynchodaeum. A nerve ring thus encircles the rhynchodaeum. A pair of lateral nerve trunks, lying near the surface or deep, passes back to the posterior end, where they are connected by an anal commissure. A complex set of commissural and subsidiary longitudinal nerves may be present

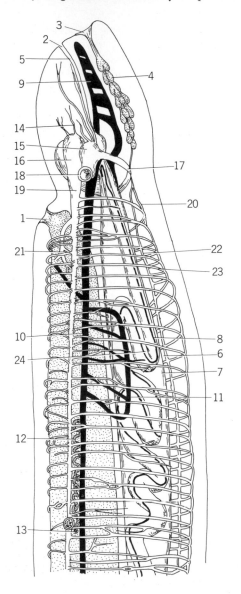

(Fig. 7.37). The nemertines are evidently more highly cephalized, and also have a far more extensive set of nerves to go with the more highly developed musculature.

Reproductive System. Considering the complexity of the rest of the organs, the reproductive system is surprisingly simple. The many gonads arise from aggregations of parenchymal cells that differentiate into sacs filled with developing gametes. As gametes ripen, each gonad develops a lateral gonopore. Sexes are almost always separate, and in the few hermaphroditic species, self-fertilization is prevented by early development of the male gonads (protandry).

Males and females shed gametes at the same time, probably in response to chemical stimulation. They may shed gametes only when in contact, or two sometimes enclose themselves in mucus before shedding gametes. Fertilization is sometimes external, and in other species sperm enter the ovaries and fertilize the ova internally. Some species are viviparous, the young developing in the ovaries. More often the ova are enclosed in a capsule and extruded in gelatinous masses or threads.

EMBRYONIC DEVELOPMENT

Cleavage is holoblastic, spiral, and determinate, but differs from endolecithal turbellarian development in producing micro-

Fig. 7.37. Anatomy of a Pelagic Nemertine. *Neuronemertes.* (After Coe.) *External features:* 1, mouth; 2, proboscis pore; 3, pore of frontal gland; 4, frontal gland. *Proboscis:* 5, rhynchodaeum; 6, proboscis sheath; 7, rhynchocoel; 8, proboscis. *Circulatory system:* 9, cephalic lacuna; 10, lateral blood vessel; 11, rhynchocoel vessel. *Nephridial system:* 12, nephridium; 13, nephridiopore. *Nervous system:* 14, cephalic nerve; 15, dorsal ganglion; 16, ventral ganglion; 17, dorsal commissure; 18, cerebral organ; 19, lateral nerve cord; 20, middorsal nerve; 21, foregut nerves; 22, lower dorsal nerve cord; 23, transverse commissure; 24, proboscis nerve.

meres that are as large and sometimes larger than the macromeres. Ectomesoderm generally arises from the micromeres, and endomesoderm from a mesendoblast, usually 4d. A coeloblastula is formed, which gastrulates by invagination or by polar ingression to form either a hollow or solid gastrula. In any event, the typical gastrula has an apical sense organ, endomesodermal cells in the old blastocoel, and an archenteron open through the blastopore.

Heteronemertines pass through a free-swimming larval stage, the pilidium, formed by the downward growth of lateral lobes to enclose the blastopore region (Fig. 7.38A). Invagination continues, producing midgut and foregut regions. The last cells to turn in are probably ectodermal. Development from this point is remarkable. Discs produced by ectodermal invagination detach and move into the interior. They grow and unite to form a larva around the pilidium gut (Fig. 7.38B,C). There are three pairs of discs, cephalic, cerebral, and trunk, and sometimes unpaired dorsal and proboscis discs. The discs are somewhat reminiscent of the masses from which young Turbellaria develop. Eventually, the larva within the pilidium escapes and develops into a young worm.

Phylogenetic Relationships

Four major ideas about the origin of flatworms have been developed, the ctenophore-polyclad theory, the ctenophore-trochophore theory, the planuloid-acoeloid theory, and the ciliate-turbellarian theory. There are difficulties with all, and as no final decision can be made, it may seem bootless to discuss them. Yet, a good controversy is always interesting, and one can learn a great deal about how animals

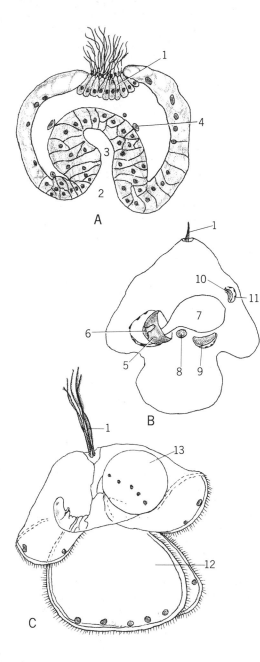

Fig. 7.38. Nemertine Development. **A.** A late gastrula of *Cerebratulus*. **B.** A pilidium, showing the fields which will develop into a larva. **C.** A pilidium containing a larva. (A, after Wilson. B, after Salensky. C, after Verrill.) 1, apical sense organ; 2, blastopore; 3, primitive gut; 4, endomesoderm; 5, cephalic disc; 6, proboscis invagination; 7, midgut; 8, disc for cerebral organ; 9, trunk disc; 10, dorsal disc; 11, amnion; 12, oral lobe of pilidium; 13, young larva within pilidium.

are built and how they behave, if not about ancestry, by going back to the original discussions. Readings in these topics can be highly absorbing and profitable.

The ctenophore-polyclad theory was especially developed by Lang (1881), who pointed out the many similarities between the platyctene ctenophores and polyclads: 1) large stomodaeal invaginations at the center of the ventral surface; 2) a pair of tentacles; 3) determinate cleavage; 4) a free-swimming larva with eight lobes; and 5) radial arrangement of polyclad intestinal trunks and nerves. But the platyctenes are so aberrant and highly specialized that they seem scarcely to have the adaptive potential needed to form the base for most of the animal kingdom. Besides, polyclads are considerably more advanced than some of the other flatworm groups, which must then be explained as degenerate forms. On the whole, this idea has declined in popularity in recent years.

The ctenophore-trochophore theory depends on certain similarities between the ctenophores and the trochophore larva characteristic of some of the higher invertebrate phyla. The similarities are far less obvious than those between ctenophores and flatworms, and the theory skips all the phyla between ctenophores and annelids. Flatworms, in this case, must be degenerate, or alternatively, larval flatworms must be considered to be more primitive kinds of trochophore larvae. Unfortunately, it is not until trochophores are fully developed that they achieve ctenophore-like traits, so the second possibility is weak. Of the first, Hyman (1959) says, "We are asked to believe the Turbellaria have lost their coelom, lost their anus, lost their nephrostomes. This is asking too much of anyone's credulity." Most zoologists would sympathize with Hyman's complaint.

The ciliate-turbellarian theory has had several recent adherents, notably Marcus (1958), Jägersten (1955), and Hadzi (1963). It is based on the idea that a bilaterally symmetrical, multinucleate ciliate became a metazoan by cytoplasmic cleavage to form a multicellular animal. It is weakest in its attempt to account for the Cnidaria, which can only be explained as degenerate flatworms. As Anthozoa are the most bilateral cnidarians, they are considered to be the primitive cnidarian form, from which Scyphozoa and Hydrozoa must be obtained. To paraphrase Hyman, we are asked to believe that Cnidaria lost a well-developed endomesoderm and replaced it with an ectodermal mesogloea, lost their protonephridia, lost their reproductive system, and invented a sexually reproducing medusa from a well-established, exclusively polypoid ancestor. This, too, seems incredible, and the idea has been severely criticized by several zoologists.

This leaves the planuloid-acoeloid theory as the most acceptable. It is based on the considerable similarities of planula larvae and acoels. Planuloid ancestral stocks are thought to have developed a mouth and an oral-aboral axis, and to have shifted the body axis to bring the mouth to the ventral surface and the brain to the anterior end. The theory is persuasive, largely because similar shifts occur in the axes of developing turbellaria, because it places the simplest flatworms as the stem group, and because it permits the animal kingdom to develop from simpler to more complex without deriving any large and successful phyla by degeneration.

The fact remains, however, that the origin of most phyla will probably remain mysterious in the predictable future, both because they appeared so long ago, and because animals are so adaptable and so plastic. Embryos are only slightly more dependable than adults when one is looking for clues to relationship. This is an area in which the questions are more important than the answers and are likely to last longer.

The relationships within the phyla are somewhat uncertain but easier to account for than the origin of the phyla. If acoels

Table 7.2. Primitive and advanced traits in turbellaria

Enteron:	None	Saccate	Straight, without diverticula.	Straight, with diverticula.	Branched into several trunks.
	Acoels	Rhabdocoels	Rhabdocoels	Alloeocoels	Triclads, Polyclads.
Pharynx:	None	Simple	Bulbous	Plicate	
	Acoels	Acoels, rhabdocoels, alloeocoels.	Rhabdocoels, alloeocoels.	Alloeocoels, triclads, polyclads.	
Protonephridia:	None	One or two, unbranched.	Branched, with accessory nephridiopores.	Reticulate, with many nephridiopores.	
	Acoels	Rhabdocoels, alloeocoels.	Alloeocoels, polyclads?	Triclads	
Nerve Trunks:	Indefinite, primarily a plexus.	Many, biradially arranged.	Five pairs.	Simplified, with one to four pairs present.	Deeply placed, in parenchyma.
	Acoels	Polyclads	Rhabdocoels, alloeocoels, triclads.	Rhabdocoels, alloeocoels, triclads.	Terrestrial triclads.
Ovary:	Indefinite	One or two pairs of germovitellaria, producing endolecithal ova.	Many germovitellaria, producing endolecithal ova.	One or two, with yolk follicles, producing ectolecithal ova.	One or two, with separate yolk glands, producing ectolecithal ova.
	Acoels	Rhabdocoels	Polyclads	Rhabdocoels, Alloeocoels.	Rhabdocoels, alloeocoels, triclads.
Testes:	Indefinite	Definite, one pair.	Definite, many pairs.		
	Acoels	Rhabdocoels, alloeocoels.	Polyclads, triclads.		

Some of the directions of turbellarian evolutionary trends are indicated in the chart, with the more primitive condition on the left and the more advanced condition on the right. Acoels are consistently the most primitive, and triclads are consistently among the most advanced. The other groups, however, differ considerably in position and are often spread over several levels of advancement. It is clear that within any one group there may be considerable difference in the rate at which different organ systems undergo evolutionary change. It is equally clear that groups which are more progressive in one system may not be equally progressive in another. To make the situation even more difficult, one cannot always distinguish between simplicity that is primitive and secondary simplicity resulting from loss of parts, and concentration or centralization of a system is many times a progressive trait. It is because of these factors that detailed evolutionary relationships are so difficult to work out, and are subject to so much controversy. In recent times, quantitative methods have been applied to differences of this type, and have sometimes proved of value in untangling possible relationships within a genus or family.

249

are the stem forms, they probably gave rise along independent lines to polyclads and to rhabdocoels. Rhabdocoels appear to have been really important stem forms, for they lead easily to the alloeocoels and so to triclads, and they strongly resemble monogenetic trematodes. They resemble rediae, and parasitic rhabdocoel stocks may have developed independently into the digenetic trematodes. Cestodes were once thought to have developed from trematodes, but differences in the arrangement of parts in the reproductive system make it more probable that they arose as an independent stem from rhabdocoels.

Nemertines have been considered as degenerate annelids, but the similarity of their sense organs, nervous system, parenchyma, and excretory organs to turbellarians makes this seem improbable. Hyman (1951) suggests that the nemertine proboscis may be a development of the kalyptorhynchid proboscis or something like it. In this case, rhabdocoels would qualify as the probable ancestral stock for nemertines also.

Whatever their origin, the flatworms and nemertines are remnants of a stock of animals that must have had an enormous influence on the course of animal evolution. Bilateral symmetry, cephalization, and the establishment of organ systems familiar throughout the animal kingdom appear to have begun with animals at this grade of organization. Within this group of animals, the major adaptive trends that have culminated in the bigger part of the animal kingdom appeared and made their initial impact on animal form.

References

Baer, J. G. 1952. *Ecology of Animal Parasites.* Univ. of Illinois Press, Urbana, Ill.

Barlowe, C. H. 1925. The life history of *Fasciolopsis buski. Am. Jour. Hyg. Monogr.* 4.

Böhmig, L. 1898. Beitrage zur Anatomie und Histologie der Nemertinen. *Ztschr. wiss. Zool.* 64: 479.

Brand, T. von. 1957. Recent trends in parasite physiology. *Exp. Parasitol.* 6: 233.

Bronsted, H. V. 1955. Planarian regeneration. *Biol. Rev.* 30: 65. (G)

Clark, R. B., and J. B. Cowey. 1959. Factors controlling the changes of shape of certain nemertean and turbellarian worms. *Jour. Exp. Biol.* 35: 731. (B)

Coe, W. R. 1943. Biology of the nemerteans of the Atlantic Coast of North America. *Trans. Conn. Acad. Arts and Sci.* 35: 129.

Dawes, B. 1946. *The Trematoda, with Special Reference to British and other European Forms.* Cambridge Univ. Press, Cambridge, Eng.

Graaf, L. v. 1911. Acoela, Rhabdocoela, and Alloeocoela des Ostens der Vereinigten Staaten von Amerika. *Ztschr. wiss. Zool.* 99: 1.

Hadzi, J. 1963. *The Evolution of the Metazoa.* Pergamon, New York.

Hanson, E. D. 1958. On the origin of the eumetazoa. *Syst. Zool.* 7: 16.

Hanström, B. 1926. Uber den feineren Bau der Nervensystems der Tricladen Turbellarien auf Grund von Untersuchungen an *Bdelloura candida. Acta Zool.* 7: 101.

——. 1928. *Vergleichende Anatomie des Nervensystems der wirbellose Tiere.* Springer, Berlin.

Hovey, H. B. 1929. Associative hysteresis in marine flatworms. *Phys. Zool.* 2: 322.

Hyman, L. H. 1951, 1959. *The Invertebrates,* Vols. 2, 5. McGraw-Hill, New York.

Jägersten, G. 1955. On the early phylogeny of the metazoa. *Zool. Bidr.* 30: 321.

Jennings, J. B. 1957. Studies on feeding, digestion, and food storage in free-living flatworms. *Biol. Bull.* 112, 63.

——. 1962. Further studies on feeding and digestion in triclad turbellaria. *Biol. Bull.* 123: 571.

Kenk, R. 1944. The fresh-water triclads of Michigan. *Misc. Publ. Mus. Zool. Univ. Mich.* 60: 1.

Kepner, W., and J. F. Barker. 1924. Nematocysts of Microstoma. *Biol. Bull.* 47: 239.

Kromhout, G. A. 1943. A comparison of the protonephridia of fresh-water, brackish-water, and marine specimens of *Gyratrix hermaphroditis*. *Jour. Morph.* 72: 167.

Lang, A. 1881. Untersuchungen zur vergleichenden Anatomie und Histologie des Nervensystems der Plathelminthen, IV. Das Nervensystem der Tricladen. *Mitt. Zool. Stat. Neapel* 3: 53.

La Rue, G. 1957. The classification of digenetic trematoda. *Exptl. Parasitol.* 6: 306.

Marcus, E. 1958. On the evolution of the animal phyla. *Quart. Rev. Biol.* 33: 24.

McCoy, O. R. 1935. The physiology of helminth parasites. *Physiol. Rev.* 15: 221.

Olmsted, J. D. 1922. The role of the nervous system in the locomotion of certain marine polyclads. *Jour. Exp. Zool.* 36: 57.

Ruebush, T. K. 1941. A key to the American fresh-water turbellarian genera, exclusive of the tricladida. *Trans. Am. Micr. Soc.* 60: 29. (F)

Smyth, J. D. 1947. The physiology of tapeworms. *Biol. Rev.* 22: 214.

——, and J. A. Clegg. 1959. Egg-shell formation in trematodes and cestodes. *Exp. Parasit.* 8: 286.

Steinbock, O. 1926. Zur Ökologie der Alpinen Turbellarien. *Ztschr. Morph. Ökol. Tiere* 5: 424.

Stephenson, W. 1947. The physiology of *Fasciola hepatica*. *Parasit.* 38: 116.

Thomas, A. P. 1883. The life history of the liver fluke (*Fasciola hepatica*). *Quart. Jour. Micr. Sci.* 23: 99.

Ullyott, P. 1936. The behaviour of *Dendrocoelum lacteum*. *Jour. Exp. Biol.* 13: 253.

Wardle, R. A., and J. A. McLeod. 1952. *The Biology of Tapeworms*. Univ. of Minn. Press, Minneapolis. (B)

8
The Pseudocoelomates

Organs cannot move freely unless they lie in a body cavity, and if they are embedded in a solid parenchyma they are squeezed or stretched every time the body moves. The parenchyma of flatworms interferes with the exchange of materials between the viscera and the body wall. In all of the remaining animal phyla the organs lie in a body cavity of some kind, making them more independent of the body wall.

Two kinds of body cavities may be distinguished. A coelom is found in vertebrates and higher invertebrates. A pseudocoelom or pseudocoel is found in a number of simpler invertebrates. A coelom forms in the mesoderm during development and is lined with peritoneum; it is sometimes called the peritoneal cavity. A pseudocoel appears between the gut and the body wall and is not lined with peritoneum. Animals with a pseudocoel lack a true coelom and can with justice be called acoelomates, as some zoologists prefer. However, from a functional point of view there are important differences between animals with a solid parenchyma and those with a pseudocoel.

Eight distinctive types of animals have a pseudocoel: Acanthocephala, Rotifera, Gastrotricha, Kinorhyncha, Priapulida, Nemathelminthes, Nematomorpha, and Entoprocta. The middle six of these have many similarities and are sometimes included in the phylum Aschelminthes. However, they do not share a common organizational plan, and to indicate their similarities as well as their differences, they are gathered here in the superphylum Aschelminthes, and each of the six placed in a separate phylum. As Hyman (1951) has pointed out, the eventual disposition of these groups is as yet uncertain. Perhaps two or three distinctive phyla can eventually be assembled from the members of the superphylum. Several such attempts have been made, but none appear wholly satisfactory.

The phyla discussed in this chapter have the pseudocoel as their most important unifying characteristic. All have a body wall composed of epidermis, muscles, and a fairly extensive dermis, within which the pseudocoel lies. The digestive tube and gonads are suspended in the pseudocoel and bathed in a perivisceral fluid.

Phylum Acanthocephala

Acanthocephala, commonly known as thorny-headed worms, are parasitic pseudocoelomates, without a digestive tract and with a proboscis, armed with recurved hooks, that can be retracted into a proboscis receptacle. Larvae are parasites of arthropods, and adults are parasites of vertebrates. No free-living larval stages are known. Over 500 species have been described, from marine, fresh-water, and terrestrial hosts.

The general form of an acanthocephalan is shown in Fig. 8.1. The body is divided by a cuticular furrow into an anterior presoma, consisting of a neck and proboscis, and a posterior trunk region. The trunk and proboscis vary in shape and size, and the body is often armed with spines. The proboscis armature is extremely variable, but characteristic of the species.

The body wall is composed of a thin cuticle, a thick, syncytial epidermis, a thin dermis, and a thin layer of circular and longitudinal muscle. The epidermis is made up of several fibrous layers and contains a constant number of giant nuclei or many small nuclear fragments. Two flaps of the body wall, the lemnisci, project into the pseudocoel at the neck region. A system of longitudinal or branching lacunae runs through the epidermis and into the lemnisci. The function of the lacunar system is unknown; perhaps it aids in food distribution, with the lemnisci serving as reservoirs for the fluid when the proboscis is retracted.

The proboscis is a formidable organ, often causing serious damage to the host intestine. A retractor muscle attaches the proboscis tip to the receptacle wall. Muscles can only pull blindly; evidently the proboscis retractor is as likely to pull the receptacle up as the proboscis down. This is prevented by the receptacle retractor, actually a continuation of the proboscis retractor, which attaches the receptacle to the body wall. Neck retractors connect the neck and body wall; they often surround the lemnisci, serving as lemnisci compressors.

Acanthocephala come close to being ultimate parasites, able to concentrate entirely on the business of reproduction. Sense organs have declined to a few bulbous endings in the reproductive organs and a single sensory pit at the proboscis tip; sometimes an additional pair of sensory pits lie in the neck. The brain is a simple ganglion in the proboscis receptacle, issuing nerves to the muscles and the proboscis sense organ. A pair of lateral nerve trunks course along the body wall, sending branches to the genital organs. A ring commissure in the base of the penis contains a pair of genital ganglia.

Acanthocephala have no digestive system or respiratory system. Food enters through the body surface and energy release is probably anaerobic. Some have a pair of short protonephridia which drain into the end of the genital tract. Each protonephridium has three large nuclei, and numerous, cytoplasmic flame bulbs.

One or two ligament sacs attach to the proboscis receptacle and the genital organs. A ligament, thought to be a vestige of the endoderm, runs in the ligament sac wall. Sexes are separate, and the relationship of ligament and ligament sacs to the genital organs differs in the two sexes.

The two testes are attached to the ligament in a ligament sac (Fig. 8.1A). Muscles from the body wall join the ligament sac below the testes, forming a genital sheath that encloses the sperm ducts and associated parts. Sperm accumulate in spermiducal vesicles in the sperm ducts or a seminal vesicle at the base of the common sperm duct. A constant number of cement glands, usually six or eight, surround the sperm ducts. Cement passes through cement ducts, sometimes after storage in a cement reservoir, into the common sperm duct near the base of the penis. Urine also drains into the common sperm duct if protonephridia are present. The urogenital duct thus carries cement, urine, and sperm, and may, as Haffner has suggested, be the vestige of an ancestral cloaca which included the gut. The endodermal origin of the ligament supports this point of view. The penis projects into a bursal cavity with a heavily muscled bursal cap, and sometimes connected with a fluid-filled sac, called Saefftigen's pouch.

Acanthocephala are unique in so many ways that it is not surprising to find fertilization and early development peculiar. During mating, the muscles of the bursal cap contract and fluid is injected from Saefftigen's pouch, if it is present. The bursa everts and grasps the female. Sperm are injected into the vagina, which is then plugged with cement. Sperm travel up the genital duct and escape into the pseudocoel.

The ovary forms in a ligament sac, but breaks into fragments which float as ovarian balls in the pseudocoel. As ova mature, they escape from the ovarian balls and are fertilized. A fertilization membrane forms within the egg membrane, and development begins.

Cleavage is distorted, but is reminiscent of the spiral, determinate cleavage of flatworms and is complicated by the formation of polar bodies at what seems to be the vegetal pole. A stereoblastula forms, and the cell membranes break down to produce a syncytial embryo. The only vestige of gastrulation is the inward movement of a small group of nuclei that will enter the primordia of gonads and ligament sacs. Differentiation does not proceed far in the mother's body. The embryo develops six hooks, and a shell forms between the fertilization membrane and the egg membrane. The shelled larva is known as an acanthor (Fig. 8.1B) and is ready to be freed. The female genital tract becomes involved for the first time.

The ligament sacs attach to the upper end of the female tract. The upper end of the tract is the uterine bell, a remarkable muscular funnel that swallows shelled larvae and sorts them out as ripe or unripe (Fig. 8.1C). Immature ones return to the pseudocoel through a ventral pore, but mature ones enter the uterine tube through one of the bell pouches. The shelled larvae pass through the uterus and genital pore, and escape with the host feces.

When the shelled larva is eaten by a suitable arthropod it emerges from the shell and works through the intestinal wall to the blood spaces. Here it becomes an acanthella (Fig. 8.1D), a growing embryo that gradually becomes a juvenile acanthocephalan, with all of the adult organs but the reproductive system. Development stops, and will not begin again until the juvenile is eaten by a suitable host. In some cases the final host does not ordinarily eat the larval host, and the juvenile worm passes through several transport hosts, reencysting each time it is eaten.

Acanthocephala are biologically interesting. No animal group is more completely parasitic, and the internal organs are so degenerate that their affinities to other kinds of animals cannot be determined with certainty. The phenomenon of cell constancy, common among pseudocoelomates, presents exciting biological problems. Proboscis hooks and nuclei are constant in number. The development of giant nuclei is most unusual and raises questions of ploidy, of nuclear specialization, and of the controls that determine how nuclei behave.

The Superphylum Aschelminthes

The aschelminths are a diverse group of animals, tantalizingly similar and yet different. Each group is to some degree distinctive in a fundamental way; one cannot describe an organizational plan common to all. Yet all share important traits with

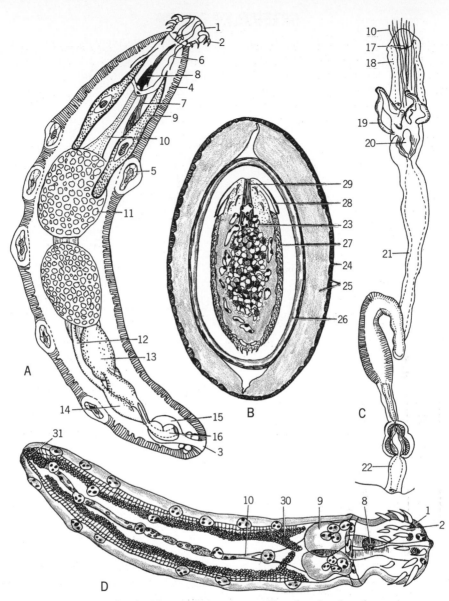

Fig. 8.1. Acanthocephala. **A.** *Neoechinorhynchus rutili* male, showing the main organs in position. **B.** A shelled acanthor embryo of *Macracanthorhynchus hirudinacea*. **C.** The female reproductive system of *Bolbosoma*. **D.** An acanthella of *M. hirudinacea* from a beetle larva. (A, after Biehler, from Goodchild in Brown. B, after Meyer. C, after Yamaguti. D, after Van Cleave.) *External features*: 1, proboscis; 2, proboscis hook; 3, cloacal opening; 4, cuticle; 5, giant nucleus. *Proboscis*: 6, proboscis receptacle; 7, retractor muscle of proboscis. *Internal parts*: 8, brain; 9, lemniscus; 10, suspensory ligament. *Male reproductive system*: 11, testis; 12, sperm duct; 13, cement gland; 14, seminal vesicle; 15, genital bursa; 16, cirrus. *Female reproductive system*: 17, ligament sac; 18, uterine bell; 19, bell pocket; 20, ventral pore; 21, uterus; 22, vagina. *Larvae*: 23, epidermal nuclei; 24, original egg membrane; 25, shell; 26, fertilization membrane; 27, larval spines; 28, larval hooks; 29, larval retractor; 30, body-wall musculature; 31, urogenital primordium.

255

other groups. It is convenient neither to group them in one phylum nor to divide them into different phyla. Some of the groups are certainly more closely related than others, but until more information is available it seems preferable to leave them all in separate phyla under the superphylum Aschelminthes.

Aschelminths are all somewhat wormlike and are not highly cephalized. The body is covered by a cuticle, lying on a cellular or syncytial epidermis. Generally the body wall does not contain the circular and longitudinal layers so characteristic of most animals. Aschelminths have a pseudocoelom, and when a digestive tract is present, it is predominantly epithelial but may have a delicate network of muscles. They have no respiratory or circulatory system. All but the nematodes have a protonephridial system. Urinary, reproductive, and digestive systems join terminally in a cloaca, a common chamber through which gametes, urine, and feces pass, but female nematodes have a separate gonopore. Most undergo determinate cleavage, and there is a strong tendency toward eutely, or constancy in the number of cells in each organ.

Phylum Rotifera

The study of rotifers is a study of ladies, sometimes beautiful, often capricious, and always fascinating. Males are uncommon and have never been seen in many species. Rotifers are delightful, minute creatures, usually between 100 and 500 μ in length. About 2000 species have been described, from fresh-water habitats of all kinds, marine littoral regions, and from semi-terrestrial environments among mosses and lichens.

Rotifers may be characterized as minute pseudocoelomates, unsegmented, and with a ciliated region, the corona, at the anterior end. They usually have a complete digestive tract, with an anterior mouth, a highly differentiated pharynx containing movable pieces that act as jaws, and a posterior cloaca, joined by typical protonephridia with terminal flame bulbs and by the female reproductive tract. Females usually produce two kinds of eggs, one that develops parthenogenetically, and another that requires fertilization.

What does one look for in a rotifer? How are they identified? The major points, other than general body shape and habits, are the form and details of the head structures, especially the corona and jaws, and the nature of the cuticular covering. A considerable technical vocabulary has been developed, and it is necessary to have some familiarity with its terms and the structures they represent. Rotifer anatomy is best understood from side views, but unfortunately the animals do not usually co-operate. The anatomy of a fairly typical rotifer is summarized in Fig. 8.2, and should be studied before undertaking an examination of classification and variability within the phylum.

CLASSIFICATION

If Rotifera is considered a class rather than a phylum, the groups listed below will be reduced to suborders and orders.

Class Seisonacea. Marine rotifers, living on the surface of Crustacea; body elongated, with a long neck; mastax fulcrate; corona small; gonads paired; without vitellaria; males common; females do not form parthenogenetic ova. Examples: *Seison* (Fig. 8.3E).

Class Bdelloidea. Swimming or creeping forms, with retractible anterior end; corona with two trochal discs or some modification of this pattern; mastax ramate; foot often with more than two toes, and with spurs; with more than two pedal glands; males unknown, females with two germovitellaria. Example: *Philodina* (Fig. 8.3C).

Class Monogononta. Swimming or sessile; mastax not ramate; males more or less reduced and with one testis; females with one germovitellarium.

Order Ploima. Swimming forms with normal corona; foot reduced or with two toes and two pedal glands. Examples: *Epiphanes* (Fig. 8.2); *Asplanchna* (Fig. 8.3D).

Order Flosculariaceae. Sessile or swimming; corona often circular or lobed, with trochal and cingular circlets; foot without toes; males much reduced. Example: *Limnias* (Fig. 8.3B).

Order Collothecaceae. Sessile rotifers with anterior end modified as a funnel and

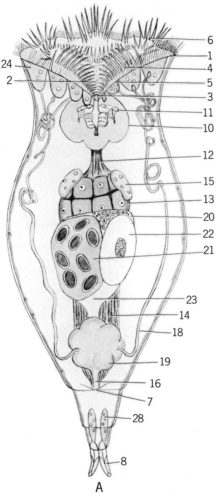
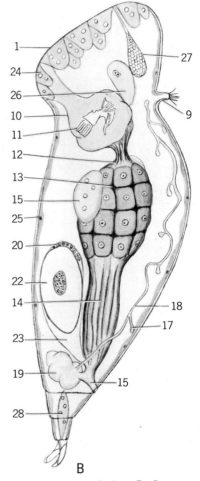

A   B

Fig. 8.2. Rotifer Anatomy. **A.** Scheme of *Epiphanes senta*, as seen in ventral view. **B.** Same, from side view. *External features* (composite): **1,** corona; **2,** mouth; **3,** infra-oral part of the buccal field; **4,** pseudotroch; **5,** circumapical band; **6,** tuft of cirri; **7,** site of cloacal opening; **8,** toe; **9,** dorsal tentacle. *Digestive system:* **10,** mastax; **11,** trophi; **12,** esophagus; **13,** stomach; **14,** intestine; **15,** digestive gland; **16,** cloaca. *Nephridial system:* **17,** flame bulb; **18,** protonephridial tubule; **19,** bladder. *Reproductive system:* **20,** ovary; **21,** vitelline gland; **22,** egg; **23,** oviduct. *Other internal parts:* **24,** coronal matrix; **25,** epidermal syncytium; **26,** brain; **27,** retrocerebral sac; **28,** pedal gland.

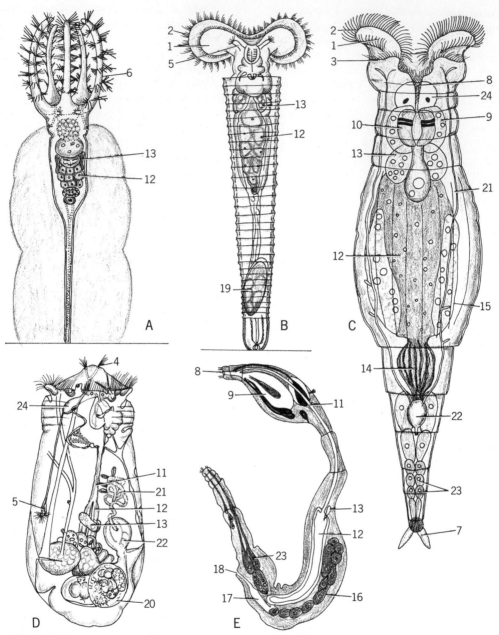

Fig. 8.3. Some Representative Rotifers. Rotifers may be divided into three classes: Seisonacea, Bdelloidea, and Monogonanta. *Seison* (E) is an example of Seisonacea, characterized by epizoic habits, the presence of normally developed males, and a poorly developed corona. *Philodina* (C) is a bdelloid, characterized by two germovitellaria, a retractile anterior end, and the total absence of males. The remaining examples belong to the Monogonanta, which have a single germovitellarium and more or less reduced males. *Asplanchna* (D) belongs to the order Ploima, which have a normal corona and foot. *Limnias* (B) is an example of the order Flosculariaceae,

258

without definite ciliary circlets; often with immobile bristles; foot without toes; males much reduced. Example: *Stephanoceros* (Fig. 8.3A).

GENERAL BODY FORM

The rotifer body is divided into a head bearing the corona, a trunk, and a posterior region called the tail or foot. A neck may separate head and trunk.

The central part of the head is without cilia, and is known as the apical field. The ciliated corona encircles the apical field (Fig. 8.2A). Projections with sensory bristles and one or two papillae with pores of the retrocerebral organs lie on the apical field. Retrocerebral organs may be homologous to the frontal glands of Turbellaria. Each consists of a pair of subcerebral glands near the brain and a retrocerebral sac between them (Fig. 8.4A). Either sac or glands may be missing, and both vary markedly in size and form. The function of the retrocerebral organ is unknown.

The form of the corona determines the appearance of the head. The coronal cilia beat metachronously, giving the impression of a revolving circle; from this the name rotifer or "wheel-bearer" is derived. The corona of primitive, creeping species is an evenly ciliated buccal field around the mouth and a circumapical band which encircles the apical field (Fig. 8.4B). All resemblance to the primitive form is lost in highly specialized species. Tufts of cilia may be present at the sides of the buccal field; from these, lateral projections known as auricles may develop. Swimming rotifers usually have a reduced buccal field, divided into suboral and supraoral fields (Fig. 8.2A). Stiff bristles, probably motionless cilia, form a pseudotroch in the supraoral field of some species. The apical field of some rotifers is bilobed, and in bdelloids is separated into two fields (Fig. 8.4C-H). Cilia at the anterior and posterior margins of the ciliated field are enlarged, forming two special circlets, an anterior trochus and posterior cingulum. The apical field of sessile Flosculariacea is lobed, with the trochus more prominent than the cingulum. The Collothecacea, also sessile, have a funnel-shaped apical field, usually with marginal lobes bearing filamentous setae (Fig. 8.3A), and with coronal cilia missing or reduced. Protozoa and algae are guided into the funnel by the setae; the funnel then closes to bring the prey to the mouth.

The cylindrical or flattened trunk is covered by a variously modified cuticle. The cuticle of swimming species often forms an immovable case, the lorica. The cuticle of creeping species is divided into telescoping rings, which allow the body to extend and contract. Single or paired dorsal antennae occur at the anterior end of the trunk, and lateral antennae may be found on the posterior end of the trunk. The middorsal anus lies at the union of trunk and foot.

The foot of most rotifers is covered by cuticular rings. It ends in an adhesive disc in sessile species, but in creeping and swimming rotifers ends in one to four movable toes containing pedal glands. The pedal glands secrete an adhesive used to attach

which have a corona with trochal and cingular circlets and are often sessile. The foot has no toes. *Stephanoceros* (A) is an example of the order Collothecaceae, which are sessile and have the corona modified into a funnel equipped with bristles but no cilia. (A,B, and D, after Edmondson. C, after Hickernell. E, after Plate.) *External features:* 1, trochal disc; 2, trochus; 3, cingulum; 4, apical sense organ; 5, lateral antenna; 6, coronal lobe; 7, toe. *Digestive system:* 8, mouth; 9, mastax; 10, trophi; 11, esophagus; 12, stomach; 13, gastric gland; 14, intestine. *Reproductive system:* 15, germovitellarium; 16, ovary; 17, oviduct; 18, female gonopore; 19, egg; 20, embryo. *Other parts:* 21, protonephridial tubule; 22, bladder; 23, cement gland; 24, brain.

the animal permanently, or temporarily for feeding or creeping.

The body wall is constructed of cuticle, epidermis, and subepidermal muscles. The cuticular scleroprotein covers the body surface and forms the lorica, spines, or other surface structures. The syncytial epidermis contains a constant number of nuclei, forming constantly placed epidermal cushions that contain one or several nuclei. The modified coronal epidermis contains the ciliary root systems and large epidermal cushions and is termed the coronal matrix. The subcerebral glands, pedal glands, and other surface glands are epidermal in origin. The foot epidermis or pedal glands

secrete the material used to make the tubes of sessile rotifers and the gelatinous envelopes of some pelagic rotifers.

Rotifer muscles are not arranged in layers as in acoelomates. Visceral muscles occur in some organs. Cutaneo-visceral muscles extend from the body wall to the viscera. Subepidermal muscles form the body wall musculature, consisting of circular muscle bands that constrict and lengthen the body, and longitudinal ones that shorten the body or retract the corona and foot. Circular muscles are complete rings or laterally placed, transverse arcs, and are much reduced in loricate species (Fig. 8.5). Longitudinal muscles pass over

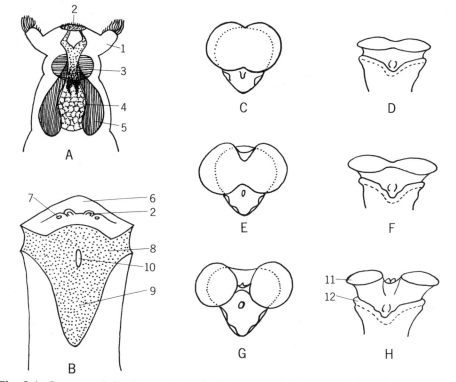

Fig. 8.4. Corona and Cerebral Region. **A.** The retrocerebral organs of *Notommata*, a genus in which they are unusually prominent. **B.** Ventral view of the primitive corona. **C-D.** Front and ventral views of the basic corona. **E-F.** Front and ventral view of the floscularian type of corona. **G-H.** Front and ventral views of the bdelloid type of corona. (All after de Beauchamp.) 1, auricle; 2, openings of the retrocerebral organs; 3, brain; 4, retrocerebral sac; 5, subcerebral glands; 6, apical field; 7, apical eye; 8, circumapical band; 9, buccal field; 10, mouth; 11, trochus; 12, cingulum.

several cuticular rings in creeping forms, or are detached for many rings and joined to the cuticle near the head or foot as retractors.

Circular muscle fibers lie just below the epidermis and are without nuclei. This may mean that they are a part of the epidermis and comparable to cnidarian epitheliomuscular fibers. Longitudinal muscles each have a nucleus. Both smooth and striated muscles occur, but usually without obvious functional significance. Swimming spines and other rapidly moving parts have striated fibers, however.

The spacious pseudocoel appears as mesoderm differentiates into muscles or becomes part of the viscera. It lacks peritoneum, and no mesenteries attach the viscera to the body wall. It is filled with a perivisceral fluid and a loose syncytial reticulum composed of amoeboid cells.

THE ORGAN SYSTEMS

Digestive System. The mouth usually lies in the buccal field or below a supraoral field. Sphincter and dilator muscles may open and close it. Raptorial species usually have oral dilator muscles and a mouth opening directly into the pharynx. Other species have a ciliated buccal tube leading to the pharynx.

The pharynx or mastax is a unique rotifer feature. It is a muscular chamber containing a set of jaws, formed of cuticularized trophi. Jaw structure is complex. A median fulcrum and pairs of rami, unci, and manubria make up the major parts. The fulcrum and rami together form the incus; the unci and manubria compose the malleus. The intricate jaw architecture is adapted along a variety of patterns, associated with the kind of food eaten and feeding habits, but the component parts remain recognizable. Jaw homologies have been worked out in detail, and illustrate the possibilities of the comparative approach in invertebrate anatomy (Figs. 8.6-7). Jaw structure is sometimes important in tax-

onomy, and is interesting as an example of detailed adaptive changes. The characteristics and uses of the types of rotifer jaws are summarized below.

MALLEATE. (Fig. 8.6A-C). The most primitive type, and common. Malleate trophi may be used to grasp food, but are

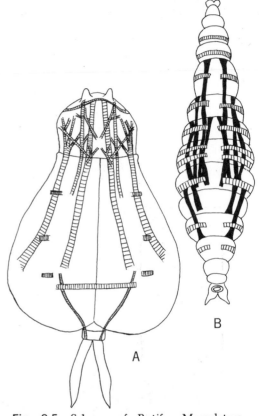

Fig. 8.5. Scheme of Rotifer Musculature. A. *Euchlanis*, in dorsal view. B. A typical bdelloid in ventral view. (A, after Stossberg. B, after Zelinka.) Note the effect of the lorica upon the musculature. In loricate rotifers the circular muscles are reduced; the longitudinal muscles are long; serving primarily for corona retraction. The worm-like bdelloids, on the other hand, have a segmented cuticle, and the musculature takes on a segmental character. Circular and longitudinal muscles are arranged for creeping movements, acting as antagonists. Circular muscles extend the body, with the fluid in the pseudocoel serving as a hydraulic fluid.

primarily for grinding. All parts are present and all are relatively strong.

VIRGATE. (Fig. 8.6D,E). The unci are used to pierce prey, and contractions of the powerful hypopharyngeal muscle pumps food in. Food is usually small plankton and plant cells. A common type.

CARDATE. (Fig. 8.6F,G). A rare type, found only in *Lindia* and related forms. Another kind of sucking apparatus, but without the hypopharyngeal muscle, suction being caused by movements of the unci which roll the trophi. The chief foods are detritus and plants.

FORCIPATE. (Fig. 8.6H,I). A grasping jaw, with slender parts. The fulcrum and rami, assisted by the unci, form a forceps, which is thrust out of the mouth and carries the prey back into the pharynx. It occurs only in the Dicranophoridae.

INCUDATE. (Fig. 8.7A,B). Another grasping jaw, but with very small mallei and with unci and rami differently related than in forcipate jaws. It is rotated 90° to be extruded, grasps prey, and pulls it to the mouth. A dorsal sac in the mastax sucks the food in. Found only in *Asplanchna* and related forms.

RAMATE. (Fig. 8.7C,D). A heavy, grinding type of jaw, with rigid unci, character-

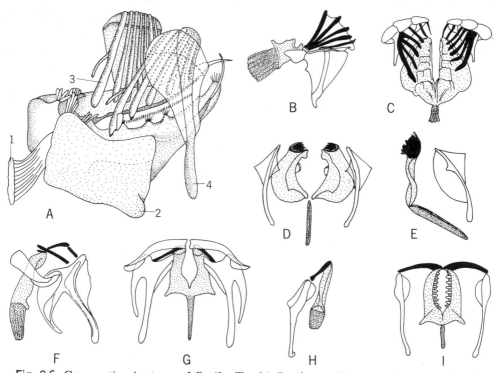

Fig. 8.6. Comparative Anatomy of Rotifer Trophi. Rotifer trophi are excellent examples of homologous parts, modified during divergent evolution, adapting the organism to different kinds of food and feeding habits. A. An oblique view of malleate trophi, showing the arrangement of the component parts. B-C. Lateral and dorsal view of malleate trophi of *Epiphanes senta*. D-E. Lateral and dorsal views of virgate trophi of *Synchaeta*. F-G. Lateral and ventral views of cardate trophi of *Lindia*. H-I. Lateral and ventral views of forcipate trophi. (A, adapted from Stossberg by Edmondson. B-I, adapted from various sources.) 1, fulcrum (dark stipple in B-I); 2, ramus (light stipple in B-I); 3, uncus (black in B-I); 4, manubrium (unshaded in B-I). Certain accessory pieces are also unshaded.

istic of the bdelloids. It was originally named with the idea that the large parts were rami.

MALLEORAMATE. (Fig. 8.7E). Another grinding pharynx, found in Flosculariaceae. The trophi are intermediate between the malleate and ramate type, with heavy unci overlying the reduced rami.

UNCINATE. (Fig. 8.7F,G). This kind of jaw occurs only in the Collothecaceae, which eat large prey and have a spacious mastax. It is used to lacerate organisms or detritus taken into the mastax, but is sometimes too weak to be useful. The unci have few teeth and the manubria are vestigial.

FULCRATE. (Fig. 8.7H). This kind of jaw occurs only in Seisonaceae, and is entirely unlike other rotifer trophi. Leaf-like manubria, with other small pieces attached to it.

The mastax is lined with cuticle and composed of a syncytial epithelium. It se-cretes the trophi, and produces the muscles that operate them. Food leaving the mastax is fully macerated. Rotifers are the first animals discussed to have a system for food fragmentation as a part of the stomodaeum region, an important progressive trait.

Food passes through an esophagus into the stomach, a thick-walled, ciliated sac or tube composed of a constant number of cells. A delicate mesh of circular and longitudinal muscles covers the surface, and a pair of syncytial gastric glands opens into it. The gastric glands probably secrete enzymes for extracellular digestion; in rotifers known to digest food intracellularly, the gastric glands are reduced. Carbohydrate digestion is apparently limited. Digestion is very rapid; within 15 to 20 minutes, protein spherules and fatty droplets begin to accumulate in the stomach wall, where they may be stored for some time. The

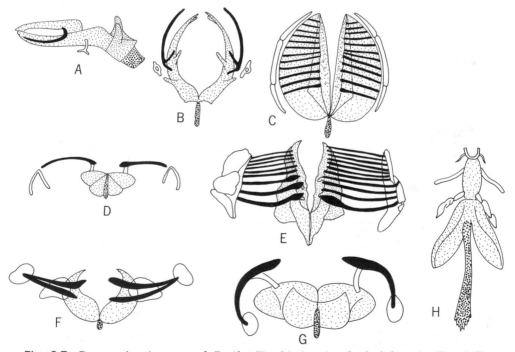

Fig. 8.7. Comparative Anatomy of Rotifer Trophi (continued; shaded as in Fig. 8.6). A-B. Lateral and dorsal views of incudate trophi. C-D. Dorsal and posterior views of ramate trophi. E. Anterior view of malleoramate trophi. F-G. Dorsal and posterior views of uncinate trophi. H. Dorsal view of fulcrate trophi. (Adapted from various sources.)

bdelloid stomach is a heavy, syncytial mass, pierced by a narrow, ciliated tube. Food enters the syncytium to be digested intracellularly.

The thin-walled, syncytial intestine is sometimes ciliated. It receives the protonephridia and oviducts near the anus, continuing as the cloaca. The dorsal anus often has dilator muscles. Cutaneovisceral muscles attach the various parts of the digestive tube to the body wall.

Respiration. Little is known of respiratory physiology. Swimming and creeping rotifers have high oxygen requirements and some live in habitats with little free oxygen. Presumably these have some ability to respire anaerobically.

Excretory System. Rotifers have two coiled, syncytial protonephridial tubules, which usually fork anteriorly. Fine capillary tubules terminate in flame bulbs. Sometimes a transverse tubule connects the two main tubules. The protonephridia drain into the cloaca, by way of a common duct or a bladder. Flame-cell activity varies with the osmotic pressure of the environment, and the protonephridial system is probably primarily a water-regulating device.

Sense Organs. A variety of sensory projections occur on the body surface, especially in the apical field (Fig. 8.8B). Stiff bristles (styles) along the anterior edge of the circumapical band have one or two sensory cells at their bases. Paired ciliated pits, probably chemoreceptive, occur on the apical field of some rotifers, and palps or other projections with sensory bristles are commonly found.

Rotifer eyes are unusual. A mass of red pigment granules forms an intracellular pigment cup with a refractive spherule (Fig. 8.8C). Rotifers may have cerebral eyes, coronal eyes, or lateral eyes, depending on whether the eye cell is on or in the brain, the coronal matrix, or endodermal cushions lateral to the corona. The eye cells are evidently not homologous to the retinal cells of Radiata or acoelomates. Rotifers respond positively or are indiffer-

ent to light. When positively phototactic, general body sensitivity to light induces swimming toward the light at a speed inversely related to the wavelength, and stimuli received by the eyes control movements to maintain a predetermined angle toward the light rays.

Most rotifers have a dorsal antenna, and some have lateral antennae. Antennae are tactile organs and may be conspicuous tentacles or reduced, in some cases to a single style.

Nervous System. Rotifers have a pair of longitudinal, ventrolateral nerve trunks, arising from the sides of a bilobed brain. Pairs of body ganglia are connected to the brain or nerve trunks (Fig. 8.8A). The anterior end of each nerve trunk bears a small anterior ganglion and a large geniculate ganglion. The nerve trunk continues posteriorly, ending in a pedal ganglion associated with the foot and a vesicular ganglion associated with the urinary bladder. The two ganglia may be united as a caudovesicular ganglion. The nervous system is bilaterally symmetrical, with similar nerves and ganglia on each side of the body. Sensory and motor nerves are distinct, and most body ganglia are wholly motor or sensory.

A mastax ganglion lies on the surface of the pharynx and is connected to the brain by pharyngeal nerves; visceral nerves to the intestine issue from the mastax ganglion. The cephalic sense organs and dorsal antennae are innervated from the brain. Lateral antennae receive nerves from the geniculate ganglia. Any caudal sense organs present are innervated by nerves from the pedal or caudovesicular ganglion. Motor nerves from the brain innervate the salivary glands and anterior retractor muscles. Posterior retractors receive motor nerves from the geniculate ganglia or the ventral nerve trunks. A scalar nerve from the geniculate ganglion goes to the circular muscles of the body wall; it contains a ganglion cell in each muscle band. The coronal sphincter receives a motor nerve from the geniculate ganglion or nerve trunk on each side of the body.

The outstanding features of the nervous system of rotifers are the clear separation of sensory and motor elements and the phenomenon of cell constancy. Brain cells and nerve cells, like epidermal syncytium, are constant in number and position, providing a remarkable consistency in the nervous system of each species.

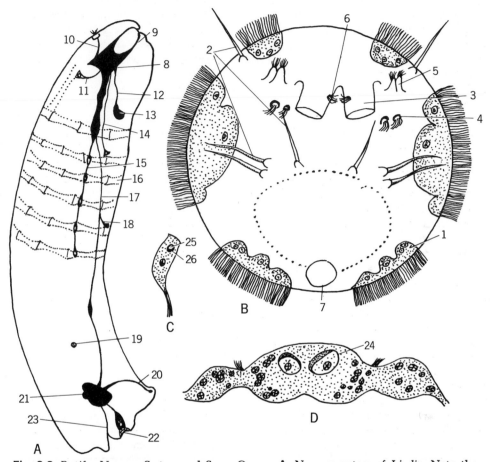

Fig. 8.8. Rotifer Nervous System and Sense Organs. A. Nervous system of *Lindia*. Note the partially segmental character, related to the partially segmental arrangement of the musculature. B. Scheme of the corona of *Euchlanis*, showing the position of the sense organs. C. Frontal eye of *Euchlanis*, containing an intracellular lens and pigment cup. D. Section through the brain of *Synchaeta*, passing through the cerebral eyes. (A, after Deihl. B and C after Stossberg. D, after Peters.) *Corona:* 1, coronal matrix; 2, tactile styles; 3, opening of retrocerebral organs; 4, ciliated pits; 5, tactile papillae; 6, apical sense organ; 7, mouth. *Nervous system:* 8, brain; 9, sensory nerves to anterior end; 10, sensory nerve to dorsal antenna; 11, motor nerve to dorsal retractor; 12, pharyngeal nerve; 13, mastax ganglion; 14, nerve to gastric gland; 15, scalar nerves containing ganglia in circular muscles; 16, circular muscle; 17, ventral nerve cord; 18, nephridial nerve; 19, lateral antenna; 20, nerve to sphincters of pedal glands; 21, caudovesicular ganglion; 22, caudal antenna; 23, nerve to anal sphincter. *Eyes:* 24, cerebral eye; 25, lens; 26, pigment.

Reproductive System. Most rotifers are females, and all bdelloids are females, producing only parthenogenetic ova. Seisonaceae are exceptions, for males are always present and females cannot reproduce parthenogenetically. Monogononta males appear only rarely, so nearly all rotifers are females.

The female reproductive organs are very simple. Monogononta females have a single, syncytial ovary and a syncytial vitellarium, enclosed in a membrane which continues as the oviduct and opens into the cloaca (Fig. 8.2). Bdelloids have a pair of germovitellaria and a common oviduct (Fig. 8.3C). Seisonaceae females have paired ovaries but no vitellaria.

Males are only a quarter the size of females or less, in most cases. Monogononta males have a single testis, opening into a sperm duct ending in the male gonopore (Fig. 8.9A). The last part of the

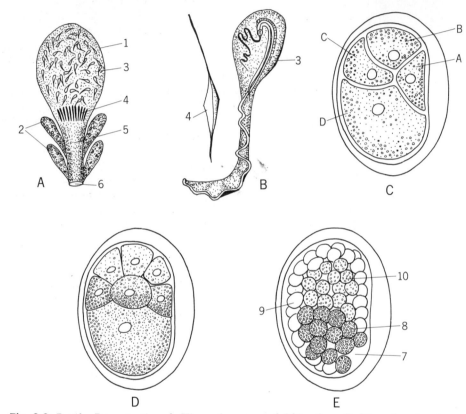

Fig. 8.9. Rotifer Reproduction. **A.** The male system of *Rhinoglena*. **B.** Normal and rod sperm of *Sinantherina*. **C-E.** Three stages in the development of *Monostyla*. C, the four-cell stage. **D.** The 8-cell stage, with A, B, C, and d¹ filled with yolk and forming a germ ring. **E.** Gastrulation by epiboly and involution. Ectodermal cells have covered the surface of the embryo; the derivatives of D, with a moderate amount of yolk, have moved away from the blastopore, and the derivatives of A, B, C, and d¹, filled with yolk, lie near the blastopore. Derivatives of D will form the ovary and vitellarium. (A, after Wesenberg-Lund. B, after Hamburger. C-E, after Pray.) **1,** testis; **2,** prostatic gland; **3,** typical sperm; **4,** rod sperm; **5,** cirrus; **6,** gonopore; **7,** blastopore; **8,** yolk-laden derivatives of A, B, C, and d¹; **9,** ectoderm; **10,** derivatives of D.

sperm duct is sometimes modified as a cirrus, and some males have a part of the body wall specialized as a penis. Impregnation is usually hypodermic. Sperm mature during embryonic development, and are of two kinds, normal, ciliated sperm and rod-shaped sperm (Fig. 8.9B). The latter probably help to pierce the cuticle. The Seisonaceae male system is quite different. Testes are paired, and the sperm duct forms chambers and tortuous coils as it passes through a syncytial mass. The sperm are cemented together into a packet, the spermatophore, in the syncytium.

REPRODUCTION

Reproduction is simple enough in bdelloids, for the females all produce ova that develop parthenogentically into parthenogenetic females. It is simple in the Seisonacea also, for the females produce only ova that must be fertilized and develop into a male or female. Female Monogononta, however, produce three kinds of ova. During most of the year the females are all diploid, and produce diploid amictic eggs, which develop into more diploid, amictic females without fertilization (Fig. 8.10). The form of amictic females gradually changes during the year, no doubt in response to environmental conditions. At critical seasons, just before the species is to become quiescent or in response to striking environmental changes, the amictic eggs develop into diploid mictic females, morphologically unlike amictic females. Mictic females produce haploid mictic ova which may develop parthenogenetically into haploid males, but if fertilized form a thick-walled case and remain dormant as diploid winter eggs until favorable environmental conditions return.

EMBRYOLOGY

Until recently, embryonic development has been best known in *Asplanchna*, an aberrant genus without anus or cloaca.

Recent descriptions of the development of *Ploesoma* and *Monostyla* provide information about more typical species.

Cleavage is holoblastic. In the four-cell stage (Fig. 8.9C) there are three smaller blastomeres (A,B,C) and one large one (D). D divides unequally; the smaller daughter (d^1) comes to lie at about the same level as the A, B, and C cells. These also divide unequally, giving rise to three smaller, granular blastomeres, which with d^1 form a germ ring, and three larger, clear blastomeres above them (Fig. 8.9D). The descendants of these clear blastomeres form the ectoderm, and can be recognized easily in later stages. The descendants of the densely granular blastomeres of the germ ring, and of the less granular D cell, can also be recognized easily in later stages (Fig. 8.9E).

The blastopore forms opposite the ectodermal cells, and epiboly and involution results in the clear ectodermal cells covering the surface, while the descendants of D and of the germ ring blastomeres move into the anterior. Eventually the blastopore closes as ectodermal cells meet. The

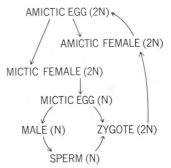

Fig. 8.10. Rotifer Generations Typical of the Ploima. During most of the year, diploid amictic females produce amictic eggs that develop into young amictic females without fertilization. At certain times, under as yet unspecified conditions, the amictic eggs develop into diploid mictic females that produce haploid mictic eggs. These develop rapidly into haploid males, or, if fertilized by males, become zygotes that develop into diploid amictic females.

progeny of the D cell form the germo-vitellarium, and the yolk-rich cells from the germ ring form the digestive tube from esophagus to intestine. The mastax arises from a part of the stomadaeum, and the foot from ectoderm at the opposite end of the embryo.

It was difficult to interpret the earlier studies of development based on *Asplanchna*, especially insofar as gastrulation and germ layers are concerned. It is clear, however, that more typical rotifers undergo a modified spiral cleavage of the determinate type. This strengthens the evidence which allies them with other Aschelminthes.

BIOLOGICAL PECULIARITIES

Rotifers have some remarkable peculiarities. Cell constancy, shared with some other aschelminths, is a most interesting biological phenomenon. It destroys all capacity to repair injury and poses embryological as well as physiological problems of great theoretical importance. What makes the cells stop dividing, and how can a syncytial animal differentiate? The controls which determine whether amictic females are to produce mictic or amictic eggs remain uncertain. Cyclomorphosis, the changes in form of the females during the year, raise questions of how genes and environment co-operate to determine form and function. Rotifers living in mosses can withstand dessication. The wrinkled, contracted rotifers emerge rapidly when water is available and return to dormancy when dry conditions return. Some survive three or four years in dry conditions and become active in a few minutes. Curiously, the dried forms must undergo some metabolism, for they are killed by oxygen deprivation. It would be highly desirable to have information on the nature of the reduced metabolism. The many peculiarities of rotifers make them promising research material for people interested in a variety of biological fields.

Table 8.1. Numbers of nuclei in Epiphanes senta

Epidermal Syncytium	
Coronal	172
Trunk and foot	108
Pedal gland	19
Muscle Tissue	
Circular body wall muscle	22
Longitudinal muscle	40
Pharynx musculature	42
Protonephridial tubules	28
Digestive tract	
Lining of mastax	63
Esophagus	15
Stomach	39
Gastric glands	12
Intestine	28
Reproductive System	
Ovary (not constant)	
Yolk gland	8
Oviduct	3
Nervous System	
Brain	183
Ganglia and sense organs	63

Phylum Gastrotricha

Gastrotrichs are microscopic animals, common enough in lentic fresh-water environments and in seashore sands. Their bristly, worm-like bodies are familiar to all who have examined many collections of fresh-water material. They attach themselves for a moment with posterior adhesive tubes and then swim on, or suddenly curl up like diminutive hedgehogs. They usually glide along, retaining contact with the substrate. They are rather like rotifers, but have no corona or mastax and generally have a characteristic scaly or spiny body. Two orders are recognized: *Macrodasyoidea* and *Chaetonotoidea*. The former are marine and live among vegetation or in sand. The later include all of the fresh-water and a few marine species.

Macrodasyoids have a body with a smooth outline, while chaetonotoids usually have a definite head, a somewhat constricted neck, a convex trunk, and a forked caudal end (Fig. 8.11A,B). The head and ventral surface are ciliated in various pat-

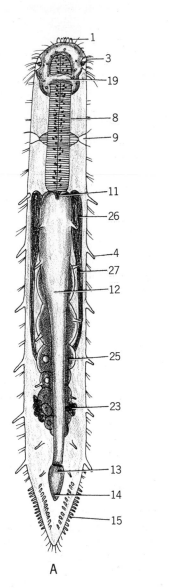

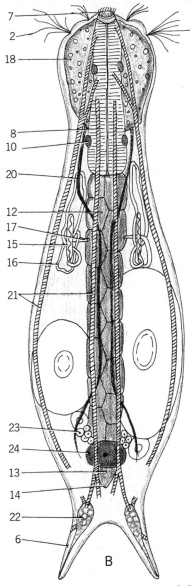

Fig. 8.11. Gastrotrich Anatomy. A. Structure of *Macrodasys*, a marine gastrotrich of the order Macrodasyoidea. B. Structure of a chaetonotid gastrotrich. (A, after Remane. B, after Pennak.) *External features:* 1, oral hooks; 2, sensory bristles; 3, piston pit; 4, lateral adhesive tube; 5, posterior adhesive tube; 6, caudal ramus or furca. *Digestive tract:* 7, buccal capsule; 8, pharynx; 9, pharyngeal pore; 10, salivary gland; 11, pharyngeal plug; 12, stomach-intestine; 13, rectum; 14, anus. *Nephridial system:* 15, solenocyte; 16, protonephridial tubule; 17, nephridiopore. *Nervous system:* 18, brain; 19, dorsal commissure; 20, longitudinal nerve. *Other internal parts:* 21, muscle strand; 22, cement gland. *Reproductive system:* 23, ovary; 24, X organ; 25, eggs in uterus; 26, testis; 27, sperm duct.

terns. Several tufts of sensory cilia usually project from the head surface. The dorsal surface is covered with abutted or overlapping cuticular scales, usually ornamented with short or long spines (Figs. 8.12A,B). Caudal adhesive tubes are characteristic of gastrotrichs. They open through the furca, sometimes known as toes, in chaetonotids, and occur in marginal posterior rows or in clusters in the head end in macrodasyoids.

The epidermis is syncytial and secretes the cuticle and its derivatives. Circular muscle fibers lie just below the epidermis and are used to operate the movable bristles. Dorsal, ventral, and ventrolateral longitudinal muscle strands retract the adhesive tubes and shorten or curl the body. A small space, the pseudocoel, separates the body wall and digestive tube.

Detritus, algae, and Protozoa are swept into the mouth by the head cilia. They enter through a cuticular buccal cavity, often ridged or toothed, which leads to the elongated, muscular pharynx. The pharynx (Fig. 8.12C) is sometimes dilated to form a bulb and contains unicellular salivary glands. It has a triangular lumen and is remarkably like the pharynx of nematodes (p. 283). Food passes to the midgut, a straight, tubular organ without external glands but with gland cells thought to secrete enzymes in its walls. Digestion appears to be extracellular. A short rectum leads to the anus.

Only chaetonotids are known to have protonephridia. A long, flame bulb containing a flagellum-like flame opens into a coiled tube on each side of the body (Fig. 8.11B); each empties through a separate nephridiopore. The protonephridia are thought to be primarily hydrostatic in function.

The cephalic bristles and ciliary tufts appear to be sensitive to touch and water currents. Clusters of red pigment bodies in some brain cells are probably photosensitive. Ciliated pits on the sides of the chaetonotid head appear to be modifications of the piston pits of macrodasyoids (Fig. 8.11A). They are probably chemoreceptors. The central nervous system consists of two lateral ganglia, connected by a narrow or broad dorsal commissure. A lateral nerve trunk issues from each ganglion.

Macrodasyoids are hermaphroditic; probably this is the primitive gastrotrich plan. The male system consists of one or two testes, with sperm ducts opening through a male gonopore, a common gonopore, or the anus. Some macrodasyoids are so extremely protandric that they are almost separately sexed. All chaetonotids, however, are parthenogenetic females. A few vestiges of testes have been reported in some species. The female system of chaetonotids is not very well understood. There are one or two ovaries, without a covering capsule. As ova mature, they move into a space called the uterus, but there is so little evidence of an oviduct that many doubt its existence. A nutritive tissue is present and is called a vitellarium. Ripe eggs move into a sac, the X-organ, and eventually escape through a ventral gonopore, the shell hardening after the eggs emerge. Chaetonotids produce thin-walled "summer" ova and thick-walled "winter" ova, both of which develop parthenogenetically. Summer ova are formed under more favorable environmental conditions by younger animals, and thick-walled ova by older females in less favorable environments. Most females produce only four or five eggs.

Embryonic development has not been worked out in detail. Cleavage is holoblastic and at least somewhat determinate. A coeloblastula invaginates as two blastomeres move into the interior (Fig. 8.12D). A stomodaeum and proctodaeum are formed, from which the pharynx and anal region develop respectively. There are no larval stages, the young looking like diminutive adults at hatching. They develop rapidly, becoming mature in two to three days.

Phylum Kinorhyncha

It has been almost 125 years since Dujardin (1851) described the first kinorhynch, and although about 100 species have been found since, much of their basic biology remains unknown. They occur in antarctic and temperate regions, and are probably far more common and widespread than the scanty literature would suggest.

Some species live among algae and feed on diatoms, but they cannot swim and this is not the preferred habitat. Most of these tiny, yellowish to brownish, jointed worms live their inconspicuous lives in ocean mud in shallow waters. Mud dominates their lives. They feed on organic detritus in mud. They hitch themselves forward by laboriously thrusting their spiny heads forward as anchors and pulling their bodies forward with retractor muscles. When disturbed, the head is pulled back into the trunk, and they lie quietly in the protective mud cover.

Kinorhynchs, also known as echinodera, have a body of 13 or 14 segments, known as zonites. The first is the head, which has circlets of curved spines (scalids) and an oral cone containing the mouth and a whorl of oral styles (Fig. 8.12B). Retractor

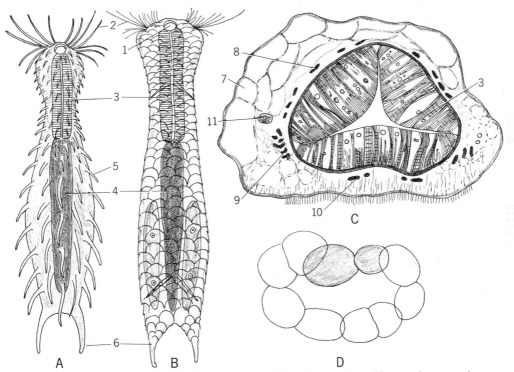

Fig. 8.12. Gastrotrichs. A. A fresh-water gastrotrich, *Chaetonota*, with conspicuous spines. B. *Lepidodermella*, a chaetonotid with surface scales. C. Section through the pharynx of *Macrodasys*. Note the triangular lumen and radial muscles, which strongly resemble the lumen and musculature of nematodes. D. Sagittal section through a gastrotrich embryo at the time of gastrulation, with the invaginating cells darkened. (A-B, after Hyman. C, after Remane. D, after de Beauchamp.) 1, buccal capsule; 2, sensory bristle; 3, pharynx; 4, midgut; 5, cuticular spine; 6, caudal furca; 7, epidermis; 8, dorsal muscle strand; 9, ventrolateral muscle strand; 10, ventral muscle strand; 11, nerve cord.

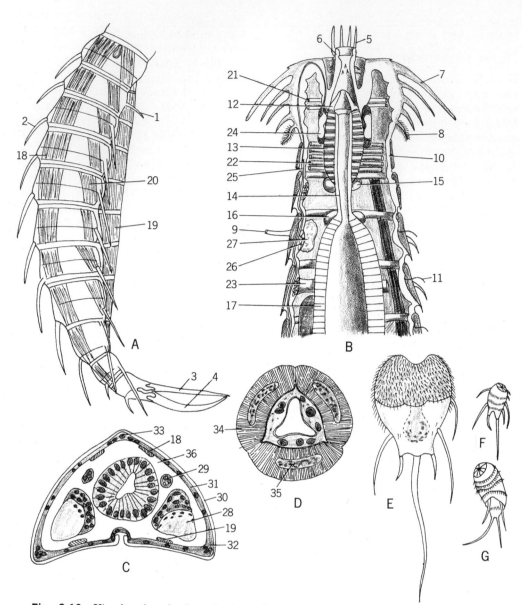

Fig. 8.13. Kinorhyncha. A. Lateral view of *Campylodera*, with the introvert retracted. B. Scheme of kinorhynch anatomy, with the introvert extended. C. Section through the intestinal region of a kinorhynch, *Pycnophyes*. D. Section through the pharyngeal region of *Pycnophyes*. E-G, three stages in the development of a kinorhynch, *Echinoderella*, showing the addition of cuticular rings as the body grows. This form of growth is reminiscent of that seen in metameric animals. (A, C, and D, after Zelinka. E-G, after Nyholm. B, after Remane, in Kükenthal and Krumbach.) *External features:* 1, lateral spine; 2, dorsal spine; 3, lateral end spine; 4, median end spine; 5, oral style; 6, oral cone; 7, scalid; 8, trichoscalid; 9, adhesive tube; 10, placid; 11, tactile hair. *Digestive system:* 12, crown of pharynx; 13, pharynx; 14, esophagus; 15, salivary gland; 16, digestive gland; 17, midgut. *Muscles:* 18, dorsolateral

muscles haul the head back into the next zonites. Three major groups, possibly suborders, can be distinguished by the equipment to protect the withdrawn head. Only the head segment of Cyclorhagae can be withdrawn, and large plates on the second zonite close the opening. The first two zonites of Conchorhagae are retracted, and the third zonite has a pair of cuticular shells that protects the retracted segments. Homalorhagae also retract the first two zonites, but close the opening with one dorsal and three ventral plates on the third zonite.

The ten unmodified trunk segments have a single dorsal cuticular plate, the tergite, and a pair of ventral plates, the sternites. With the appearance of independent segmental plates on the body surface, the muscles have assumed a metameric arrangement (Fig. 8.13A). Dorsoventral muscles, derived from the circular muscles, connect the tergite and sternites and flatten the body, forcing the eversion of the head by increasing the internal pressure of the perivisceral fluid. Pegs and sockets hold the plates in line in some species. The last body segment, typically the eleventh, is often modified. Conspicuous movable spines with special muscles are found, and sometimes a median movable spine is also present.

The somewhat syncytial epidermis extends into the spines and projects into the pseudocoel as epidermal cushions. It also forms middorsal and lateral epidermal chords, resembling the epidermal chords of nematodes (Fig. 8.13C). Circular muscle forms rings in the first two zonites and intersegmental, diagonal muscles are found in the trunk.

The anterior end of the digestive tract is highly specialized. The oral cone contains the buccal cavity, ending posteriorly in a pharyngeal crown (Fig. 8.13B). The tapered, tubular pharynx has a triangular lumen and resembles the nematode and gastrotrich pharynx, but has the radial muscle outside the epithelial lining (Fig. 8.13D). The oral cone is protruded during feeding. The oral stylets penetrate the detritus, and the pharynx sucks the food in. The narrowed anterior part of the gut is the esophagus and receives secretions of the salivary glands. The wider midgut receives secretions from the pancreatic glands. A mesh of circular and longitudinal muscles covers the midgut, and a series of sphincters divide the gut regions into discrete functional chambers. The hindgut is divided by a sphincter into anterior and posterior parts, and as the posterior part is lined with cuticle, it is probably derived from the proctodaeum. The cuticular lining of the esophagus probably means that it is derived from the stomodaeum.

Kinorhynchs have a protonephridial system, with a single, large, multinucleated solenocyte on each side of the eleventh zonite. A solenocyte differs from a flame bulb in having a flagellum rather than a ciliary tuft. Kinorhynch solenocytes contain one long and one short flagellum.

Little is known of kinorhynch sense organs. One species has eyes with a red pigment cup and a lens. Some bristles appear to be sensory. The nervous system is epidermal. A circumenteric nerve ring with many dorsal ganglion cells gives rise to a midventral nerve cord with ganglia in each zonite. The middorsal and lateral epidermal chords also contain masses of ganglion cells, but these are not united by longitudinal nerve trunks. The kinorhynch

muscle; 19, ventrolateral muscle; 20, diagonal muscle; 21, circular head muscle; 22, circular muscle of neck; 23, dorsoventral muscle. *Nervous system:* 24, brain; 25, ventral nerve cord; 26, ganglion on ventral cord. *Other parts:* 27, adhesive gland; 28, gonad. *Histology:* 29, protonephridium; 30, cuticle; 31, epidermis; 32, lateral chord; 33, dorsal chord; 34, muscle layer of pharynx; 35, nucleus; 36, pseudocoel.

nervous system is a modification of an epidermal or subepidermal nerve plexus. The nerve ring around the gut resembles the circumenteric ring of other aschelminths, but the segmentation of the cuticle into zonites, with associated segmental arrangement of the muscles, has resulted in the nervous system's assuming a segmental appearance. Something of the same sort has occurred in rotifers with cuticular rings, where ganglia associated with the divisions of the scalar nerve arise (Fig. 8:8A). Evidently segmentation of the cuticle favors the development of segmentally arranged muscles, and these, in turn, favor the development of a segmental nervous system.

Male and female kinorhynchs are similar. The paired, saccate gonads lie in the thirteenth zonite and have paired gonoducts, each leading to a separate pore. The epithelial covering of the gonad, the nutritive tissue of the ovary, and the gametocytes are all derived from an apical cell in each gonad. The syncytial ovary contains germinal and nutritive nuclei. As ova develop, they take up the nutritive material. The short oviduct has a diverticulum, the seminal receptacle, and ends at the gonopore. The short sperm duct connects testis and gonopore and contains two or three cuticular rods (spicules), probably used in copulation.

Little is known about development, but the youngest larvae appear to be composed of the first three zonites (Fig. 8.13F). As they grow, new zonites are added.

Phylum Priapulida

Priapulids are curious little mud-dwellers with a predilection for cold or cool waters. The longest are said to reach about 8 cm. in length. Priapulids are found in the littoral mud and up to depths of about 500 m. in the North Atlantic, the Baltic, and North Sea, and in corresponding lati-

tudes around Patagonia and adjacent islands. Only five species are known. In the Americas they occur no further south than Massachusetts.

Priapulids burrow in the slime, usually lying quietly with their open mouths flush with the surface of the bottom mud. They explore the surroundings with the front part of the body when hungry, or, according to Lang, (1948), plow about at random through the mud. They are carnivores, capturing and swallowing whole their slowly moving prey.

The priapulid body is divided into a presoma and trunk (Fig. 8.14A). The barrel-shaped, proboscis-like presoma is usually extended, but retractor muscles can pull it in quickly in an emergency. It ends in a spiny, circumoral region, sharply set off from the rest of the presoma by a smoother collar (Fig. 8.14B). The spiny trunk is ringed, and contains an anus and a pair of urogenital pores at the posterior tip. *Priapulus* has one or two branched, caudal appendages with hollow, vesicular twigs, covered by a wall histologically like the body wall (Fig. 8.14C). They look like gills, but *Priapulus* seems undisturbed by their removal and merely grows a new set.

The thin, layered cuticle covers a curious epidermis with fluid-filled spaces between the cells. The body wall contains an outer layer of circular muscle and an inner layer of longitudinal muscle. The spacious body cavity is anomolous, for a thin, non-cellular layer lines the body wall, covers the viscera, and forms mesentery-like sheets attaching the gut to the body wall. It lies in exactly the same position as the peritoneum of coelomates; its non-cellular nature seems to preclude its being homologous with a peritoneum, but no other pseudocoelomates have anything like it. While the priapulids resemble pseudocoelomates rather more than coelomates, their body organization is more or less intermediate, and their assignment to the Aschelminthes is temporary, awaiting further information about them. The body cavity contains a perivisceral fluid, useful in transport but more important as a hydraulic fluid for the operation of the extrusible anterior end. The perivisceral fluid contains many rounded cells which take up injected particles and convey them to the protonephridia, functionally resembling athrocytes.

A toothed cuticle lines the muscular pharynx, which leads to the straight midgut. The midgut lining is deeply folded and is separated by a constriction from the cuticularized hindgut. Nothing is known of digestive physiology.

Priapulids have no respiratory organs. The protonephridial system is linked with the gonads to form a urogenital organ. Thousands of nucleated solenocytes arise from one side of the urogenital duct. The solenocytes take up injected carmine and are apparently excretory in function. The gonads are tortuous tubules, which produce gametes.

The priapulid and kinorhynch nervous systems are built on the same plan. The nerve ring, continuous with the epidermis, encircles the body in the collar region and gives rise to a midventral nerve trunk and a system of peripheral nerves and ring commissures (Fig. 8.14E).

Early cleavage stages are said to be somewhat rotifer-like. At hatching, a tiny, rotifer-like larva emerges. The body is covered with a lorica of dorsal, ventral, and three pairs of lateral plates (Fig. 8.14G). *Halicryptus* larvae have a ring of spines like the adhesive tubes of gastrotrichs. *Priapulus* larvae have two pairs of tactile spines that resemble the larval antennae of rotifers, and a terminal foot (Fig. 8.14D), which is also rotifer-like. The caudal appendages arise from the branches of the foot, which suggests the remarkable conclusion that the caudal appendages of *Priapulus* may be homologous to rotifer toes. Larvae live as juveniles for some time, after which they shed the lorica by molting, and thereafter gradually acquire adult characteristics by a series of molts.

Phylum Nematoda

Nematodes have been enormously successful. On the basis of known ratios of free-living to parasitic species and of parasitic species to potential host species, Hyman (1951) estimates that there may be as many as 500,000 nematode species, of which 10,000 are known. Nematode specialists will be kept busy for some time to come. Perhaps more truthfully than with any other group, one must say that nematodes occur everywhere, from hot springs to polar regions, and from deserts to ocean depths. They are almost unbelievably abundant: 90,000 in a single rotting apple; 36 species and 1074 individuals in 6.7 cc. of mud from the Italian coast; 527,000 per acre in the top 3 inches of beach sand in Massachusetts; and from three to nine billion per acre in good farm land from northern China, Austria, and the United States! They abound in soils containing dead plant or animal material; they parasitize plants and animals; and they feed on the roots of plants (e.g., 13 species around the roots of a single 10 cm. wheat seedling). They even live in the pitchers of pitcher plants.

Their abundance can be partly explained by their ability to resist factors toxic to other animals and by their general adaptability. The vinegar eel, *Turbatrix aceti*, is often abundant in vinegar. It endures an acetic acid concentration of 13.5 per cent, but can also tolerate a pH of 11.5 and can live for several hours in mercuric chloride concentrations instantly fatal to most animals. There is no sharp distinction between aquatic and terrestrial species, and some of the same species occur in Dutch lowlands and Austrian highlands. To complete the picture of diversity, some species occur in specialized habitats from restricted localities.

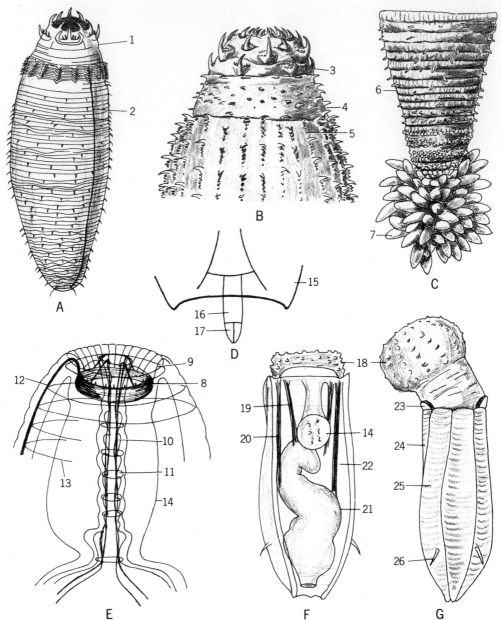

Fig. 8.14. Priapulids. **A.** *Halicryptus spinulosus*, which lacks the caudal appendage. **B.** The everted anterior end of *Priapulus*. **C.** The rear end of *Priapulus caudatus*, showing the caudal appendage. **D.** Posterior end of a *Priapulus larva*, showing the rotifer-like tail. **E.** The nervous system of the anterior end of *Halicryptus*. **F-G.** Larva of *Priapulus caudatus*, with the anterior end extended and withdrawn. (A, after Shipley. B-C, after Theel. D, F, and G, after Lang. E, after Apel.) *External features:* 1, proboscis; 2, external ridge caused by the ventral nerve cord; 3, circumoral spine; 4, collar; 5, rib of papilla on proboscis; 6, trunk ring; 7, caudal appendage. *Nervous system:* 8, circumenteric ring; 9, nerve from ring to body wall; 10, nerve

Their success does not depend on specialization, but rather on minor modifications of an effective organizational plan. The modifications are so minor that species identifications tend to be tedious and difficult.

Simplicity rather than complexity characterizes the organizational plan. The body is composed of a system of tubes. The body wall is a covering tube, composed of a resistant cuticle, an epidermis that forms four longitudinal chords, and groups of peculiar, wholly longitudinal muscles. A pseudocoel containing the perivisceral fluid separates the body wall and viscera. The gut has no transport function and is a simple tube, with some regional specialization. The excretory system is unique; there are no flame cells or protonephridia, but a system of tubes developed from renette cells is present. Specialized circulatory and respiratory systems are missing. The sense organs are relatively simple, including tactile bristles or papillae and characteristic pouches, the phasmids, at the posterior end of the body and amphids at the anterior end. A circumenteric nerve ring is associated with a bilobed brain; with middorsal and midventral nerve trunks it serves as the nerve center. Sexes are usually separate, and the tubular gonads pass directly into gonoducts. The male gonoduct joins the gut near the anus, but the female gonoduct ends in a separate gonopore. Nematodes are compactly organized animals, but ill adapted for large size. Many are microscopic; few are more than a few centimeters long.

Ascaris, a large parasitic nematode, is best for dissection, and small, transparent species of *Rhabditis* or *Turbatrix* are excellent as an introduction to nematode form. The anatomy of *Rhabditis* is summarized in Fig. 8.15, and should be examined carefully before undertaking a study of the phylum as a whole.

CLASSIFICATION

Nematode classification is by no means stable, for nematodes were studied independently by animal parasitologists, plant pathologists, and those interested in free-living animals. Serious attempts to bring all nematodes into a single classification are relatively recent, and not all agree on details. Some disagreements grow out of the homogeneity of the group. A confusing array of different combinations of minor variations makes it difficult to decide whether a category should be considered an order or a superfamily. The system used here was devised by the Chitwoods (1937), and is based on the tendency of nematodes with well-developed amphids to be without phasmids, and of those with phasmids to have simple or reduced amphids. Only a few of the more important orders are listed below.

Subclass Aphasmidia. Usually small, free-living nematodes with conspicuous sensory bristles or papillae on the head; large amphids of circular, spiral, or goblet shape, opening behind the lips; reduced amphids in parasitic groups; no phasmids, although caudal glands may be present; many pseudocoelocytes in the pseudocoel; the excretory system rudimentary or missing.

Order Enoploidea. Predominantly marine nematodes with a smooth, often bristled, unringed cuticle; head with six sensory papillae on the lips and 10 to 12 sensory bristles in one or two circlets; cyathiform amphids and a pair of cephalic slits. Example: *Pelagonema* (Fig. 8.16B).

to pharynx from ring; 11, nerve ring in pharynx; 12, ventral nerve cord; 13, segmental nerve to trunk; 14, pharynx. *Larval features:* 15, dorsal lorica plate; 16, foot; 17, toe; 18, presoma; 19, short retractor; 20, long retractor; 21, intestine; 22, pseudocoel; 23, small ventral lorica plate; 24, large ventral plate; 25, lateral lorica plate; 26, lateral tactile organ.

Order Dorylaimoidea. Small, common in fresh water and soil, with smooth cuticle lacking bristles; head with an inner circlet of six and an outer circlet of ten sensory papillae; a piercing apparatus derived from a modified tooth (odontostylet) in the oral region; goblet-shaped (cyathiform) amphids; posterior part of

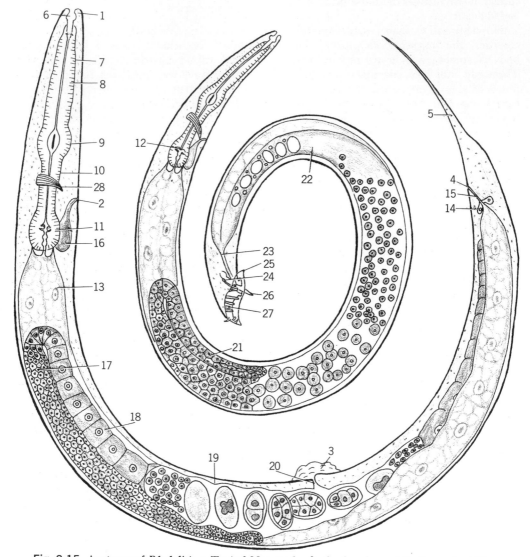

Fig. 8.15. Anatomy of *Rhabditis*, a Typical Nematode. **A,** the female, and **B,** the male. (After Hirschmann, in Sasser and Jenkins.) *External form:* 1, lip; 2, excretory pore; 3, vulva; 4, anus; 5, phasmid. *Digestive system:* 6, stomodaeum; 7, pharynx; 8, procorpus of pharynx; 9, median pseudobulb of pharynx; 10, isthmus of pharynx; 11, bulb of pharynx; 12, pharyngeal valve; 13, intestine; 14, rectal gland; 15, rectum. *Excretory system:* 16, renette cell. *Female reproductive system:* 17, germinal zone of ovary; 18, growth zone of ovary; 19, uterus; 20, vagina. *Male reproductive system:* 21, testis; 22, sperm duct; 23, cloaca; 24, gubernaculum; 25, caudal alae; 26, spicule; 27, genital papilla. *Nervous system:* 28, nerve ring.

pharynx enlarged. Example: *Actinolaimus* (Fig. 8.16C).

Order Chromadoroidea. Predominantly marine, with smooth or ringed cuticle; cuticle usually ornamented and often with bristles; pharynx with a posterior bulb; spiral amphids. Example: draconematids.

Order Trichiuroidea. Mouth without lips; pharynx very long and narrow, with a short, anterior muscular region and a long posterior region embedded in a glandular column (stichosome); with body narrowed in the pharyngeal region; females with one ovary and males with one or no copulatory spicule. *Trichinella.*

Subclass Phasmidia. Often parasitic nematodes, with phasmids and no caudal glands and with reduced amphids; few pseudocoelocytes in pseudocoel; a well-developed reproductive system.

Order Rhabditoidea. Small, transparent, free living or parasitic; pharynx with posterior and sometimes an anterior bulb; amphids are small pockets; with or without a buccal stylet. Examples: *Rhabditis* (Fig. 8.15); *Turbatrix* (Fig. 8.16A); *Heterodora.*

Order Oxyuroidea. Small or medium-sized nematodes without cervical papillae; pharynx with posterior bulb; terminal part of female reproductive tract heavily muscled and females usually with a slender tail; males with one or two copulatory spicules, and often with alae forming a bursa. Example: *Oxyuris.*

Order Ascaroidea. Usually large, parasitic nematodes, with a mouth surrounded by three, rarely six, lips; with cervical papillae; pharynx with or without a bulb, but never valvulated; often with caeca from pharynx, intestine, or both; without a buccal capsule; females with short, curved tail; males with two equal copulatory spicules and usually without alae. Example: *Ascaris.*

Order Strongyloidea. Parasitic nematodes with a simple, lipless mouth or with a buccal capsule; pharynx without a bulb; females usually with an ovejector and males with a usually conspicuous copulatory bursa supported by 13 muscular rays. Example: *Necator.*

Order Filaroidea. Filiform nematodes with a simple, lipless mouth and usually without a buccal capsule; without a pharyngeal bulb; females larger, with an anterior vulva and a long, tubular vagina; males with two unequal spicules and with or without alae; usually in blood or lymphatic system and transmitted by blood-sucking insects. Example: *Wuchereria.*

BODY FORM AND ORGANIZATION

The body is circular in cross section, tapering toward the mouth and posterior end. Occasionally it is dilated regionally, as in the draconematids (Fig. 8.22). There is no definite head, but the brain is anterior, and sense organs are concentrated around the mouth. The anus is ventral, and the body continues as a tail, sometimes narrowed or curved. Depressions known as phasmids may be found at the posterior end; they are sometimes reduced to papillae. Many free-living nematodes have a pore for caudal glands at the posterior tip of the body. The glands appear to be comparable to the adhesive glands of rotifers and gastrotrichs.

Nematodes are bilaterally symmetrical, but in fitting into the narrow, elongated body, internal organs are often coiled or one member of a pair is often lost. Externally, nematodes have a strong tendency to have radially arranged parts. Many sessile animals tend to develop radial symmetry, and it is thought that primitive nematodes were aquatic, attaching themselves to submerged objects by caudal cement glands and waving their bodies sinuously to obtain food. (Fig. 8.22).

Radial tendencies are best seen in a front view of the head (Fig. 8.17A). Primitive, marine nematodes have strong hexamerous tendencies. Six lips, three on

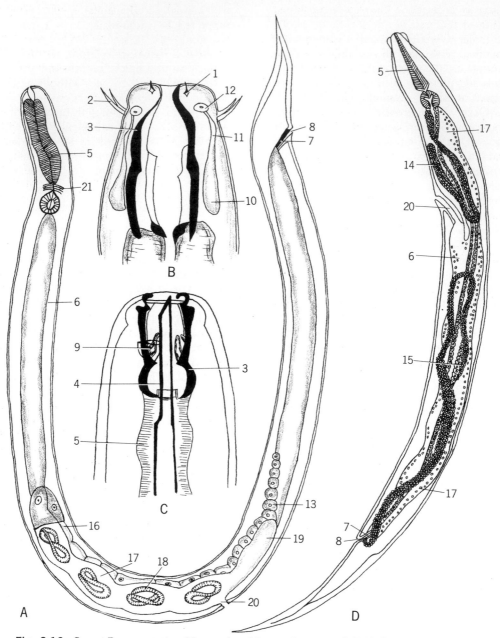

Fig. 8.16. Some Representative Nematodes. Nematodes are subdivided into the subclass Phasmidia, with phasmids and reduced amphids, and subclass Aphasmidia, with well-developed amphids and no phasmids. A. *Turbatrix aceti*, the "vinegar eel," is a commonly studied member of the Phasmidia; it belongs to the relatively primitive order Rhabditoidea. B. *Pelagonema*, a marine aphasmid which belongs to the primitive order Enoploidea. C. *Actinolaimus*, another aphasmid nematode, which belongs to the order Dorylaimoidea. They have a piercing apparatus used in feeding, and are common in fresh water and soil. D. *Enterobius vermicu-*

each side, surround the mouth. Each lip (labium) bears a sensory bristle or papilla; together they form the inner ring of labial papillae. An outer ring of labial papillae surrounds the inner ring or attaches to the cephalic region around the lips. An outer circlet of four cephalic bristles or papillae completes the primitive complement of head sense organs. The circlets are combined, papillae are lost or fused, and lip structure is varied, making head structure useful in taxonomy. The amphids are paired and the excretory pore is midventral, so a definite sagittal plane is defined in spite of the radial tendencies. The triangular lumen of the pharynx is a continuation of the hexamerous lip arrangement.

Body organization is best seen in cross section (Fig. 8.17B). The body wall consists of layers of cuticle, epidermis, and muscle. Except in the pharynx, the gut wall is a single layer of epithelial cells. The reproductive organs lie in the pseudocoel.

Cuticle. The cuticle is not the simple body covering it seems. Actually, the external covering of an animal is never an insignificant part of its equipment. Whatever the organism learns of its surroundings, and often much of what it absorbs or liberates, passes through the surface. It protects the animal from mechanical and chemical injury and provides support; it often serves as a site of muscle attachment. The nematode cuticle is a remarkable product of the epidermal cells. It is elastic, but provides support; tough, yet permits increase or decrease of body volume without changes in the fluid pressure of the pseudocoel. It is readily permeable to water, yet protects the animal against many toxic compounds.

The cuticle is sometimes smooth and featureless, and sometimes ornamented with bristles or protuberances used as sense organs or in locomotion. In several groups, the cuticle is ringed, sometimes so deeply as to cause pseudosegmentation. The cuticle is structurally complex, consisting of a cortex, a homogeneous layer, two or three fiber layers, and a basement membrane (Fig. 8.17C). The collagenous fibers of each fibrous layer are parallel, but the direction differs with layers. In three-layered cuticle, the top and bottom layers have parallel fibers. Fibers make an angle of about 70° with the longitudinal axis, permitting the cuticle to relax when the muscle tone of the body wall muscles falls. The relaxed cuticle permits body expansion without increasing fluid pressure in the pseudocoel, an important factor in filling the intestine. Volume changes are sometimes remarkable. *Rhabditis* can lose 30 per cent of its length in hypertonic solutions, and *Onchocerca*, a microfilarian, increases in length up to 55 per cent when removed from isotonic glucose. Water comes in through the cuticle, but is not discharged through it. *Ascaris* cuticle is permeable to respiratory gases, chloride, and perhaps to such small ions as ammonium, but impervious to volatile organic compounds. *Ascaris* cuticle has a cortex composed of a thin, osmiophilic lipid layer and inner and outer cortical layers, perhaps composed of quinone-tanned proteins, for it resists digestion.

Epidermis. Flattened epidermal cells lie just below the cuticle and project inward

laris is a parasitic member of the Phasmidia; it belongs to the order Oxyuroidea. (A, after De Man. D, after Goodchild, from Brown. B, after Kreis. C, after Filipjev.) *External features:* 1, labial papillae; 2, outer circlet of bristles. *Digestive tract:* 3, buccal capsule; 4, odontostyle; 5, pharynx; 6, intestine; 7, rectum; 8, anus. *Amphids:* 9, amphid; 10, amphidial gland; 11, amphidial duct; 12, amphidial pore. *Female reproductive system:* 13, ovary; 14, anterior ovary; 15, posterior ovary; 16, oviduct; 17, uterus; 18, developing larvae; 19, seminal receptacle; 20, vagina. *Nervous system:* 21, nerve ring.

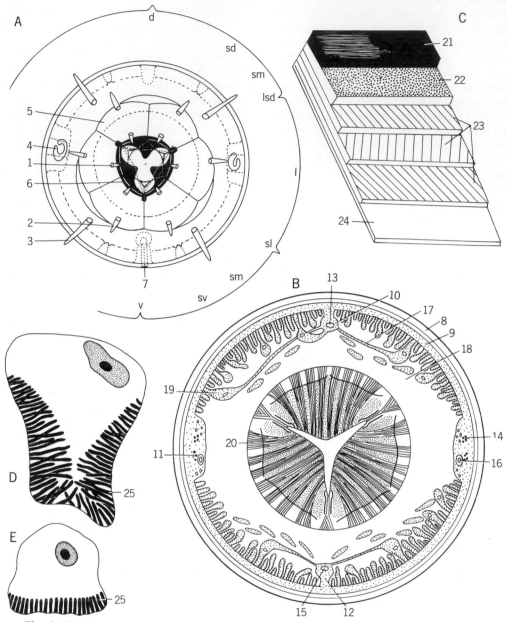

Fig. 8.17. Nematode Structure. A. Scheme of front view of nematode head. B. Scheme of cross section through *Ascaris* in the pharynx region. C. Scheme of layers of *Ascaris* cuticle. D. Scheme of coelomyarian muscle cell. E. Scheme of platymyarian muscle cell. (A, after de Coninck. B, after Hirschmann. C, after Fairbairn, in Sasser and Jenkins. D-E, after Chitwood.) *Head form:* **1**, inner labial papilla; **2**, outer labial bristle; **3**, cephalic bristle; **4**, amphid; **5**, lip; **6**, buccal capsule; **7**, excretory pore; **d**, dorsal; **sd**, subdorsal; **sm**, submedian; **lsd**, laterosubdorsal; **l**, lateral; **sl**, sublateral; **sv**, subventral; **v**, ventral. *Histology:*

as four ridges, known as chords (Fig. 8.17B). The dorsal and ventral chords are less prominent, and may disappear near the ends of the body. The chords enclose the nerve trunks and excretory canals, and divide the musculature into four fields. Small nematodes have all of the epidermal nuclei in the chords, and flattened extensions of the cells, without nuclei, connect the chords. Large nematodes, like *Ascaris*, have a syncytial epidermis in which the original nuclei have fragmented to form many small nuclei.

Muscle. A constant number of large, longitudinal muscle cells lie in fields between the epidermal chords. Many nematodes have only two to five muscles in each field and are meromyarian. Others have many muscle cells in each field and are polymyarian. The bulging, cytoplasmic part of the muscle cells contains supporting fibrils, and contractile fibers next to the epidermis (platymyarian) or extending up the periphery of the cell (coelomyarian) (Fig. 8.17D,E). Nematode muscle cells are unique in having innervation processes which extend to the nerve trunks in the epidermal chords (Fig. 8.17B).

ORGAN SYSTEMS AND PHYSIOLOGY

Digestive System. The digestive tube consists of a stomodaeal buccal cavity and pharynx, a midgut consisting of the intestine, and a proctodaeal rectum or cloaca. The inconspicuous to large buccal cavity is often highly differentiated. It is lined with cuticle, often thickened to form ridges, plates, or teeth. When highly specialized, the buccal cavity may be divided into an anterior chamber enclosed by the lips, a long protostome, and a

small telostome (Fig. 8.16B,C; Fig. 8.18). Plant parasites have an oral stylet, used to puncture plant cells so the contents can be ingested. The style is sometimes formed by the modified lining of the buccal cavity (stomatostyle) and sometimes from a highly modified tooth (odontostyle). The Chitwoods (1937) have worked out mouth-part homologies on the assumption that *Rhabditis* and *Plectus* are primitive aphasmids and phasmids, but more information about embryonic origins is needed to determine how profitable these will prove.

The pharynx is termed the esophagus by most nematologists, but appears equivalent to the pharynx of other invertebrates. In its simplest form, the pharynx is an unspecialized tube, but in most nematodes it undergoes regional specialization (Fig. 8.18). Various distinctive patterns of muscular and glandular regions are recognized, and are important taxonomically. The pharynx has a characteristic histological structure, with a triangular lumen and strong radial muscle fibers (Fig. 8.17B).

The pharyngeal glands aid in penetration of host tissues and are important in food acquisition. Enzymatic secretions are ejected from the mouth and soften and predigest food before ingestion. The food ingested is often wholly or largely fluid, and many nematodes have developed a pharyngeal pump. A pharyngo-intestinal valve at the union of pharynx and intestine remains closed while the pharynx fills. It opens and the mouth closes while the pharyngeal muscles force food into the intestine.

In most nematodes the intestine is a simple epithelial tube without regional specialization. It is composed of a rela-

8, cuticle; **9,** epidermis; **10,** dorsal epidermal chord; **11,** lateral epidermal chord; **12,** ventral epidermal chord; **13,** dorsal nerve; **14,** lateral nerve; **15,** ventral nerve; **16,** lateral excretory canal; **17,** innervation process; **18,** pseudocoel; **19,** muscle cell; **20,** pharyngeal radial muscle. *Cuticle layers:* **21,** cortex; **22,** homogeneous layer; **23,** fiber layers; **24,** basement membrane. *Muscle:* **25,** contractile band.

tively small number of cells in small nematodes, 18 to 64 in rhabditids, and 16 to
24 in tylenchids. In some nematodes, an
anterior ventricular region, a mid-region,

and a posterior prerectal region can be
distinguished on histological grounds.

Little, if any, intracellular digestion occurs. Details of the digestive processes are

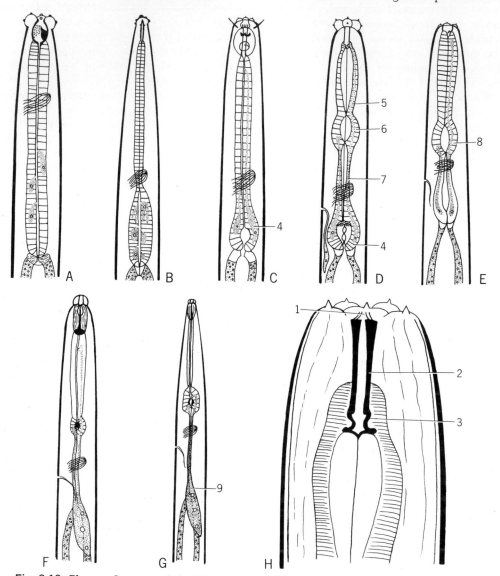

Fig. 8.18. Pharynx Structure. A-G. Scheme of the pharynx structure in nematodes of various
types. A, cylindrical type (*Mononchus*); B, dorylaimoid type (*Dorylaimus*); C, bulboid type
(*Ethmolaimus*); D, rhabditoid type (*Rhabditis*); E, diplogasteroid type ʼ(*Diplogaster*);
F, tylenchoid type (*Helicotylenchus*); G, Aphelencoid type (*Aphelenchus*). H, Buccal capsule
of *Rhabditis*. (A-G, after Hirschmann, in Sasser and Jenkins. H, after Stekhoven and Tenuissen.) 1, cheilostome; 2, prostome; 3, telostome; 4, end bulb; 5, corpus; 6, median pseudobulb; 7, isthmus; 8, median bulb; 9, pharyngeal gland.

not well known. Microvilli thickly clothe the inner surface of the *Ascaris* intestine, and secretory bulbs can be seen on its surface (Fig. 8.19). The digestive processes are far more varied than in the carnivorous phyla so far discussed. Some nematodes are plant parasites, and others are phytophagous. Even parasites absorb food only through the digestive tube and

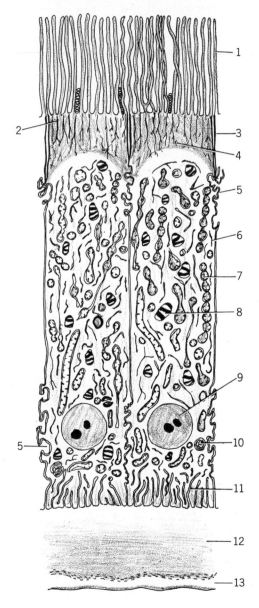

have not been cultured successfully in media containing only dissolved foods. The intestine stores food as well as absorbs it. Glycogen and fat reserves in the intestinal cells are used during starvation and molting, and in some species food is accumulated in large amounts at specific periods of the life cycle, preparing for critical waiting periods or periods of intensive development.

The rectum is a proctodaeal region, derived from the ectoderm and lined with cuticle. It leads from an intestino-rectal valve to the slit-shaped anus. A muscle lifts the lip of the anus and rectal wall to aid in defecation. Large, unicellular rectal glands are common in parasitic species. The male reproductive tract joins the rectum, forming a chamber known as the cloaca, although it is not joined by the urinary system. The cloaca is highly modified to provide copulatory organs, discussed with the male system.

Fig. 8.19. Scheme of Intestinal Cell of Ascaris (as seen in electron micrographs). (After R. G. Kessel *et al.*) It is evident that the epithelial cells of organisms at this level of organization have developed all of the major types of specializations found in more highly organized animals. The striated border is composed of surface-amplifying microvilli, and their fibrillar rootlets, and ends in a terminal web of filaments. Interdigitating folds of the cell membrane at the upper and lower end of the cells attach adjacent cells, and add to the integrity of the tissue as a whole. Desmosomes in the forms of terminal bars occur at the upper ends of the cells, where they come in contact with other cells. Infoldings at the base of the cell seat it firmly on the basement membrane. Note the thin mesenterial layer of non-cellular material outside the basement membrane. 1, microvilli; 2, rootlets of microvilli; 3, desmosomes (terminal bars); 4, terminal web of filaments; 5, infoldings of the cell membrane; 6, endoplasmic reticulum; 7, mitochondrium; 8, lipid inclusion; 9, nucleus; 10, granule; 11, basal infoldings of the cell membrane; 12, basement membrane; 13, mesenterial membrane.

Respiration. Nematodes have no special respiratory organs. Haemoglobin occurs in the periatisceral fluid of some parasitic nematodes. It is evidently formed by the organism, as it differs from host haemoglobin, and haemoglobins of different properties sometimes occur in the body wall and perivisceral fluid.

A considerable amount of information about nematode respiration is now available. The general principles undoubtedly apply to lower invertebrates generally, although specific details may differ in different groups.

Oxygen is the final hydrogen-acceptor in aerobic respiration. Hydrogen is removed from molecules with the aid of dehydrogenases, and is transferred to oxygen by way of a hydrogen transport system, typically a cytochrome-oxidase system sensitive to cyanides plus a limited amount of other, iron-free, and cyanide-

insensitive oxidases. Anaerobic respiration, on the other hand, produces a variety of end products (Fig. 8.20). Many of these products are somewhat toxic. As aerobic respiration completely oxidizes the substrate, it provides more energy per unit of substrate consumed. Aerobic respiration thus has two great advantages over anaerobic respiration; it leads to a more efficient use of food and produces less toxic or more easily handled end products.

Most invertebrates are aerobic, but can survive short periods of oxygen deprivation. Evidently some capacity for anaerobic respiration is generally present, but this capacity is inadequate to permit normal activity and survival for long periods of time when oxygen is not available. Most aerobic animals take up larger quantities of oxygen immediately after oxygen deprivation. This is the so-called oxygen debt phenomenon. The debt must be paid

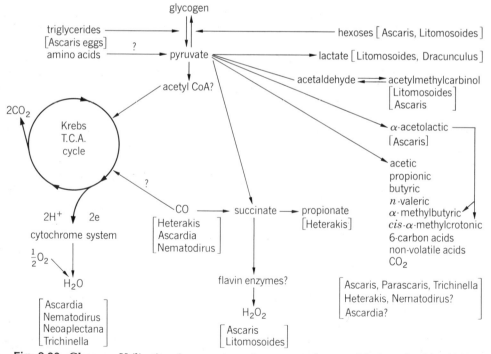

Fig. 8.20. Glycogen Utilization (as seen in various nematodes parasitic in animals). (After Rogers, from Fairbairn, in Sasser and Jenkins.)

to oxidize the end products of anaerobic respiration that have piled up in the tissues. An animal perfectly adapted to anaerobic life builds up no oxygen debt, for it is able to handle the end products of its anaerobic energy release. In such organisms, oxygen may be toxic. *Ascaris*, for example, is sensitive to high oxygen tensions, probably because it produces H_2O_2 and lacks a catalase system for its disposal. An anaerobic organism that did not produce H_2O_2 might find oxygen non-toxic.

Both aerobic and anaerobic energy release produce toxic compounds, and the ability to survive either kind of respiration depends on the respiratory patterns that are followed, and on the ability to exchange end products with the environment. The end products, and therefore the sensitivity of the animal to the presence or absence of oxygen, depend qualitatively on the nature of the enzyme systems that determine respiratory patterns. They depend quantitatively on the modifications of the body, intestinal, or other surfaces which cope with the respiratory end products. Complete anaerobes or aerobes are uncommon. Trematodes, cestodes, and nematodes that live as intestinal parasites are predominantly anaerobic, but all can use oxygen when it is available.

The ability of an animal to shift from anaerobic to aerobic respiration or the reverse is important in its distribution. Small amounts of oxygen are available in many habitats and considerable seasonal fluctuation is common. Bacterial decomposition in dirty waters or at the bottom is rapid at some seasons, and oxygen becomes scarce. In colder seasons, bacterial decomposition is slower and more oxygen can dissolve in the water, so oxygen tensions rise. When a sheet of ice covers a pond, however, and especially if snow on the ice prevents light penetration and photosynthesis, oxygen levels fall sharply. Wet soils are characterized by low oxygen levels, and many soils vary in

moistness and oxygen levels with the season. Adaptability to such changing respiratory situations is an important factor in survival. Nematodes live in all of these environments, and many species are widely distributed, occurring in areas with high and low oxygen tensions.

One method of assessing the respiratory physiology of animals is to experimentally reduce the amount of oxygen available and determine the rate of oxygen absorption. As oxygen tension falls to some critical level, the rate of oxygen uptake begins to fall. Nematodes 0.05 mm. in diameter find oxygen tensions of 16 mm. Hg critical; 32 mm. Hg oxygen tension is critical for worms 0.14 mm. in diameter, showing the effect of reduced surface-volume ratios in larger animals. Animals too large for the environmental oxygen supply are forced to tolerate a constant state of oxygen deprivation in deeper tissues. The difference between the environmental oxygen tension and the critical oxygen tension provides a safety factor. The organism can tolerate this much reduction of environmental oxygen (or increase its activity a corresponding amount) before it must curtail its aerobic respiration. Most lower invertebrates have a small safety factor, if they are large. A sea anemone, for example, normally lives in an environment providing too little oxygen; it is larger than the maximal size for internal physiological efficiency.

Selective pressures favoring respiratory adaptations arise from low oxygen tensions in parasitic environments and in the environments of bottom-dwellers or animals living in wet soils. They also arise as the result of increased size and activity. There are several possibilities. Anaerobic respiratory enzymes may be amplified, with accompanying modification of the body, gut, or excretory surfaces for disposal of the end products. Parasitic species, and probably many species living in oxygen-poor environments, often adapt in this manner. Many free-living species adapt by remaining small, by living on a narrow margin with little or no safety factor, by adjusting activity to levels suitable for a low oxygen uptake, or by developing special methods of increasing the efficiency of the oxygen uptake system or the oxygen transport system. The last is dependent, for full implementation, on the development of special respiratory or circulatory organs. The various avenues of adaptation are clearly illustrated by lower invertebrates. Flatworms and nematodes remain small, in part because of the absence of respiratory organs. The pseudocoel of nematodes and the circulatory system of nemertines undoubtedly improve respiratory transport. Respiratory pigments are beginning to make their appearance in the circulating fluid of nemertines and in the perivisceral fluid of some nematodes. Such changes lower the critical oxygen tension at which aerobic respiration must be curtailed, increase the safety factor, and permit occupation of oxygen-poor habitats. It is customary to think of respiratory adaptation as centering about gills, lungs, and a circulatory system, but this is only partly true. Enzyme systems and biochemical specializations are also important. And, in a sense, nematodes and all other animals are adapting to a respiratory situation, more or less directly as the case may be, in growing to a certain size, in being active at certain seasons, and in living where they do.

Respiratory adaptation by way of enzyme systems is clearly shown in nematodes (Fig. 8.20). The Krebs cycle has been identified in some nematodes, but is known to be absent in Ascaris. Cytochrome-cytochrome oxidase is present in Trichinella and absent in Ascaris, although a similar system is found. The anaerobic respiration of carbohydrates releases a variety of end products, and some nematodes liberate an amazing complex of five- and six-carbon acids that is difficult to explain. The addition of oxygen to the environment reduces the output of organic acids in some nematodes and has little effect on others, especially parasitic forms like Ascaris and Trichinella. Undoubtedly the metabolic plasticity that the studies on a few forms have shown reflects an adaptability that has had much to do with the success of nematodes as a group.

Excretion. Primitive, marine nematodes have a glandular excretory system, and other nematodes have a tubular system based upon it. There are no flame bulbs or cilia of any kind in the nematode excretory system; it is evidently not protonephridial.

The glandular cell (renette cell) making up the unicellular excretory system of Enoplus is on the ventral midline, and opens through a midventral, anterior pore. Closely related parasitic and fresh-water species also have a renette. Phasmidia have a tubular excretory system. Rhabditids have an H-shaped system, associated with two renette cells (Fig. 8.21). Changes in the excretory system have resulted in the loss of the renette cells, and the loss of arms of the H-shaped system of tubes. As renette cells appear during the development of nematodes with a tubular system, it may be concluded that the renette cells are primitive.

Excretory physiology is poorly understood. The predominant nitrogenous wastes are ammonia and urea. Some nematodes are ammonotelic, but release some urea. Cavier and Savel found that Ascaris excretes more urea when water is scarce. When water is restricted, Ascaris excretes 52 per cent of its nitrogen as urea, and with normal water availability, only 7 per cent. If this ability to change excretory patterns with water availability is general, it may help to account for the adaptability of nematodes, especially to water deprivation in dry soils or in dehydrating organic matter. Urea is ordinarily formed from ammonia released during deamination by way of an ornithine cycle known to be centered in the intestine. Urease is also present and can convert urea to ammonia. The biochemical equipment needed to shift excretion products is present, but the way in which it is controlled is not understood.

Nematode cuticle is permeable to water entering, but not leaving, the animal. Nevertheless, many nematodes adjust to a wide range of salinities. Osmoregulation depends in part on control of salts, but also on the ability of nematodes to discharge water from the excretory pore. Direct evidence of changing activity of the excretory parts with osmotic stress indicates that they are hydrostatic organs. If the intestine is the primary seat of nitrogen excretion and the excretory system primarily hydrostatic, the nematode system is functionally comparable to that found in other aschelminths.

Pseudocoel and Perivisceral Fluid. The pseudocoel is derived from the blastocoel and contains the gut and reproductive organs. It is filled with the perivisceral fluid and fibrous, lacy material that invests the gut and reproductive organs and lines the body wall. The fibrous material contains nuclei in some nematodes. In *Ascaris* and some other parasites, a single large cell above the pharynx produces fenestrated membranes covering the body wall and digestive tube. Fixed cells are present in other nematodes. Among parasites, only two to six are found, but in free-living species they are more numerous. They are constant in position and are often highly

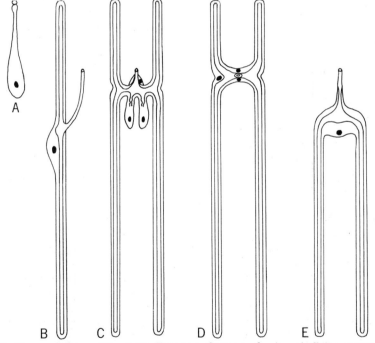

Fig. 8.21. Form of Some Nematode Excretory Systems. A. A unicellular renette system. B. One-sided tylenchoid type, with renette cell and excretory tube, and with a median excretory pore. C. Rhabditoid system, with paired renette cells and an H-shaped system of excretory tubules. D. Oxyuroid system, with H-shaped excretory tubules and no renette cells. E. Ascaroid type, without anterior excretory tubules. The renette cells appear to be primitive, and to have been wholly replaced in some nematodes by a system of excretory tubules, at one time associated with the renette cell system. (All after Hirschmann, in Sasser and Jenkins)

branched. These cells are called pseudo-coelocytes; they do not take up particles or move but may be oxidative centers.

The perivisceral fluid is chemically complex in *Ascaris*, the only nematode in which it has been carefully studied. It contains a variety of mono- and di-valent ions, with sodium the predominant cation and chloride the predominant anion. A deficiency of anions is probably balanced by organic acids, and possibly by bicarbonates. Proteins, fats, and carbohydrates are present, with proteins predominant. Urea, ammonia, and some free amino acids have been recovered, and a small amount of haemoglobin is present. The chemical complexity reflects its function. Bathing body wall and internal organs, the perivisceral fluid is an important transporting medium. Body movements agitate the fluid and increase its effectiveness.

Locomotion and Movement. The unusual longitudinal muscles have been described. Alternate contractions of the muscles on each side of the body produce the characteristic lashing movements of the body.

The absence of circular muscle makes it impossible to stretch the body by direct muscle action. The crossed cuticular fibers permit a lengthening and shortening of the body, depending on the fluid pressure of the pseudocoel and the tone of the longitudinal muscles. Some nematodes with a rough cuticle move by alternately stretching and contracting the body, rather like earthworms. These movements undoubtedly depend on the give of the cuticle and the tone of longitudinal muscles. Sinuous, serpentine movements are made by some nematodes, and they produce good forward locomotion, especially when combined with roughened cuticle. Sinuous movements result from muscle contractions involving parts of the body. Draconematids (Fig. 8.22) have long stilt bristles with adhesive glands and inch along by attaching the head bristles and stilt bristles alternately, or creep on the

stilt bristles by alternately lengthening and contracting the body. In general, however, nematodes thrash about and get nowhere. Undoubtedly they randomly sample the environment, but at a considerable expenditure of energy. It should be remembered, however, that they are usually observed in a less viscous medium than their normal environment.

Sense Organs. So little is known of the

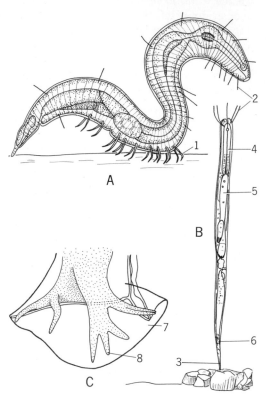

Fig. 8.22. A. A draconematid. Draconematids are characterized by the enlarged, head-like anterior end and stilt bristles containing adhesive tubes, used in locomotion. B. A marine nematode, attached by the posterior caudal glands. C. The bursa of a hookworm, *Ancylostoma duodenale*. (A, after Steiner, from Rauther, in Kükenthal and Krumbach. B, after Steiner. C, after Looss, from Chandler and Read.) 1, stilt bristles; 2, head bristles; 3, adhesive tube; 4, pharynx; 5, intestine; 6, adhesive gland; 7, bursa; 8, bursal ray.

functions of nematode sense organs that we have no good idea of the world they inhabit. Only a few aquatic nematodes have eyes; when present they are pigment cup ocelli with cuticular lenses. The cephalic bristles and papillae (Fig. 8.17A) are evidently sensory and are complex histologically. Some must be tactile, but specific functions can only be guessed. Amphids may be chemoreceptors. Although they differ in shape, all have about the same components, an external pore, a duct, and an amphidial pouch (Fig. 8.16B). An amphidial nerve forms a cluster of nerve endings and the unicellular amphidial gland opens into the pouch. Phasmids are variable. When fully developed they consist of a gland, a pore, and nerve endings. They are evidently glandulo-sensory organs, but of unknown function.

Responses to single environmental stimuli have not been intensively studied. *Dorylaimus* and *Rhabditis* from sewage beds give no definite responses to temperature, light, or chemicals from capillary tubes. One species of *Rhabditis* is attracted by dilute acids. Many nematodes appear to be wholly insensitive to nearby prey and must touch them with the lips before reacting. On the other hand, nematodes which feed on or enter plant roots locate roots from a distance and aggregate around them.

Nervous System. The central nervous system consists of a circumenteric nerve ring, several associated ganglia, and a system of longitudinal nerves (Fig. 8.23). The ring is predominantly formed of nerve fibers, and the nerve-cell bodies are located predominantly in ganglia. Paired lateral and single or paired ventral ganglia are attached to the ring. A variable group of smaller ganglia are associated with the nerve ring and nerves. Mixed motor and sensory nerves pass to the cephalic papillae, and a pair of amphidial nerves, containing amphidial ganglia, arise from the lateral ganglia. The predominantly motor

dorsal nerve cord runs in the dorsal epidermal chord. The predominantly sensory lateral nerve trunks run in the lateral epidermal chords, passing through lumbar ganglia and terminating at the anus. The main body nerve is the ventral nerve trunk, in the ventral chord. It is formed by the union of two trunks behind the excretory pore at a ganglion and continues posteriorly to the single or paired anal ganglia. Commissural connectives are often present, and some nematodes have additional longitudinal trunks. Visceral nerves pass to the esophagus from the circumenteric ring and from the anal ring in the rectal region.

Little is known of nerve physiology. Acetylcholine causes muscle contraction, but no cholinesterase is present, so contractions are prolonged. Acetylcholine can be demonstrated in nematode tissues and is more abundant anteriorly. Probably neurohumors play some role in the nematode nervous system.

Although small and simple in form, nematodes have a number of sense organs and several muscles for special purposes, such as moving the bristles, papillae, and parts of the reproductive organs. Selective pressures are adequate to maintain a good nervous system, even in parasitic forms. Probably the most important development is the appearance of definitely specialized dendritic and axonic branches of the bipolar neurons. Nerve impulses move in a definite direction in flatworms because of neuron placement, but in nematodes, receiving and transmitting ends of the neurons are differentiated.

Reproduction. A few nematodes are hermaphroditic, with ova and sperm formed in the same gonad and with self-fertilization the rule. Most nematodes are dioecious, with sex determined by environmental or hereditary mechanisms. Fresh-water and soil nematodes tend to be predominantly female, and parthenogenetic development is common. An outstanding peculiarity is the continuity of

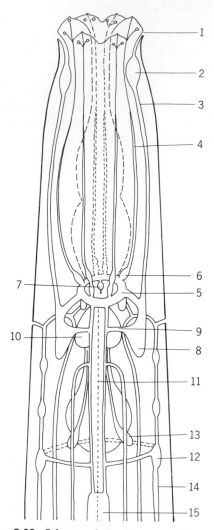

Fig. 8.23. Scheme of the Nervous System of *Rhabditis terricola*. (After the Chitwoods, from Hirschmann, in Sasser and Jenkins.) Note the nerve ring and the relatively large number of ganglia and ring commissures. 1, amphidial pore; 2, amphidial pouch; 3, amphidial nerve; 4, subventral papillary nerve; 5, nerve ring; 6, cephalic ganglion; 7, dorsal ganglion; 8, lateral ganglion; 9, lateroventral commissure; 10, subventral ganglion; 11, dorsal nerve; 12, posterolateral ganglion; 13, posterosubventral ganglion; 14, lateral nerve; 15, retrovesicular ganglion.

gonads and gonoducts, with a continuous epithelial capsule enclosing both. Many nematode gonads have a terminal stem cell, from which all gametes arise.

The Male System. Most male nematodes have a single testis, but some have anterior and posterior testes which join at the origin of the sperm duct. The testis consists of an apical germinal zone, a middle growth zone, and a terminal zone where gametes mature and are dissociated (Fig. 8.16). The sperm duct usually dilates near the origin as a seminal vesicle with glandular walls, forming the cement used during mating. The seminal vesicle opens into the ejaculatory duct, a nonglandular, muscular region that joins the rectum. Prostatic glands may open into the end of the ejaculatory duct. Depressions in the cloacal wall, the spicule pouches, secrete cuticular rods (copulatory spicules) used in mating. Most nematodes have two equal or unequal spicules, but a few have one. The spicule pouch sometimes secretes a piece, the gubernaculum, which guides the spicule to the anus. Hookworms and some other nematodes have a prominent bursa, an umbrella-shaped affair, formed of cuticular flanges (alae) and supported by radiating, muscular bursal rays, arranged like the ribs of an umbrella (Fig. 8.22C). The bursa clasps the female during mating. The form of the spicules, gubernaculum, and bursa are important in species determination.

The Female System. Most nematodes have an anterior and a posterior ovary, but some species have one and in one family there may be as many as eleven. The ovary, like the testis, is divided into a germinal zone, growth zone, and terminal zone (Fig. 8.15). The terminal zone leads quickly into the dilated uterus. The upper end of the uterus serves as a seminal receptacle, and eggs are fertilized as they pass through it. Shell formation and the early part of embryonic development take place in the uterus. In some nematodes, the eggs hatch into larvae in the uterus, but these ovoviviparous species are in the minority. The two uteri join at the vagina. Nematodes with one ovary have a diverticulum serving as a seminal receptacle at this position. It is probably the vestige of a second oviduct. The heavily muscled vagina has a cuticular lining, and may be modified at the end to form an ovejector that expels the ova. The female gonopore is a slit-shaped, midventral vulva, often equipped with special dilator muscles.

EMBRYONIC DEVELOPMENT

A fertilization membrane forms at fertilization. This membrane later thickens to form the shell, and a lipid membrane is deposited on its inner surface. Glands in the uterine wall add protein material at the surface, so the egg-shell is usually three-layered. Some eggs have a break in the shell (operculum), through which the embryo escapes, and many free-living nematodes attach the ova with threads or branched filaments to submerged objects.

The first cleavage division produces a germ cell and a somatic cell, termed P_1 and S_1 respectively. S_1 divides into blastomeres A and B, and P_1 divides into S_2 and P_2. The four cells arrange themselves into a rhomboid (Fig. 8.28), with A anterior, B dorsal, S_2 ventral, and P_2 posterior. A and B give rise to the ectodermal covering of the body, and S_2 is a stem cell for the endoderm, mesoderm, and stomodaeum. It divides into blastomeres E and MSt at its first division, and MSt divides into M and St at the next division, thus segregating as single blastomeres the future endoderm (E), mesoderm (M), and stomodaeum (St). The daughters of E move into the interior at gastrulation and develop into a chain of cells that will form the midgut. The daughters of M form a strand of cells on each side of the endoderm cells, and will form all of the mesodermal tissue. St de-

velops into a group of cells that becomes the stomodaeum and establishes the foregut. The P line continues to produce one P cell and one S cell at each division for a time: P_2 divides into P_3 and S_3; P_3 into P_4 and S_4, etc. The P cell is a germinal cell, eventually producing the stem cell of ovaries or testes. The S cells are somatic; S_3 and S_4 form the posterior epidermis and proctodaeum, and in some nematodes form some ectomesoderm. The

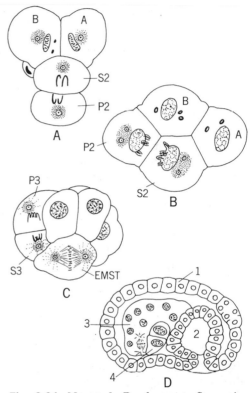

Fig. 8.24. Nematode Development. Stages in the development of *Parascaris equorum* (after Boveri). A. The T-shaped, four-cell stage. B. The four-cell stage, after rearrangement into the rhomboid form. C. The seven-cell stage, showing the stem cell for the endoderm, mesoderm, and pharynx. D. Sagittal section of an embryo at the time of stomodaeum formation. The numbered cells are as described in the text. 1, epidermis; 2, stomodaeum; 3, midgut endoderm; 4, germ cell.

nervous system and sense organs arise from the ectodermal cells, and the renette cells are also ectodermal. Cleavage is not spiral, but is determinate.

Late in embryonic development, nuclear divisions cease and all future growth results from changes in cell size. The only exceptions are the cells which produce the reproductive organs. The result is a great cell constancy, extending to all parts of the nematode body except the reproductive system. The nematode nervous system, for example, is formed of the same number of cells in each member of a species. Each ganglion consists of the same number of cells, and each cell is in a constant position, with its axon extending to a predetermined point.

LIFE CYCLES

Fully developed, but juvenile, worms emerge from the eggs at hatching. Some changes in form occur during their growth, especially at the anterior end, where the pharynx may undergo progressive specialization, and the reproductive system develops gradually. Four molts occur during growth and maturation. The entire cuticle is shed at molt, so the larva loses the lining of the buccal capsule, pharynx, vagina, rectum, and cloaca. Each molt terminates one growth period and begins another; they often separate distinctive phases of the life cycle. Parasites sometimes remain in a stage, awaiting introduction to an appropriate host, where they will molt immediately and begin a new phase of growth. The cuticle shed at the second molt of some nematodes is not discarded, but forms a sheath around the third stage larva, increasing its resistance to unfavorable environmental conditions (Fig. 8.25B). After the fourth molt, the worms mature, but may grow somewhat in length.

Physiological and ecological adaptation of the shelled or free larval stages, and the development of parasitic habits in

larvae and adults cause a great diversity of life cycles. Most nematodes are free living and develop directly into adults, but specialized behavior and growth produces specific and varied life cycles. These often center on specialized food habits.

Phytophagous nematodes are small, and the plants on which they feed are relatively huge. The line between normal foraging on one or a few plant species and parasitism is indistinct, but eventually the association of nematode and food organism becomes so intimate that the borderline is passed and the nematode must be considered parasitic. Larvae, adults, or both may be parasitic. The form of the life cycle depends on which stages are parasitic and how extensive the parasitism may be. Every life cycle involving incipient or full-fledged parasitism instead of

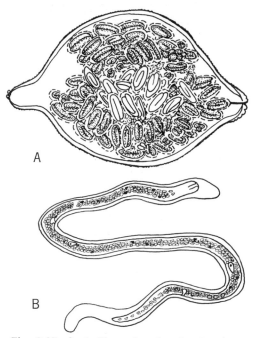

Fig. 8.25. A. A *Heterodora* female after conversion into a cyst, filled with inactive larvae. B. A sheathed larva of *Wuchereria*. The cuticle from the preceding molt has remained in place, forming a sheath. (A, after Waggenti and Allen, from the Nobles.)

random feeding represents a profound adaptational adjustment of the reproductive cycle to physical and biotic environmental factors. Specific behavior patterns that bring the parasite to the host and enable it to enter, physiological adjustments to the conditions encountered in the host, and often structural changes upon which critical behavior patterns depend, are all involved. Nematode life cycles are far too varied and complex to be fully discussed here, but they are well worth further study, not only by parasitologists but also by general zoologists as examples of detailed adaptive changes in animal stocks.

Some nematode species are becoming phytoparasites today, while others have a long history of phytoparasitism. Every stage of adaptation can be observed among living species. An early stage of parasitism is seen among species that have larvae that attach to but do not enter plant roots. Adults produce soil-inhabiting larvae that find their way to new roots. Some nematode larvae enter the plant tissues, causing necrotic areas in which the adults feed and grow. Some ability of adults and larvae to live freely in the soil is to be expected in the initial phases of parasitism, and some species are facultative parasites and may or may not enter plants. Eventually parasitism becomes obligatory and the final stages of phytoparasitism are attained, establishing selective pressures favoring intensive specialization of the parasite. The second-stage larvae of *Heterodora*, for example, enter the host plant and pierce and suck out the contents of cells, creating a gall. Larvae become mature in the gall. Male nematodes remain normal in form, and embark from the home gall into the soil to seek other infected plants, where they fertilize the females and die. The females become more and more plump, losing all resemblance to the cylindrical larvae, and several hundred ova form within them (Fig. 8.25A). The gravid females die, but their cuticle remains as a cyst membrane around the eggs, which can remain alive for years before germination.

Insects feeding on the host plant may transport larvae from plant to plant, and on this relationship complex and detailed life cycles may be based. Thus, adult females of *Tylenchinema oscinellae* live in the haemocoel of fruit flies. Their larvae enter the fly gut and are deposited on oat plants parasitized by the fly. Larval flies and larval nematodes develop independently on the oat plant, and as the nematodes mature, the females enter the fly larvae after mating, while the males die.

One avenue to zooparasitism is the habit of feeding on feces. Many soil forms aggregate in regions of high organic content, and some have specific preferences for fecal material. Dung beetles and flies that visit feces become transporters of some *Rhabditis* species. This habit is fixed in the life cycle of some, whose third-stage larvae remain quiescent until they have been carried by insects to fresh dung. It is not far from this hitch-hiking to endoparasitism. Diplogasterid larvae are transported to the galleries of bark beetles by attaching to the insects, and some enter the gut or haemocoel of the insect. Only the larvae of mermithids are parasitic. The eggs are eaten by grasshoppers, and develop in its body. They emerge, complete the final molt, and grow to maturity in the soil. Scavenging adults may have larvae that enter the body of an animal and await its death to mature, as in *Rhabditis maupasi*. The young live in the soil; they enter and leave earthworms freely, but do not mature until the earthworm has died. They feed on the carcass, producing larvae that live freely in the soil.

A number of nematodes parasitize man and his domestic animals. The details of their life cycles can be found in texts on parasitology. A variety of patterns of life cycles can be recognized. *Ascaris* eggs

leave the host with the feces and are infective for new hosts. They hatch into
larvae when eaten. The larvae migrate
through the blood to the lung, where
they pause and molt twice. After the last
molt they pierce the lung wall, migrate
up the respiratory tree, enter the pharynx,
and are swallowed, eventually becoming
mature in the intestine. *Trichinella* females release from 1350 to 1500 live
larvae, which migrate through the lymphatics and blood stream and eventually
encyst in striated muscle tissue. Here they
remain until the muscle is eaten by an
acceptable host; they emerge from the
cysts and reach maturity in the intestine.
Hookworm eggs leave the body with the
feces and hatch to form larvae that live
in the soil. They eventually become infective larvae that penetrate the skin, migrate along avenues like those followed by
Ascaris, and mature in the intestine. Here
they attach to the intestinal lining and
feed on blood from the wounds produced
by their teeth. *Wuchereria* adults live in
the lymphatics and give rise to larvae
known as microfilariae. The larvae enter
the blood, and are taken with blood by
blood-sucking arthropods, in whose body
they become infective larvae. When the
arthropod takes another blood meal, the
larvae enter the vertebrate host and develop into maturity in the lymphatics.

These examples illustrate the diversity
of life cycles, and the many ways the
nematode adult and larval stages can be
fitted to a parasitic mode of life. Nowhere
in biology does the interplay of environmental, physiological, and morphological
factors determine selective pressures and
evoke adaptations involving detailed suit-
abilities of animal, behavior, and environment so clearly as in the minutiae of
parasitic life cycles.

Phylum Nematomorpha

Horsehair worms do not come from horse-
hairs as people once thought, but they
look as if they should have. They are
sometimes called the Gordiacea, and they
fully live up to this name, both because
they are in many ways perplexing, and
because they can tie themselves up into
a knot of Gordian proportions. There are
two orders, Gordioidea and Nectonema-
toidea. Members of the first order parasitize insects when juvenile and emerge
into fresh water when adult. The second
order includes only the genus *Nectone-
mua.* These animals parasitize crabs when
juvenile and emerge into salt water when
adult.

One must examine the nematomorphs
closely to find any external features. They
have a very thick cuticle, with an outer
homogeneous layer often containing
rounded or polygonal thickenings (are-
oles), and with as many as 45 fibrous
layers below. Some species have two or
three caudal lobes at the posterior end
(Fig. 8.26B), and all have a posterior
cloacal pore. The head is not set off from
the rest of the body, but a lighter head
calotte containing the mouth is usually
present (Fig. 8.26A). The mouth is small
and functionless, for the adults do not
feed; their whole business is reproduction.
They usually mate soon after being freed,
but may overwinter if they emerge from
the larval host in late fall. Males die immediately after mating and females after
egg-laying.

The digestive tract is no more useful
to the larva than to the adult, for both
absorb food through the body surface.
The adult gut is greatly reduced. The
pharynx is a solid cord of cells, and the
intestine a diminutive epithelial tube
(Fig. 8.26C,D). Its cells look like the
cells of an insect Malpighian tubule, an
excretory organ, and as there is no other
excretory organ, it may be that the gut
has become one. The reproductive organs
join the posterior end of the intestine,
converting it to a cloaca.

As there are no circulatory, respiratory,
or excretory systems, and as the digestive

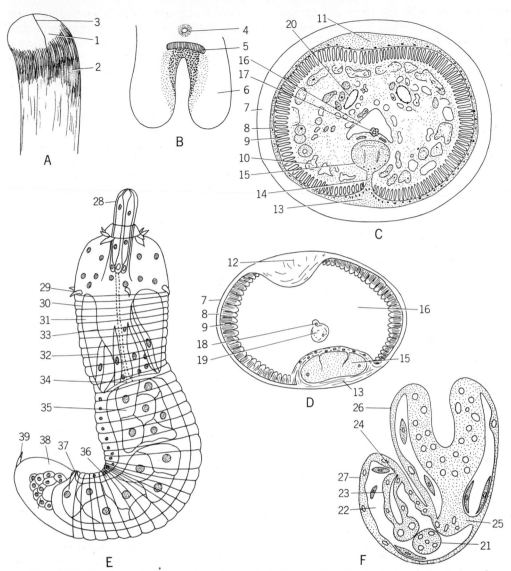

Fig. 8.26. Nematomorpha. **A.** Anterior end of *Paragordius*, **B.** Posterior end of a male *Gordius*. **C.** Section through a gordioid nematomorph, *Paragordius*. **D.** Section through a nectonematoid nematomorph, *Nectonema*. **E.** Larva of *Gordius aquaticius*. **F.** Older larva of *Paragordius*. (**A**, after May. **B**, after Heinze. **C**, after Montgomery. **D**, after Bürger, **E**, after Mühldorf. **F**, after Montgomery.) *External form:* 1, head calotte; 2, pigment ring; 3, pharynx; 4, anus; 5, postanal crescent; 6, caudal lobe. *Histology:* 7, cuticle; 8, epidermis; 9, muscle layer; 10, mesenchyme; 11, dorsal epidermal thickening; 12, dorsal cord; 13, ventral cord; 14, lamella connecting the epidermal cord and the nerve cord; 15, nerve cord; 16, pseudocoel; 17, intestine; 18, pharynx; 19, syncytium accompanying the pharynx; 20, testis. *Embryonic form:* 21, gland; 22, pseudocoel; 23, intestine; 24, anus; 25, septum; 26, presoma; 27, trunk. *Larva:* 28, proboscis; 29, spines; 30, body wall; 31, pseudocoel; 32 retractor muscle; 33, pharynx; 34, septum; 35, gland; 36, intestine; 37, anus; 38, mesenchyme; 39, end spine.

system is vestigial, the anatomy is not complex. The epidermis below the cuticle has a single ventral chord, resembling the nematode epidermal chords, except in *Nectonema*, which has middorsal and midventral chords. All muscle fibers are longitudinal, and in *Nectonema* they resemble the coelomyarian muscles of nematodes. Gordioid muscle has contractile fibers all the way around the central cytoplasmic region. *Nectonema* has a spacious pseudocoel, and gordioids have a greatly reduced pseudococoel around the gut and gonads.

Gordioid males recognize females at a distance and respond to touch; evidently there are sense organs but no definite information is available. Presumably, some of the bristles and papillae are sensory. Nerve endings in the calotte look like touch receptors. *Paragordius* has a heavily innervated sac containing fusiform cells suspended in a coagulated fluid; it has a dark pigment ring behind it. If it is an eye it is unique, for no other animals, including other nematomorphs, have eyes of this type.

The central nervous system consists of a circumenteric nerve ring in the head calotte and a midventral trunk, which forms in the epidermis. In the more primitive *Nectonema* it remains in this position, but it migrates inward in gordioids, becoming attached to the epidermal chord (Fig. 8.26C,D). Neuroglial partitions divide the nerve trunk into three tracts. Giant neurons at the union of nerve ring and nerve trunk probably coordinate long regions of the worm.

Males have a pair of long, tubular testes that open independently into the cloaca through short sperm ducts. A seminal vesicle sometimes lies at the end of the testis. The cloacal wall of some species is armed with bristles and may serve as a cirrus. Young ovaries resemble the testes, but as they mature form lateral diverticula in which the ova ripen. As many as 4000 diverticula may occur. The ovary is left vacant and serves as a uterus, storing the ripened ova. The two oviducts combine to form a common antrum, from which a seminal receptacle arises. The antrum opens into the cloaca.

The male wraps his body around the female and deposits sperm near the female cloacal opening. Sperm migrate into the seminal receptacle. When ova are mature, they emerge in long strings, which may contain several million ova. Cloacal secretions provide the binding material for the strings.

Accounts of embryonic development differ, suggesting generic differences in growth patterns. The egg undergoes holoblastic, equal cleavage, and passes through nematode-like three- and four-celled stages. A coeloblastula undergoes a typical gastrulation, before or after the blastocoel is invaded by mesodermal cells. An ectodermal presoma invaginates to form a proboscis with several spines and three long stylets (Fig. 8.26F). The anterior part of the primitive gut forms a gland, and the posterior part an intestine, blind anteriorly but open posteriorly at the blastopore. The larva (Fig. 8.26E) resembles a kinorhynch or priapulid and is sometimes called an echinoderid larva.

The larva penetrates any convenient water animal soon after hatching, but continues its development only when it reaches a suitable host, typically an insect. How it reaches the host is not entirely clear. In the proper host it grows gradually, without a sharp metamorphosis, into a juvenile worm. It emerges when the host is near water and molts, losing the last traces of larval structure.

Phylum Entoprocta

Entoprocts are curious, sessile creatures, superficially resembling hydroids. They are predominantly marine, but one genus, *Urnatella*, occurs in fresh water in the United States and India. Less than a hundred species are known, but they are widely distributed and more will probably be recognized. They have caused a good deal of confusion. They are often classified in the phylum Bryozoa or Molluscoidea with the ectoprocts, which they resemble superficially. However, ectoprocts have a coelom and entoprocts have a pseudocoel, and such a basic difference in organization justifies recognizing the entoprocts as a distinct phylum.

The body is divided into a main mass, the calyx, borne at the end of a stalk (Fig. 8.27C). The stalk usually ends in a pad-like basal plate or sends out lateral stolons, from which other stalks arise, forming a colony. However, some have stalks that attach by secretions from pedal glands.

A whorl of ciliated tentacles encloses the upper surface of the calyx; it is usually called the tentacular crown or lophophore. This is actually the ventral surface, but will be called the upper surface for sake of clarity. It contains four midsagittal openings: mouth, nephridiopore, gonopore, and anus, in that order. The mouth and anus lie near the tentacles, and the gonopore and nephridiopore usually lie in a definite depression (vestibule), used as a brood chamber for the developing young. The tentacles can be folded into the vestibule, and so enclosed by the velum, a marginal flange.

The calyx wall consists of a cuticle, a cellular epidermis, and a few longitudinal muscle strands. Transverse muscles below the stomach compress the body, and muscles from the base of the calyx to the vestibule retract the calyx. The tentacles are simple extensions of the body wall, without a cuticle, and are moved by subepidermal, longitudinal muscles.

Entoprocts are ciliary feeders. Long lateral cilia waft diatoms, Protozoa, and bits of detritus over the calyx surface, and short cilia on the inner face of the tentacles capture them, sweeping them downward toward the ciliated vestibular groove

(Fig. 8.27B) and eventually into the mouth.

The U-shaped gut nearly fills the calyx. It is heavily ciliated; food slowly revolves in the ciliary currents. Food accumulates in the buccal cavity and is swallowed by contractions of the esophagus. A glandular region of the stomach secretes enzymes and mucus, and food particles are trapped in clumps or strands. The upper surface of the stomach is an excretory organ and contains brownish inclusions of uric acid and guanin that are discharged into the stomach lumen. Ciliated tracts revolve the food strings and move them into the narrowed intestine. Digestion is extracellular, and absorption occurs in stomach and intestine. A sphincter at the junction of intestine and rectum and at the anus isolates the rectal region. Food is held here for some time when the animal is not gorged with food; probably some absorption occurs here also.

A pair of flame bulbs lies just above the stomach, opening into a protonephridial tubule surrounded by large amoeboid athrocytes. The two tubules join just before reaching the nephridiopore.

The tentacles and velum have many tactile cells. On each side of the oral end of some endoprocts is a tuft of bristles resembling the lateral antennae of rotifers. The brain is a ganglion above the stomach, probably corresponding to the subenteric ganglia of other pseudocoelomates. Pairs of nerves pass to the body wall, gonads, and stalk, and three pairs of nerves branch and connect with ganglia at the base of each tentacle.

The stalk of primitive entoprocts has a sheath of longitudinal muscles, but the muscles are usually concentrated in swollen sections of the stalk (Fig. 8.28A). This limits movement to a quick flitting of the calyx when the otherwise straight stalk is bent at the muscular region. Large or small colonies are formed by stolonic branching, and in many cases the stalk also branches at the muscular enlarge-

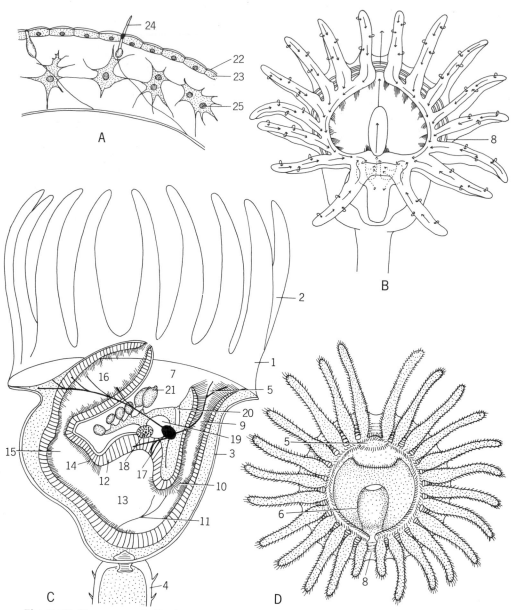

Fig. 8.27. Entoprocta. **A.** Section through the surface of a tentacle. **B.** The tentacular crown of *Loxosoma*, showing ciliary currents associated with feeding. **C.** Scheme of organization of entoprocts, based largely on *Pedicellina*. **D.** Scheme of the upper surface of *Pedicellina*. (**A,** after Harmer. **B,** after Atkins. **C,** composite. **D,** after Marcus, in Grassé.) *External features:* **1,** tentacular membrane; **2,** tentacle; **3,** calyx; **4,** stalk; **5,** mouth; **6,** anal papilla; **7,** embryophore; **8,** atrial sphincter. *Digestive system:* **9,** buccal tube; **10,** esophagus; **11,** tract of long cilia at stomach entrance; **12,** glandular area on stomach roof; **13,** stomach; **14,** long cilia at intestinal entrance; **15,** intestine; **16,** rectum. *Other parts:* **17,** brain; **18,** testis; **19,** ovary; **20,** nephridiopore; **21,** developing larvae. *Histology:* **22,** cuticle; **23,** epidermis; **24,** sensory nerve cell; **25,** mesenchyme.

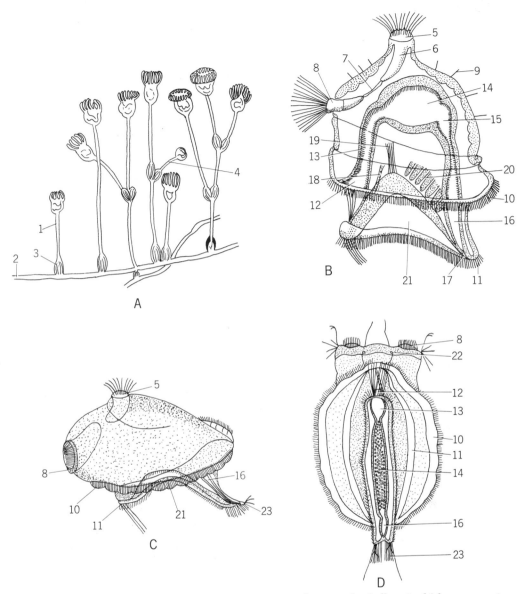

Fig. 8.28. **A.** Part of a colony of *Barentsia*, showing the muscular bulbs, at which movement and budding occurs. **B.** Larva of *Pedicellina*, somewhat like a trochophore, although with extensive peculiarities. **C-D.** Larva of *Loxosomella* seen from the side and below. Note the resemblance to a rotifer. (A, after Hyman. B-D, after Cori, from Marcus, in Grassé.) 1, stalk; 2, stolon; 3, muscular bulb; 4, bud at muscular bulb. *Larval parts:* 5, apical sense organ; 6, ganglion of apical sense organ; 7, commissure; 8, oral sense organ; 9, tactile sensory bristle; 10, prototroch; 11, preoral ciliary band; 12, mouth; 13, esophagus; 14, midgut; 15, intestine; 16, rectum; 17, anus; 18, nephridium; 19, retractor muscle; 20, atrial gland; 21, atrium; 22, eye; 23, toes.

ments. The stalk is a continuation of the body wall. It contains a pseudocoel filled with gelatinous material, through which amoebocytes wander. A constriction at the calyx base is filled with a plug of cells that separates stalk and calyx pseudocoels.

Asexual reproduction occurs by budding. Solitary species form buds in the calyx while colonial species produce buds only on the stalks or stolon. Buds contain only epidermis and mesoderm, and the new digestive tube is formed from an epidermal vesicle. Stalks regenerate new calyces, and in unfavorable conditions a large number of headless stalks are sometimes found; new calyces form under improved conditions.

Dioecious entoprocts have a single pair of saccate gonads with short gonoducts that unite near the gonopore. Monoecious species have an additional pair of gonads and gonoducts, but all gonoducts unite near the common gonopore.

Eggs are fertilized in the ovaries or gonoducts. On their way out, the prominent eosinophilous glands cover them and form a stalk by which they are attached. The stalk adheres to the depressed vestibular wall in a region known as the embryophore (Fig. 8.27). The thickened embryophore wall of *Pedicellina* is filled with food inclusions used by the embryos. Each embryo pushes the next in line further along, so a regular series, decreasing in age, is formed.

A highly modified, spiral determinate cleavage occurs. Five quartets of micromeres and one set of macromeres are formed. Cell 4d gives rise to endoderm and mesoderm, and the first quartet of micromeres forms the ciliated girdle of the larva. The mouth forms at a stomodaeal invagination near the blastopore, and a proctodaeal invagination also occurs.

The larvae are curious creatures, with some resemblance to annelid trochophores. The larva of *Loxosoma* is rotifer-like, and has a bifurcated tail resembling a rotifer foot (Fig. 8.28C,D). It swims or creeps

about for a time, and then attaches by the ciliated girdle. The complex metamorphosis is described in detail by Hyman (1951) and by Cori (1936).

Pseudocoelomate Developments

The presence of a pseudocoel profoundly alters body organization. Except at openings, the body wall and viscera are disconnected and can move or adapt independently. The perivisceral fluid permits a more efficient distribution of materials in the body. Yet these advantages appear to be more theoretical than real. Gut musculature remains delicate, and peristalsis is less important than cilia for food conduction. The digestive system is a true digestive system without extensive diverticula for food distribution, indicating the effectiveness of the pseudocoel in transport. None of the pseudocoelomates have a circulatory system, but they are almost all small and it is not certain whether size or the effectiveness of the pseudocoel has been the most significant factor in militating against a circulatory system. It is clear that the pseudocoel has not led to a significant increase in body size, for most pseudocoelomates are as small or smaller than acoelomates.

The greater independence of the body wall and the presence of a cuticle have favored the development of pseudosegmentation. This is frequently accompanied by segmentation of the body wall musculature, and the nervous system shows a tendency to develop ganglia associated with the muscular segments. While it is improbable that any modern pseudocoelomate groups are directly ancestral to metameric animals, their tendency toward pseudosegmentation may reveal the kind of changes that produced segmented animals.

Phylogenetic Relationships

A great deal of paper has been wasted on discussing the phylogenetic relationships of pseudocoelomates. They are perplexing animals. Only rotifers and nematodes have been very successful, and the other groups are all small. They give the impression of highly specialized end twigs of groups that were established long ago. They are probably remnants of an archaic fauna that might have been abundant but are no longer able to cope with modern competitors. This idea cannot be checked as none have left a fossil record.

The entoprocts are obviously mavericks in this assemblage of worms. Many entoprocts have larvae that are like those of annelids, and the pseudocoel and flame bulbs relate them to lower invertebrates. Are they degenerate products of more highly organized ancestors, or progressive progeny of less highly organized ancestors? Both views have been expressed. They have a strong resemblance to ectoprocts, which are coelomate animals, but differences in nephridia and cleavage patterns lead many to seriously doubt that they are related. Sessile rotifers resembling Collothecaceae, with the corona drawn out into tentaculate processes and a reduced mastax, would be possible ancestral stocks, and the rotifer-like larva of some entoprocts has been emphasized by those who believe them completely independent of entoprocts. No firm conclusions are justified at present.

Acanthocephala and nematomorphs have often been placed with nematodes in the phylum Nemathelminthes. Rotifers and gastrotrichs have been put together in the phylum Trochelminthes. The closeness of these relationships is questioned today.

Acanthocephala are particularly problematic, for their development resembles cestode development in many ways, but cell constancy, the pseudocoel, and the proboscis appear to relate them to other pseudocoelomates. Arguments for allying them with flatworms and pseudocoelomates are about equally strong.

The remaining aschelminths are irritatingly similar and yet different. Some similarities are too profound to be dismissed as superficial, but some of the differences are by no means inconsequential. Much more information is needed about embryonic development before solid conclusions can be drawn. Nematodes and nematomorphs have many similarities, but the curious echinodera larva of nematomorphs is puzzling. The similarity of nematode and nematomorph cleavage is an argument in favor of their relationship. If they are related, they undoubtedly differentiated into separate stems long ago. Similarities of the gastrotrich and nematode pharynx are very strong, and the adhesive caudal glands of primitive nematodes provide another good reason to think them related.

Kinorhynchs and priapulids are similar in having an introvert at the anterior end of the body, but otherwise are quite different. Similarities between the nematomorph larva and that of priapulids and kinorhynchs seem too extensive to be accidental. Probably these stems have some relationship but diverged very long ago.

The rotifers appear more remotely related to the other aschelminths, although the rotifer-like larvae of some groups provide some evidence of relationship. Rotifers appear more primitively organized than other aschelminths.

One might, very tentatively, hypothesize an ancestral line leading from small turbellarians, which tended to restrict cilia to the anterior and ventral surfaces and developed a cuticle, anus, and pseudocoel, as ancestral to rotifers. Sessile rotifers, developing early as a distinctive stem, may have given rise to the entoprocts. Another ancestral line, probably stemming from very early rotifer stocks, might have given rise to the remaining aschelminths. This line may have devel-

Table 8.2. Summary of traits of pseudocoelomates

	ACANTHOCEPHALA	ROTIFERA	GASTROTRICHA	KINORHYNCHA	PRIAPULIDA	NEMATODA	NEMATOMORPHA	ENTOPROCTA
Cleavage	bilateral determinate	modified spinal determinate	holoblastic determinate	?	rotifer-like	modified spiral, determinate	as in nematodes	modified spiral, determinate
Larvae	acanthor, parasitic	none	none	unique, three-segmented, segments added at molts	rotifer-like proboscis and lorica present	juvenile molts, but much like adult.	rather like priapulid, parasitic.	trochophore-like
Mouth	none	yes	stomodaeal, near blastopore.	stomodaeal	stomodaeal	stomodaeal, near blastopore.	stomodaeal, near blastopore.	stomodaeal, at blastopore.
Pharynx	none	epidermal, mastax and trophi present.	stomodaeal, tubular, bulbs ± triradiate.	stomodaeal, triradiate	stomodaeal	stomodaeal, triradiate, bulbs ±	reduced	tubular
Anus	none	yes	proctodaeal	proctodaeal?	proctodaeal	proctodaeal, near blastopore.	from blastopore	proctodaeal
Excretory system	flame bulb	flame bulb	solenocyte	solenocyte	solenocyte	renette and canal system	none	flame bulb
Pseudosegmentation	±	yes	no	pronounced	yes	±	no	no
Circular muscle	a sheath	separate strands	strands	strands	rings	none	none	reduced.
Longitudinal muscle	a sheath	strands	strands	strands	sheath, and strands	strands	strands	reduced, but a sheath in stalks
Body cavity	pseudocoel	pseudocoel	pseudocoel	pseudocoel	pseudocoel? non-cellular lining.	pseudocoel	reduced	pseudocoel
Brain	ganglion in proboscis receptacle	bilobed, dorsal	ganglia and dorsal commissure	epidermal nerve ring	epidermal nerve ring	ring with dorsal and ventral ganglia	epidermal nerve ring	ganglion, bilobed?
Nerve trunks	lateral	ventral, paired	ventrolateral	midventral	midventral	midventral and middorsal cords	midventral	none

oped into one gastrotrich stem that remained small, became parthenogenetic, and emphasized ventral ciliation in adaptation. From this line, after caudal adhesive glands were developed, a general nematode line may have appeared. Their cylindrical shape and perhaps sessile habits favor the development of biradial form, and these early biradial forms may have diverged, before the loss of protonephridia, into a line that was ancestral to kinorhynchs, priapulids, and nematomorphs. One stem lost the protonephridia and developed into nematodes. All of these ideas are highly speculative, and it is profitless to go deeply into arguments for and against them until more evidence is available.

References

Ahlstrom, E. H. 1938. Plankton Rotatoria from North Carolina. *Jour. Elisha Mitchell Sci. Soc.* 54: 88.

Atkins, D. 1932. The ciliary feeding mechanism of the endoproct polyzoans and a comparison with that of the ectoproct polyzoans. *Quart. Jour. Micr. Sci.* 75: 393 (G)

Bayliss, H. A. 1924. Systematic position of Nematodes. *Ann. Mag. Nat. Hist.* 13: 165.

———, and R. Daubney. 1926. A *Synopsis of the Families and Genera of Nematoda.* Brit. Mus. Nat. Hist., London.

Berg, K. 1934. Cyclic reproduction, sex determination, and depression in Cladocera (and Rotifera). *Biol. Rev.* 9: 139.

Berzins, B. 1951. On the collothecacean Rotatoria. *Ark. Zool.* 1: 565.

Brunson, R. B. 1949. The life history and ecology of two North American gastrotrichs. *Trans. Am. Micr. Soc.* 68: 1.

Camerano, L. 1897. Monografia dei Gordii. *Mem. R. Accad. Sci. Torino* 2: 339.

Cavier, R., and J. Savel. 1945. Étude de quelques aspects du metabolisme intermédiare des acides aminés chez l'Ascaris du porc (*Ascaris lumbricoides* Linné 1758). *Bull. Soc. Chim. Biol.* 36: 1631.

Chitwood, B. G., and M. B. Chitwood. 1937. *An Introduction to Nematology.* B. G. Chitwood, Baltimore. (B)

Cobb, N. A. 1914. The North American free-living fresh-water nematodes. *Trans. Am. Micr. Soc.* 33: 69.

———. 1935. A key to the genera of free-living nemas. *Proc. Helminth. Soc. Wash.* 2: 1. (F)

Cori, C. 1936. Kamptozoa. In H. G. Bronn (ed.), *Klassen u. Ordnung des Tier-Reichs, Bd. IV, Abt. II, Buch 4.*

Dobers, E. 1915. Über die Biologie der Bdelloidea. *Int. Rev. Biol. Suppl.* 1: 1.

Dujardin, F. 1851. Sur un petit animal marin, l'Echinodére. *Ann. Sci. Natur. Zool. Ser.* 3, p. 15.

Edmondson, W. T. 1940. The sessile Rotatoria of Wisconsin. *Trans Am. Micr. Soc.* 59: 433.

———. 1946. Factors in the dynamics of rotifer populations. *Ecol. Monogr.* 16: 357. (E)

Ferguson, M. S. 1943. Migration and localization of an animal parasite in the host. *Jour. Exp. Zool.* 93: 375.

Goodey, T. 1951. *Soil and Freshwater Nematodes.* Methuen, London.

Grundspan, T. 1910. Die Süsswassergastrotrichen Europas. *Ann. Biol. lac.* 4: 211.

Harring, H. K., and F. J. Myers. 1922. The rotifer fauna of Wisconsin. *Trans. Wis. Acad. Sci. Arts and Lett.* 20: 553.

Harris, J. E., and H. D. Crofton. 1957. Structure and function in the nematodes. *Jour. Exp. Biol.* 34: 116.

Harwood, P. D., and J. H. Brown. 1934. *In vitro* consumption of oxygen by parasitic nematodes. *Jour. Parasit.* 20: 128.

Heinze, K. 1937. Die Saitenwurmer (Gordioidea) Deutschlands. *Zeitschr. Parasitenk.* 9: 263.

Hickernell, L. M. 1917. A study of desiccation in the rotifer *Philodina roseola*, with special reference to cytological changes accompanying desiccation. *Biol. Bull.* 32: 343.

Hudson, C. T., and F. H. Gosse. 1889. *The Rotifera.* Longmans, Green, London.

Jennings, H. S. 1900. Rotatoria of the U.S., especially the Great Lakes area. *Bull. U.S. Comm. Fish.* 19: 67.

Johnson, G. E. 1913. On the nematodes of the common earthworm. *Quart. Jour. Micr. Sci.* 58: 605.

Kunike, G. 1925. Nachweis und Verbreitung organischer Skeletsubstanzen bei Tieren. *Ztschr. Vergl. Physiol.* 2.

Lang, K. 1848. Contribution to the ecology of *Priapulus. Ark. Zool.* 41A, Art. 5.

May, H. G. 1919. Contributions to the life histories of *Gordius robustus* and *Paragordius varius* (Leidy). *Ill. Biol. Monogr.* 5: 1.

Miller, H. M. 1931. Alternation of generations in the rotifer *Lecane inermis* Bryce. Life histories of the sexual and non-sexual generations. *Biol. Bull.* 60: 345.

Montgomery, T. H. 1903. On the morphology of the rotatorian family Flosculariidae. *Proc. Acad. Nat. Sci. Phila.* 55: 363.

Nachtwey, R. 1925. Untersuchungen über die Keimbahn, Organogenese und Anatomie von *Asplanchna priodonta* Gosse. *Ztschr. wiss. Zool.* 126: 239.

Northrop, J. H. 1926. Resistance of living organisms to digestion by pepsin and trypsin. *Jour. Gen. Physiol.* 9: 497.

Pennak, R. W. 1940. Ecology of the microscopic metazoa inhabiting the sandy beaches of some Wisconsin lakes. *Ecol. Monogr.* 10: 537.

Rahm, P. G. 1923. Beiträge zur Kenntnis der Moosfauna. *Zeitschr. Allg. Physiol.* 20: 1. (F)

Sachs, M. 1955. Observations on the embryology of an aquatic gastrotrich, *Lepidodermella squammata. Jour. Morph.* 96: 473.

Shull, A. F. 1929. Determination of types of individuals in aphids, rotifers, and cladocerans. *Biol. Rev.* 4: 218. (G)

Stauffer, H. 1929. Die Lokomotion der Nematoden. *Zool. Jahrb. System.* 49: 1.

Stephen, A. C. 1941. The Echiuridae, Sipunculidae, and Priapulidae. *Discovery Rep.* 21: 235.

Stossberg, K. 1932. Zur Morphologie der Radertiergattungen *Euchlanis, Brachionus,* and *Rhinoglena. Ztschr. wiss. Zool.* 142: 313.

Pray, F. A. 1965 Early development of the rotifer *Monostyla cornuta* Müller. *Trans. Am. Micr. Soc.* 84: 210.

Van Cleave, H. J. 1932. Cell constancy and its relation to body size. *Quart. Rev. Biol.* 7: 59. (B)

Wesenberg-Lund, C. 1923. Contributions to the biology of the Rotifera, I. The males of rotifers. *D. Kgl. Vidensk. Selsk. Skr. Naturv. Mat.* 4: 189.

———. 1930. Contributions to the biology of the Rotifera, II. The periodicity and sexual periods. *D. Kgl. Vidensk. Selsk. Skr. Naturv. Mat.* 2: 1.

9
Introduction to Coelomates

Much of the history of the animal body can be inferred from the study of lower invertebrates. The first animals probably developed from simpler creatures in which the elements of cell structure had been evolved. They were probably masses of protoplasm containing one or several packages of DNA, or nuclei, at the organizational level of modern Protozoa. It is reasonable to suppose that the adaptive radiation of Protozoa reflects the early response of animals to the factors responsible for the evolution of the animal body. Three outstanding developments occurred among Protozoa: 1) the development of three distinctive lines of feeding: autotrophic, saprobic, and holozoic, and of organelles suitable for each nutritional habit; 2) consolidation of nuclear architecture and development of mitotic nuclear division; and 3) development of sexual methods of reproduction. Many other kinds of protoplasmic specializations appeared in Protozoa, of course, but the three mentioned prepared the way for the development of multicellular animals along the particular paths they followed. The photosynthetic and saprobic lines either came to nothing or led off into parts of the plant kingdom, while the holozoic line established the basic relationship of animals to their environment insofar as nutrition is concerned. Furthermore, only detailed changes in the mechanism of mitosis or meiosis have occurred in all of the multicellular animals.

The mechanisms responsible for adaptive radiation in Protozoa are the same as those operating on other kinds of animals. A modification of form that improves the probability of survival or success in reproducing, whether a specifically inherited trait or a potentiality resulting from the interaction of many protoplasmic and environmental factors, tends to be fixed in an animal stock by success. Although exceptions can be found, most of the successful changes tend to improve metabolism by introducing further division of labor and specialization of parts, and to lead toward habitat diversification and withdrawal of stocks from intense competition with one another. In general, the most critical physiological processes are the ones which can be changed with the most profit, and among free-living Protozoa these have centered primarily on problems associated with nutrition and food-gathering, and with reproduction.

Protozoa that develop a colonial habit are exposed to the same evolutionary forces as isolated Protozoa. Division of labor and specialization of zooids in a protozoan colony lead toward multicellularity. If the embryological evidence of cleavage and blastula formation be given much weight, protozoan colonies appear to be the most probable source of multicellular animals.

The first multicellular animals were relatively unspecialized. They probably were characterized by a limited cellular anarchy, rather like modern sponges, with each component cell far more self-sufficient and capable of a wider spectrum of activities than in more highly organized animals. Evolutionary change has compensatory aspects; with greater functional specialization, cells tend to lose some potentialities. Sponge cells are often competent to undergo profound structural and functional transformations, leading to a variety of appearances and a variety of roles in the life of the organism. The direction of evolutionary change, however, has been toward a loss of great plasticity in favor of a more marked metabolic specialization, as backwoodsmen are replaced by hundreds of kinds of technicians in human cultures undergoing progressive specialization and division of labor. Tissue cells become permanently transformed, by processes not clearly understood. *Hydra* can be turned inside out; when this is done, the epidermis and gastrodermis cells change places to reconstitute the animal. Evidently the substitution of structure and function of the cells belonging to one layer for the structure and function of the other layer has become impossible, and the cells must return to their places to assume their functions in the economy of the whole organism. The obvious inference is that restrictions on structural and functional peculiarities of cells were among the first adaptations to multicellular life. Neverthe-

less, in the simplest metazoans a number of cells remain more or less unspecialized trouble-shooters. They replace lost, injured, or senile cells, and regenerative powers are very great.

The first multicellular animals may have been somewhat solid, with external sensory-locomotor cells and inner nutritive cells. Covering cells live in a polarized environment; one surface is exposed to the surrounding medium and the other to the internal cells. The universal polarity of epithelial cells undoubtedly favored their early specialization. Even in the most aberrant sponges, covering cells appear more determined than most. The covering layer, exposed to the world outside, tends to adapt along lines suitable for its position. Cilia or flagella at the body surface are responsible for movement and for maintaining currents used in feeding. The locomotor functions of the covering layer extend to muscle, for while muscles play a limited role in the movement of lower invertebrates, the first muscle forms in epithelial cells, and the first mesogloeal muscle cells are derived from the ectoderm. Sensory and coordinating functions also develop in surface cells. The epidermis is, therefore, the part of the organism in which protective layers, sense organs, nerve, muscle, and ciliary or flagellar locomotor parts center, and most of these arise from the ectoderm of more highly organized animals. The internal cells, on the other hand, are primarily reproductive in some colonial Protozoa, and tend to assume the tasks of digesting and storing food.

With the development of a mouth and digestive cavity, the multicellular animals become simple, but recognizable, metazoans. Sponges have evolved in a unique direction, with the internal cavity system used to capture food and with embryological peculiarities that may be associated with this unusual organization. Other metazoan groups have an enteron or digestive cavity open to the exterior by way of a mouth, unless it is lost as a result of adaptation to parasitism. The cells that line the digestive cavity are polarized by exposure to cells at one surface and to the gut cavity at the other, and acquire the usual peculiarities of epithelial cells. The basic animal form is determined with the appearance of two epithelial layers, an outer locomotor-sensory-coordinating layer and an inner nutritive layer, corresponding to the ectoderm and endoderm of the embryo.

The two epithelial layers of the first true metazoa appear to have been separated by a somewhat gelatinous or fibrous matrix, soon populated by cells from the inner and outer epithelial layers. It is a general tendency for sense organs and nerves to move to internal positions. Muscles have also moved inward; it is not surprising that the first mesoderm was preponderantly ectomesoderm. In modern cnidaria it is formed partly by wandering cells and partly by insinking of primitively superficial elements. This is an informal process in cnidarians, but in flatworms mesoderm formation becomes a formal part of embryonic development and the new endomesoderm appears. Ectomesoderm is not abandoned; it contributes to a greater or lesser degree to the body of all acoelomates and pseudocoelomates, but endomesoderm is evidently becoming more important.

A true mesoderm contains far more cells than the mesogloeal mesoderm of sponges and Radiata. Respiratory needs rise dramatically. Waste materials are liberated by cells not exposed to the digestive cavity nor to the external medium. The inner cells need food for energy release and growth. The problems of internal transport, in one way or another, remain critical throughout the lower invertebrates. Internal transport is at first achieved by diffuseness of organs. The enteron is highly branched, especially in larger species. Its ramifications, almost of capillary dimensions, extend to all parts of the body. The protonephridial system is extensively branched in most of the larger flatworms.

Organ ramification is inadequate for large animals, however, and the only really large members of lower phyla are sponges and cnidarians with mesogloea containing few cells.

Two experiments in transport are seen in the lower invertebrates. A system of tubes containing a circulating fluid, propelled by pulsations of the major vessels, occurs in nemertines. Haemoglobin in the blood cells is an important aid to respiration in these creatures, permitting them to occupy habitats poor in oxygen, and some of them are relatively large. The protonephridia become intimately associated with the blood vessels, but the digestive tube usually retains some diverticula. This establishes one of the important methods of solving the problem of internal transport.

Pseudocoelomates solve internal transport problems by transforming much or all of the parenchyma into great, spongy spaces or into open spaces containing a perivisceral fluid. Protonephridia become less diffuse and are associated with the pseudocoel; they can serve the whole body even when collected in a small region, as in priapulids and Acanthocephala. Lateral diverticula for food distribution do not occur. The gut becomes a simple tube, with one-way traffic between the mouth and anal openings. The body wall is far more independent, and pseudosegmentation of the cuticle and body wall musculature sometimes occurs. No special respiratory or circulatory systems appear, perhaps because the pseudocoel suffices for transport. But pseudocoelomates remain small or moderate in size. The lack of a peritoneum may be critical, for the peritoneal lining of many coelomates bears cilia or flagella and keeps the coelomic fluid circulating rapidly enough to effect adequate transport.

Many coelomates are as small as or smaller than some of the acoelomates and pseudocoelomates, but with the appearance of a true coelom important new potentialities arise. Body wall and visceral wall architecture become more complex and more stable. Blood vessels often develop in the mesenteries, and the excretory system and gonoducts tend to develop a stable relationship to the new body cavity. Before undertaking the study of the coelomate phyla, it is helpful to consider some of the more important aspects of their body organization.

The Coelom

The first cavity to appear in embryos, and possibly in ancestral metazoan stocks, is the blastocoel, sometimes termed the primary body cavity. The formation of a gut reduces the blastocoel, but some remnant of the space between endoderm and ectoderm remains. It is in this part of the body that the solid parenchyma of acoelomates forms. The pseudocoel is a cavity left by the failure of the parenchyma to completely fill the space between the body wall mesoderm and the gut wall; it is a derivative of the blastocoel. No peritoneum lines the pseudocoel walls; the gut and gonads are at least partly bathed in the perivisceral fluid.

The coelom is a secondary body cavity; it forms as a new space in the mesoderm and is completely surrounded by mesodermal tissue. As the coelom increases in size, the outer part of the mesoderm becomes intimately associated with the body wall, and the body wall is lined by the parietal or somatic mesoderm that becomes the parietal peritoneum. The inner mesoderm becomes intimately associated with the gut wall and other viscera, and the coelom is lined with visceral or splanchnic mesoderm, which forms the visceral peritoneum. The organs which lie in the coelom are connected to the body wall by mesenteries, actually continuations of the peritoneum connecting parietal and visceral layers (Fig. 9.1C). The coelomic fluid in the coelomic cavity does not come directly in contact with either the gut or body wall, but is separated from both by the peritoneal epithelium.

How did the coelom originate? Four major theories have been stated. They may be called the enterocoel, gonocoel, nephrocoel, and schizocoel theories. All have had, and to some extent still have, their proponents.

Perhaps the most controversial of these is the enterocoel theory, which explains the coelom as a derivative of a partitioned enteric cavity, as seen in Anthozoa and Scyphozoa. The idea is that the tips of the gastric pouches were cut off to form coelomic cavities. As gonads are often found in the mesenteries of sea anemones or the septa of scyphozoans, this would explain the relationship of the gonads to the coelomic wall. However, although neat, this explanation lacks persuasiveness, as it involves the derivation of the lower cnidaria from more highly organized cnidarian forms, and as the mechanics of enteric pocket formation differ from the mechanics of coelom formation. Enterocoelous coelom formation occurs as the result of outpocketings of the gut, while the mesenteries or septa of cnidarians grow inward to divide the coelenteron into gastric pockets. Hyman (1959) and others have severely criticized this idea. For a discussion of the theory and reasons for it, the writings of Marcus and Jägersten should be consulted.

The gonocoel theory visualizes the coelom as arising from the lumen of the gonads (Fig. 9.1A,B). This theory also accounts for the relationship of gonads to the coelomic wall and has a number of adherents. A regular series of gonads occur in some flatworms and nemertines, and alternate with the lateral diverticula of the gut. If the branches of the gut were withdrawn, presumably as an anus forms, and if the gonads expanded into cavities containing the gametes to fill in the resulting space, a series of coelomic pouches surrounding the gut could appear. This idea, first expressed by Hatschek (1878), has been further developed by Lang (1904) and Meyer (1901). It has some serious drawbacks, for it would link the origin of the coelom with metamerism and leave no explanation for unsegmented coelomates. Lang's idea was strengthened in his times by the discovery of a turbellarian with large testes in a regular series between the gut diverticula. It was common then to dwell heavily on similarities of living adult species to organizational plans of other phyla, and a number of supposed missing links were turned up. A peculiar rotifer, *Trochospaera*, has a superficial resemblance to a trochophore larva, but is probably nothing more than an unusual rotifer. The flattened, platyctene ctenophores are probably meaningless insofar as flatworm phylogeny is concerned, although there are convergent similarities between them and polyclads. Today it is generally agreed that for clues to relationships we must look to the most primitive rather than the most specialized members of phyla, and sometimes to larval forms and embryonic stages where they are not too highly modified to yield useful clues.

The nephrocoel theory sees the coelom as the derivative of the inner, expanded ends of nephridia. Its principal disadvantages are the absence of any real supporting evidence, and the total absence of nephridia in some coelomates.

The schizocoel theory assumes that spaces appeared independently in the mesoderm, rather than as derivatives of gonads, nephridia, gastric pouches, or any pre-existing part. The best features of this idea are that it does not demand that any major phylum be derived by degeneration from some more highly organized phylum, and that it is flexible enough to explain the appearance of a single, large coelomic space or segmental coelomic spaces. Hyman (1951) suggests that the coelom may have appeared as a site for the accumulation of fluid, possibly dissolved wastes. Fluid does tend to accumulate in aquatic organisms,

and it seems no more difficult to visualize the appearance of fluid-filled schizocoelous cavities than the appearance of a fluid-filled pseudocoel. It may be that the coelom first appeared, like the pseudocoel, as a space which facilitated transport of all kinds of substances, but unlike the pseudocoel, as a true mesodermal space, surrounded on all sides by mesodermal epithelium.

However the coelom may have appeared in the first coelomates, it arises in two major ways in modern forms (p. 101), and by a third method in *Phoronis* and the ectoprocts. In annelids, molluscs, and arthropods it appears as spaces in the mesoderm. This type of coelom is known as a schizocoel, and is characteristic of the protostomes. In echinoderms, chordates, and related phyla, the coelom appears as outpocketings of the gut, and is thus derived from the enteron. This type of coelom is termed an enterocoel, and is characteristic of a group of phyla known as deuterostomes. Mesenchyme cells rearrange themselves to form the *Phoronis* and ectoproct coelom and develop into a peritoneal lining. Whether this last type is degenerate or preserves traces of a method more primitive than either the schizocoelous or enterocoelous method of coelom formation remains uncertain.

Protostomia and Deuterostomia

Two main evolutionary lines of coelomates are recognized, the Protostomia and Deuterostomia. Protostomia includes the great invertebrate phyla: flatworms, molluscs, annelids, and arthropods, in addition to several minor phyla. Deuterostomia includes the echinoderms, chordates, and several minor, related phyla.

Protostomes are so named because the adult mouth is derived from the primitive embryonic mouth, the blastopore. Phyla with a mouth derived from a stomodaeum formed at the anterior border of a closed blastopore are included in the Protostomia. Protostomes generally undergo determinate embryonic development, initiated by spiral, determinate cleavage or some modification of it. Mesoderm generally arises from a special blastomere, typically 4d, closely associated with a stem endoderm cell. In annelids, the stem mesoderm cell gives rise to two bands of mesodermal cells in which the coelom eventually forms. Among arthropods no teloblasts can be recognized,

but similar mesodermal bands are formed. Protostomes generally have a schizocoel, the coelomic cavity first appearing as a series of splits in the mesodermal bands.

Among deuterostomes, the anus arises from or near the blastopore and a new mouth arises from a stomodaeum formed at a distance from the anterior border of the blastopore. Among these animals with a secondary mouth, cleavage is usually indeterminate and radial. Specific blasto-

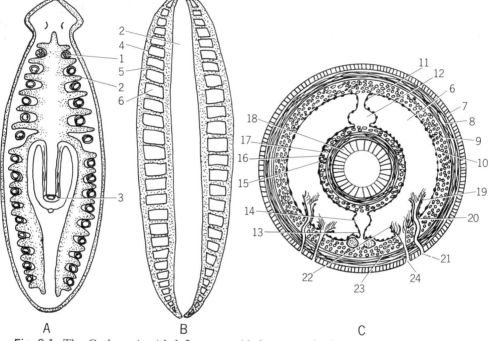

Fig. 9.1. The Coelom. A triclad flatworm with large gonads alternating with the intestinal diverticula, as shown at A, might become coelomate, like the annelid shown at B, if the gonads were to expand to form coelomic spaces and the intestinal diverticula were retracted with the formation of an anus. This view of coelomic development is known as the gonocoel theory. The basic scheme of a coelomate in cross section, showing the typical layers of the body wall, gut wall, and the gonoducts and nephridia, is seen at C. If the coelom developed from an expanded gonad, the gonoduct is presumably the original duct leading to the coelom, and the nephridium a separate duct. To the extent that nephridia and gonoducts are of mesodermal origin, open to both coelom and exterior, they may be termed coelomoducts. (After Hyman.) 1, gonad; 2, gut; 3, pharynx; 4, body wall; 5, septum; 6, coelom; 7, epidermis; 8, circular muscle; 9, longitudinal muscle; 10, parietal peritoneum; 11, dorsal mesentery; 12, dorsal blood vessel; 13, ventral mesentery; 14, ventral blood vessel; 15, visceral peritoneum; 16, longitudinal visceral muscle; 17, circular visceral muscle; 18, gut mucosa; 19, gonostome; 20, gonoduct; 21, gonopore; 22, nephrostome; 23, nephridium; 24, nephridiopore.

meres cannot be trusted to form a particular part of the body; their destiny can be changed experimentally, and a whole larva may be formed by one blastomere of a two-celled or four-celled embryo. The mesoderm is formed by outpocketings of the gut, and the coelom, as a result, is an enterocoel.

The study of higher invertebrates is largely a consideration of the evolutionary outcomes of these two great branches of the animal kingdom. The two branches appear to meet in creatures known as the lophophorates, which are somewhat anomalous, vacillating between protostomes and deuterostomes in their general attributes.

The Trochophore Larva

The trochophore larva has occasionally been mentioned in discussing pseudocoelomates. The trochophore larva is the basis for an important idea about the phylogeny of the protostomes, developed especially by Hatschek (1878). He considered it a stem larval form, from which the larvae of most of the bilaterally symmetrical phyla have been derived.

The trochophore larva is especially characteristic of annelids and molluscs. It is typically formed after a spiral determinate cleavage, similar in general outline to the spiral cleavage of flatworms (p. 211), which might well be reviewed at this point. Blastomeres form a characteristic annelid rosette and cross during later cleavage stages (Fig. 9.2A). A similar cross of blastomeres, known as the molluscan cross, forms in molluscs (Fig. 13.7B). The annelid and molluscan crosses are superficially similar, but include different blastomeres. The annelid rosette is formed by blastomeres la^{111}-ld^{111}, and the cross by the sister cells, la^{112}-ld^{112}. The molluscan cross is formed of blastomeres la^{12}-ld^{12}. The annelid cross is thus interradial in position and the molluscan cross radial.

The four quartets of micromeres and their descendants give rise to remarkably consistent parts of the adult and of the trochophore larva, not only in annelids and molluscs, but also in flatworms (p. 212). Blastomeres la-ld form the ectoderm near the animal pole of the blastula, and give rise to the apical part of the trochophore larva. They give rise to the apical sense organ, to the cerebral ganglia which develop near the apical sense organ, and to the apical ectoderm, and they may make some contributions to the head kidneys or nephridia. The blastomeres la^2-ld^2 are the primary trochoblasts, and give rise to four ciliary tufts. Later, other blastomeres, known as secondary trochoblasts, develop cilia to complete a ciliary band around the trochophore larva known as the prototroch (Fig. 9.2G). The blastomeres of the second quartet, 2a-2d, contribute to the surface ectoderm and to the stomodaeum. Among annelids, 2d is known as the primary stomoblast, and gives rise to the greater part of the trunk ectoderm, including the ventral nerve cord. Blastomeres 3a-3d give rise to the circumanal ectoderm, and descendants of $3c^2$ and $3d^2$ give rise to most of the larval excretory organs, or archinephridia. The endoderm arises from 7 blastomeres, 4a-c and 4A-D, which eventually invaginate and form the endoderm of the stomach and intestine. Blastomere 4d gives rise to a few endodermal cells, but its most important contribution to the embryo is two cells which divide repeatedly to form the mesodermal bands on each side of the embryo, in which the coelom forms (Fig. 9.2B-G).

The fully formed trochophore (Fig. 9.2H) is essentially biconical, with a band of cilia, the prototroch, passing just above the mouth. A second ciliated band, the paratroch, may encircle the anus. The U-shaped gut, lined with a ciliated endoderm, protrudes into the upper hemisphere and is surrounded by remnants of the blastocoel, partially occluded by ectomesodermal cells and muscles derived from the ectomesoderm.

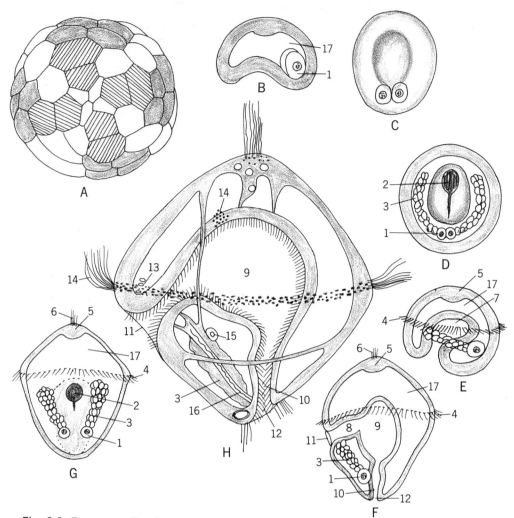

Fig. 9.2. Protostome Development. **A.** The embryo of an annelid, *Arenicola*, in the 64-cell stage. Protostomes typically undergo spiral cleavage. During annelid development, an annelid cross and rosette appear.The cross is darkened in the figure. It is composed of blastomeres la^{112}-ld^{112} and some cells from the second quartet. The annelid rosette at the pole is composed of blastomeres la^{111}-ld^{111}. A similar cross, composed of different blastomeres, is formed during molluscan development. **B-G.** Scheme of transformation of a gastrula into a trochophore larva, as it occurs in polychaetes. In **B** and **C**, gastrulation is seen from the left and the animal pole. The teloblasts are darkened. Later (**D, E**), the teloblasts develop into mesodermal bands, and a primitive gut forms. Externally, a locomotor band, the prototroch, appears. Still later (**F, G**), the apical tuft of cilia appears and a proctodaeum develops. It comes in contact with the gut and breaks through to complete gut formation. The mouth arises from the blastopore directly, or from its anterior margin. In the fully developed trochophore (**H**), a larval nephridium containing a single solenocyte and other differentiated parts are formed. (**A,** after Child. **B-G,** after Korscheldt, from Dawydoff, in Grassé. **H,** after Shearer.) **1,** teloblast; **2,** blastopore; **3,** mesodermal band; **4,** prototroch; **5,** apical plate; **6,** apical tuft; **7,** primitive gut; **8,** stomodaeum (foregut); **9,** midgut; **10,** proctodaeum (hindgut); **11,** mouth; **12,** anus: **13,** ectomesoderm; **14,** eye; **15,** statocyst; **16,** larval nephridium; **17,** blastocoel.

314

A main nerve ring encircles the larva below the prototroch, and connects to a variable number of radial nerves that pass from the apical ganglion at the base of the apical sense organ. A pair of endomesodermal bands, derived from the teloblasts, parallels the digestive tube. The lower hemisphere contains a pair of nephridia, terminating in one or several solenocytes.

The occurrence of a trochophore larva in annelids, molluscs, and other related phyla has made it the center of various phylogenetic schemes. The trochophore is at about the same level of organizational complexity as a rotifer, and one theory derives the trochophore from ancestral rotifer stocks. This idea cannot be accepted today for a variety of reasons, of which the most consequential are the gross difference in embryonic derivation of parts and the rotifer cleavage pattern, which is not similar to typical spiral cleavage. The ctenophore-trochophore theory explains the origin of bilateral animals from radial animals by deriving the trochophore from a ctenophore. The ctenophore embryo also develops a cross of blastomeres, similar superficially to the annelid cross, and the apical sense organ and radial nerves of ctenophores and of the trochophore larvae have some similarities. The greatest difficulty in this idea is its failure to account for flatworms except as degenerate annelids, a possibility that seems too remote to be persuasive.

In any case, the trochophore larva serves as a link between annelids and molluscs, and certainly resembles larvae seen in other protostome phyla in many respects. It may be more remote from rotifers than Hatschek (1878) thought, but it may nevertheless be reminiscent of an ancestral stem that was once at this level of organization. At the present, it seems preferable to think of the trochophore as a generalized and perhaps important ancestral larval form, reflecting as yet unanalyzed relationships between a number of protostome phyla.

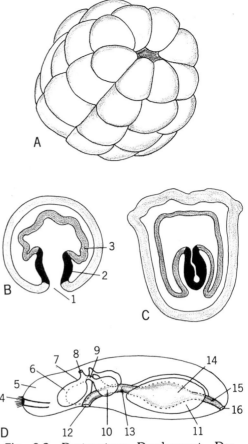

Fig. 9.3. Deuterostome Development. Deuterostomes typically undergo radial cleavage, as seen in the sea cucumber embryo shown at A. Mesoderm formation is enterocoelous. The inner end of the primitive gut expands and develops into mesodermal pouches, as seen at B and C. These become detached from the gut. The old blastopore disappears during mesoderm formation, and a new opening for the mouth is eventually formed. The outstanding larval characteristics are summarized in the hypothetical dipleurula larva, which shows the three pairs of coelomic compartments typical of the deuterostomes. (A, after Runnström, from Dawydoff, in Grassé. B-C, after McBride. D, after Bather.) 1, blastopore; 2, presumptive gut; 3, coelom; 4, apical sense organ; 5, preoral lobe; 6, axocoel; 7, hydropore; 8, hydroporic canal; 9, stone canal; 10, hydrocoel; 11, somatocoel; 12, mouth; 13, esophagus; 14, stomach; 15, intestine; 16, anus.

The Dipleurula Larva

The curious and provocative echinoderm larva is no less significant in phylogenetic thinking than the trochophore larva. Echinoderms begin life as bilaterally symmetrical larvae, and through a complex metamorphosis assume a secondary radial symmetry. Bather (1900) developed the idea of a dipleurula larva as an ancestral stem form for echinoderms and certain related phyla. The dipleurula is a synthetic larva, based on similarities seen in various bilaterally symmetrical echinoderm larvae. The generalized dipleurula (Fig. 9.3D) is an elongated, bilaterally symmetrical creature without the skeleton typical of echinoderms. On each side of the simple digestive tract are paired coelomic cavities, called by Heider (1912) the axocoel, hydrocoel, and somatocoel, and more recently termed the protocoel, mesocoel, and metacoel. All of these are derived as a result of lateral evaginations of the archenteron (Fig. 9.3B-C). Radial rather than spiral cleavage precedes the formation of the dipleurula type of larva (Fig. 9.3A), each blastomere giving rise to daughters that lie directly in line. Early cleavage is indeterminate rather than determinate, and embryonic induction rather than cell differentiation is basic to the organization of the early embryo.

The concept of a dipleurula larva makes a good deal of sense, as otherwise divergent echinoderms do pass through dipleurula-like, bilaterally symmetrical stages, and related phyla sometimes have larval types which might be considered modified dipleurulae. As an ancestral larval type, however, the dipleurula larva is inadequate for several reasons, best discussed in conjunction with echinoderm phylogeny (p. 451). Yet, with all of its problematical aspects, the dipleurula larva helps to explain a relationship between primitive chordates and echinoderms, for the tornaria larva (Fig. 12.6B) of the hemichordates shows obvious similarities to young echinoderm larvae. It is at least partially valid to distinguish the Protostomia and Deuterostomia as being characterized by trochophore and dipleurula larval types.

References

Bather, F. A. 1904. The echinoderms. In R. Lankester (ed.), A *Treatise on Zoology*, Vol. III. Adam and Charles Black, London.

Hatschek, B. 1893. Studien über Entwicklungsgeschichte der Anneliden. Ein Beitrag zur Morphologie der Bilaterien. *Arb. Zool. Inst. Wien* 3: 277.

Heider, K. 1912. Über Organverlaterung bei den Echinodermen-Metamorphose. *Verh. Deutsch. Zool. Gesellsch.* 22: 239.

Lang, A. 1904. Beiträge auf einer Trophocöltheorie. *Jena. Ztschr. Naturw.* 38: 1.

Meyer, E. 1901. Studien über den Körperbau der Anneliden, v. Das Mesoderm der Ringelwürmer, *Mitt. Zool. Stat. Neapel* 14: 247.

10
The Lophophorate Coelomates

Three phyla of coelomate animals, Phoronida, Ectoprocta, and Brachiopoda, are characterized by a crown of ciliated tentacles, the lophophore, used for food capture. The lophophore is a complex structure and provides strong evidence of relationship. Other aspects of their form give further evidence of relationship, particularly the divisions of the coelom. The three groups of animals have become so specialized, however, that relationships are not obvious on superficial examination.

Lophophorates are especially interesting because although they are protostomes, with a mouth derived from the blastopore or formed near it, a number of traits link them with deuterostomes. Protostomes usually undergo spiral, determinate cleavage and have a trochophore-like larva. Deuterostomes usually undergo indeterminate, radial cleavage and have a dipleurula-like larva. Phoronids undergo either spiral or radial cleavage, depending on the species, and have a larva resembling a trochophore in many respects. Ectoproct cleavage is highly modified or radial, and the larvae only remotely resemble a trochophore. Brachiopods undergo radial cleavage and have no larval stage truly comparable

to a trochophore. Protostomes are generally schizocoelous, and derive mesoderm from teloblasts arising from 4d or a comparable blastomere, or from mesodermal bands. Deuterostomes are usually enterocoelous, with mesoderm arising as an outpocketing of the primitive gut. The phoronid coelom is formed by the rearrangement of endomesodermal mesenchyme, and so is somewhat like the protostomes. Ectoproct development is highly modified; the mesoderm is all ectomesoderm, and the coelom forms more or less as in phoronids. Brachiopod mesoderm arises in several ways, depending on the species. Some brachiopods are definitely enterocoelous, the mesoderm arising as an outpocketing from the primitive gut. The dipleurula larva is described as having three pairs of coelomic sacs, the protocoel, mesocoel, and metacoel, and some deuterostomes have the body divided into a protosome, mesosome, and metasome containing the corresponding coelomic parts. Lophophorates have a coelom divided into two parts, corresponding to the mesocoel and metacoel of deuterostomes, and some have a partially separated coelomic compartment that may be comparable to the protocoel. The typical protostome is highly cephalized, while deuterostomes are often uncephalized, like lophophorates.

Lophophorates are far too specialized to be considered ancestral to deuterostomes, but the many similarities suggest that lophophorates and deuterostome ancestral stocks may have diverged from the protostome line at about the same time, and may, perhaps, have remained together for a short period.

Phylum Phoronida

Aggregations of worm-like phoronids attach to pilings, build tubes in mud, or burrow in calcareous rocks and shells in shallow coastal waters, especially in temperate regions. Similar tubes are found in great numbers in early paleozoic sandstones, so phoronids may have been extremely abundant in past ages. Not many survive today; only about 15 species are known. Phoronids live quiet lives, for they never emerge from their tubes. The tentacles are thrust out for feeding, and when disturbed the animal merely retreats into its tube. Some species form aggregations by asexual reproduction, but most phoronids cannot reproduce asexually.

The outstanding characteristics of the phoronids are:

1. A bilaterally symmetrical, often spirally coiled lophophore at the anterior end.

2. A true coelom, lined with peritoneum and with mesenteries to the digestive tube; divided by a septum into a mesocoel and metacoel, and with evidences of a protocoel in the episteme, a flap which covers the mouth.

3. A circulatory system with contractile vessels and blood containing haemoglobin in corpuscles.

4. A metanephridial excretory system, with nephrostomes opening into the coelom.

5. A complete, U-shaped digestive tract, with mouth and anus at the lophophore end.

6. A simple, subepidermal nervous system with an anterior nerve ring.

7. Simple gonads associated with the peritoneum, with gametes escaping through the nephridia.

8. Irregular to spiral cleavage, producing an actinotroch larva, which resembles a trochophore.

The slender, worm-like body expands in an end bulb that anchors it in the tube (Fig. 10.1A). A constriction or collar sets the trunk off from the upper end, on which the lophophore and all conspicuous external features are placed. The body wall is very thin, as in many other animals protected by a tube. The circular muscles are delicate, but the longitudinal muscles are strong and complexly folded, crowding many fibrils in a single muscle strand (Fig. 10.1C). A delicate peritoneum invests the muscle layers and lines the coelom (Fig. 10.2).

The lophophore is the most conspicuous feature of the body. New tentacles are formed at a median gap, where several short, growing tentacles may be found. Each arm of the lophophore is double, with inner and outer ridges, bearing inner and outer rows of tentacles (Fig. 10.1B). Space for tentacles is increased by spiral coiling; as many as 500 tentacles may be present in some species. A ciliated buccal groove between the lophophore ridges leads to the corners of the crescentic mouth. Strong cilia on each tentacle face the buccal groove and produce downward currents. Particles are caught in mucus as flies are caught on fly paper. Cilia in the buccal groove deliver the mucous string with its food particles to the mouth.

The slender tentacles are hollow; their wall is a continuation of the body wall and contains weak longitudinal muscles permitting limited movements. The thickened basement membrane supports the tentacles and makes them rather stiff. Each tentacle encloses a coelom, continuous with the coelom of the lophophoral ridge. A flap-like extension of the body wall, the epistome, covers the mouth and contains a coelomic cavity, also continuous with the coelom of the lophophore. The ring coelom of lophophore, tentacles, and epistome is divided from the trunk coelom by a slanting septum extending from the body wall to the esophagus.

The lophophore coelom is termed the mesocoel, and this part of the body may be called the mesosome. The trunk coelom

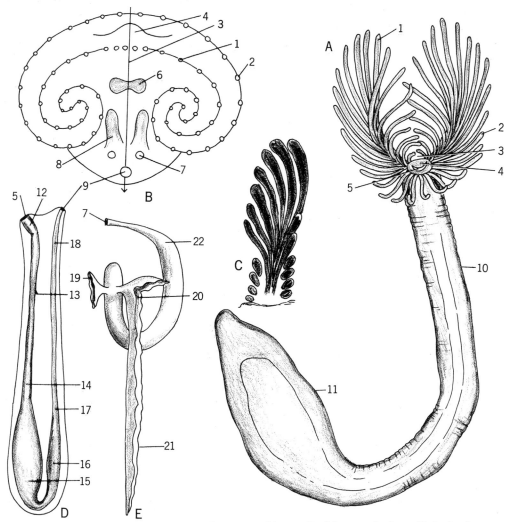

Fig. 10.1. Phoronids. **A.** A young *Phoronis architecta*. **B.** Scheme of phoronid lophophore organization. **C.** Muscle bundle of *Phoronopsis pallida*, showing infolding with the associated multiplication of muscle fibers. **D.** Scheme of the digestive tract of a phoronid. **E.** A metanephridium, showing two funnels. (**A**, after Wilson. **B**, after Sélys-Longchamps, from Dawydoff and Grassé, in Grassé. **C**, after Silén. **D**, after Hyman. **E**, after Benham.) *External features:* 1, inner tentacle; 2, outer tentacle; 3, gap where new tentacles are formed; 4, epistome; 5, mouth; 6, ganglion; 7, nephridiopore; 8, lophophore organ; 9, anus; 10, trunk; 11, end bulb. *Digestive tract:* 12, buccal tube; 13, esophagus; 14, prestomach; 15, stomach; 16, wide intestine; 17, intestine; 18, rectum. *Nephridium:* 19, narrow nephrostome; 20, wide nephrostome; 21, funnel appendage; 22, nephridial tube.

is the metacoel, and the trunk may be termed the metasome. These body regions and coelomic compartments resemble the same body regions and coelomic compartments of some deuterostomes, particularly the hemichordates (p. 425). The epistome may be considered a reduced protosome, and its coelom the equivalent of the protocoel, but this correspondence is more controversial.

The coelomic fluid is a hydraulic skeleton and is undoubtedly important in internal transport. It contains albuminous material and a number of kinds of coelomocytes, as well as haemocytes containing haemoglobin.

A ventral mesentery is formed during the growth of the coelom, and a dorsal and two lateral mesenteries are usually added. The middle part of the trunk coelom is thus divided into two dorsolateral and two ventrolateral compartments, usually confluent at the two ends of the trunk (Fig. 10.2).

Food passes from the buccal tube into

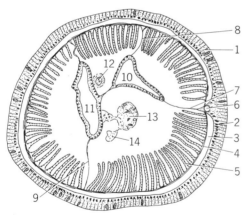

Fig. 10.2. Transverse section through the trunk of *Phoronopsis harmeri*. Note the deep muscular ridges. (After Pixell.) 1, epidermis; 2, gland cell; 3, basement membrane; 4, circular muscle; 5, longitudinal muscle; 6, lateral nerve; 7, lateral mesentery; 8, dorsal mesentery; 9, ventral mesentery; 10, intestine; 11, prestomach; 12, median vessel; 13, vasoperitoneal tissue; 14, lateral vessel.

the esophagus, which is attached to the body wall by radial muscle fibers and has heavily folded, glandular walls. The prestomach, which makes up the rest of the descending arm of the digestive tube, has thinner walls (Fig. 10.1D). The stomach lies in the end bulb. A strip of strong cilia begins in the prestomach and passes through the stomach. There are few gland cells in the adult stomach, and a pair of syncytial regions known to carry on intracellular digestion in larvae persist in the adult, so digestion is probably predominantly intracellular. The ascending arm of the digestive tract is made up of the three regions of the intestine, a wide intestine in the end bulb, a long, ascending narrow intestine, and a short rectum ending in the anus.

There are no special respiratory organs, but the circulation of blood through the tentacles undoubtedly oxygenates the haemoglobin.

Phoronids have a pair of metanephridia. Metanephridia differ from protonephridia by having the inner end open to the coelom. Animals without a true coelom never have metanephridia, although some coelomates have protonephridia. Metanephridia however, are the characteristic excretory organs of coelomate animals. Phoronid metanephridia open to the coelom through one or two ciliated funnels, the nephrostomes (Fig. 10.1E). The metanephridial tubules open to the exterior through a pair of nephridiopores located near the anus. Gametes as well as wastes escape by way of the nephridia. Excretory physiology is unknown, but dark inclusions in the nephridial wall, believed to be wastes, have been seen emerging from the nephridiopore.

Phoronids have a simple circulatory system, containing blood with red corpuscles holding haemoglobin. Each tentacle contains a single blood vessel (Fig. 10.3A), in which blood ebbs and flows. Blood is drained from the tentacle vessels by an efferent lophophore vessel, which lies in the lophophore ridge. Two vessels from the efferent lophophore vessels join to form the ventral vessel after passing through the septum. The ventral vessel runs to the stomach, where it branches to form a haemal plexus on the stomach wall. Blood from the haemal plexus drains into the dorsal vessel, which carries blood straight to the lophophore, connecting with an afferent lophophore vessel that runs parallel to the efferent lophophore vessel. A number of capillary caeca branch from the ventral vessel. Gonads cluster about the caeca during their development.

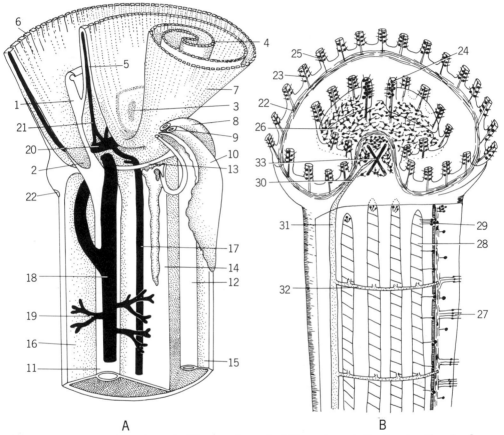

A B

Fig. 10.3. Phoronid Structure. A. The anterior end of *Phoronis australis*, showing the circulatory system and major organs. B. Scheme of the phoronid nervous system. (A, after Benham. B, after Silén.) *External features:* 1, epistome; 2, mouth; 3, lophophore organ; 4, spiraled lophophore; 5, inner tentacle; 6, outer tentacle; 7, fused bases of tentacles; 8, nephridial ridge; 9, anus; 10, rectal ridge. *Digestive tract:* 11, esophagus; 12, intestine. *Coelom:* 13, septum; 14, lateral mesentery; 15, dorsal mesentery; 16, ventral mesentery. *Circulatory system:* 17, median vessel; 18, lateral vessel; 19, capillary caeca of lateral vessel; 20, lophophore ring vessel; 21, tentacular vessel. *Nervous system:* 22, nerve ring; 23, neurosensory cells of tentacles; 24, lophophoral sense organs; 25, tentacular nerve; 26, main nervous field; 27, trunk neurosensory cell; 28, longitudinal muscle of trunk; 29, neurons serving the upper ends of muscle bundles; 30, decussation of giant fibers; 31, lateral nerve (giant fiber); 32, transverse branch of giant fiber; 33, anal decussation.

There is no heart; the major vessels are contractile and force the blood along.

The nervous system has many primitive characteristics. It is a subepidermal nerve plexus, conducting impulses in all directions. The nervous layer is thickened to form a preoral nervous field, from which a ring paralleling the outer ridge of the lophophore arises (Fig. 10.3B). Nerve fibers pass from the ring to the outer circle of tentacles, and the inner tentacles are innervated from the preoral field. Motor fibers pass through the septum to the anterior end of the body-wall muscle tracts. There is only one nerve, the lateral nerve, typically on the left side of the body. It is a giant fiber, originating on the right and crossing to the left side of the nerve ring, then turning to course along the body wall. The giant fiber coordinates the longitudinal muscles for rapid withdrawal into the tube; when it is cut, the muscles below the cut fail to contract.

At appropriate seasons, the peritoneal cells near the capillary caeca and ventral vessel are transformed into gametes, forming the gonads. Hermaphroditic and dioecious species are known. Gametes escape through the nephridia. The depression between the arms of the lophophore serves as a brood chamber in some species. A ciliated groove connects each nephridiopore with the lophophore organ, a glandular region secreting cement used to attach ova to the brood chamber wall. The sperm of other phoronids are trapped in the secretion of the lophophore organs, and it probably helps them reach the coelom, where fertilization occurs.

Vestiges of spiral cleavage are reported in *Phoronopsis viridis*, but radial or irregular cleavage patterns have also been described. In any case, a coeloblastula is formed. It gastrulates by invagination and develops an apical sensory tuft. Mesoderm cells move into the blastocoel during gastrulation. A preoral lobe grows over the originally large blastopore, enclosing a vestibule that opens into the stomach. The intestine ends in an anus, formed without a proctodaeal invagination. A ciliated band appears, along which hollow projections, the larval tentacles, develop (Fig. 10.4A). A posterior ciliated band, the telotroch, forms. Larval tentacles continue to develop and the larva becomes a fully developed, free-swimming actinotroch (Fig. 10.4B).

Unfortunately, coelom formation is not well understood. It seems to arise as a single space that curves around the intestine and meets, ventrally, to form a single, ventral mesentery. The septum dividing the mesocoel and metacoel is formed very early. A preoral septum partly separates a preoral coelom from the mesocoel. Thus the coelom may be divided into three chambers, which may be comparable to the protocoel, mesocoel, and metacoel of deuterostome larvae, but unpaired rather than paired and therefore only doubtfully homologous. For a discussion of the details of metamorphosis, Hyman's (1955) description is recommended. It includes references to the more important investigations.

Phylum Ectoprocta

At every organizational level, some highly successful phylum emerges. Lophophorates have had two great successes, the ectoprocts and brachiopods. In modern times ectoprocts are more successful, for about 4000 species are known. Despite their small size, ectoprocts are common fossils; about 4000 fossil species have been described. Ectoprocts occur in fresh-water and marine habitats everywhere in the world. They live in shallow waters and to depths of about 6000 m., and are abundant in polar and tropical seas.

Like phoronids, ectoprocts secrete a covering for themselves, but whereas the phoronid and its tube remain separate, the ectoproct case is an integral part of the body wall. All ectoprocts are colonial. Colonies either form gelatinous or firm encrusting masses or are arboreal. Ectoprocts have a number of traits in common with phoronids:

1. A lophophore constructed like the phoronid lophophore and used for the same purpose.

2. A coelom divided by a septum into a mesocoel and metacoel.

3. A U-shaped digestive tract with mouth and anus near the lophophore and the anus outside of the tentacular crown.

4. Simple gonads derived from the peritoneum.

Traits in which ectoprocts differ from phoronids are:

1. Exclusively colonial habits with very high capacity for asexual reproduction.

2. Lack of nephridia and circulatory system.

3. A nervous system with a ganglion in the ring coelom of the mesocoel, and with other characteristics less primitive than those of phoronids.

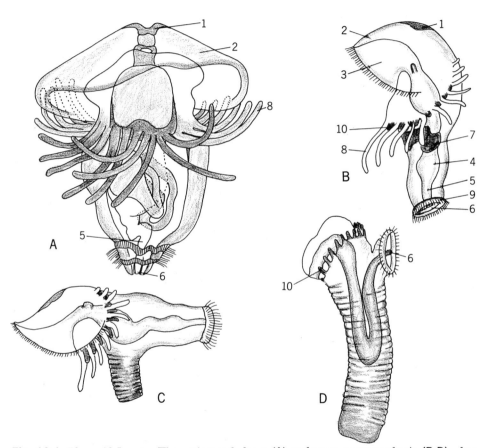

Fig. 10.4. Phoronid Larvae. The actinotroch larva (A) undergoes metamorphosis (B-D), during which the adult tentacles bud out between the gradually degenerating larval tentacles. The trunk region develops a metasome pouch that grows down into a stalk-like extension of the larval trunk and eventually becomes the greater part of the adult animal. (A, after Sélys-Longchamps. B-D, after Meeck, from Dawydoff and Grassé, in Grassé.) 1, apical sense organ; 2, preoral lobe; 3, vestibule; 4, stomach; 5, intestine; 6, anus; 7, metasome pouch; 8, larval tentacle; 9, telotroch; 10, buds of definitive tentacles.

Table 10.1. Summary table of ectoproct traits

	CTENOSTOMATA	CHEILOSTOMATA	CYCLOSTOMATA	PHYLACTOLAEMATA
Lophophore	circular	circular	circular	horseshoe-shaped
Epistome	none	none	none	present
Body wall	complete, no communication between coeloms of adjacent zooids	complete	complete	incomplete; adjacent zooids with coeloms in communication.
Body wall muscles	none	none	none	present
Zoecium	flexible, without operculum, sometimes with pleated membrane	calcified and box-like; orifice subterminal, with operculum	calcified, circular, without operculum	not calcified
Polymorphism	autozooids and kenozooids	autozooids, kenozooids, avicularia, and vibracula	autozooids, kenozooids, and gonozooids.	none
Statoblasts	none	none	none	floatoblasts, sessoblasts, and spinoblasts
Distribution	predominantly marine	marine	marine	fresh water

Ectoprocts are divided into two classes, Gymnolaemata and Phylactolaemata. The former are almost exclusively marine, and the latter live only in fresh water. Nearly all fossil ectoprocts are gymnolaemates, but the phylactolaemates appear somewhat more primitive today. *Cristatella* is a common fresh-water species, and shows the general features of ectoprocts (Fig. 10.5). It should be examined closely before undertaking a study of classification or the organs and their functions.

Early students of ectoprocts thought each zooid to be two animals, a case-forming cystid and a feeding polypide. Although cystid and polypide appear independent, they are parts of the same animal. The cystid is the highly modified trunk and its exoskeleton; the polypide is the lophophore and the digestive tract which hangs down from it, the muscles which manipulate it, and the nervous

centers. The cystid contains a capacious cavity, the trunk coelom or metacoel. As in phoronids, the lophophore also contains a coelom, the mesocoel, and in fresh-water species the epistome contains another coelom, the protocoel. The protocoel intrudes between the main mesocoel and the coelom of the inner tentacles; these tentacles contain a coelomic cavity connected to the main mesocoel by forked canals that pass on each side of the protocoel (Fig. 10.5).

The cystid wall, or zoecium, of marine ectoprocts is complete, but may contain pores which permit contact between the living tissues of adjacent zooids. The cystid wall of fresh-water species is always somewhat incomplete, so the metacoel of adjacent zooids is continuous, and sometimes the many polypides hang down into a common open coelom. *Cristatella* shows the many similarities between phoronids

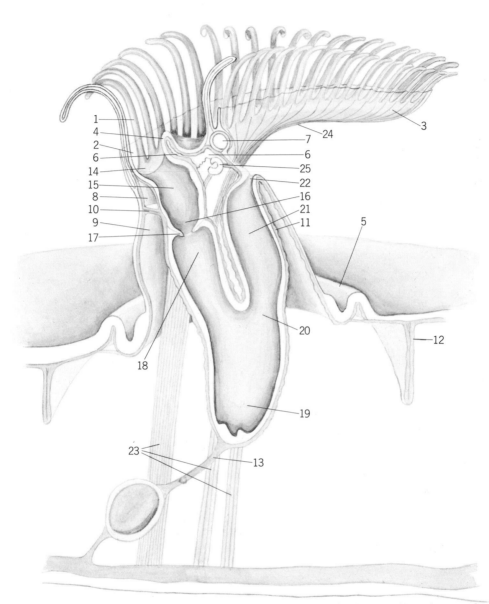

Fig. 10.5. Scheme of Ectoproct Anatomy (adapted from Cori). *External form:* **1,** tentacle; **2,** intertentacular membrane; **3,** ridge of lophophore; **4,** epistome; **5,** fold of the body wall. *Coelom and septa:* **6,** protocoel; **7,** sac of forked canal; **8,** mesocoel; **9,** metacoel; **10,** septum between mesocoel and metacoel; **11,** peritoneum; **12,** septum between zooids; **13,** funiculus containing young statoblast. *Digestive tract:* **14,** mouth; **15,** pharynx; **16,** esophagus; **17,** cardiac valve; **18,** cardiac region of stomach; **19,** gastric caecum; **20,** pyloric stomach; **21,** intestine; **22,** anus. *Muscles:* **23,** retractor muscles; **24,** branches of lophophore retractor. *Nervous system:* **25,** brain.

and ectoprocts. The lophophore and U-shaped digestive tube are similar. The mouth lies between the two sides of the lophophore, and the anus just outside of the lophophore ring. Ectoprocts are much smaller and have no circulatory or excretory organs, but otherwise the principal differences between phoronids and ectoprocts are in the nature of the trunk body wall. The phoronid body wall is delicate for such large organisms; they are protected by their tubes. Fresh-water ectoprocts have a body wall with a delicate musculature, especially in species with gelatinous zoecia. Marine ectoprocts with firm continuous zoecia are without a body wall musculature.

CLASSIFICATION

Endoprocts and ectoprocts were long classified together in the phylum Bryozoa or Polyzoa, which many still prefer. The lack of a coelom in endoprocts recommends that they be classified in a separate phylum, but the term bryozoan remains a useful common name. When endoprocts are placed in the same phylum as ectoprocts, they are usually placed in a separate subphylum.

Class Gymnolaemata. Lophophore circular, without epistome; body wall musculature absent; without direct connections between the coeloms of adjacent zooids; almost exclusively marine.

Order Ctenostomata. With a simple, flexible case of chitinous material, having a terminal or subterminal orifice; without a closing plate, but often with a pleated membrane on the diaphragm which occludes the vestibule; polymorphism restricted to ordinary feeding zooids and specialized zooids for stolonic attachment; mostly marine, but including some fresh-water forms. Example: *Victoriella* (Fig. 10.6A); *Aeverillia* (Fig. 10.7J).

Order Cheilostomata. With membranous or calcareous, box-like cases, variously arranged to form colonies, but with separate wall between zooids; case with a subterminal opening and typically with a hinged lid, the operculum; sometimes with a collar containing a secondary, permanently open orifice; commonly polymorphic, with specialized zooids for grasping (avicularia) and for sweeping the colony surface (vibracula); marine. Examples: *Bugula* (Fig. 10.6D); *Membranipora* (Fig. 10.6F).

Order Cyclostomata. With tubular, fully calcified cases having a terminal, typically circular, orifice, without an operculum but closed by a perforated membrane; coelom divided by a membranous sac into inner and outer regions used in lophophore extrusion; polymorphism common, with formation of gonozooids and kenozooids; many young formed by polyembryony from a single embryo in a brood chamber. Example: *Crisia* (Fig. 10.6E).

Class Phylactolaemata. Zooids with a horseshoe-shaped lophophore; with an epistome; body wall with musculature; cases incomplete and not calcified; coelom of adjacent zooids continuous; without polymorphic zooids; exclusively fresh-water species. Examples: *Cristatella* (Fig. 10.5); *Fredricella* (Fig. 10.6C).

ZOOID STRUCTURE

Zooid form is extremely variable. The cystid may be gelatinous, membranous, or strongly calcified. The mechanism for withdrawing and extruding the lophophore varies with the flexibility of the zoecium and involves extensive modification of the form of the cystid wall and the details of the attachment of the cystid and polypide. The arrangement of the few internal organs is quite stable; differences in the lophophore, epistome, cystid, and connection between the cystid and polypide are responsible for most ectoproct diversity. An important source of variability is the extensive polymorphism of some marine ectoprocts. The following description relates only to the unmodified, feeding polyp (autozooid).

Zoecium. A formidable vocabulary is used to describe detailed differences in the case, or zoecium, of different ectoproct orders, and much of classification depends on zoecium traits. The zoecium can only be discussed meaningfully for each group separately.

Phylactolaemata are fresh-water species with a delicate or tough, membranous zoecium, although some form massive colonies with gelatinous zoecia. Membranous zoecia are built of chitin. Each zoecium is tubular, with a circular to subcircular orifice, through which the polypide protrudes. The zoecium wall is never complete, so the coelom of the whole colony is continuous, but partial divisions are usually present (Fig. 10.5).

Gymnolaemate zoecia are more complete. The zooids are still connected by tiny interzooidal pores in the zoecial wall, but these openings are plugged by small rosettes of epidermal cells. The gymnolaemate body wall contains no muscle, and is composed only of the zoecium wall, epidermis and peritoneum (Fig. 10.7A).

The simplest zoecia are seen in some Ctenostomata. They are simple, cylindrical, or vase-shaped cases with a thin, chitinous wall and no calcareous layer (Fig. 10.7J). They are considered the most primitive gymnolaemates.

The zoecium provides protection and support; both are increased by thickening the zoecial wall. Many zoecial traits are adaptations that increase support or protection. A common cheilostome trait is a hinged lid (operculum) that can cover the orifice when the polypide is withdrawn. The major adaptational trend has been toward the strengthening of the zoecial wall by calcification. This interferes with the mechanism for extruding the lophophore, always achieved by a hydraulic system. Pressure is exerted on the coelomic fluid, forcing the polypide out like a jack-in-the-box. Phylactolaemates and cteno-

stomes have an elastic zoecial wall, which can be easily compressed to cause lophophore extrusion. Where the zoecial wall is inelastic, however, a special mechanism is required.

All but the ventral zoecial wall of many cheilostomes is calcified. The ventral wall remains an elastic frontal membrane (Fig. 10.6D; 10.7B,C), which covers all or part of the surface. Parietal muscles attach to the firm zoecial wall and the frontal membrane; they depress the frontal membrane to force the polypide out. The frontal membrane, however, is the weak point in the cystid wall. Many species partially protect it by spiny outgrowths of the hard parts of the zoecium. Some cheilostomes have a calcareous shield, the cryptocyst, below the frontal membrane (Fig. 10.7D, E). Parietal muscles pass through openings (opesiules) and attach to the frontal membrane, permitting the same mechanism of lophophore extrusion as in species without a cryptocyst. The spiny protection over the frontal membrane is consolidated to form a continuous cover in some cheilostomes, and the frontal membrane is replaced by a compensation sac (Fig. 10.7F-H). When parietal muscles depress the floor of the compensation sac, the polypide is forced out and water rushes into the compensation sac from without.

The tubular zoecium of cyclostomes is completely calcified and has no frontal membrane or compensation sac. An entirely different system of polypide extrusion is used. The orifice is covered by a terminal membrane, turned in to line a vestibule (Fig. 10.7I). The coelom is divided into inner and outer parts by a membrane. When the dilator muscles extend the vestibule, coelomic fluid around the vestibule in the outer coelomic chamber is forced down around the membrane surrounding the inner coelomic sac. This increases pressure in the inner coelomic sac and forces the polypide out.

The operation of the coelomic hydraulic system to extrude the polypide lophophore

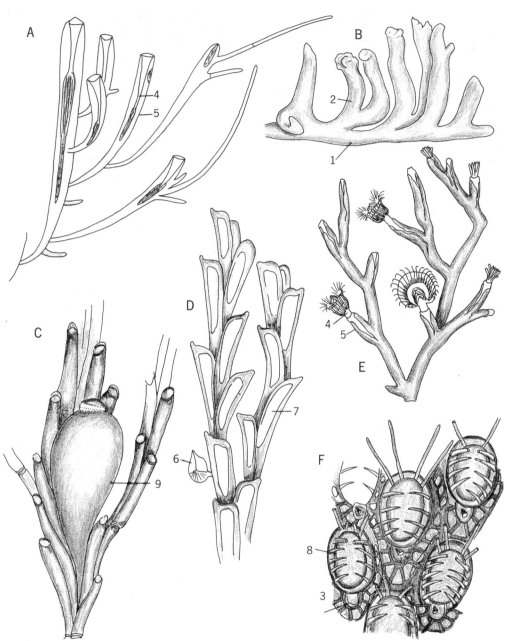

Fig. 10.6. Representative Ectoprocts. The ectoprocts are divided into two classes, the predominantly marine Gymnolaemata with an essentially circular lophophore, and the fresh-water Phylactolaemata with a horseshoe-shaped lophophore. *Victoriella* (**A**) is an example of the gymnolaemate order, Ctenostomata, with a simple, chitinous zoecium. *Paludicella* (**B**) is another example. *Victoriella* is often found in brackish water, and *Paludicella* occurs in fresh water. Members of the large gymnolaemate order, *Cheilostomata*, have box-like cases, usually with an aperture protected by an operculum. Some members form arborescent colonies, like

demonstrates some of the advantages of a hydraulic system. Muscles can only shorten and pull on an object; they can never push something directly. This is a severe limitation when something must be lifted from the body surface. Some method of transforming a pull into a push is necessary. Two major methods are used. One is a lever and fulcrum system, as in the bones and joints of vertebrates. The other is a hydraulic system, in which pressure on a fluid enclosed in a water-tight compartment is transmitted to a movable part. A hydraulic system is considerably more flexible than a mechanical system of levers, for the pressure can be applied in any direction, depending on the configuration of the water-tight compartment and the way a movable part is free to move. The coelomic space within the tentacles of the lophophore inflates the tentacles as the lophophore is extruded. To achieve the same result, a very complex arrangement of levers would be required. Hydraulic systems are very common. The extension of the body of creeping rotifers is caused by the constriction of circular muscles of the body wall, applying pressure on the perivisceral fluid and forcing the extension of the body, for example.

The ectoproct body wall is everywhere firmly attached to the zoecium, as epidermis clings to the cuticle of other kinds of animals. The zoecium is, in a sense, a highly modified, cuticular covering.

Polypide. The ectoproct lophophore is so like the phoronid lophophore that it need not be described in detail. The crescentic to horseshoe-shaped phylactolaemate lophophore carries more tentacles than the circular gymnolaemate lophophore, and an epistome is found only in phylactolaemates. Ciliated currents caused by the lophophore have been described in detail. The cilia on the lateral surfaces of the tentacles pull water down and out between the tentacles, directing particles toward the mouth (Fig. 10.8A). Large particles are rejected by retraction or muscular movements of the tentacles, and small particles are delivered to the mouth by ciliary currents at the lophophore base.

The short, ciliated pharynx leads to a long, delicately muscled esophagus (Fig. 10.5). A cardiac valve usually separates the esophagus and stomach. Some ctenostomes have a gizzard, containing grinding denticles, at the base of the esophagus (Fig. 10.7J). Other ectoprocts have three stomach regions, a cardia, caecum, and pylorus. The caecum forms the bottom of the U, and the rectum is sharply set off from the pylorus.

Bryozoans are active feeders. Food accumulated in the pharynx is swallowed by the esophagus. The stomach and caecum are very active, and food moves back and forth between the caecum and pylorus. According to Silén (1944), food is formed into an elongated mucous cord that is rotated by ciliary currents up to 150 times per minute in the caecum and pylorus. Digestion is very rapid in phylactolaemates; Marcus (1934) reports that food, when plentiful, may be no more than an hour in the digestive tract. Digestion is correspondingly inefficient, however, for an occasional rotifer or nematode will shake itself and swim away after having been through the whole process. Digestion is wholly extracellular in phylactolaemates, but food vacuoles are formed in

Bugula (D), while others form incrusting colonies, like those of *Membranipora* (F). The third order, *Cyclostomata*, is characterized by more or less cylindrical zoecia with a circular aperture and without an operculum, like *Crisia* (E). The phylactolaemates are far less numerous than the gymnolaemates, but include some species that form massive colonies, and others that undergo arborescent branching, like *Fredricella* (C). (A, after Braem. B and C, after Rogick, in Edmondson. D, after Hyman. E and F, after Robertson.) 1, stolon; 2, zooid; 3, orifice; 4, polypide; 5, zoecium; 6, avicularium; 7, frontal membrane; 8, calcareous spine; 9, ovicell.

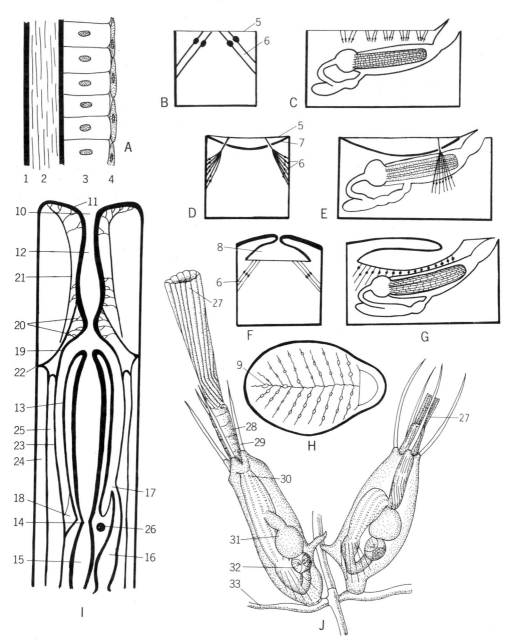

Fig. 10.7. **A.** Scheme of the body wall of an entoproct. (Note the absence of muscle layers.) **B-I.** Scheme of the extrusion mechanisms of various types of entoprocts. **B-C,** end and side views of a simple zoecium with a frontal membrane. When the frontal membrane is depressed by parietal muscles, the polypide is extruded. **D-E,** end and side views of a zoecium with a cryptocyst wall beneath the frontal membrane. In such ectoprocts, the extrusion mechanism is the same as in forms with a simple frontal membrane, although the parietal muscles must pass through the concave cryptocyst wall. **F-G,** end and side views of a zoecium with a compensation sac. In this case, parietal muscles depress the lower membrane of the compensation

the cardiac and caecal epithelia of some gymnolaemates. The rectum forms residues into mucous fecal balls, an important progressive step and useful, as the anus is so close to the lophophore. The lophophore is bent away at the time of defecation.

Starch is digested slowly and deposited as glycogen in the gymnolaemate, *Zoobotryon*. Proteins are hydrolyzed in the stomach and are probably absorbed there. Fat globules are phagocytized by stomach epithelial cells. Glycogen and fat is eventually distributed throughout the body, and food reserves are laid down in the stolon as fat, glycogen, and protein masses.

Respiratory exchange occurs at the body surface, no doubt largely through the lophophore. There are no excretory organs, although Cori (1941) has suggested that the forked canals connecting the bases of the inner tentacles to the mesocoel may be vestiges of nephridia. Not many have accepted this, but there is evidence that nitrogenous wastes build up there and are ejected. Yellowish inclusions in the stomach wall are also generally thought to be wastes, and coelomocytes appear to pick up wastes for storage excretion. The cyclical dying down of colonies with the for-

mation of brown bodies (p. 336) may represent a physiological response to the accumulation of wastes and may be a method of disposing of stored waste materials.

Ectoprocts are small, and the coelomic fluid is adequate for internal transport. The peritoneum is partially ciliated, and a constant, definite circulation of coelomic fluid is maintained (Fig. 10.8B).

Ectoprocts have few muscles but are very busy insofar as their limited capacity for movement permits. This consists largely in withdrawing or extruding the polypide and manipulating the lophophore. Special muscles close the operculum and move the epistome, when it is present. The most conspicuous muscles, other than the parietal muscles previously mentioned, are the lophophore retractors, large strands of muscle on each side of the polypide, connecting the lophophore base to the bottom or sides of the zoecium.

An unusual ability to move is seen in some gelatinous phylactolaemates. The circular and longitudinal muscles on the bottom of the body wall are strongly developed, forming a creeping sole (Fig. 10.9A). Young colonies creep about, apparently by alternate contraction and relaxation of these muscles, sometimes with

sac. Water flows into the compensation sac and coelomic pressure rises, forcing the polypide out. H. Top view of a zoecium with a compensation sac, showing pores between the partially consolidated costae that protect it. I. Scheme of cyclostome construction, showing extrusion mechanism. Contraction of the vestibule dilators forces fluid from the distal, outer coelomic space into the proximal, outer coelomic space. This raises pressure in the inner coelomic space and forces the polypide out. Note that in all these extrusion mechanisms, a hydraulic system is used to change the direction of movement, very much as a lever may be used for the same purpose. This is one of the important advantages of a hydraulic system. J. Two *Aeverilla* zooids, showing the pleated membranes often seen in the gymnolaemate order, Ctenostomata. (A-I, modified, from various sources. J, after Marcus.) *Body layers:* 1, cuticle; 2, calcareous layer; 3, epidermis; 4, peritoneum. *Extrusion mechanisms:* 5, frontal membrane; 6, parietal muscle; 7, cryptocyst wall; 8, compensation sac; 9, pores between costae. *Cyclostome structure:* 10, orifice; 11, terminal membrane; 12, vestibule; 13, tentacular crown; 14, mouth; 15. pharynx; 16, intestine; 17, anus; 18, ring coelom; 19, diaphragm; 20, diaphragm sphincter; 21, vestibule dilator muscle; 22, ligament of membranous sac; 23, membranous sac; 24, outer proximal coelom; 25, inner coelomic sac; 26, ganglion. *Ctenostome structure:* 27, pleated collar; 28, vestibular membrane; 29, spines; 30, retracted tentacles; 31, digestive tract; 32, gizzard; 33, stolon.

the aid of currents produced by the lophophores.

There are no special sense organs, but sensory cells provide for reception of tactile, chemical, and water current stimuli. The nervous system is simple. Gymnolaemates have a nerve ring around the pharynx. A small cephalic ganglion, with peripheral neurons and central neuropile, is attached to the ring and lies against the lophophoral coelom. Two motor and two sensory fibers pass to each tentacle from the ring. Pairs of sensory and motor fibers pass to the tentacle sheath from the ganglion, probably connecting with the subepidermal nerve plexus. Motor nerves to the various muscles and to the gut arise from the tentacle sheath nerve or cephalic ganglion. The cystid wall contains a nerve net, and in some cases the nerve nets of adjacent zooids are connected by fibers passing through the pore canals.

The nervous system of phylactolaemates is somewhat different. The cerebral ganglion is similar to the gymnolaemate ganglion and lies in a peritoneal vesicle open to the mesocoel. A pair of gangli-onated tracts parallels the lophophore, issuing sensory and motor nerves to the tentacles (Fig. 10.9B). The epistome on the one side and the mouth and pharynx on the other interfere with the innervation of the tentacles in the middle of the lophophore. Two nerve rings, a circumoral ring and an epistomial ring around the epistome, surmount this difficulty. Nerves to the tentacle sheath, pharynx, and body muscles arise from the ganglion.

Gymnolaemates are hermaphroditic or dioecious; not uncommonly, different members of a colony are of different sexes. The gonads develop in the peritoneum of the metacoel, on the body wall, gut, or funiculus, an extension of the body wall containing muscle fibers and attaching to the stomach caecum. All phylactolaemates are hermaphroditic, with ovaries on the body wall and testes on the funiculus. There are no gonoducts.

POLYMORPHISM

Bryozoa have been colonial organisms since Cambrian times, and demonstrate some of

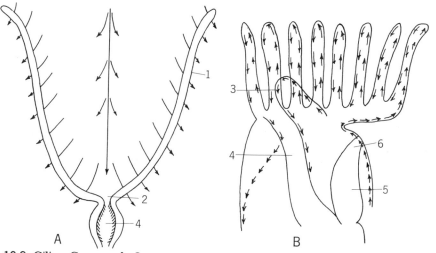

Fig. 10.8. Ciliary Currents. A. Currents in a gymnolaemate lophophore, sweeping food in and toward the mouth. B. The coelomic ciliary currents in the lophophore of a phylactolaemate, *Pectinatella.* (A, after Borg. B, after Oka.) 1, tentacle; 2, mouth; 3, epistome; 4, foregut; 5, intestine; 6, anus.

the typical consequences of colonial life. They have high powers of asexual reproduction and regeneration; the individual zooids are small; and in some cases, specialization of zooids for particular functions has occurred. Ordinary zooids are called autozooids; so far only this type has been mentioned. There are four important types of modified zooids (heterozooids): avicularia, vibracula, kenozooids, and various modifications for brooding the young, which may be termed gonozooids.

Avicularia are found only in cheilostomes: they are essentially overgrown opercula attached to greatly reduced zooids. Typical avicularia consist of a peduncle of variable length, attaching the zooid to the colony, a head which is actually the modified zoecium, and a mandible which is a modified operculum (Fig. 10.10A,B). Avicularian form is variable, and sometimes several kinds occur in a single species. The reduced parts of the polypide and cystid can be seen in the interior (Fig. 10.11A). The most conspicuous internal

elements are the opening (abductor) and closing (adductor) muscles. Avicularia snap viciously when disturbed; they grasp and hold small organisms that visit the colony, and probably prevent fouling of the colony surface by other sessile organisms.

Vibracula (Fig. 10.10C) are also highly modified zooids with the operculum altered into a long, movable bristle. Muscles similar to those of avicularia manipulate the bristle, sweeping the colony surface free of particles or organisms that cling to it.

Kenozooids are extremely variable. All are modified zooids that serve as stolons, rhizoids, or other hold-fast parts.

REPRODUCTION

A few ectoprocts shed ova into the sea, but most marine and all fresh-water species brood the young. Phylactolaemates breed in late spring and early summer. The gametes unite in the metacoel and the

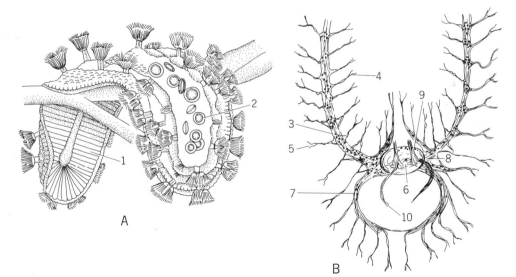

Fig. 10.9. A. *Cristatella mucedo*, creeping over a twig. Note the muscular creeping sole of the colony. B. Nervous system of *Cristatella*. (A, based on Allmann. B, after Gewerzhagen.) 1, sole; 2, statoblast; 3, lophophoral tract; 4, nerves to inner tentacles; 5, nerves to outer tentacles; 6, ganglion; 7, epistomial ring to inner tentacles; 8, circumoral ring; 9, dorsal nerve to tentacle sheath; 10, ventral nerve to tentacle sheath.

young develop in an embryo sac which develops on the body wall near the ovary. Holoblastic cleavage produces a coeloblastula; early embryology is highly modified and not well understood. No endoderm seems to be formed. Mesoderm arises from the ectoderm, and rearranges itself to form a coelom. The early embryo is a cystid, which buds off one or more polypides, develops cilia, and emerges as a free-swimming larva (Fig. 10.11A). It

settles down after a brief migratory phase and develops into a new colony.

Gymnolaemates often have highly modified brooding zooids. Most cheilostomes have ovicells, essentially a hood-like device into which ova are deposited (Fig. 10.6C). Ova removed from ovicells do not develop normally; evidently a special environment is maintained for the young. Cyclostome ova develop in gonozooids, forming a germinal ball that develops surface lobes, pinched off to form secondary embryos. The formation of several embryos from a single ovum is called polyembryony. This may be a device compensating for the many ova that never develop, for only ova that attach to a polypide that becomes a gonozooid develop, severely reducing the number of successful ova.

Gymnolaemate cleavage is radial or biradial, and produces a coeloblastula (Fig. 10.11B). Four cells elongate and move into the interior, giving rise to endoderm and endomesoderm. Large trochoblast cells form a girdle around the embryo, an apical organ begins to form, and several ectodermal invaginations appear. These become an adhesive sac and a pyriform organ. A vibratile plume develops in connection with a ciliary cleft. Ova developing externally form a cyphonautes larva (Fig. 10.11D,E), a highly modified trochophore. The modified cyphonautes larvae formed by brooding species are less trochophore-like. After swimming about for a time, the larva uses the vibratile plume as a sensory tuft in selecting a suitable site for attachment. The adhesive sac is everted and sticks the larva to the spot selected. The pyriform organ may also secrete an adhesive substance.

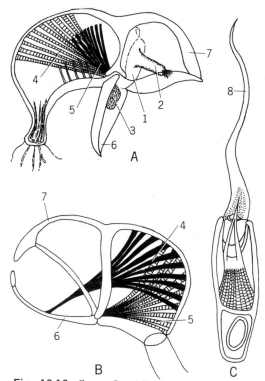

Fig. 10.10. Some Specialized Zooids. A. An avicularium of *Bugula*, with the mandible open, showing the reduced polypide within. B. A *Bugula* avicularium with the mandible closed. Antagonistic muscles are contrastingly shaded. C. A vibraculum of *Scrupocellaria*. (A, after Calvert and Marcus, from Cori in Kükenthal and Krumbach. B-C, after Hincks.) 1, polypide; 2, setiferous organ; 3, tendon of adductor; 4, adductor muscle; 5, abductor muscle; 6, mandible (operculum); 7, rostrum; 8, seta.

COLONY DEVELOPMENT

After attachment, the larva deteriorates into a mass of cells covered by the protoecium wall. The ancestrula (Fig. 10.11F) forms from the cell mass. It grows upward, and buds off daughter zooids in whatever pattern is characteristic of the species. Budding patterns are complex and varied, so a great variety of colony forms are known.

Some of the factors involved in budding and colony formation are known. The stolon grows at the tip, producing new ectodermal and mesodermal tissue. Buds appear at some distance from the tip, suggesting that a maturation process is involved. Buds begin as ectodermal outgrowths, but later develop some mesodermal cells. A septum forms only after the bud has appeared. The patterns of bud formation are evidently under precise regulation by internal factors (Fig. 10.12F).

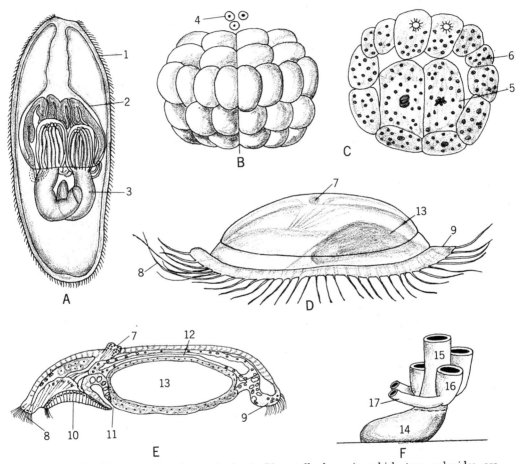

Fig. 10.11. Ectoproct Development. A. A *Plumatella* larva in which two polypides are developing. B. A *Bugula* embryo in the 64-cell stage. C. Section through a *Frustrellidra* embryo during gastrulation. D. A cyphonautes larva of *Frustrella*. E. Sagittal section through a cyphonautes larva. F. Scheme of early development of a *Prasopora* colony. (A, after Brien. B, after Correa. D, after Barrois. C and E, after Pace. F, after Cumings.) 1, mantle; 2, future cystid wall; 3, digestive tube of polypide; 4, polar bodies; 5, endoderm cell; 6, ectoderm; 7, apical sense organ; 8, vibratile plume; 9, ciliary girdle; 10, pyriform organ; 11, pharynx; 12, stomach; 13, internal adhesive sac; 14, protoecium; 15, ancestroecium; 16, first generation bud; 17, second generation bud.

BROWN BODIES

Polypides do not live long and are replaced by regeneration. An exhausted polypide contracts powerfully; its tissues break down and some are phagocytized, but the stomach tissue balls up to form a brownish mass, the brown body. During life the stomach wall builds up dark inclusions,

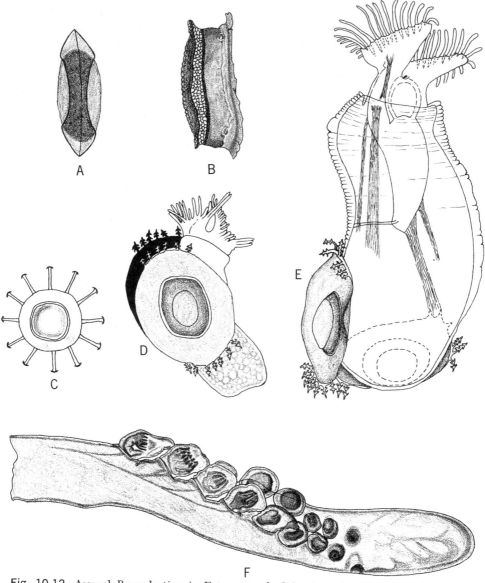

Fig. 10.12. Asexual Reproduction in Ectoprocts. **A.** Side view of a *Plumatella* floatoblast. **B.** Side view of a *Plumatella* sessoblast. **C.** Top view of a *Cristatella* statoblast. **D-E.** Two stages in the germination of a statoblast of *Lophopodella*. **F.** Spiral budding pattern on the stolon of *Bowerbankia*. (A-B, D-E, after Rogick. F, after Brien and Huysmans.)

perhaps of an excretory nature, which give the brown body its color. A bud from the cystid wall develops into a new polypide. In some species the brown body remains in the metacoel; sometimes several are present, attesting to several cycles of degeneration and regeneration. In others, the brown body is surrounded by the forming gut and is eventually discharged through the anus. Senility and physiological depression resulting from poor environmental conditions cause degeneration of the polypide, but some believe that it also is caused by accumulation of excretory products. Whatever causes degeneration, brown body formation is an unusual kind of storage excretion, for waste materials appear to be incorporated into a body part that will eventually be shed or be retained in an inert condition.

PHYLACTOLAEMATE ASEXUAL REPRODUCTION

Fresh-water ectoprocts reproduce asexually during colony formation, but also reproduce asexually by means of statoblasts. Buds appear on the funiculus. They grow and differentiate into a dark, resistant covering and a mass of yolky, undifferentiated, germinal cells. Three kinds of statoblasts are recognized, floatoblasts with air-filled cells making up the capsule wall, sessoblasts, attached to the zoecium wall by cement, and spinoblasts with spiny projections (Fig. 10.2A-C). Statoblast form is characteristic of the species and is used in species identification. Statoblasts are liberated when polypides degenerate. They are resistant and protect the species during the winter or when low water levels make conditions unfavorable. They are also important in the dissemination of the species. Sexually produced larvae do not swim far, and in any case cannot reach another pond or lake. Statoblasts can be carried by air or water currents for long distances, can pass unharmed through the digestive tract of some aquatic animals, and can cling to the surface of animals, thus spreading the species widely.

The internal cells, rich in stored food, begin to protrude from the capsule walls of germinating statoblasts (Fig. 10.12D,E). The young polypide develops within the capsule walls, using the stored food materials and gradually emerging as it grows. The primary zooid produces new zooids by budding to establish a new colony.

Phylum Brachiopoda—The Lamp Shells

At the beginning of the Cambrian era, about 600,000,000 years ago, brachiopods were abundant and the two main divisions of the phylum were already established. Their clam-like shells make good fossils and have kept paleontologists busy; some 30,000 extinct species have been described. They are not abundant today; only about 200 species are still alive. These are sporadically distributed around the world, as last members of once widespread animal groups tend to be. A great deal more is known about brachiopod shells than about the animals that occupy them.

Like other lophophorates, brachiopods lead quiet lives. Sessile and slow-moving animals often develop a protective covering. Each lophophorate group has developed a protective sheathing along independent lines: phoronids secrete tubes, ectoprocts form a zoecial case, and brachiopods secrete a clam-like shell. Brachiopod shells are only superficially like clam shells, but until about a hundred years ago, they were classified as molluscs. The symmetry of brachiopod and clam shells differs. The midsagittal line passes between the two parts, or valves, of a clam shell, and bisects the two valves of brachiopod shells (Fig. 10.13A,B).

Brachiopods resemble other lophophorates in possessing the following:

1. A lophophore, constructed along lines similar to other lophophorates.
2. A coelom divided into indistinct pro-

tocoel, mesocoel, and metacoel compartments.

3. Simple gonads formed from peritoneal cells.

They also have unique characteristics, including:

1. A bivalved shell secreted by two folds of the body wall known as the mantle.

2. Attachment to the substrate by a pedicel.

3. One or two pairs of metanephridia.

4. An open circulatory system with a pulsating dorsal vesicle.

Brachiopods are divided into two classes, Articulata and Inarticulata. Inarticulates have a long posterior pedicel, and the hingeless valves are held together by muscles only. They burrow in sand or mud flats and pull the body out of danger by contracting the pedicel (Fig. 10.13H). Other inarticulates are permanently attached to objects by the ventral valve, like oysters. Interlocking processes form a hinge in articulate shells. The pedicel passes through a notch in the valves at the hinge line, or through an opening in the ventral (pedicel) valve. The dorsal (brachial) valve is usually smaller and the ventral valve curves up as a beak. When

this tendency is advanced, the hinge is displaced toward the anterior edge, the pedicel is directed dorsally, and the animal attaches upside down (Fig. 10.13D).

CLASSIFICATION

Brachiopod classification is at present unsatisfactory. The two classes are distinct, but the subdivisions of the predominantly extinct class Articulata are controversial.

Class Inarticulata. Shell held together by muscles only; lophophore without a skeletal support; digestive tract complete, with anus.

Order Atremata. With the pedicel attached to the ventral valve, but both valves modified to permit its passage; shell mineral is calcium phosphate. Example: *Lingula* (Fig. 10.13H).

Order Neotremata. Without a pedicel, or with pedicel emerging from a notch or foramen in the ventral valve; some attached directly to objects by the ventral valve; shell minerals are calcium carbonate or calcium phosphate. Example: *Crania* (Fig. 10.13G).

Class Articulata. Valves hinged by interlocking processes; pedicel emerging

Table 10.2. Summary of brachiopod traits

	ATREMATA	NEOTREMATA	ARTICULATA
Pedicel	attached to ventral valve; very long	none, or passing through notch in ventral valve	passing through ventral valve foramen
Hinge	muscles only	muscles only	hinge of interlocking teeth and sockets
Lophophore	without a skeleton, spirolophous	without a skeleton, spirobolous, or schizolophous	with a skeletal support, spirolophous, ptycholophous, schizolophous, trocholophous, and plectolophous
Anus	present	present	absent
Shell	elongate, thin valves; chitin and calcium phosphate	more or less circular; sometimes attached by the ventral valve; chitin, calcium phosphate and calcium carbonate	usually circular to broad; calcium carbonate
Mantle	not reversed during development	not reversed during development	reversed during development

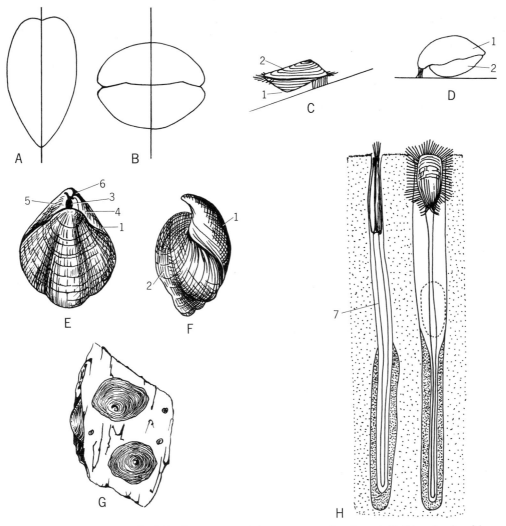

Fig. 10.13. Brachiopods. **A-B.** Comparison of the symmetry of a clam shell **(A)** and a brachiopod shell **(B)**. The plane of symmetry passes between the valves of a clam, and bisects the valves of a brachiopod. **C-D.** Comparison of the positions assumed by neotremate inarticulates and articulates. The pedicel passes through a notch in the neotremate pedicel valve; there is no calcareous hinge arrangement, and muscles hold the valves together. It attaches with the pedicel valve down and the brachial valve up. The articulate valves, however, meet in a specialized hinge, and the pedicel valve extends beyond the hinge. It attaches with the pedicel valve up and the brachial valve down. **E-F.** Dorsal and side views of the shell of *Hemithrys psittacea*, an articulate. Note the prolonged pedicel valve and the opening for the pedicel. **G.** Three *Crania* attached to a rock. They have no pedicel, but like other neotremate inarticulates attach with the pedicel valve downwards, using calcareous secretions. **H.** Two views of the atremate inarticulate, *Lingula*, imbedded in the mud. The contractile pedicel secretes mucus; when contracted it pulls the body down into position indicated by the dotted outline on the right. (C-D, based on Morse. E-F, after Blochmann. G, after Shipley. H, after François.) 1, pedicel valve; 2, brachial valve; 3, foramen; 4, palintrope; 5, deltidial plate; 6, beak; 7, pedicel.

through ventral valve; shell mineral, calcium carbonate; lophophore with skeletal support; digestive tract incomplete; without anus. Example: *Hemithyris* (Fig. 10.13E,F).

ANATOMY AND PHYSIOLOGY

A forbidding vocabulary, useful primarily to paleontologists, has grown up about the details of shell structure. It will be avoided here. The shell is tightly adherent to the two mantle folds, extensions of the body wall. Shell and mantle are intimately associated; tubular papillae from the mantle penetrate the shell, reaching the uppermost horny layer, the periostracum (Fig. 10.14B). Alternating layers of chitin and phosphate occur in the *Lingula* shell. The calcareous shell of most species has an outer, laminated and an inner, prismatic layer of carbonates. The shell begins as a small plate, the protegulum. As additional shell is laid down, the protegulum lies at the growth center of the shell (apex). Additional material cannot be added to the periostracum or outer calcareous layer, but the inner prismatic layer is thickened throughout the life of the animal.

Hinge teeth on the ventral valve of articulate shells fit into dental sockets on the dorsal valve. The dorsal or brachial valve extends out as a cardinal process between the lateral dental sockets. The hinge teeth serve as rocking surfaces when the shell opens or closes (Fig. 10.14A). Adductor muscles attached to dorsal and ventral valves close the shell, and diductor muscles attached to the ventral valve and the cardinal process of the dorsal valve open the shell. Diductor muscles work at a mechanical disadvantage and are larger than adductors. The shell cannot be opened widely, but sufficient space to permit food-laden water to enter and leave is provided. Additional muscles, known as adjustors, pass from the ventral valve to the pedicel (Figs. 10.14 C-E). They tilt the shell with respect to the pedicel. In-

articulates can make more complex shell movements and have correspondingly more complex muscle arrangements.

The inner surface of the dorsal valve is often sculptured to accommodate the lophophore, and in articulates bears the brachidium or lophophore skeleton, often of complex form (Fig. 10.15A-D).

The relationship of the shell and body is explained by development. The young animal has an anterior lobe, from which most of the body will arise, and a mantle fold that projects posteriorly (Fig. 10.16A-C). The mantle folds bend forward, enclosing the head in a mantle cavity. When the shell is completely formed, the anterior two-thirds encloses the mantle cavity, bounded by the mantle folds attached to its inner surface. The main mass of the body occupies only the posterior third of the space between the valves, and the pedicel emerges from the posterior end at the hinge. The trunk metacoel extends into the mantle, but the upper and lower layers of the mantle unite as it matures, leaving a number of tubular coelomic channels, known as mantle canals. The edge of the mantle bears prominent, stiff setae, supposedly protective and sensory in function.

The simplest brachiopod lophophores, are discoid. The number of tentacles is increased by lobulation of the lophophore, as indicated in Fig. 10.16D-H. Additional space is obtained by adding lobes or by extending the lateral arms of the lophophore. The plectolophous type, with two simple, lateral arms, and a median arm, is most common in modern articulates, and the spirolophous type, without a median arm but with spirally coiled lateral arms, is seen in modern inarticulates. A brachial fold extends over the mouth and is thought to represent a modified epistome; in inarticulates it contains a coelom, presumably a protocoel, open to the lophophore mesocoel. The articulate brachial fold is solid. Details of mesocoel construction vary with the lophophore type and need

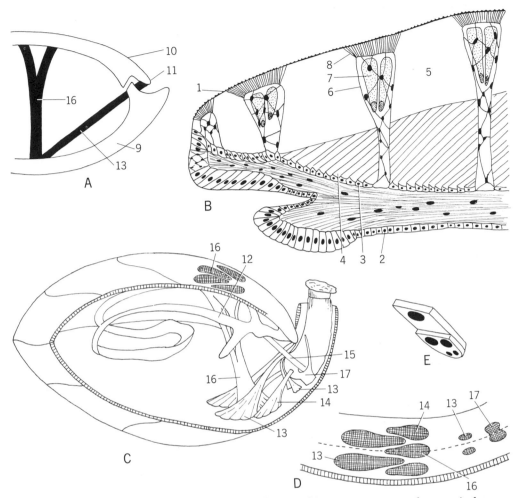

Fig. 10.14. Structure of Brachiopod Shells. **A.** The hinge arrangement of an articulate brachiopod. The rocking surface of the hinge leads to the opening of the valves when the diductor muscle is contracted, and the closing of the valve when the adductors are contracted. **B.** Scheme of a longitudinal section through the mantle and valve of an articulate brachiopod. Note the papillae which extend into the calcareous and fibrous parts of the shell, conferring a characteristic porous texture. **C-E.** The muscles and muscle scars of a modern articulate, *Magellania*. The muscle scars of the brachial valve are shown in C; of the pedicel valve in D, and of the cardinal process in E. (B, after Williams. C-E, after Hancock.) *Histology:* **1**, periostracum; **2**, inner epidermis of mantle; **3**, outer epidermis of mantle; **4**, prismatic layer of valve; **5**, fibrous calcareous layer of shell; **6**, mantle papilla; **7**, secretory cell of papilla; **8**, brush connecting papilla and periostracum. *Shell and muscle:* **9**, pedicel valve; **10**, brachial valve; **11**, cardinal process; **12**, calcareous loops supporting the lophophore; **13**, diductor muscle, which opens shell; **14**, ventral adjustor muscle, which moves the shell with respect to the pedicel; **15**, dorsal adjustor muscle; **16**, adductor muscle, which closes the shell; **17**, protractor muscle, which moves the pedicel.

341

not be discussed here. As in other lophophorates, the tentacles contain extensions of the mesocoel.

The brachiopod lophophore captures food like other lophophores. The shell valves are held apart during feeding. Lateral tracts of cilia produce lateral intake currents and a median exhaust current (Fig. 10.17A). The tentacles are held high and large particles drop to the mantle, to be ejected by mantle cilia or the sudden clapping of the valves. A brachial groove at the base of the tentacles collects the food particles brought to it by frontal cilia on the tentacles. The brachial groove cilia convey the food particles, trapped in

mucus, to the mouth (Fig. 10.17B). The brachial fold projects over the mouth, perhaps helping to direct traffic inward.

Food passes into the dorsally arched esophagus and is pushed by peristalsis to the dilated stomach (Fig. 10.18). Conspicuous paired diverticula arise from the stomach wall. They are called digestive glands or the liver, but nothing of importance is known of their function. They are probably sites of intracellular digestion. Articulates have a narrow, blind intestine, but the inarticulate intestine curves or loops in the metacoel and ends in the anus.

There is no evidence that respiratory deficiencies limit brachiopod size. Very large species once existed; shells over a foot in diameter have been recovered, and some modern species are considerably more bulky than the cylindrical, elongated pseudocoelomates. Evidently a solution to the problem of internal respiratory transport has been found, but it is not well understood. A respiratory pigment known as haemerythrin occurs in coelomic fluid cells. It does not take up oxygen as readily as haemoglobin, but gives it up very readily, and is no doubt involved in respiratory transport. The movement of the fluid containing the respiratory pigment is an important factor, and brachiopods offer some interesting physiological problems in this area.

Brachiopods have two circulating body fluids, blood and coelomic fluid. Blood circulates in an open circulatory system. The mesocoel and metacoel are only partially separated by a diaphragm at the level of the esophagus. Branches of the mesocoel extend into the tentacles, and of the metacoel extend into the mantle. Coelomic fluid flows throughout the coelomic system.

Peritoneal cilia or flagella circulate the coelomic fluid. The fluid moves rapidly in the narrow passageways of the mantle and tentacles, and was once thought to be blood.

The main blood vessel is middorsal, and

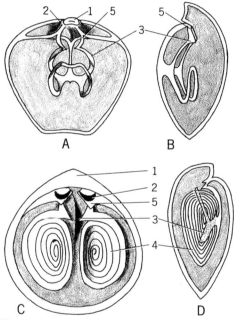

Fig. 10.15. Brachiopod Shell Structure. A, B. Top and side views of the brachial valve of *Magellania*, showing the calcareous support for the lophophore. C. Interior view of the brachial valve of *Atrypa*, with a spiraled brachial support (brachidium). D, Side view of the brachial valve of *Athyris*, showing a spiraled brachidium. (A, B, and D, after Davidson. C, after Shrock and Twenhofel.) 1, cardinal process; 2, dental socket; 3, jugal process; 4, spiralium; 5, crura.

contains a pulsating vesicle. The middorsal vessel divides into two anterior branches, each communicating with an extensive sinus around the gut and continuing to the lophophore, where branches reach each tentacle. The middorsal vessel bifurcates posteriorly, forming dorsal and ventral mantle vessels, which branch extensively in the mantle. The ventral mantle vessel also communicates with sinuses in the nephridia and gonad. The pulsating vesicle beats slowly and circulation is sluggish. Nothing is known of details of circulation; presumably the blood ebbs and flows. The difference between blood and coelomic fluid is probably more academic than real, for they communicate extensively through tissue spaces, and blood and coelomic fluid must exchange components everywhere.

The lophophoral and mantle cilia ventilate a large exposed surface. Within the tentacles and mantle the coelomic fluid circulates rapidly and blood moves more sluggishly. At least the coelomic fluid contains haemerythrin; presumably the blood does also. The two body fluids reach all other organs, providing a system that can effectively provide for respiratory transport.

The nephridia lie in the metacoel. The ruffled, flagellated nephrostomes are supported by the lateral mesenteries that support the gut. The tubular part of the nephridium narrows as it approaches the nephridiopore, which opens into the mantle cavity. Finger-like processes occur on the nephridia of *Terebratulina caputser-*

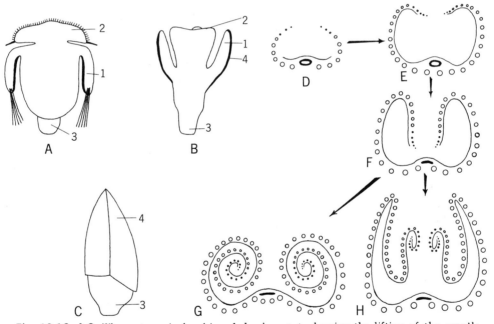

Fig. 10.16. A-C. Three stages in brachiopod development, showing the lifting of the mantle lobes to enclose the anterior lobe of the larva, which then develops into the greater part of the body. D-H. Scheme of lophophore evolution in brachiopods. Tentacles are shown as circles, with decreasing age indicated by decreasing size. The primitive type (D) gains tentacles by becoming bilobed (trocholophous) as shown at E. Further changes in this direction produce the schizolophous type (F), with two recurved arms. From this type, either the highly spiraled spirolophous type (G) or the horseshoe-shaped and spiraled plectolophous type (H) may develop. (A, after Shipley. B-C, after Kowalevsky. D-H, after de Beauchamp, in Grassé.) 1, mantle fold; 2, anterior lobe of larva; 3, pedicel; 4, developing valves.

pentis (cf. Fig. 10.19); their function is unknown. Particulate material is taken up by coelomic phagocytes and by peritoneal cells that detach and disintegrate. Streams of particles move to the nephridium and are taken up by the epithelial lining, eventually to be discharged, suspended in mucous strands, from the nephridiopore. Particles of nitrogenous waste may be expelled in this way, but nothing is known of the release of soluble wastes.

The sensory cells and nervous system are imperfectly described. The inarticulate nervous system appears to be in the epidermis and the articulate nervous system below the epidermis. A circumenteric ring connects the larger subenteric and smaller supraenteric ganglia. Nerves to the lophophore issue from the supraenteric gan-

glion, and nerves to the mantle, pedicel, and shell muscles arise from the subenteric ganglion. Nothing is known of nerve physiology.

Gametes arise from the peritoneum, forming indistinct and sometimes extensive gonadal masses. Four pairs of gonads are usually present. Gametes usually depart through the nephridia and develop in the sea, but a few species brood young in the mantle cavity, nephridia, or the lophophore arms.

DEVELOPMENT

Embryonic development has been followed in articulates and inarticulates. Early development involves holoblastic, radial cleavage, somewhat modified in the articulates, *Terebratulina* and *Terebratella*. A coeloblastula forms, which usually gastrulates by invagination. Accounts of mesoderm and coelom formation do not agree; apparently there are species differences. *Lingula* mesoderm arises as two masses from the sides of the archenteron and later hollows out to form two coelomic pouches. *Lingula* is evidently schizocoelous. In other brachiopods, the mesoderm arises as lateral, anterior, or posterior pouches of the archenteron, and the coelom is evidently enterocoelous. The blastopore closes, and the mouth arises from the anterior end of the resulting groove, as is typical in protostomes. More comparative work is needed in this area.

Later development of inarticulates and articulates differs markedly. In inarticulates, a mantle fold differentiates from the body mass, divides into dorsal and ventral lobes, and partly encloses the body (Fig. 10.20A). The body develops lobulations for the future lophophore, and as the larval tentacles form, an epistome that grows into the brachial fold appears. The larval tentacles never surround the mouth, for a median tentacle appears above the mouth, and new tentacles form at this point, gradually moving laterally as new

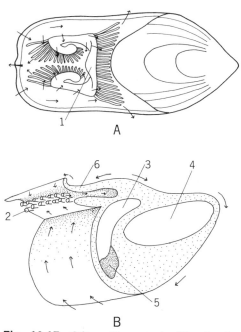

Fig. 10.17. Ciliary Currents in *Lingula*. **A.** Ciliary currents in the mantle cavity, as seen in ventral view. **B.** Ciliary currents over one arm of the *Lingula* lophophore. (After Chuang.) **1,** mouth; **2,** cut end of tentacle; **3,** small arm canal; **4,** large arm canal; **5,** brachial muscle; **6,** brachial fold.

ones form. The pedicel appears as a posterior bud when the mantle lobes begin to form a shell, resulting in the typical bivalved, free-swimming larva.

Articulate embryos develop three body regions: anterior, middle, and posterior. The posterior lobe becomes the pedicel, the anterior lobe the lophophore and most of the body. The mantle lobe grows posteriorly, at first as a ring but later bifurcating and bending forward to enclose the body, as mentioned earlier (Figs. 10.16A-C).

Lophophorate Relationships

The lophophorate phyla are linked by the lophophore, the somewhat consistent division of the coelom into compartments, and the simple reproductive system without gonoducts. It would not be difficult to visualize convergence producing several kinds of tentacular crowns as feeding devices, but that independently developed lophophores should consistently contain the same part of a divided coelom seems highly improbable. The evidence, therefore, supports the idea that the lophopho-

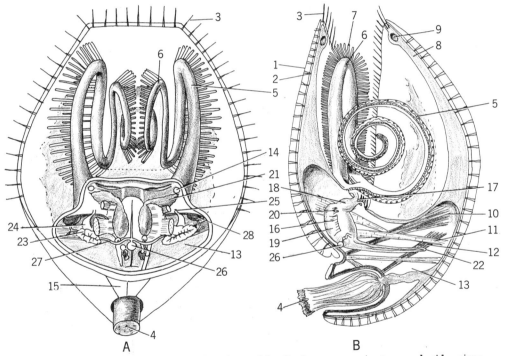

Fig. 10.18. Brachiopod anatomy, based on *Magellania*, as seen in top and side views. (After Delage and Hérouard, from de Beauchamp, in Grassé.) *External features:* 1, shell; 2, mantle papilla; 3, setae; 4, peduncle; 5, lateral arm of lophophore; 6, median arm of lophophore, with tentacles removed, in side view; 7, tentacle; 8, mantle; 9, mantle sinus. *Muscles:* 10, diductor muscle; 11, adductor muscle; 12, adjustor muscle. *Coelom:* 13, metacoel; 14, aperture of lophophore coelom; 15, dorsal mesentery; 16, gastroparietal ligament. *Digestive tract:* 17, mouth; 18, esophagus; 19, stomach; 20, duct of digestive gland; 21, digestive gland; 22, intestine. *Excretory system:* 23, nephrostome; 24, nephridium; 25, nephridiopore. *Circulatory system:* 26, heart; 27, mental vessel. *Reproductive system:* 28, gonad.

rates are related. The relationship is undoubtedly extremely ancient, and the three groups have diverged markedly since their appearance. Embryonic development has been modified, largely in connection with shell formation in brachiopods and the cystid-polypide construction of ectoprocts. Serious disturbances of ordinary mesoderm and coelom formation have occurred, and the scant available observations suggest that lophophorates have been quite experimental about development.

Phoronids appear to be the most primitive lophophorates; their form suggests that they originated from burrowing, worm-like ancestral stocks. Whatever other traits ancestral stocks may have had they were undoubtedly protostomes, for the least modified lophophorate larvae resemble a trochophore. Once the lophophore became really effective it dominated further evolutionary development. Food capture became a sedentary occupation, and adaptation fitted lophophorates to a quiet life, following avenues seen elsewhere in the animal kingdom. External protection is important if one cannot flee, and the three basic lophophorate lines are related to three different schemes for protection—producing the tubiculous phoronids, the encased ectoprocts, and the shelled brachiopods.

As the animal's life came to be dominated by the activity of extending the lophophore for feeding and pulling it back for protection, the head, a product of active movement, tended to decline and the neurosensory system, as in other animals, fitted itself to the body contour and to the range of activities necessary and profitable for the organism to pursue.

An acephalized, worm-like, relatively inactive stock of this kind could have led off toward tubiculous, enterocoelous animals, like the hemichordates. Lophophorate ancestors must have been coelomate when the lophophore appeared, for the constancy with which the coelom extends into the lophophoral ridge and tentacles could not easily be explained otherwise. If tendencies toward experimentation in coelom formation and division of the coelom into compartments were characteristic of the ancestral stocks as of modern lophophorates, they might well have given rise to an enterocoelous animal stem. There are serious difficulties in homologizing between the unpaired protocoel, mesocoel, and metacoel of lophophorates and the paired coelomic divisions in enterocoels. The brain, for example, is typically in the protocoel region in enterocoelous animals

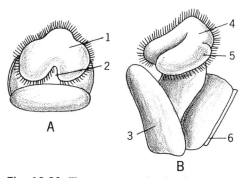

Fig. 10.20. Two stages in the development of an inarticulate, *Lingula*. (After Yatsu.) In A, the development of the mantle lobes is shown. In B, the developing body extends upward from the mantle lobes, and the developing median tentacle and lophophore lobes are evident. 1, anterior lobe; 2, mantle lobe; 3, stomodaeum; 4, median tentacle; 5, lophophore lobe; 6, shell.

Fig. 10.19. The Nephridia of *Terebratulina retusa*. (After Heller.) 1, nephridiopore; 2, glands; 3, nephrostome.

and in the mesocoel region in lophophorates. It is probably unimportant for the coelomic compartments of lophophorates and enterocoelous animals to correspond in detail; the tendency of an animal stem to form non-metameric coelomic compartments is in itself a significant link with enterocoels. Probably the ancestral lophophorates and enterocoels were very similar and for a short time may have been identical.

References

Allan, R. 1940. A revision of the classification of the terebratelloid brachiopods. *Rec. Canterbury Mus. N. Z.* 4.

Allman, J. 1856. A *monograph of the freshwater Polyzoa.* Ray Soc., London.

Brooks, W., and R. Cowles. 1905. *Phoronis architecta*: its life history, anatomy and breeding habits. *Mem. Nat. Acad. Sci.* 10.

Brown, C. J. D. 1933. A limnological study of certain fresh-water Polyzoa with special reference to their statoblasts. *Trans. Am. Micr. Soc.* 52: 271.

Chapman, G. 1958. The hydraulic skeleton in the invertebrates. *Biol. Rev.* 33: 338. (G)

Chuang, S. 1956. The ciliary feeding mechanisms of *Lingula. Proc. Zool. Soc. London* 127.

Clarke, F. W., and W. C. Wheeler. 1922. The inorganic constituents of marine invertebrates. *U.S. Geol. Surv., Prof. Pap.* 124.

Cori, C. Die Nephridien von *Cristatella. Ztschr. wiss. Zool.* 55: 626.

———. 1941. Bryozoa. In W. Kukenthal and T. Krumbach (eds.), *Handbuch der Zoologie*, Vol. 3, Pt. 2, lf. 15–16. W. de Gruyter, Berlin.

Hurrell, H. 1927. Ecology of fresh-water Polyzoa in East Anglia. *Jour. Roy. Micr. Soc.* 47.

Ikeda, I. 1901. Development, structure and metamorphosis of *Actinotrocha. Jour. Coll. Sci. Tokyo U.* 13.

Lynch, W. E. 1949. Acceleration and retardation of the onset of metamorphosis in *Bugula. Jour. Exp. Zool.* 111: 127.

———. 1956. Synergism and antagonism in the induction of metamorphosis of *Bugula* larvae. *Biol. Bull.* 109: 82.

Maturo, F. 1957. Bryozoa of Beaufort, North Carolina. *Jour. Elisha Mitchell Scient. Sci.* 73: 11. (F)

McDougall, K. 1943. Sessile marine invertebrates at Beaufort, North Carolina. *Ecol. Monogr.* 13.

Orton, J. 1914. On ciliary mechanisms in brachiopods, annilids, and molluscs. *Jour. Mar. Biol. Assoc.* 10: 283.

Rogick, M. 1935. Bryozoa of Lake Erie. *Trans. Am. Micr. Soc.* 34: 245. (F)

———. 1935a. Development of *Lophopodella carteri. Ohio Jour. Sci.* 35: 457.

———. 1937. The finer anatomy of *Lophopodella carteri. var. typica. Trans. Am. Micr. Soc.* 56: 367.

———. 1956. Bryozoa of the U.S. Navy Antarctic Expedition. *Proc. U.S. Nat. Mus.* 105: 221.

———, and H. Van der Schalie. 1950. Michigan Bryozoa. *Ohio Jour. Sci.* 50: 136. (F)

Silén, L. 1944. Division and movements of the alimentary canal of Bryozoa. *Ark. Zool.* 35A: 1.

Termier, H., and G. Termier. 1949. Sur la classification des brachiopodes. *Bull. Soc. His. Nat. Afr. d. Nord.* 40: 51.

Yatsu, N. 1902. Development of *Lingula. Jour. Coll. Sci. Tokyo U.* 17: 112.

———. 1902. On the habits of Japanese *Lingula. Annot. Zool. Jap.* 4: 61.

11

The Echinoderms

Nothing more certainly symbolizes the sea than starfish, sea urchins, and sand dollars. There is good reason for this, for all echinoderms have one deficiency; they cannot adequately control the water content of their bodies, and so have never been able to invade fresh-water habitats.

Echinoderms though exclusively marine are very successful. They are found at all depths and in all climates. They have been with us for a long time, for they were well established at the start of the Cambrian, perhaps 600,000,000 years ago, and are still one of the more important phyla of animals. About 6000 modern species and over 20,000 fossil species have been described.

Many animal phyla can be assembled in superphyla with other, somewhat similar phyla. This is not true of echinoderms. No other animals resemble them closely. Like sponges, they have unique characteristics that set them apart from other animal groups. Unlike sponges, however, they diverged from the major lines of animal ancestry after becoming fairly highly organized. The deuterostome stem, from which they branched, is probably the one that also produced the vertebrates.

The most outstanding feature of echinoderms is their radial symmetry, impressed as an afterthought, as it were, on a primitive bilateral symmetry. No other animals begin life as bilaterally symmetrical creatures and metamorphose into radial forms. They are predominantly pentamerous, as the typical five arms of a starfish or five petals on the surface of a sand dollar testify. Only a few fossil forms, apparently older than radial symmetry, show no evidence of radial tendencies. Several modern groups of echinoderms, however, have taken up a free-moving life and show tendencies to replace the ancestral, secondary radial symmetry with a tertiary bilateral symmetry.

Aside from their unique symmetry, echinoderms have the following outstanding characteristics:

1. They are unsegmented, enterocoelous animals, with an endomesoderm derived from the archenteron.

2. They have an endoskeleton of calcareous ossicles, covered by an epidermis, usually ciliated.

3. The spacious coelom is complexly partitioned, and during development gives rise to haemal and ambulacral systems.

348

4. They have a unique hydraulic system, the ambulacral or water-vascular system, derived from the coelom and equipped with tube feet or podia used for respiration, movement, and sensory reception.

5. They are uncephalized; and have an oral-aboral axis.

6. The body surface is usually composed of five fields containing podia (ambulacra) alternating with five fields without podia (interambulacra).

7. They usually have a complete digestive tract, but no anus or intestine occurs in Ophiuroidea.

8. They have a simple circulatory or haemal system, which runs through a system of coelomic sinuses.

9. They have a diffuse, uncentralized nervous system, typically composed of three nerve rings around the digestive tube and radiating peripheral nerves.

10. They have no excretory organs, and completely independent types of respiratory adaptations occur in different groups.

11. They are typically dioecious and have simple reproductive organs with simple gonoducts.

12. Development primitively involves holoblastic, radial cleavage and a series of ciliated larval stages which metamorphose to become radially symmetrical.

Some of these traits are chordate-like: the enterocoelous coelom with mesoderm derived from the archenteron, and the mesodermal endoskeleton. Some of the traits are unique: the water-vascular system and the curious indecision about symmetry. Some traits may be considered more or less degenerate: the lack of cephalization and, sometimes, the lack of an anus or intestine. Other traits may be considered primitive: the poor development of the circulatory system and the absence of a definite respiratory system characteristic of the phylum as a whole. The odd hodge-podge of highly specialized, progressive, retrogressive, and primitive traits marks the echinoderms as one of the most interesting of all animal phyla from a theoretical point of view.

The five major types of modern echinoderms are generally familiar to people interested in biology; each represents a distinctive class of the phylum. Each is easily recognized by the normal orientation of the body, and by the distribution of the alternating ambulacral fields containing the podia of the water-vascular system, and interambulacra, fields without podia. The mouth lies at the center of the oral surface and the anus is usually placed at the opposite surface; typical echinoderms have an oral-aboral axis like cnidarians. Echinoids (sea urchins, sand dollars, and heart urchins) normally lie with the mouth down, and have the ambulacra and interambulacra on the sides of the body. Holothurians (sea cucumbers) also have the ambulacra and interambulacra on the general body surface, but usually lie on their side, with the oral-aboral axis parallel to the substrate (Fig. 11.1). In all other echinoderms, the ambulacra extend along arms or rays, which attach to a central, discoid body mass. Crinoids (sea lilies, feather stars) are attached at the aboral surface by a stalk, and so are normally oriented with the mouth up. Asteroids (starfish) normally lie with the mouth down, and have open ambulacra extending along the rays. Ophiuroids (brittle stars) also lie with the mouth down, but have narrow, flexible rays or arms, with the ambulacra enclosed and so not visible from without.

Although predominantly radial, all echinoderms retain vestiges of bilaterality. The ambulacral system opens to the exterior through a water pore or a madreporite, and even if the anus and mouth are centered on opposite ends, the madreporite cannot also be centered. It is not uncommon for the mouth or anus to be eccentric also. To describe this bilaterality, Carpenter (1884) devised a method of designating the radii and interradii which is generally applicable to echinoderms.

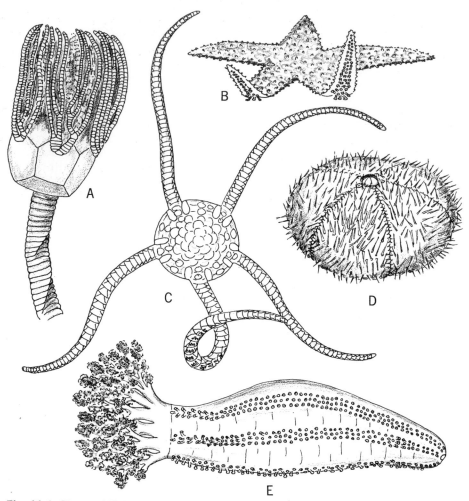

Fig. 11.1. Types of Echinoderms. Echinoderms are generally characterized by a pentamerous radial symmetry and have five ambulacra from which the podia or tube feet arise. The position of the ambulacra, the relative length of the oral-aboral axis, the presence or absence of arms, and the normal attitude of the body serve to distinguish the major echinoderm groups. Attached echinoderms (Pelmatozoa) are represented today only by the crinoids (A), some of which are attached only as juveniles and later move about freely. All, however, normally live with the oral surface upwards, and have arms on the oral surface of which the open ambulacra lie. The remaining four modern groups of echinoderms are unattached (Eleutherozoa). In two of these groups, arms extend from the flattened central disc of the body. Asteroids or starfish (B) normally live with the oral surface down, and have ambulacra located in grooves on the arms and central disc. The wide arms are not sharply set off from the central disc. Ophiuroids or brittle stars (C) also live with the oral surface downwards, but have narrow arms, sharply set off from the central disc, and internal ambulacra, wholly invisible from the outside. Arms are absent in two of the groups. The oral-aboral axis of the holothurians or sea cucumbers (E) is elongated, and they normally lie on one of the ambulacra, which course over the surface of the leathery body. The echinoids or urchins (D) are spherical to flattened, and normally lie with the oral surface down. The ambulacra run over the hard body surface, although they are often obscured by spines.

The entrance to the ambulacral system always lies on an interradius. A line drawn from the madreporite to the center of the opposite ray defines the plane of symmetry (Fig. 11.2). This ray is designated A, and the remaining rays are lettered clockwise, as seen in oral view. Interradii are always interambulacra; they are designated by the letters of the rays or ambulacra that enclose them: AB is the interradius between rays A and B. An eccentric anus usually lines up with the mouth and madreporite, conforming to Carpenter's scheme. If the animal is cut at right angles to the plane of symmetry, the body is divided into an anterior, three-rayed part, the trivium, and a posterior, two-rayed bivium. The trivium contains rays A, B, and E, and the bivium contains rays C and D. Sea cucumbers lie on radius A, so the trivium is ventral and the bivium dorsal. Starfish may move in any direction, so the bivium and trivium are insignificant unless one needs to specify a ray or interradius. Carpenter's system is very simple to use; one need only remember that the madreporite lies on the center of the bivium.

Classes of Echinoderms

The skeletal plates of echinoderms make good fossils, and we know more of their history than is generally true of animal phyla. Classification is complicated by extinct groups which cannot be ignored entirely because of their phylogenetic interest, but which are ordinarily seen only by paleontologists. The figures in this book will give some idea of what they were like. They are not discussed here, however, and those who wish to learn more about them should consult a book on invertebrate paleontology.

Subphylum Pelmatozoa. Predominantly extinct forms attached as juveniles or permanently, usually by an aboral stalk; both mouth and anus are on the upturned oral surface. They have a calcareous test or theca containing the internal organs; ambulacra serving as food grooves and usually extending out on body projections known as arms or rays; podia devoted primarily to food capture; and a predominant aboral nervous system.

Class Heterostelea. Extinct Pelmatozoa without radial symmetry, and typically without arms; apparently held horizontally by a stalk, at least partly composed of a double row of ossicles; theca flattened and non-porous; often with marginal plates. Cambrian to Lower Silurian. Example: *Dendrocystites* (Fig. 11.3B).

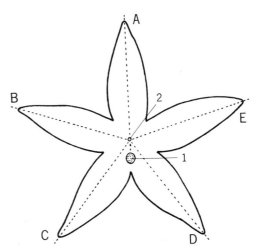

Fig. 11.2. Carpenter's System of Designating Radii and Interradii. In all echinoderms, the entrance to the ambulacral system is on an interradius. In starfish, it is marked by a madreporite (1). The line running from the opposite radius through the madreporite divides the organism into bilateral halves. Carpenter designated this radius A. The remaining radii are lettered B, C, D, and E, counting clockwise from A with the oral surface up, or counterclockwise when viewed from the aboral surface. The mouth or anus (2) may be centered or eccentric, but in the majority of echinoderms falls on the line from the entrance to the ambulacral system and radius A. Interradii are termed AE, AB, or by whatever radii bound them. In starfish, the two rays C and D contain the interradius on which the madreporite lies and constitute the bivium. Rays A, B, and E make up the trivium.

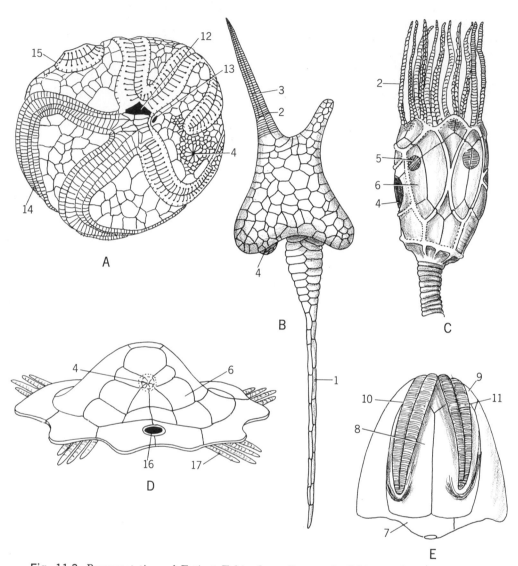

Fig. 11.3. Representatives of Extinct Echinoderm Groups. A. *Edrioaster bigsbyi*, a member of the Edrioasteroidea. B. *Dendrocystites scotica*, an example of the Heterostelea. C. *Cheirocrinus walcotti*, a member of the Cystidea. D. *Volchovia*, restored, a member of the Ophiocistoidea. E. *Pentremites*, an example of the Blastoidea, with the brachioles removed. (A, B, after Bather. C, after Jaeckel, from Cuénot, in Grassé. D, after Haecker. E, after Hyman.) 1, stem plates; 2, brachiole; 3, food groove; 4, anus; 5, rhomb; 6, thecal plate; 7, basal plate; 8, radial plate; 9, deltoid plate; 10, ambulacrum; 11, side plates with grooves leading to the brachioles (not shown); 12, mouth; 13, hydropore; 14, cover plates for ambulacra; 15, floor plates of ambulacra; 16, gonopore and hydropore?; 17, podia.

Class Cystidea. Somewhat globose, extinct Pelmatozoa, usually without pentamerous symmetry, attached directly or by an aboral, hollow stalk; theca of rigid plates, with all or some pierced by canals, often in fields called rhombs; primitively with three ambulacra, becoming five by division of the two laterals; ambulacra extend out on arm-like extensions, brachioles, which are not pinnate and lie on each side of the food groove. Middle Ordovician to Middle Devonian. Example: *Cheirocrinus* (Fig. 11.3C).

Class Blastoidea. Extinct, bud-shaped Pelmatozoa, attached directly or by an aboral stalk; theca pentamerous, with 13 primary plates in three cycles: three basals to which the stalk attaches; five radials, notched for the ambulacra and composing most of the theca; and five deltoids, forming the oral surface; with five ambulacra, floored by a lancet plate with lateral plates bearing sometimes pinnate brachioles; food groove extending on brachioles; characteristic respiratory structures, hydrospires, made of folds extending into the thecal cavity beside or below the ambulacra. Ordovician to Permian. Example: *Pentremites* (Fig. 11.3E).

Class Crinoidea. Sea lilies and feather stars. Strongly pentamerous, living and extinct Pelmatozoa, typically stalked but with most modern species leaving the stalk to become free-moving adults; body of five, often branched, pinnate or nonpinnate arms, arising from radial ossicles incorporated into the upper margin of the cup-shaped, aboral theca; theca of regularly arranged, pentamerous plates; oral surface covered by a membranous or skeletized tegmen; ambulacra extend along arms and pinnules; mouth and anus on oral surface. Ordovician to present.

Class Edrioasteroidea. Extinct, discoid Pelmatozoa, with a somewhat flexible theca of small, irregular plates; free, or sessile aborally, but without a stalk; five straight or curving ambulacra, typically formed of many small floor plates with pores between them for the emergence of podia, and covered by a double series of cover plates. Example: *Edrioaster* (Fig. 11.3A).

Subphylum Eleutherozoa. Free-moving, typically pentamerous echinoderms, without a stalk and normally lying on one side or with the mouth down, ambulacral system used primarily for locomotion; the anus usually centered on the aboral surface or missing; the oral nervous system predominant.

Class Holothuroidea. Sea cucumbers. Leathery, vermiform echinoderms, with the endoskeleton missing or reduced to scattered spicules or platelets; elongated along the oral-aboral axis and lying on one side; not uncommonly with dorsal and ventral sides differentiated, conferring a tertiary bilateral symmetry; podia usually emerge from five ambulacra on the sides of the body, but often somewhat diffuse; a circlet of tentacles derived from podia around the mouth; a single, non-radial gonad.

Class Echinoidea. Sea urchins, sand dollars, and heart urchins. Spherical to flattened Eleutherozoa without arms and enclosed in a solid test of compactly arranged skeletal plates; test of alternating ambulacral plates pierced by podial pores and imperforate interambulacral plates; mouth centered on oral surface or displaced toward anterior end, and anus centered on aboral surface or displaced toward posterior end; pentamerous symmetry, sometimes modified by tertiary bilateral symmetry; gonads pentamerous.

Class Asteroidea. Starfish. Flattened, flexible, star-shaped Eleutherozoa with an endoskeleton of ossicles separated by connective tissue; typically with five rays rising from a central disc, not sharply set off from base of rays, a prominent system of ambulacral grooves extending out on rays; ambulacral grooves floored with ambulacral plates, with pores for podia between them; mouth centered on oral surface and anus on aboral surface; gonads radially arranged.

Class Ophiuroidea. Brittle stars. Flattened, star-shaped Eleutherozoa, with long, slender, sometimes branched, flexible rays, sharply set off from central disc; arms with solid endoskeletal ossicles, formed by the fusion of ambulacral plates below the ambulacral groove; without an ambulacral groove, and podia much reduced; often with ten bursal sacs opening at the sides of the rays, used for respiration and discharge of gametes; digestive system incomplete, without anus; gonads arranged radially.

Class Ophiocistoidea. Extinct, discoid Eleutherozoa, free-moving on the oral surface; oral surface with central peristome and five ambulacra, alternating with interambulacra; ambulacra with a few pairs of pores for giant podia, covered by small scales; aboral part of theca not pentamerous, and with an anal pore. Example: *Volchovia* (Fig. 11.3C).

Crinoidea—Sea Lilies and Feather Stars

Crinoids are the only living remnant of the subphylum Pelmatozoa. At their peak in the Middle Mississippian period, about 350,000,000 years ago, they must have been amazingly abundant, for many sedentary rocks are very rich in crinoid fossils. Three of the four crinoid orders are extinct. About 5000 extinct species have been described, and it is easy to think of crinoids as a nearly extinct group. Actually, they are a flourishing animal group, with over 600 modern species. As many as 10,000 feather stars were taken in a single haul of the *Albatross*'s nets.

As all modern crinoids belong to the order Articulata, the classification of crinoids will not be discussed. Modern crinoids are stalked sea lilies, belonging to the suborders Isocrinida or Millericrinida, or are feather stars, belonging to the suborder Comatulida, stalked as juveniles,

but breaking free and moving about on the bottom. Isocrinid sea lilies have projections known as cirri on the stalks (Fig. 11.4A). Millericrinids have smooth stalks; cirri, when present, occur only at the attachment point (Fig. 11.4B). Feather stars are among the most beautifully colored animals. They creep about awkwardly on the aboral cirri or swim weakly but gracefully by undulating movements of the arms. Sea lilies are usually found in deep waters, and are pale or colorless. Feather stars from deep water are also pallid.

Crinoid stalks have the usual holdfast adaptions: root-like extensions, basal discs, or anchoring hooks. The stalk looks jointed, for it is supported by a series of hollow skeletal ossicles known as columnals. The longer nodal columnals have whorls of movable cirri attached to facets. Between them are many internodal columnals without cirri or facets. Cirri look jointed, too, for they are supported by a series of ossicles known as cirrals. Cirri were primitively located only at the base of the stalk, as in millericrinids, but have spread upwards, eventually reaching the aboral surface of the calyx. Comatulid cirri attach directly to facets on the aboral body surface; they vary greatly in form, depending on whether the feather star perches on rocks, creeps about on the bottom, or clambers about on algae.

The main part of the body is the corona. It is covered by an aboral calyx, formed of close-fitting skeletal ossicles, and a membranous, oral tegmen, often containing small skeletal ossicles. The arms arise at the junction of calyx and tegmen.

The primitive crinoid calyx was simple; it became complex and is secondarily simplified in modern species. The primitive calyx contained two cycles of plates: basals, to which the stalk attached, and radials, reaching to the arms. Later, a cycle of infrabasals intervened between basals and stalk, and other plates were

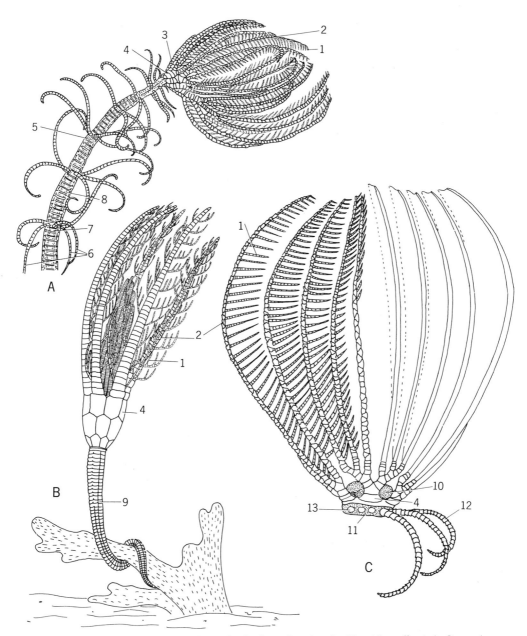

Fig. 11.4. Some Representative Crinoids. **A.** A modern isocrinoid, with stalk cirri, *Cenocrinus asteria*. **B.** A Devonian crinoid without stalk cirri, *Eifelocrinus dohmi*. **C.** A comatulid, *Neometra acanthaster*, with cirri attached to the calyx. (**A**, after Carpenter. **B**, after Haarmann, from Cuénot, in Grassé. **C**, after Clark.) **1**, pinnule; **2**, arm; **3**, lower brachial; **4**, calyx; **5**, stalk columnal; **6**, whorl of cirri; **7**, node; **8**, internode; **9**, prehensile stalk; **10**, tegmen; **11**, centrodorsal plate; **12**, cirral; **13**, facet for cirrus attachment.

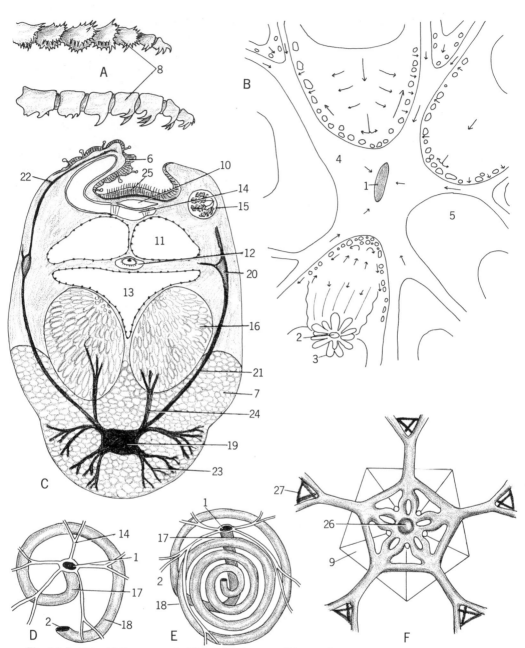

Fig. 11.5. Crinoid Structure. A. The ends of comatulid pinnules, showing pinnulars and spination. B. Ciliary currents on the oral surface of *Antedon*, a feather star. Note the cleansing currents and the food-collecting currents in the food grooves. C. Scheme of a crinoid arm in cross section. D. Scheme of endocyclic digestive system, characteristic of crinoids with a central mouth. E. Scheme of exocyclic digestive system, characteristic of crinoids with an eccentric mouth. F. Aboral nerve center of *Antedon*. (A, after Clark. B, after Gislén. C and F, composite. D and E, after Carpenter.) *External features:* 1, mouth; 2, anus; 3, anal papilla;

sometimes added. The infrabasals of modern crinoids are missing or greatly reduced, but the stalk is modified for attachment to them. When comatulids detach from the stalk, the upper columnal remains attached to the calyx, forming the large centrodorsal plate, and leaving the radials as the only major calyx plates.

Primitive crinoids had only five arms, but most modern species have more. The primary arms fork to form ten, or fork repeatedly to form as many as 200 arms. Diminutive branches (pinnules) attached to the arm margins give them a feathery appearance. The skeleton of arms and pinnules is jointed; brachial ossicles support the arms and pinnulars the pinnules. Details of skeletal form and articulation are characteristic of species. Those interested in skeletal minutiae can have a jolly time with crinoids, and a formidable vocabulary is available to describe the finer details. Unfortunately, considerably less is known of the soft parts.

Food Capture and Digestion. The crinoid ambulacral groove system corresponds functionally to a lophophore. Primitive Pelmatozoa had no arms, but ambulacral grooves converged at the mouth and were no doubt used for ciliary feeding, as in modern species. Arms are body extensions that increase the length of the crinoid trap line; the oral faces of the arms and most pinnules bear ambulacral grooves. A hungry feather star clings to a rock with its arms spread wide and its pinnules at attention. If food is added to the water, arms and pinnules thrash about and the three-branched podia at the margins of the ambulacral grooves push food particles into the groove. Diatoms, algae,

Protozoa, and small plankters are staple items of the diet. The epidermis is thin over most of the body surface, but is tall and heavily ciliated in the ambulacral grooves. Food is caught in mucus, and the mucous strings move along the ambulacral groove like conveyer belts (Fig. 11.5A). Interambulacral cilia on the tegmen surface cause cleansing currents that sweep toward the grooves, turn, and run peripherally just outside of the grooves. The system is so effective that parasitic polychaetes (myzostomes) live almost exclusively on crinoids, feeding on the moving mucous strands in the ambulacral grooves.

The digestive tract is simple, consisting of an esophagus, midgut or intestine, and hindgut or rectum. The whole gut lining is ciliated except for the rectum; food is propelled and stirred by ciliary currents. Circular muscles form a sphincter at the start of the midgut. The intestine may be somewhat dilated, may have several diverticula, or may be a simple tube externally indistinguishable from the esophagus (Fig. 11.5D,E). When the mouth is central the gut arches aborally in a single, clockwise turn. When the mouth is eccentric the intestine is longer, making four coils. An anal cone lifts the anus above the tegmen surface. Fecal balls, bound together with mucus, are ejected and drop away from the oral surface or fall when the animal moves.

Coelom. The crinoid coelom is reduced by webs of connective tissue, often containing calcareous spicules, and it is complexly compartmented. All coelomic compartments are lined with cuboid peritoneum, and all communicate to some degree.

4, ambulacral groove; 5, interradial area; 6, podium. *Skeleton:* 7, brachial ossicle; 8, pinnular ossicle; 9, radial plate. *Coelom:* 10, hyponeural sinus; 11, subtentacular coelomic canals; 12, genital canal containing genital cord; 13, aboral coelomic canal. *Ambulacral system:* 14, radial water canal; 15, saccule. *Muscle:* 16, flexor muscle. *Digestive system:* 17, esophagus; 18, intestine. *Nervous system:* 19, main brachial nerve; 20, lateral brachial nerve; 21, commissure between main and lateral brachial nerves; 22, podial nerve; 23, sensory nerves; 24, motor nerve; 25, radial nervous epidermis; 26, nerve cup; 27, decussation of fibers.

A space, the axial sinus, surrounds the esophagus, and opens aborally into the perivisceral coelom, which fills most of the corona. Each arm contains four intercommunicating but distinct coelomic spaces (Fig. 11.5C). The large aboral coelomic canal arises from the perivisceral coelom. Paired subtentacular coelomic canals branch from a common stem rising from the axial sinus. A tiny genital coelomic canal houses the genital cord, along which primordial germ cells migrate to the arms and pinnules, where gonads form. The coelomic canals branch with the arms, and continue into the pinnules. Here heavily ciliated pits of unknown function occur; similar pits may occur in the arm canal. The rest of the coelom is cut off as the chambered organ (Fig. 11.5F), embedded in the cup-shaped center of the aboral nervous system. Branches from its five separate compartments extend into the cirri, and in stalked crinoids extend as a five-chambered canal throughout the stalk, giving off branches to any cirri that may be present.

Coelomocytes occur everywhere in the coelom, and wander through the connective tissue of the corona. Some are phagocytic. They probably participate in food transport, waste elimination, and other processes, as in other echinoderms.

Haemal System and Axial Gland. The haemal system is the echinoderm circulatory system. It is generally associated with an axial gland, variously formed and developed in different echinoderm groups. Other coelomic derivatives are also important in internal transport, and the haemal system is generally poorly developed for organisms as large and complex as echinoderms.

Crinoid connective tissue contains many spaces and the haemal lacunae can be recognized only because they contain the coagulated haemal fluid. As a result, their distribution is imperfectly known. A plexus of haemal tubes occurs around the esophagus and another just below the teg-

men. The subtegminal plexus communicates with the genital tubes of the arms. At the aboral end of the periesophageal plexus, the lacunar walls thicken and merge with a "spongy organ," of unknown function. Many lacunae connect the spongy organ to the axial gland, a group of ductless glandular tubules. The function of this gland is unknown in crinoids. An endocrine function has been suggested, but there is no supporting evidence for this theory.

Water-Vascular System. The basic form and mechanics of the ambulacral or water-vascular system are similar in all echinoderms, despite differences in its relationship to the body wall. The system centers in a ring canal around the stomodaeum (Fig. 11.6). It gives off one or more calcareous stone canals, through which water may enter, and five radial canals, each serving as the center of an ambulacrum. They pass into the arms or on the body wall, depending on the body form. Lateral canals attach the podia to the radial canals. The podia of most echinoderms are provided with sac-like ampullae within the body, but crinoid podia have no ampules. When muscles of the internal canals or ampullae are contracted, water is forced into the podia. When muscles of the podia are contracted, water is forced back into the canals or ampullae.

The crinoid ring canal is hexagonal, running around the margin of the oral depression. Branches to the large oral podia arise from the ring canal, and radial canals to the arms branch with the ambulacral grooves. Crinoids have treble podia (Fig. 11.6B) containing sensory endings; they are used to push food into the ambulacral groove. Many small stone canals arise from the ring canal, hanging free in the coelom. Small ciliated funnels pierce the tegmen, drawing sea water into the coelom.

Neurosensory Apparatus. Little is known of crinoid sense organs. Crinoids react to touch and right themselves when overturned. Many are sensitive to light, choosing dark or moderately lighted areas. Comatulids are well-coordinated, creeping about with the cirri or clutching rocks or other objects. Some, like *Antedon*, can swim for short distances by undulating movements of the arms.

Echinoderms have three nervous systems: the oral, or ectoneural, system, the deep oral, or hyponeural, system, and the aboral, or entoneural, system. All communicate somewhat through an extensive subepidermal plexus. The oral system is located superficially on the oral surface, centering in a nerve sheath around the esophagus and giving rise to radial nerve bands in the epidermis of the ambulacral grooves (Fig. 11.5C). The deep oral system centers in a hexagonal ring in the tegmen, external to the ring canal, and gives rise to nerves to the tegmen, oral podia, and to the lateral brachial nerves of the arms. Motor nerves to the podia

and water canals rise from the lateral brachials, and a commissure connects them with the main brachial nerves arising from the aboral nerve center. The aboral nervous system is predominant in crinoids. It forms a nervous cup containing the chambered organ and gives rise to a nerve cylinder that runs through the center of the stalk (Fig. 11.5F). The nerve center lies in the radial plates of the calyx and sends branches to the cirri. Stalk cirri are innervated from the nerve cylinder.

Reproduction. Crinoid gonads are indefinite masses of gametes in the arms or pinnules. Genital pinnules usually lack an ambulacral groove, and in some species have a cement gland used to attach the ova to the body surface. Primordial germ cells arise elsewhere and reach the arms through the genital cords.

Gametes are usually shed into the sea. As it is a large ocean, it is imperative that

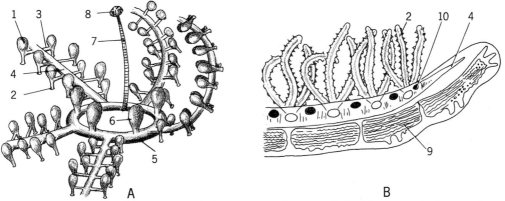

Fig. 11.6. A. Generalized scheme of the water-vascular or ambulacral system. A ring canal encircles the stomodaeum. From this, five radial water canals arise, attached by lateral canals to the podia. In echinoderms with arms, the radial canals extend into the arms, as on the left. In forms without arms, the radial canals run along the inner surface of the body wall. In most echinoderms, each podium is equipped with a saccate ampulla. A stone canal extends to a hydropore or, more often, a porous plate, the madreporite. Polian vesicles or other compensation sacs may arise from the ring canal, irregularly or on the interradii as shown in the figure. B. Podia and saccules on the pinnule of a crinoid. Note the clusters of three podia, which lack ampullae. (B, after Chadwick.) 1, ampulla; 2, podium; 3, lateral canal; 4, radial canal; 5, ring canal; 6, polian vesicle; 7, stone canal; 8, madreporite; 9, pinnular ossicle; 10, saccule.

ova and sperm be released at the same
time and in the same neighborhood. Generally males shed sperm first; this apparently stimulates the females to shed ova.
Evidently some environmental stimulus
coordinates the ripening of male and female gametes, ensuring that both will be
ready at the same time, but the details of
the controlling factors are unknown. Environmental stimuli also help to coordinate spawning. Almost all *Comanthus
japonicus* spawn between 3 and 5 p.m. on
the same day during the last half of October, with the moon in the first or last
quarter. Even when they are held in the
laboratory, spawning occurs at this time.
The controls must be independent of
temperature or chemical factors in the
water.

Fertilized ova form a fertilization membrane, sometimes heavy and spiny. Embryonic development will be discussed
with the development of other echinoderm groups.

Class Asteroidea—Sea Stars

Sea stars, or starfish, have a world-wide
distribution, occurring abundantly in cold
as well as tropical seas. They prefer a
stern and rockbound coast, but also live
in deep waters. Some species are widely
distributed, while others are local. Nearly
all of New Zealand's thirty littoral species
are endemic, for example. Starfish first
appeared in the Ordovician, and although
they do not fossilize as well as some
echinoderms, a number of fossil species
are known. About 2000 modern species
have been described. They are certainly
the best known and most universally
studied eleutherozoans.

Starfish are usually pentamerous, with
the five rays or arms not sharply set off
from the central disc. Variations in the
number of rays and their distinctness from
the disc lead to considerable diversity in
body form (Fig. 11.9). Starfish also vary

in texture. Most are roughened by conspicuous spines, but others are nearly
smooth and some are outlined by definite
marginal plates. Many are drab but some
are brightly colored, with characteristic
banding or mottling.

The body wall bears many minute appendages. Papulae (Fig. 11.10A) are inconspicuous, thin-walled, sac-like extensions of the coelom, used for respiration.
They occur on the aboral or on both body
surfaces. Among and around them are
pedicellariae. These jaw-like parts snap at
intruders on the surface, and protect the
delicate papulae. There are three kinds:
pedunculate (stalked); sessile (attached
directly to skeletal ossicles and often composed of several spines); and alveolar
(somewhat insunk, sitting in small depressions). Pedunculate pedicellariae may
be cross-jawed or straight-jawed, and have
special musculature (Fig. 11.8).

One of the most conspicuous features
of the aboral surface is the often brightly
colored madreporite, through which water
enters the ambulacral system. It lies in the
bivium, opposite arm A. The anus is also
on the aboral surface, usually slightly eccentric on interradius BC.

The mouth is centered on the oral surface, surrounded by a membranous peristome and encircled by protective spines.
A conspicuous ambulacral groove extends
from the border of the peristome to the
tip of each ray. It contains two or four
rows of podia and a single, terminal
podium at the tip. A red spot, the optic
cushion, lies at the tip of the ray.

Endoskeletal plates support the rays
and central disc. The two sides of the
ambulacral groove are formed of ambulacral ossicles (Fig. 11.7A,B), which
rest on adambulacral ossicles at the edge
of the groove. Muscles between the ossicles flatten or deepen the groove. Inframarginal and supramarginal ossicles support the sides of the rays, and specialized
carinate ossicles sometimes lie at the
middle of the aboral surface of the rays.

Some starfish have specialized inframarginal and supramarginal plates that outline the body margin. One group of starfish has skeletal ossicles known as paxillae, with many small, movable spines on the expanded external face (Fig. 11.7B). The spines are also endoskeletal ossicles, and they have special muscles at the base which move them slightly.

A skeletal ring, the mouth frame, is formed by the ambulacral and adambulacral plates at the margin of the peristome. An ambulacral mouth frame is composed predominantly of ambulacral ossicles; in an adambulacral mouth frame the adambulacral plates predominate (Fig. 11.7C,D).

CLASSIFICATION

The features mentioned will suffice to comprehend the characteristics of starfish

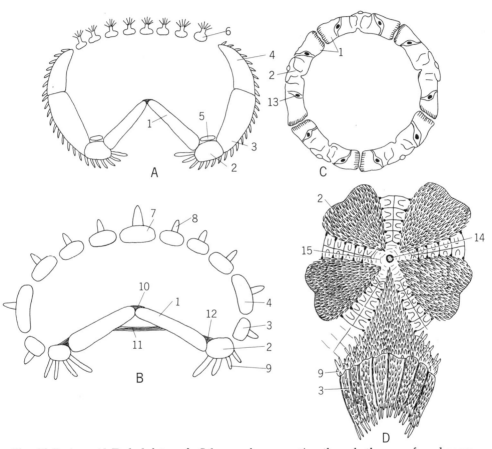

Fig. 11.7. Asteroid Endoskeleton. A. Scheme of cross section through the ray of a phanerozonic starfish. B. Scheme of cross section through the ray of a forciculate starfish. C. Peristomial ossicles of the ambulacral mouth frame of *Astropecten*, seen from without. (A, B, and D, after Hyman. C, after Chadwick.) 1, ambulacral ossicle; 2, adambulacral ossicle; 3, inframarginal ossicle; 4, supramarginal ossicle; 5, supra-ambulacral ossicle; 6, paxillae; 7, carinal ossicle; 8, tubercle; 9, adambulacral spine; 10, upper transverse ambulacral muscle; 11, lower transverse ambulacral muscle; 12, lateral transverse ambulacral muscle; 13, pore for first podium; 14, mouth; 15, peristome.

orders. Only the three modern orders are included. The omitted extinct orders are the *Platyasterida*, with wide, low ambulacral grooves and no definite mouth frame, and the *Hemizonida*, also without a definite mouth frame, but with deep ambulacral grooves.

Order Phanerizonida. Arms with conspicuous rows of aboral supramarginal and oral inframarginal plates; sessile or alveolar pedicellaria; papulae on aboral surface; adambulacral mouth frame. Example: *Ctenodiscus* (Fig. 11.9D).

Order Spinulosa. Usually without conspicuous marginal plates; pedicellaria usually wanting; aboral skeleton not uncommonly with paxillae; mouth frame adambulacral; podia with suckers and single or bifurcated ampullae. Example: *Solaster* (Fig. 11.9A).

Order Forcipulata. Without conspicuous marginal plates; spines not grouped and aboral skeleton usually reticulate; papulae on oral and aboral surfaces; pedunculate pedicellariae; podia usually in four rows, with suckers; mouth frame ambulacral. Example: *Asterias* (Fig. 11.9C).

THE BODY WALL

The body wall consists of cuticle, flagellated epidermis, a nerve plexus at the base of the epidermis, a delicate basement membrane, a dermis containing the skeletal ossicles, a delicate layer of circular muscle and a thicker layer of longitudinal muscle, and a cuboid, flagellated peritoneum. Asteroids have a generalized body wall, with all of the elements represented in fair quantities, whereas most other echinoderms have a preponderance of skeletal or soft elements.

Four kinds of body-wall appendages are found: spines, papulae, podia, and pedicellariae. Spines are covered with epidermis and surrounded by dermis at the base. Slips of body-wall muscle insert on movable spines. The sessile and alveolar pedicellariae are characteristic of Phanerozonia, and pedunculate pedicellariae are characteristic of Forcipulata, while Spinulosa generally lack pedicellariae. Papulae are composed of epidermis, dermis, muscle, and peritoneum, but these layers are very thin (Fig. 11.10A). Delicate muscles permit papula retraction and extrusion, and the constant beating of epidermal and peritoneal flagella ventilate the external surface and circulate coelomic fluid through the papular lumen, hastening respiratory exchange. Small canals ramify through the dermis and form a ring at the base of each papula (Fig. 11.10A).

Asteroid podia have ampullae within the body, above the ambulacral plates. The podial tube projects outward between the ambulacral plates. Where there are two rows of podia the lateral canals are equal in length, but where there are four rows of podia, longer and shorter lateral canals alternate (Fig. 11.10B). The podial and ampullar walls are continuous with the body wall, and contain the same tissues. Each podium is, in a sense, an oddly shaped blister in the body wall, connected to a canal system.

COELOM

The asteroid coelom is complexly partitioned, and all of its derivatives are lined with flagellated peritoneum. The central disc and rays contain a spacious perivisceral coelom. The floor of the ambulacral grooves bulges into the coelom; the cardiac part of the stomach is attached to the ambulacral plates by gastric ligaments, which partially divide the coelom into oral and aboral parts. Each arm coelom is continuous with the aboral coelom. A system of coelomic sinuses enclose the lacunae of the haemal system. This system centers in the axial sinus, which surrounds the stone canal and axial gland (Fig. 11.10C). At its oral end, the axial sinus opens into the inner hyponeural sinus, a ring-shaped channel just inside the mouth frame. A slanting partition

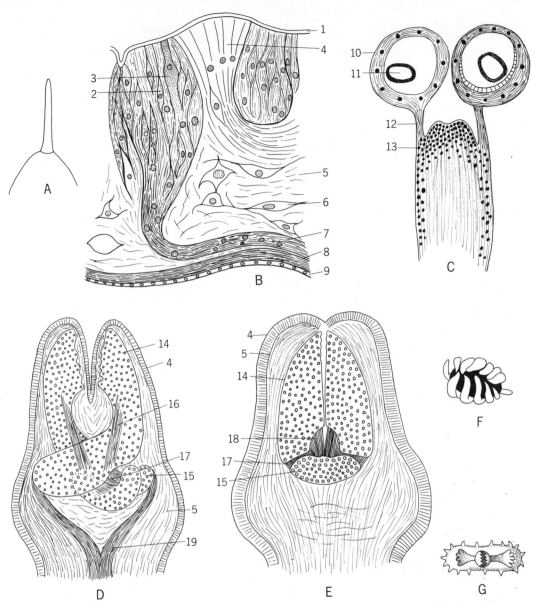

Fig. 11.8. Some Body-Wall Appendages and Sense Organs of Echinoderms. A. A papillate sea cucumber podium with the sensory filament extended. B. Section showing sensory buds in the oral tentacle of a sea cucumber, *Caudina*. C. Statocysts of a sea cucumber, *Caudina*. D. A cross-jawed pedicellaria of *Asterias*. E. A straight-jawed pedicellaria of *Asterias*. F. Sessile pedicellaria of *Astropecten*. G. Alveolar pedicellaria of *Hacelia*. (A, D, and E, after Hyman. B, after Gerould. C, after Clark. F, after Fisher. G, after Cuénot, in Grassé.) 1, cuticle; 2, sensory bud; 3, gland cell; 4, epidermis; 5, dermis; 6, connective tissue cells; 7, branch of tentacular nerve; 8, longitudinal body wall muscle; 9, peritoneum; 10, statocyst; 11, statolith; 12, statocyst nerve; 13, radial nerve; 14, valve; 15, basal piece; 16, long adductor muscle; 17, abductor muscle; 18, short adductor muscle; 19, ligament.

A

B

Fig. 11.9. A. *Solaster,* a starfish belonging to order Spinulosa. The absence of pedicellariae generally and of conspicuous marginal plates characterizes the Spinulosa. B. View of the ambulacral groove of *Asterias,* showing the tube feet and marginal ossicles along the groove. Note the suction cups at the tip of the podia.

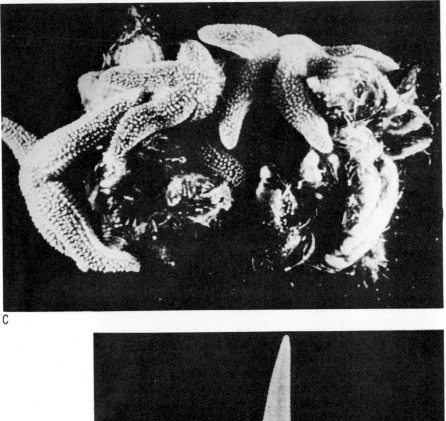

C

D

C. A cluster of *Asterias forbesi*. *Asterias* is a familiar genus of the order Forcipulata, members of which have no conspicuous marginal plates but do have pedicellariae. D. A phanerozonid starfish. *Ctenodiscus*. Note the conspicuous marginal plates, which are characteristic of the phanerozonids. (Courtesy of the General Biological Supply Co.)

divides the inner hyponeural sinus from the somewhat larger outer hyponeural sinus, through which the ring vessel of the haemal system passes. Radial hyponeural sinuses enter each ray, running along the ambulacral groove just outside of the ambulacral plates (Fig. 11.10D). Delicate branches pass to the marginal sinuses just above the marginal nerve cord at the edges of the ambulacral groove. The axial sinus opens aborally into a pentagonal genital sinus, from which branches extend into the rays. The young gonads lie in the genital sinuses of the rays. A dorsal sac, containing the head of the axial gland, also arises from the sinus.

THE HAEMAL SYSTEM

The haemal system is closely associated with the coelomic sinus system. An oral haemal ring lies in the septum dividing the inner and outer hyponeural ring sinus. It gives rise to radial haemal sinuses, from which branches pass to the podia (Fig. 11.10C). The brownish or purplish axial gland lies in the axial sinus, with its head in the dorsal sac. One or more haemal tufts connect the axial gland with the haemal sinus system of the digestive tract. The axial gland tissue is spongy and contains many coelomocyte-like cells. The haemal lacunae have incomplete walls, and contain amoeboid cells indistinguishable from amoeboid coelomocytes.

The haemal system has no heart, although the axial gland was initially described as a heart. Some circulation occurs, however, and contractions of the head process, the aboral haemal ring, and gastric tufts have been described.

FOOD CAPTURE AND DIGESTION

Starfish are carnivorous, and while some species have definite food preferences, most will take any kind of animal food they can get. Clams, oysters, snails, and other shelled molluscs are staple items,

but brachiopods and hermit crabs are eaten, and inactive or dying fish are not ignored.

Some starfish swallow food whole. The anus is too small to accommodate empty shells, and the remains are necessarily ejected through the mouth. Other starfish evert the stomach through the mouth. It is pressed against the food organism, enzymes are secreted to soften the food, and the predigested tissues are swallowed. In this case there is little residue to egest, and the anus becomes unimportant. It is lacking in some deep sea, cribelloid Phanerozonia. Everting the stomach increases the number of animals that can be eaten, for the stomach can be pressed against sessile animals, like corals, digesting them in place. The struggle between a starfish and clam or oyster has often been described. The starfish grasps the shell with its podia and exerts a steady pressure, while the mollusc holds the shell closed. The problem is for the starfish to get its stomach inside the shell. According to the classical view, the hydraulic system of the starfish permits it to exert a long, steady pull that the oyster cannot match. Measurements of the amount of pull exerted by individual podia and the pull an oyster can resist fail to justify this explanation. The probability is that with most starfish, as with *Asterias*, it takes very little space for the stomach to enter. A space as small as 0.1 mm. suffices, and small irregularities of the shell margin may be enough to make the tug-of-war unnecessary. Probably the later gaping of the shell occurs as enzymes weaken the oyster's muscles.

Some starfish, especially those living on muddy bottoms, are ciliary feeders. Starfish known to feed in this way stay alive and healthy in aquaria when denied large food organisms, while other species starve under identical conditions.

The starfish digestive system consists of an esophagus, a stomach divided into cardiac and pyloric parts, large diverticula

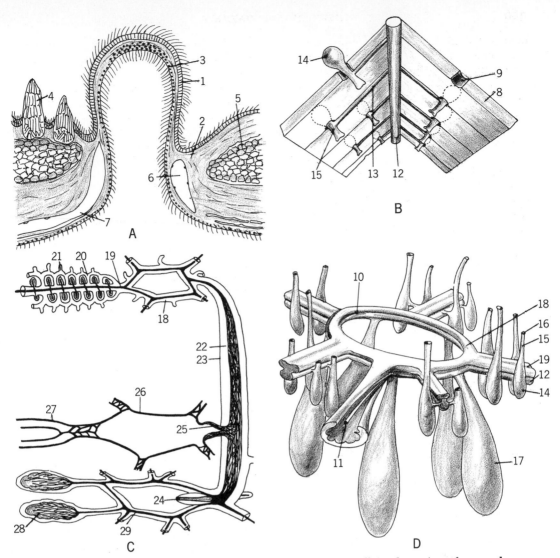

Fig. 11.10. Asteroid Anatomy. A. Scheme of asteroid body wall in the region of a papula.
B. Scheme of ambulacral groove, with one row of podia on the left and two rows on the right.
C. Scheme of the haemal and perihaemal sinus system of an asteroid, with the oral surface
upward. Note the arrows indicating direction of flow. D. Ambulacral system near the mouth,
with the oral surface upward. (A and C, after Cuénot, in Grassé. D, after Delage and
Hérouard.) *Histology:* 1, epidermis; 2, dermis; 3, peritoneum; 4, spine; 5, ossicle; 6, ring sinus
around papula; 7, intertegumentary sinus. *Ambulacral system:* 8, ambulacral plate; 9, podial
pore; 10, ring water canal; 11, stone canal; 12, radial water canal; 13, lateral canal; 14, ampulla; 15, podium; 16, sucker; 17, polian vesicle. *Coelom and haemal system:* 18, oral
coelomic ring sinus containing oral haemal ring; 19, radial hyponeural sinus containing radial
haemal canal; 20, marginal sinus; 21, connections between marginal sinus and intertegumentary sinuses; 22, axial gland; 23, axial sinus; 24, dorsal sac containing head of axial gland;
25, gastric haemal tufts; 26, haemal absorptive ring; 27, absorptive haemal canal on pyloric
caecum; 28, genital organ receiving haemal branches; 29, aboral coelomic ring sinus containing
aboral haemal ring.

367

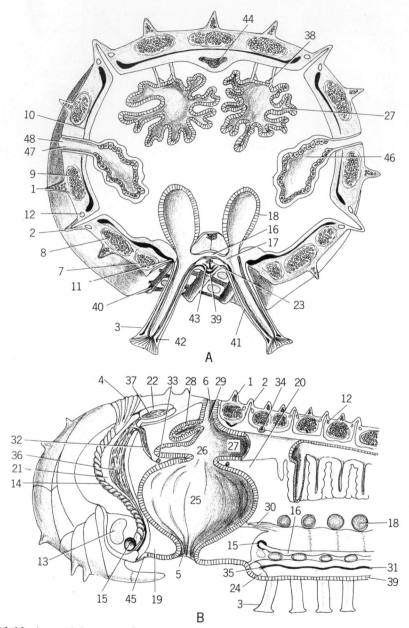

Fig. 11.11. Asteroid Anatomy. **A.** Section of asteroid ray. **B.** Section through the central disc and the base of a ray (composite). *External features:* **1**, spine; **2**, papula; **3**, podium; **4**, madreporite; **5**, mouth; **6**, anus. *Body wall:* **7**, adambulacral ossicle; **8**, inframarginal ossicle; **9**, supramarginal ossicle; **10**, intradermal (intertegumentary) sinuses of body wall; **11**, communicating canal between intradermal sinuses and marginal sinus; **12**, ring sinus at base of papula; **13**, interradial muscle. *Ambulacral system:* **14**, stone canal; **15**, ambulacral ring canal; **16**, radial water canal; **17**, lateral canal; **18**, ampulla. *Coelom:* **19**, oral part of perivisceral coelom; **20**, aboral part of perivisceral coelom; **21**, axial sinus; **22**, dorsal sac;

known as digestive glands, or pyloric caeca, and a short intestine, giving off intestinal caeca, and leading to the anus (Fig. 11.11B).

Some starfish also have ten esophageal pouches, and in some a Tiedemann's pouch, of unknown function, rises from the cardiac stomach.

The gut wall is built of an inner gastrodermis (mucosa) with a nerve plexus at its base, a layer of connective tissue, circular and longitudinal muscle layers, and a peritoneum continuous with the peritoneum of the gastric ligaments. Regional specialization of various areas is accomplished by modifying the thickness or nature of the wall tissues.

THE NEUROSENSORY APPARATUS

The epidermis is everywhere supplied with neurosensory cells, providing sensitivity to touch, chemicals, and light. Mechanical stimuli cause contraction of papulae and podia. Acids cause contraction of papulae and podia when applied locally, but evoke a flight response when applied to the aboral surface. The presence of food arouses positive reactions. A sudden light ray causes contraction of podia and papulae, and may evoke coordinated responses of the whole animal as well.

Asteroids have a typical echinoderm nervous system, with a predominant ectoneural (oral) system, a reduced hyponeural (deep oral) system, and a much modified entoneural (aboral) system, which may not be wholly homologous to the crinoid entoneural system. The oral nervous system centers in a pentagonal nerve ring in the peristomial membrane, giving off a radial nerve at each radius. The radial nerve extends to the tip of the ray in the floor of the ambulacral groove (Fig. 11.11A), and connects with the subepidermal nerve plexus. The plexus is thickened in sensitive areas, and at the margins of the ambulacral grooves, where it forms marginal nerves. Motor nerves to the ambulacral muscles and to the nerve plexus of the coelomic lining which controls the body-wall muscles arise from the marginal nerves, which in this sense correspond to the entoneural nervous system of other echinoderms. The only remnant of the hyponeural nervous system is a plate of nerve tissue known as Lang's nerve, which lies on the oral wall, separated from the oral nerve ring by a delicate septum. Predominantly motor branches from Lang's nerve run above the hyponeural coelomic sinuses.

REPRODUCTION

The common starfish has ten gonads, two in each ray, lying free in the coelom except at the gonoduct. Gonopores open near the interradius on the ray margin. Some starfish have many gonads in each arm, with a series of marginal gonopores or a collecting duct leading to a normally placed gonopore. Each gonad is enclosed within the delicate walls of a genital sinus, arising as a branch from the genital coelomic ring.

Sexes are usually separate, but an occasional hermaphroditic asteroid occurs. Some species appear to be dioecious because of marked protandry. Gametes are

23, hyponeural sinus containing radial haemal vessel; 24, circumoral coelomic ring sinus. *Digestive tract:* 25, cardiac stomach; 26, pyloric stomach; 27, digestive gland or pyloric caecum; 28, rectal sac; 29, intestine; 30, gastric ligament. *Haemal system:* 31, radial haemal vessel; 32, gastric tuft; 33, ring vessel around gut; 34, aboral haemal ring; 35, oral haemal ring; 36, axial gland; 37, head of axial gland; 38, absorptive haemal lacunae. *Nervous system:* 39, radial nerve; 40, marginal nerve; 41, podial nerve; 42, podial nerve ring; 43, deep oral radial nerve; 44, apical nerve; 45, oral nerve ring. *Reproductive system:* 46, gonad; 47, gonoduct; 48, gonopore.

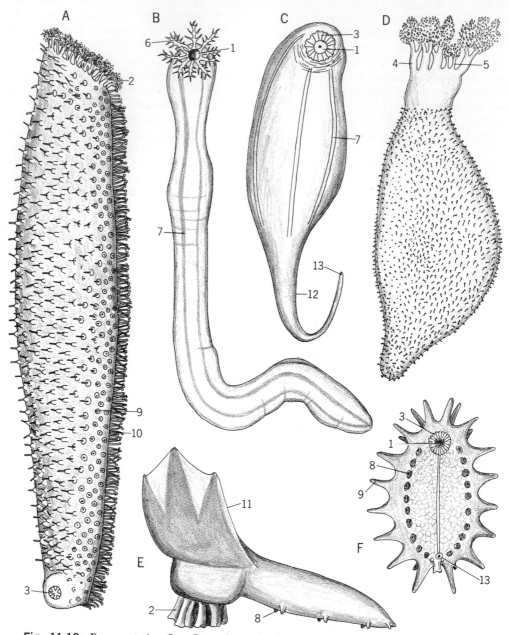

Fig. 11.12. Representative Sea Cucumbers. **A.** *Actinopyga aggasizi*, an aspidochirote sea cucumber, characterized by peltate oral tentacles and many podia. They cannot withdraw the oral region. **B.** *Leptosynapta*, an apod sea cucumber, characterized by the absence of podia and the reduction of the water vascular system. **C.** *Molpadia musculus*, a molpadonian sea cucumber, characterized by the reduction of podia to a few anal papillae and digitate oral tentacles. The posterior end tapers to a caudal region. **D.** *Thyone*, a common dendrochirate sea cucumber, characterized by dendroid oral tentacles and an oral region modified as an

usually released into the sea and fertilization is external, but some species have developed brooding habits. The females cup their body over the egg mass, retaining this position without feeding while the young develop. The stiffer body of Phanerozonia prevents this habit, but the young of some species implant themselves among the paxillae of the aboral surface. Some forcipulates, the Heliasteridae, have a nidamental chamber, floored with many papulae, used for brooding the young and for respiration. Brooding starfish produce larger ova with more yolk. Evidently the chances of development are increased by brooding, for brooders produce only a few dozen to several hundred ova while nonbrooding females may release millions of ova.

External Form and Classification of Other Echinoderms

Echinoderms are particularly interesting from a comparative point of view, for they have retained a remarkably stable set of organ systems although the external form and habits have undergone an extensive set of changes. The crinoids, the only living Pelmatozoa, and the asteroids, one of the modern classes of Eleutherozoa, have been described. The internal organs of the remaining classes will be discussed comparatively, after considering their external form and habits separately.

CLASS HOLOTHUROIDEA—SEA CUCUMBERS

Pliny mentioned the *cucumis marinus*, and it is customary to use this as the beginning of our knowledge of sea cucum-

bers, but the Chinese were undoubtedly gathering them for soup long before Pliny's day. Sea cucumbers are familiar littoral animals throughout the world, but they are not restricted to shallow waters. A rich deep-water fauna extends to depths of about 6000 m. Most sea cucumbers are of moderate size, well-named as cucumbers, but the group as a whole varies from the smallest gherkins to a truly noble watermelon. *Stichopus variegatus*, from the Philippines, reaches a meter in length and 21 cm. in diameter. Most species are dull, but an occasional one is brightly colored.

The soft leathery body is elongated, with an anus at or near the aboral end and the mouth at or near the oral end. The standard five ambulacral regions usually mark the sides of the body, but sea cucumbers lie on one side and dorsal and ventral surfaces are often differentiated. They lie on their trivium, with ray A on the midventral line. The ventral surface is sometimes flattened, and the dorsal surface arched. Some glide on a creeping sole, propelled by muscular waves and locomotor podia (Fig. 11.12E,F). The mouth tends to migrate to the ventral and the anus to the dorsal surface. The bilateral symmetry of some elasipods is emphasized by sail-like extensions of the body, used in floating. These creatures have an amazing symmetrical history. Bilateral larvae become secondarily radially symmetrical, and later return to a tertiary bilateral symmetry.

The mouth is surrounded by modified podia known as oral tentacles. They may be digitate (finger-like), dendritic (arboreally branched) pinnate (with side branches on a central axis), or peltate

introvert. E. *Peniagone*, an elasipod, one of the deep-sea forms tending toward bilateral symmetry, with peltate oral tentacles and unable to retract the oral region. F. *Deima*, in ventral view, another elasipod. (A and D, after Hyman. C, after Clark, B, after Coe. E and F, after Théel.) 1, mouth; 2, peltate tentacle; 3, digitate tentacle; 4, normal dendritic tentacle; 5, dwarfed mid-ventral tentacle; 6, pinnate tentacle; 7, ambulacrum; 8, locomotor podia; 9, papillae; 10, creeping sole; 11, sail; 12, tail; 13, anus.

(flattened, with a short stalk and terminal disc, often with horizontal branches). The tentacles can be withdrawn and the body wall closed over them for protection. Some sea cucumbers have a definite collar around the oral end, forming an introvert that can be pulled in by retractor muscles. In others, a simple tentacular collar folds over the withdrawn tentacles.

Usually the body wall contains microscopic skeletal ossicles, but a few species have a protective layer of small, close-fitting plates. Various warty prominences, papillae, and other projections may mark the surface. Many are modified podia, connected to the water-vascular system. The anus is often surrounded by special anal papillae.

There are approximately 500 species, arranged in five orders. The anatomy of a sea cucumber is summarized in Fig. 11.21, and should be examined before considering the classification and details of the body wall.

Order Aspidochirota. Holothurians with many podia, peltate oral tentacles, respiratory trees, and without oral retractor muscles. Example: *Actinopyga* (Fig. 11.12A).
Order Elasipoda. Deep-sea holothurians with many podia, peltate oral tentacles, and without oral retractor muscles or respiratory trees. Examples: *Deima* (Fig. 11.12F); *Peniagone* (Fig. 11.12E).
Order Dendrochirota. Holothurians with many podia, dendroid oral tentacles, oral retractor muscles, and respiratory trees. Example: *Thyone* (Fig. 11.12D).
Order Molpadonia. Holothurians with digitate oral tentacles, and respiratory trees; podia reduced to anal papillae, and posterior region tapering to a caudal region. Example. *Molpadia* (Fig. 11.12C).
Order Apoda. Holothurians with oral tentacles and a reduced water-vascular system, without podia or respiratory trees. Example: *Leptosynapta* (Fig. 11.12B).

The holothurian body wall consists of a cuticle, epidermis, dermis, circular and longitudinal muscle layers, and peritoneum. The tiny, bizarrely shaped ossicles lie in the dermis (Fig. 11.13A). All echinoderm ossicles are fenestrated, but this is seen most easily in the lacy form of holothurian ossicles. The outer part of the dermis is loose, but the deeper parts are strengthened by collagenous fibers (Fig. 11.13B), forming a strong, protective layer. Strands of longitudinal muscle interrupt the sheath of circular muscles at each ambulacrum. Circular muscles are strengthened as sphincters at the mouth and in the collar or behind the introvert. The oral region is supported by a calcareous ring, the aquapharyngeal bulb (Fig. 11.21B), to which the retractor muscles attach. The unusually strong body-wall musculature of sea cucumbers is associated with the absence of a skeletal sheath.

CLASS ECHINOIDEA—THE URCHINS

Sea urchins and sand dollars are among the familiar animals of sea coasts, and exemplify the differences between the regular and irregular echinoids. Sea urchins are regular echinoids, with a radially symmetrical, globose test and forbidding spines. Sand dollars are irregular echinoids, with flattened test, less prominent spines, and fairly marked evidences of bilateral symmetry.

Echinoids occur in all climatic regions, and from the littoral zone, where they are abundant, to depths of 5000 m. or more. Fossil echinoids date back to the Middle Ordovician. Deep-sea forms live on slimy bottoms, but regular echinoids usually prefer hard bottoms and rocky areas, while irregular echinoids prefer muddy or sandy bottoms. Sea urchins often lie in protected, rocky crannies; boring urchins enlarge these spaces with the teeth and spines when they are too tight for comfort. There are two major types of irregular echinoids, sand dollars and heart urchins (Fig. 11.14). The greatly flattened sand dollars are round

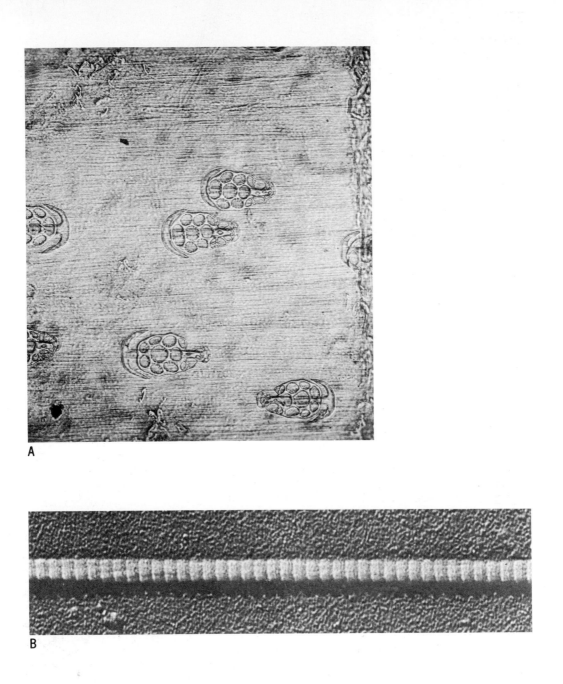

Fig. 11.13. A. Ossicles from the body wall of a sea cucumber, *Synapta*. The fenestration of skeletal ossicles is characteristic of echinoderms generally, but can be seen most clearly in the holothurians. **B.** Electron micrograph of a collagenous fiber from the body wall of a sea cucumber, *Thyone*. (From Andrew.)

373

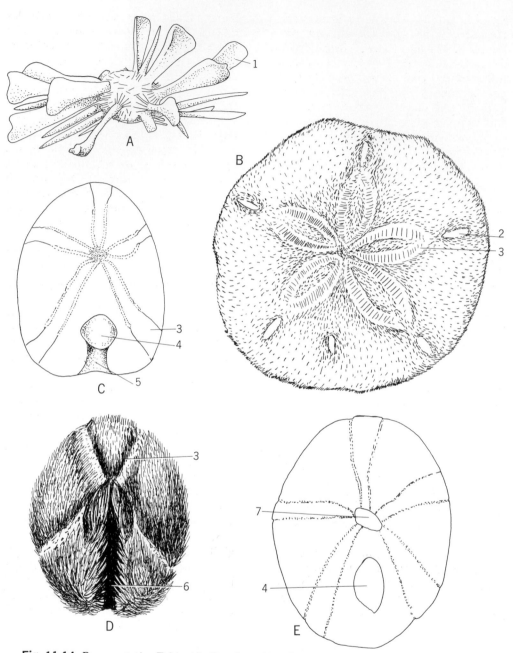

Fig. 11.14. Representative Echinoids. Regular echinoids are the sea urchins, which are divided into several orders. The Cidaroidea, a single large spine encircled by smaller spines on each ambulacral plates, as in *Cidaris blakei* (A). The irregular urchins include the heart urchins or spatangoids, like *Echinocardium* (D), with the oral ambulacrum insunk and tending toward bilateral symmetry, and the more flattened forms commonly known as sand dollars. The true sand dollars are clypeastroids, with small spines, an oval to circular test, and petaloid ambulacra,

to oval in outline, while heart urchins are indented at one ambulacrum and are deeper, with more evident bilateral symmetry. Sand dollars live just below the surface of the sand. When exposed, they bury themselves by piling sand in front of them and moving into it. Heart urchins burrow in the mud; the burrows are strengthened with mucus, preventing their collapse.

The firm shell, with its projecting spines, pedicellaria, podia, and gills, is characteristic of echinoids. The membranous periproct, containing the anus, is centered on the aboral surface of regular echinoids (Fig. 11.16A). A large membranous peristome at the center of the oral surface contains the mouth. The mouth and periproct of some irregular echinoids have moved backward or forward in association with bilateral symmetry. The test is often thickened at the rim of the peristome where jaw muscles attach; this is the perignathic girdle. Viewed from the oral surface, the periphery of the test is the ambitus. The ambitus is round to oval in regular urchins and irregular or bilaterally symmetrical in irregular echinoids.

Radial water canals lie just beneath the test. Pores for the podia make distinctive ambulacral regions, not always evident until the spines are removed from sea urchins. The ambulacra are often petal-shaped (petaloid) in irregular urchins, forming a flower-like design on the test.

Echinoid spines are important tools and are specialized for diverse functions. *Arbacia* has spines of only one size, but many sea urchins have larger spines known as primaries, smaller ones known as secondaries, and still smaller ones known as tertiaries. Each spine sits on a complex tubercle. The very short spines of irregular urchins form an almost hair-like covering. Heart urchins have tracts of specialized, racket-shaped, ciliated spines (clavules) which generate cleansing currents, keeping the test free of mud.

An intricate set of jaws, known as Aristotle's lantern, is a unique echinoid feature. They are strong enough to chew up the cases of sessile ectoprocts and calcareous algae, and to bore in rocks. The lantern is beautifully designed, and stands among the most remarkable structures to be found among invertebrates (Fig. 11.24). An extinct subclass of echinoids, Bothriocidaroidea, was without Aristotle's lantern, but it occurs in most modern groups. Extinct orders are not included in the classification below.

Subclass Regularia. Sea Urchins. Globose echinoids with circular ambitus and pentamerous symmetry; test with two rows of interambulacral plates between the ambulacra; periproct surrounded by an apical system of plates; with an Aristotle's lantern.

Order Lepidocentroida. With a flexible test of separated plates and ambulacral plates which cross the peristome to the mouth rim; mostly abyssal forms today, but predominantly extinct. Example: *Calveriosoma.*

Order Cidaroidea. Test rigid, with two rows of narrow, simple ambulacral plates and two rows of interambulacral plates, continuing to the mouth rim, perignathic girdle marked by interradial muscle attachments; each ambulacral plate with a single, large spine, encircled by small spines; without gills or balance organs; tridentate and globiferous pedicellariae. Example: *Cidaris* (Fig. 11.14A).

as in *Mellita* (B). *Apatopygous* (C), shown in aboral view, is an example of the Cassiduloida, which have the mouth central or somewhat anterior, and guarded by modified plates forming a floscelle. *Echinoneus* (E) is one of the holectypoids, with a regular test and central peristome, but without petaloid ambulacra. (A, after Mortenson. C and E, after Hyman. D, after MacBride.) 1, fan-shaped primary spines; 2, lunule; 3, petaloid ambulacrum; 4, periproct; 5, groove to periproct; 6, anterior ambulacrum; 7, peristome.

Fig. 11.15. Some Echinoids. **A.** *Eucidaris metularia*, a regular echinoid belonging to the Cidaroidea. The presence of heavy spines on each of the adambulacral plates is characteristic of the cidaroids. B and E. Dorsal and ventral views of *Meoma ventricosa*, a spatangoid. The

376

D

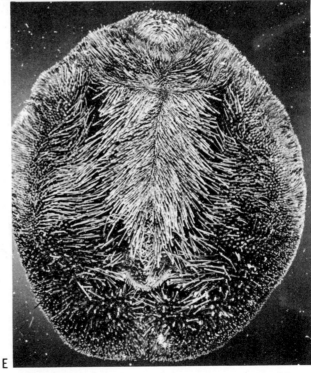

E

petaloid ambulacra are found on the dorsal surface, while the ventral surface is considerably modified, showing strong tendencies toward bilateral symmetry. C and D. *Astropyga magnifica*, a diademitid regular echinoid. (Courtesy of the Smithsonian Institution.)

Order Diadematoida. Test globose, with two rows of interambulacral plates and two rows of compound ambulacral plates, both ending at the peristome margin; muscle attachments on the perignathic girdle radial; gills and small bodies on the ambulacra thought to be balance organs (sphaeridia); all types of pedicellaria or without globiferous pedicellaria. Example: *Arbacia, Astropyga* (Fig. 11.15).

Subclass Irregularia. Test flattened, with oval to circular or bilaterally symmetrical ambitus; periproct posterior, on oral or aboral surface, having moved back on one interradius; apical plates at aboral pole; mouth centered or eccentric, displaced anteriorly, ambulacra often petaloid, and podia usually not for locomotion.

Order Holectypoida. Test regular, with apical plates centered at aboral pole; anus somewhat separate from apical plates; peristome central; ambulacra not petaloid; mostly extinct. Example: *Echinoneus* (Fig. 11.14E).

Order Cassiduloida. Test round to oval; periproct variable in position; peristome central or slightly anterior; ambulacral plates modified at peristome as petal-like phyllodes and interambulacral plates with prominences known as bourrelets, the whole forming a flower-like pattern, the floscelle; ambulacra petaloid, but open at margin; without a lantern in recent species but mostly extinct. Example: *Apatopygous* (Fig. 11.14C).

Order Clypeastroida. Sand dollars. Test flattened and oval or circular at ambitus, usually densely covered by small spines; test often supported by internal strutting; peristome and apical system usually central; petaloid ambulacra with a single sphaeridium near the peristome; without phyllodes or bourrelets; with a lantern and without gills. Example: *Mellita* (Fig. 11.14B).

Order Spatanguloida. Test oval or cordiform, bilaterally symmetrical about the long axis; peristome displaced anteriorly, with oral ambulacrum insunk and not petaloid and remaining four ambulacra petaloid; phyllodes present, but bourrelets wanting; with posterior interambulacrum often modified as a plastron on the aboral surface, with short spines, some modified as clavules and forming fascioles; without gills or lantern. Example: *Echinocardium* (Fig. 11.14D).

The Test. The test is best examined with all spines and other surface structures removed. A denuded sea urchin test is a beautifully symmetrical object, for the tubercles for spine attachment occur in meridional rows, adding symmetrical ornamentation to an otherwise symmetrically arranged set of plates. The test is built of 20 rows of plates; each radius centers on a double row of ambulacral plates containing paired pores for the podia, and each interradius centers on a double row of interambulacral plates with conspicuous tubercles.

The skeletal plates are straight on three sides and V-shaped on the fourth. The plates of a row meet at two of the flat sides; two adjacent rows of ambulacrals or interambulacrals meet at the V-shaped ends, and so are set alternately, as a mason lays bricks, increasing the strength of the test (Fig. 11.16B). The margins of the double rows of interambulacrals and ambulacrals meet in a straight line.

Echinoid podia have an inner canal to the water canal and an outer canal to the ampulla; each ambulacral plate is pierced by a pair of pores for each podium. Simple ambulacral plates are very narrow, with a single pore pair. Compound plates, formed by the fusion of simple plates, are common and several patterns of fusion are recognized. Interambulacral plates are larger than ambulacral plates and have larger tubercles for spines.

The test is modified at oral and aboral ends. The membranous periproct is surrounded by an apical system of plates, consisting of five larger genital plates on the interradii and five smaller terminals on the radii. The madreporite lies in a modified genital plate. Genital plates are pierced by gonopores, and terminal podia pass through the terminal plates. The periproct and peristome may contain small plates but they remain flexible. The ambulacral and interambulacral plates of most echinoids end at the margin of the peristome, but continue across the peristome in cidaroids; in lepidocentroids only the ambulacrals cross the peristome. Most echinoids have a thickening around the peristome where jaw muscles attach (perignathic girdle). The peristome may be strengthened at the interambulacra by apophyses or at the ambulacra by auricles.

The flat test of irregular echinoids is not not so impressively designed, but is strong because internal struts extend from oral to aboral surface. The spines are small and the regularly symmetrical pattern of tubercles is missing. Clypeastroids have wider ambulacrals and spatangoids have wider interambulacrals. The petaloid ambulacra

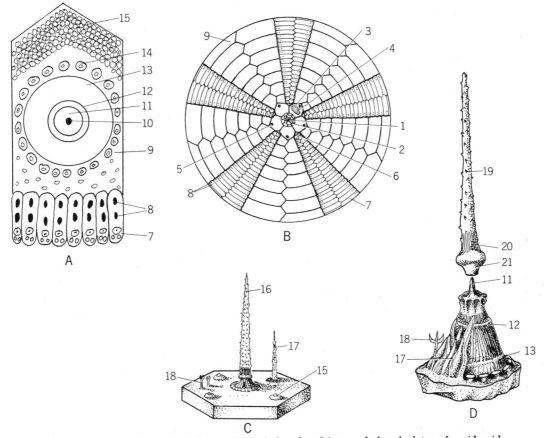

Fig. 11.16. Echinoid Test and Spines. **A.** Ambulacral and interambulacral plates of a cidaroid, *Eucidaris*, showing tubercles. **B.** Scheme of the test of a regular echinoid. **C.** Scheme of a coronal plate, showing pedicellaria, tubercles, and spines. **D.** Tubercle and spine. (A, after Hyman. C, after Jackson. D, largely after Prouho.) **1**, anus; **2**, periproct; **3**, genital plate; **4**, madreporite; **5**, gonopore; **6**, terminal plate containing pore for terminal podium; **7**, ambulacral plate; **8**, podial pore; **9**, interambulacral plate; **10**, perforation; **11**, mamelon; **12**, base; **13**, areole; **14**, scrobicular tubercle; **15**, tubercles for secondary spines; **16**, primary spine; **17**, secondary spine; **18**, pedicellaria; **19**, shaft of spine; **20**, milled ring; **21**, base of spine.

of many irregular echinoids are formed by very narrow ambulacral plates and their podial pores (Fig. 11.14B). Some irregular echinoids have expanded ambulacrals forming petal-like phyllodes around the mouth, and prominences on the interambulacrals (bourrelets) may produce a flower-like foscelle around the mouth (Fig. 11.17).

The tubercles of regular echinoids consist of a basal spine, the boss, raised to form a ring around a central knob (mamelon) (Fig. 11.16D). The spine ends in a flange-shaped condyle that pivots on the mamelon. A circular area (areole) around the boss provides a site for muscle attachments. Tubercle size varies with spine size. Primary tubercles are usually much larger than secondaries, but some species have intergrading sizes. Cidaroids have very large tubercles for the huge primary spines, surrounded by a ring of scrobicular tubercles for the secondary scrobicular spines (Fig. 11.16C).

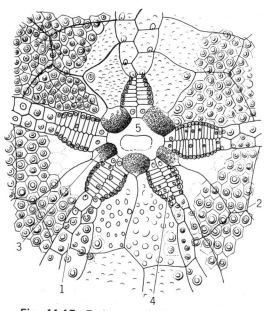

Fig. 11.17. Peristome of *Cassidula*, showing the floscelle. (After Lovén.) **1**, ambulacrum; **2**, interambulacrum; **3**, bourrelet; **4**, phyllode; **5**, peristome.

Body Wall Appendages. Echinoids have a simple body wall, composed of an external ciliated epidermis, a dermis composed almost entirely of skeletal plates, and a flattened peritoneal lining. As in other encased animals, body-wall muscles have disappeared except for specialized slips; in echinoids these are associated with the body-wall appendages.

Spines, pedicellaria, podia, gills, and sphaeridia are the body-wall appendages. Sphaeridia are small, transparent, stalked bodies, thought to be balance organs and probably derived from spines. They lie along the ambulacra of regular echinoids, and in depressions near the peristome or on the aboral surface of irregular echinoids. A circle of gills occurs on the peristomial border of all regular echinoids. They are thin-walled extensions of the peristome. Irregular echinoids lack gills entirely.

Spines are used as levers for locomotion and for digging, and are protective. Sea urchins are surprisingly dexterous with their levers. An exposed *Evechinus choroticus* can cover itself with small pebbles in a few minutes, using spines and pedicellaria. Spine shape, size, and form vary with spine function. Longer spines are more effective than small ones for movement and protection and spade-like ones are best for digging. The clavules of spatangoids are racket-shaped and heavily ciliated; they generate currents that cleanse the body surface. Some echinoids have poisonous spines and can cause painful puncture wounds.

Echinoid podia are like locomotor podia of other echinoderms, but attach to the ampullae and water canals by a double canal system. Diadematoids have ten specialized buccal podia, used in food manipulation. Podia are more highly specialized in heart urchins. Digitate or discoid sensory podia lie in the anterior ambulacrum. Leaf-like branchial podia from the petaloids serve as gills. Penicillate podia arise from the phyllodes; they correspond to buccal podia of regular echinoids and are

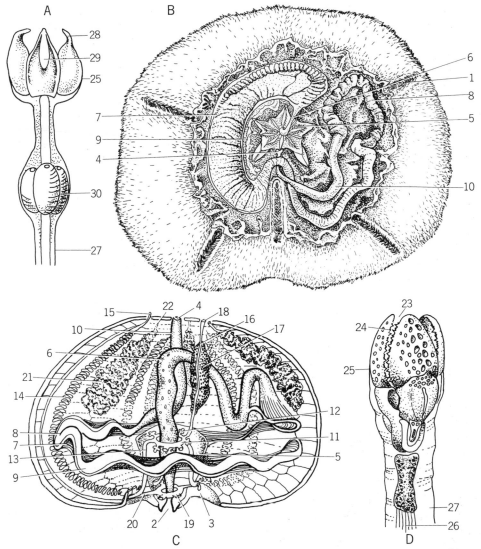

Fig. 11.18. Echinoid Anatomy. A. Poisonous globiferous pedicellaria of *Sphaerechinus*.
B. Anatomy of *Mellita pentapora*. C. Scheme of internal organization of *Arbacia*. D. Ophiocephalous pedicellaria of *Arbacia*. (A, after Cuénot, in Grassé. B, after Coe. C, after
Petrunkewitch. D, after Reid, from Reid, in Brown.) *External features:* 1, lunule; 2, mouth;
3, peristomial membrane; 4, anus. *Digestive system:* 5, Aristotle's lantern; 6, esophagus;
7, stomach; 8, intestine; 9, siphon; 10, rectum. *Ambulacral system:* 11, ring canal; 12, polian
vesicle; 13, radial water canal; 14, ampullae; 15, terminal podium; 16 stone canal; 17, axial
gland; 18, madreporite. *Nervous system:* 19, nerve ring; 20, radial nerve. *Genital system:*
21, gonad; 22, gonopore. *Pedicellariae:* 23, aperture; 24, teeth; 25, valve; 26, skeletal rod;
27, stalk; 28, terminal tooth; 29, valve gland; 30, stalk gland.

381

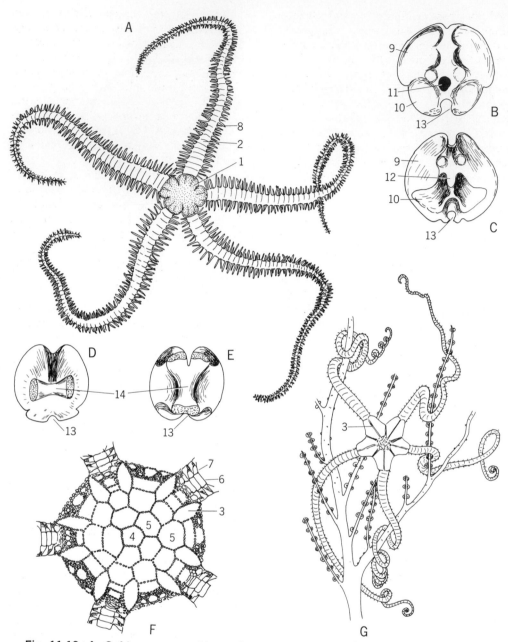

Fig. 11.19. A. *Ophiocoma*, an ophiurous brittle star with scaly arms, moving only in one plane. B-C. Proximal and distal surfaces of ophiurous brittle star vertebrae, showing the zygospondylous articulations that permit movements in a horizontal plane only. D-E. Proximal and distal surfaces of the vertebrae of an euryalous brittle star, showing the hour-glass articulations of the streptospondylous type, permitting arm movements in all directions. F. The aboral surface of the disc of *Ophiolepus*, with the primitive concentric arrangement of plates. G. *Asteronyx excavata*, an euryalous brittle star with arms that can twine about objects.

used for food manipulation and chemo-reception. Sand dollars have only branchial podia and simple, suckered podia used for locomotion and food-gathering.

Four major types of pedicellariae are found among echinoids: dentate, foliate, ophiocephalous, and globiferous. Dentate pedicellariae are the most common; they usually have three jaws (tridentate), but sand dollars have two-jawed dentates, and some echinoids have dentates with four or five jaws (Fig. 11.22A). Ophiocephalous pedicellariae occur on the peristome (Fig. 11.18D). They are clamped shut by a special valve when closed. Dentate and ophiocephalous pedicellariae drive off or grasp intruders at the surface and may be used in food capture. Foliate pedicellariae usually have three jaws, although some sand dollars have two-jawed foliates. They are used to keep the test clean. Globiferous pedicellariae (Fig. 11.18A) have jaws and ducts specially formed to deliver poison from the poison sacs. They snap viciously at intruders, paralyzing small organisms, and are toxic enough to make starfish withdraw from combat.

CLASS OPHIUROIDEA—BRITTLE STARS

Brittle stars or serpent stars are smaller, more agile, and on the whole more successful than asteroids. About 1600 species have been described, but they are inconspicuous and less well know than asteroids and many more species will probably be found. Although abundant in the littoral zone they are often overlooked, for they hide in the sand or under objects, and some live in sponges or in other colonial animals. They occur from tropical to polar regions, and have been collected from depths of 6000 m.

There are two orders: Ophiurae and Euryalae. Ophiurae have simple arms, supported by skeletal ossicles with zygospondylous articulations (Fig. 11.19B,C), permitting only horizontal arm movements. The arms and disc are usually scaly. Euryalae have simple or branched arms, with streptospondylous articulations, permitting the arms to twine about objects. They do not have conspicuous scales on arms or disc (Fig. 11.19D,E).

Brittle stars are not as diverse in appearance as most other echinoderm groups. The arms can be simple or branched, longer or shorter in relation to the disc size, and smooth or scaly. Most are dull, but there is some variation in color and pigmentation patterns. The most striking forms are basket stars, with arms that branch repeatedly.

During late development the epidermis is invaded and largely replaced by mesenchyme. Gland cells are scant, except on the podia. Cilia or flagella occur only in small tracts or patches, usually on the oral surface of the disc or arms. Epidermal cells cover the sense organs and form a normal covering on the podia.

The dermis and the superficial elements of the skeleton form most of the surface. In many species, especially the Euryalae, the spines and granules of the superficial skeleton are obscured by dermis. Spines are relatively sparse, occurring only at the arm margins, or on the central disc also. Larger spines attach to tubercles and are movable.

The deeper skeleton of the aboral disc of a young ophiuroid consists of a central plate, surrounded by a series of concentric rings of plates with five plates to a ring (Fig. 11.19F). This primitive arrangement is so modified by secondary plates that the

(A, F, and G, after Hyman. B-E, after Lyman.) *External features:* 1, disc; 2, arms; 3, radial shields; 4, central plate; 5, primary concentric plates; 6 aboral arm shields; 7, lateral arm shields; 8, arm spines. *Ossicles:* 9, fossa for upper intervertebral muscles; 10, fossa for lower intervertebral muscles; 11, central depression; 12, central projection; 13, canal for radial nerve; 14, hour-glass projection.

pattern is wholly obscured in many species; in others, granules of the superficial skeleton conceal it. The most conspicuous and constant of the secondary plates are the radial shields on each side of the arm bases.

The arms appear jointed, each joint corresponding to one of the arm vertebrae. The margins of the vertebrae are thinner, providing space for muscles, and meet at special articulating surfaces. Oral and aboral pairs of muscles lie between adjacent vertebrae. The mechanics of arm movement are determined by the articular surfaces; the hour-glass form of the streptospondylous articulation permits movement in all directions. More combinations of directional muscle pulls are possible than skeletal flexibility will actually permit in the Ophiurae. Conspicuous arm shields are associated with each vertebra: one oral, one aboral, and two lateral shields. The two lateral shields are the most important, and are often enlarged at the expense of the oral and aboral shields. They are homologous to the adambulacral ossicles of asteroid arms and bear the arm spines. The extremely variable arm spines are of value in species identification. Little is known of the functional significance of variations in arm spines; presumably they roughen the surface and so aid in clinging to surfaces and in locomotion.

The arm continues across the oral surface to the mouth (Fig. 11.20). The oral and lateral shields are modified at the mouth border. The mouth frame is composed of five wedge-shaped interradial jaws, built of two half-jaws composed of the first two ambulacral plates and lateral arm shields. They bear spines modified to form teeth. A maxiller plate lies across the tips of the half-jaws; through this plate the muscles operating the teeth pass. The oral and two aboral shields conceal a considerable part of the jaw apparatus of most species. One of the oral shields is the madreporite. Bursal slits at the bases of the arms open to the genito-respiratory bursal pits. Two genital plates lie beside each bursal pit.

Internal Anatomy

The internal anatomy of the echinoderm groups is varied but retains a uniquely echinoderm character throughout the phylum. It is particularly characterized, as in crinoids and asteroids, by coelomic compartments, a haemal system associated with the axial gland or its homologue, a watervascular system, and a diffuse nervous system with three somewhat independent centers. The digestive tract is more variable than other systems, having undergone modifications associated with eating habits and dietary differences.

THE COELOM

Some peculiarities of the complexly partitioned echinoderm coelom arise from the way in which it is formed during development; others are associated with its adaptation as a hydraulic system. Although the coelom varies in the different echinoderm groups, it shows certain consistencies that emphasize the unity of the phylum (see Table 11.1).

The main coelomic space is the perivisceral coelom, spacious in echinoids, holothurians, and asteroids, but infiltrated with connective tissue in crinoids and encroached upon by bursal sacs in ophiuroids (Fig. 11.22). The perivisceral coelom extends into the rays of crinoids, asteroids, and ophiuroids, and is partly partitioned by mesenteries supporting the organs. The remainder of the coelom consists of small, more to less discrete spaces associated with the nervous and haemal systems and with the gonads. Three coelomic ring sinuses are generally present. Their basic arrangement is seen most clearly in asteroids (Fig. 11.10C). A hyponeural ring sinus is separated from an epineural ring sinus by a thin membrane in which the nerve ring

Fig. 11.20. Oral View of an Ophiuroid. Note the openings into the bursal sacs at the margins of the arms, and the modified spines forming the teeth around the oral region. The arms continue across the disc and have no open ambulacral groove.

Table 11.1. Derivatives of echinoderm coelomic pouches

	CRINOIDS	HOLOTHURIANS	ECHINOIDS	ASTEROIDS	OPHIUROIDS
Right					
axocoel	not formed	missing	lumen of axial gland and aboral coelom into which axial gland extends	dorsal sac?	right side of axial sinus
hydrocoel	not formed	missing	missing	missing	missing
somatocoel	aboral part of the perivisceral coelom; chambered organ; aboral or genital coelomic canals	aboral part of the perivisceral coelom; perianal sinus	aboral part of the perivisceral coelom; periproctal, perianal, and aboral sinuses.	aboral part of the perivisceral coelom; mesenteries of pyloric caeca; aboral coelom	aboral part of the perivisceral coelom; aboral sinus
Left					
axocoel	axial sinus; hydropore	stone canal?	hydroporic canal; ampulla	axial sinus; inner hyponeural sinus	left side of axial sinus?; hydroporic canal
hydrocoel	water-vascular system; hydroporic canal	water-vascular system; hydroporic canal	water-vascular system; hydroporic canal, in part	water-vascular system; hydroporic canal	water-vascular system; hydroporic canal
somatocoel	oral part of perivisceral coelom; subtentacular coelomic canals	oral part of perivisceral coelom; peribuccal and peripharyngeal sinuses	oral part of perivisceral coelom; peripharyngeal cavity and gill cavities	oral part of perivisceral coelom; outer hyponeural sinus; radial hyponeural sinus	oral part of perivisceral coelom; periesophageal ring sinus; arm coeloms; peristomial ring sinus

Table 11.2. Summary of asteroid characters

	PHANEROZONIA	SPINULOSA	FORCIPULATA
Mouth Frame	adambulacral	adambulacral	ambulacral
Pedicellariae	sessile or alveolar if present	usually none	pediculate
Papulae	aboral	in nidamental chamber	oral and aboral
Marginal plates	with infra- and supramarginals	no conspicuous marginals	no conspicuous marginals
Podia	often without suckers	with suckers	with suckers

lies. The hyponeural ring sinus is connected by an axial sinus, containing the axial gland and stone canal, with an aboral coelomic ring sinus. Radial channels arise from the ring sinuses. The channels from the aboral coelomic ring enclose the gonads, and the channels from the hyponeural ring sinus lie just within the radial nerves. As asteroids have open ambulacral grooves, they have no epineural radial sinuses, but epineural radial sinuses external to the radial nerves are found in echinoids and in holothurians.

The basic arrangement is nearly universal in echinoderms, but is somewhat modified or reduced in some cases. The aboral ring sinus of crinoids is the chambered organ, associated with the cirri and stalk (Fig. 11.5F), and the hyponeural radial sinuses of asteroids are divided by an incomplete partition into two channels.

Holothurians have a small perianal sinus at the aboral end, but the gonads are not radially arranged and there are no radial genital sinuses. Regular echinoids have a complex set of aboral ring sinuses, consisting of a small perianal sinus, a periproctal sinus divided from the main coelom by a ring mesentery supporting the rectum, and a genital ring sinus system. The three ring sinuses tend to be united into a single aboral sinus ring in irregular echinoids. Ophiuroids have an aboral sinus system like that of asteroids.

In holothurians, the epineural sinus lies in the buccal membrane and is termed the peribuccal sinus. Small epineural radial sinuses lie external to the radial nerves. There is no hyponeural ring sinus, but hyponeural radial sinuses lie just beneath the radial nerves. Echinoids have exactly the same arrangement.

Table 11.3. Summary of holothurian characters

	ASPIDOCHIROTA	ELASIPODA	DENDROCHIROTA	MOLPADONIA	APODA
Podia	numerous	numerous	numerous	only as anal papillae	none
Oral tentacles	peltate	peltate	dendritic	digitate	simple, digitate, or pinnate
Oral retractors	none	none	present	none	±
Respiratory tree	present	present	present	present	absent
Cuverian tubules	±	none	none	none	none

Table 11.4. Summary of echinoid characters

	LEPIDOCENTROIDA	CIDAROIDEA	DIADEMITOIDA	HOLECTYPOIDA	CASSIDULOIDA	CLYPEASTROIDA	SPATANGOIDA
Test	flexible; with overlapping or separated plates	rigid, globular	rigid, globular	flattened, rigid	rigid, flattened	rigid, flattened	rigid, convex
Ambulacral plates	pass over peristome to mouth	pass over peristome to mouth	cease at edge of peristome	without petaloids	somewhat petaloid aborally	petaloid aborally	four of five petaloid aborally
Peristome	central	central	central	central	with floscelles	usually central	displaced anteriorly; usually with phyllodes
Apical plates	central	central	central	central	usually central	usually central	displaced anteriorly
Periproct	central	central	central	somewhat displaced from apical plates to aboral	touching apical plates to far displaced	in the posterior ambulacrum	far displaced; on oral surface
Spines	hollow, some very poisonous	large primary on each inter-ambulacral plate; many small secondaries	variable; usually solid	short, dense	small, dense	small, dense	small, dense, but some are larger and from tracts
Podia	mostly for locomotion	weakly developed for locomotion	special buccal podia; mostly locomotor	small	branchial podia aborally	aboral podia branchial	aboral podia branchial; others specialized for other functions
Gills	variously developed	none	well-developed	none	none	none	none
Lantern	well-developed	present	present	only in juveniles	only in juveniles	present	none

388

A part of the perivisceral coelom of echinoids and holothurians is cut off as a peripharyngeal coelomic sinus, lying in the aquapharyngeal bulb of holothurians (Fig. 11.21B), and in Aristotle's lantern in regular echinoids (Fig. 11.24). The chamber so formed helps in manipulating the oral tentacles and the peristomial gills of regular echinoids. Irregular echinoids have no peristomial gills, and are without a peripharyngeal coelomic sinus.

THE HAEMAL SYSTEM

The echinoderm haemal system is closely associated with the coelom and the axial gland. The asteroid system (Fig. 11.10C) illustrates the basic pattern. A system of haemal vessels on the oral side consists of a haemal ring in the hyponeural coelomic sinus and radial branches passing out in the hyponeural radial sinuses. The aboral haemal system consists of a similar aboral haemal ring in the aboral coelomic ring sinus, and radial genital lacunae that run in the genital sinuses. The oral and aboral systems are connected by a large axial gland, containing haemal passageways, from which haemal tufts to the digestive tract arise. The axial gland lies in the axial sinus, and has a head lying in a special coelomic sac, the dorsal sac.

Several modifications are seen in echinoids. The axial gland is free in the perivisceral coelom. In regular echinoids it is a long, dark body, ending blindly at the oral end, and projecting aborally as a finger-like process enclosed in a small coelomic compartment. In irregular echinoids it is much shorter, and contains a plexus of water canals as well as a plexus of haemal vessels. A system of genital haemal lacunae arises from an aboral haemal ring, associated with the aboral coelomic ring sinus, as in asteroids. An oral haemal ring passes around the pharynx, and gives rise to radial haemal lacunae that cross the peristome and run between the water canals and the hyponeural coelomic si-

nuses on the body wall, giving off branches to the podia. A series of short haemal sinuses run to spongy bodies, of unknown function, on the interradii between the radial lacunae. Two main haemal vessels arise from the oral ring, passing on opposite sides of the gut. These are the inner and outer marginal sinuses. In some sea urchins, a contractile, collateral haemal sinus, connected to the outer marginal sinus by many branches, parallels the marginal sinuses for a considerable part of their length.

Holothurians are unusual in having, at the most, only vestiges of an axial gland. Several axial gland homologues have been described, but they may turn out to be sites of coelomocyte formation in the walls of the haemal vessels. Sea cucumbers have no radially arranged, aboral gonads, and the aboral haemal ring and system of genital haemal vessels are missing. Otherwise, the system is much like that of echinoids. A haemal ring encircles the pharynx and gives rise to radial haemal vessels that lie beneath the radial nerves and give rise to podial branches. Two haemal vessels associated with the gut arise from the oral ring. One lies on the mesentery side of the gut. This is the dorsal haemal sinus, the only contractile part of the haemal system. It is not attached to the intestinal wall, but gives rise to many tufty branches, making up the rete mirabile (Fig. 11.21A), an important organ in digestion. A collecting vessel parallels the rete mirable, and gives rise to many small branches attaching it to a haemal plexus in the intestinal wall. On the opposite side of the intestine, a ventral haemal sinus lies.

The ophiuroid haemal system presents some interesting variations of the basic plan seen in asteroids. The oral haemal ring and radial haemal vessels are essentially like those of asteroids. The aboral haemal ring (Fig. 11.22) is long, following the aboral coelomic sinus. On the radii it lies on the aboral side of the central disc,

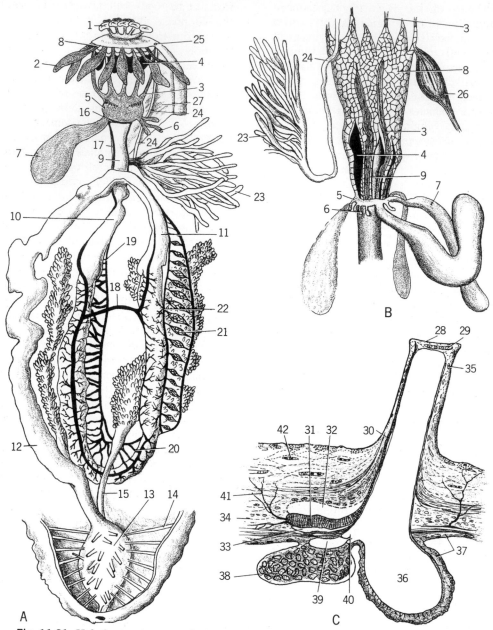

Fig. 11.21. Holothurian Anatomy. **A.** Internal anatomy of *Holothuria tubulosa*. **B.** Calcareous ring and aquapharyngeal bulb of *Thyone sacellus*. **C.** Section of podium and ambulacrum of *Holothuria*. (**A**, after Cuénot. **B**, after Selenka. **C**, after Delage and Hérouard.) *Ambulacral system*: **1**, oral tentacle; **2**, ampullae of tentacle; **3**, radial water canal; **4**, opening between peripharyngeal and perivisceral coelomic spaces; **5**, circumoral water ring; **6**, stone canal and madreporite; **7**, polian vesicle; **8**, calcareous ring. *Digestive tract*: **9**, pharynx; **10**, descending intestine; **11**, ascending intestine; **12**, large intestine; **13**, cloaca; **14**, cloacal dilators;

just below the lateral shields, but on each interradius it turns orally, looping down near the oral shields. The aboral haemal ring vessel gives rise to branches to the bursal sacs and to the gonads, and receives a branch from the haemal plexus of the stomach on each radius. Because of the unusual course of the aboral ring, the axial gland turns orally from the oral haemal ring to reach the aboral ring. It lies in an axial sinus, divided by a central partition into right and left compartments. The left compartment is homologous to the axial sinus of the starfish, and the right compartment to the dorsal sac of starfish.

THE DIGESTIVE SYSTEM

Ophiuroids have the simplest of echinoderm digestive tracts. The mouth lies in the middle of the peristomial membrane, covered by the modified arm skeleton forming the jaw apparatus. The short esophagus opens into a saccate stomach. The stomach pouches out between the bursae, nearly filling the cavity of the central disc. There is no intestine or other digestive structures.

Echinoids and holothurians have an elongated digestive tract. Holothurians with short tentacles do not capture food, but eat the mud or sand around them, digesting out whatever suitable material it may contain. This lazy system of feeding means that a great deal of mud must be processed to avoid starvation. A *Paracaudina* handles up to 140 pounds of mud every year, and according to Crozier, in one Bermuda bay the sea cucumbers pass from about 350 to 500 tons of sand through their digestive tracts per square mile per year. The dendritic tentacles of some species are covered with mucus and are used to catch algae, diatoms, and small plankton organisms. The tentacles are licked off in a regular series, one by one, as a small boy might lick sugar from his fingers. The pharynx passes through the aquapharyngeal bulb and emerges in the main body cavity (Fig. 11.21). The main part of the gut is the intestine, but in some species a slender esophagus and stomach lie between the pharynx and intestine. The intestine is far too long to fit in the body without coiling in most sea cucumbers. It is arranged in a clockwise spiral, viewed from the oral end, descending to the aboral end of the coelom, and it ascends to a sharp aboral bend, the beginning of the rectum. The rectum is often dilated with a load of sand or mud. It leads directly to the cloaca, which is attached to the body wall by dilator muscles. Respiratory trees, highly branched diverticula of the cloaca, are used for respiration (p. 403). Water is pumped in and out of them by the muscles of the cloaca wall and the dilator muscles. Three mesenteries, often lacy and incomplete, support the gut. The dorsal mesentery arises from the middorsal interradius (CD) and supports the anterior part of the intestine. The left mesentery arises from the left dorsal interradius (DE) and supports the ascending part of the intestine. The ventral mesentery usually attaches at the ventral interradius (AB), and supports the rectum.

The echinoid digestive system consists

15, respiratory tree. *Haemal system:* 16, haemal ring; 17, ventral haemal sinus; 18, transverse connection between ventral haemal sinuses; 19, dorsal haemal sinus; 20, lacunar plexus in intestinal bend; 21, rete mirabile; 22, collateral vessel. *Reproductive system:* 23, gonad; 24, gonoduct; 25, gonopore. *Other parts:* 26, retractile muscle; 27, dorsal mesentery. *Histology:* 28, terminal disc of podium; 29, nervous plexus; 30, podial nerve; 31, radial nerve; 32, epineural sinus; 33, hyponeural sinus; 34, dermis; 35, podial muscles; 36, ampulla; 37, peritoneum; 38, radial longitudinal muscle; 39, radial water canal; 40, valve; 41, motor nerve; 42, skeletal ossicle.

of a pharynx, surrounded by Aristotle's lantern, an esophagus below the lantern, an intestine, often divided into two parts, and a rectum. A caecum usually occurs at the union of the esophagus and intestine. It is very large in spatangoids. The intestine coils about the test and is festooned by mesenteries. In regular echinoids it makes nearly a complete counterclockwise turn, bends back on itself to return in an aboral circuit, and then turns upward at the rectum to end at the anus (Fig. 11.18C). A similar coiled arrangement is seen in irregular echinoids. A curious feature is the siphon, a narrow,

ciliated tube branching from the first part of the intestine. It runs parallel to the intestine and rejoins it near the point of its recurvature (Fig. 11.18B). It is thought to carry water past the first part of the gut, concentrating food and enzymes in this region.

Aristotle's lantern is a unique feature of echinoids. It is a complex structure, with 40 ossicles in addition to the teeth. The main external framework is dominated by five large pyramids, each consisting of two half-pyramids tightly joined (Fig. 11.24B). At the aboral end, ten epiphyses form complete or incomplete

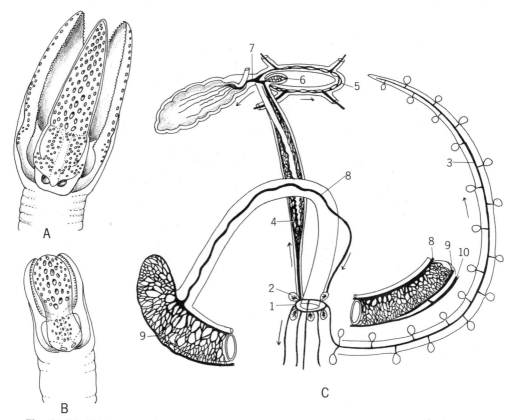

Fig. 11.22. Echinoid pedicellariae and haemal system. A. Tridentate pedicellaria of *Arbacia*. B. Triphyllous pedicellaria of *Arbacia*. C. Scheme of the haemal system of *Echinus*. (A and B, after Reid, in Brown. C, after Cuénot, in Grassé.) 1, oral haemal ring; 2, spongy body; 3, radial haemal lacunae in radial coelomic sinus; 4, axial gland in axial sinus; 5, aboral haemal ring; 6, terminal sinus; 7, genital haemal lacuna in genital coelomic sinus; 8, collecting sinus; 9, inner marginal sinus; 10, collateral sinus.

bars across the top of the pyramids. Three types of sea urchins are distinguished by the epiphyses. Aulodonts have widely separate epiphyses, and the lantern teeth have no keel. Stirodonts have epiphyses that are not joined at the top of the pyramids and have keeled teeth. *Arbacia* is a common stirodont. Camarodonts have the epiphyses fully united as a bar and often have a recess that holds the teeth in place. *Strongylocentrotus* is a camarodont. The compasses extend radially over the upper surface of the lantern. Each is composed of an inner and outer ossicle. Below the compasses, usually hidden by muscles, are the five rotules, rather heavy plates arranged radially. The long teeth are supported by the pyramids. At the aboral end they become membranous and extend into the dental sacs of the peripharyngeal sinus. The musculature is as complex as the ossicle arrangement. Commintator muscles between the pyramids rock them back and forth. Small inner

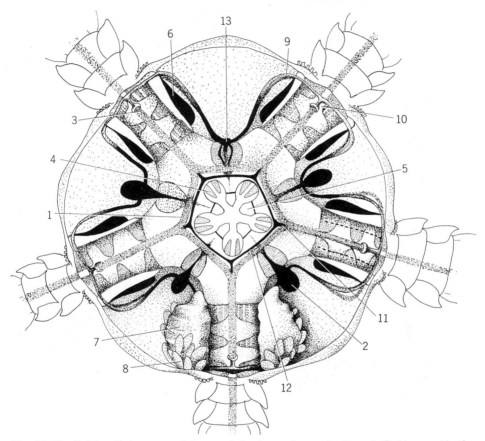

Fig. 11.23. Ophiuroid Anatomy. Scheme of the internal organization of *Ophiura*, with the digestive system and all but one pair of bursae removed. (After Cuénot, in Grassé.) *Ambulacral system:* 1, circumoral water ring; 2, polian vesicle; 3, radial water canal; 4, oral podium. *Mouth:* 5, tooth. *Bursal system:* 6, bursal slit; 7, bursa. *Reproductive system:* 8, gonad. *Haemal system:* 9, aboral coelomic sinus, containing the aboral haemal sinus; 10, efferent haemal lacuna from the gastric diverticula; 11, radial haemal channel; 12, oral coelomic ring sinus and enclosed haemal ring; 13, axial sinus containing axial gland.

and outer rotular muscles transfer the pyramid movements to the teeth; they connect the epiphyses and rotules. Lantern protractors from the epiphyses to the perignathic girdle move the whole lantern forward, extruding the teeth, and lantern retractors withdraw the lantern. They attach to the inner ends of the pyramids and to the ambulacral auricles.

The rear part of the lantern of sea urchins is used for respiration. The cavity of the peristomial gills is continuous with the peripharyngeal coelomic sinus. A flat sheet of muscle forms a pentagonal ring, connecting the compasses; its contraction elevates the compasses, increasing the volume of the sinus and collapsing the gills. Narrow compass depressors pass along the margins of the protractor muscles. When they are contracted, coelomic fluid is forced back into the gills. Only sea urchins have a fully developed lantern. Clypeastroids also have a lantern, but they have no peristomial gills, compasses, or compass musculature. The lantern is broader, lower, and star-shaped (Fig. 11.18B).

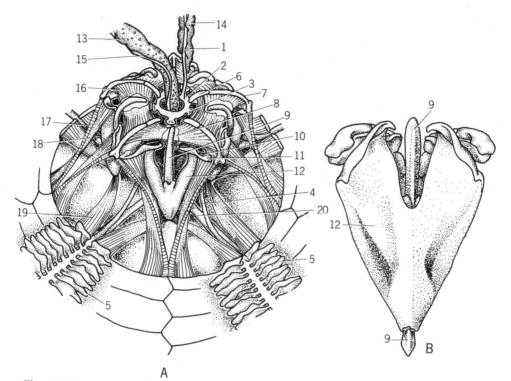

Fig. 11.24. Aristotle's Lantern. A. The lantern and musculature of *Arbacia punctulata*. B. Lantern ossicles of *Arbacia punctulata*, showing the relationship of tooth and pyramid. (After Reid, in Brown.) *Ambulacral system:* 1, madreporic canal; 2, ring canal; 3, polian vesicle; 4, radial canal; 5, ampullae. *Lantern ossicles:* 6, proximal compass ossicle; 7, distal compass ossicle; 8, dental capsule; 9, tooth; 10, rotula; 11, epiphysis; 12, alveolus. *Digestive tract:* 13, esophagus. *Haemal system:* 14, axial organ; 15, inner marginal haemal sinus. *Muscles:* 16, compass elevator; 17, compass depressor; 18, lantern protractor; 19, lantern retractor. *Nerves:* 20, radial nerve.

THE WATER-VASCULAR SYSTEM

The water-vascular system is one of the most stable elements of echinoderm anatomy, although the position of the radial water canals differs in the various echinoderm groups. The radial water canals extend into the arms of asteroids, orphiuroids, and crinoids, and lie on the inner surface of the body wall in echinoids and holothurians. In any case, the podia are attached to the radial water canals by lateral canals, and while crinoid and ophiuroid podia have no ampullae, the mechanics of their operation remain the same throughout the phylum. The principal differences lie in the number and arrangement of the stone-canal system, the position of the madreporite, and the number and kinds of compensation sacs associated with the radial water canal around the stomodaeum.

The ring water canal of sea cucumbers encircles the pharynx behind a calcareous ring (Fig. 11.21B). One or more sac-like polian vesicles hang from the ring canal, serving as expansion sacs when the fluid is put under pressure. Elasipods and molpadonians have a single stone canal attached to the ring canal, and in elasipods it sometimes reaches the body surface. In other holothurians the stone canal is branched and several or many porous, ciliated madreporic bodies hang in the coelom. Apoda are unique among modern echinoderms in having no radial canals. All other holothurians have five radial canals that arch up over the aquapharyngeal bulb, enter the bulb near the oral end, and give off branches to the oral tentacles. They continue, much diminished, over the surface of the body wall beneath the ambulacra. Each radial water canal ends in a terminal podium, often associated with a system of anal papillae at the aboral end of the body.

Echinoids have a very similar system. The ring water canal lies at the aboral end of the lantern, or near the mouth if there is no lantern. A stone canal parallels the axial gland, connecting the madreporite, located in one of the genital plates at the aboral end of the test, with the water canal. The radial water canals lie just within the ambulacral plates and extend aborally to terminal podia which pierce the terminal plates. At each interradius a small canal connects a mass of lymphoid tissue, the spongy body, to the ring water canal.

Ophiuroids may have a single hydropore in the oral shield on interradius CD, or may have a madreporite in each of the interradii. Typical ophiuroids have a pore canal between the hydropore and an ampulla. The ampulla and ring canal are connected by a stone canal that passes through the axial sinus. The ring canal gives rise to polian vesicles on all of the interradii except the one occupied by the stone canal (Fig. 11.22). Special branches from the ring canal pass to the ten oral podia, and radial water canals extend into the rays. The radial water canals pass along the aboral surface of the vertebrae in a notch (Fig. 11.25C). The water canal is expanded in each ossicle, and paired podial canals arise from these regions to the podia. The podia are small, papillate structures, richly supplied with gland cells.

The basic form and mechanics of podia remain much the same, regardless of the function of the podia or the presence or absence of ampullae. The lateral canals which connect the podia and water canals usually have a valve, preventing back-flow into the main water canal. The ampule projects into the coelom. The podium and ampullae are essentially spaces in the body wall, attached to the water-canal system and lined with the coelomic epithelium of the water-vascular system. Each podium contains the normal elements of the body wall: epidermis, dermis, muscle, and a lining of ambulacral peritoneum. Perivisceral peritoneum, connective tis-

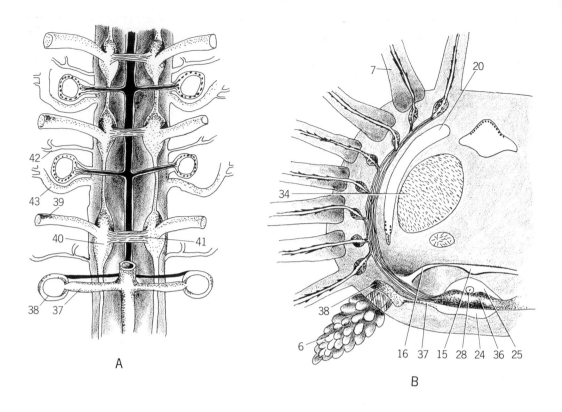

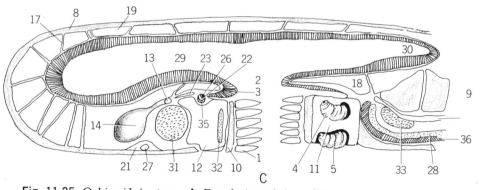

Fig. 11.25. Ophiuroid Anatomy. **A.** Dorsal view of the radial nerve and associated structures in *Ophiocomina*. **B.** Section through the arm of *Ophiothrix*. **C.** Scheme of a section through the central disc of an ophiuroid, passing through an interradius on the left and a radius on the right. (A, largely after Ludwig. B and C, after Cuénot, in Grassé.) *External features:* 1, teeth; 2, mouth; 3, peristome; 4, oral podium; 5, second podium; 6, arm podium; 7, spine; 8, body wall. *Skeletal system:* 9, vertebral ossicle; 10, maxiller; 11, ambulacral ossicle; 12, adambulacral ossicle. *Ambulacral system:* 13, circumoral water ring; 14, polian vesicle; 15, radial water canal; 16, lateral water canal. *Coelom:* 17, gastric mesentery; 18, perieso-phageal coelomic cavity; 19, perivisceral coelomic cavity; 20, arm coelom; 21, aboral coelomic sinus; 22, hyponeural ring canal; 23, epineural ring canal; 24, epineural coelomic sinus;

sue, muscle, and the lining peritoneum form the wall of ampullae (Fig. 11.21C). When the valve of the lateral canal is closed, contraction of the ampullar muscles forces water into the podium. It is prevented from dilating by connective tissue in the wall and so must lengthen. When the longitudinal muscles of the podial wall contract, the podium shortens as fluid is forced back into the ampulla. The degree of podial expansion is actually determined by the tone of ampullar and podial muscle and the amount of fluid on the podial side of the valve. Evidently, if the longitudinal muscle of one side of the podium contracts, the podium will bend. If its terminal sucker is attached, a certain amount of leverage is applied to the whole animal. It is a common misconception that podia pull the animal forward. Most starfish and echinoid podia push the animal forward in a step much like that of a land vertebrate; pulling movements are most common in heavy-bodied echinoderms.

The locomotor podia of echinoids, holothuroids, and asteroids end in a plate of thickened epithelium. Marginal extensions of the epidermis and connective tissue usually form sucker-discs at the tip. A podial nerve from the oral part of the radial nerve connects with a general epidermal nerve plexus in the podial wall and ends in a terminal nerve pad at the podial tip. One or more nerve rings may pass around the podium, most commonly near the tip. Sensory podia are without terminal suckers, and are often set in papillae in sea cucumbers (Fig. 11.8A). They are especially abundant on the dorsal surface of holothurians, and in ophiu-

rids and echinoids. Irregular echinoids have flattened, saccate branchial podia, used in respiration, on the dorsal surface. Special oral podia, larger and more powerful, occur in ophiurids and echinoids. The oral tentacles of sea cucumbers are modified podia.

NEUROSENSORY APPARATUS

The nervous system and sensory apparatus are extremely diffuse in echinoderms. The subepidermal nerve plexus extends everywhere on the body surface, and every projection from the body surface is richly supplied with sensory cells. Podia, papulae, pedicellariae, and spines react when stimulated. Special sense organs, however, are not abundant.

The neurosensory cells of echinoderms are like those of other invertebrates, terminating in sensory tips and having basal fibers that make contact with the nerve plexus. In some cases they form sensory buds (Fig. 11.8B), especially common in the jaws of globiferous echinoid pedicellariae, and in apod holothurians in the oral and anal regions, or in papillate projections of the body surface. Generally speaking, neurosensory cells are concentrated on the peristomial membrane or around the mouth opening, and are also abundant near the anus.

The light-sensitive cells of most echinoderms are scattered over the body surface. Asteroids often have an optic cushion at the tip of each ray, consisting of a cluster of small, pigment cup ocelli. Diadematid sea urchins have bright-blue bodies on the genital plates, and in some species similar blue bodies are found on the peristome.

25, hyponeural coelomic sinus. *Haemal system:* 26, oral haemal ring; 27, aboral haemal ring; 28, radial haemal channel. *Digestive system:* 29, stomach; 30, gastric diverticulum. *Muscles:* 31, external interradial muscle; 32, internal interradial muscle; 33, lower radial muscle; 34, flexor muscle. *Nervous system:* 35, nerve ring; 36, radial nerve; 37, podial nerve; 38, podial ring ganglion; 39, motor nerve to intervertebral muscles; 40, motor ganglion of deep oral nervous system; 41, commissure between the motor ganglia; 42, lateral nerve; 43, sensory nerve to body wall.

In *Astropyga radiata,* they form stalked bodies which histologically resemble a compound eye. Although there is good evidence for a light-receptive function of asteroid optic cushions, the echinoid "eyes" are not definitely shown to be light receptors.

Some echinoderms have balance organs. Apod, elasipod, and Molpadonian sea cucumbers have interesting statocysts, set on stalks and hanging like hammers over the nerve ring or the base of the radial nerves (Fig. 11.8C). Many echinoids have somewhat similar sphaeridia. Geotactic responses, however, occur in echinoderms without balance organs, presumably as a result of tactile stimulation of the upper or lower surface (p. 406).

Most echinoderms have some remnants of the three major nerve rings, the oral (ectoneural), deep oral (hyponeural) and aboral (entoneural). Except for the crinoids, however, the oral system predominates. The aboral nervous system has disappeared entirely in holothurians. It is much reduced in ophiuroids, but some have a definite aboral nerve ring that gives rise to nerves to the gonads. In echinoids, also, the aboral ring supplies the genital region with nerves. Asteroids have a well-developed aboral nerve ring associated with a subperitoneal plexus that operates the muscles of the body wall appendages on the aboral surface.

The oral and deep oral systems are closely allied. The oral system gives rise to sensory and motor fibers, while the deep oral system is at least predominantly motor. In ophiuroids the oral and deep oral systems are about equally well developed. The main nerve ring lies between the epineural and hyponeural ring sinuses, and the radial nerves as well as the nerve ring are divided by a median septum into oral and deep oral parts. The deep oral nerve band produces only motor nerves to the intervertebral muscles, while the oral nerve band is larger, and gives rise to motor and sensory nerves to podia and to the body surface.

Holothurians have a greatly reduced deep oral system. The oral system centers in a nerve ring in contact with the peribuccal coelomic sinus and gives rise to radial nerves that lie just external to the water canals. The deep oral system consists only of delicate motor nerves lying on the inner surface of the oral radial nerves. They innervate the body-wall muscles and make contact with the subepidermal plexus. The deep oral fibers do not reach the nerve ring. In echinoids, the oral system centers in a nerve ring around the pharynx, and gives off nerves to the peristome and mouth region and five radial nerves that lie between the epineural and hyponeural coelomic sinuses. The radial nerves give off branches to the podia and make contact with the rich subepidermal plexus. The plexus is strongly developed, forming rings around the spines and pedicellariae. Five nerve masses on the pharyngeal wall just internal to the oral ring appear to be the vestiges of the hyponeural system. They innervate the lantern musculature.

Echinoderm Physiology

In spite of marked differences in external form, the internal organ systems are relatively stable. They provide a good opportunity to observe how functions are modified during the evolutionary divergence of organisms with a rather definite organizational plan.

Perhaps the most outstanding peculiarity of echinoderms is the informality of their way of doing things. Except for the well-developed body wall and endoskeleton and the unique water-vascular system, echinoderm organization is rather simple. There is no excretory system, and respiratory arrangements are little more than jury-rigged expedients. The digestive system is sometimes incomplete, and although echinoderms are relatively large, the circulatory system is quite simple and ineffective. The reproductive system is simple, and the diffuse nervous system has nothing remotely like a brain. Nevertheless, they have been remarkably successful for a long time.

OSMOREGULATION

Echinoderms have little ability to control the entry or exit of water or salts. The sea cucumber, *Paracaudina*, swells in diluted sea water and loses weight if returned to normal sea water. Pieces of the body wall are fully permeable to water and to inorganic cations and anions. Various asteroids (*Asterias, Solaster,* and *Astropecten*) have demonstrated the same inability to control water intake but have some control over ions, for more potassium and hydrogen ions occur in the coelomic fluid than in sea water. They can survive some dilution of sea water, but only by tolerating a more dilute coelomic fluid, a swollen body, a softer body wall, and other morphological changes. Echinoids imbibe water when placed in a dilute medium but cannot swell, as they are enclosed within a test. The coelomic fluid of some echinoids has a higher potassium, sodium, and chloride content than the external medium, as well as a lower pH.

In a chemical sense, echinoderms evidently live in glass houses. Their metabolism is accomplished without the chemical screen that the body wall of most animals provides. If they are to remain alive it is imperative that cells be able to retain ions. There is strong evidence that this is the case. Many ions are more concentrated in tissues than in coelomic fluid. This situation contrasts with the usual arrangement in animals, where the body fluid provides a controlled isotonic environment for tissue cells. Echinoderm cells undoubtedly spend more energy for the control of inorganic cations and anions than is the case in most animals.

The inability to control the internal ionic and water content is associated with the restriction of echinoderms to marine habitats. Most do not venture into brackish water, and they avoid estuaries. It is unimportant that crinoids have a porous tegmen, through which sea water is free to enter the body cavity, for other echinoderms are scarcely better protected.

INTERNAL TRANSPORT

Where water and salts pass freely through the body wall, how effective can coelomic fluid be in internal transport? Peritoneal cilia or flagella agitate the coelomic fluid of all echinoderms, and there can be no doubt that this agitation is useful in the transport of materials. The use of coelomic compartments as a hydraulic skeleton and as a hydraulic system for moving gills or other parts changes, but does not wholly destroy, definite currents in the perivisceral coelomic cavity and its extensions into the arms. Coelomic currents have been described in a number of echinoderms. In sea cucumbers, the coelomic fluid flows aborally along the inner surface of the body wall, and returns centrally; in the tentacles the current passes toward the tip at the oral surface and back on the outer side. The coelomic fluid of starfish tends to flow distally along the aboral surface and center of the central disc and arms, and to return along the margins of the rays.

The flowing coelomic fluid sweeps coelomocytes along and aids in the distribution of oxygen. What of food distribution? There is little organic material in the coelomic fluid, except in the form of coelomocytes. Amino acids injected into the digestive tract of a sea cucumber, *Arbacia*, appear in the coelomic fluid. Sugars injected into the gut may or may not appear in the coelomic fluid, but sugars injected in the coelom are rapidly converted into glycogen and disappear as soluble sugar. Amino acids have been recovered from the coelomic fluid of feeding starfish. The organic content of sea cucumber coelomic fluid is also low. The gut wall is wholly impermeable to chlorides, sulphates, glucose, and sucrose, and food absorption is difficult to explain.

The evidence points to a limited role of the coelomic fluid in the distribution of foods, particularly of dissolved carbohydrates. When present, they disappear rapidly. The coelom is too close to the ocean; there are too many thin-walled podia, gills, and other structures and the danger of losing hard-won food is too great. The coelomic channels and haemal system they contain may be an adaptation that slows down losses and preserves some passageways that approach equilibrium with sea water more slowly. There is little real evidence to support this, but what information is available is consonant with it. The potassium content of the water-vascular system of some echinoderms is higher than that of the coelom. As potassium is highly mobile, it may be a good test. The second line of adaptation is use of coelomocytes in transport. They occur in the gut lumen, in the coelom, in the haemal system, and in the dermis of the body wall. They are often filled with food inclusions, supporting the idea that they are important in food transport. A third line of adaptation leads to storage of food in the gut wall. This is most clearly demonstrated in asteroids, where specially differentiated storage cells occur in the walls of the pyloric caeca.

The close relationship of the haemal system and the gut, as evidenced by the extensive haemal sinus system of holothurians and echinoids, and to a lesser extent in other echinoderms, suggests that the haemal system may be important in food distribution. In this sense the haemal system is truly an incipient circulatory system. In holothurians it contains haemocytes, and so plays a role in oxygen distribution also, but in no echinoderms has the haemal system become an effective circulatory system, perhaps because extensive currents in the perivisceral coelom tend to make its further development unprofitable. Movement of fluids in the haemal system is caused by cilia or flagella on the peritoneal lining, to some extent aided by contractility of parts of the haemal walls. The head of the axial gland contracts in some asteroids, the dorsal haemal sinus of holothurians is contractile, and the collateral sinus of some echinoids is also contractile. In some instances a local circulation is established in the haemal vessels and plexus associated with the gut. The walls of the haemal system are incomplete; all of the coelomic spaces communicate more or less directly, varying in intimacy with the group. Internal transport occurs to some extent in the coelomic sinuses and the perivisceral coelom, to some extent in the water-vascular system, and to some extent in the haemal system. The physiological diffuseness is typical of echinoderms, and is seen in most of their organ systems.

DIGESTION

The stomodaeum is associated with the reception of food and its conduction to the midgut, and sometimes has adaptations for food storage and the mechanical trituration of food. Its development varies considerably in different echinoderm groups. In ophiuroids, for example, modifications of the arm skeleton and spines enter into jaw structure, while the echinoid lantern is associated with the stomodaeum.

Food is moved along the gut by muscular action and by cilia or flagella. Some ciliation of the gastrodermis occurs in all echinoderms, but it is sparse in holothurians, which eat large quantities of mud or sand and have more muscular intestinal walls than most echinoderms. Peristaltic waves move along the *Synaptula* intestine at intervals of about two seconds, pushing the food along. Crinoids, on the other hand, depend more than most echinoderms on ciliary currents, probably in association with the habit of ciliary feeding. Usually cilia and muscle cooperate in moving food materials and digestive juices in the gut. The intestinal caeca of *Asterias* pulsate rhythmically, for example, the muscular movements helping the cilia to propel food particles and digestive juices.

Strong musculature develops in forms that evert the stomach for feeding and egestion. Starfish mouth muscles are relaxed by acetylcholine and contracted by adrenalin. The relaxation of the mouth is accompanied by contraction of the body-wall muscles, increasing pressure and forcing the stomach out. The stomach is withdrawn by active contraction of the gastric musculature and relaxation of the body wall, presumably as a result of muscles that respond antagonistically to neurohumoral substances.

The kind of food that can be eaten profitably depends on the complement of digestive enzymes. Enzymes have been specified for several echinoderms; no great consistency is observed, as might be expected in view of the dietary differences among them. As a rule, protein digestion is very active, and carbohydrate digestion reasonably so. Lipases seem in short supply.

Echinoderm gland structure tends to be primitive, with little evidence of surface amplification through the formation of compound glands. Only asteroids have very large gut diverticula, and while the gastric caeca secrete enzymes, they are also used in absorption and intracellular digestion. Evidently the species that evert the stomach must secrete large quantities of enzymes for preliminary digestion of food. In other echinoderms, unicellular glands are intermingled with ciliated epithelial cells. They occur abundantly in the pharyngeal, and sometimes in the gastric region, of holothurians, in the esophagus of echinoderms, and in the esophagus and stomach wall of asteroids.

They are sparse in the holothurian intestine, and appear to be completely absent in the intestine of echinoids. Gland cells have not been described in the digestive tract of ophiuroids. Compound glands are occasionally seen, as in the esophagus of echinoids, but are rare.

Extracellular digestion is evidently important in asteroids that evert the stomach. The relative scarcity of gland cells in the gut wall of the other echinoderms suggests that some other source of digestive enzymes may be important. The transparent mucous covering of food balls in the echinoid intestine include bacteria, and an agar-dissolving bacterium has been recovered from the intestine of *Strongylocentrotus*. The haemal plexus of sea cucumbers contains the same enzymes as the intestine. It is thought that coelomocytes from the haemal plexus enter the gut, bringing enzymes, and load up with food for the journey out. Intracellular digestion may occur in the coelomocytes. It is probable, in view of the dearth of gland cells, that the microbial flora and coelomocytes play an important role in digestion. A *p*H gradient is evident in the echinoderm digestive tube, with the acid end at the stomach or the beginning of the intestine and the basic end at the rectum. As enzymes are active in definite *p*H ranges, some sequentialism of extracellular digestive processes probably results.

Modifications of the digestive tract are sometimes clearly related to function. The decline of the intestine in asteroids that feed by stomach eversion, and in asteroids and ophiuroids that egest shells or hard fragments through the mouth, is an evident case. Too little is known of the details of digestion to determine the exact functions of diverticula. Pyloric caeca of asteroids amplify surface for secretion, absorption, and intracellular digestion, but the function of other diverticula is unknown. The paucity of gland cells suggests that the festoons of the ophiuroid stomach must be associated with absorption rather than secretion, and that the lengthening of the digestive tube of crinoids, echinoids, and holothurians must also be associated with something other than secretion. Peculiarities of the absorptive process, however, make it uncertain to what extent absorptive surface is increased by lengthening of the digestive tube. It is possible that some of the modifications in gut shape are important in delaying the explusion of food, giving more time for the rather informal digestive processes to be finished.

RESPIRATION

Echinoderms are aerobic. Most echinoderms are not very effective in respiratory exchange. Oxygen uptake of starfish and echinoids is dependent on oxygen tension; under ordinary conditions they have no safety factor. The sea cucumber, *Paracaudina*, also takes up oxygen at rates dependent on the oxygen tension, but *Thyone* oxygen consumption remains constant until oxygen tension has fallen to about one-seventh of normal figures. Evidently some echinoderms have a more effective system of respiration, but the activities of most are limited by the availability of oxygen. Considering their relatively inactive life, it is clear that the respiratory arrangements are poor.

Echinoderm ancestral stocks must have been without respiratory organs; presumably relatively small size and inactivity made the body surface adequate for respiratory exchange. Respiratory adaptations differ in each class and sometimes in smaller subgroups, from which one may infer that respiratory adaptations appeared late, after the major aspects of body form had been stabilized. Most respiratory modifications seem to be structural afterthoughts, mere expedient solutions to respiratory problems that may have appeared with increased size or activity. They involve surface amplifications bringing the coelomic fluid in close proximity to the sea, or a pumping device that "breathes" sea water, especially at the end of the hindgut.

Crinoids have no special respiratory structures. Water enters the coelom through pores in the tegmen, but this exchange is small and serves primarily to maintain coelomic pressure. Respiratory exchange occurs at the podia, but the rest of the body surface must also play a minor role. Podial respiration is important in all echinoderms, even when other respiratory structures are present. In starfish, for example, the covering of one ambulacral groove reduces respiratory exchange by about 10 per cent. Undoubtedly body surface and podial respiration are the primitive mode in the phylum.

Currents in the ambulacral grooves or on the general body surface ventilate the podia and surface epithelium and hasten respiratory transfer. The thin podial walls bring the fluid of the water-vascular system close to the exterior, and podia are excellently adapted for gaseous exchange. They are not primarily for respiration, however, and the aerated fluid in the water canals does not reach many tissues, although oxygen in it can pass into the coelomic fluid. Where no other respiratory structures are found, podia may be specially modified for respiration. The irregular echinoids have flattened or ruffled branchial podia extending from the petaloid, aboral ambulacral regions.

More commonly, however, echinoderms have resorted to non-podial respiratory adaptations. Special body-wall appendages, with podia-like walls, occur in some. Asteroids have papulae, and regular echinoids have peristomial gills. Both are thin-walled evaginations of the body surface, containing coelomic fluid agitated by peritoneal flagella, and are equipped with external flagella that ventilate the outer surface. Starfish papulae occur over most of the body surface, or on the major part of the aboral surface. The peristomial gills of echinoids occur in a circlet on the peristome.

The elevation and depression of the compasses of Aristotle's lantern by the lantern musculature raise and lower the aboral membrane bounding the peripharyngeal coelomic sinus and pump coelomic fluid in and out of the gills, replacing or augmenting the flagellary agitation of the coelmic fluid by muscular movements. The substitution of muscular control for ciliary or flagellar control of ventilating surface membranes is a general tendency of larger and more complex invertebrates. A somewhat similar mechanism has developed in some phanerozonian starfish. The upper surface of these starfish is a false front, so to speak, consisting of a membrane supported by the outer ends of the aboral paxillae. A spacious nidamental chamber lies beneath, with a floor consisting of the main body wall covered by many papulae. The upper wall of the chamber is pierced by a large, central osculum and many minute pores (spiracles). Openings also occur at the ray margins. Water is pumped in and out of the nidamental chamber, entering through the marginal openings and spiracles, and departing through the osculum. With each pulsation, the papulae expand and contract.

Most ophiuroids have a different respiratory mechanism, consisting of ten bursal sacs, open to the exterior through bursal slits. Ciliary currents carry water into and out of the bursae. In some ophiuroids, disc movements pump water in and out of the bursae once or twice a minute. The bursae are sometimes very large and partially united, encroaching on the perivisceral coelom.

Molpadonian, dendrochirote, and aspidochirote sea cucumbers have extensively branched diverticula of the hindgut know as respiratory trees. These are filled and emptied by pumping movements of the cloaca. The anus is opened, and contractions of dilator muscles fill the cloaca. The anus is closed, the cloacal wall contracts, a valve at the base of the respiratory trees opens, and water is forced into the respiratory trees. The respiratory trees contract, often simultaneously with body-wall muscles, to expel the water. When the respiratory trees are lost by evisceration, cloacal pumping continues to move water into and out of the coelom.

Muscular respiratory movements are not rhythmic in most echinoderms, but holothurians with respiratory trees maintain a regular rhythm that can be modified in response to changed respiratory needs. Cloacal pumping is disturbed by stimulation of the oral tentacles, but the main regulatory mechanisms lie in the aboral end. The beat of the cloaca ceases if it is separated from the body wall; evidently the body-wall nerve plexus is in charge. A reduction in oxygen tension increases the vigor of pumping in isolated strips of cloaca, but if it falls too low, pumping ceases rapidly. The ability to adjust respiratory movements to respiratory demands is an important step in respiratory evolution.

If a sea cucumber anus is covered by a rubber membrane, oxygen consumption falls by half or more immediately. The animal extends its oral tentacles fully and stretches its body out in a reflex that favors oxygen absorption at the surface. Anal pumping is not unique in sea cucumbers. Some crinoids pump water in and out at the anus, and this activity also occurs in some other animal phyla. This method of increasing oxygen intake may have an ancient history, at least in echinoderms.

The diversity of respiratory arrangements indicates that independent responses to a physiological need have led to similar selective pressures, but with diverse end results, even though all echinoderms have a somewhat similar internal organization. Evidently similar selective pressures evoked by similar problems may lead to either evolutionary convergence or divergence.

Despite the diversity in respiratory adaptations for gaseous exchange, special internal transporting mechanisms have not been developed by most echinoderms. Haemoglobin occurs in haemocytes in the coelomic fluid and haemal channels of holothurians. It gives the coelomic fluid a reddish color, and probably plays a role in oxygen transport. Sea cucumbers have rather low oxygen requirements, and it is not surprising that some have reached the point where respiration can continue at the same rate in spite of reduced oxygen tensions. Coelomocytes in the water canals of one species of brittle star have been reported to contain haemoglobin, but this has not been confirmed. Other pigments found in coelomocytes have proved not to be respiratory.

EXCRETION

Echinoderms have no excretory organs, and excretion is carried out informally. They release relatively small amounts of nitrogenous wastes, and there is a considerable discrepancy in the reports available. Echinoderms are ammonotelic, but some excrete significant percentages of other compounds. It appears that echinoderms have been experimental about excretion, as about some other physiological functions. Uric acid and allantoin are common excretory products of purine metabolism; both have been recovered in small amounts from echinoderms. When the enzyme uricase is present, uric acid is converted to urea. Uricase has been obtained from some echinoderm tissues, and a number of echinoderms excrete significant quantities of urea. All urea does not stem from uric acid, however, as ammonia may be formed from urea or urea from ammonia. In Asterias, the ratio of ammonia to urea nitrogen released is approximately 4 to 1. Some echinoderms apparently liberate significant amounts of

amino acids. Creatine and creatinine have been reported, and as these are also liberated by vertebrates, they have been considered to be phylogenetically significant. These compounds are relatively unimportant in echinoderms, however. The over-all impression is that echinoderms are ammonotelic, with urea the next most important excretory product. Uric acid is not excreted in large amounts, and amino acids are often more significant. Creatine and creatinine are very minor elements of excretion. In individual cases, however, the percentages may be shifted considerably. Asterias, for example, liberates about one-fourth of its nitrogen as amino acid.

Soluble wastes leave at the body surface, and perhaps at the intestinal surface. Insoluble wastes are picked up by amoebocytes for disposal in various ways. Many amoebocytes contain brownish inclusions that may be urates. Special devices capitalizing on the phagocytic capacities of coelomic amoebocytes are sometimes found. Apod holothurians have ciliated urns in the peritoneal lining. Here coelomocytes accumulate to form masses that pass into the body wall or fall into the coelom as brown bodies. Loaded amoebocytes leave asteroids through the papulae or podia, and echinoid amoebocytes also leave through the podia. The axial gland seems to be an important station on the way out, for loaded amoebocytes are abundant there. They may make their way out through the madreporite. The amoeboid coelomocytes seem to be the major method of discharging insoluble wastes. They take the most convenient route out, whether through podia, gills, or madreporite.

The coelomocytes are evidently important agents in echinoderm economy. They enter actively into food and waste transport, may participate in digestion, and sometimes deliver enzymes to the digestive tube. Special haemocytes probably enter into respiratory transport in holothurians. The dependence upon wandering cells to carry out so many functions is evidently a primitive trait. Perhaps the capacities of the coelomocytes have tended to reduce or eliminate selective pressures that might have resulted in more effective organ systems.

ECHINODERM RESPONSIVENESS

Echinoderms respond to the stimuli they are able to receive. Sensory reception occurs in neurosensory cells dispersed in the epidermal covering, sometimes clustered to form sensory buds. They are closely associated with the body-wall appendages: spines, papulae, podia, and pedicellariae. The body surface is sensitive to the usual range of stimuli—to touch, light, chemicals, and water currents. Sensory cells are connected with the subepidermal nerve plexus and may initiate local responses or coordinated responses involving the whole organism.

Special sense organs are not abundant. Optic cushions at the tip of asteroid rays contain a number of pigment-cup ocelli each. Some sea urchins have blue bodies on the genital plates of the apical system or on the peristome, thought to be photosensitive. Stalked statocysts occur in holothurians, and echinoid sphaeridia are also thought to be balance organs. There is some evidence of special chemical sensitivity of oral podia and oral tentacles of echinoids and holothurians.

Local responses vary with the part stimulated. Most pedicellariae respond positively to moderate contact but bend away from strong mechanical stimuli, but pedicellariae with poison glands are not repelled by strong mechanical force. They attack fearlessly, and shear off, if necessary, still clamped to the intruder. Echinoid spines have a double musculature, one to set the spine in position and one to manipulate it. Touching a spine causes contractions that set it, but the holding muscles relax, and manipulating muscles come into play when the body surface at the base of the spine is touched. Reactions of this kind are wholly controlled by local reflexes in the subepidermal nerve net, and are not disturbed by removal of all traces of the radial nerves. The echinoderm subepidermal nerve plexus is in no way comparable to the nerve net of cnidarians. It transmits impulses in all directions, but is thickened as definite, often ring-shaped, ganglia at the bases of spines and pedicellariae and in the podia.

The oral (ectoneural) nervous system is both sensory and motor, and is closely associated with the subepidermal nerve net. The deep oral (hyponeural) is motor, innervating the podia and muscles of the body wall. Except in crinoids, the aboral (entoneural) nervous system is largely concerned with the innervation of the gonads and gonoducts. There is nothing comparable to a brain. The nerve rings are essentially condensation of a peripheral nervous system.

Despite the diffuseness of the nervous systems, effective coordination is achieved. Echinoid movement calls for the coordination of podia and spines; asteroid movement involves hundreds of podia and sometimes the body-wall muscles; and holothurian movement depends on body-wall muscles and podia. Asteroid podia respond to stimuli as individual parts. They contract when exposed to strong illumination and may bend if touched lightly. Podia step toward the oral ring in isolated arms, but step toward the tip in arms containing parts of the nerve ring. Whichever happens to be the leading arm gains dominance over the others, which then step in its direction. Cutting the nerve ring isolates an arm functionally; it loses coordination with other arms, although it can use its own podia in a coordinated fashion. Destruction of the radial nerve destroys the coordination of an arm. Essentially similar relationships are found in other echinoderms, insofar as evidence is available.

The podia of an isolated arm, like a well-trained army squad, march in unison. Policy decisions can be made by the non-commissioned officers of the radial nerves, but the heavier brass of the nerve ring takes over for general coordination. Some of the most interesting studies of coordination concern righting movements. Touching the aboral surface of a starfish or brittle star evokes a "dorsal reflex," consisting of an aboral curvature of the arms caused by contractions of aboral muscle strands. An overturned starfish begins to right itself with a strong dorsal reflex, curving the body so that the podia at the tips of the arms eventually make contact with the substrate. Then it moves off on two or three arms, the body flopping over when it has progressed far enough. Brittle stars right themselves by extending two adjacent arms in opposite directions, while the other three tilt the disc up and flip it over. Echinoids right themselves by attaching suitable podia and pulling themselves over. Sea cucumbers twist the body, bringing ventral podia in touch with the surface, and move off with the twist progressing along the body as it advances.

Asteroid righting has been most intensively studied. According to some studies, righting cannot depend on podial stimulation, for starfish deprived of podia can still right themselves. It cannot depend on the nerve ring, for isolated arms, and even pieces of arms, if of suitable shape, can right successfully. It cannot be dependent on contact of the aboral surface with the substrate, for it will take place despite removal of the aboral surface, nor can it be evoked by the sag of the stomach, since internal organs can be removed without interfering with it. The issue is in doubt at present. Perhaps several or all of these factors enter into the reaction to some degree.

Responses to light vary; some echinoderms are photonegative and others photopositive. Strong light usually evokes con-

tractions of gills and podia and affects the individual reactions of most body-wall appendages. Two kinds of light reception occur in starfish: reception by ocelli and at the body surface. Oriented responses depend on the ocelli, while choice of a suitably illuminated background is dependent on general body surface and is phobotactic. An isolated starfish arm exhibits a beautiful orientation to light, curving its tip up toward the cut end, thus pointing the optic cushion at the light source and stepping off purposively toward the light. Generally, sensitivity to light declines in species that live in deeper water.

Brittle stars and feather stars use the arms or arms and cirri in movement. Arm movements are mediated by the radial nerves, while cirral movements of comatulids depend on the aboral nerve center. Movements are highly coordinated and graceful.

Some studies have been directed toward the ability to modify behavior as a result of past experience. Starfish can be trained to right with arms not normally used, and they retain the modified behavior for several days. They have also been trained to draw back from a boundary they would normally cross, but this is difficult and retention is short. Brittle stars have been similarly trained. A very moderate ability to learn may be characteristic of echinoderms, despite the absence of a brain.

Development

Echinoderms are well suited to the needs of experimental embryologists. Sea urchins and starfish have been used in classical studies of fertilization, of cleavage, and of early development, most of which go beyond the scope of this discussion. An excellent résumé of the results of work on sea urchins is available (Harvey, 1956).

Development involves periods of cleavage, gastrulation, and larval formation, followed by a larval development that may entail several changes in larval form. A final period of metamorphosis transforms the last larval stage into a juvenile with many of the adult characteristics. Some echinoderms brood the young. They usually form larger, yolkier eggs, which undergo modified types of cleavage, and development is shortened by the omission of some larval stages. These alterations do not materially change the derivation of important body parts, and will be ignored here. Relationships are most clearly seen in species with relatively primitive, unmodified types of development.

CLEAVAGE

Echinoderms undergo radial or biradial, holoblastic cleavage, as is typical of most enterocoels. The first cleavage divisions are indeterminate, the blastomeres of two- or four-cell stages can each give rise to diminutive larvae. This, too, is typical of

enterocoels. Cleavage ends in a coeloblastula with a capacious blastocoel.

GASTRULATION

Invagination at the vegetal pole produces a small archenteron during gastrulation. Sometimes, as in crinoids, invagination is preceded by the unipolar ingression of some cells, Mesenchyme cells move into the blastocoel during gastrulation (Fig. 11.26C). They arise from the forming primitive gut or its margins, and give rise to the skeletal spicules of the larvae.

LARVA FORMATION

The blastopore becomes the larval anus. It will be convenient to call this the posterior end. The archenteron is the future coelom and gut cavity; the anterior end of the archenteron produces coelomic pouches and the middle part forms the midgut and part of the foregut. Larva formation involves: 1) the origin of coe-

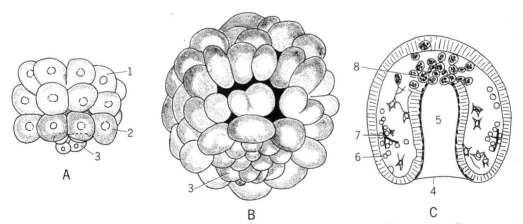

Fig. 11.26. Early Development. A. Embryo of *Paracentrotus*, a sea urchin, at 32-cell stage. Note the radial cleavage, and the micromeres at the vegetal pole. B. Later cleavage stage of *Psammechinus*, another sea urchin, showing the field of micromeres at the vegetal pole. C. *Paracentrotus* embryo at the end of gastrulation. Primary mesenchyme from the borders of the blastopore have begun to fill the blastocoel and form skeletal spicules, and secondary mesenchyme is forming from the inner end of the primitive gut. (A and C, after Boveri. B, after Selenka.) 1, mesomere; 2, macromere; 3, micromere; 4, blastopore; 5, primitive gut; 6, primary mesenchyme; 7, forming spicule; 8, secondary mesenchyme.

lomic primordia; 2) the completion of the larval gut; and 3) the development of one or more locomotor bands at the surface. The timing of these events differs somewhat in different groups, and in different species in the same group. As the three are more or less independent events they may be considered separately.

Coelom formation is especially interesting from a phylogenetic point of view. It is similar in all echinoderms, although differences in the shape of the compartments and the times of their appearance sometimes obscure the similarities. The similarities are far more important than the differences, and as it is easier to consider the whole course of coelom development as a unit, the changes up to the time of metamorphosis will be discussed together. Those interested in the particulars of timing and sequence of events in a given species should consult original articles.

The coelom arises from the anterior tip of the archenteron (Fig. 11.27) and then divides into right and left compartments. Each compartment lengthens and is cut into anterior and posterior parts, although these may remain attached for a time. The posterior compartments eventually form the right and left somatocoels, from which the perivisceral coelom develops. The anterior compartments are the axohydrocoels, and become partially separated to form an axocoel and hydrocoel on both sides of the embryo. The right and left axohydrocoels are not symmetrical; in two groups of modern echinoderms, the crinoids and holothurians, the right axocoel and hydrocoel never appear. Only four coelomic compartments form, right and left somatocoels, left axocoel, and left hydrocoel. The left hydrocoel grows into an arc, which becomes scalloped as five evaginations develop. These are the beginning of the ring canal and the radial canals. A stone canal connects the left hydrocoel with the axocoel, and the axocoel opens to the exterior by way of a hydropore and pore canal. The right and

left axocoel and right hydrocoel are much reduced. Typically the madreporic vesicle arises from the right axocoel. The relationship of these first compartments of the coelom to the adult coelomic divisions is summarized in Table 11.1.

The gut is completed while the coelomic compartments are being partitioned off. A stomodaeum develops at the surface and makes contact with the enteric sac, the part of the expanded archenteron left when the coelomic primordia form. The larval anus develops from the blastopore and the larval mouth from the stomodaeum. The foregut contains the stomodaeum and part of the enteric sac. The midgut or stomach is formed by the rest of the enteric sac, and the hindgut or intestine by the posterior end of the primitive gut. The larval gut is functional in free-swimming larvae; only in modified embryos developing from yolky eggs does it remain functionless until metamorphosis.

The embryo is at first covered by cilia or flagella. While the early steps in coelom formation take place, the surface cilia disappear except in one or a few bands. It is not clear how many types of larvae have cilia and how many have flagella, but it may be safely assumed that some species said to have cilia actually have flagella, for they are not always distinguished precisely. Larvae of different types appear in different echinoderm groups. As they are often common in plankton samples, it is well to be familiar with the major types.

LARVAL STAGES

The development of a locomotor band transforms the embryo into a larva. The simplest larval form is the auricularia of holothurians (Fig. 11.28A). A single locomotor band curves forward as a preoral loop, and forms a similar anal loop at the posterior end. Parts of the band degenerate and the remaining parts are rearranged into three to five transverse locomotor bands, resulting in a doliolaria larva (Fig. 11.28 B-C). The first crinoid larva is a doliolaria, similar to the holothurian doliolaria (Fig. 11.28D). The first starfish larva is a bipinnaria, which resembles an auricularia when young, but develops a number of larval arms and loses its auricularian form (Fig. 11.28E). The bipinnaria swims about for several weeks, and eventually develops three brachiolar arms to become a brachiolaria (Fig. 11.28G). Ophiuroids and echinoids have a pluteus larva, termed ophioplutei and echinoplutei to distinguish them. The echinopluteus develops as the gastrula becomes flattened on the future oral sur-

face. The locomotor band follows the margin of an oral lobe that bends over the oral surface, and the young pluteus grows two pairs of arms, a postoral pair and an anterolateral pair. More arms develop during later growth; most echinoplutei have five pairs, but spatangoids have six pairs of well-developed arms (Fig. 11.29A). The ophiuroid gastrula develops a ciliated girdle, and arms form more slowly. Only four pairs appear, and nearly three weeks are required to complete them (Fig. 11.29C). The arms of echinoplutei and ophioplutei contain skeletal supports. Many are pigmented, and the larvae are unusually attractive as well as suited for many kinds of experimentation.

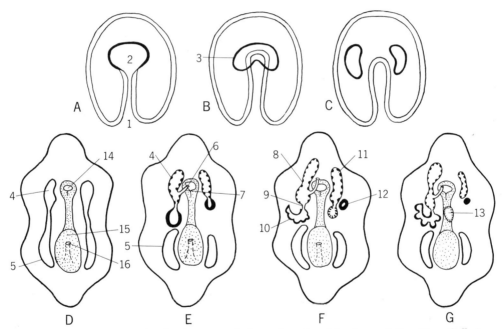

Fig. 11.27. Scheme of the development of the coelom in echinoderms (after Dawydoff, in Grassé.) The coelom is cut off from the inner end of the primitive gut (A, B) and divides into right and left compartments (C). While the gut forms, the right and left coelomic compartments elongate and eventually divide into a posterior somatocoel on each side and an anterior axohydrocoel (D,E). The small right axohydrocoel, sometimes not formed, is further reduced during development. The left axohydrocoel divides into an axocoel that opens to the outside through a hydropore, and a hydrocoel, connected to the axocoel by a stone canal. The hydrocoel on the left develops into the water vascular system (E-G). 1, blastopore; 2, primitive gut; 3, coelom; 4, left axohydrocoel; 5, left somatocoel; 6, hydropore; 7, canal to the hydropore; 8, left axocoel; 9, stone canal; 10, left hydrocoel; 11, right axocoel; 12, right hydrocoel; 13, madreporic vesicle; 14, mouth; 15, midgut; 16, anus.

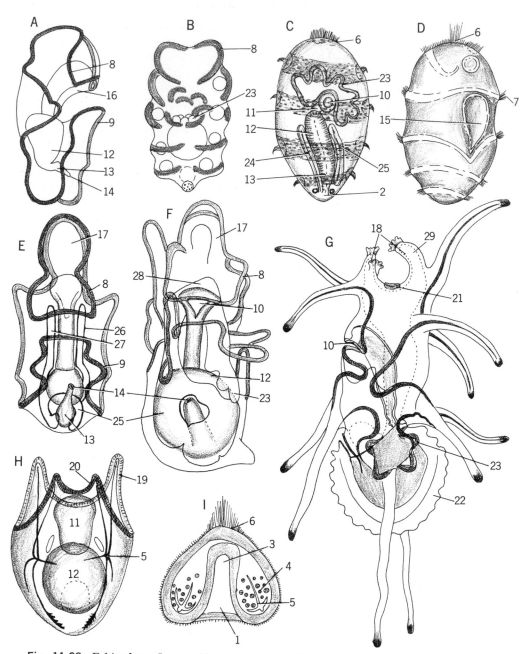

Fig. 11.28. Echinoderm Larvae. The auricularia is the simplest larva (A), and occurs in holothurians and asteroids. By partial degeneration of the locomotor bands and their rearrangement, the auricularia of holothurians becomes a doliolaria (B-C). Crinoids do not form an auricularia, but have a doliolaria larva much like that of holothurians (D). The young asteroid larva develops arms to become a bipinnaria (E-F). Later, brachiolar arms and a sucker develop, transforming the bipinnaria into a brachiolaria (G), which attaches and metamorphoses into a starfish. Echinoids do not go through an auricularia stage; the gastrula flattens and develops

410

METAMORPHOSIS

All echinoderm larvae undergo metamorphosis. Starfish and crinoids attach to metamorphose, but holothurians, echinoids, and ophiuroids continue to swim about, eventually sinking as they become too heavy to swim.

It is not possible to discuss the details of metamorphosis in all echinoderm groups here. It may suffice to indicate the main changes in a crinoid, as an example of a pelmatozoan, and a starfish, as an example of an eleutherozoan.

An attachment organ develops at the anterior end of the crinoid doliolaria, and the larval anterior end becomes the adult aboral end. A 90° rotation of internal parts brings the mouth to the future oral surface and rearranges the coelomic compartments. The long anterior part of the larva becomes the stalk. As parts rotate, the right somatocoel comes to occupy an aboral position and sends five extensions down into the stalk as the primordia of the chambered organ (Fig. 11.30). The larval mouth closes, and the stomodaeum becomes a flattened chamber, the vestibule, which moves to the apex of the attached larva. The right hydrocoel and axocoel never form. The left hydrocoel forms an arc with five primordia of the radial canals. These protrude into the vestibule, and the crescentic hydrocoel surrounds the esophagus. The stone canal connects the hydrocoel with the axocoel, which opens by an external hydropore. Primitively, a central extension from the axocoel extends into

the stalk. It forms the axial sinus, and in free-moving species ends at the aboral end of the body, connecting with the chambered organ.

A starfish larva ready for metamorphosis feels about for a suitable site with the brachiolar arms. It eventually attaches with an attachment organ between them. The adult starfish forms from the rounded, posterior part of the brachiolaria, the arms and anterior part of the larva deteriorating during metamorphosis. The left side becomes the oral surface and the right side the aboral surface. As the old anterior part of the larva degenerates, the crescentic hydrocoel rounds out to make a five-lobed disc around the esophagus, as in crinoids (Fig. 11.30C-E). It is attached to the left axocoel by the stone canal. The axocoel opens to the exterior through the hydropore. A small remnant of the right axocoel becomes the dorsal sac in which the head of the axial gland lies, and the axial gland develops in the coelomic compartment of the left axocoel, paralleling the stone canal. As the left hydrocoel completes the water ring, the first buds grow out to form the first podia. Shortly afterwards, the young asteroid moves away from the sucker, which had attached it during metamorphosis, and takes up an independent existence.

PHYLOGENETIC RELATIONSHIPS

The common character of echinoderms shines through the considerable differences in their appearance and modes of life. The strong similarity of the organ systems; the

into a young pluteus larva (H-I). (A-B and H-I, after Mortensen. C, after Runnström. E and F, after Hörstadius. G, after Mead.) 1, blastopore; 2, closed blastopore; 3, primitive gut; 4, mesenchyme; 5, primary skeletal spicule; 6, apical sensory tuft; 7, locomotor ring; 8, preoral locomotor loop; 9, anal locomotor loop; 10, mouth; 11, esophagus; 12, stomach; 13. intestine; 14, anus; 15, vestibule; 16, site of mouth formation; 17, preoral lobe; 18, brachiolar arm; 19, postoral arm; 20, anterolateral arm; 21, adhesive region; 22, part of larva that will form adult body; 23, hydrocoel developing tentacular lobes; 24, right somatocoel; 25, left somatocoel; 26, right axohydrocoel; 27, left axohydrocoel; 28, fused anterior coelomic compartments; 29, coelom extending into brachiolar arms.

unique water-vascular system; the total absence of excretory organs; and the fenestrated skeletal ossicles attest to their common ancestry. The curious embryonic development, with a common although complex pattern of coelomic partitioning and the biologically ridiculous metamorphosis that transforms the posterior end of a bilaterally symmetrical larva into a radi-

ally symmetrical adult, is further proof of their homogeneity.

The relationship of echinoderms to other animal phyla will be postponed until other deuterostomes have been examined. Relationships within the phylum are by no means easy to determine, in spite of the discreteness of the phylum. It is not surprising to find the crinoids, the only living

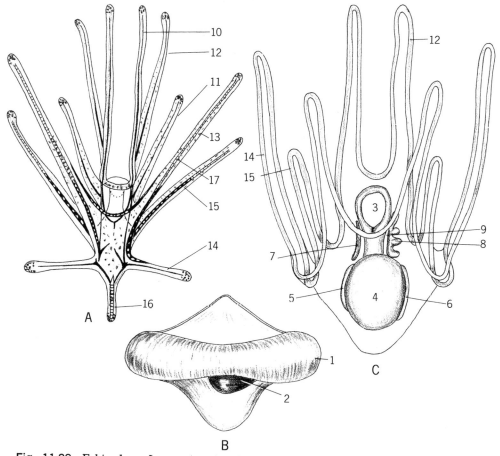

Fig. 11.29. Echinoderm Larvae (continued). Echinoid plutei are known as echinoplutei (A). The one shown is a spatangoid with six pair of arms. Plutei of ophiuroids are known as ophioplutei (C). They develop directly from a motile gastrula (B) and are structurally similar to echinoplutei. Skeletal spicules have been omitted from the ophiopluteus shown here. (A, after Mortensen. B, after MacBride. C, after Narasimhamurti.) 1, locomotor band; 2, blastopore; 3, esophagus; 4, stomach; 5, right somatocoel; 6, left somatocoel; 7, right axohydrocoel; 8, left hydrocoel with tentacular lobes; 9, left axocoel; 10, preoral arm; 11, anterodorsal arm; 12, anterolateral arm; 13, postoral arm; 14, posterolateral arm; 15, posterodorsal arm; 16, aboral spike; 17, skeletal rod.

Pelmatozoa, distinctly separated from the more modern Euleutherozoa. On this point there is general agreement. Two points of view have been expressed about the other groups. One sees the brittle stars and asteroids as the distinctive branches of an armed stem, which became separated very early, certainly by the end of the Cam-

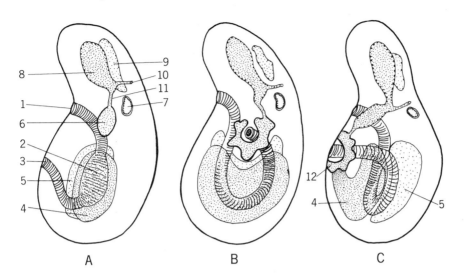

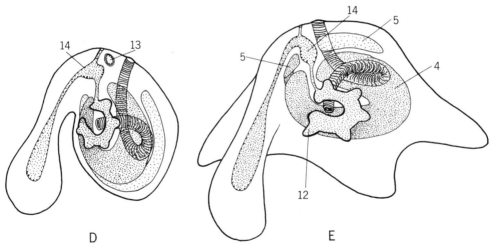

Fig. 11.30. Scheme of Metamorphosis of an Asteroid. The basic relationships of the digestive tube and coelomic compartments are shown at **A**, as seen from the left side. As a result of flexion, the larva becomes asymmetrical and the anus comes to lie on the aboral surface. The left hydrocoel encircles the mouth **(B)** and develops, eventually, into the water-vascular system. The left somatocoel is carried to the oral surface **(C-E)** and comes to form the oral part of the perivisceral coelom. The right somatocoel forms the aboral part of the peri-visceral coelom. (After Heider, from Dawydoff, in Grassé.) **1**, mouth; **2**, midgut; **3**, anus; **4**, left somatocoel; **5**, right somatocoel; **6**, left hydrocoel; **7**, right hydrocoel; **8**, left axocoel; **9**, right axocoel; **10**, hydropore; **11**, stone canal; **12**, left hydrocoel developing into water ring and radial canals; **13**, madreporic vesicle; **14**, axial sinus.

brian. Echinoids and holothurians are seen as closely related, with the holothurians descending, perhaps, from the Edrioasteroidea, and the echinoids arising from similar stocks before or after the holothurians had separated from the edrioasteroids. The alternative view would see the holothurians as more closely related to the crinoid stem, perhaps paralleling it during early times. Starfish are derived from this stem at an early period. Echinoids and ophiuroids are seen as stemming from some common ancestral group, or as arising from an early echinoderm stem group and following parallel lines of early development. It is evident that the second point of view emphasizes larval relationships, while the first emphasizes adult structure. Holothurians and crinoids are associated through the doliolaria and asteroids and holothurians because of the similarity of young bipinnaria to auricularia. The similarity of the pluteus larvae of ophiuroids and echinoids serves to link them. It may seem strange to separate the rayed asteroids and ophiuroids so completely, but the starfish arm with its open ambulacral groove is far more primitive than the ophiuroid arm, with the water-vascular system deeply imbedded and the ambulacral groove closed.

Although one may feel, for one reason or another, that one point of view is more persuasive than the other, there is insufficient evidence to warrant a firm commitment to either. The fact is that entirely differing and somewhat inconsistent pictures of echinoderm evolution are gained by stressing adult morphology of modern species, embryonic development, or fossil forms.

References

Anderson, J. M. 1960. Histological studies on the digestive system of a starfish, *Henricia*, with a note on Tiedemann's pouches. *Biol. Bull.* 119: 371.

Boolotian, R. A., and A. C. Giese, 1959. Clotting of echinoderm coelomic fluid. *Jour. Exp. Zool.* 140: 207.

Budington, R. A. 1942. The ciliary transport system of *Asterias forbesi*. *Biol. Bull.* 83: 438.

Carpenter, W. B. 1884. On the nervous system of the crinoidea. *Proc. Roy. Soc. London* 37: 67.

Clark, H. L. 1917. The habits and reactions of *Tropiometra carinata*. *Carn. Inst. Wash., Papers., Dept. Mar. Biol.* 11.

Coe, W. R. 1912. Echinoderms of Connecticut. *Conn. Geol. Nat. Hist. Surv. Bull.* 19: 1. (F)

Deichmann, E. 1938. Holothurians from the western coasts of lower California and Central America, and from the Galapagos Islands. *Zoologica.* 23.

Fell, H. B. 1948. Echinoderm embryology and the origin of the chordates. *Biol. Rev.* 23: 81. (G)

Fisher, W. K. 1911–20. Asteroidea of the North Pacific and adjacent waters. *Bull. U.S. Natl. Mus.* 76: 1. (F)

Gemmillis, J. F. 1919. The rhythmic pulsation in the madreporite vesicle of young ophiuroids. *Quart. Jour. Micr. Sci.* 63: 537.

Gislén, T. 1930. Affinities between echinoderms, enteropneusts, and chordates. *Zool. Bidrag.* 12: 197.

Glaser, O. 1907. Movement and problem-solving in ophiura. *Jour. Exp. Zool.* 4: 203.

Gregory, W. K. 1946. The role of motile larvae and fixed adults in the origin of the vertebrates. *Quart. Rev. Biol.* 21: 248. (G)

Harvey, E. B. 1956. *The American Arbacia and Other Sea Urchins.* Princeton Univ. Press, Princeton. (B)

Hawkins, H. L. 1931. The first echinoid. *Biol. Rev.* 6: 443.

Jennings, H. S. 1907. Behavior of the starfish, *Asterias forbesi*. *Univ. Calif. Publ. Zool.* 4: 53.

Kerkut, G. A. 1953. The mechanisms of coordination of the starfish tube feet. *Behav.* 6: 206.

Koehler, R. 1924–27. *Les Echinodermes des*

Mers de'Europe. Paris Libr. Oct. Doin, Paris.

Millott, N. 1953. Color pattern and the definition of the species. *Experentia* 9: 9.

———, and M. Yoshida. 1960. The shadow reaction of *Diadema antillarum. Jour. Exp. Biol.* 37: 363.

Moore, A. R. 1924. The nervous mechanism of coordination in *Antedon. Jour. Gen. Physiol.* 6.

Mortensen, T. H. 1927. *Handbook of Echinoderms of the British Isles.* Clarendon Press, Oxford.

Nichols, D. Histology and activities of the tube feet of *Antedon bifida. Quart. Jour. Micr. Sci.* 101: 105.

Parker, G. H. 1931. Color changes in *Arbacia. Proc. Nat. Acad. Sci.* 17:594.

Pearse, A. S. 1908. Behavior of *Thyone. Biol. Bull.* 15: 259.

Pople, W., and D. W. Ewer. 1955. Circum-oral conduction in *Cucumaria, Jour. Exp. Biol.* 32: 59.

Smith, J. E. 1950. The motor nervous system of the starfish *Astropecten irregularis. Phil. Trans. Roy. Soc.* 234: 521.

Tao, L. 1930. Ecology and physiology of *Caudina. Proc. 4th Pac. Sci. Congr.* 3: 7.

Yamanuchi, T. 1939. Ecological and physiological studies on the holothurians in the coral reef of Palao. *Palao Trop. Bio. Sta. Stud.* 4: 603.

12
Other Deuterostomes

Echinodermata and Chordata are the two most important deuterostome phyla. The other three, Chaetognatha, Pogonophora, and Hemichordata, are biologically interesting but contain relatively few species. As members of the stem that includes the vertebrates, all have a special significance.

Deuterostomes form a new mouth at some distance from the blastopore and the anus arises from or near the blastopore. They are enterocoelous, forming mesoderm from the wall of the primitive gut. During mesoderm formation, the coelom appears. Its cavity is originally continuous with the primitive gut. The coelom is usually partitioned into a protocoel in the head region (protosome), a mesocoel, and a metacoel in the posterior region of the body (metasome). The three coelomic regions correspond in position and are probably homologous with the axocoel, hydrocoel, and somatocoel of echinoderms.

Phylum Chaetognatha—Arrowworms

About fifty species of small, predaceous, typically planktonic organisms make up the phylum Chaetognatha. The long, transparent body has lateral and caudal fins. The animals dart about so swiftly that they live up to their name in both form and behavior. They are most abundant in warm, shallow seas, where they sometimes swarm in enormous numbers and are influential planktonic predators. Some species live in polar waters, however. They center in the Indo-Pacific region, but are not uncommon along the coasts of Europe and North America.

Chaetognaths are all much alike. Differences in the position and number of lateral fins, the shape of the caudal fin, and detailed differences in head construction and in the seminal vesicles are the most important taxonomic characters. The bilaterally symmetrical body is divided into head (protosome), trunk (mesosome), and tail (metasome). One or two pairs of lateral fins on the trunk and anterior tail region, and a tail fin, are built of epidermis strengthened by fin rays (Fig. 12.1A).

A ventral depression on the head, the vestibule, leads to the mouth (Fig. 12.1B). Most species have anterior and posterior rows of teeth. Raptorial bristles extend from the sides of the head. A conspicuous hood folds over the head between feeding periods; it reduces friction and protects the teeth and bristles. During feeding, the hood is retracted, the mouth-parts extruded, and the teeth and bristles spread. They snap shut with startling speed to capture prey. The histological structure of eyes, vestibular organs, vestibular pits, and retrocerebral organs suggests that they are sense organs. Each of the paired compound eyes is formed of a large, lateral pigment-cup ocellus and four smaller, medial ocelli. They are inverse eyes, with turbellarian-like photosensory cells (Fig. 12.1D). The vestibular organs are rows of papillae on each side of the head. Many chaetognaths also have glandular vestibular pits. The retrocerebral organs are deep sacs, reaching the cerebral ganglia. They are enclosed by a connective tissue sheath but receive fibers from ganglion cells. They open by paired ducts that unite before reaching a middorsal pore.

The corona ciliata (Fig. 12.1C), an oval or sinuous ciliated loop, lies at the front of the middorsal trunk surface. The *Spadella* corona has an outer zone of flagellated cells and an inner zone of glandular cells that take up and eject dyes and may have an excretory function. The corona of some species is a rheoreceptor, and is probably chemoreceptive also.

The body wall is composed of cuticle, epidermis, basement membrane, and muscle layers. There is no peritoneum, although the body cavities arise from what appear to be coelomic compartments of the embryo. The cells lining the coelomic pouches give rise to muscle and connective tissue. The basement membrane is thickened to form capsules for the eyes, and lateral and ventral head plates between the cuticle and epidermis stiffen the head covering. Muscles have their origins on the thickened basement membrane.

A head-trunk septum divides a small head coelom (protocoel) from the trunk coelom (mesocoel). Muscles and other head structures encroach on the protocoel, reducing it significantly. A trunk-tail septum divides the mesocoel from the metacoel

and defines the trunk and tail regions. The gut is held by a dorsal and ventral mesentery, formed of double layers of basement membrane. A similar mesentery divides the tail coelom into right and left compartments (Fig. 12.1A). The coelomic fluid contains no coelomocytes, but small granules circulate slowly, passing through the lacy mesenteries, as a result of the beating or large cilia (flagella?) on the inner surface of the body wall.

Chaetognaths are strongly cephalized and have an intricate head musculature. Muscles can be recognized without sectioning, through the transparent body wall. Many of the head muscles listed in Table 12.1 can be identified in Fig. 12.1B. A careful study is rewarding for those interested in detailed invertebrate anatomy, as they provide a good example of specialized invertebrate musculature.

The trunk and tail muscles are simple. Circular muscles are absent. Two dorsolateral and two ventrolateral longitudinal muscle bands bend the body, forcing the fins against the water and causing rapid, darting movements. Histologically, the muscle is like nematode muscle, with feathery bands of fibers arranged along the margins of cells.

The circular or T-shaped mouth opens into a glandular pharynx, ending in a bulb at the level of the head-trunk septum. The lining of the straight intestine contains more gland cells anteriorly and more absorptive cells posteriorly, indicating some sequentialism in digestion. The last part of the intestine is histologically differentiated as a rectum, with strengthened circular muscles and a ciliated lining.

Chaetognaths are voracious. Lebour (1923) says *Sagitta bipunctata* swallow baby herring as large as themselves. They usually swim about actively, pouncing on prey with a quick, flashing movement and a rapid snap of the bristles, but *Spadella* attaches to the substrate with adhesive caudal papillae, waiting for prey. Little is known of digestive physiology, for these

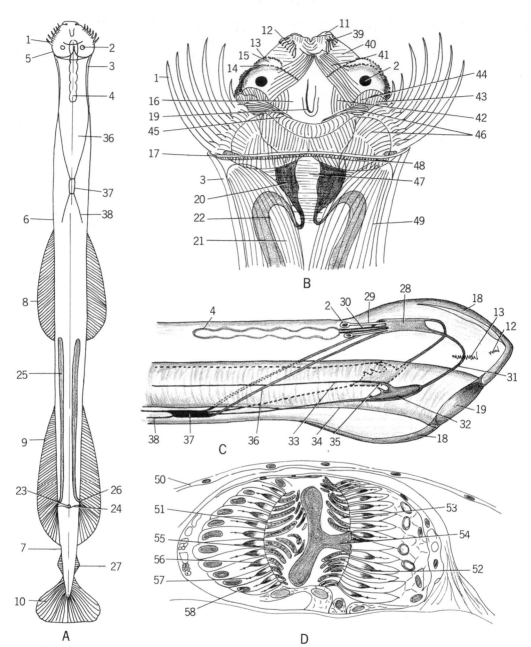

Fig. 12.1. Chaetognatha. **A.** Ventral view of *Sagitta elegans*, showing general body form. **B.** Ventral view of the head of a chaetognath. Note the highly developed musculature. **C.** Scheme of organization of the anterior end of a chaetognath. Note the ganglia and nerves associated with the gut, presumably similar to the stomatogastric nervous system of higher invertebrates. **D.** Section through the eye of *Sagitta*. (**A**, after Ritter-Záhoney. **B** and **C**, composite. **D**, after Hesse.) *External features:* **1**, raptorial spines; **2**, eye; **3**, collarette; **4**, ciliary loop (corona ciliata); **5**, head; **6**, trunk; **7**, tail; **8**, anterior lateral fin; **9**, posterior lateral

animals are difficult to keep alive in the laboratory. The pharynx secretes an adhesive substance that entangles, but does not stun, prey and probably prepares it for swallowing. *Spadella* gulps sea water after swallowing food, probably sending enzymes into the rear part of the intestine, where food usually lodges. Digestion seems to be

Table 12.1. Chaetognath muscles

MUSCLE	POSITION	ACTION
protractor preputii	rim of hood	extends hood
retractor preputii	from dorsal skeletal plates to deep connective tissues	retracts hood
expansus superior	median lamella, transversely to teeth	erects teeth
expansus inferior	behind expansus superior	erects teeth
obliquus capitus brevis	transverse, in front of expansus muscles	depresses teeth
adductor uncinorum	lateral, dorsal head muscles	closes grasping spines
obliquus capitus longus	from anterior lateral plates obliquely to back of head	shortens head
obliquus superficialis	external obliques forming triangle at back of head	help to retract hood
transversus dorsalis	lateral to superficial obliques	help to open grasping spines
rectus coli externus	at sides of neck, from dorsolateral plates to ventral plates	nods head
constrictor oris primus	ventral, curving in front of mouth	constrict mouth
constrictor oris alter	beside mouth	constrict mouth
dilator vestibuli externus	lateral to mouth constrictor in ventral view	dilates mouth and vestibule
complexus lateralis	ventral, lateral, at back of head	changes shape of head and spreads grasping spines
bicornis	transverse, behind vestibule	changes shape of head and spreads grasping spines

The heavy lamellae and skeletal plates of the head, together with the movable head parts, have provided a great stimulus to the development of specific muscles, with definite origins, insertions, and actions. In the head region, the relatively simple body-wall musculature has been divided into many slips, with specific functions.

fin; 10, tail fin; 11, anterior ends of lateral plates; 12, anterior teeth; 13, posterior teeth; 14, vestibular ridge; 15, vestibular pit; 16, vestibule; 17, site of attachment of ventral hood; 18, hood; 19, mouth. *Digestive system:* 20, bulb of pharynx; 21, intestine; 22, intestinal diverticulum; 23, anus. *Coelom:* 24, trunk-tail septum. *Reproductive system:* 25, ovary; 26, gonopore; 27, seminal receptacle. *Nervous system:* 28, brain; 29, optic nerve; 30, coronal nerve; 31, frontal connective; 32, vestibular ganglion; 33, lateral esophageal nerve; 34, ventral esophageal nerve; 35, esophageal ganglion; 36, circumenteric connective; 37, ventral (subenteric) ganglion; 38, posterior nerve. *Muscles:* 39, obliquus capitis brevis; 40, expansus superior; 41, constrictor oris primus; 42, constrictor oris alter; 43, dilator vestibuli externus; 44, dilator vestibuli internus; 45, bicornis; 46, complexus lateralis; 47, transversus ventralis; 48, hood protractor; 49, ventrolateral longitudinal muscle. *Histology:* 50, epidermis; 51, lateral ocellus; 52, upper medial ocellus; 53, lower medial ocellus; 54, common pigment cup; 55, retinal bulb; 56, refractive body; 57, neurofibril; 58, retina cell.

wholly extracellular. Only glycogen-and starch-splitting enzymes have so far been reported. Digestion is rapid, taking from 40 minutes to four hours in various species.

Respiration apparently occurs at the body surface. No true excretory organs are found, but the corona may have an excretory function. Soluble wastes probably escape through the body surface.

Chaetognaths have a complex nervous system, in keeping with their active life and complex musculature. A frontal commissure connects the bilobed dorsal ganglion to a pair of ventral, vestibular ganglia. A subpharyngeal commissure completes the circumenteric ring (Fig. 12.1C). Nerves to the eye and corona arise from the dorsal ganglion. A pair of subenteric connectives pass ventrally and posteriorly to a large subenteric ganglion. Nerves to the pharynx, vestibular border, and head musculature arise from the vestibular ganglion. Pairs of nerves from the subenteric ganglion extend to the subepidermal plexus of the trunk and tail.

Chaetognaths are hermaphroditic. Paired testes lie behind the trunk-tail septum. Masses of spermatogonia enter the tail coelom, and when mature, pass into the funnel-shaped openings (gonostomes) of the sperm ducts. Each of the sperm ducts ends in a seminal vesicle, which bulges the body wall out near the base of the tail fin. Adhesive secretions mold the sperm into spermatophores in a sac at the anterior end of the seminal vesicle (Fig. 12.1A).

Ovaries lie at the posterior end of the trunk coelom, attached by a mesentery to the body wall. Chaetognath oviducts are unique. Each oviduct is double, formed of an outer tube, the oviduct proper, and an inner tube that opens to the exterior by way of a short vagina and is expanded posteriorly to form a seminal receptacle. The oviduct proper has no opening to the ovary nor the outside.

Some species are self-fertilizing, while others outbreed. In either case, spermatophores are attached to the body surface,

and sperm eventually enter the vagina and move into the seminal receptacle. Ova are accompanied by two nurse cells when they leave the ovary. The nurse cells form a hollow stalk that pierces the inner oviduct and conducts sperm to the ovum. The ova develop externally; either a duct forms to permit their departure or they break through the body wall.

Equal, holoblastic cleavage produces a blastula with a small blastocoel. The endoderm invaginates, coming in contact with the ectoderm to destroy all traces of the blastocoel. A pair of primordial germ cells arise early and remain unchanged during early development. Lateral folds of the primitive gut form and are cut off, starting at the anterior end, to establish a coelom. The front end of the coelom is cut off as a head coelom, and the trunk and tail coeloms separate later. The mouth and pharynx form from an anterior stomodaeum.

The newly hatched chaetognath is a diminutive adult and undergoes no metamorphosis. Each primordial germ cell divides once during early development, and one daughter cell comes to lie in each mesocoel and metacoel compartment. They later develop into the testes and ovaries. The sperm ducts arise from the epidermis, but the gonoducts are true coelomoducts, developing from mesoderm.

Phylum Pogonophora—Beardworms

Pogonophora live predominantly as abyssal tube-dwellers and were not seen before the twentieth century. Much interest has been shown in them in recent years, for they have a number of unique characteristics. The following are some of the major peculiarities of pogonophores:

1. The body is divided into a protosome containing a protocoel, a mesosome containing paired mesocoels, and a metasome containing paired metacoels, like chaetognaths and hemichordates.

2. Pinnate tentacles on the protosome form a food-capturing apparatus.

3. They have no trace of a gut, and no blastopore forms during development.

4. A pair of coelomoducts connects the protocoel with the exterior.

5. They have a circulatory system with a heart.

6. They have a primitive, epidermal nervous system.

Pogonophora all live in chitinous, secreted tubes. They are remarkably slender; larger species may be a foot long and no more than 2 mm. in diameter. The body is clearly divided into protosome, mesosome, and metasome, but no external constriction between protosome and mesosome occurs in some species. A cephalic lobe on the protosome contains the cerebral ganglion. Species of *Siboglinum* have a single tentacle, very long and much coiled, extending forward from the side of the protosome opposite the cephalic lobe. Other genera have numerous tentacles; some species have over two hundred. Each tentacle contains an extension of the protocoel and bears a double row of delicate pinnules, each an extension of one epidermal cell (Fig. 12.2D). In some cases, tentacles arise from a U-shaped ridge or are fused at the base. The cephalic lobe and tentacle bases define opposite surfaces, but no one is certain which side is dorsal. Ivanov's (1956) view that the cephalic lobe is dorsal is followed here; there are good arguments, however, for considering it ventral.

The bridle is a pair of oblique ridges of thickened cuticle on the mesosome. It may be used to engage the tube rim when the body is extended. The very long trunk is divided into preannular and postannular parts by a pair of ridges, the belts (Fig. 12.2C). A deep groove bordered with prominent papillae usually extends on the midventral preannular surface part of the way to the belts, and a dorsal ciliated strip lies above it. The papillae may secrete material for the tube or an adhesive substance. Two orders of Pogonophora are recognized: *Thecanephria* with postannular adhesive papillae arranged in transverse rows, and *Athecanephria* with fewer, irregularly scattered papillae behind the belts.

Pogonophora are unique in being the only free-living metazoa without a trace of a digestive system. There is no evidence of mouth, anus, or gut. No one knows how they obtain food. They cannot store food as larvae, like nematomorphs, for the larvae also lack a gut. Ivanov (1955) has suggested that the tentacles trap food with the aid of cilia at the bases of the pinnules. He suggests that when sufficient food has been assembled, the animal may retire into the tube to digest it, pouring enzymes on the food and absorbing it through the thin-walled, highly vascular pinnules. The pinnules contain no gland cells, but enzymes may be brought to the tentacles from glands located elsewhere. Another idea is that they are saprobic, absorbing food materials prepared by bacterial action through the general body surface. It is probable that the pinnules are important absorptive parts, whether food is absorbed directly from the mud or digested outside of the body.

The circulatory system centers in dorsal and ventral vessels lying in the mesentery. Blood flows posteriorly in the dorsal vessel and anteriorly in the ventral vessel. Afferent vessels to the tentacles arise from the ventral vessel and send branches into the pinnules (Fig. 12.2E). Efferent pinnular vessels empty into an efferent tentacle vessel, which returns blood to the dorsal vessel. Some species also have lateral vessels. The ventral vessel is enlarged to form a heart in the protosome. The heart is surrounded by a pericardial sac in Athecanephria, but not in Thecanephria. The blood flow is opposite to the flow in other somewhat similar animals; this is one of the arguments for considering the cephalic lobe ventral instead of dorsal.

The nervous system is epidermal. The dorsal brain extends laterally to give rise to tentacular nerves, and may also give off a middorsal nerve to the ciliated band of the metasome. Jägersten (1956) has seen a midventral connection, suggesting that a circumenteric ring exists. No ventral or lateral nerve cords have been seen. Jägersten has also described a nerve ring in the mesosome-metasome septum.

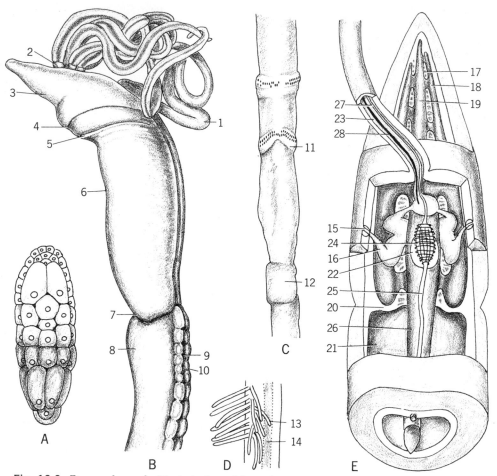

Fig. 12.2. Pogonophora. A. Ventral view of late cleavage stage of *Siboglinum*. B. Anterior end of *Birsteinia vitjasi*. C. Middle region of the body of *Siboglinum caulleryi*, showing the belts. D. A part of the distal region of tentacle of *Galathealinum*, showing the pinnules. E. Scheme of organization of *Siboglinum*, showing protocoel and anterior end of mesocoel. (A, B, C, and E, after Ivanov. D, after Southward.) *External features:* 1, tentacle; 2, fused base of tentacles; 3, cephalic lobe; 4, protosome-mesosome boundary; 5, bridle; 6, mesosome; 7, mesosome-metasome boundary; 8, metasome (trunk); 9, midventral groove; 10, adhesive papilla; 11, belt; 12, dorsal shield; 13, pinnule; 14, ciliated band. *Coelomoducts:* 15, nephridiopore; 16, nephridium. *Coelom:* 17, muscle bands; 18, lateral protocoel channel; 19, ventral protocoel channel; 20, protocoel-mesocoel septum; 21, mesocoel; 22, pericardial cavity; 23, extension of coelom into tentacle. *Circulatory system:* 24, heart; 25, ventral vessel; 26, dorsal vessel; 27, afferent vessel to tentacle; 28, efferent vessel to tentacle.

The sexes are separate. Males have a pair of testes in the posterior half of the trunk. Long ciliated, glandular sperm ducts extend forward to the mesosome-metasome septum, where they open ventrally. Spermatophores crowd the sperm ducts. They are fusiform in Athecanephria and flattened in Thecanephria. Ovaries lie in the anterior metacoel, and open through short oviducts through gonopores located near the middle of the metasome.

The elongated, yolky eggs undergo holoblastic, unequal cleavage. Young are brooded in the tube, and the basic pattern of development is now known. An elongated blastula (Fig. 12.2A), probably without a blastocoel, has larger blastomeres at the ventral and vegetal surfaces. Gastrulation is by delamination. Three inner cells appear to represent the endoderm. Coelom formation is enterocoelous, beginning at the anterior end and progressing posteriorly. The protocoel, and later the mesocoel, are cut off as in chaetognaths. A larva with three definite body regions, each with a band of cilia, is formed. A small anterior pit may be a vestige of an ancestral mouth.

Phylum Hemichordata—Acorn Worms and Pterobranchs

Hemichordates are more or less worm-like animals, living in tubes in the bottom mud or among rocks or masses of plant material. The more familiar acorn worms are solitary, but pterobranchs are social, and some form definite colonies. The two are so dissimilar that it was not until the end of the nineteenth century that their affinities were recognized.

The more outstanding hemichordate characteristics include the following:

1. The body is divided into a protosome containing an unpaired protocoel, a mesosome containing paired mesocoels, and a metasome containing paired metacoels.

2. A middorsal nerve center in the mesosome is hollow, reminiscent of the tubular nerve cord of chordates.

3. One or more pairs of gill slits usually connect the pharynx lumen with the anterior, as in chordates.

4. They have a fairly well-developed circulatory system, usually with a contractile heart.

5. They have no nephridia.

It is evident that hemichordates have several chordate-like traits, but the absence of a notochord separates them sharply from the true chordates. They are often called prochordates.

CLASSIFICATION

Class Enteropneusta. Acorn worms. Solitary, worm-like hemichordates with a straight gut and many gill slits and without arms on the mesosome.

Class Pterobrancia. Aggregative or colonial hemichordates living in a zoecium and with a U-shaped gut that may or may not have gill slits; with arms bearing tentacles.

Order Rhabdopleurida. Colonial pterobranchs, each living in a tubular zoecium secreted by the epidermis and connected to other members by a living stolon; with two tentacular arms and without gill slits.

Order Cephalodisca. Pterobranchs living in a common zoecial mass, but without a living stolon connecting the members of the aggregation; with one pair of gill slits and four to nine pairs of arms with tentacles.

Class Planctosphaeroidea. A class known only by its large, transparent larva, of the tornaria type but with highly branched, ciliated bands at the surface. It has been collected several times, but cannot be related to any known hemichordates. Evidently some type of hemichordate which has never been recognized must somewhere exist (Fig. 12.3).

THE ENTEROPNEUSTA

Most acorn worms are moderate in size, up to about a foot or so long, but *Balanoglossus gigas* may reach a length of 2.5 m. They are slimy, beige to pinkish worms, very sluggish and so soft that they break easily when handled. Many smell like iodoform. Some live in tubes and eat sand or mud; others are ciliary-mucus feeders that do not secrete tubes. Differences in habit have little effect on general appearance. Two constrictions divide the body into an anterior, conical, or elongated proboscis (protosome), a middle collar (mesosome), and a long, worm-shaped trunk (metasome).

The ciliated epidermis is richly glandular, composed of tall, slender cells that vary considerably in different body regions. Gland cells are mucus-secreting goblets or

Fig. 12.3. Representative Hemichordates. **A.** *Planctosphaera*, the organism for which the class Planctosphaeroidea was erected. **B.** A typical enteropneust, *Saccoglossus kowalewski*. (**A**, after Spengel. **B**, after Bateson.) **1**, protocoel; **2**, horns of protocoel; **3**, hydropore; **4**, site representing apical plate; **5**, posterior depression; **6**, mouth; **7**, esophagus; **8**, anus; **9**, ciliary band; **10**, proboscis; **11**, collar, **12**, branchial region of trunk; **13**, gill slit; **14**, genital region of the trunk; **15**, abdominal region of trunk.

coarsely granular or reticulated mulberry cells. The collar is often marked by five transverse bands of alternating glandular and non-glandular epithelium. A thick nervous layer at the base of the epidermis lies immediately above the tough basement membrane. The outer circular and inner longitudinal muscle layers are strong in the proboscis and collar, but the trunk musculature is thin and almost wholly longitudinal.

Proboscis. The conical to elongate proboscis is the only active part of the body. It probes inquisitively into the mud or sand and collects food in mucous strands, which are carried to the margin of the collar for swallowing. The proboscis does the excavation work for tube-dwelling species. It is thrust into the sand; cilia move sand and mucus back over the surface to the collar (Fig. 12.4B). The sand and mucus may be swallowed, or may slow down and push back over the collar surface to form a ring around the body. Body cilia slowly move the sand ring back as sand is added at the front. The tubes are U-shaped, with one or more front entrances and a back doorway. The proboscis is thrust from the tube entrance for feeding and the anus from the back for defecation. A great deal of sand is eaten, and the spiral fecal mounds are a tell-tale clue to the presence of enteropneusts in a mud flat.

The proboscis contains the remnants of the protocoel (Fig. 12.4B). The embryonic peritoneum differentiates into muscle and connective tissue, so the coelom is partly filled with tissue. The proboscis has rather delicate circular muscles. Prominent strands of longitudinal muscles, sometimes arranged in a fan and often mixed with diagonal fibers, nearly fill the anterior part of the protocoel. The protocoel widens posteriorly, but is invaded by the buccal diverticulum, a highly modified preoral gut long thought to be a notochord. The buccal diverticulum is covered by peritoneum and is attached to the proboscis floor by a midventral mesentery, partly dividing the protocoel into right and left chambers. A canal of the protocoel extends into the proboscis stalk on each side of the buccal diverticulum. Here the peritoneum is sometimes frilly, forming the "cauliflower organ." A proboscis canal connects the protocoel with a proboscis pore. Extensions of the mesocoel extend forward to meet the posterior canals of the protocoel. Where they meet, the coelomic peritoneum forms chondroid tissue, reminiscent of vertebrate cartilage. The coelomic linings disintegrate and disappear as chondroid tissue forms. The basement membrane is thickened in the proboscis, and muscles insert on it. It is thickened at the proboscic base to form the proboscis skeleton, consisting of a median plate and two anterior horns.

Collar and Mesocoel. Adults have no definite proboscis-collar septum, but the protocoel and mesocoel are not openly confluent. The mouth lies on the ventral side, between the proboscis base and the collar margin, here flared out as the collarette (Fig. 12.4A). A buccal tube extends through the collar. The rest of the space in the collar is occupied by the mesocoel, considerably reduced by connective tissue and muscle fibers. *Protoglossus* is considered the most primitive enteropneust genus; it has right and left mesocoel chambers divided by a median septum. In other forms the mesentery, especially on the ventral side, is incomplete. The mesocoel opens to the exterior on each side through a collar canal leading to a collar pore, located in the first gill slit. The collar musculature varies. Radial muscles attached to the body wall and buccal tube, and longitudinal muscles are usually present, but some species have only a feeble collar musculature. A deep constriction divides collar and trunk; here the collar-trunk septum lies. Although simple in *Protoglossus*, it is complicated in other forms by one or two pairs of metacoel pouches which extend through the septum. Perihaemal spaces extend forward over the top of the buccal tube, with the dorsal blood vessel in the septum between them. In some species a pair of flattened peribuccal folds containing an extension of the metacoel extends forward on each side of the buccal tube.

Trunk and Metacoel. The long trunk is usually divided into regions. A series of pairs of branchial pores mark the dorsolateral surface of the genitobranchial region of the trunk (Fig. 12.3B). The number of pores is variable, for new ones are added as the animal grows. The gonads lie in this part of the trunk, and genital ridges can often be seen on the surface. The anterior part of the postbranchial region is sometimes darkened by the hepatic part of the gut; in this case it is termed the hepatic region. The metacoel is partly divided into compartments by a mesentery, but the dorsal mesentery is incomplete. It does not communicate with the exterior by a canal and pore. The coelomic fluid of the protocoel and mesocoel must approach the composition of sea water as the chambers are open to the outside, but the metacoel contains a coelomic fluid with many coelomocytes.

Digestive System. The straight gut has no conspicuous dilations and usually is without intrinsic muscle, but it is connected to the body wall by radial muscles. The mouth and buccal tube lie in the collar, and the pharynx and intestine in the trunk.

The buccal diverticulum is a unique part, interesting historically because Bateson (1886) believed it a notochord and so classified enteropneusts as chordates. It was not until recent times that it was found to be a preoral extension of the buccal cavity associated with the central sinus of the circulatory system, and with a mass of blind peritoneal tubes known as the glomerulus. The buccal diverticulum, central sinus, and glomerulus together form the proboscis complex. The glomerulus is probably excretory; brownish crystals occur in glomerular cells, and the peritoneum adjacent to the proboscis complex is also brownish and seems to have an athrocytic function in some species.

Food collects in the collarette and is diverted into the mouth. Strong cilia in the buccal tube cause a current that flows toward the gills. The horns of the proboscis skeleton extend along the upper surface of the buccal tube, which is often evaginated as a groove at this point.

The digestive tube widens to form a pharynx in the trunk. Here gill slits open to the exterior; their cilia help to pull water through the anterior part of the gut. The gill slits are primitively a food-gathering device, no doubt assuming a secondary respiratory function. As no gills are associated with enteropneust gill slits, they must be concerned primarily with food procurement.

The esophagus has a relatively large lumen and in some species is histologically differentiated into several regions. In two families, esophageal canals lead to esophageal pores at the body surface. These are probably abortive gill slits. The anterior part of the intestine is the hepatic region. The dorsal epithelium is filled with brownish or greenish inclusions, and in some species is thrown into sacciform projections. This part of the intestine is richly vascular (Fig. 12.5), and one species has a siphon reminiscent of the echinoid intestinal siphon. The next part of the intestine has a wide lumen and a low epithelial lining. Dorsoventral ciliated bands are sometimes found. In some species a midventral band of cells extends between the two leaves of the ventral mesentery. This band of cells, sometimes hollow and often interrupted, has been called the pygochord because its vacuolated cells bear some resemblance to notochord cells. The intestine ends in a dilated or histologically differentiated rectum, opening through an anus which is sometimes guarded by a sphincter.

Little is known of digestive physiology.

Cilia are primarily responsible for food conduction, although some peristalsis occurs in the esophagus of *Saccoglossus*. An amylase is found in the proboscis secretion and is swallowed with the mucous strings. Weak lipase and protease have been recovered from extracts of body pieces. Barrington (1940) is of the opinion that the brownish inclusions of the hepatic region are enzymatic, but there is no direct evidence to support this idea.

Respiration. Respiratory exchange occurs at the body surface and to some extent in the branchial apparatus and the foregut epithelium. No gills are attached to the gill slits, but they will be considered a part of the respiratory system.

An epibranchial ridge usually attaches the dorsal ends of the gill slits. The paired gill pores open into a series of branchial cavities (Fig. 12.4D), in some species merged as a single long chamber on each side. Ciliary currents force water from the pharynx through the gills slits and branchial chambers to the outside. The gill pores are usually guarded by sphincter muscles and open in the genitobranchial groove on each side of the body. Gill slits are oval at first, but a tongue bar pushes down from the dorsal side during development, giving them a chevron shape. Each tongue bar contains an extension of the coelom. A series of septa divide the gill slits. Each septum is supported by a skeleton, originally composed of two U-shaped pieces, with one prong in the septum and one in the tongue bar (Fig. 12.4C). Fusion of the two pieces in each septum converts them into three-pronged supports. In some species, small septa known as synapticules attach the tongue bars and adjacent septa, holding the tongue bars firmly in place.

Circulatory System. The circulatory system consists of closed vessels, lacunar spaces, and a definite pulsating organ, generally known as the heart. The blood contains no or very few cells and no respiratory pigment. Most of the circulatory system is located between the lamellae of the basement membrane and the leaves of the mesentery.

The dorsal vessel conducts blood forward, and the ventral vessel back (Fig. 12.5). The dorsal vessel is dilated at the front of the collar, forming a venous sinus that empties into a central sinus above the preoral gut. Blood from the central sinus enters the glomerular sinuses of the proboscis complex. A contractile epidermal sac, the heart vesicle, lies immediately above the central sinus. No blood enters it; it is not comparable to a true heart, but its contractions help to force the blood from the central sinus. Dorsal and ventral blood vessels also contract and force blood along.

All of the blood flows through the glomerulus, where it is presumably cleared of nitrogenous wastes. Paired efferent glomerular vessels run back along the sides of the proboscis complex and then turn ventrally, as peribuccal arteries, meeting below to form the ventral blood vessel. The ventral vessel continues into the tail region.

A series of circulatory arcs arise from the major vessels. The proboscis arc is formed by a middorsal proboscis artery and midventral proboscis artery arising from the glomerulus, and paired lateral proboscis veins that empty into the central sinus. A body wall arc receives blood from the ventral vessel, never far from the body wall and sometimes in contact with it. Blood enters a lacunar plexus in the body wall and returns to the dorsal vessel through many small branches. Short branches from the ventral vessel bring blood to a similar lacunar plexus in the gut wall; the blood enters the dorsal vessel through similar short branches.

The lacunar plexus of the collar body wall is continuous with the buccal lacunar plexus at the mouth and at the constriction between the collar and trunk, where definite ring vessels occur. Blood from the ventral vessel reaches this double plexus by branches in the collar-trunk septum and drains into the dorsal vessel by small

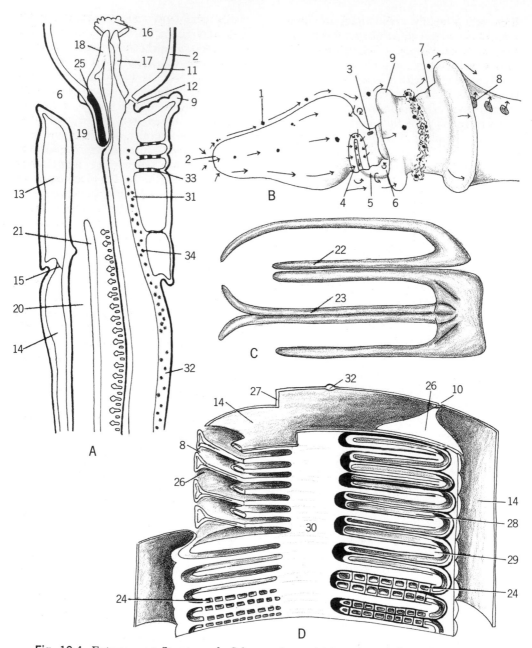

Fig. 12.4. Enteropneust Structure. **A.** Scheme of a sagittal section of *Saccoglossus pusilus*. **B.** Anterior end of *Protoglossus köhleri*, showing the ciliary currents used in feeding and burrowing. The proboscis is used in burrowing, and slime-trapped particles move back to the peduncle. Here fine particles move in a slime strand into the mouth, while coarser particles move back over the collar, and eventually to the posterior end of the body. **C.** Skeletal rods supporting the branchial region, from *Saccoglossus kowalewski*. **D.** Scheme of the gill region. (**A,** after Bullock. **B,** after Burdon-Jones, in Kükenthal and Krumbach. **C,** after Spengel.

branches. A ventral collar vessel also supplies blood to the collar plexus; it extends forward from the point where the peribuccal arteries unite.

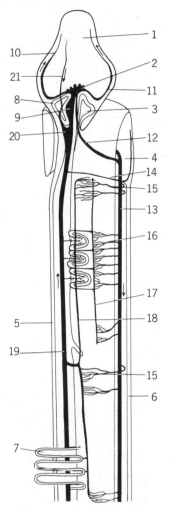

The pharyngeal lacunar plexus is modified as a branchial circulatory arc. The pharynx is composed of a dorsal branchial region and a ventral digestive region. A lateral pharyngeal vessel at the junction of the two pharyngeal regions appears in the lacunar plexus. It gives rise to an afferent branchial to each gill septum, which in turn gives off a branch that curves ventrally to enter the tongue bar. The lacunae of the branchial region empty into efferent branchials, formed by branches from the septum and tongue bar (Fig. 12.5).

Neurosensory Apparatus. The enteropneust body surface is supplied with neurosensory cells of the usual invertebrate type. The only special sense organ is thought to be a U-shaped depression on the posterior face of the proboscis, which may be chemoreceptive.

The nervous system is composed primarily of an epidermal plexus, just external to the basement membrane. Thickened strands of the plexus form a middorsal

Fig. 12.5. Scheme of Enteropneust Circulation. (After van der Horst, in Kükenthal and Krumbach.) *Body parts:* 1, proboscis; 2, glomerulus; 3, buccal diverticulum; 4, collar; 5, dorsal nerve cord in trunk; 6, ventral nerve cord; 7, hepatic diverticulum. *Circulatory system:* 8, heart vesicle; 9, central sinus; 10, dorsal proboscis artery; 11, ventral proboscis artery; 12, peribuccal artery; 13, ventral vessel; 14, ring vessel in collar-trunk septum; 15, lacunar network in body wall; 16, lacunar network in digestive tube; 17, lateral pharyngeal vessel; 18, lateral longitudinal vessel; 19, dorsal vessel; 20, venous sinus; 21, lateral proboscis vein.

D, after Delage and Hérouard from van der Horst, in Kükhenthal and Krumbach.) *External features:* 1, sand grain; 2, proboscis; 3, peduncle; 4, preoral ciliary organ; 5, fine particles in mucous strand; 6, mouth; 7, collar; 8, gill pore; 9 collarette; 10 branchiogenital groove. *Coelom:* 11, protocoel; 12, proboscis pore; 13, mesocoel; 14, metacoel; 15, collar-trunk septum. *Proboscis complex:* 16, glomerulus; 17, heart vesicle; 18, buccal diverticulum. *Digestive system:* 19, buccal tube; 20, pharynx; 21, parabranchial groove. *Skeleton:* 22, skeletal support of tongue bar; 23, skeletal support of septum; 24, synapticule; 25, proboscis skeleton. *Branchial apparatus:* 26, branchial sac; 27, body wall; 28, septum; 29, tongue bar; 30, dorsal wall of pharynx. *Nervous system:* 31, collar cord; 32, dorsal nerve cord of trunk; 33, dorsal strands of collar cord; 34, giant cells.

nerve cord, extending the length of the body, and a midventral nerve cord that starts at the collar-trunk constriction and continues posteriorly. The nerve plexus is also thickened at the base of the proboscis, forming an anterior nerve ring, and again at the junction of the collar and trunk, where a circumenteric nerve ring connects the dorsal nerve cord with the start of the ventral nerve cord.

The dorsal nerve cord in the collar, sometimes called the collar cord (Fig. 12.4B) is especially interesting, for it lies in the mesocoel instead of outside of the basement membrane and is hollow, in some species opening by anterior and posterior neuropores to the exterior. In other species the cavity is discontinuous, consisting of scattered spaces. The collar cord arises from the epidermis, but has sunk in to take a deeper position. Its similarity to the chordate nerve cord, formed by invagination of the nervous ectoderm at the dorsal midline, is evident.

The collar cord, and sometimes the anterior part of the dorsal cord in the trunk or nerve ring, contains giant neurons. Each gives off a single large nerve fiber which crosses to the other side of the body and runs through the circumenteric ring to the ventral nerve cord. In some species giant neurons at the front of the collar cord cross over and enter the proboscis. The number of giant neurons varies from about 10 to 160. They are responsible for rapid conduction of stimuli leading to quick retraction of body parts.

A nerve plexus below the gut epithelium is most highly developed in the buccal region, forming a diffuse oral ring. It becomes less conspicuous posteriorly. It tends to be thickened into a midventral tract and in some species into a lesser middorsal tract.

Although the collar cord is the most complex part of the nervous system, it is no more than a conduction path and the site of giant neuron formation. The proboscis is dominant and activity is greatly reduced when it is removed. Conduction in the plexus is diffuse, as is typical of nerve nets. Digging movements are hampered but not totally inhibited by transsection of the dorsal proboscis cord. Sudden startle contractions, much more rapid than ordinary peristaltic movements, are not disturbed by transsection of the dorsal nerve cord of the trunk, but are interrupted by transsection of the collar cord or ventral cord, where the giant fibers are found. Evidently giant neurons conduct impulses rapidly and are responsible for rapid, coordinated reactions of the body as a whole, as in a shortening reflex. The normal peristaltic body movements are disturbed but not totally destroyed by transsection of the dorsal and ventral cords. The epidermal plexus can control peristaltic movement, but less effectively than the nerve cords.

Reproduction. Sexes are separate, and male and female reproductive systems are simple. Each of the many gonads open through a gonopore, typically located beside the gill pores in the genitobranchial groove. The gonads sometimes extend into the genital ridges or genital wings on the sides of the body.

Little is known of spawning habits. In some species, females shed gametes first, releasing 2000 to 3000 eggs about half an hour after the tide has ebbed. Males release sperm about half an hour later. The eggs are imbedded in mucus, but are scattered by the returning tide.

Enteropneusts fragment easily and regenerate reasonably well. Trunk pieces regenerate a new proboscis and collar, but the isolated proboscis and collar cannot regenerate a new trunk. At least one species reproduces asexually by transverse constrictions, which cut off pieces of the trunk.

Development. One family (Harimaniidae) produces large, yolky eggs, but most enteropneusts produce small ova with little yolk. The small ova undergo indirect development through a ciliated, tornaria larva stage that strongly resembles some echino-derm larvae.

Cleavage is equal, holoblastic, and usu-ally radial. A coeloblastula gastrulates by invagination. The blastopore soon closes, but marks the posterior end of the embryo. The embryo elongates and develops a covering of cilia and escapes from the fertilization membrane after a day or so of development. At hatching, a long apical tuft of cilia is present (Fig. 12.6A). The tuft and surface ciliation declines as a loco-motor band develops. This sinuous band transforms the embryo into a young tor-naria larva, with an apical plate at the site of the former ciliary tuft (Fig. 12.6B).

The locomotor band forms a preoral and ventral loop. Later a circumanal loop, com-pletely separated from the first band, is formed. Tentacles appear at the margins of the locomotor band of some species. Tor-naria larvae are not uncommon in plank-ton samples, and are interesting from a structural and functional point of view. More kinds of tornaria have been described than species of enteropneusts, so it may be assumed that several undescribed species must exist. The fully grown tornaria has a pair of pigment-cup ocelli at the sides of the apical plate and a new, shorter tuft of cilia on the plate. The tornaria eventually regresses, becomes constricted, foreshadow-ing the proboscis-collar constriction, and becomes worm-like as the locomotor band gradually declines (Fig. 12.6C,D).

The protocoel arises from the anterior tip of the archenteron. A pore canal and pore, remarkably like the hydropore of echinoderms, form during development; these become the proboscis canal and pro-boscis pore. The mesocoel and metacoel arise in a variety of ways, depending on the species. The principal methods are: 1) the protocoel gives rise to two lateral exten-sions that grow backward and are cut off as right and left mesocoels and metacoels; 2) solid mesodermal cords on each side of the gut are divided into collar and trunk

regions, hollow out, and become mesocoels and metacoels; 3) the mesocoels and meta-coels arise independently as either solid or hollow outgrowths of the gut wall; 4) they appear independently as spaces in groups of mesenchyme cells. The mesocoels, like the protocoel, become open to the exterior by pore canals and pores.

The enteric sac, left after coelom forma-tion, becomes the primitive gut. A stomo-daeum makes connections with it, and the foregut, midgut, and hindgut develop as in echinoderms. The fully-formed larval gut is U-shaped. Unlike echinoderms, enterop-neusts derive the adult mouth and anus from the larval mouth and anus.

THE PTEROBRANCHS

Pterobranchs are odd, ectoproct-like crea-tures, largely confined to antarctic and subantarctic regions, but reaching into the tropics in the Indo-Pacific region. They are poorly known, for they are usually taken only on collecting expeditions. Only three genera have been described: *Atubaria*, *Cephalodiscus*, and *Rhabdopleura*. *Atu-baria* is known from a single dredging near Japan and is unique in having no tube or case, attaching by its stalk to colonial hy-droids (Fig. 12.7A). The solitary individ-uals apparently cannot reproduce asexually. The members of the other two genera live in tubes imbedded in a common case, the coenecium. They reproduce asexually to produce new members of the coenecium and sexually to form new coenoecia. *Ceph-alodiscus* zooids (Fig. 12.7B) are not con-nected; they live in tubes as independent as separate apartments in an apartment house. *Rhabdopleura* are permanently at-tached to the common stolon from which they arose as buds.

A glandular region on the discoid proto-some secretes the coenecium. The *Cephalo-discus* coenecium is a soft, gelatinous mass. It may be stiffened by firmer spines or have filamentous projections, giving it a plant-like appearance. Each zooid inhabits a

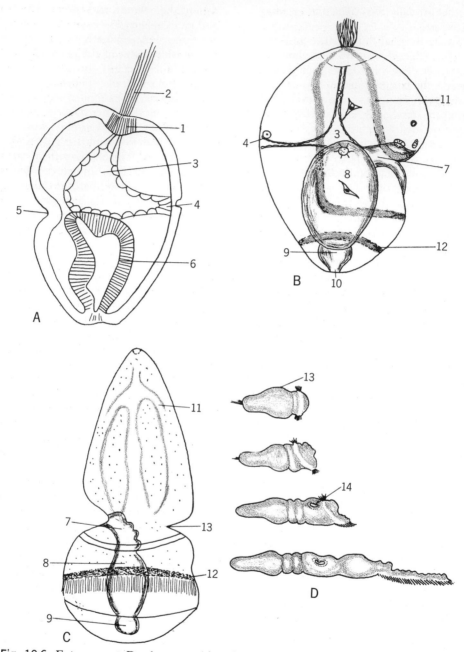

Fig. 12.6. Entcropneust Development. After the protocoel has arisen from the inner tip of the primitive gut, the protocoel comes to open to the exterior through a hydropore (A), destined to become the proboscis pore of the adult. Mouth and anus formation is like that of echino-derms, and a ciliary band develops, closely resembling the locomotor bands of echino-derm larvae, converting the larva into a tornaria (B). During later development, the anterior end of the larva loses its locomotor bands, is separated from the posterior part by a proboscis-

firmer, darker tube imbedded in the coenecium. The *Rhabdopleura* coenecium is a branching tube, giving off upright tubes for the zooids. The creeping tube is somewhat irregular, and contains the black stolon, formed of a firm tube containing a cellular column from which new buds arise. The upright tubes are built of regular, successive rings.

Each zooid is composed of a cephalic shield (protosome), collar (mesosome), and trunk (metasome), and contains the same five coelomic compartments as enteropneusts (Fig. 12.8A). The protocoel opens to the exterior through paired pore canals and paired pores at the base of the arms. The mesocoel also opens through paired pore canals and collar pores.

The flattened cephalic shield of *Cephalodiscus* always is crossed by a red band of unknown function. The shield is highly muscular, with radiating subepidermal muscles and radial muscle fibers attached to the shield-collar septum and crossing the protocoel. A buccal diverticulum complex, essentially like that of enteropneusts, thrusts into the protocoel from the shield-collar septum.

The mouth is on the ventral side of the collar and can be closed by the cephalic shield. Flanges of the body wall (oral lamellae) guide food into the mouth. It is collected by four to nine pairs of arms, with marginal fringes of 25 to 50 tentacles and ventral ciliated grooves. Mucous glands on the dorsal sides of the arms help to trap food. The collar coelom (mesocoel) extends into the oral lamellae and arms.

The trunk narrows posteriorly into a long, muscular stalk. A single pair of gill slits, without skeletal supports, opens just behind the collar-trunk septum. The trunk coelom (metacoel) is nearly filled by gonads and the digestive tube in front and by muscles and connective tissue in the stalk. The stalk ends in an adhesive region, where the zooid is attached to its tube. Zooids are freely movable. They leave the tubes and cling to the coenecium surface while feeding.

Pterobranch organ systems closely resemble enteropneust organ systems, and need not be described in detail. The digestive system is U-shaped instead of straight, as is common in sessile organisms. It consists of buccal tube in the collar, a pharynx with a pair of gill slits in the anterior part of the trunk, a short esophagus, a saccate stomach, and an intestine that curves dorsally to end in an anal slit. The main circulatory channels have no cellular walls. A dorsal sinus above the esophagus and pharynx receives blood from the gonadal sinuses and lacunar plexus of the gut. It runs into a central sinus in front of the buccal diverticulum. A contractile heart vesicle lies over the central sinus, but the sinus is also contractile. A large, ventral shield sinus arises from the posterior tip of the central sinus; it gives off the peribuccal sinuses that join to form the main ventral sinus at the collar-trunk septum. Folds in the wall of the ventral shield sinus constitute the glomerulus. The nervous system of *Cephalodiscus* is wholly epidermal. There is no hollow collar cord, but an indefinite, solid collar ganglion joins middorsal and laterodorsal thickenings of the nerve plexus in the cephalic shield. Circumenteric connectives at the collar-trunk boundary pass from the collar ganglion to the midventral nerve cord. A short middorsal nerve trunk

collar groove, and develops into the proboscis. The posterior part of the larva forms the collar and trunk (C). Some enteropneusts develop directly, without passing through a tornaria stage. They, however, undergo a similar metamorphosis to develop the three body regions characteristic of the group (D). (A, after Heider. B, after Stiasny. C, after Morgan. D, after Burdon-Jones.) 1, apical plate; 2, apical tufts; 3, protocoel; 4, hydropore; 5, stomodaeum; 6, primitive gut; 7, esophagus; 8, stomach; 9, intestine; 10, anus; 11, ciliary band; 12, telotroch; 13, proboscis-collar groove; 14, gill pore.

extends from the collar ganglion to the anal region.

The stalk epidermis forms buds that receive an extension of the stalk coelom and of the dorsoventral mesentery. The cephalic shield of the bud grows large first and the trunk develops later. The arms arise as buds, the anterior pair first and the rest in serial order. The heart vesicle arises differently than in enteropneusts, deriving from the protocoel.

The saccate gonads lie in front of the stomach. Short gonoducts open behind the collar-trunk boundary. Sexes are usually separate, but males and females look alike. Hermaphroditic forms are not uncommon.

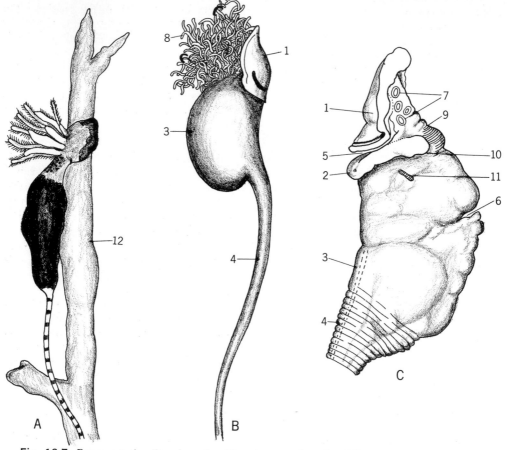

Fig. 12.7. Representative Pterobranchs. The tiny pterobranchs differ markedly in the stalk and zoecium. While *Rhabdopleura* has a common stolon attaching all members of a colony, the order Cephalodiscida is characterized by a stalk that ends blindly, so each member of a colony is free. A and B. *Cephalodiscus hodgsoni*. At A, an individual zooid is outside its compartment, clinging to the zoecium with its stalk. C. *Atubaria heterolopha*, with the arms removed to show the body form. *Atubaria* produces no zoecium, the individuals clinging to colonial animals with their stalks. (A, after Andersson. B, after Ridewood, from van der Horst and Helmeke, in Kükenthal and Krumbach. C, after Sato.) 1, cephalic shield; 2, postoral lamella; 3, trunk; 4, stalk; 5, mouth; 6, anus; 7, cut ends of cephalic arms; 8, tentacles; 9, genital region; 10, site of pore to coelom; 11, gill slit; 12, zoecium.

Members of one coenecium may be of the same or different sex.

Rhabdopleura zooids resemble *Cephalodiscus*, but have no gill slits and only one pair of arms. The stalk is permanently attached to the stolon, so they are tethered when they emerge from the tube to feed. The dark brown zooids are only about 1 mm. long, and have a cephalic shield with a red pigment band but without a marginal notch.

Little is known of their embryology. The large, yolky eggs develop indirectly. A tornaria-like larva is formed. The primordium of the cephalic shield develops early; its gland cells are thought to secrete the coenecium.

Phylum Chordata—The Chordates

Phylum Chordata is one of the most successful animal phyla from the standpoint of number of species and size of its members. Most chordates are vertebrates, and so fall outside of the scope of this book. Two subphyla, Cephalochordata and Urochordata, include invertebrate chordates. Amphioxus is so universally studied in vertebrate anatomy courses that it will be omitted here, but Urochordates are sometimes neglected, and are important enough to deserve discussion.

CLASSIFICATION

Among the most outstanding chordate characteristics are the following:

1. A supportive structure, the notochord, is present at some stage of embryonic development, and may persist in the adult.

2. The nervous system centers in a dorsal, tubular nerve cord, formed by the invagination of a strip of nervous ectoderm on the dorsal midline.

3. Gill slits open into the pharynx at some time during development, and may persist in adults.

4. They are enterocoelous.

5. They have a ventral, pulsating heart.

6. A postanal tail contains extensions of the nerve cord, notochord, and body-wall musculature.

Subphylum Urochordata. Tunicates. Chordate characteristics developed only in the larvae; usually metamorphosing into highly modified, sessile or pelagic adults without a coelom or traces of metamerism; notochord in the tail region only; without bony tissue; body wall forming a secreted case, usually rich in a cellulose known as tunicin.

Class Larvacea. Appendicularians. Tunicates retaining the larval organization as adults; pelagic, secreting a temporary house through which water is circulated to capture food. Example: *Oikopleura* (Fig. 12.8B,C).

Class Ascidiacea. Ascidians or sea squirts. Sessile, solitary, or colonial tunicates with a heavy tunic; adults without a tail and with degenerate nervous and muscle systems; pharynx with several gill slits usually subdivided to form a pharyngeal basket; an atrial cavity receives water from the gill slits, and discharges it through an atrial pore. Examples: *Molgula* (Fig. 12.10A.); *Botryllus* (Fig. 12.9A).

Class Thalliacea. Salps. Pelagic tunicates with a transparent tunic, and an atrial cavity discharging water through a posterior aperture. Examples: *Salpa* (Fig. 12.9D,E); *Pyrosoma* (Fig. 12.9B,C); *Doliolum* (Fig. 12.9F).

THE LARVACEA

Larvacea are relatively common plankton organisms from polar to tropical seas. They are most common at depths of 100 m. or less, but have been collected at depths of 3000 m. They are probably neotenic larvae, but may reveal something of the nature of ancestral stocks from which urochordates stemmed.

They are tiny, transparent animals, often scarcely visible unless the gut, gonads, or

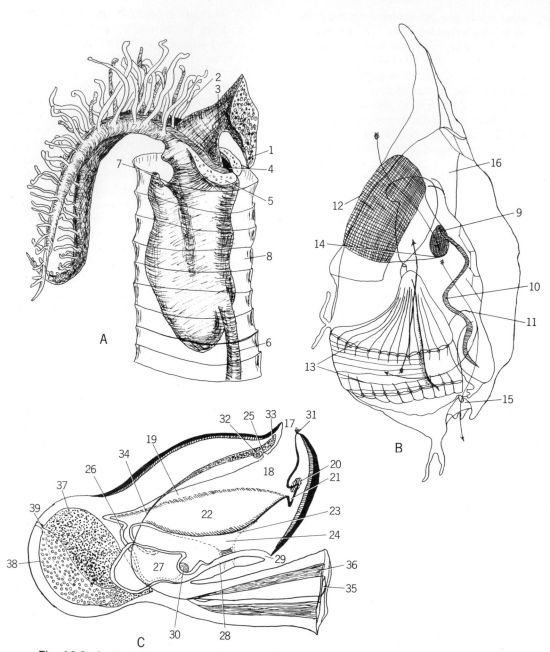

Fig. 12.8. A. *Rhabdopleura normani*, a typical pterobranch. B. *Oikopleura albicans*, an appendicularian, in its house. The animal is much smaller than its house. It drives water through the house by lashing movements of its tail. Food is filtered out as the water passes through, and as pressure builds up, the door at the posterior end opens; as water leaves the house it forces the house forward. When the filters are clogged, the animal escapes from its house through an exit and secretes a new house. C. An optical section of *Oikopleura*, showing a

other parts are pigmented; bright-red and violet shades predominate. The asymmetrical, U-shaped body consists of a dilated trunk and an elongated tail, attached to the ventral trunk surface and twisted 90°, bringing the dorsal surface to the left (Fig. 12.8C). The tail contains a central notochord, a dorsal nerve cord with swellings for each muscle region, and two lateral muscle bands that tend to be broken into incipient metameres. A large ganglion swells the nerve cord at the base of the tail.

The mouth opens into a dilated pharynx with a short, tubular, ventral endostyle, containing longitudinal rows of gland cells (Fig. 12.8C). A single pair of simple, ciliated gill slits open into short, funnel-shaped atrial canals that open ventrally. The rest of the alimentary tract consists of a short esophagus, a saccate stomach, and an intestine that curves anteriorly to an anus on the right side of the ventral surface in front of the gill slits. A large ganglion gives rise to a solid nerve cord that extends into the tail. A richly ciliated, tubular process corresponding to the dorsal tubercle of ascidians (p. 444) is attached to the floor of the cerebral ganglion and hangs down into the pharynx. An eye and statocyst lie on the left side of the brain. Except in *Kowalevskia*, a heart lies in front of and below the stomach. There are no blood vessels; blood circulates in a haemocoel derived from the blastocoel. They are usually protandrous hermaphrodites. The unpaired testis and ovary lie at the back of the trunk.

The most remarkable appendicularian feature is the house, a transparent affair secreted very rapidly by oikoblasts at the body surface (Fig. 12.8B). It is far larger than the animal that makes it, permitting free movement within. Lashing movements of the tail drive water through the house. Water enters at an incurrent pore, guarded by a fibrous mesh that filters out large particles, and circulates through passageways that act as a second filter system. The particles that gather on the inner filters are eaten. An excurrent pore is normally closed by a hinged door, that opens suddenly as pressure builds up in the house; the sudden jet of water propels the house and animal through the water. An added feature is the escape hatch or emergency door, through which the animal leaves when the filters are clogged. New houses are secreted very frequently, every few hours in some species.

THE ASCIDIANS

Ascidians occur in oceans everywhere, from pole to pole and from shallow to deep water. Some are solitary and others form colonies of large size. Some individual ascidians are very small, while others are about a foot long. Colonial species usually have relatively small zooids.

Ascidian structure is best studied in solitary species. A soft or tough tunic clothes the body, and is attached at a permanent base located at the posterior part of the left side of the body. At the opposite end, an oral siphon marks the anterior tip of

part of the tail. (A, after Delage and Hérouard. B, after Lohmann. C, after Herdmann.) *Cephalodiscus:* 1, cephalic shield; 2, tentacle; 3, neck; 4, mouth; 5, boundary of metasome; 6, stalk; 7, anus; 8, coenecium. *Oikopleura house:* 9, body of animal; 10, tail of animal; 11, tail chamber; 12, entrance filter; 13, filtering channels; 14, duct to mouth; 15, posterior opening propelling the house; 16, escape chamber. *Oikopleura: Digestive tract:* 17, mouth; 18, pharynx; 19, epipharyngeal ridge; 20, oral gland; 21, endostyle; 22, branchial sac; 23, hypobranchial ridge; 24, atrium; 25, ciliated funnel; 26, esophagus; 27, stomach; 28, intestine; 29, anus. *Circulatory system:* 30, heart. *Neurosensory apparatus:* 31, sense organ; 32, otocyst; 33, brain; 34, nerve cord. *Tail:* 35, notochord; 36, longitudinal muscle. *Reproductive system:* 37, testis; 38, ovary; 39, gonoduct.

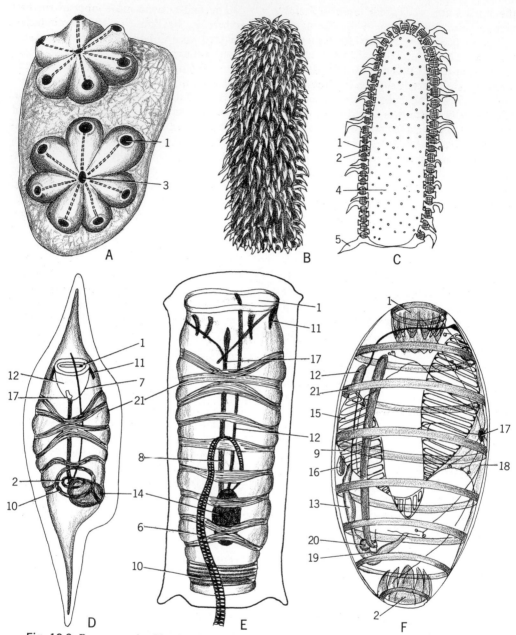

Fig. 12.9. Representative Urochordates. Urochordates are divided into three classes, Larvacea, Ascidacea, and Thaliacea. Ascidians are solitary or colonial, and sessile as adults. *Botryllus violaceus* (A) is one of the colonial forms made up of systems of individuals surrounding a central and common exhalant pore. The Thaliacea are pelagic, and may be colonial or solitary. *Pyrosoma* (B, C) is a colonial form composed of many individuals arranged in the form of an open cylinder. It is propelled by water passing into the central cavity from the many members of the colony, and emerging through the opening at one end of the colony. *Salpa* is a

438

the body and a cloacal siphon the dorsal margin.

Tunic. The tunic is an epidermal secretion, but amoeboid cells from the mesenchyme invade it and differentiate into pigment cells, stellate cells, and vacuolated cells, and sometimes secrete calcareous spicules that stiffen the tunic. The tunic matrix is composed largely of a cellulose known as tunicin, found only in tunicates and some hemichordates. The tunic is often colored, taking its colors from pigment cells and blood corpuscles. Blood sinuses enter the tunic and ramify through it, ending near the surface in terminal knobs. They are abundant enough to aid in respiration, and in some cases pulsate and aid in blood flow.

Body Wall. The mantle or body wall is beneath the tunic. An epidermis covers a thick dermis containing homogeneous and fibrous connective tissues. Smooth muscles run in all directions; their contraction somewhat modifies body shape. The siphons have strong sphincter muscles. The siphons are lined with tunic and epidermis, turned in at the siphon margins. Tunic stimulation evokes responses, indicating the presence of a body-wall nerve plexus. Stimuli spread in all directions and can spread around cuts. The body-wall nerve plexus is independent, for destruction of the central nervous system causes relaxation of the body-wall muscles but does not destroy the normal reflexes.

Pharynx and Atrium. Water enters the oral siphon and leaves through the cloacal siphon, having passed through the pharynx, the gill slits, and atrial cavity (Fig. 12.10A). The epidermal lining of the oral siphon stops at the whorl of oral tentacles. Neurosensory cells in the oral tentacles evoke reflex contractions of body-wall muscles, clearing the siphon of particles or irritating substances by ejecting a stream of water. The pharynx is the largest organ. It is lined by tissues derived from larval endoderm, but the lining may arise from other germ layers during asexual reproduction. It begins just beyond the oral tentacles.

The pharynx wall is supported by a system of bars, through which the branchial lacunae of the circulatory system pass (Fig. 12.10B,C). The bars are arranged in patterns characteristic of species. Internal, longitudinal bars support a delicate grid of transverse and longitudinal bars. The primary gill slits become subdivided, often very intricately, to form many stigmata. Stigmata are often so modified that they are lacy or spiral. A deep midventral groove, the endostyle, runs the length of the pharynx, ending in a posterior caecum. The pharynx wall is joined to the mantle below the endostyle; everywhere else it is surrounded by the atrium (Fig. 12.10B). Four rows of mucous glands lie in the endostyle, as in amphioxus. The thyroid primordium of ammocoetes larvae also has four rows of gland cells, indicating that the endostyle is the homologue of the vertebrate thyroid. A median row of long flagella and laterally placed tracts of cilia push mucus from the endostyle up on the pharyngeal basket.

The ciliated bands of the endostyle diverge behind to form ciliated ridges (retropharyngeal bands) that extend dorsally to

transparent pelagic thaliacean which may occur in chains (D) or as single individuals (E), depending on the stage of the life cycle. *Doliolum* (F) is another transparent thaliacean with a complex life cycle. (A, after Milne-Edwards. B, D, and E, after Herdmann. C, after Grobben. F, after Neumann, in Grassé.) *External features:* 1, oral siphon; 2, cloacal siphon; 3, common cloacal siphon; 4, common cloacal chamber; 5, velum; 6, stolon with buds. *Pharynx:* 7, peripharyngeal band; 8, dorsal lamina (gill); 9, stigmata of gill; 10, atrial muscle; 11, branchial muscle; 12, endostyle. *Internal parts:* 13, digestive tube; 14, visceral mass; 15, pharynx; 16, heart; 17, ganglion; 18, peripheral nerve; 19, testis; 20, ovary; 21, muscle bands.

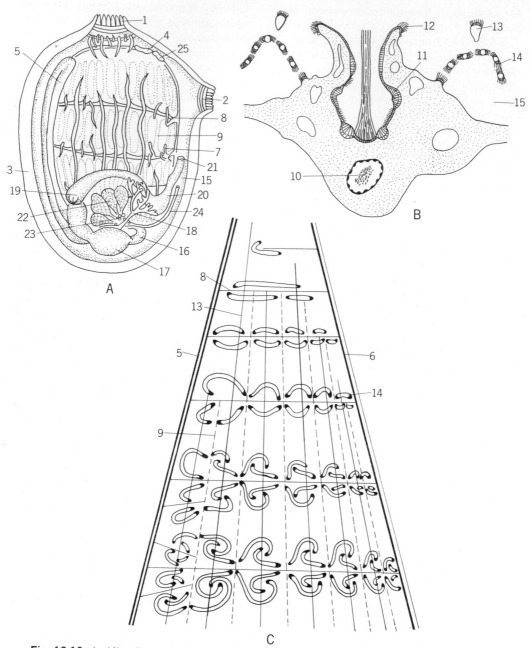

Fig. 12.10. Ascidian Structure. **A.** Anatomy of *Molgula*, a solitary ascidian. **B.** Scheme of section through the endostyle of an ascidian. **C.** Scheme of development of the stigmata in a *Molgula*. The primary protostigmata is subdivided to form a complex pharyngeal wall with a series of spiraled stigmata. Divisions along the developing horizontal sinuses produce pairs of stigmata, and divisions along the longitudinal sinuses result in the number of rows of stigmata characteristic of the species. Ribs support the stigmata between the longitudinal

the junction of pharynx and esophagus. A second ciliated ridge may parallel them, forming retropharyngeal grooves. Ciliated bands (peripharyngeal bands) emerge from the front of the endostyle. They cross the pharynx, dividing the peribranchial from the branchial pharynx. The peripharyngeal bands meet a middorsal sheet of tissue, the dorsal lamina. A fringe of small tentacles (languets) forms the margin of the dorsal lamina.

The pharynx is a ciliary-mucous food-gathering device. Cilia at the margins of the stigmata pull water into the pharynx and send it into the atrium. Some tunicates move several thousand times their body volume of water through the pharynx in a day. Mucus from the endostyle moves up across the pharyngeal bars, and food particles stick to it. Strands of mucus are delivered to the dorsal lamina, which bends over to form a tube or groove along which food moves to the esophagus.

Water leaving the pharynx goes into the atrium, formed by the union of two ectodermal invaginations from the surface and lined with epidermis throughout. Cords of tissue attach the outer wall of the atrium to the pharynx, preventing excessive expansion. The gonoducts and anus enter at the upper end of the atrium, converting it into a cloaca. Water from the atrium departs through the cloacal siphon.

Digestive Tract. The pharynx opens into an esophagus, usually a short, descending arm of the U-shaped digestive tract (Fig. 12.10A). A dilated stomach lies at the turn of the U. The tubular intestine ascends to open into the atrium at the anus. Circular muscles form a sphincter at both ends of the stomach, but the gut wall is not highly

muscular and food conduction depends on ciliary currents. The stomach wall contains gland cells, mucous cells, and absorptive cells. Digestive glands arise from the posterior end of the stomach. Enzymes have not been studied carefully; proteolytic enzymes have been found. Digestion appears to be wholly extracellular, and appears to occur in the stomach. The intestine appears to be the primary absorptive part, based on histological evidence. A high, dorsal ridge, the typhosole, increases the absorptive surface. Surface is sometimes further amplified by increase in intestinal length and coiling. Food is stored in the intestinal wall, primarily as glycogen.

Respiration. The rich lacunar plexus of the pharyngeal wall suggests that most respiratory exchange occurs there. Some respiratory exchange undoubtedly occurs in the tunic lacunae also. Tunicates have no respiratory pigment, but their inactive life requires little oxygen. Less than 10 per cent of the available oxygen is absorbed from water passing through the gills. Critical oxygen tensions have not been determined; presumably they pass so much water through the body for feeding that respiration is not a physiological problem.

Excretion. About 90 per cent of the nitrogen excreted is in the form of ammonia. Presumably it leaves at the pharynx, tunic, or any other handy surface. A considerable quantity of uric acid and urates are also produced. These are picked up by amoebocytes and built into intracellular concretions. Cells containing such insoluble wastes settle on the surface of various organs, especially the gut and gonads. Special centers for storage excretion some-

sinuses. (A, after Van Name, from Kleinholtz, in Brown. B, after Herdmann. C, after Sélys-Longchamps, in Grassé.) *External features:* 1, oral siphon; 2, cloacal siphon; 3, mantle. *Pharynx:* 4, dorsal tubercle; 5, endostyle; 6, dorsal raphe; 7, dorsal languet; 8, horizontal sinus; 9, longitudinal sinus; 10, ventral sinus; 11, glandular tract in endostyle; 12, lip of endostyle; 13, longitudinal rib; 14, stigmata; 15, peribranchial (atrial) cavity. *Digestive tract:* 16, esophagus; 17, stomach; 18, intestinal gland; 19, intestine; 20, rectum; 21, anus. *Reproductive system:* 22, testis; 23, ovary; 24, gonoduct. *Nervous system:* 25, ganglion.

times occur. They are most often delicate, clear-walled vesicles in the intestinal loop. In the absence of definite information, it may be guessed that these wastes are end products of purine metabolism. An erroneous impression of the excretory situation would be obtained if only released compounds were taken into consideration. No doubt the same principle applies in many invertebrates where storage excretion is less obvious.

Circulatory System. The tunicate circulatory system is almost wholly open. Blood flows through spaces rarely lined with endothelium. The heart is unusual from morphological and physiological viewpoints, and the blood has some unique properties.

A pericardium and pericardial sac are formed from endodermal tissue during development. Some consider the pericardial cavity a vestige of the coelom. The pericardial cavity lies at the base of the digestive loop, or at the base of the postabdomen in species with a long postabdominal region. Its wall is folded to make a more or less U-shaped tube, the heart. The heart has no wall comparable to the heart wall of other chordates, and also lacks a lining.

Three lacunar plexi connect the three principal blood sinuses. The subendostylar sinus arises from the ventral end of the heart and is connected to the ventral side of the lacunar plexus of the pharyngeal basket. The ventral abdominal sinus is connected to the dorsal end of the heart. It opens into an extensive lacunar plexus over the gut and viscera, and issues two branches to the tunic. The median dorsal sinus is connected with the lacunar plexus of the viscera and runs over the dorsal midline of the pharynx, where it is attached to the pharyngeal lacunar plexus. It also receives branches from the lacunar plexus of the tunic.

The circulatory system is essentially triangular. Blood can (and does) flow either way through the triangle. The heart pulsates, each beat a peristaltic wave beginning at one end and passing to the other. There are no valves; blood is milked along by the advancing wave of constricting muscle. For several minutes, perhaps a hundred beats, contractions begin at the dorsal end, forcing blood into the subendostylar sinus, through the pharynx, into the median dorsal sinus, from this into the tunic and viscera, to return by way of the dorsal abdominal sinus. The beat gradually slows and stops. Then the heart beats again, but in the opposite direction, forcing blood to flow through the system in the opposite direction. This arrangement is unique. Neither its functional significance nor the factors that cause it is understood. The heartbeat appears to be myogenic, originating in the heart muscle itself, for isolated hearts continue to beat and the removal of the brain has little effect in most of the tunicates tested. A pacemaker of ganglion cells may lie in the heart, but discrepant results have been obtained in histological studies of the heart wall. It has been suggested that back pressure causes reversal of beat, but isolated hearts in which back pressures should be missing continue to reverse. When a heart is forced to beat by electrical stimuli, the threshold of excitation rises with each successive beat, suggesting that the pacemaker may undergo changes, gradually becoming less sensitive. In this case the pacemaker at the opposite end of the heart may gain dominance. Whatever the causes, the unique heartbeat and blood-flow in tunicates is a curious and interesting feature.

Tunicate blood plasma is isotonic or only slightly hypertonic to sea water, but some inorganic ions are regulated. They concentrate vanadium enormously, sometimes as much as half a million times. It is accumulated in the blood plasma of *Cionides* and *Diazonides,* and in blood corpuscles known as vanadacytes in some other tunicates. The vanadium is not involved in respiratory transport, as it remains in the reduced state within cells. The pyloric glands, which open into the stomach, are thought to excrete calcium. A full analysis of ionic regulation of tunicates is not available.

The blood corpuscles are numerous and strikingly colorful. They contain red, yellow, green, brown, blue, or white inclusions. Some are amoeboid, and some are known to be phagocytic. They move through tissues, and apparently pick up uric acid to initiate storage excretion.

Coelom. Tunicates never have a coelom, but are so evidently related to coelomates that the coelom must have been lost secondarily. The pericardial cavity and epi-

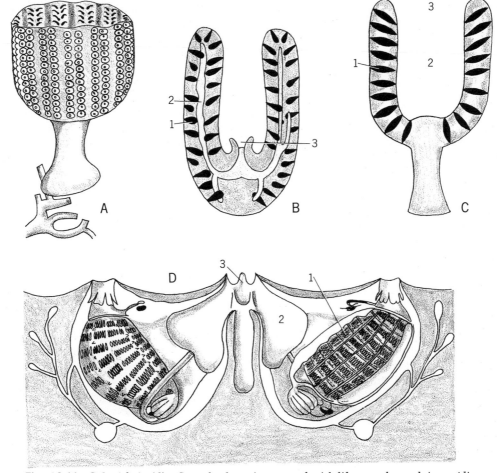

Fig. 12.11. Colonial Ascidia. Several adaptations to colonial life are observed in ascidians. Some, like *Botryllus* (D), retain the U-shaped gut and develop a common cloacal chamber, opening through a cloacal siphon common to the zooids in a single system. Others become lineal, with the oral siphon on the outer surface of the colony, and the cloacal siphon opening into an interior common cloacal cavity. In such forms, the colonies assume characteristic shapes, such as the goblet-shaped *Cyathocormus* (A and B) or *Coelocormus* (C). (A-C, after Okada, in Grassé. D, after Delage and Hérouard.) 1, zooid; 2, common cloacal chamber; 3, common cloacal pore.

cardium may be vestiges of the coelom. The epicardium is one tube or a pair of tubes arising from the base of the pharynx. When a pair of tubes is present, they usually unite. The epicardium extends along one side of the digestive tract, and in tunicates with a long postabdomen reaches the base and extends into the stolon. Its function is problematic. It contributes tissue to buds formed in this region, introducing an endodermal derivative into the bud, but many tunicates bud successfully without any endodermal tissue in the bud primordia.

As the epicardium arises from the digestive tube, it may be the vestige of an enterocoelous coelom. This view is somewhat supported by epicardial development in *Ciona*. The two epicardial sacs remain separate, one on each side of the digestive tube. They are greatly enlarged, surrounding the internal organs in the same manner as the coelomic pouches of other animals.

Neurosensory Apparatus. The motile larvae have good sense organs, but adults do not. Neurosensory cells of the invertebrate type occur on the body surface, especially in the siphon regions and in papillae on the inner surface of the branchial apparatus. They are probably important in regulating water-flow, and in clearing the siphons of particles by evoking ejection reflexes. A light stimulus inside of a siphon causes closing of the other siphon. A stronger stimulus causes the closure of the other siphon and body-wall contractions that eject a particle in the offending siphon.

A large, usually somewhat elongated, ganglion lies between the two siphons. Nerves arise from each end, passing to the siphons, the viscera, and the gills, where they innervate the languets, dorsal lamina, and dorsal tubercle. The cerebral ganglion seems to be of little importance in controlling the body activities. Its removal destroys the crossed siphon reflexes, but other activities are unchanged.

The subneural gland is a small mass of gland cells below the cerebral ganglion. A narrow duct connects it with a ciliated funnel located in the dorsal tubercle, a prominence in the dorsal pharyngeal wall. Dorsal tubercles vary greatly in form and are useful in taxonomy (Fig. 12.10). The subneural gland has been thought an excretory organ, a mucous gland, and a lymph gland, but no satisfactory demonstration of a function has been achieved. Extracts of the subneural gland cause effects like those caused by pituitary hormones when tested on other animals. This is interesting, as it lies at the same place as the hypophysis of vertebrates. The vertebrate pituitary rises from a double primordium, a depression on the brain floor and a pocket extending upward from the stomodaeum. The subneural gland and dorsal tubercle also arise partly from the pharynx and partly from the ganglion, supporting the idea that they are a pituitary homologue.

Reproduction. Nearly all ascidians are hermaphroditic. Most have a single ovary and testis in the center of the digestive loop. Each is served by a gonoduct. The parallel gonoducts, sometimes a double tube, run to the atrial wall and open into the cloaca. The lumen of the saccate ovary is continuous with the gonoduct. The testis is usually composed of many tubular branches. Sperm mature in the tubule wall and enter the tubule lumen, which leads to the gonoduct. *Molgula* and some other ascidians have paired ovaries and testes. The second ovary and testis lie against the right body wall, and have separate gonoducts to the cloaca. Some species are protandrous or protogynous, thus avoiding self-fertilization, but ova and sperm mature simultaneously in other species.

Colonies. Colony formation by asexual reproduction is important in tunicates as in most other sessile animals. The relationship between the zooids of a tunicate colony varies in intimacy with the nature of the budding process and the extent to which they share a common tunic. Discrete zooids are attached by a stolon in the simplest colonies. A common tunic partly unites the base of zooids in some stolonic colonies. The zooids are wholly enclosed in a common tunic in other types of colonies. In this case, zooids tend to be regularly arranged, perhaps as an adaptation preventing the discharge of excreta from the cloacal siphon of one zooid toward the oral siphon of another. This trend results in colonies with a definite shape, with all oral siphons at one side and all cloacal siphons at the other.

It is a short step from such an arrangement to the development of a common atrial chamber for all of the zooids, discharging water through a common atrial pore (Fig. 12.11B,C). Another type of common atrial chamber is seen in *Botryllus*, where regular systems of small zooids share a common cloacal siphon (Fig. 12.11D). One large colony may have many such systems.

Asexual Reproduction. Solitary ascidians do not reproduce asexually, but colonial forms are active budders. Colonial

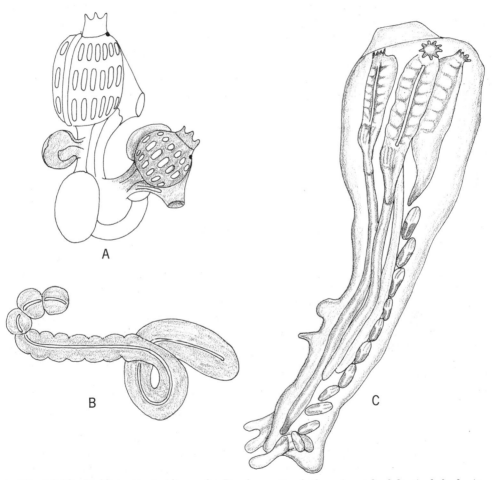

Fig. 12.12. Budding in Ascidians. **A.** Development of thoracic and abdominal buds in Dideminidae, which together will make a single zooid. **B.** Postabdomen of *Colella*, containing the epicardial tube, undergoing strobilation. **C.** Strobilation in a young colony of *Circinalium*. (**A**, after Salfi. **B**, after Caullery. **C**, after Brien, in Grassé.)

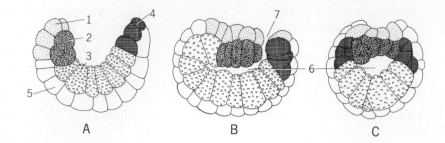

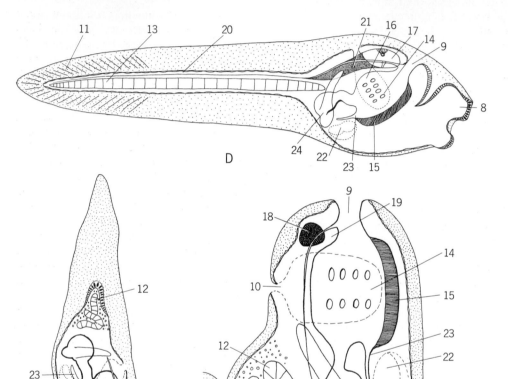

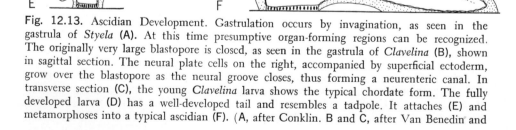

Fig. 12.13. Ascidian Development. Gastrulation occurs by invagination, as seen in the gastrula of *Styela* (A). At this time presumptive organ-forming regions can be recognized. The originally very large blastopore is closed, as seen in the gastrula of *Clavelina* (B), shown in sagittal section. The neural plate cells on the right, accompanied by superficial ectoderm, grow over the blastopore as the neural groove closes, thus forming a neurenteric canal. In transverse section (C), the young *Clavelina* larva shows the typical chordate form. The fully developed larva (D) has a well-developed tail and resembles a tadpole. It attaches (E) and metamorphoses into a typical ascidian (F). (A, after Conklin. B and C, after Van Benedin and

species also regenerate well, while solitary forms do not. Tunicates have developed surprisingly diverse methods of budding. As a result they are valuable experimental material for the study of factors controlling certain aspects of growth and morphogenesis. Berrill's (1961) excellent review is recommended. Here only a few points can be mentioned.

The tissues present in buds differ surprisingly. All buds contain epidermis, but the other components vary remarkably. Some contain only epidermal tissue; others include mesenchyme; and still others have one or another kind of endodermal derivative, usually the epicardium. In *Botryllus*, only the atrial epithelium and epidermis are used in bud formation. In *Salpa*, on the other hand, buds contain epidermis, part of the endostyle and mesenchyme, so all germ layers are represented. *Diazona* buds contain part of the intestine, epicardium, and reserve cells in addition to epidermis. Evidently germ layers mean very little in developing buds, however important they may be during embryonic differentiation.

Budding occurs at stolons, along the epicardium in the postabdominal region of elongated ascidians, or from the atrial wall in flattened colonies without a stolon. Regions of bud formation are first seen as centers of rapid growth, which disrupt the over-all organization and continuity of the organism. As the growth rate falls somewhat, these areas become morphogenetic fields which gain integrity and independence, differentiating into new organisms. Rapidly elongating parts, such as a stolen or the epicardium of a young ascidian, often divide repeatedly

to form a chain of buds (Fig. 12.12 A,B). The young bud is a blastozooid. Its organogeny has been described in detail, and differs from group to group. Its development is sometimes delayed until the stolon breaks away from the colony or has grown enough to become distant from the parent, thus gaining the autonomy needed for differentiation.

Embryonic Development. Ova differ considerably in size and form. As in other groups, brooding species produce large ova with more yolk, undergoing more direct development, and smaller ova show more primitive patterns of development. Cleavage is complete and unequal. The destiny of blastomeres is determined very early, and regions that will participate in formation of some body parts can be distinguished in the ovum. A somewhat flattened coeloblastula invaginates to form a flattened gastrula (Fig. 12.13A). The blastopore shrinks and closes as the embryo elongates. A typical neural groove forms at the middorsal surface, sinks in as a neural groove, and closes to form a neural tube (Fig. 12.13C). Cords of cells on each side of the archenteron serve as primordia of the mesenchyme. They at no time contain a coelom.

The larva is sometimes called a tadpole, for it is shaped like an amphibian tadpole. Diagrams of its metamorphosis into an adult tunicate are shown in Fig. 12.13. The larva is completely enclosed in a tunic, and so cannot feed until metamorphosis is over. The larva is more highly organized than the adult, indicating that adaptations leading to a sessile life have involved the loss of external bilateral symmetry, cephalization, and the maintenance of muscular

Julin. D-F, after Seeliger, in Grassé.) The presumptive areas are indicated by similar shading in A-C. **1**, (presumptive) neural plate; **2**, (presumptive) notochord; **3**, endoderm; **4**, (presumptive) mesoderm; **5**, superficial ectoderm; **6**, primitive gut; **7**, blastopore. *Larva:* **8**, adhesive papillae; **9**, oral siphon; **10**, cloacal siphon; **11**, caudal muscle; **12**, degenerating tail; **13**, notochord; **14**, branchial sac; **15**, endostyle; **16**, peribranchial cavity; **17**, cerebral vesicle; **18**, cerebral ganglion; **19**, neural gland; **20**, neural tube; **21**, visceral ganglion; **22**, heart; **23**, epicardium; **24**, digestive tube; **25**, stolon.

and nervous systems at a typical chordate level.

Budding is an important reproductive process in ascidians and salps. The larva develops into an oözooid, while buds are blastozooids. The two develop differently. The oözooid often develops buds very early, so the free-swimming larva has several precociously formed buds and is already a small colony when it settles and undergoes metamorphosis. Odd budding habits are sometimes seen in precocious buds. In Diademinidae, for example, each of the first two buds to form on the oözooid make half of the first asexual daughter, the anterior bud forming the pharynx, atrium, and siphon region and the posterior bud the organs of the trunk (Fig. 12.12A).

THE THALIACEA

Thaliacea is divided into three subclasses: Pyrosomidea, Doliolidea, and Salpidea. All have a posterior atrial pore, resembling some of the colonial ascidians with a common atrial chamber, Although organ placement is somewhat modified, the basic anatomy is like that of ascidians.

Pyrosoma, the only genus of the Pyrosomidea, is colonial, forming cylindrical colonies with a common atrial chamber open at one end and closed at the other

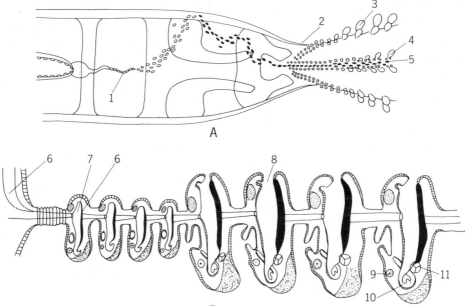

Fig. 12.14. Budding in Salps. A. The stolon of *Doliolum,* showing the formation of probuds and their migration to the stolon, where they form three bands of buds, the two lateral bands becoming nutritive zooids (gastrozooids) and the center band becoming nurse zooids (phorozooids) and definitive buds which will continue their development on the stolon of the phorozooids. B. Scheme of stolon of *Salpa,* showing the formation of three generations of individuals. Diminutive buds formed at the base of the stolon develop; at the end of the stolon they are fully formed, and may break free to take up an independent existence or remain in small groups, attached by the original stolon. (A, after Barrois, in Grassé. B, after Brooks.) 1, probud; 2, base of stolon; 3, developing gastrozooid; 4, developing phorozooid; 5, definitive buds; 6, endostyle; 7, pharynx; 8, cloaca; 9, ganglion; 10, digestive tract; 11, heart.

(Fig. 12.9B,C). The oral siphons are on the external surface, and the atrial siphons discharge into the atrial chamber. The stream of water emerging from the open end of the common atrium propels the colony slowly through the water. *Pyrosoma* are most common in warm seas and may become very large; some are said to reach 4 m. in length. They are brilliantly luminescent. Mosely remarks, "I wrote my name with my finger on the surface of a giant *Pyrosoma* as it lay on the deck in a tub at night, and my name came out in a few seconds in letters of fire." The stimulus spreads; even a flash of light directed on the surface may make a whole colony glow. Rounded gland cells at the end of the pharynx are the luminescent organ. *Pyrosoma* have a pigment cup with retinal cells, evidently a visual organ, imbedded in the brain.

Doliolidea are solitary, cask-shaped animals with eight or nine muscle bands around the body (Fig. 12.9F). Contraction of the circular muscles forces water out of the posterior cloacal opening, propelling the animal.

Salpidea are similar, transparent animals, but without complete circular muscle bands and with two large, open gill slits (Fig. 12.9D,E). Not many species of salps are known, but they are widespread, occurring abundantly in cold seas and deep water.

Remarkable life cycles are characteristic of Thaliacea. Sexual reproduction gives rise to a zooid that reproduces asexually. Asexual reproduction eventually leads to the appearance of sexual individuals. Sexual and asexual animals are very similar in organization, and the salpian life cycle is clearly metagenetic.

Pyrosoma produces a large, yolky egg that undergoes meroblastic cleavage in the parent atrium. No tailed larva are formed, and the embryo develops into a cyathozooid that never completes its development. It forms a stolon that produces four buds, the tetrazooids. As these appear, the embryonic colony leaves the parent. The cyathozooid is a nurse zooid; it digests the yolk and develops a heart and blood vessels that distribute food to the growing tetrazooids. The atrium of the cyathozooid becomes very large, eventually becoming the primordium of the common atrium of the colony. When the tetrazooids mature, they bud off new zooids and the colony continues to grow.

The solitary *Salpa* is an oözooid, arising from a zygote. When mature, a stolon forms at the end of the endostyle. The stolon constricts to form a series of blastozooids attached to it. These develop while still attached, forming chains of animals with the eldest at the tip (Fig. 12.14B). The chain trails behind the parent salp, and clusters of young blastozooids break off from time to time. Blastozooids are substantially like oözooids internally, but are rounded and have tubular papillae that attach them together. They may separate early or remain attached until mature. They eventually produce ova and sperm. The zygote develops in the parent atrium, receiving nourishment through a placental arrangement. When mature it separates from the parent and eventually produces a stolon of new blastozooids.

Of all Thaliacea, *Doliolum* has the most complex life cycle. Zygotes develop in the sea, becoming typical tailed larvae. The tails are lost as they metamorphose into oözooids. Mature oözooids have a complex posterior stolon and a dorsal process. Prebuds formed on the stolon migrate to the dorsal process, where they attach in three rows (Fig. 12.14A). The parent organism becomes modified to support the young. Internal organs are largely lost, but the muscles remain strong and the parent becomes a motile raft on which the young develop. Prebuds do not develop directly into zooids. The two lateral rows of prebuds develop into nutritive zooids (gastrozooids) and remain permanently attached to the oözooids. Some of the buds in the middle row develop into *Doliolum*-like

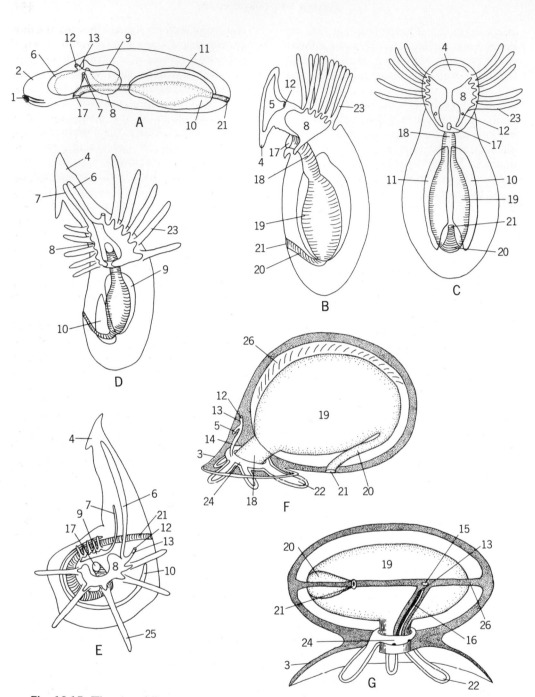

Fig. 12.15. Theories of Deuterostome Phylogeny. Bather designed the hypothetical dipleurula (A) as a bilateral ancestor of the echinoderms and, presumably, a basic deuterostome type. The dipleurula is characterized by the three coelomic compartments on each side, with the axocoel open to the outside by way of a hydropore. Grobben has suggested that echinoderms might

phorozooids which detach and swim away. While attached, however, other buds from the middle row (gonozooids) migrate to the stalk of the phorozooid and are carried away with it. These buds become sexually mature gonozooids, assume a *Doliolum* shape, and detach from the phorozooid. This unique specialization of buds is a remarkable adaptation at a stage when one least expects it. The controls responsible for modifying bud development in this manner remain unknown.

Deuterostome Affinities

Interest in the phylogenetic relationships of deuterostomes is heightened because they include the vertebrates. The various phyla have long been distinct and have become extremely diverse, so embryonic development provides some of the best clues to relationship.

The contrast between the usually radial, indeterminate cleavage of deuterostomes and the usually spiral, determinate cleavage of protostomes has already been discussed. Deuterostomes tend to form mesoderm twice, once from the lip of the primitive gut during gastrulation, and later from the tip of the primitive gut as coelomic pouches are formed, whereas protostomes generally produce mesoderm from a definite stem cell derived from the endoderm. The coelom, especially, provides the most detailed

and convincing evidence of relationship among the main deuterostome groups. Echinoderms have three coelomic pouches, axocoel, hydrocoel, and somatocoel, primitively formed on each side of the body. Elongated deuterostomes tend to have a protocoel, corresponding to the axocoel, a mesocoel, corresponding to the hydrocoel, and a metacoel, corresponding to the somatocoel. In most of the elongated deuterostomes the body forms three regions, protosome, mesosome, and metasome, containing the corresponding parts of the coelom. The pore canals and pores connecting the protocoel and mesocoel with the exterior are reminiscent of the hydropore of echinoderms. Similarity of echinoderm larvae to tornaria larvae of hemichordates adds to the over-all impression of relatedness.

If one tries to think of other phyla that resemble deuterostomes, only the lophophorates come to mind. The body tends to show three divisions, not unlike the protosome, mesosome, and metasome of many deuterostomes. The epistome of phylactolaemate ectoprocts, brachiopods, and phoronids contain a coelom, not clearly set off from the coelom of the mesocoel, but still similar to the cephalic-shield coelom of *Rhabdopleura*. The tentaculate arms of *Rhabdopleura* are reminiscent of a lophophore, and pterobranchs were once thought to be aberrant ectoprocts. In early development the lophophorates show tendencies

have arisen from an ancestral stock like the pterobranchs (B-E), with the cephalic disc becoming the adhesive region of the echinoderm larva and the ambulacral system developing from the five lophophoral tentacles on the left side, with the right lophophoral tentacles becoming reduced as radial symmetry developed. Semon, and later Bury, conceived of a hypothetical type, the pentacula (F, G), with five oral tentacles containing extensions of the coelom, which may have developed into the water-vascular system. (A, after Bather. B-E, after Grobben. F and G, after Bury.) *External features:* 1, apical sense organ; 2, preoral lobe; 3, vestibule; 4, cephalic shield. *Coelom:* 5, axocoel (protocoel); 6, left axocoel; 7, right axocoel; 8, left hydrocoel; 9, right hydrocoel; 10, left somatocoel; 11, right somatocoel; 12, hydropore; 13, hydroporic canal; 14, stone canal; 15, dorsal sac; 16, axial gland. *Digestive system:* 17, mouth; 18, esophagus; 19, stomach; 20, intestine; 21, anus. *Other parts:* 22, primary tentacles becoming the radial canals of the water-vascular system; 23, tentacles of the lophophore, containing extensions of the protocoel; 24, ring canal of the water-vascular system; 25, primary podia; 26, dorsal mesentery.

toward radial cleavage, and coelom formation in some resembles coelom formation in deuterostomes. Yet lophophorates are not truly deuterostomes; they have traits which associate them with protostomes as well, particularly in the relationship of the blastopore and mouth. No modern lophophorate could be considered an ancestor of deuterostomes, but the similarities are too strong and extensive to be ignored. It is probable that the general line of animals from which the lophophorates developed must have greatly resembled, and perhaps been identical with, the line from which deuterostomes arose.

Lophophorates and deuterostomes tend to approach the problems of survival in similar ways. Lophophorates are sessile or tube-dwelling ciliary feeders. Primitive echinoderms were stalked or sessile ciliary feeders, and tube-dwelling and sessile habits are seen in Pogonophora, hemichordates and urochordates. The tendency to live sedentary or sessile lives has had important consequences in lophophorates and most deuterostomes. A motile larva is an almost indispensable adjunct of sedentary habits. Sessile animals tend to form aggregations or colonies by asexual reproduction, and to retain relatively high capacities for regeneration. Sedentary and sessile animals tend not to develop a head, or to reduce the head if one is present. In the low degree of cephalization, lophophorates resemble most deuterstomes. It is probable that some similarities of lophophorates and deuterostomes are convergent, arising as a result of somewhat similar habits, but it seems improbable that all of the similarities can be explained in this way.

If the primitive lophophorate and deuterostome stocks were the same or very similar, and ran through parallel early adaptations, they must have arisen more or less simultaneously from some pre-existing group. The ancestral forms must have been coelomate, but without a long history of having had a coelom. Considerable diversity in the methods of coelom formation of lophophorates may reflect early experimentation. Some zoologists have strongly believed that the first coelomates were enterocoelous, and that all coelomate stocks arose from primitive enterocoels. It is more probable, however, that the first coelomates formed the coelom in a variety of ways, perhaps vacillating in much the same manner as modern lophophorates. Certainly the primitive coelomates must have diverged very early along distinctive schizocoelous and enterocoelous lines, and it is not impossible that the two lines were never parts of a common stem.

It seems certain that early denterostomes were bilaterally symmetrical, for echinoderm metamorphosis cannot be accounted for otherwise. They probably had two coelomic compartments on each side of the body and very early developed a tendency to subdivide the more anterior of these into separate protocoels and mesocoels. Bather (1900) designed a hypothetical ancestor, the dipleurula (Fig. 12.15A), on the basis of common characteristics of different kinds of echinoderm larvae. The dipleurula is supposed to have had a locomotor band, a foregut, midgut, and hindgut, arranged more or less in a straight tube, and three pairs of coelomic pouches derived from the primitive gut (p. 316). Bather explained echinoderms by postulating the attachment of the dipleurula on the right side of the oral end, resulting in the reduction of the right side of the body. The migration of the mouth toward the original posterior end twisted the digestive tract and, associated with the torsion of the body, rearranged the coelomic spaces to form oral and aboral coelomic compartments, which gave the hydrocoel a circular shape. Bather's view has several weak points. Modern echinoderm larvae attach at the oral end, but not on the right side. Torsion occurs during metamorphosis, but does not cause the crescentic shape of the hydrocoel. Bather also thought that the water-vascular system resulted from the covering over of three ciliated grooves, with two later being subdivided to make five. Such a history is in no way reflected during the differentiation of the water-vascular system.

Bury (1895) conceived of a hypothetical echinoderm ancestor called a pentacula, with five tentacles (Fig. 12.15F,G). The five tentacles contained a coelomic cavity, derived from a hydrocoel and connected with the exterior by a stone canal and hydropore. If the original pentacula were bilaterally symmetrical, the tentacles might resemble a lophophore. Torsion of such a form would produce an organism not unlike a potential ancestral echinoderm. Bury's idea has deficiencies also. It begs the question of how a water-vascular system formed, for the problem is solved by starting with an ancestor already equipped with a hydropore. Bury's concept has the advantage of bringing echinoderm and lophophorate stocks close together, but it must be remembered that the extension of the coelom into tentacles is mechanically advantageous and might result from convergence of originally dissimilar stocks.

The remarkable similarity of the coelom of hemichordates and echinoderms cannot be easily explained by convergence. The system of pore canals and pores connecting the protocoel and mesocoel of hemichordates with the exterior is echinoderm-like. The heart vesicle of hemichordates arises like the madreporic vesicle of echinoderms and is similar in its association with the haemal system. It is generally agreed that pterobranchs are more primitive than enteropneusts, and their tentaculated arms resemble a lophophore. Presumably the enteropneusts lost their tentacles secondarily. Grobben (1923) has suggested that the echinoderms could have arisen from a pterobranch-like ancestral stock instead of a pentacula (Fig. 12.15 B-E). The cephalic shield might have elongated as a stalk, and the lophophore and mesocoel might have become the echinoderm hydrocoel and water-vascular system. Grobben's idea, like Bury's, emphasizes the relative closeness of the body organization of lophophorates, echinoderms, and hemichordates.

Unfortunately, primitive echinoderms,

as revealed by fossils, refuse to cooperate with any of these ideas. The Heterostelea (Fig. 11.2A) have food grooves, but are not radially symmetrical and have no apparent podial pores. In fact, podial pores are seen only in the Edrioasteroidea among extinct Pelmatozoa. On the whole, the organization of echinoderms appears to have become more rather than less lophophorate-like during their fossil history. Evidently all the theories are somewhat inadequate. They are important in the sense that they show similarities too striking to ignore, but until we know a great deal more about the most primitive echinoderms, we are likely to emphasize the wrong traits in devising hypothetical ancestors.

The ancestral stocks that gave rise to hemichordates were also ancestral to the chordates. The gill slits associated with the pharynx are clearly chordate-like. It is probable that the more active of the ancestral stocks gave rise to the first chordates.

Pogonophora resemble hemichordates. The loss of the gut is undoubtedly secondary, and justifies their being placed in a phylum of their own. The absence of pores for the protocoel and mesocoel suggests an early division of the Pogonophora and worm-like hemichordates. It is not yet clear whether the Pogonophora tentacles are homologous to the pterobranch tentacles.

This leaves the chaetognaths unaccounted for. They have many aschelminth traits: (1) bands of longitudinal muscle in the body wall; (2) the pharyngeal bulb; (3) the absence of a peritoneum; and (4) the cuticular covering. These must be superficial resemblances, however, for the embryo produces a coelom with anterior and posterior compartments, and the lack of a peritoneum occurs as a secondary development in some other coelomates. Although they do not reproduce asexually, they have high powers of regeneration. A head piece grows a new tail, and under proper conditions, a tail piece may grow a new head. It has been suggested that they are the most primitive of the bilaterally symmetrical deuterostomes. Certainly they are not too far removed from what one might expect if a bilaterally symmetrical, primitive deuterostome stock were to adapt to an active rather than a tube-dwelling or sedentary life.

References

Azema, M. 1937. Recherches sur le sang et l'excretion chez les Ascidies. *Ann. l'Inst. Ocean. Paris* 17: 1.

Barrington, E. 1940. Observations on feeding and digestion in *Glossobalanus. Quart. Jour. Micr. Sci.* 82: 227.

Berrill, N. J. 1950. *The Tunicata.* Ray Soc., London.

———. 1955. *The Origin of the Vertebrates.* Clarendon Press, Oxford.

Bone, Q. 1960. The origin of the chordates. *Jour. Linn. Soc. Zool.* 44: 252.

Bullock, T. H. 1945. The anatomical organization of the nervous system of the Enteropneusta. *Quart. Jour. Micr. Sci.* 86: 55.

Bumpus, D., and E. Pierce. 1955. The hydrography and the distribution of chaetognaths over the continental shelf of North Carolina. *Deep Sea Res.* 3 (suppl). (E)

Burdon-Jones, C. 1952. Development and biology of the larva of *Saccoglossus. Phil. Trans. Roy. Soc. London* 236: 553.

Burfield, S. 1950. Chaetognatha. *Sci. Res. Great Barrier Reef Exp.* 5: 459.

Clarke, G., *et al.* 1943. Distribution and reproduction of *Sagitta elegans* on Georges Bank. *Biol. Bull.* 85: 201. (E)

Cowles, R. 1930. Ecological studies of the offshore waters of Chesapeake Bay. *Bull. U.S. Bur. Fish.* 46.

Dunbar, J. 1941. The breeding cycle in *Sagitta elegans arctica. Can. Jour. Res. D.* 19.

Esterly, C. 1919. Reactions of various plankton animals with reference to their diurnal migration. *Univ. Calif. Publ. Zool.* 19: 1. (E).

Garstang, W. 1929. The morphology of the Tunicata and its bearing on the phylogeny of the Chordata. *Quart. Jour. Micr. Sci.* 72: 51.

Gilchrist, J. D. 1917. On the development of *Cephalodiscus. Quart. Jour. Micr. Sci.* 62: 189.

Hess, W. 1936. Reaction to light in *Ptychodera. Carn. Inst. Wash. Pap. Tortugas Lab.* 31: 77.

Horst, C. J. van der. 1935. *Plantosphaera* and *Tornaria. Quart. Jour. Micr. Sci.* 78: 605.

Ivanov, A. V. 1955. The main features of the organization of the Pogonophora. *Syst. Zool.* 4: 170.

———. 1959. The nervous system of Pogonophora. *Syst. Zool.* 8: 96.

———. 1962. *Pogonophora.* Consultants Bureau, New York. (!)

Jägersten, G. Larva of *Siboglinum. Zool. Bidgrag.* 32: 67.

John, C. 1931. Anatomy of the head of *Sagitta. Proc. Zool. Soc. London* 1931: 1307. (G)

———. 1933. Habits, structure and development of *Spadella. Quart. Jour. Micr. Sci.* 75: 625.

Jorgesen, C. B. 1950. Quantitative aspects of filter feeding in invertebrates. *Biol. Rev.* 30: 391. (G)

Knight-Jones, E. W. 1953. The feeding of *Saccoglossus. Proc. Zool. Soc. London* 123: 637.

———, and R. Millar. 1949. Bilateral asymmetry shown by the metachronal waves in the protochordate gill slits. *Nature* 163: 137.

Komai, T. 1951. The homology of the notochord in pterobranchs and enteropneusts. *Amer. Nat.* 85: 270.

Krijgsman, B. J. 1956. Contractile and pacemaker mechanisms in the heart of tunicates. *Biol. Rev.* 31: 288.

Meyer, A. 1927. Cölombewimperung und cölomatische Kreislaufsysteme bei Wirbellosen. *Ztschr. wiss. Zool.* 129. (G)

Orton, J. H. 1913. The ciliary mechanisms on the gills and mode of feeding in *Amphioxus,* ascidians, and *Solenomya togata. Jour. Mar. Biol. Ass.* 10: 19.

Webb, D. A. 1939. Observations on the blood of certain ascidians with special reference to the biochemistry of vanadium. *Jour. Exp. Biol.* 16: 499.

13
Phylum Mollusca

The deuterostomes have been followed out of sight into the vertebrate realm, and it is time to return to the protostomes. All of the remaining protostomes are coelomate, although the coelom is secondarily reduced in some. Several small phyla are recognized, but the great bulk of the animal kingdom falls into three large phyla, Mollusca, Annelida, and Arthropoda. Two major lines can be distinguished. One includes the molluscs, and is characterized by lack of segmentation. A recent find of a metamerically organized mollusc, however, has raised anew the question of primitive segmentation in the molluscan ancestral stock. The annelid-arthropod stem is characterized by segmentation. Both lines have been extremely successful, in ancient as well as in modern times.

Most kinds of higher invertebrates are too conspicuous to escape notice, and so are, to some extent, familiar to all. Molluscs include familiar animals, some beautiful and some bizarre. Snails, clams, squids, and octopi are familiar to all who have eyes for the living things around them. No one knows exactly how many species of molluscs are alive today, but estimates run from about 80,000 to 150,-

000. At least 35,000 fossil species have been described. Certainly they are among the most successful of animal types. They are found in the abyssal depths of the ocean and above high-tide line, and are common in fresh-water everywhere. Some have become reasonably common in moist, terrestrial habitats. Their shells are collected by amateur and professional alike, and some rare and beautiful species bring a good price. Molluscan shells have always been economically important. They have served as money and can be fashioned into jewelry and buttons. Shells of molluscs are important components of the kitchen middens of prehistoric man. Scallops, oysters, claims, squids, and octopi are important food animals today, and considerable money is provided for their study and conservation. All in all, it is not surprising that we have a more complete picture of molluscs than of any other invertebrate phylum.

Nevertheless, it is not easy to start a study of molluscs. For one thing, they are very old. All of the major groups were established before the end of the Cambrian, and long, independent adaptation of the diverse lines has so modified the primitive organizational plan that some of the modern molluscs appear to have little in common. A clam, a garden slug, and an octopus are all molluscs, but it is not so simple to explain the evidence that links them together. It is not hard to list the common features of all modern molluscs, but it is difficult to understand their significance. Another approach is to explain all modern molluscs as highly specialized descendants of an ancestral stem form with a certain organizational plan, a plan that is not fully preserved in any modern mollusc. Understanding the primitive plan helps us to see the phylum as an organic whole rather than as a hodge-podge of animals that do not fit conveniently anywhere else. Both approaches have their shortcomings, so both will be tried.

The outstanding common characteristics of molluscs are the following:

1. With the exception of a single, aberrant species, recently discovered, molluscs are non-segmented.

2. They are strongly cephalized, with a definite head and special cephalic sense organs.

3. The coelom is reduced, and the body wall is thick and muscular.

4. The ventral side of the body wall is specialized as a muscular foot, generally used for locomotion.

5. The dorsal body wall is extended as one or a pair of folds, the mantle or pallium, which secretes a shell and encloses a mantle cavity, typically containing the gills.

6. The anus and excretory pores usually open into the mantle cavity.

7. A well-developed, regionalized digestive tract is present. A sclerotized buccal cavity almost always contains a toothed, proboscis-like radula. The esophagus arises from the stomodaeum, and usually includes specialized regions for food storage and fragmentation. The midgut forms a stomach, and a pair of large digestive glands, often called the liver. The hindgut consists of an often long intestine that ends at the anus.

8. A circulatory system with a well-defined heart is almost universally present. One or more collecting chambers, known as auricles, convey blood to a median ventricle. Although definite blood vessels occur, the blood usually circulates through open spaces, the perivisceral lacunae and sinuses, which encroach upon the coelom. The blood typically contains a respiratory pigment, haemocyanin.

9. A single pair of metanephridia, sometimes reduced to one, are closely associated with the pericardial cavity, in which the heart lies.

10. A circumenteric nerve ring is associated with two pairs of nerve cords, one to the foot and one to the viscera and mantle. Ganglia are usually associated with the nerve ring and nerve cords, and an extensive subepidermal nerve plexus is also present.

11. Where ova are small and contain little yolk, cleavage is spiral and determinate, and the characteristic larva is a trochophore.

Some exceptions can be found to almost all of these, but all molluscs have so many of these characteristics that there can be no doubt that they are all derived from a common ancestral stock in which these traits appeared. In attempting to reconstruct a hypothetical ancestral stock, these traits, especially as they appear in the most primitive of the various classes, are emphasized.

One design of an ancestral mollusc is shown in Fig. 13.1. Perhaps no such animal ever crept about on the rocky shores of an ancient sea, but something not too unlike it must have lived there. It had a definite head, with cephalic tentacles containing the eyes. The ventral surface was modified to form a creeping sole, known as the foot, and the dorsal part of the body projected upward as a visceral mass or hump. A fold of the body wall, known as the mantle, covered the hump and secreted calcareous spicules or a shell. At the posterior end, the mantle enclosed a mantle cavity, into which the nephridiopores and anus opened. A pair of gills of unique design, known as ctenidia, extended back from the anterior end of the mantle cavity. Each gill consisted of a central axis, from which flat filaments extended on each side, and was supported by dorsal and ventral membranes. Water flowed forward below the ventral membrane, so this space may be termed the inhalant passageway. It flowed back above the dorsal membrane in the exhalant passageway, flushing the feces and urine out of the mantle cavity. Afferent and efferent blood vessels brought blood, probably containing haemocyanin or some other respiratory pigment, to and from the gills. The mouth opened into a buccal cavity, surrounded by a muscular buccal mass. A chamber known as the radula sac opened into the buccal cavity. It contained a toothed belt, the radula, which could be projected from the mouth and used to scrape bits of algae from the rocks over which the animals crept. Salivary glands opened into the buccal cavity, secreting mucus that helped bind the bits of food together as they passed toward the esophagus. The mucous string containing food was probably swept down the esophagus by cilia into a stomach that had a ciliary sorting field, where bits of rock and sand were separated from the food material. The stomach also contained a sclerotized grinding region, where harder particles could be squeezed and partially crushed, and ended in a style sac, where water and smaller particles were squeezed out of the stomach contents for use, and condensed material was conveyed to the intestine for ejection. A pair of large digestive glands opened into the stomach. They may have secreted enzymes for extracellular digestion in the stomach, or may have been sites of intracellular digestion, but probably there was little absorption of food in the intestine. An important intestinal function was the condensation of feces into solid masses, preventing the fouling of the gills in the mantle cavity. Blood from the gills flowed into a pair of auricles, which discharged into a median ventricle. An aorta ran forward, discharging blood into open spaces around the viscera and in the tissues. The coelom probably consisted of two broadly confluent compartments, one surrounding the heart and the other a part of the intestine. A pair of metanephridia opened into the pericardial cavity through nephrostomes, and discharged wastes into the mantle cavity through nephridiopores. They probably had a simple nervous system, consisting of a subepidermal plexus, a circumenteric nerve ring associated with a pair of cerebral ganglia and a pair of pleural ganglia, and two pairs of nerves, one pair passing to the foot tissues and one to the viscera. The gonads were located in the coelom, and gametes were discharged through the nephridia, entering by way of the nephrostomes.

An ancestral stem form of this kind could evolve into all of the modern molluscs, although in the process some of the primitive features would be lost. Meanwhile, the various body regions would have become so greatly changed that in some cases the resemblance to the stem form would be obvious only after careful study.

Classification

Each molluscan class includes some familiar forms that are widely known. These are given as examples below, although in most cases other less well-known representatives of the class could be mentioned that would evoke a somewhat different image of the group. The exception is the Monoplacophora, a recently discovered group that is sometimes included as an order in the Amphineura.

Class Amphineura. The chitons (Fig. 13.9). Bilaterally symmetrical, oval to worm-like molluscs with a rudimentary head having neither tentacles nor eyes; a mantle covers the whole dorsal surface and secretes separate spicules or a shell of eight pieces; a ventral foot, typically broad and flat and encircled by a groove-like mantle cavity, but sometimes reduced; a number of pairs of gills in the mantle cavity; an anterior mouth, radula, and posterior anus; nervous system without definite ganglia and with a circumenteric ring from which pedal and palliovisceral nerves arise; sexes usually separate; a trochophore larva typically formed during development.

Class Monoplacophora (Fig. 13.13). Newly discovered deep-water molluscs, resembling amphineurans somewhat, but with metamerically arranged nephridia discharging wastes through nephridiopores associated with the paired gills; metamerically arranged muscles to the foot; and paired auricles draining into paired ventricles, one on each side of the intestine.

Class Gastropoda. Snails (Fig. 13.16). Molluscs whose primitive bilateral symmetry is lost to a greater or lesser degree as a consequence of torsion, the twisting of the visceral mass during development; they have a definite head, with eyes and tentacles; a flattened, ventral foot; a mantle cavity containing gills, or with a wall modified as a lung; and usually a solid, spirally coiled shell. The buccal cavity contains a radula; the nervous system is centralized and has cerebral, pleural, and visceral, and usually pedal, ganglia; a pair of visceral nerves passes to the viscera. They may be hermaphroditic or dioecious, oviparous or ovoviviparous, and often develop through a trochophore stage.

Class Scaphopoda. Tusk shells (Fig. 13.43). Bilaterally symmetrical, elongated molluscs with a rudimentary head on which paired processes drawn out into prehensile filaments attach; no eyes; a conical foot adapted for burrowing; mantle folds fused to form a cylindrical mantle cavity; no ctenidia; radula present; circulatory system reduced; nervous system with cerebral and

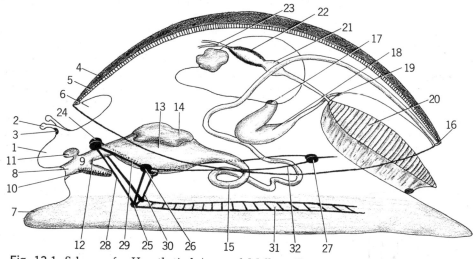

Fig. 13.1. Scheme of a Hypothetical Ancestral Mollusc. *External form:* 1, head; 2, tentacle; 3, eye; 4, shell or spicules; 5, mantle; 6, opening of mantle cavity; 7, foot. *Digestive tract:* 8, mouth; 9, buccal cavity; 10, radula in radular sac; 11, salivary gland; 12, esophagus; 13, stomach; 14, gastric gland; 15, intestine; 16, anus. *Nephridial system:* 17, nephrostome; 18, nephridium; 19, nephridiopore. *Respiratory system:* 20, ctenidium. *Circulatory system:* 21, auricle; 22, ventricle; 23, aorta. *Nervous system:* 24, cerebral ganglion; 25, pedal ganglion; 26, pleural ganglion; 27, visceral ganglion; 28, cerebropedal connective; 29, cerebropleural connective; 30, pleuropedal connective; 31, pedal nerve; 32, visceral nerve.

pleural ganglia; dioecious, with a trocho-phore larval stage.

Class Pelecypoda. Clams (Fig. 13.34). Bi-laterally symmetrical molluscs having a rudimentary head without eyes or ten-tacles; body compressed laterally and en-closed by a pair of mantle folds that secrete a bivalve shell; valves meet in a dorsal hinge and are closed by adductor muscles; a large mantle cavity contains a blade-shaped foot and a pair of much-enlarged, modified ctenidia, usually used for filter-feeding; mouth flanked by a pair of labial palps; radula absent; nervous system with cerebral and pleural ganglia, sometimes united, and with pedal and pallial ganglia; almost exclusively dioecious, with trocho-phore and veliger stages usually formed during development of marine species.

Class Cephalopoda. Octopi (Fig. 13.44). Bilaterally symmetrical molluscs with a well-developed head containing remark-ably prominent and often complex eyes, and encircled by prehensile tentacles, in part derived from the foot; a mantle in-vests the body, enclosing a mantle cavity containing one or two pairs of ctenidia and opening through a funnel-shaped siphon derived from the foot; water is ejected through the siphon to propel the animal; primitively with a chambered shell, but shell internal and much reduced in most modern species; radula present; nervous system complex; dioecious, forming yolky ova that develop directly without larval stages.

Some General Molluscan Features

Although there is a bewildering variety of molluscs, adapted for extremely diversified habitats and living in remarkably different ways, some general features serve to link all of them. These general features are not always obvious, for they are affected by the habits and habitat. Molluscs offer particu-larly good material for the study of ecologi-cal physiology and morphological modifica-tions that fit originally similar organisms to different conditions of life. A discussion of some of the more important aspects of molluscan organization is valuable to intro-duce the major groups and to prevent repe-tition.

Body Wall. The molluscan body wall is extremely plastic. Exposed to the world in which the animal lives, it forms a protec-tive barrier on the one hand, and is respon-sible for receiving sensory stimuli on the other. To a far greater extent than in most animal groups, the molluscan body wall is responsible for locomotion, and with this responsibility it has been stimulated to de-velop extensive muscle tissue. Each dif-ferent group of molluscs uses the body wall in its own way, and in each it has re-sponded by evolving characteristic struc-tural features. It may be drawn out to form tentacles, folded to form a mantle, or thickened to form a foot. Tentacles may be sensory or prehensile; a mantle may be a secretory device which produces a protec-tive shell, or itself serve as a protective cover, or, in some cases, serve as a swim-ming organ. Such adaptations are not mere changes in shape. Each different function depends upon the presence of histological elements that are properly proportioned and have the physiological qualities re-quired for the activities upon which the functions depend. In this sense the body wall of modern molluscs provides a most interesting and instructive story of the re-sponse of a complex layer of cells to the evolutionary forces that have encouraged diversity in choice of habitat and way of life.

The outer layer of the body wall is the epidermis. As in other animals, the epi-dermis tends to develop specialized cells for secretion, for sensory reception, and for evoking currents. Molluscan epidermis is rich in gland cells. Considering the phylum as a whole, mucous glands predominate. Molluscs, like other animals, find many uses for slime. It is used in trapping food particles, and helps to prevent evaporation at the body surface in terrestrial species. It also lubricates the foot surface, an important factor in the locomotion of snails, chitons, and slugs. Special glandular regions derived from the epidermis provide secretions for specific uses, the most important of which is the elaboration of the shell. Byssal threads, secreted by glands derived from the epidermis, attach some mussels to rocks or other submerged objects, and specialized epidermal glands provide cement for attaching ova to surfaces or for other reproductive activities. Special cells for sensory reception are described elsewhere, but it should be pointed out that a considerable variety occurs among molluscs. Patches of epidermis are ciliated, generating currents that are important factors in feeding, in respiration, and sometimes in other ways.

Below the epidermis is the dermis, consisting of connective tissue and muscle tissue. In molluscs, these tissues are rarely arranged in definite layers, but are interwoven in complex masses. Rings of circular muscle and strands of longitudinal muscle are the exception rather than the rule. The evolutionary trend away from alternating layers of circular and longitudinal muscle is undoubtedly associated with the complex movements required of the body wall in different types of molluscs. Adaptation of the body wall, however, has gone beyond the rearrangement of connective tissue and muscle tissues. Special types of connective tissue, and muscles with differing physiological properties, have evolved with complex body-wall functions.

Connective tissues may be tough or spongy, and each type has its role to play. Molluscs with heavy protective shells have had little reason to emphasize the protective qualities of connective tissue, but those with reduced shells often have a very firm type of connective tissue, known as chordoid tissue. Chordoid tissue is built of vesicular cells, which can become firm through turgor, like the notochord cells of chordates. Molluscan chordoid tissue is

quite varied, and in some cases different parts of the same animal are supported by chordoid tissues of different form. Relatively tough, fibrous connective tissue is found in areas where great tensile strength is valuable. Loose, spongy connective tissue is especially important in molluscs. A snail tentacle, for example, can be withdrawn by the contraction of a retractor muscle, but how can it be extended once again? Animals with a spacious coelom often use a hydraulic system for such purposes, forcing coelomic fluid into a tentacle in coelomic canals, but molluscs, with reduced coelomic spaces, cannot use this system. This adaptive challenge is met by the development of a loose, spongy tissue, filled with blood vessels or blood lacunae. When charged with blood the tissue expands and becomes firm, thrusting the part outward. Such tissue is the adaptive parallel to the erectile tissues of vertebrates, and is responsible for such diverse tasks as extension of a snail tentacle and the effective operation of the foot of a clam. It is evident that such a function can be successfully discharged only if a supply of blood can be maintained in the spongy tissue. Special valves are sometimes present, holding the blood in the tissues throughout the period of activity.

Muscle tissue is irregularly distributed in the body wall of molluscs. It is abundant in the foot if the foot is used for locomotion, and also in the mantle of species with reduced shells, especially where the mantle is used in locomotion. Body-wall muscle is especially important in locomotion, for molluscs are usually too large to move by means of cilia. Some molluscs move very little or not at all, while others are among the best swimmers in the animal kingdom. It is clear that the demands placed on muscle tissues must be very unequal in such organisms as an oyster, permanently attached to a rock, and a pelagic squid, dependent on its ability to swim rapidly to get food. As muscle fibers have not been discussed in the last few phyla, it may be timely to consider some of the properties of muscle fibers in general, and of molluscan muscles in particular.

When properly stimulated, muscle fibers move the body or a part by shortening. Some muscles contract and relax very rapidly, while others contract slowly but remain contracted for a relatively long time. A muscle exposed to a series of stimuli contracts with each stimulus, unless they are delivered so rapidly that a relaxation between stimuli is impossible. In this case, the contractions fuse. A fused contraction of fast muscle tissue requires the delivery of stimuli at high frequency, while a fused contraction of slow muscle tissue requires stimuli at a far lower frequency. The speed of contraction and relaxation and the frequency of stimulation required for fused contractions are important properties in suiting muscles to specific tasks. A few examples may help to clarify the nature of the problem. It is important, and often critical, that a clam be able quickly to clap its shell shut in an emergency, but no less important that it be able to hold the shell shut for a long time. On the other hand, scallops swim by opening and closing the shell valves rapidly. They have an entirely different problem, and a muscle that can hold a clam shell shut for a long time would be useless for swimming movements like those of a scallop, while a muscle that can close a clam shell rapidly would not be suited for holding it shut.

Two general classes of muscles are recognized, phasic muscles that contract and relax rapidly, and tonic muscles that contract slowly and maintain contraction for a relatively long time. Fast phasic muscles are usually striated, while the slower, tonic muscles are usually unstriated. Some idea of the variety of properties seen in molluscan muscles is shown by their time properties. The muscles used by a scallop for swimming are striated, and have a contraction time of 0.046 sec. and a half-relaxation time of 0.04 sec. A squid swims with the aid of mantle muscles that have a contraction time of 0.07 sec. and a half-relaxation time of 0.11 sec. The unstriated muscle fibers in the tentacle retractor of a snail have a contraction time of 2.5 sec. and a half-relaxation time of 25 sec.

Evidently, none of these muscles would do the job for a clam, closing the shell rapidly and holding it shut for a long period. Molluscan muscles that hold as well as contract rapidly are unusual in having very small fibers, 50 Å in diameter, and large ones up to 1500 Å in diameter (Fig. 13.2A). The small fibers contain actomyosin, the element normally responsible for shortening during contraction, while the large fibers contain paramyosin. The evidence suggests that the holding mechanism depends on a "catch" principle, operating in the large fibers. Some action of these fibers, such as crystallization when the fast muscle fibers have contracted, is thought to be responsible for the long holding of tension. This avoids the problem of prolonged tetanic contraction of muscle fibers and the concomitant problem of fatigue.

The full details of the histological construction of the body wall are known for only a few species of molluscs. The physiological characterization of the component cells and tissues is even more incomplete. Yet, enough is known to indicate clearly that the evolution of the body wall is a remarkably complex problem. The cell populations that constitute the body-wall tissues vary from species to species and from region to region in the same organism, both in relative numbers and in the nature of the individual cells. The development of a foot like a snail's foot, used for creeping, involves the subtle interaction of gross morphological changes and modifications in the kinds and proportions of the cells present. To describe and explain evolutionary adaptation and the behavioral and environmental factors that have evoked it will require all of the ingenuity of morphologist, ecologist, cytologist, and physi-

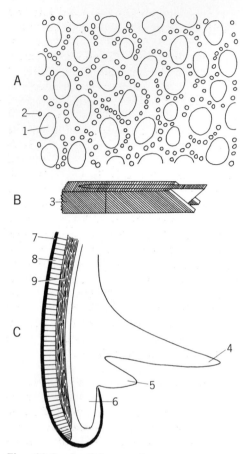

Fig. 13.2. A. Scheme of transverse section through a muscle fiber of an oyster, showing thick fibers containing paramyosin and thin fibers containing actomyosin. B. Crossed lamellar shell structure, showing three highly magnified primary lamellae, each composed of slanted secondary lamellae, with alternating direction of slant in each lamella. C. Scheme of the edge of shell and the mantle of a clam, showing the relationship of shell layers and mantle edge. (A, based on a micrograph by Hanson and Lowy. B, after Newell. C, composite.) 1, paramyosin fibril; 2, actomyosin fibril; 3, primary lamella composed of slanted secondary lamellae; 4, inner mantle fold; 5, middle mantle fold; 6, outer mantle fold; 7, periostracum; 8, ostracum or prismatic layer; 9, hypostracum or nacreous layer.

ologist, working together as they have rarely succeeded in doing.

Shell. The shell is secreted by the outer, glandular surface of the mantle. Where the shell is internal, the mantle is turned back on itself (reflected) so that the shell is completely surrounded by the glandular epithelium. Amphineuran shells have a different structure than the shells of other molluscs and will be discussed elsewhere. Other molluscan shells are essentially similar, although they differ in mineralogical detail. The outer layer is the periostracum and is composed of a horny substance, conchiolin (Fig. 13.2C). It is secreted by a fold of the mantle edge, and so is laid down only at the shell margin, where growth occurs. The periostracum of the older portions of old molluscs is often badly worn. The rest of the shell is calcareous and is known as the ostracum. It is laid down in layers. In most molluscs, two layers can be recognized, an outer ostracum (prismatic layer), and an inner ostracum (nacreous layer). The prismatic layer is built of densely packed, polygonal prisms of calcareous material, separated by delicate membranes of conchiolin. It is laid down by the thickened glandular margin of the mantle, and so grows only at the margin of the shell as the animal grows. In areas where the mantle is reflected, however, secondary additions of prismatic substance may be added to the outer surface, forming such external structures as the callus in snail shells. Nacreous material is secreted constantly by the whole mantle surface and so becomes thicker throughout the life of the animal. Nacreous material is laminated. Thin plates of calcareous material are laid down parallel to the shell surface. When these lamina are straight and thick, the shell lining is dense and porcelaneous. If they are thin and wavy, however, the lining of the shell is iridescent and pearly. Sometimes a crossed lamellar structure is seen. In this case the primary lamina are composed of secondary lamellae laid down at a characteristic angle (Fig.

13.2B). When particles come to lie between the inner shell surface and the mantle, they are covered with nacre; when composed of pearly nacre and well formed, the resulting pearls are among the most treasured of precious stones. Some gastropods make pearls, but commercial pearls are obtained from pelecypods, especially from the pearl oyster, *Pinctada*. It is not ridiculous to think of pearls as precious stones, for mineralogically they are stone, as is the calcareous substance of which the prismatic and nacreous layers are formed. The inner and outer ostracum is calcite or arragonite, differing in different species, and sometimes in the two layers of a single shell.

The shell first appears during the veliger larva stage, and grows throughout life. Growth at the margin of the shell produces regular growth lines, which parallel the contour of the margin. Additional sculpturing is common and is sometimes very complex. Whether the shell is simple or complexly sculptured, its growth is remarkably regular and provides excellent examples of proportionate growth. The aperture of a shell grows with the animal, and the shell thus provides a growth history of the animal as a whole. Some suggestions about the analysis of shell growth are found in the remarkably entertaining book by D'Arcy Thompson (1945), *Of Growth and Form*, and are very valuable to those interested in the analysis of growth.

Body Cavities. Because of the terminology used, it is easy to be confused by the system of cavities in a mollusc. The lumen of the nephridia and their ducts are sometimes called the nephrocoel, and the lumen of the gonads and gonoducts are sometimes called the gonocoel. The spaces through which the blood flows are, collectively, the haemocoel. These spaces are not to be confused with the coelom, or peritoneal cavity, for their origin and role in the organization of the animal are entirely different. The coelom of molluscs is always somewhat reduced in size because of the large haemo-

coel, and in some cases has been very sharply reduced. In molluscs, the coelom is more or less distinctly separated into two chambers, a pericardial cavity, in which the heart lies, and a perivisceral coelom, in which the viscera lie. The pericardial cavity is never very large, and the perivisceral coelom is very small when the haemocoelic sinuses around the internal organs are large. Both coelomic compartments are lined with peritoneal tissue, derived from the lining of the coelomic cavity of the larva or embryo. They are always connected, and in most cases are broadly confluent. Although the coelom is differently arranged in different groups of molluscs, it remains a characteristic molluscan feature, for no other group of animals have a coelom quite like that of molluscs. Molluscs are the first large phylum that has been discussed in which metanephridia occur. The metanephridia are tubules, typically open to the exterior by way of nephridiopores, and open to the coelom by way of a nephrostome. Even in molluscs with a single nephridium, the nephridium retains its relationship to the coelom, and a renopericardial canal connects the lumen of the excretory organ with the pericardial cavity. In no other phylum are the nephridia consistently associated with the pericardial cavity. The gonads of coelomate animals lie in the coelom, and gametes reach the exterior through ducts connecting the coelom with the exterior. In some cases the nephridia serve to discharge the gametes. In other cases gonoducts are present. As will be seen during the study of annelids, gonoducts are often coelomoducts, which means that they are, at least in part, derived from the peritoneum and connect the coelom with the exterior. Traces of this relationship are seen in various molluscs, where the gonoducts are associated with the nephridia.

Digestive Tract. By the time one has studied the lower metazoa and deuterostomes, some comprehension of the general trends to be seen in the evolution of the digestive tract is unavoidable. In its constant association with the embryonic endoderm and in its origin from some kind of primitive gut, the digestive tract is remarkably conservative, but in its sensitivity to adaptations associated with diverse feeding and dietary habits it is remarkably progressive. With the development of increasingly complex organization in the higher invertebrates, the digestive tract shows more clearly the tendency for food processing and absorption to become a sequential program, with special regions responsible for special steps in these processes. Development of special cilia or musculature to move food along becomes more important, and water reabsorption or other methods of feces condensation appear as an important feature of digestive function. Molluscs are remarkably diversified and are among the most highly differentiated of invertebrates. The study of details in the capture, ingestion, digestion, and absorption of food and the study of feces formation, in relation to the ecological factors and behavior of molluscs, are particularly rewarding.

Molluscs have a complex digestive tract, divided into discrete, functionally specialized regions. Like other animals, they have a foregut, derived from the stomodaeum, a hindgut, derived from the proctodaeum, and a midgut, derived from the primitive gut and lined with cells originating from the endoderm. Despite the great differences seen in different groups with different eating habits, the important features of the digestive tract are stable enough to make a preliminary discussion profitable.

The foregut consists of the buccal cavity, esophagus, and the parts derived from them. It is, primarily, the region for the reception of food, and its adaptation is closely correlated with the method used for food capture and the nature of the food itself. While some molluscs feed on large plants or animals and some are ciliary feeders, most molluscs gain their livelihood by scraping surfaces. The hypothetical

stem form is thought to have fed on algae and detritus scraped from the surface of rocks. One reason for confidence in this supposition is the radula apparatus, the most characteristic feature of the molluscan buccal cavity. It is found in nearly all molluscs in one form or another, and is peculiarly suited for scraping food particles from a surface, although it assumes other functions in molluscs with different eating habits. The radula apparatus consists of the radula, a toothed belt that passes over a supporting rod, the odontophore, and the radula sac in which the radula typically lies (Fig. 13.3A). When the radula is used for scraping, the odontophore is thrust out of the mouth by the contraction of the protractor muscles, and the radula is applied to the surface that is to be scraped. The odontophore is a firm piece, composed of chordoid tissue, and hence suitable for pressing the radula against the detritus-covered rock. When in place, the radula may be moved back and forth across the odontophore by muscles attached to the belt, while the recurved teeth engage particles, pulling them away from the surface as the odontophore is retracted. Obviously, teeth used in this way have a short life expectancy. New teeth are constantly being formed by odontoblasts at the back of the radula. They move forward as the front end of the radula wears. In any given species a definite number of transverse rows of odontoblasts occur, so that there is a definite number of radular teeth in each row. The number, size, and shape of radular teeth are remarkably specific within a species and remarkably variable in molluscs as a whole, so the teeth are valuable in taxonomy. Typically, there is one central tooth in each transverse row, flanked by one or two lateral teeth on each side. One or several marginal teeth at each edge of the radula complete the row of teeth (Fig. 13.3B,C). At the two extremes, *Chaetoderma* has a single radular tooth, while Cooke estimates that *Umbrella* may have as many as 750,000 radular teeth.

Modifications of the radula and radular teeth are correlated with the uses to which they are put. Some snails bore through clam or oyster shells with the aid of the radula, licking the flesh from the helpless prey when the shell is pierced. Many herbivorous snails have cutting jaws, located at the aperture of the buccal cavity, and nip off pieces of vegetation, which are torn and fragmented as they pass over the radula. The radula of carnivorous snails is often borne at the tip of a proboscis that can be shot out with great speed and force. In this case the radular teeth serve as weapons. Cone shells (Conidae) have hollow radular teeth, packed with poison from poison glands. The tooth poison sac ends blindly; presumably the tip of the tooth shears off to admit poison to the wound. The poison is extremely powerful and can cause human death. Although the radula is found in most molluscs, filter feeders have no use for one. In pelecypods, the radula is wholly lost, even in species which, like the shipworms and boring clams, use a rasping surface. In these organisms, the modified shell valves serve as a rasp.

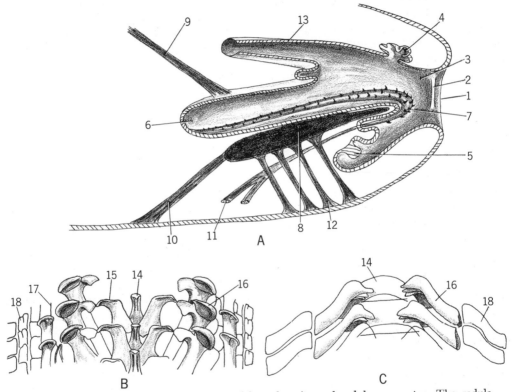

Fig. 13.3. Mouth Structure. A. Scheme of buccal cavity and radular apparatus. The radula passes over the odontophore, and can be moved back and forth. The odontophore may be extruded or withdrawn. B. Part of the radula of a *Chiton*, showing two rows of radular teeth. C. Part of the radula of a *Dentalium*, showing two rows of radular teeth. (B and C after Cooke.) 1, mouth; 2, jaw; 3, buccal cavity; 4, salivary gland; 5, subradular organ; 6, radular sac; 7, radula; 8, odontophore; 9, radular retractor; 10, odontophore retractor; 11, radular protractor; 12, odontophore protractor; 13, esophagus; 14, central tooth; 15, major lateral tooth; 16, lateral tooth; 17, major marginal tooth; 18, marginal tooth.

The esophagus is extremely variable. It is sometimes a simple tube, and in other cases has dilated regions which serve as a crop or gizzard. When small particles are swallowed, they are usually conveyed to the stomach trapped in mucous particles, while muscles are used for swallowing in forms that feed on larger particles. The specializations are best discussed in connection with the various classes.

Most molluscs have complex stomachs. Stomach structure varies in detail with the feeding habits, but some features have a special molluscan quality. It is characteristically associated with a pair of large digestive glands, which vary somewhat in function and form in the different classes.

Some gastropods feed in the primitive manner, scraping bits of algae or sponge into the mouth. These contribute much to our picture of the primitive molluscan stomach. *Diodora*, a keyhole limpet, is a good example. The salivary glands of *Diodora* secrete a copious flow of mucus, which forms a strand in which small particles of the sponge surface, or particles adhering to the sponges on which *Diodora* feeds, are caught. Cilia move the mucous strand with its load of material into the stomach. The mucous strings first encounter a sorting region, consisting of cilia and cuticular projections (Fig. 13.4). Here the food is graded into smaller particles for digestion and large ones that are rejected or sent to the crushing region. The muscular crushing mill is heavily lined with chitin, and it fragments larger particles, to be graded again and sent into the digestive region or rejected. Enzymes are secreted in the digestive glands and discharged through pores near the sorting region. While digestion is largely extracellular, absorption occurs in the ducts of the digestive glands. In some modern species, intracellular digestion occurs in the digestive glands, and it is likely that this system was used in ancestral stocks. A deep groove in the stomach wall conveys the mucous strand and rejected particles into the style sac. Cilia in the style sac rotate the mucous strand, and it is pressed by muscular action. The compacted mucous strand with the rejected particles is then guided to the intestine.

Major changes in stomach form are associated with adaptation to other kinds of feeding, but the style sac is usually retained. Clams, and some other molluscs, have a crystalline style, a transparent mass of material rich in amylase. In some cases, spirochaetes live in the crystalline style, providing other enzymes for digestion. The simplest stomachs are found in carnivorous species. Some have a simple crushing region and a digestive region, while others have a simple saccate stomach in which extracellular digestion occurs.

The hindgut is an intestine, often quite long and sometimes divided into definite regions. While it sometimes participates in absorption, it is generally most important in feces formation. Formed feces are of considerable importance because the anus is near the gills in the mantle cavity, and firm feces are less likely to foul the res-

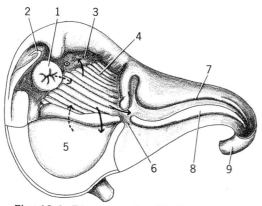

Fig. 13.4. Dissection of a *Diodora* Stomach. The *Diodora* stomach is thought to retain some of the characteristics of the stomach of primitive or ancestral forms. (From Graham and Fretter.) **1**, opening of the esophagus into stomach; **2**, spiral caecum; **3**, opening of ducts of digestive glands; **4**, sorting area; **5**, gastric shield; **6**, intestinal groove; **7**, region of style sac; **8**, typhlosole; **9**, intestine.

piratory surfaces. Feces formation generally involves the secretion of more mucus, the squeezing of the mucus and rejected material to form firm bodies, and possibly some absorption of water.

Ctenidia. The first real molluscs were probably rather bulky, not so elongated as worms, and with a body surface partly covered by spicules or a shell. In such animals the body surface is inadequate to serve for respiratory exchange, and special respiratory arrangements must appear if they are to survive and retain a reasonable level of activity. The physiological problems are similar in all organisms. The surface used for respiratory exchange may be amplified, or made more effective, or both. The principal methods of increasing the effectiveness of a surface for respiratory exchange involve the ventilation of the outer surface, or the development of methods to more rapidly drain off oxygen as it enters and to deliver carbon dioxide to the surface. The latter solution involves the movement of a body fluid through the tissues below the respiratory surface, or the development of a respiratory pigment which will increase the carrying capacity of the fluid, or both. The whole system works better if greater respiratory stress evokes feedback mechanisms that lead to an increase of the ventilation of the respiratory surface, or of the rate of circulation, or of both. Molluscs include the most highly developed invertebrates, and it is not surprising that they have utilized all of these techniques in meeting their respiratory needs.

Nearly all molluscs have a shell of some kind, and it seems probable that the shell was a factor in preventing molluscs from using simple external gills for respiration. This idea is particularly persuasive because some molluscs that have no shells or have much-reduced shells have lost primitive gills and use the body surface, or have simple external gills. In any case, the first molluscs must have developed a characteristic gill before they began to diverge toward the various modern groups, as the same kind of gill is seen repeatedly in molluscs of diverse types. The typical molluscan gill is called a ctenidium. Its simple form is highly effective, permitting the easy passage of a quantity of water over a large respiratory surface. A long, usually flattened central axis contains incurrent and excurrent blood vessels (Fig. 13.5). A series of flattened gill filaments are attached to the axis, separated enough to permit water to flow freely between them, but close enough so that cilia on adjacent filaments can co-operate in generating water currents. Blood circulates through the gill filaments while cilia on their surface swirl water over the filament and remove foreign particles. Skeletal rods support the filaments and prevent their collapse. The ctenidia are located in the mantle cavity, attached by membranes above and below. Cilia in the mantle cavity generate inhalant currents, bringing water in below the ctenidia, and exhalant currents, flushing water out from above them. Special cleansing cilia sweep particles off the filaments, and hypobranchial glands in the roof of the mantle cavity secrete mucus in which the particles are trapped, to be discharged through the opening of the mantle cavity. Respiratory exchange is most efficient if the blood and water flow in opposite directions. Molluscs discovered this principle of counterflow long before man, for the diverse respiratory systems are engineered in accordance with it. Water is brought up to the ctenidium from below, while blood is brought in from above. In each gill filament, the water passes upward and the blood courses downward, making for the most effective use of the gill.

Many molluscs have adapted to freshwater and some to terrestrial life. Marine species living in the intertidal zone are exposed alternately to air and water, and are thus faced with constantly changing respiratory problems. As might be expected, the ctenidial system has undergone many kinds of adaptations. Some aquatic species have lost the ctenidia entirely, depending on the body surface or on vacularized tufts extending from the surface. Some snails without ctenidia have a rich blood supply in the wall of the mantle cavity itself, converting it into a "lung." Actually, a lung of this kind can function in either air or water.

The common tendency for larger or more complex animals to replace ciliary mechanisms with muscular ones is seen in the respiratory arrangements of many molluscs. The clam, *Yoldia*, for example, has muscle fibers in the membrane attaching the ctenidium to the roof of the mantle cavity. The muscles relax each time a pulse of blood enters the gills, and the gill moves

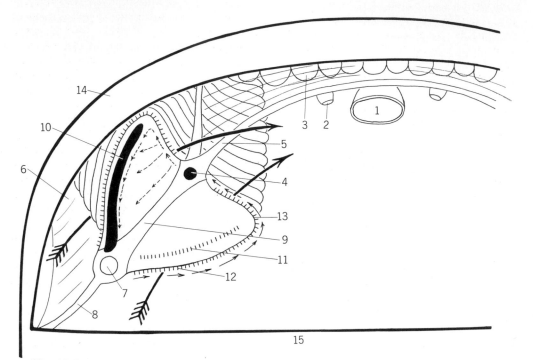

Fig. 13.5. Scheme of Arrangements in Mantle Cavity of a Hypothetical Ancestral Mollusc. The mantle cavity opens to the rear. Water enters, passes forward in the dorsolateral mantle compartment and between the filaments of the ctenidium, as indicated by the large arrows. Feces from the anus and wastes from the nephridiopores are also discharged into the mantle cavity, to be ejected with the exhalant current in the medial part of the mantle cavity. Each ctenidial gill filament is supported by skeletal rods, and has cilia on its face. The lateral cilia bring water up between the gill filaments, and the frontal and abfrontal cilia cleansing currents (the small, solid arrows), bring particles upward for discharge by the exhalant current. Blood flows through the filaments in a direction opposite to that of water flow (dotted arrows in the left filament), making most efficient use of the equipment for oxygen absorption. Hypobranchial glands in the roof of the mantle cavity secrete mucus that traps particles for discharge into the exhalant current. (Somewhat modified from Graham and Fretter.) **1**, anus; **2**, nephridiopore; **3**, hypobranchial gland; **4**, afferent blood vessel; **5**, afferent ctenidial membrane; **6**, dorsolateral mantle compartment; **7**, efferent blood vessel; **8**, efferent ctenidial membrane; **9**, axis of ctenidium; **10**, skeletal rod supporting ctenidial filament, shown only on the left; **11**, lateral cilia, shown only on the right; **12**, frontal cilia; **13**, abfrontal cilia; **14**, mantle and shell; **15**, foot.

downward. The gill is lifted each time the blood drains from it. These movements help ventilate the gill filaments. More highly organized systems are sometimes used. Some pelecypods have no gills, and in their place are muscles that pump water into the exhalant passageway and draw it into the mantle cavity. The vascularized mantle-cavity wall serves for respiratory exchange. Many swimming molluscs aerate the gill surface as a result of swimming movements, resulting in an automatic adjustment of the rate of gill ventilation with changes in the animal's activity.

Pulmonate snails have no ctenidia, and the mantle-cavity wall contains a rich supply of blood vessels converting it to a lung. This change in snails is especially correlated with terrestrial habits and air breathing. Cilia cannot generate air currents, and the mantle cavity has a muscular, dome-shaped floor, raised and lowered by alternate contraction and relaxation of muscles. With the changing volume of the mantle cavity, air rushes in or out through a narrow opening, the pneumostome. When air enters, the pneumostome is closed and the muscles relax. The elasticity of the tissues tends to compress the mantle cavity, increasing the partial pressure of oxygen and facilitating oxygen absorption. The pneumostome is then opened and air rushes out.

The development of regulatory mechanisms for adjusting the ventilation of respiratory surfaces for temporary changes in respiratory demands is an important step in respiratory evolution. The rate of oxidation varies with environmental factors such as temperature, and with the activity levels of the organism. An animal that cannot regulate its respiration is seriously handicapped if it moves for short periods into an environment with less than the usual oxygen supplies, if it is exposed to high temperatures that raise metabolic rates (and in aquatic habitats lower oxygen solubility), or if it is required to exert

itself to avoid enemies or capture food. Unless it has so much respiratory surface that it can meet the highest peaks of demand without regulatory mechanisms, it must tolerate anaerobic energy release for the duration of the emergency or be forced into inactivity to balance its respiratory accounts.

Respiratory regulation is seen most clearly in pulmonate gastropods with lungs. Some of the pulmonates have returned to aquatic habitats. *Helisoma* and *Lymnea* are fresh-water pulmonates that surface to breathe, presumably when the oxygen supply reaches a critical level. They remain submerged three times as long in water containing 6 cc. of O_2/l. as in water with 2 cc. of O_2/l. They remain submerged 22 times as long at 11° C. as at 21° C. They regulate respiration, at least partly, by the regulation of behavior. Pulmonates can also regulate respiration by changing the frequency and amplitude of breathing movements. The most important internal clues in animals that regulate breathing, generally, are low oxygen levels or high carbon dioxide levels. Pulmonates appear to be sensitive to both, and change both frequency and amplitude of breathing movements. *Limax*, a slug, and *Helix*, a land snail, adjust the opening of the pneumostome in accordance with carbon dioxide levels. When the air contains 3 to 5 per cent carbon dioxide, the pneumostome is held open constantly. At this point their regulatory system breaks down, for the permanently open pneumostome undoubtedly reduces the ability to absorb oxygen, as the pressure in the lung cavity can no longer be raised by muscular relaxation while the pneumostome is closed. Up to this point, the dilation of the pneumostome results in increased frequency of breathing movements and exchange of a higher percentage of lung air with each breath. A more significant change in lung ventilation results from changes in the muscle contractions of the lung wall. At reduced oxygen levels, muscles along the sides as well as the floor of the lung contract, increasing the amplitude of breathing movements.

Excretion. Primitively, the molluscan excretory system consists of a pair of U-shaped, tubular metanephridia, open to the pericardial cavity by way of nephrostomes, and to the mantle cavity by way of nephridiopores. Segmented animals, such as annelids, increase the number of nephridia with the number of body segments, but few molluscs have more than one pair of nephridia. Only in Monoplacophora and the cephalopod *Nautilus* is the number of nephridial pairs increased, As a matter of fact, it is not uncommon for molluscs to lose one member of the pair.

As many molluscs are relatively bulky, it is clear that they must have found some way to compensate for the small number of nephridia. Only two lines are open: biochemical accommodation to nitrogen compounds, or morphological and physiological amplification of the nephridium and its functional capacity, perhaps with the assumption of excretory functions by other body parts. Molluscs have used all these methods.

Aquatic species can eliminate ammonia through the body surface or gill surface as well as through the nephridia, thus compensating for lack of nephridial excretory surface. Ammonia is relatively toxic, and few animals can tolerate much of it in their blood. Molluscs appear to have a rather higher tolerance for ammonia than most animals. Some measure of this tolerance is provided by comparisons of normal ammonia levels in the blood. Cold-blooded aquatic vertebrates usually excrete a significant amount of ammonia, but normal blood ammonia levels are below 0.1 mg./100 ml. Comparable figures for the cuttlefish, *Sepia*, are 2.8 to 4.8 mg., and snails vary from about 2.3 to 3.0 mg. The blood ammonia concentrations of molluscs run about 1000 times as high as mammals, about 30 times as high as fish, and twice as high as lobsters. *Sepia*, aquatic snails,

and clams excrete about half of their nitrogenous wastes as ammonia.

A second line of biochemical accommodation is to convert nitrogenous wastes to relatively insoluble, non-toxic compounds. This is the common technique for terrestrial species, which cannot excrete ammonia at the body surface effectively. Nitrogen is eliminated as amino acid or uric acid. Amino acids make up almost a fifth of the nitrogen excreted by the land slug, *Arion*; *Sepia* excretes less than 10 per cent of its nitrogen as amino acid. Amino-acid excretion tends to vary sporadically, and uric-acid excretion reveals excretory adaptation more clearly. Osmotic stress appears to have a decided effect upon nitrogen excretion, for snails from fresh water tend to be more like terrestrial than marine species. This is clearly shown in comparisons of the uric-acid content of nephridia from marine, fresh-water, and land snails. The uric-acid content of terrestrial snails, as shown by dry-weight measurements, is from 10 to 300 times as high as marine snails, and species living in the intertidal zone and sometimes exposed to air are intermediate. Some fresh-water snails are pulmonates, with a prior history of land life, and some are operculates, which entered fresh water from the sea. It is not surprising to find fresh-water pulmonates with uric-acid concentrations as high as land species, but it is not so clear why operculate fresh-water snails should also tend to excrete uric acid as an adaptation to fresh-water life. Differences in the availability of water associated with seasonal or other environmental changes sometimes evoke changes in the patterns of nitrogen excretion. *Pila*, an amphibious snail, for example, has 1.68 mg. of uric acid/g. of nephridium when freshly collected, but when it is estivating under dry conditions comes to have up to 102 mg. uric acid/g. of nephridium.

Molluscs are peculiar in having little or none of the enzymes associated with the ornithine cycle, the pathway of urea production in other animals. Adjustments to water availability and osmotic stress are made without developing urea excretion. Clams depend heavily on ammonia excretion, although appreciable amounts of amino acids are excreted, and some clams release trimethylamine oxide, a soluble, non-toxic nitrogenous compound.

Without reference to the biochemical details, we can distinguish four principal avenues by which nephridial capacity is increased. 1) In a metanephridial system, wastes can enter the nephrostome from the coelomic fluid. Development of the nephrostomal apparatus can increase excretion. 2) Wastes also enter the nephridium through the "glandular" region of the tubule. Increases in the surface of the glandular nephridium increase excretory capacity. 3) Wastes can reach the nephridium by way of the circulatory system. The development of close association between the nephridium and the circulatory system can increase excretory capacity. 4) Urine is concentrated, in part, by the reabsorption of water from the nephridial contents. Improvements in the reabsorptive mechanisms can also improve excretory efficiency. The molluscan body plan tends to minimize the importance of the nephrostome. Animals with a relatively thin body wall and a spacious coelom can dump nitrogenous wastes into the coelomic fluid from the tissues of the digestive tube and body wall effectively, and in such animals the nephrostome can be of considerable functional importance. Molluscs have a reduced coelom, and the heavily muscled body wall contains tissues some distance away from the coelom. Wastes enter the blood rather than the coelomic fluid, and the functional significance of the nephrostome diminishes. The nephrostome of most gastropods and cephalopods is a simple opening into the renopericardial canal. The canal often empties far down on the nephridium, close to the ureter, instead of at the primitive position at the head of the nephridial tubule. Sometimes, however,

the heart wall or pericardium contains a glandular region that, on histological evidence, appears to process nitrogenous compounds. In such cases, the remains of the nephrostome undoubtedly play a role in bringing wastes into the nephridium.

Nephridial surface, and especially the glandular and absorptive parts of the surface, can be increased by lengthening of the tubule and folding of the tubule wall. These modifications are seen repeatedly in different molluscan groups. Amphineura have very large, greatly folded nephridia, with diverticula that extend out into the haemocoel. The gastropod nephridium, although differently placed, has a similarly expanded surface. The walls are alveolar, and the original tubular nature of the nephridium is masked. The nephridium in cephalopods is also compact. A blood vessel runs through it, and masses of glandular epithelium surround the vessel, apparently removing wastes from the blood. Although cephalopods have a relatively large coelom, the nephrostome remains a small pore, indicating that the new relationship of the nephridium with the circulatory system is functionally more important than its primitive relationship with the coelom.

Circulatory system. Considering the diversity seen in other organ systems, the circulatory system is remarkably stable. There are detailed differences in the arrangement of vessels and heart associated with different groups of molluscs, and within groups associated with differences in size and activity. But although differently located, the heart and major blood vessels are quite stable and retain about the same relationships with the main organs of the animal.

A few gastropods and pelecypods have blood containing haemoglobin, but most molluscs depend on haemocyanin as a respiratory pigment. Haemocyanin, a copper compound with a high molecular weight, is dissolved in the blood plasma. It is colorless when reduced, and bluish when loaded with oxygen. Mollusc blood

is a very effective oxygen-carrier by invertebrate standards, combining with about 1 to
7 mg. O_2/100 ml. Most cold-blooded vertebrates have blood which will combine with
between 6 and 15 mg./100 ml., so the best
molluscan blood is somewhat superior to
the least effective vertebrate bloods. Before
the properties of haemocyanin were understood, molluscs with red blood were
thought to have unusual respiratory capacities. Some of the resulting reasoning may
serve as a warning to modern theoreticians.
A common snail, *Planorbis*, has haemoglobin, but shows no unusual activity; it
was suggested that it needed haemoglobin
because it breathed the stagnant air of the
marshlands! This not only ignored the
existence of other snails in the same vicinity with colorless blood, but was also
based on the erroneous idea that haemoglobin was the only respiratory pigment.
Actually *Planorbis* blood carries only about
0.15-0.9 mg. O_2/100 ml., and so falls below
most snails with haemocyanin. The oxygen-
carrying capacity, however, does tend to
be associated with activity. The copper
content of the blood is distinctly greater
in highly active cephalopods than in
smaller and less active molluscs.

Remarkably little is known of blood corpuscles. The little available information
indicates a fair population of blood cells,
but classification of the cell types has not
progressed far. It appears that lymphocytes
with limited amoeboid locomotion, and
granulocytes with high phagocytic capacities are standard equipment in molluscs.
Some molluscs have neutrophils and eosin-
ophils. The blood of the large conch, *Busycon*, contains blood cells that divide. It is
probable that the differentiation of blood
cells occurs in the blood itself, although
some lymphoid tissues have been reported
in molluscs. In at least some molluscs,
phagocytic cells enter the gut and ingest
small food particles, apparently for intracellular digestion. This does not appear,
however, to be a very significant factor in
digestion or absorption. Inclusions of excretory material have been seen within
oyster blood corpuscles, and it is not
impossible that some of the blood cells
are actually mobile nephrocytes. Nearly
all of the blood protein is haemocyanin,
so it is not surprising that molluscan bloods
do not clot. The clumping of blood cells at
injuries, however, may aid in reducing
bleeding.

The blood circulates in part through
large haemocoel channels or lacunae, and
in part through blood vessels. The proportion of blood vessels and lacunae varies
somewhat in different groups, but the general course of circulation remains quite
stable. Blood which has passed through the
haemocoel lacunae around the viscera and
the body wall is collected in one or two
sinuses that convey the blood to the gills.
It passes through an afferent vessel to the
gill, through lacunae or capillaries in the
gill filaments, and into an efferent branchial vessel. This vessel takes blood to the
auricle associated with the gill. The blood
then passes into the heart, to be distributed
to the tissues by way of an anterior aorta
and its branches, and in some cases, a
posterior aorta as well. One of the stable
features is the close relationship of the
gills and auricles. Except in Monoplacophora and Amphineura, which have many
gills served by a collecting vessel on each
side of the body, each gill drains into its
own auricle. The majority of molluscs have
a single pair of gills and a single pair of
auricles, but there are some modifications
(Fig. 13.6 A-G). The asymmetrical gastropods tend to lose one gill, and with it lose
one of the auricles. *Nautilus* has two pairs
of gills and two pairs of auricles. The relatively stable design of the circulatory system of molluscs is one of the features that
give a degree of homogeneity to the members of the phylum.

Because lacunae and haemocoel sinuses
are so important in the circulatory system
of clams and snails, it is easy to over-
emphasize the importance of open spaces
in molluscan systems and underemphasize

the blood-vessel design. Some molluscs are large creatures, and some of the most active animals are cephalopods. Blood-flow is necessarily rapid in large, active animals, and a reasonable blood pressure is maintained. An octopus has a blood pressure of 40 to 60 mm. Hg at the heart, and 5 to 6 mm. Hg in the gill veins. This is a higher pressure than is found in many fishes, and far higher than the pressure in small molluscs. The snail, *Helix*, has a blood pressure of only 1.1 mg. Hg at the heart and about 0.4 mm. Hg in the gill veins, and a large clam has a blood pressure of about 4.4 mm. Hg at the heart. The maintenance of high blood pressures depends in part on the strength of the heart, and partly on the effectiveness of the retaining walls around the blood. Small arteries have an endothelial lining that can detach to form blood cells (Fig. 13.6H,I) and both large and small arteries have a thick basement membrane below the endothelium. The basement membrane is the primary source of strength in smaller arteries, but large arteries have smooth muscle fibers and a large amount of connective tissue. While the arteries deliver blood into lacunar spaces rather quickly in some molluscs, the arteries of cephalopods divide and redivide, eventually emptying into true capillary beds in some organs, especially the gills.

The high development of the molluscan circulatory system is associated with a reduction in the importance of the coelomic fluid in internal transport. As in vertebrates, the heavy body wall limits the value of coelomic transport. The development of the haemocoel compensates, and has the additional advantage of connecting with lacunae in the body wall. In bulky animals, the circulatory system cannot be efficient without a heart, and the further development of bulky animals depends upon the effectiveness of the heart.

The evolution of an effective heart involves the solution of a number of physiological problems. A heart is essentially a muscular tube, whose contraction forces blood along. A single contraction is ineffective; it must contract repeatedly and rhythmically to maintain blood-flow. Furthermore, blood must go in a definite direction, rather than ebb and flow. This is made possible by valves that prevent backflow. To be fully effective, it is important that the rate of flow be adjusted to the physiological needs of the organism at any given time, requiring feedback regulatory mechanisms. Two obvious possibilities for stimulating heart muscle to contract repeatedly in a coordinated beat exist, and two kinds of hearts are found, one using each method. One possibility is the delivery of repeated stimuli to the heart, so that the rhythmicity of heartbeat depends on rhythmic firing of nerves. Hearts of this type are said to be neurogenic. The other possibility is to develop muscle that will spontaneously contract in a rhythmic way. Hearts built of such muscle are myogenic. Mollusc hearts are of the second type, and will beat if completely separated from the nervous system. This does not mean that the heart is completely independent of nerve stimuli, however, even though the beat originates in the heart muscle itself. Nerve cells in the heart wall of gastropods and cephalopods modify the rate of beat. In most animals with myogenic hearts, some part of the heart wall is dominant and serves as a pacemaker. Apparently the heartbeat of most molluscan hearts can start anywhere; there is no localized pacemaker.

Various kinds of mechanisms can adjust the heartbeat to meet physiological demands. The properties of the heart muscle, itself, are important. The heart muscle of clams, mussels, and octopi, like most muscles, contracts more when stretched. Both the frequency and power of contraction are increased by the stretching of the muscle. In the intact animal, this means that the amplitude and frequency of heartbeat rises with increased venous return resulting from greater activity. Control from

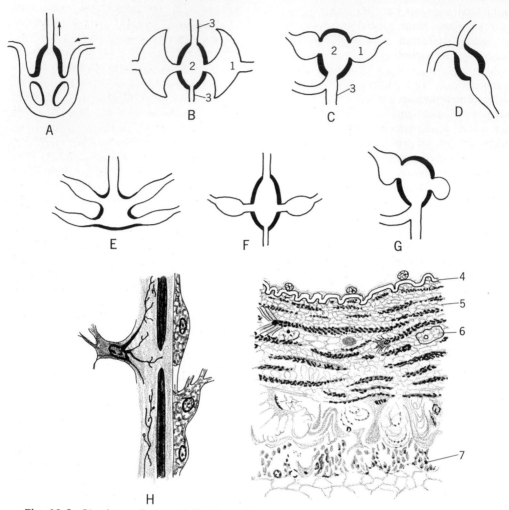

Fig. 13.6. Circulatory System. A-G. General arrangement of the heart in different kinds of molluscs. A, as in *Chiton*, with an anteriorly directed aorta, and auricles on each side, collecting blood from the row of ctenidia on each side. B, as in clams, with anterior and posterior aortae, and large auricles on each side, collecting blood from the large gills. C, as in a prosobranch with two gills, with the two auricles anterior to the heart as a result of torsion. The aorta divides into anterior and posterior branches, but emerges from the posterior end of the ventricle. D, as in a prosobranch with a single pair of gills, showing concomitant reduction of one auricle. E, as in an opisthobranch, with the auricle brought forward by detorsion. F, as in a cephalopod with two gills, with anterior and posterior aortae. G, as in a nautiloid, in which a second pair of gills and a second pair of auricles are present. H. Section through a part of an *Octopus* artery. Note the heavy walls of connective tissue and muscle, with an intima. I. Section through the foot artery of a clam, with considerably less developed walls. (H, after Dahlgren and Kepner. I, after Schneider, from Dahlgren and Kepner.) 1, auricle; 2, ventricle; 3, aorta; 4, intima; 5, connective tissue fibers; 6, nucleus of muscle cell; 7, longitudinal muscle fiber.

without is no less important. Stimuli which inhibit and augment beat are provided by neurosecretions from special neurons to the heart. Molluscan heart tissue is inhibited by acetylcholine and excited by serotonin, in general, and there is good evidence that an acetylcholine-serotonin system of neuronal secretions regulates the heartbeat of most molluscs. Cephalopods have some other system, the details of which are not yet worked out. The neurons responsible for regulation do not fire at random, of course. They are the final steps in a feedback mechanism which must depend on some internal clue that activates the central nervous system. Details of the feedback system are as yet unknown. The system probably rests upon some of the same kinds of factors that are important in other animals—blood pressure, carbon dioxide levels, and, perhaps, oxygen levels.

Neurosensory Apparatus. In general, molluscs are well equipped with sense organs, but they are so variable that they are best discussed in connection with the various classes. The primitive equipment probably included cephalic tentacles containing ocelli and sensory patches associated with the ctenidia (osphradia), used to sample water that entered the mantle cavity.

Annelids and arthropods usually have many ganglia, but molluscs tend to have very few. Primitive molluscs probably had four pairs of ganglia, for these are found in most molluscan groups. A pair of pedal ganglia is associated with the pair of pedal nerves which innervates the foot (Fig. 13.1). A pair of palliovisceral nerves arises in a pair of pleural ganglia and ends in a pair of visceral ganglia. Sometimes a pair of parietal ganglia lies between the pleural and visceral ganglia on the palliovisceral nerves. A pair of cerebral ganglia is associated with the circumenteric nerve ring. The cerebral, pleural, and pedal ganglia form a nervous triangle on each side of the body, connected by cerebropedal, cerebropleural, and pleuropedal connectives. In the more highly developed molluscs, the cerebral, pleural, pedal, and parietal ganglia tend to crowd together and, to a greater or lesser extent, unite to form a complex brain. Cephalopods have the most highly developed nervous system. Their brain compares favorably with the brain of lower vertebrates in size and complexity, and their behavior is correspondingly complex.

Development. Reproductive systems vary from simple to complex, and are best considered with the various classes. The course of development also varies, for some molluscs produce large, yolky ova that undergo modified development. Where eggs are small a typical spiral cleavage occurs, almost identical with the spiral cleavage of annelids and polyclad flatworms. Spiral cleavage has been described in connection with general protostome characteristics (p. 312) and need not be discussed here.

Gastrulation varies with the yolk content of the macromeres. Invagination and epiboly are the most common techniques used, but some species gastrulate by ingression. The embryo differentiates rapidly after gastrulation, forming a trochophore larva (Fig. 13.7C-E). The blastopore narrows, and ectoderm cells turn in at the margin of the blastopore to form an ectodermally lined stomodaeum. Two teloblasts arise from blastomere 4d. These lie on each side of the primitive gut and divide to form a band of mesodermal cells. A ciliated band, the prototroch, forms a girdle anterior to the stomodaeum, and an apical plate bearing an apical tuft of cilia develops at the anterior end of the larva. The larva elongates, and in most molluscs becomes a veliger. As veliger larvae differ in different classes, they will be discussed later. It may suffice here to note that the post-trochophore stages show no signs of the segmentation so prominent in the annelid post-trochophore larvae (Fig. 13.7F,G). It is during this period that the fundamental differences in annelid and molluscan architecture are determined. The

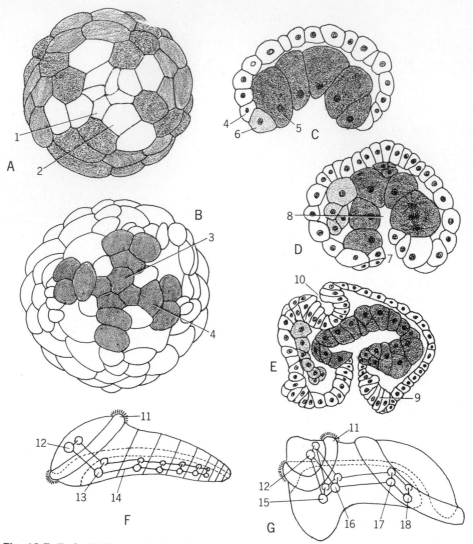

Fig. 13.7. Early Molluscan Development. **A.** Cleavage stage of an annelid, *Arenicola*, showing annelid rosette and annelid cross. The annelid cross is interradial in position. **B.** Cleavage stage of a mollusc, *Crepidula*, showing the molluscan rosette and cross. The molluscan cross is radial in position. **C-E.** Stages in the development of *Littorina*, showing gastrulation and early changes leading toward the trochophore larva, including the early proliferation of the mesoderm stem cell. **F.** Scheme of the post-trochophore larva of an annelid. As segments are added the nerve cord and paired ganglia increase in number. **G.** Scheme of the post-trochophore larva of a mollusc. There is no evidence of segmentation, and a mantle forms over the posterior part of the body. (**A**, after Child. **B**, after Conklin. **C-E**, after Delsman, from Korschelt. **F** and **G**, after Naef.) **1**, annelid rosette composed of blastomeres la^{111}-ld^{111}; **2**, annelid cross, composed of blastomeres la^{112}-ld^{112}; **3**, molluscan rosette and cross, the latter composed of cells la^{12}-ld^{12} and second quartet cells. (Note that it is abutted to the arms of the rosette instead of between them, as in annelids.) **4**, ectoderm; **5**, endoderm; **6**, mesoderm stem cell; **7**, blastopore; **8**, primitive gut; **9**, stomodaeum; **10**, shell gland; **11**, prototroch; **12**, cerebral ganglia; **13**, ventral ganglion; **14**, nerve cord; **15**, pedal ganglion; **16**, pleural ganglion; **17**, parietal ganglion; **18**, visceral ganglion.

476

close similarity of annelid and mollusc trochophores, however, attest to ther relationship.

Class Amphineura

Amphineura has been briefly characterized with the other classes of molluscs. It contains two orders, whose members are so different that they are best discussed separately. The orders are:

Order Polyplacophora. The chitons. Oval amphineurans with a dorsal mantle that extends down as a heavy girdle around the edge of the broad, flat, ventral foot; shell composed of eight plates arranged in a longitudinal series; many pairs of ctenidia in a groove-like mantle cavity encircling the foot; internal organization relatively primitive. Example: *Chaetopleura* (Fig.13.9).

Order Aplacophora. Elongated, worm-like amphineurans with the mantle expanded laterally to cover most or all of the ventral surface; foot absent or reduced to a midventral ridge without a shell, but with calcareous spicules imbedded in the mantle; mantle cavity missing or greatly reduced; without ctenidia or radula in some species. Example: *Chaetoderma* (Fig. 13.8 A); *Paramenia* (Fig. 13.8B).

Order Polyplacophora—The Chitons

Most chitons are inconspicious, drab creatures, only a few inches long at the most, but under a lens they often turn out to be beautifully patterned. The dull shades are valuable camouflage, helping them to blend with the rocks on which they live. The largest species is *Ishnochiton* (*Amicula*) *stelleri*, found on the Pacific coast of North America. It is brick red and reaches up to about 0.3 m. long. About 600 species are known. Chitons occur in the sea in all climates and at all depths up to about 4000 m. Although some live high in the intertidal zone,

moistened only at full tide, they are especially abundant in shallow water in rocky areas.

Chitons are homebodies, and move about very little unless they are disturbed. They usually stray away from a definite home site only to make short foraging expeditions and come back unerringly to the exact spot they call home, and to which they may have adapted by slight shell modifications. *Nuttallina* is even less of a gadabout, and lives permanently in depressions that fit its body almost perfectly. These niches appear to have been carved in the rock by past generations of *Nuttallina*, living like today's crop on whatever food fate happens to bring to their niche. Chitons tend to be photo-

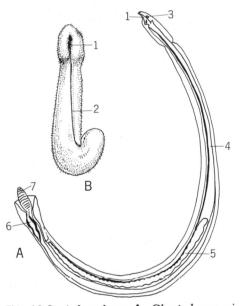

Fig. 13.8. Aplacophora. A. *Chaetoderma nitidulum*, a chaetodermomorph aplacophoran. They have no distinct ventral groove, and a posterior cloacal chamber with two gills. B. *Paramenia cryophila*, a neomeniomorph aplacophoran. They have a ventral pedal groove and are without gills. (A, after Wirén. B, after Pelseneer, from Pelseneer, in Lankester.) **1,** mouth; **2,** pedal groove; **3,** cerebral ganglion; **4,** digestive tract; **5,** digestive gland; **6,** heart; **7,** gill.

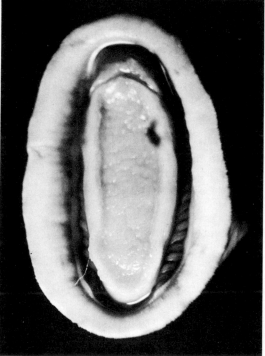

Fig. 13.9. Dorsal and Ventral Views of *Chaetopleura*, a Chiton. Notice the gills in the elongated mantle cavity, and the foot and head region. The sculpturing of the shell valves is formed, in part, by the aesthetes.

negative, and many species will crawl slowly to the underside of their rock if it is turned over. They adhere to the rocks with the broad flat foot unless one tries to detach them, when the tough girdle is thrust against the rock and the foot is retracted. This forms a suction cup and enables them to hold tenaciously. If they are detached from their rock, ,they roll up like an armadillo, with their dorsal plates forming a continuous protective covering.

Shell. The shell is formed of eight valves arranged in a longitudinal row. The front margin of each of the last seven plates extends below the plate in front of it. Special articulating surfaces mark the overlapping regions of the valves (Fig. 13.10C-E). The middle six plates are similar, but the anterior (cephalic) and the posterior (anal) plates are differentiated, as they do not articulate with valves in front or behind them.

The shell is made of two layers, somewhat different from the layers of other mollusc shells. The upper layer is the tegmentum. It is composed of conchiolin impregnated with calcium carbonate. The lower layer is the articulamentum, which is wholly calcareous. The edge of the mantle turns back over the edges of the valves, and in some cases covers the valves entirely. Shell characteristics are valuable in species identification and an extensive vocabulary has developed to describe the form and sculpturing of the valves (Fig. 13.10A).

The tegmental sculpturing is not mere ornamentation. It is caused by epidermal canals associated with sense organs known as aesthetes (Fig. 13.10B). The development of these surface sense organs is undoubtedly associated with the reduction of the head and the fact that it is completely enclosed by the girdle and covered by the shell. Some chitons have only simple, tactile aesthetes, but many also have large, visual aesthetes. These shell eyes vary from simple ocelli to highly differentiated eyes with a calcareous cornea and a lens. Some species have thousands of eyes, but as the tegmentum gradually wears away, the visual sense declines. In this case the older animals are indifferent to light. Branches of the visceral nerve innervate the aesthetes.

Mantle and Mantle Cavity. The ventral edge of the mantle forms the tough girdle that completely encircles the body. The color and ornamentation of the girdle are important factors in taxonomy. On the ventral surface a pallial groove separates the girdle and the foot. This groove is the mantle cavity, and contains a series of pairs of gills attached to its roof (Fig. 13.9). Amphineura have many primitive characteristics, but the mantle cavity and ctenidia are highly specialized. The primitive, posterior mantle cavity has been reduced, probably in connection with the flattening of the body; in compensation the mantle cavity has spread forward as a trough around the body. It is not clear whether the original single pair of gills was subdivided or whether more pairs were added. In either case the gill apparatus was fitted into the available space. The edge of the mantle is lifted slightly in front, permitting water to enter. Drawn in by the ciliated mantle wall, water passes posteriorly between the gills and the mantle. Cilia on the gill filaments cause currents that sweep the water up over them. As the water reaches the exhalant space between the gills and the foot, it continues to flow posteriorly, departing at one or two points at the rear, where the mantle is slightly lifted.

Digestion. Chitons feed as the hypothetical ancestor is thought to have eaten, scraping algae and other material from the rocks. The foregut retains its primitive character. Seven jaws usually lie just inside of the buccal cavity, but the radula does most of the heavy work of food procurement. The radula is very long, often reaching back beyond the beginning of the stomach, and has many transverse rows of 17 teeth. Typically, each row is made up of three central teeth, three lateral teeth on each side, and three marginal teeth on each side (Fig. 13.3B). Immediately below the opening of the radula sac is the subradular sac (Fig. 13.3), which contains a chemoreceptor,

the subradular organ. A hungry chiton extends the subradular organ from time to time to survey the situation. When food is located, it is withdrawn and the radula is extruded. Mucus from the salivary gland lubricates the radula and catches small particles as they are loosened from the

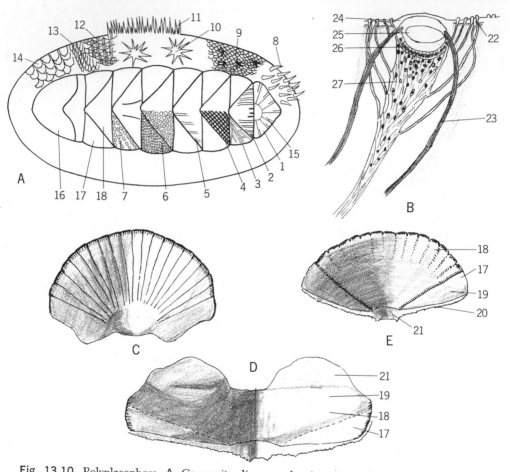

Fig. 13.10. Polyplacophora. A. Composite diagram, showing some of the variations in the sculpture and girdle ornamentation in polyplacophorans. B. Section through an aesthete of a polyplacophoran, *Acanthopleura*. C-E. Anterior, middle, and posterior valves of the shell of a polyplacophoran. (A, after Turner. B, after Mosley, from Pelseneer, in Lankester. C-E, after Cooke.) *Shell sculpture:* 1, radially ribbed; 2, ribbed; 3, divaricating radially; 4, graduated in quincunx; 5, sulcate; 6, granose; 7, radially nodulose. *Girdle ornamentation:* 8, calcareous spines; 9, scales and spiculose bunches; 10, sutural tufts; 11, spiculose fringe; 12, scale striate; 13, scales smooth; 14, scales mucronate. *Valves:* 15, anterior valve; 16, posterior valve; 17, lateral area; 18, central area; 19, tegmentum; 20, articulamentum; 21, sutural lamina, covered by the valve in front when in place. *Aesthete:* 22, micraesthete; 23, pigmented capsule; 24, cornea; 25, lens; 26, retinal cell; 27, optic nerve.

rocks. The mucus forms strings, containing food particles, which are swept toward the stomach by cilia in a ventral groove of the esophagus. Amylase is poured over the food from a pair of esophageal glands as it moves along the groove.

The oddly shaped stomach contains no sorting areas like those found in *Diodora*. Proteolytic enzymes from the large digestive gland pour into the stomach through two ducts. Food and enzymes are mixed by peristaltic movements of the stomach. The food eventually passes into the slightly expanded anterior intestine, where it remains for a time, held back by the intestinal valve. Absorption and digestion occur in the stomach and anterior intestine. Both contain mucous glands, and by the time residues reach the posterior intestine, they are heavily charged with mucus. Each time the intestinal valve opens and closes, a fecal pellet is stamped out and passes into the posterior intestine. The pellets are further condensed by reabsorption of water as they move toward the anus. Water currents in the mantle cavity waft the feces away as they are released.

Excretion. Chiton nephridia have been carefully described, but little is known of excretory physiology. Urease has been reported from *Chiton*, so presumably urea is transformed into ammonia for excretion.

Chitons have the primitive arrangement with a pair of nephridia open to the pericardial cavity through nephrostomes. Each nephridium is U-shaped (Fig. 13.11A) and expands rapidly beyond the nephrostome. They run forward, curve down and back, and end at the nephridiopores situated well back in the pallial groove. Chitons are too large to find a simple pair of nephridial tubules adequate for excretion. The nephridial surface is greatly amplified by median and lateral diverticula and complex folding of the glandular walls. Urine production is undoubtedly favored by the intimate relationship of the nephridia and haemo-

coel, resulting from the diverticula extending into the haemocoel.

Circulatory System and Transport. The circulatory system so closely resembles the primitive system that it need not be discussed in great detail. Two bilaterally symmetrical auricles, located at the back end of the body, open independently into the ventricle through from one to four openings. The ventricle drives blood forward in the aorta. It emerges into a system of sinuses which serve the head region and body wall and surround the internal organs. This blood eventually drains into two pallial sinuses, which run back at the junction of the mantle and foot (Fig. 13.11A). Afferent branchial vessels extend to the medial side of the gill axis from the pallial sinuses. Aerated blood is returned by an efferent branchial vessel on the lateral side of the gill axis, and empties into the gill veins that pass back to the auricles.

Neurosensory Apparatus. Chitons are sedentary animals, and show the usual tendency toward reduction of the head and sense organs. The rudimentary head has no cephalic tentacles and no eyes, and there are relatively few special sense organs. The subradular organ is the principal chemoreceptor. Some chitons have sensory patches on the palps around the mouth. The mantle cavity has a number of sensory patches, thought to be homologous to the osphradia of other molluscs. Epidermal neurosensory cells provide sensitivity to touch and temperature changes, and the aesthetes are the principal tactile and, in some cases, photosensitive receptors of the dorsal surface.

The nervous system is relatively diffuse and decentralized for animals as large as the chitons. There is very little evidence of ganglion formation. The nervous system consists of a subepidermal plexus, a circumenteric ring, a pair of palliovisceral nerves, and a pair of pedal nerves. Commissures run between the two pedal nerves and connect the pedal and palliovisceral nerves (Fig. 13.12D). A small nerve ring arising from the circumenteric ring innervates the radula sac, and may contain a pair of tiny radular ganglia. A somewhat larger ring associated with the buccal cavity sometimes contains a pair of small buccal ganglia. The rings and ganglia are part of the sympathetic (stomatogastric) nervous system.

It is evident that the chiton nervous system is no more centralized than that of flatworms. If, as appears probable, ancestral stem forms had cephalic tentacles containing ocelli, they probably had a nervous system that was somewhat more centralized. It is probable that the chiton nervous system is partly primitive and partly somewhat degenerate, with degeneration related to the assumption of more sedentary habits.

Reproduction. In chitons, the two gonads unite to form a single large organ

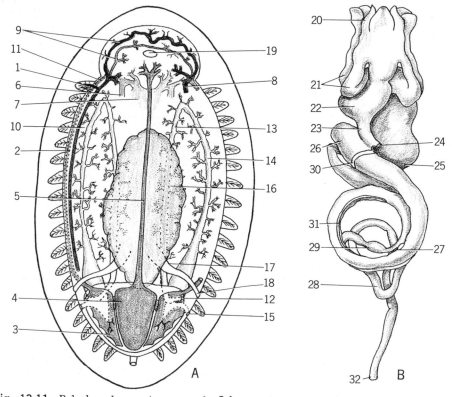

Fig. 13.11. Polyplacophoran Anatomy. A. Scheme of internal organization of a polyplacophoran, somewhat generalized and with the digestive tract omitted. B. Digestive tract of *Lepidochiton.* (B, after Fretter.) *Circulatory system:* 1, efferent branchial vessel; 2, gill vein; 3, auricle; 4, ventricle; 5, aorta; 6, pedal sinus; 7, perivisceral sinus; 8, neuropedal sinus; 9, cephalic sinus; 10, marginal sinus; 11, afferent branchial vessel. *Excretory system:* 12, nephrostome; 13, ascending branch of nephridium; 14, descending branch of nephridium; 15, nephridiopore. *Reproductive system:* 16, gonad; 17, gonoduct; 18, gonopore. *Digestive tract:* 19, mouth; 20, buccal gland; 21, sugar gland; 22, esophagus; 23, dorsal canal; 24, ducts of digestive gland; 25, stomach; 26, anterior intestine; 27, anterior intestinal valve; 28, posterior intestine; 29, posterior intestinal valve; 30, transverse ciliary band; 31, longitudinal ciliary band; 32, anus.

with paired gonoducts. The gonoducts open into the mantle cavity through gonopores that lie just in front of the nephridiopores. A few species, however, retain paired gonads. Sexes are separate, but there is no sexual dimorphism.

Sperm are shed into the mantle cavity. As chitons are gregarious, some sperm reach neighboring females. Females do not shed ova until the males have shed sperm, presumably shedding in response to some chemical stimulus. Ova are generally deposited singly, in masses, or in strings. In several species, the sperm enter the oviducts, fertilization is internal, and

the young are brooded in the oviduct. These species have larger, yolkier eggs, and development is modified.

Development to the trochophore larva follows the usual molluscan pattern. Chitons do not pass through a veliger stage, and the trochophore metamorphoses directly into juveniles. The posterior end of the larva elongates as the shell starts to form. The coelom appears as spaces in the mesodermal bands on each side of the body, derived from cell 4d. The buccal cavity and much of the esophagus arises from the stomodaeum, but the proctodaeum forms late, and appears to give rise to only a small part of the intestine. Ctenidia appear late in development, with the most posterior pair appearing first. The apical cilia and prototroch decline during metamorphosis, and the young chiton sinks to the bottom and takes up life as a juvenile.

SUBCLASS APLACOPHORA— THE SOLENOGASTERS

Aplacophora are small (2.5 cm. or less), worm-like, aberrant Amphineura living in

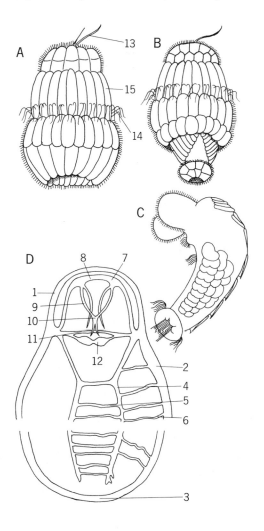

Fig. 13.12. A-C. Three stages in the development of an Aplacophoran, *Myzomenia*. **A** and **B** are younger and older trochophore larvae, and show the test of large cells. **C** is an advanced larva, as it appears after the test cells have been shed. **D**. Dorsal view of the nervous system of *Acanthochiton*. The middle portion is omitted. Note the absence of ganglia, except for small ones associated with the stomatogastric or visceral nervous system. (A-C, after Pruvot. D, after Pelseneer, in Lankester.) *Nervous system:* **1**, cerebral commissure; **2**, pallial nerve cord; **3**, pallial commissure; **4**, pedal nerve cord; **5**, pedal commissure; **6**, commissures between pedal and pallial nerves; **7**, upper buccal ganglion; **8**, upper buccal commissure; **9**, stomatogastric commissures; **10**, stomatogastric ganglion and radular nerves; **11**, labial commissure; **12**, subradular ganglion and commissure. *Larvae:* **13**, apical tuft; **14**, velum; **15**, ciliated test cell.

the sea at depths of about 30 to 1800 m., or sometimes at somewhat greater depths. They fall naturally into two groups, the Neomeniomorpha, closely associated with colonial hydroids and corals on which they feed, and the Chaetodermomorpha, which burrow in the mud. They are quite unlike chitons. The most outstanding feature that links them with chitons is the appearance of dorsal plates during larval development (Fig. 13.12C). In chitons they are the beginning of the shell, but are shed in aplacophorans. As a group, the aplacophorans are not very well known.

The foot of the Neomeniomorpha is reduced to a ventral ridge (Fig. 13.8A). The mantle nearly encloses the animal, and there is little to choose between anterior and posterior ends. The mouth opens at the anterior end and the cloaca at the posterior end. Secondary gills, which are not ctenidia-like, lie in the cloacal chamber. The paired nephridia unite on the midline, and open through a single pore below the anus. There is no solid shell, but the mantle is studded with spicules. The digestive glands are reduced to patches of secretory epithelium in the stomach wall and the intestine is a simple, straight tube. The circulatory system is much reduced, consisting largely of sinuses about the organs. Haemoglobin occurs in blood corpuscles. They are hermaphroditic animals. Gametes are released into the pericardial cavity and escape to the exterior through the nephridia. Larval development has been followed (Fig. 13.12A-C). The young larvae are striking, because a test of ciliated cells, derived from the velum, encloses the larva. These test cells are suddenly shed shortly before metamorphosis begins. During metamorphosis a transitory set of dorsal plates, similar to those of chitons appears.

The Chaetodermomorpha are still more extensively modified. The foot is missing entirely, and the mantle forms a cylindrical tube around the body. The anterior and posterior ends are marked by constrictions (Fig. 13.8B). The posterior end is expanded as a bell-shaped cloacal region containing a pair of large ctenidia. Large digestive glands open into the gut just anterior to the intestine. The ciliated, U-shaped nephridia open on each side of the anus. The circulatory system is like that of Neomeniomorpha.

The Aplacophora have a nervous system that is somewhat more centralized than that of chitons, with definite cerebral and pedal ganglia. They do not appear to be degenerate polyplacophorans, but much work remains before their affinities can be determined.

Class Monoplacophora

This new class has been erected for *Neopilina galathea*, taken off the west coast of Mexico at a depth of 3600 m. It is an exciting find, and when it is better known, many hope that it will shed new light on the original molluscs.

Neopilina is flat, with a dome-shaped, solid shell. The shell is like the shell of a limpet, and evidences of coiling have been noted in the younger shells, so that in this sense it resembles some of the gastropods. It has a shallow mantle cavity that runs around the broad, flat foot, much as in chitons and limpets. The five pairs of gills in the mantle cavity are a chiton-like characteristic. There is no sign of the torsion that is characteristic of gastropods. It is evident that *Neopilina* is a curious creature, with affinities with the two most primitive groups of molluscs, but not fitting comfortably into either group.

The internal structure is even more remarkable. The nervous system is chiton-like, but the other organ systems have unique characteristics, although all are evidently molluscan in character. The coelom is rather large and contains two pairs of gonads. A pair of nephridia is associated with each pair of gills, and the

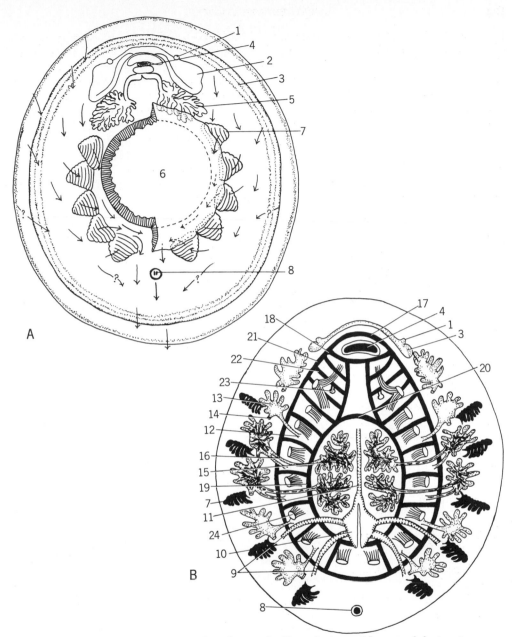

Fig. 13.13. *Neopilina*, the Monoplacophoran. **A.** Ventral view, with part of foot cut away and the probable course of currents indicated by arrows. **B.** Internal organization. (From Lemche and Wingstrand, in Grassé.) *External features:* **1**, preoral tentacle; **2**, velum; **3**, pallial groove; **4**, mouth; **5**, tuft of tentacles; **6**, foot; **7**, ctenidium; **8**, anus. *Circulatory system:* **9**, atrium; **10**, ventricle; **11**, aorta. *Excretory system:* **12**, nephrostome; **13**, nephridium; **14**, nephridiopore. *Reproductive system:* **15**, gonad; **16**, gonoduct to nephridium. *Nervous system:* **17**, cerebral commissure; **18**, subcerebral commissure; **19**, pedal nerve cord; **20**, pedal commissure; **21**, lateral (pallial) nerve cord; **22**, commissures between pedal and pallial nerve cords; **23**, statocyst; **24**, segmental muscles (foot retractors).

485

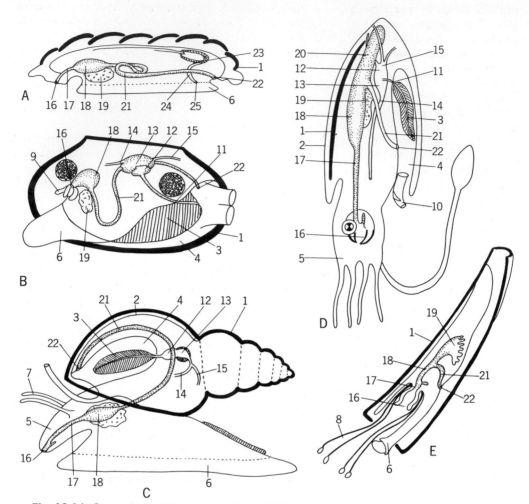

Fig. 13.14. Comparison of the Organization of Different Types of Molluscs. The Amphineura (A) have a flattened form, and the chitons a shell composed of eight valves arranged longitudinally. The head is reduced, and the ctenidia lie in a pallial groove which encircles the foot. The Pelecypoda (B) have a bivalve shell, with a dorsal hinge. The blade-shaped foot is thrust between the valves, but they are not highly mobile; and the head is reduced. Large gills hang in the mantle cavity, which fills most of the space between the two folds of the mantle lying on the inner surface of the shell valves. In gastropods (C), the visceral mass has become very tall and extends into the usually spiraled shell. The broad ventral foot is large, and the head is well developed. In cephalopods (D) also the visceral mass has become very tall. While they may be spiraled, like gastropods, most modern cephalopods have a tall, conical shape, with the shell enclosed within the mantle. The head is ventrally placed, and a siphon, derived from the foot, opens into the mantle cavity. The original dorsoventral axis has become elongated and is functionally the anteroposterior axis. The head is well developed in these active forms, and is encircled by tentacles. In scaphopods (E), the conical shell is open at both ends, as in a clam with the valves fused ventrally and open at anterior and posterior ends. The much-reduced head is provided with captacula used in feeding, and the cylindrical foot extends through the anterior opening of the shell. *External features:* 1, shell; 2, mantle; 3, gill;

486

nephridiopores lie near the bases of the gills. The gametes escape through the middle pairs of nephridia, which are connected with the gonads. Regular paired muscles go up to the shell. The most remarkable feature of the internal organization is the occurrence of regularly paired parts. It is not surprising that bilaterally symmetrical animals should have paired parts, but it becomes remarkable when there are similar numbers of pairs of gills and nephridia, and when paired muscles alternate with the nephridia. This kind of arrangement is seen in segmented animals, and is known as metameric. Cell lineage studies of the determinate spiral cleavage of annelid and mollusc embryos and similarities in their larvae attest to the close relationship of the two groups of animals. Molluscs, however, are not segmented, while annelids are. It is, therefore, of some importance to know whether the first molluscs were unsegmented, arising from the the protostome stem before metameric organization appeared, or segmented. *Neopilina* may be an independent molluscan venture into metameric organization, or it may be evidence of a primitive metamerism that has been suppressed in all other molluscs. It is too early to draw any firm conclusions, but *Neopilina* will remain a most important find, whatever they may be.

Class Gastropoda

Since gastropods first appeared during early Cambrian times, they have spread to all parts of the oceans, adapted to life in fresh-water ponds and streams, and invaded land wherever a reasonable amount of moisture is available. About 15,000 fossil and 35,000 modern species are known. Their success need not be calculated on the basis of the number of species alone. Anyone who has visited a mudflat, where one can scarcely step without crushing some snails, or marveled at the many limpets attached to the rocks in the intertidal zone, can testify to the success of individual species.

The road to success, however, has not been a smooth one. Gastropods have had to live with, and adjust to, two characteristics that would disqualify most animals for successful competition with other organisms. Most of them live with the body coiled up in a spiral. As if this were not enough, while they are embryonic the visceral mass is suddenly twisted about, bringing the back end to the front. Most of them remain permanently twisted, and while a few partially untwist during later growth, all show its results. These two features of gastropod structure can never be ignored, for they explain a great deal about the course of gastropod evolution and enter into the organization of the organ systems.

Before considering the specifics of coiling and twisting in gastropods, it will be helpful to consider the relationship of the various molluscan stocks to the organization of the hypothetical ancestral stocks. Animals belonging to the various classes look quite different, but the ancestral type can be converted into them rather easily (Fig. 13.14). Primitive organization is relatively simple. The foot is a platform, on which the viscera lie, covered by the mantle and shell. Flattening the visceral mass and extending the mantle cavity forward as a groove around the foot leads to the basic form of the Amphineura, as previously described. En-

4, mantle cavity; 5, head; 6, foot; 7, tentacle; 8, captaculum; 9, labial palp; 10, siphon. *Circulatory system:* 11, gill vein; 12, auricle; 13, ventricle; 14, anterior aorta; 15, posterior aorta. *Digestive system:* 16, mouth; 17, esophagus; 18, stomach; 19, digestive gland; 20, caecum; 21, intestine; 22, anus. *Excretory system:* 23, nephrostome; 24, nephridium; 25, nephridiopore.

larging the mantle and dividing it into symmetrical halves, hanging down on both sides of the body, enlarging the gills in the now huge mantle cavity, and extending the foot downward between the mantle folds as a blade-like structure, leads to the body form of pelecypods. Tusk shells (scaphopods) can be derived in much the same manner, with the additional sealing of the mantle margins below to form a tubular structure secreting a tubular shell, and elongating the body to fit the tubular enclosure. The other two classes ventured along an entirely different path. The visceral mass grew higher, becoming a tall visceral hump, with the great digestive gland at the apex. As the hump grew tall it tended to coil, in both gastropods and cephalopods. The squid is a common type of cephalopod, and is a tall cone, not coiled but straight, with the head and foot united. Many extinct cephalopods, and the modern chambered nautilus, have coiled bodies, however. The gastropod stems that gave rise to the modern species were all coiled, although some ancient gastropods were

straight. Gastropods, unlike cephalopods, have a distinct head and foot, and so more closely resemble the primitive stem forms.

Evidence that this series of changes occurred in gastropods is provided by fossil species. The first gastropods did not have coiled shells, but were conical (Fig. 13.15A,B). They belong to the wholly extinct order Cynostraca, literally the dog shells, so named because they resemble a dog's tooth. The first gastropods must have encountered some difficulty in balancing the tall spire, for the shell peak tended to sag and coil. The first coiled gastropods were not twisted. Their bodies were bilaterally symmetrical and coiling was largely restricted to one plane. (Fig. 13.15C). The first coiled gastropods belong to the order Cochleostraca, which may be translated as "spiral shell," also wholly extinct. These two orders make up the Protogastropoda and include the fossil species that might have been coiled but were never twisted. They are old-fashioned molluscs; the last traces of them are found in the late Carboniferous and Permian deposits.

The growth of snail shells is a fascinating subject and involves factors that might be ignored without careful consideration. A gastropod is a living, growing animal, and the opening of the shell is proportionate to its body size. The shell grows with the body. New shell is laid down at the aperture, and reflects the growing size of the body. If the body stops growing or grows more slowly, the shell usually stops or slows its growth also. If a snail hibernates or is stunted by a bad environment, shell growth slows down or stops. As a result, if the shell were unwound, it would often be a simple cone with a straight edge. In other species the body grows more rapidly than the shell grows in length, and the uncoiled shell would flare out like a trumpet. Shells of conical gastropods are of both types.

However, modern gastropods do not

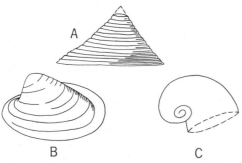

Fig. 13.15. Protogastropoda. These first gastropods did not undergo torsion and had a posterior mantle cavity. Primitively conical, as the visceral mass became taller they developed a spiral shell. **A.** *Palaeacmea,* a late Cambrian form with a simple, conical spire. **B.** *Scenella,* a lower Cambrian form with a bent spire. **C.** *Pelagiella,* the oldest known coiled gastropod, appearing in the lower Cambrian. (All after Shimer and Shrock.)

have conical shells, but spiraled ones. What is a spiral, and how is it formed? Few of us ever study spirals, and the mathematics of spirals is largely neglected, so a consideration of snail shells is generally a profitable undertaking. If two points are a certain distance apart, and one moves around the other, a circle is generated. The circle is transformed into a spiral if the moving point approaches or moves away from the central point as it revolves. The moving point may be considered the point at the middle of the shell aperture, moving with respect to the apex of the shell as the animal grows. As spiraling of the shell accompanies growth, only spirals formed by a point moving away from the center point need be considered. Two general cases can be distinguished. The moving point may move away from the center point at a constant rate. In this case, each new whorl of the spiral is the same breadth as the preceding whorl. Or the moving point may accelerate as it moves. In this case, each new whorl will be broader than the last if the acceleration is positive, or narrower if the acceleration is negative. The rate of movement of the moving point away from the center is, therefore, an important factor in determining the form of the spiral. The second factor is the direction of the movement of the moving point. The point may move away from the center in a straight line, remaining in the same plane. This simple outward movement results in a flat, plane spiral (Fig. 13.16A), with each whorl the same breadth if it moves at a constant rate, or each new whorl broader if it accelerates as it moves. Plane spirals with exactly equal whorls are never found, although some snail shells approach this form. Plane spirals with the whorls becoming larger with each revolution are common, but if the acceleration is great the shell form is greatly modified, as in *Haliotus*. The point might move downward in a straight line, generating a tubular, helical spiral (Fig. 13.16L). If the moving point does not accelerate, a spring-like form results, and if it accelerates, the whorls become farther and farther apart, so that they appear twisted rather than spiraled. This type of spiral is never perfectly achieved by gastropods, although some shells approximate it. In most cases, the moving point moves both outward and downward, and generates a conical spiral (Fig. 13.16D). If the rate of movement outward and down is constant, or if the rates remain proportionate throughout, a straight-sided spiral shell of conical form results. In many cases, however, movement outward and downward are not proportionate because of acceleration in one direction, or unequal acceleration in the two directions. If the outward movement accelerates more rapidly than the downward movement, a conical spiral with concave sides results (Fig. 13.16J). If the downward movement accelerates more rapidly than the outward movement, a conical spiral with convex sides results (Fig. 13.16G). In *Of Growth and Form*, D'Arcy Thompson (1945) offers a most interesting discussion of the kinds of spiral growth seen in snails and other plants and animals.

As is so often the case in biological material, the relationships revealed by simple mathematical statements of directions and rates of change may tell us something important about the dynamics of a biological system, but so austerely that it requires genuine creative imagination to translate the mathematical symbols into the active process of living and meeting the emergencies that life involves. Consider the nature of the organisms within the spiral shells that have been described. A bilaterally symmetrical animal can fit into a plane spiral shell if it is properly oriented. But even if the aperture of the shell were a perfect circle, and all of the whorls were circular in cross section, the only way that a bilaterally symmetrical animal could be fitted into a conical spiral

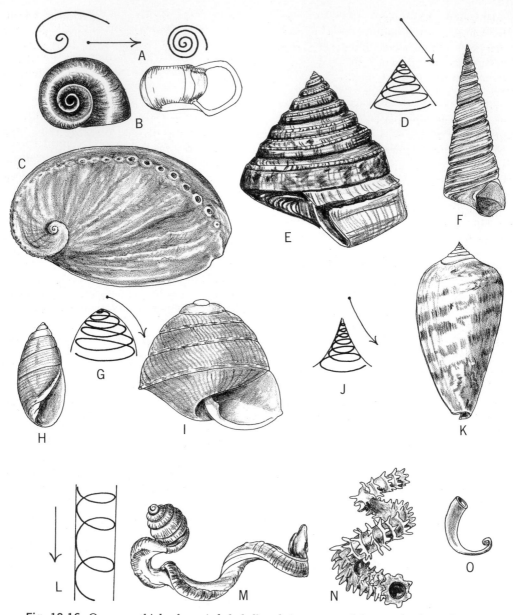

Fig. 13.16. One may think of a spiraled shell as being generated by a point located at the center of the last whorl and moving as the animal grows. The central point of the spiral is at the protoconch, the initial larval shell. A plane spiral (A) results when the generating point moves outward only. If it moves outward at a nearly constant rate, each whorl is of nearly the same diameter, as in *Helisoma* (B), while if it accelerates rapidly, a great increase in whorl breadth results, as in *Haliotus* (C). If the generating point moves downward as it moves outward, a conical spiral results. A straight-sided conical spiral (D) results when there is no acceleration or deceleration in the downward movement. Such straight-sided conical spirals may be relatively low and broad, as in *Pleurotomaria* (E) or high and narrow, as in

shell would be by twisting the body along the whorl, and the only way that the shell margin could be secreted would be by having the animal turn constantly with respect to the aperture. Snails do not behave this way, and, indeed, most conical snail shells would not permit any kind of bilaterally symmetrical animal to be fitted into them. As soon as gastropods began to grow conical spiral shells, they entered into a completely new and complex biological maze. Right and left sides must grow unequally, and in such a manner that a compact and manageable spiral results, if they are not to be handicapped by the shell. The achievement of the delicately balanced growth rates of whorl diameter, and of the outward and downward growth of the whorls as they coil, required for shells of acceptable design has been a remarkable biological phenomenon. An infinite variety of shell shapes results from slight changes in the rate and direction of growth, but for every one that produces a reasonably efficient shell, there are many that produce monstrosities. For example, if the growth of the whorl diameter does not keep pace with the outward and downward coiling, the shell falls apart as a spiral and becomes so unwieldy that the animal must, perforce, adapt its habits to its house. A few species have survived, despite such abnormalities (Fig. 13.16M,N).

In spite of all of the growth problems that the conical spiral shell introduced, it was more compact than a plane spiral

shell, and there are mechanical advantages that have apparently outweighed the disadvantages. At no time in geological history have plane spiral shells disappeared, but the conical spiral appeared early in gastropod history and is the predominant snail form today.

The next big event in gastropod history was the appearance of torsion. If our fossil record is adequate, it happened for the first time during the upper Cambrian. Torsion happens to modern gastropods when they reach the veliger stage. By this time the mantle has appeared, and a broad, ciliated region, the velum, forms the anterior end of the embryo. The body is curved, with both head and foot protruding from the mantle (Fig. 13.18D,E). The visceral hump has already begun to form a spiral. The whole visceral mass revolves 180°. It may take a few minutes, or far longer. In *Haliotus*, torsion occurs in two movements, a fast 90° twist, followed by a much slower second twist of 90°.

The results of torsion are drastic (Fig. 13.18A-C). Before torsion, the esophagus opens normally into the stomach, but after torsion, it comes into the stomach from behind. Before torsion, the mantle cavity, containing the gills and anus, is posterior, but after torsion it is anterior. Before torsion, the visceral nerves and ganglia form a simple loop, but after torsion they are twisted into a figure of eight. As the twist is counterclockwise, the left visceral nerve passes dorsal to the right. As the twist occurs between the pleural and parietal ganglia,

---

Turitella (F), depending on the ratio of outward to downward movement. If the outward movement of the generating point decelerates, a convex-sided conical spiral results (G), as seen in *Pupa* (H) and *Laoma* (I). If the outward movement accelerates, a concave-sided conical spiral results (J), as in the spire of *Conus* (K). Acceleration of the downward movement of the generating point (L) results in the whorls losing contact, as in *Siliquaria* (M) or *Cyclosaurus* (N). A plane spiral may also fall apart, if the whorls do not grow in diameter as rapidly as they grow outward, as seen in *Cylindrella* (O). Through such combinations of spiral patterns, the considerable variation in whorl diameter, sculpturing and pigmentation of the shell, the thousands of specifically different kinds of gastropod shells are formed. (B, after Walker, in Edmondson. H and I, after Suter. E, M, N, and O, after Cooke.)

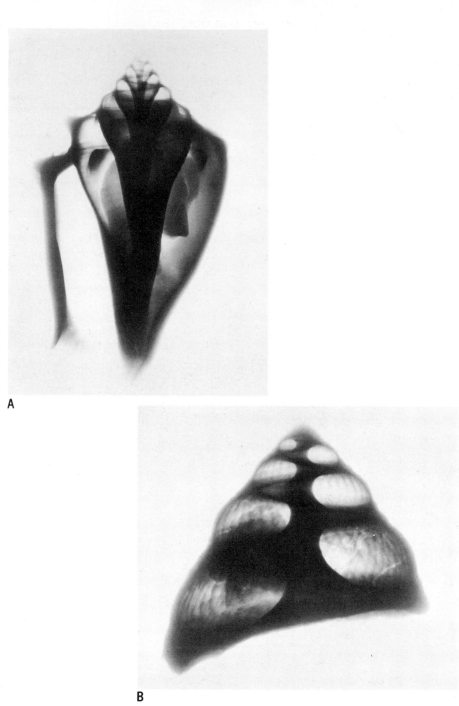

A

B

Fig. 13.17. X Rays of the Shells of Two Snails. A. *Strombus pugilis*. B. *Trochus olivaceous*. The relationship of the whorls of the shell become much more evident in X rays. The whorls wind around the central columella. Each whorl may make up the whole region external to the columella at each level, or whorls may overlap each other, as in the *Strombus*. In either case, however, the shell grows without modification of its external shape or its internal structure.

the pleural ganglia are not affected, but the left parietal is carried upward to become the supraparietal ganglion, while the right one is carried ventrally to become the infraparietal ganglion.

Are there advantages to this peculiar arrangement? There is evidence that there must be, for all of the gastropods that do not undergo torsion have died out, while the twisted ones have become highly successful. It may be that torsion is a mechanical side-effect of forming conical spirals, but this idea is not persuasive, as the first group of gastropods to undergo torsion were predominantly equipped with plane spiral shells. Gar-

stang (1928) has suggested that the veliger larva gains by torsion, as after torsion it can pull the velum into the shell and fall to the bottom if pursued by enemies. There are serious objections to this idea. As molluscan cilia are generally under nervous control the velum need not be retracted to stop swimming movements. Furthermore, torsion does not occur in other classes of molluscs but their larvae have been able to survive. The mantle cavity is quite plastic, and a far more simple solution would have been to expand the mantle cavity a little to accommodate the velum. If the larva does not profit from torsion, presumably

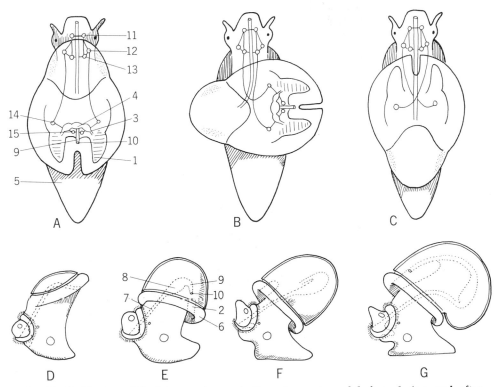

Fig. 13.18. Torsion. A-C. Scheme of organization of a gastropod before, during, and after torsion. Note that as the mantle cavity is brought forward, the visceral nerve trunks are twisted and the position of the heart is reversed. The general organization at C is that of the two-gilled prosobranchs belonging to the Archeogastropoda. D-G. Side view of the torsion of *Paludina vivipara*. (All after Naef.) 1, gill; 2, mantle cavity; 3, auricle; 4, ventricle; 5, foot; 6, mantle; 7, esophagus; 8, stomach; 9, intestine; 10, anus; 11, cerebral ganglia; 12, pleural ganglia; 13, pedal ganglia; 14, parietal ganglion; 15, visceral ganglia.

the adult must. Torsion brings the mantle cavity to the front of the body. As a result, water currents resulting from forward movement tend to bring water into the mantle cavity, while they work against water entering when the mantle cavity is behind. This would be especially important in fresh-water gastropods with the habit of moving against the current in a stream. But there are serious drawbacks to this idea also. Most gastropods are marine, and there is every reason to believe that this was true when the habit of torsion began, so orientation to water currents is probably not an important factor. Most gastropods move so slowly that currents set up by their own movements are not a very important factor. Besides, many snails have a narrow, tubular siphon for drawing water into the mantle cavity. In these snails, the opening of the mantle cavity is smaller, and any advantage coming from its anterior position is lost. As it stands, there is no really satisfactory explanation for torsion. Perhaps it is no more than a pleiotropic side-effect of some gene constellation that brought other and more important advantages. Be that as it may, there is much to show that torsion created problems.

The most obvious disadvantage of torsion is that the anus is brought directly over the head and threatens to foul the respiratory organs and the head sense organs. It is not surprising to find the first adaptational trend evoked by torsion involved attempts to get the sewer away from the front door. Evidences of this are seen in fossil forms and in some surviving forms that belong to the more primitive groups.

Torsion and the consequent anterior position of the mantle cavity gave gastropods a new look. They are no longer Protogastropoda, but Prosobranchia. The first prosobranchs are fossils from the upper Cambrian. For the next 200,000,000 years or so, until about the end of the Paleozoic, most prosobranchs belonged to

the order Archeogastropoda, characterized by a simple and direct solution of the sewage problem. The anus is bent upward, fitting into a special notch in the shell. As the shell grows, the anal notch becomes a slit band (selenizone). The most ancient prosobranchs were often flat spirals with conspicuous slit bands. (Fig. 13.19F), but then as now, there was considerable variation in shell form. In modern species with arrangements of this kind, respiratory currents enter the mantle cavity from in front, flow up between the gill filaments, and depart dorsally, past the anus, carrying away the fecal material (Fig. 13.20A). The site of the anus varies considerably in these gastropods. The anus may change position as the animal grows, fitting into a rather small notch at the margin of the shell (Fig. 13.19E), or it may remain in the original site with the slit band of the shell eventually sealing up as the animal grows, leaving the anus centrally placed (Fig. 13.19A-D), as in the keyhole limpets. *Haliotus* (Fig. 13.16C) has a series of openings in the selenizone.

Not all of the archeogastropods have a perforate shell, however. Many modern species have a solid shell, made possible by a new solution to the problem of feces disposal. The gill, auricle, and nephridium on the larval left (adult right) side are reduced and disappear. Why this adaptive tendency should have appeared is not clear, but when completed, a new routing of water through the mantle cavity becomes possible (Fig. 13.20B-D). Water enters on the left, flows over the persisting gill first, and then passes the anus and nephridiopore on its way out of the mantle cavity, sweeping the wastes away neatly enough. It is quite possible that this routing of water through the mantle cavity began before gill reduction, and itself served as a stimulus to reduction of the right gill.

Reduction and loss of the organs on the larval left side occur among some of the archeogastropods. The limpet, *Acmea*, for example, has a single gill, with water currents passing over the gill before reaching the anus and nephridiopore. The shell is imperforate, with neither a slit nor a hole for the anus. Some limpets have gone even farther, developing pallial gills in a secondary mantle cavity like the mantle cavity of chitons. Respiratory currents in these limpets are like those of chitons. Others have two gills, but with the right gill smaller, as in *Haliotus*. All of the archeogastropods, however, have two auricles. The auricle associated with the reduced gill is smaller, and where the gill has disappeared completely, the auricle is rudimentary.

Most gastropods with one gill have also lost the auricle associated with it. They belong to the Mesogastropoda, the largest gastropod order. Mesogastropods appeared first in the lower Ordovician, and may be considered at their peak today. Opisthobranchs and pulmonates are more modern forms that have been derived from the mesogastropods. As a part of the remarkable adaptive radiation of mesogastropods and the establishment of the opisthobranch and pulmonate stems, several important tendencies have appeared:

1. Many gastropods have further reduced the gill surface. The remaining left ctenidium becomes one-sided, is built into the mantle wall, and eventually may be reduced to a vascular area in the mantle wall. The vascularized wall of the mantle cavity then serves as the respiratory surface, acting as a water- or air-breathing lung.

2. Some gastropods undergo detorsion. This reverse movement occurs during development, and while it does not wholly eliminate the results of torsion, it greatly reduces them. Gastropods that have followed this line have no shells or reduced shells, and some have wholly lost the mantle cavity. In this case, the body surface is the site of respiratory exchange, and may bear simple or complex secondary gills.

3. A strong tendency to untwist the nervous system is evident. It grows naturally out of detorsion, but is also achieved by the centralization of the nervous system and the shortening of the visceral nerves.

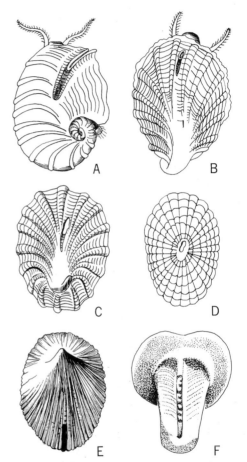

Fig. 13.19. A-D. Four stages in the metamorphosis of *Fissurella*, a keyhole limpet. It begins with a spiral shell and a slit-band. As new shell is laid down at the margin the slit-band is encircled, eventually coming to occupy a central position. Meanwhile the spire deteriorates, becoming a callosity near the aperture. E. *Emarginula*, a limpet with a marginal slit. F. A cast of *Salpingostoma*, a fossil form with a partially filled-in slit-band. (A-D, after Boutan. E, after Cooke. F, after Ulrich and Scofield.)

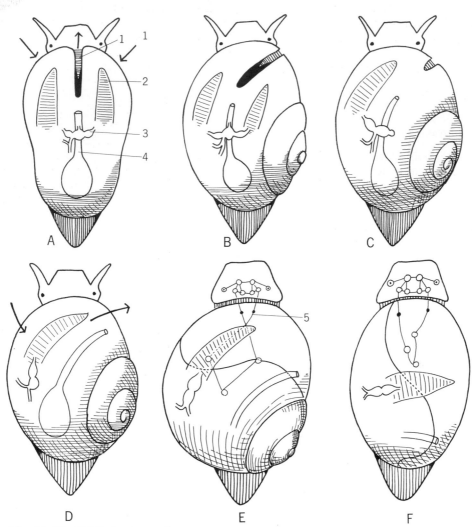

Fig. 13.20. Gill Reduction and Mantle Cavity Currents. **A.** The ancestral type of two-gilled prosobranch, with a slit-band and a plane spiral shell. Water enters the mantle cavity from both sides in front, and is discharged upward and forward. **B.** An archeogastropod with a slit-band and unequal gills. The right gill is smaller, and the shell has become somewhat conical. Water emerging from the mantle cavity no longer passes directly over the head. This type of organization is seen in *Pleurotomaria.* **C.** An archeogastropod with reduced slit-band and a single gill. The right gill is completely missing and the right auricle is greatly reduced, although still present as in *Trochus.* **D.** A mesogastropod. The slit-band is gone, and the heart has lost all traces of the right auricle, becoming more asymmetrically placed. Water enters only from the left side and emerges on the right, as in *Paludina.* **E.** an organism essentially like D, showing the streptoneurous type of nervous system, as thought to have been present in the ancestral forms leading to the opisthobranchs. **F.** An opisthobranch, showing the effects of detorsion. The shell opening now is toward the right, and the nervous system is detorted, as in *Bulla.* (All after Naef.) **1**, slit-band; **2**, gill; **3**, heart; **4**, intestine; **5**, visceral nerve cord.

The results of these evolutionary tendencies, and of those discussed previously, are reflected in the classification of the gastropods. At this time, we can have some confidence that, for the most part, major gastropod groups reflect significant and relatively homogeneous adaptive trends.

Classification

Subclass Protogastropoda. Wholly extinct gastropods showing no evidence of torsion; presumably with a posterior mantle cavity; shells conical, plane spirals, or conical spirals.

Order Cynostraca. Protogastropods with conical shells, showing no evidence of spiral coiling. Examples: *Palaeacmea* (Fig. 13.15A); *Scenella* (Fig. 13.15B).

Order Cochliostraca. Protogastropods with coiled shells. Example: *Pelagiella* (Fig. 13.15C).

Subclass Prosobranchia. Gastropods which undergo torsion, bringing gills, anus, and mantle cavity to the front; primitively with a pair of ctenidia, but usually with a single gill and auricle; primitively with a pair of nephridia, but generally with only the right nephridium retained; nervous system twisted into a figure-of-eight, which may be partially corrected by some concentration of the nerves and ganglia near the head.

Order Archeogastropoda (aspidobranchs). Prosobranchs with a primitive mantle cavity without gills, or containing a pair of ctenidia or a single ctendium; heart with a pair of auricles, although one may be reduced in size; primitively with a notch or slit in the shell for the anus and exhalant siphon, but with an imperforate shell when the ctenidia are reduced. Examples: ear shells (*Haliotus*, Fig. 13.16C); keyhole limpets (*Fissurella*, Fig. 13.19D); slit limpets (*Emarginula*, Fig. 13.19E); top shells (*Trochus*); neritas (*Nerita*); cat's eyes (*Turbo*).

Order Mesogastropoda (pectinobranchs). Prosobranchs with a single gill,

auricle, and nephridium; with or without an operculum; shell without a slit band or hole for the exhalant siphon and usually without a groove for an inhalant siphon; gill almost invariably one-sided and attached for its whole length to the wall of the mantle cavity (monopectinate); usually with a well-developed, sometimes pectinate, osphradium; sexes separate; male usually with a penis. This is the largest order of gastropods, including many marine, fresh-water, and operculate land snails. There are too many common genera to do more than list a few examples. Pelagic snails (*Janthina*, Fig. 13.23C); moon shells (*Natica*, Fig. 13.23D; *Polynices*); slipper shells (*Crepidula*, Fig. 13.23A); periwinkles (*Littorina*); worm shells (*Vermetus*); cowries (*Cypraea*); fresh-water snails of many kinds (*Valvata*, an exception with a bipectinate gill; *Campeloma*; *Vivipara*); pelagic heteropods (*Carinaria*; *Atlanta*).

Order Neogastropoda (stenoglossa). Prosobranchs like mesogastropods, but with a bipectinate osphradium; an unpaired esophageal gland, becoming a poison gland in some; a strongly concentrated nervous system; with a penis. Some examples are the boring murexes (*Murex*, *Thais*); mud snails (*Nassa*); whelks (*Buccineum*); conchs (*Busycon*, Fig. 13.28A); olive shells (*Olivo*); and cone shells (*Conus*, Fig. 13.24B).

Subclass Opisthobranchia. Marine gastropods with a single auricle and nephridium and with one or no ctenidium; often with surface gills; nervous system untwisted by detorsion and often relatively centralized; with a strong tendency toward shell reduction and a return toward bilateral symmetry.

Order Cephalaspidea. Opisthobranchs with a ctenidium and usually with a shell; male genital groove open; with a cephalic shield; usually, with a gastric shield for grinding. Example: *Bulla*, bubble shells.

Order Anaspidea. Opisthobranchs with the shell poorly developed or missing; with well-developed natatory parapodia; male genital groove open; with several gastric shields and a large radula with median tooth; ctenidium and jaws present; visceral hump attached along the foot. Example: Sea hares (*Aplysia*, Fig. 13.24D).

Order Thecosomata. Opisthobranchs with a variable shell development; with a mantle cavity, but with the gill usually reduced; with strongly developed, natatory epipodia; male genital groove open; nerve ganglia centralized and united. Example: *Clio.*

Order Gymnosomata. Opisthobranchs without a shell or mantle cavity; with gill behind heart; foot with parapodia; male genital groove open; nerve ganglia free. Example: *Clione.*

Order Acochlidiacea. Small opisthobranchs without shell, gill, or cephalic shield; with rhinophores; visceral mass distinct from foot; without jaws but with radula; without a gastric shield; with a nerve ring in front of the buccal mass. Example: *Acochlidium.*

Order Monostichoglossa. Jawless, herbivorous opisthobranchs with rhinophores; with one series of teeth in sac; male genital groove closed over; never with cnidosacs containing nematocysts; nerve ganglia but little fused. Example: *Styliger.*

Order Nudibranchiata. Opisthobranchs without a shell in adults; with visceral mass attached along the foot; without parapodia; with male genital groove closed over; with a nerve ring behind the buccal mass. Example: *Doris*; *Eolis* (Fig. 13.27E).

Order Notaspidea. Opisthobranchs with the shell usually internal; without parapodia or gastric shield, but some with chitinous spines; with one gill; male genital groove closed over; radula variable, but without radula sac. Example: *Pleurobranchia.*

Subclass Pulmonata. Predominantly terrestrial and fresh-water snails without ctenidia, the mantle cavity being modified as a respiratory sac, used for air or water breathing; with one auricle and nephrid-

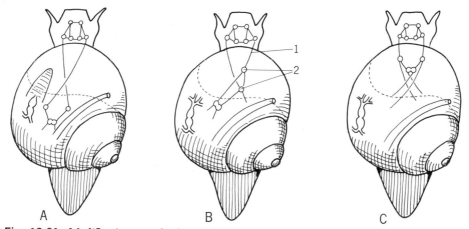

Fig. 13.21. Modifications involved in pulmonate development. Pulmonates are thought to have arisen from typical one-gilled prosobranchs, like the one shown in A. Loss of the gill, coupled with vascularization of the mantle cavity wall, converts the mantle cavity into a lung. The lung vessels have the same relationship to the heart as the gill vessels. Meanwhile, the visceral nerve is somewhat shortened, partly untwisting the visceral trunks, as seen in B. Further shortening of the visceral nerve trunks results in straightening the nervous system, resulting in the short-looped, euthyneurous condition shown in C, which is characteristic of many pulmonates. (After Naef.) 1, visceral nerve; 2, parietal ganglion.

ium; nervous system bilaterally symmetrical as a result of the concentration of nerve tissue to form complex brain; almost universally without an operculum; shell sometimes lacking; hermaphroditic, producing yolky ova that develop without passing through larval stages.

Order Stylommatophora. Almost exclusively land pulmonates with an anterior pair of tactile and probably chemoreceptive tentacles, and a posterior pair of tentacles with eyes at the tips; usually with a common genital antrum, into which both male and female organs open. Examples: Land snails, such as *Helix, Polygyra, Succinea,* and *Zonitoides;* slugs such as *Arion* and *Limax* (Fig. 13.28B).

Order Basommatophora. Predominantly aquatic pulmonates found in fresh-water, and rarely in marine, habitats; with a single pair of tentacles; usually with separate male and female gonopores. Examples: fresh-water snails, such as *Lymnea, Helisoma* (Fig. 13.16B); and *Physa,* and a few salt-water forms, such as *Melampus.*

GASTROPOD ANATOMY AND PHYSIOLOGY

Gastropods have undergone a remarkable adaptive radiation. Some are pelagic and others benthonic; they have remarkably diversified food habits, and have spread to all kinds of marine and fresh-water habitats. They are one of the few invertebrate groups to successfully invade land. In the process, every organ system has responded to selective pressures and become modified in one or another group of gastropods. The group is so varied that only a few of the most important points can be mentioned here.

Shell and External Form. The most obvious external feature of most gastropods is the shell, usually coiled and often beautifully colored and marked. The shell is extremely variable. The thousands of species can usually be recognized by shell characters alone. Identification is not

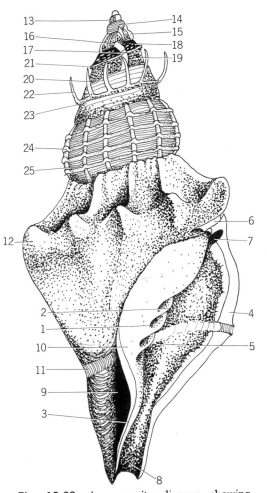

Fig. 13.22. A composite diagram showing some features of gastropod shells. (After Turner, from Shrock and Twenhofel.) The last whorl is the body whorl; the remaining whorls compose the spire. *Shell parts:* 1, inner lip, composed of 2, parietal lip and 3, columellar lip; 4, outer lip; 5, aperture; 6, sutural canal; 7, anal canal; 8, siphonal canal; 9, umbilicus; 10, callus (parietal shield); 11, selenizone; (slit-band); 12, node. *Ornamentation:* 13, pitted sculpture; 14, spiral striae; 15, boss; 16, axial costae; 17, varix; 18, beaded sculpture; 19, reticulate sculpture: 20, suture; 21, carinate ridge; 22, spine; 23, spiral ridge; 24, spiral costae; 25, spiral threads.

easy, however, and requires an extensive vocabulary, a little of which is summarized in Fig. 13.22.

The shells present some interesting problems. Some of the characteristics of shells seem functionally insignificant, but are constant for a species and appear to be genetically fixed. The mechanisms responsible for such functionless, or apparently functionless, characteristics' becoming constant within a species are not understood, and considerable work is needed along these lines. Most gastropods have a dextral shell (coiled clockwise), but some have a sinistral shell (coiled counterclockwise), and a few species may have either kind of shell. Dextral shells are easily recognized. When the shell is held with the spire up and the aperture facing the observer, the aperture is on the right. Shells are oriented in this way for study and measurement.

Shell formation begins in the larvae. It is at first a simple cap. Later it forms a plane spiral, which usually changes gradually into a conical spiral. The first embryonic whorls of the shell are the protoconch, and are often sharply set off from the rest of the shell by differences in sculpturing or in coiling. Each whorl of the shell meets the next whorl in a suture. The last or body whorl contains the aperture, through which the head and foot are extended. The aperture varies greatly in shape, influenced by the shape of the shell, the presence or absence of an inhalant siphon or anal slit, and the extent to which the mantle is reflected over its margins.

Limpets, ear shells, and slipper shells are flat; this form is characteristic of sedentary species that cling to rocks. Some flattened shells consist of a few very broad whorls, but others have lost their spiral character and are cup-shaped, resembling the cup-like protogastropods. All modern species with this kind of shell, however, begin life as definitely spiraled, snail-like juveniles, losing the spiral form as new shell is added during growth (Fig. 13.19A-D). When the shell is cup-shaped, the body is less firmly attached, for the muscle that extends up along the ordinarily spiraled columella of the shell must hold it without the aid of spiraling. Some of these have an inner partition of variable shape (Fig. 13.23A,B), which holds the body firmly in the uncoiled shell. The attachment muscles are then somewhat reduced.

The shell is a mixed blessing. It provides protection, but at the expense of adding weight. A strong tendency toward the reduction of unnecessary shell weight is seen in many of the gastropod groups. The opisthobranchs show this most clearly. The shell is reduced in association with detorsion, and the amount of detorsion is usually correlated with the amount of shell reduction. They are characterized by shell reduction and loss of spiraling; in some cases, the shell is completely lost. These trends are associated with increased mobility, for many opisthobranchs are pelagic, swimming by means of parapodia or epipodia. Others, like the nudibranchs, have greatly reduced shells or no shells but have retained the creeping habit. The shell is a greater burden on land, and land gastropods usually have a very thin shell. Many land pulmonates have greatly reduced shells; the land slugs probably represent a final step in an adaptational line tending toward reduced shell weight. Even creeping, aquatic snails sometimes have methods of reducing shell weight or making it less awkward to handle. The visceral hump sometimes withdraws from the uppermost whorls, which are broken off or drop off. Neritas, cowries, and olive shells reduce weight by resorption of the inner shell partitions. This has an added advantage, for the tight coils of the viscera relax as they conform to the larger inner space.

Unless the shell is considerably reduced, the visceral hump is completely enclosed, and all that can be seen is the head and foot. The head is generally well developed, and is distinctive The mouth is more or less terminal, and nearly all gastropods have a pair of tentacles, primitively containing eyes near their bases. Land pulmonates and some opisthobranchs have lost their tentacles, and in others the tentacles are fused together to form cephalic shields. The tentacles are important as chemoreceptors. In some opisthobranchs, the second pair of tentacles are rhinophores, with a large chemoreceptive region. As might be expected, the activity of the animal is related to the development of the head and cephalic sense organs. The head is less developed in sedentary species, but none have a head as simplified as the chiton. It is probable that the head of gastropods is more like the head of the primitive molluscs than is the case in chitons, for there is good reason to believe that the first molluscs had a pair of cephalic tentacles. The chiton head is probably simplified as a result of a long history of sedentary habits.

The foot is a ventral creeping organ in its primitive form. It is somewhat reminiscent of the creeping sole of some of the flatworms. Certainly it performs a similar task, and is subject to similar adaptive trends. It represents the end product of the trends seen in flatworms, for the larger flatworms depend less and less upon cilia for movement, and more and more upon muscle. The highly developed musculature of flatworms, however, is simple when compared with the foot musculature of molluscs, Muscle strands run in all directions, permitting a variety of movements. As in flatworms, an important part of the foot's work is secretion. A rich supply of mucous glands provides slime for lubrication. Proso-

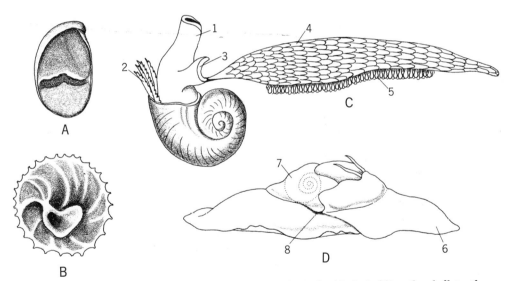

Fig. 13.23. A. Shell of *Crepidula*, showing inner shelf which aids in holding the shell to the body. B. Shell of *Crucibulum spinosum*, the cup and saucer limpet, showing another arrangement for holding the flattened shell to the body. C. *Janthina*, with a float on which eggs are carried. The float is secreted by the foot. D. A *Natica* in movement. *Natica* lives in soft sand, and has a very large foot with a propodium that covers much of the shell, serving as a sand plow. (C, after Quoy and Gaimard, from Cooke. D, after Schiemenz, from Pelseneer, in Lankester.) 1, proboscis; 2, gill; 3, foot; 4, float; 5, eggs; 6, propodium; 7, shell covered by posterior part of foot; 8, exhalant opening.

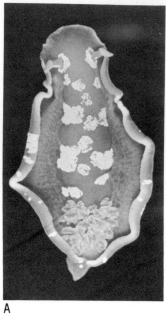

A

B

C

Fig. 13.24. Some Representative Gastropods. **A.** *Hexabranchus aureomarginatus*, an opistho-branch. Notice the rhinophores at the anterior end and the posterior gills. **B.** A textile cone, *Conus textile*, as it appears in active movement. Notice the siphon and foot. The cone shells are dangerous, as the radular teeth contain a poison. **C.** *Ariolimax columbianus*, a land slug.

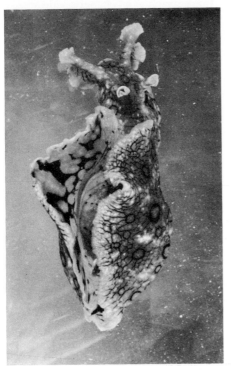

D

E

Notice the small mantle, within which the lung cavity lies. D. *Aplysia dactylomela*, a sea hare, one of the swimming opisthobranchs. E. *Polygyra*, one of the terrestrial pulmonates. Note the two pairs of tentacles, characteristic of the land pulmonates. (A, B, and D, courtesy of the Smithsonian Institution. C and E, courtesy of General Biological Supply Co.)

branchs and opisthobranchs usually have a large, anterior mucous gland, which empties into a median furrow. Mucus spreads over the foot surface from the furrow. Pulmonates have a dorsal mucous gland, which opens above the anterior border of the foot. Some terrestrial pulmonates also have mucous glands at the posterior end of the foot. The mucus produced is different in quality, hardening on contact with air or water. Some snails use this mucus to spin a filament from which the animal can suspend itself. The pelagic snail, *Janthina*, uses the secretions of the foot gland for an entirely different purpose. It is filled with air bubbles, making a float on which the eggs are attached, and which suspends the animal in the water (Fig. 13.23C).

Short, more or less rhythmic muscular waves are usually used to propel snails, but foot movements become a great deal more highly organized in some species. In *Littorina* and some land operculates, the foot is divided into functional right and left sides by a longitudinal furrow. The sides of the foot move forward alternately, so the animal skates over the surface. The foot is sometimes divided into an anterior propodium, a middle mesopodium, and a posterior metapodium (Fig. 13.23D). The propodium of *Melampus* is sharply set off by a deep transverse groove, and the animal moves by extending the propodium, attaching it, and pulling the rest of the foot after it. The propodium of species living in soft sand is usually much enlarged, and serves as a sand-plow. The rest of the foot is very broad, and the animal slides over the sand without sinking in.

Usually, the mesopodium is not separated from the metapodium by external grooves. The metapodium forms the back of the foot, and may contain special glands or other structures. An important task for the metapodium of prosobranchs is the secretion of an operculum. The operculum is often horny, but is sometimes composed of both calcareous material and conchiolin. It is a trap door, brought into position in the aperture by the withdrawal of the head and foot into the shell. Prosobranchs with flattened shells, like the limpets, do not withdraw in this manner, and the operculum has lost its usefulness. In many cases it has completely disappeared in adults, although one is formed by the young animal. The operculum is almost universally missing among opisthobranchs and pulmonates. The operculum first appears during early development, and grows with the organism by the addition of material at the margin, usually forming concentric or spiral growth lines. A curious and incomprehensible phenomenon is noted. When the opercular growth lines are spiral, they invariably wind in a direction opposite to the coiling of the shell. Nevertheless, there is a very close correlation between the rate of opercular growth and the growth of the aperture, so that the operculum fits the aperture with remarkable exactitude.

It is not uncommon for the foot to develop lateral outgrowths of one kind or another. Parapodia are outgrowths of the ventral margins of the foot, and epipodia are outgrowths of the lateral surface of the foot (Fig. 13.25A-C). They are especially well developed in opisthobranchs, where they serve as fins in swimming species (Fig. 13.25E). Heteropods are pelagic prosobranchs, whose evolutionary development has more or less paralleled that of opisthobranchs. The shell and operculum are reduced, and the mantle is progressively reduced, until in some species it is completely lost. Heteropods are characterized by varying degrees of detorsion, and a tendency to return to bilateral symmetry (Fig. 13.25F). Some of the pelagic prosobranchs, like opisthobranchs, swim with the aid of epipodia.

Digestive Tract. Gastropod adaptive radiation has resulted in remarkably varied eating habits, and as the digestive

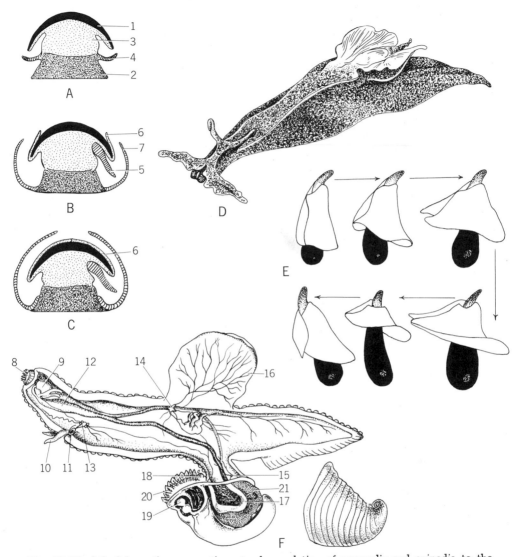

Fig. 13.25. A-C. Schematic cross sections, to show relation of parapodia and epipodia to the foot, and the enclosure of the shell by mantle folds. **D.** The sea hare, *Aplysia*, a swimming opisthobranch. **E.** Swimming movements of an opisthobranch, *Akera bullata*. **F.** *Carinaria*, a typical heteropod. It swims with the foot upward, in the position shown. The shell has been removed from the visceral mass. (A-C, after Lang. D, after Boulenger. E, after Morton and Holme. F, after Souleyet, from Pelseneer, in Lankester.) **1**, shell; **2**, foot; **3**, visceral mass; **4**, epipodium; **5**, parapodium; **6**, mantle fold; **7**, gill; **8**, mouth; **9**, odontophore; **10**, cephalic tentacles; **11**, eye; **12**, esophagus; **13**, cerebropleural ganglian; **14**, pedal ganglion; **15**, visceral ganglion; **16**, pedal fin; **17**, stomach; **18**, anus; **19**, heart; **20**, ctenidium; **21**, digestive gland.

tract is modified in accordance with the kind of food eaten and the way it is obtained the digestive system is an extremely variable one. Some gastropods, like *Diodora*, are microphagous feeders, scraping bits of food from rocks, sponges, or other surfaces, and have digestive systems that are rather primitive in nature. Some are macrophagous feeders, cropping

bits of plants or feeding on animal prey. There is little relationship between the groupings used for classification and feeding habits. Evidently carnivorous and other dietary habits have developed independently in a number of gastropod groups. In the absence of consistent adaptive lines, only a general discussion of adaptive trends can be undertaken, and

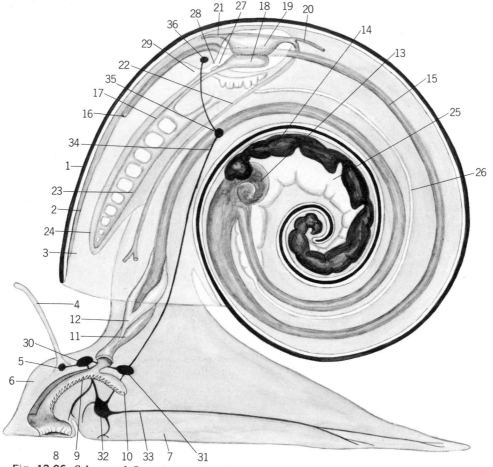

Fig. 13.26. Scheme of Organization of a Gastropod. *External features:* 1, shell; 2, mantle; 3, mantle cavity; 4, tentacle; 5, eye; 6, head; 7, foot. *Digestive tract:* 8, mouth; 9, radula; 10, radular sac; 11, esophagus; 12, salivary glands; 13, stomach; 14, digestive gland; 15, intestine; 16, anus. *Circulatory system:* 17, efferent branchial vessel; 18, auricle; 19, ventricle; 20, posterior aorta; 21, anterior aorta; 22, cephalic artery; 23, afferent branchial vessel; 24, gill. *Urogenital system:* 25, gonad; 26, gonoduct; 27, nephrostome; 28, renopericardial canal; 29, nephridiopore. *Nervous system:* 30, cerebral ganglion; 31, pleural ganglion; 32, pedal ganglion; 33, pedal nerve trunk; 34, visceral nerve; 35, parietal ganglion; 36, visceral ganglion.

the many exceptions will, of necessity, be ignored.

The most important equipment associated with the buccal cavity is concerned with the procurement and preliminary processing of food. The jaws, radula, and various glands vary in character and are developed or missing in accordance with the eating habits. Horny jaws, ridged and sculptured in patterns characteristic of species, are common in herbivores. Most carnivores lack jaws entirely, depending on the radula for food fragmentation. Opisthobranchs, however, are exceptions, for both carnivores and herbivores have large, paired jaws. Herbivorous prosobranchs usually have paired jaws, located near the mouth at the sides of the buccal cavity. Terrestrial pulmonates, on the other hand, usually have one median jaw on the roof of the buccal cavity.

Carnivores usually capture prey with the aid of a proboscis, with the radula at its tip. Proboscis form varies greatly. As in flatworms, the proboscis is formed by the infolding of the body wall to form a proboscis chamber (Fig. 13.27A,B). In general, the carnivores have fewer, larger radular teeth than herbivores, and snails with poison glands have hollow teeth filled with poison (Fig. 13.27D). In these forms, the proboscis is a formidable weapon.

A number of snails bore through the shells of oysters or other molluscs to obtain food. Oyster drills and their allies consume incredible numbers of oysters each year, and are important pests from an economic point of view. Boring is not accomplished by the abrasive action of the radula alone. A spot on the shell of the prey is soaked with a secretion from glands in the foot or proboscis. The secretion, probably a chelating agent, softens the shell so the radular rasp is more effective. Throughout the boring process the shell is alternately soaked with secretion and rasped by the radula until an opening is made. The unprotected oyster is laid out, meat on the table, to be carved into small pieces by the radula.

The glands associated with the buccal cavity vary in form and in function. Usually a single pair of salivary glands occurs, with ducts that pass through or outside of the nerve ring. The salivary glands of carnivorous prosobranchs tend to be asymmetrical, although the reason for this is not understood. Many of the opisthobranchs have more than one pair of salivary glands. The primitive salivary glands secrete mucus, and are characteristic of the forms which feed on small particles scraped up by the radula. The mucus lubricates the radula apparatus and the jaws, when they are present, and traps small particles for swallowing. Other substances, with specialized functions, are often added to the mucus, however. Some carnivorous gastropods, like *Dolium*, secrete sulfuric acid, which attacks calcareous material. The saliva of *Aplysia* contains amylase and proteolytic enzymes, and the saliva of *Murex*, a carnivore, contains a dipeptidase. Salivary enzymes are probably important in most gastropods that have a gastric mill of some kind, helping in fragmentation and preliminary processing of the food.

Snails have a long esophagus, for after torsion it enters the posterior end of the stomach. It generally contains a ciliated food groove in microphagous feeders, down which the mucous string containing food particles passes, and it is more muscular in macrophagous feeders, on the whole. Two major types of specializations are found in the esophagus, chambers for the storage or treatment of food, and glands used for the procurement or treatment of food. Not much is known of the functions of esophageal secretions. Not all of the esophageal glands are homologous. A pair of glandular pouches near the front end of the esophagus is found in many archeogastropods, while in mesogastropods and opisthobranchs, a single, median caecum or gland is often present.

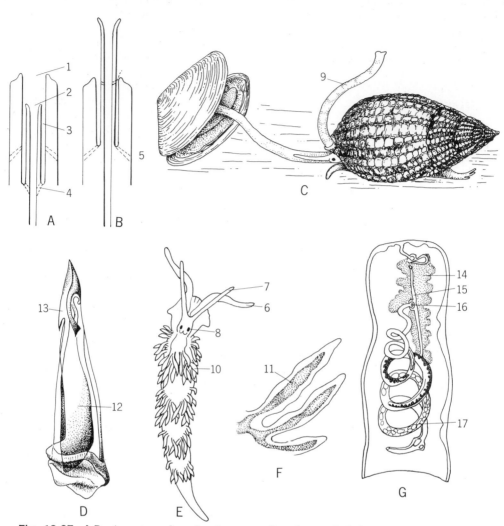

Fig. 13.27. A-B. A gastropod proboscis, retracted and extended. Note the fibrous bands which stop the withdrawal and extrusion at predetermined points. C. A *Nassarius* feeding on a dead bivalve, *Tellina*. Note the long proboscis and the nearly equally long siphon. D. The hollow tooth of a poisonous cone shell. Poison collects in the tooth, and enters prey when the barb breaks off. E. *Eolis*, a nudibranch, with cerata containing extensions of the liver. F. Several cerata, showing the liver branches extending into them. G. *Entoconcha mirabilis*, a parasitic gastropod in position in the host sea cucumber. The mouth is imbedded in the haemal sinus on the intestine of the host. (A and B, after Lankester, from Pelseneer, in Lankester. C, after Graham and Fretter. D, after Cooke. E-F, after Alder and Hancock, from Pierce, in Brown. G, after Bauer.) *Proboscis:* 1, opening of proboscis; 2, mouth; 3, proboscis chamber; 4, fibers preventing further withdrawal; 5, fibers preventing further extrusion. *External features:* 6, oral tentacle; 7, rhinophore; 8, eye; 9, siphon; 10, cerata; 11, extension of liver. *Tooth:* 12, poison duct; 13, barb. *Entoconcha:* 14, host intestine; 15, haemal vessel of host; 16, mouth of *Entoconcha*; 17, embryos.

508

In toxiglossans, like *Conus*, it is this gland which secretes the poison introduced into the teeth.

The esophagus of many gastropods is dilated to form a crop, where food is stockpiled and where some preliminary digestion may occur. A crop is common in carnivores as well as herbivores, but more is known of the events taking place in the crop of herbivorous species. Food material entering the crop is mixed with saliva and any esophageal secretions that may be formed, and enzymes that are present begin to act. This preliminary digestion is preparatory, serving principally to break up cellulose and so fragment cells, releasing protoplasmic compounds for further digestion. Cellulase has been recovered from *Helix* and *Limnea*, and is probably present in the secretions of many herbivorous snails. The beta-glucosides needed to continue cellulose digestion are present in *Helix*, and may also be widespread in herbivores. It is common for the crop to contain chitinous plates or teeth, and to have muscular walls whose contractions grind food particles against the crop armature. In such forms, the crop assumes the functions of a gizzard. Some carnivores swallow prey whole; in these the crop also functions as a gizzard.

Food passes from the esophagus into the stomach. The gastropod stomach works in close association with a pair of huge digestive glands. Stomach structure varies greatly. Carnivores usually have a simple, saccate stomach. Herbivores, however, have stomachs of complex structure. The primitive type of stomach, with a sorting device, style sac, and grinding region has been described (p. 466). These three stomach regions are differently developed in gastropods with different eating habits. The sorting region is characteristic of microphagous species only, while the style sac and grinding region are more widely distributed. Of these, the grinding region is the more variable, for it is usually missing in macrophagous herbivores with a gizzard, but present in species with unarmored crops.

The function of the style sac in microphagous feeders of primitive habits has been described. Many ciliary feeders and some microphagous herbivores have a transparent rod in the style sac, attached to a posterior, pyloric stomach chamber. This rod is a crystalline style, composed of a protein matrix on which amylase is adsorbed. It is found only in species that digest proteins intracellularly, for if the stomach were to contain proteolytic enzymes the crystalline style itself would be digested. Cilia rotate the crystalline style, rubbing it on the food, or scraping some of the material off against the cuticular grinding surfaces of the stomach. This mixes amylase with the food, so stimulating starch digestion.

Primitive molluscs have paired digestive glands. Most gastropods have a pair of digestive glands, but it is a mismatched pair as a result of unequal right and left sides associated with coiling. In dextral species, the left digestive gland is larger, while the right is larger in sinistral species. The openings of the digestive glands into the stomach vary greatly. Primitively, each gland opens through a separate duct, but the ducts are sometimes united, and in many species the duct openings are subdivided. The digestive glands play an important role in digestion. Herbivores with a crystalline style cannot digest proteins extracellularly, and small particles enter the ducts of the digestive glands, eventually reaching cells where they are taken into food vacuoles for intracellular digestion and absorption. The digestive glands of *Helix* secrete cellulase, which reaches the food in the crop, where cells are mechanically triturated and cellulose digestion further breaks them down. Absorptive cells in the digestive gland eventually take up small fragments for intracellular digestion. Even in species where digestion is entirely extracellular, most food absorption occurs in the digestive glands. The digestive glands of carnivores, for example, secrete proteolytic enzymes that act in the stomach, but most of the food is absorbed in the digestive gland.

A most remarkable adaptive line is found among the nudibranchs. Some nudibranchs have run-of-the-mill digestive glands, wholly contained within the general visceral mass. In others, the huge digestive glands have long diverticula that extend out into the surface gills (cerata). Glandular tips at the end of the diverticula secrete protease and diastase, and some intracellular digestion of glycogen may occur. These species are carnivorous, feeding in part on Cnidaria. When Cnidaria are eaten, most of their nematocysts, are digested, but the microbasic mastigophores are not attacked and eventually reach the end of the diverticula. Here they are passed to chambers at the ends of the cerata, where they form a protective organ for the mollusc (Fig. 13.27F).

After torsion, the intestine emerges from the front end of the stomach. Not much is known of the details of intestinal function. Some food absorption appears to occur, but the main task is the condensation of the feces. The intestinal wall contains many goblet cells that secrete mucus, helping to compact the fecal material. Some water absorption also occurs, and the feces are well formed when released. Some carnivores have relatively short intestines, but herbivores process a great deal more food and release more feces. They have a long intestine, often coiled, the increased length presumably helping to process the larger amounts of material. A prominent dorsal fold, the typhlosole, usually projects into the lumen. The typhlosole increases intestinal surface and, where cilia are important in moving food along, helps to move fecal material. It probably has other functions, but more work is needed to define them.

The intestine ends in the anus, which is placed at different points in different types of gastropods. It is far forward and slightly to the right in dextral prosobranchs. When the slit band disappears and respiratory currents sweep across the mantle cavity, the anus is displaced further to the right. Opisthobranchs arose from prosobranch ancestors and have a single gill. Primitively, the anus is lateral in position, but detorsion brings the anus back to a posterior position in some opisthobranchs. A rectal gland, placed somewhat in front of the anus, is found in some carnivores. Its function is uncertain. The intestine of many archeogastropods passes through the pericardial cavity as well as the perivisceral coelom, in much the same manner as in clams. In some of these, the intestine passes through the ventricle of the heart.

Parasitism is not common among gastropods, but where it occurs it has had profound effects upon the digestive system. The parasitic Pyramidellidae have no radula or jaws, but have a highly developed proboscis, used to attach to the host and pump in body fluids. They vary markedly in degree of parasitic adaptation, some showing few morphological changes, and others being greatly modified. *Entoconcha* is a worm-like snail which has no shell and lives with its proboscis permanently attached to the haemal plexus of the host sea cucumber (Fig. 13.27G).

Respiration. The primitive respiratory arrangements and the modifications associated with torsion have been described previously (p. 494). Torsion brings the mantle cavity forward, placing paired ctenidia over the head, with the anus situated between the gills. This arrangement is characteristic of the dibranchiate archeogastropods. In other archeogastropods, the right ctenidium is lost. These monobranchiate archeogastropods, however, retain some traces of the right auricle. The mesogastropods have a similar gill arrangement, but have lost all evidences of the right auricle.

The next important trend involves the reduction of the left ctenidium. It becomes attached along its whole axis to the mantle wall. In the primitive ctenidium, gill filaments are free of the mantle wall, and occur on both sides of the axis. In gill reduction, the filaments, like the axis, become attached to the mantle wall, and the filaments on one side of the axis disappear entirely. The one-sided, adherent gill is termed monopectinate. The final stages of gill reduction involve the disappearance of the remaining gill filaments, with the mantle wall coming to contain the vascular elements previously contained in the gill filaments. In such cases, the mantle wall becomes the site of respiratory exchange, functioning as an air- or water-breathing lung. This arrangement is characteristic of the pulmonates, but also occurs in some prosobranchs.

The course of gill reduction is similar as the dibranchiate snails become monobranchiate and as the monobranchiate snails develop a lung. In the dibranchiate *Haliotus*, the right ctenidium is somewhat smaller than the left. The right ctenidium of *Scissurella* is monopectinate, with gill filaments on one side of the axis and adherent to the mantle wall.

Ctenidial reduction in monobranchiate gastropods appears to be favored by exposure to air. Many mesogastropods living in the intertidal zone and alternately submerged in water and exposed to air have greatly reduced left ctenidia, and in some the ctenidium is wholly lost. In these forms a true lung, like a lung of the pulmonates, has developed. This has occured independently in several prosobranch families. The pulmonate prosobranchs can be recognized by the large opening into the mantle cavity, contrasting with the narrow opening, the pneumostome, characteristic of the pulmonates.

As detorsion and shell reduction occur, opisthobranchs tend to lose their mantle cavity. Some have a single, reduced ctenidium and a single auricle, demonstrating that they have arisen from prosobranch ancestral stocks. Many, however, have no ctenidium, depending on the body surface or secondary gills derived from the body surface for respiratory exchange.

Pulmonates have an anterior mantle cavity with highly vascular walls. Blood returns to a single auricle, giving evidence of their descent from monobranchiate prosobranchs. The mantle is closely pressed to the right side of the foot, leaving only a small opening, the pneumostome, through which air enters and leaves (Fig. 13.28B). Muscles in the floor and walls of the mantle cavity contract to pump air in and out of the lung, and the pneumostome opens and closes rhythmically (p. 495). The most remarkable lung development is seen in janellids. Tubular invaginations of the lung wall form trachea that extend into the body, penetrating the blood sinuses where oxygen absorption can occur with maximum efficiency. It is evident that the pulmonate lung developed as an adaptation to terrestrial life, but it has not restricted the pulmonates to land. Many have returned to fresh water, and a few to the sea. Some of these surface to breathe air; some have the pneumostome located at the end of a snorkel so air breathing can occur while the animal is submerged; still others pump water in and out of the lung. In water-breathers, secondary gills have tended to develop.

Excretion. Primitive gastropods have a pair of U-shaped metanephridia, open to the pericardial cavity through nephrostomes. The right nephridium is also used for the release of gametes. All of the archeogastropods except the neritas retain a pair of nephridia, but in all other gastropods the right nephridium is sharply reduced, remaining only in the form of a gonopericardial canal. This canal connects the gonoduct and pericardial cavity, or

has become an integral part of the gonoduct itself.

The nephrostomes of archeogastropods
are functional. Pericardial glands on the
wall of the heart or the pericardium appear to collect and process nitrogenous
wastes. The products pass from the pericardial cavity into the nephridium for
further treatment. In other gastropods the
nephrostome is functionally unimportant,
although the nephridium retains a connection with the pericardial cavity by way
of a renopericardial pore, the vestige of
the nephrostome. The canal connecting
the renopericardial pore with the main
body of the nephridium is the remnant of
the upper part of the nephridium, but
often empties into the nephridium near
the ureter. For some as yet unexplained
reason, pelagic gastropods tend to have
more tubular nephridia while creeping
gastropods tend to have more compact
nephridia.

As the nephrostome becomes smaller
and wastes from the coelomic cavity become an insignificant part of the excretory material, the nephridial wall becomes
the important site for excretion of wastes.
This "glandular" region of the nephridium is amplified, providing adequate excretory surface. In compact nephridia, the
glandular wall is very complexly folded,
assuming an alveolar structure. The
nephridium loses its tubular appearance,
becoming a fairly compact kidney. The
blood rather than the coelomic fluid transports wastes to the nephridium, and the
glandular part of the nephridium comes
to have a close relationship with the
haemocoel. In many gastropods, the
greater part of the blood circulates in
the nephridial wall on its way to the
gills.

Gastropods are the only molluscs to
establish themselves on land successfully,
and one of the two groups that adapted
to fresh water. Evidently they have some
capacity for the regulation of water and
salt concentration not shared by other
molluscs. As a result, their excretory physiology is of considerable interest.

When some marine gastropods are
placed in dilute sea water, they promptly
swell, showing very little control over
water intake. *Doris*, a nudibranch, and
Onchidium, a slug-like marine pulmonate,
swell and show no sign of size regulation
in 24 hours. *Aplysia* also swells in dilute
sea water, but later excretes up to 37 per
cent of its body salt, apparently through
the body surface, thus eliminating water
to regain normal volume.

Water regulation by means of salt excretion is far from perfect, but may be
a step toward adaptation to fresh-water
life. The blood concentration of fresh-
water snails and clams is distinctly lower
than in marine species. *Limnea* blood, for
example, has an osmotic concentration
equal to about 0.43 per cent NaCl. The
urine it excretes contains about 0.3 per
cent NaCl. Evidently salt is a precious
material. Adjustment to salt lost in excretion is made possible by a remarkable
capacity for selective salt absorption
through the body surface. *Limnea* can
actively absorb salt from 0.01 Ringer
solution.

Land snails have considerably more
salts in their blood than do fresh-water
snails but have poor mechanisms for controlling the concentration. A heavy rain
may reduce the salt concentration of the
blood by over a half. Water loss resulting
from excretion is held to a minimum by
excretion of uric acid (p. 470) and by a
few adaptations that reduce evaporation
at the body surface. Hibernating or estivating snails, for example, secrete a partition over the shell aperture, thus reducing
water loss during inactivity.

Circulatory System. The arrangement
of the primitive circulatory system has
been described. Paired ctenidia, located
in a posterior mantle cavity, drain into a
pair of auricles, and an anteriorly directed
aorta leads from the ventricle. After torsion, however, the auricles lie in front of

the ventricle, and the aorta extends posteriorly. This is the arrangement found in dibranchiate archeogastropods. As the right ctenidium dwindles and is eventually lost, the right auricle dwindles with it, although the monobranchiate archeogastropods retain some vestiges of a right auricle. In prosobranchs, however, all traces of the right auricle have been lost. The left auricle drains blood from the left ctenidium and the heart retains its position, with the ventricle discharging into a posteriorly directed aorta. This arrangement is retained in the pulmonates, although the auricle receives blood from the vascular mantle wall rather than a ctenidium. Among opisthobranchs, detorsion returns the auricle to a posterior position, but they have a single auricle and have evidently arisen from mesogastropod stocks.

Blood returning from the ctenidia, secondary gills, or lung is oxygenated, so the heart is an arterial heart, pumping blood to tissues for the distribution of oxygen and pick-up of carbon dioxide. The short aorta gives rise to a cephalic artery conducting blood to the head and foot, and a visceral artery, which empties into lacunae around the viscera. Blood collects in a system of sinuses that eventually return it to the gills or lung, generally by way of lacunae around the kidney. In some of the pulmonates, however, blood returns directly to the auricle from the kidney.

Maintenance of blood-flow, especially in larger gastropods, is physiologically important. So much of blood-flow occurs in open spaces and sinuses that booster hearts often play an important role. *Patella*, *Natica*, and many heteropods have muscular aortic bulbs in the pericardial cavity. *Busycon* and some other siphonate prosobranchs have a booster heart outside of the pericardial cavity, in the head region.

Sense Organs. Tactile cells are scattered over the body surface. They are concentrated in regions of high sensitivity, such as the head, the margin of the foot, and sometimes the edge of the mantle. The cephalic tentacles are well supplied with tactile cells, and other tactile projections appear sporadically in different groups. The most outstanding of these are the epipodial tentacles, found on the sides of the foot of many archeogastropods, and the cerata, which occur on the dorsal or lateral surfaces of many nudibranchs.

A patch of sensory cells, the osphradium, occurs at the base of each gill. The osphradium is often a strand of elevated sensory cells associated with the nerve to the ctenidium, but in some cases it is incorporated in the ctenidial axis. Sometimes lateral tracts of elevated cells extend on each side of a central strand, giving the osphradium a bipectinate appearance. Gastropods without ctenidia retain an osphradium if a mantle cavity and secondary gills are present. Aquatic pulmonates have an osphradium, but land pulmonates do not.

Osphradia lie in the path of inhalant respiratory currents. They are chemoreceptors, probably governing water-flow into the mantle cavity. Yonge (1934) has suggested that they may be sensitive to sediment. There is evidence that they participate in chemoreception generally. Certainly, in opisthobranchs which have lost the osphradium, the anterior cephalic tentacle is converted into a rhinophore.

Chemoreceptors are important mediators of gastropod behavior. Some gastropods make frenzied flight responses to the tube feet of starfish. This response is sometimes initiated before contact with the tube feet is made, indicating both contact and distant chemoreception. Oriented responses to food are usually well developed in gastropods. In some species, removal of osphradia destroys the ability to detect food and feed normally. Rhinophores are proving to be less effective chemoreceptors than was once thought. They are more sensitive to contact with acids and salts than are the oral tentacles,

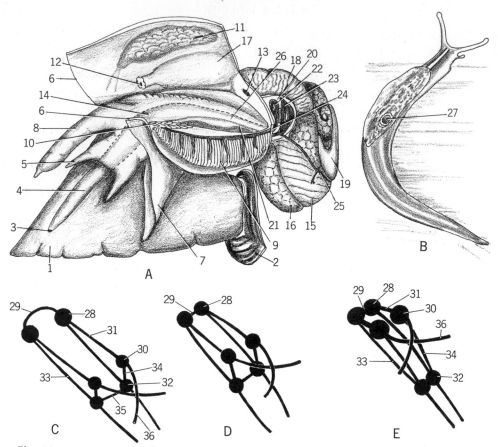

Fig. 13.28. A. *Busycon*, with the shell removed and the mantle reflected to show the gill. **B.** *Limax*, a slug. With shell reduction, the mantle is made more evident. It encloses the vascularized mantle cavity which serves as a lung. An opening, the pneumostome, permits lung ventilation. **C-E.** Scheme of the nervous triangle, as seen in various gastropods. Among the more primitive prosobranchs, the hypoathroid type of nervous triangle is found (C). In this type, the pleural ganglia are near the pedal ganglia, and the pleuropedal connectives are very short, while the connectives to the cerebral ganglia are long. In the dystenoid type (D), the pleural ganglia have shifted toward the cerebral ganglia, with corresponding shortening of the cerebropleural and lengthening of the pleuropedal connectives. In the epiathroid type (E), the pleural ganglia are near the cerebral ganglia or have united with them, and connectives to the pedal ganglia have lengthened. Among these forms, the pedal ganglia may also move toward the cerebral ganglia. There is a tendency, also, for the cerebral ganglia to move closer together, with corresponding shortening of the cerebral commissures, and for the pedal ganglia to become approximated to them. The general tendency toward centralization favors the development of a complex brain region. *Busycon external features:* **1,** foot; **2,** operculum; **3,** mouth; **4,** proboscis; **5,** cephalic tentacles; **6,** mantle; **7,** siphon; **8,** penis. *Mantle cavity:* **9,** gill; **10,** osphradium; **11,** hypobranchial gland; **12,** anus; **13,** nephridiopore. *Digestive tract:* **14,** esophagus; **15,** stomach; **16,** digestive gland; **17,** intestine. *Urogenital system:* **18,** testis; **19,** nephridium. *Circulatory system:* **20,** pericardial cavity; **21,** efferent branchial (gill vein); **22,** auricle; **23,** ventricle; **24,** aorta; **25,** visceral artery; **26,** booster heart. *Limax:* **27,** pneumostome. *Nervous system:* **28,** cerebral ganglion; **29,** cerebral commissure; **30,** pleural ganglion; **31,** cerebropleural connective; **32,** pedal ganglion; **33,** cerebropedal connective; **34,** pleuropedal connective; **35,** pedal commissure; **36,** visceral nerve.

but there is no evidence that they are stimulated by substances not in contact with them. The oral tentacles of nudibranchs prove to be more important in contact chemoreception involved in feeding. The anterior margin of the foot is also an important site of chemoreception in many aquatic gastropods.

Hollow statocysts containing calcareous concretions are almost universally present in gastropods. They are innervated from the cerebral ganglia. Generally, creeping gastropods have statocysts in the foot, while heteropods and most nudibranchs have the statocysts close to the cerebral ganglia. Details of operation of the gravity receptors have not been worked out.

Most gastropods have eyes at the base of the cephalic tentacles. Tentacle eyes (Fig. 13.29A) are converse pigment-cup ocelli. Some are simple cups, while others are complex eyes comparing favorably with the eyes of fishes. The simplest eyes are open epidermal cups, differentiated into sensory and pigment cells covered by a layer of hyaline, rod-shaped retinidia. Fibers from the sensory cells extend to the optic nerve. Further specialization of the eye leads to: (1) the appearance of a crystalline lens, varying from a few hyaline cells to a complex structure covered by an inner cornea; (2) the secretion of a vitreous body in eyes containing a lens; (3) narrowing and, eventually, closing of the cup opening, with the concomitant development of transparency of the closing tissues; (4) insinking of the eye, accompanied by the formation of a transparent cornea from the superficial epidermis; and (5) the narrowing of the retina as the eye becomes more complex, with some histological specialization and the appearance of a limiting membrane between the retina and vitreous body.

Some slug-like marine pulmonates have mantle eyes, located on tubercles on the dorsal surface. These eyes are independent developments. They are converse pigment-cup ocelli with a lens composed of a few hyaline cells. A thorough analysis of the visual capacity of snails has not been made, but most are light sensitive and do not form images. The capacity to distinguish intensities and wavelengths of light are as yet undescribed, as least in a detailed manner.

Nervous System. It is easier to understand the form of the gastropod nervous system before torsion (Fig. 13.29F). Three pairs of ganglia lie near the esophagus. The cerebral ganglia lie above the esophagus, the pedal ganglia lie below it in the anterior midline of the foot, and the pleural ganglia are more laterally placed. Cerebropedal, cerebropleural, and pleuropedal connectives link the ganglia, forming a neural triangle on each side. A pair of small buccal ganglia are attached by buccal connectives to the cerebral ganglia. A pair of pedal nerves arises in the pedal ganglia, and extend back in the foot. They are connected by cross commissures, and are ganglionated at the junction of commissures and nerves. A pair of palliovisceral nerves arise from the pleural ganglia and extend back into the visceral hump. Typically, a parietal ganglion is found on each of the palliovisceral nerves, and each nerve ends in a visceral ganglion. Cross commissures connect the two cerebral ganglia, the two pedal ganglia, and the two visceral ganglia.

Torsion brings the visceral ganglia forward, twisting the palliovisceral (also known as the visceral) nerves between the pleural and parietal ganglia, but does not affect the rest of the nervous system (Fig. 13.29G). The visceral and parietal ganglia on the larval (pretorsion) right are brought to the left side of the adult. The adult left parietal ganglion is higher than the right and is the supraparietal ganglion; the right parietal is the infraparietal ganglion. All modern gastropods undergo torsion, so it must be considered primitive for them. Undoubtedly the ancient gastropods had a nervous system that was

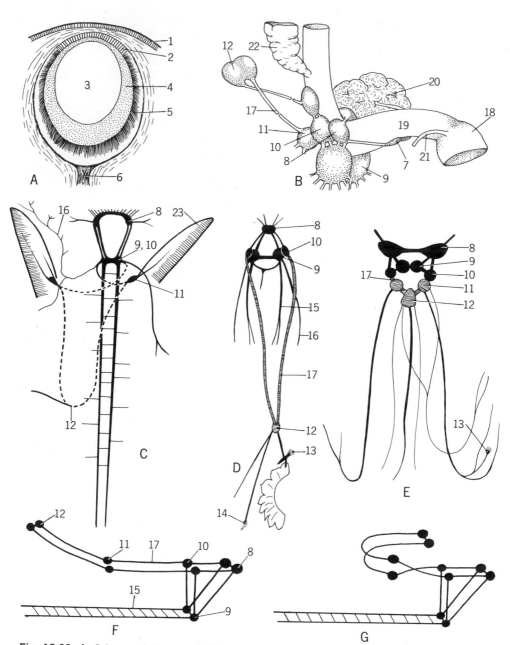

Fig. 13.29. **A.** Scheme of the eye of *Murex*. **B.** Brain of the large conch, *Busycon.* Note the rather strong centralization of the ganglia in the brain region. **C.** Nervous system of *Haliotus,* illustrative of the gastropods with a twisted visceral loop (streptoneurous), it also shows the hypoathroid type of ganglion arrangement. **D.** One method of untwisting the visceral loop is detorsion as occurs in opisthobranchs. This leaves a long, but untwisted visceral loop, as seen in the nervous system of *Aplysia,* shown here. This is known as the long-looped euthyneurous arrangement. **E.** Another method of straightening the visceral loop is by concentration of the

516

not twisted and they were organized as the larvae are before torsion.

A nervous system twisted in this manner is said to be streptoneurous, and is characteristic of the more primitive of the modern gastropods. In many gastropods, however, a more or less complete return to bilateral symmetry of the nervous system is achieved by one of two methods: (1) detorsion, which untwists the visceral nerve and brings the parietal ganglia back to their original position; and (2) shortening of the connectives between the pleural and parietal ganglia, which hauls the parietal ganglia back into a symmetrical position. In either case, the nervous system is said to be euthyneurous.

Untwisting of the visceral nerve by detorsion is characteristic of opisthobranchs. The results are seen in *Aplysia*, for example (Fig. 13.29D). Other changes somewhat complicate the picture, however, for the ganglia have tended to become concentrated at the anterior end. The pleural and cerebral ganglia have fused together and all of the prominent ganglia have disappeared from the shortened visceral nerves. Pulmonates regain bilateral symmetry by shortening the visceral loop and the connectives. As a result, the visceral ganglia unite with the pleurals and both may unite with the cerebral ganglia, forming a complex brain from which peripheral nerves pass to the various parts of the body (Fig. 13.29E).

The form of the neural triangle in the head varies with the relative length of the connectives (Fig. 13.28C-E). Most archeogastropods have the pleural and pedal ganglia close together, with short pleuropedal connectives. *Pleurotomaria* and some other prosobranchs have all of the connectives about the same length, with the pleural ganglia about halfway between the cerebral and pedal ganglia. Most mesogastropods, however, have the pleural and cerebral ganglia close together, with short cerebropleural connectives. In some cases the ganglia come in contact and unite, leaving no visible connectives.

No matter how the nervous system is organized, the connectives between the pedal and cerebral ganglia are maintained whether or not they are visible from without. The cerebropedal connection is functionally important, particularly in control of locomotion. The immediate control of peristaltic creeping movements of the foot is vested in the pedal ganglia, working through fibers in the pedal nerve, and affected by stimuli from a well-developed subepidermal plexus in the foot. Stimulation of one side of the *Aplysia* foot evokes reactions on the other side. These cross reactions are destroyed by disturbance of the connection between the two pedal ganglia, but not by destroying the commissure between the two cerebral ganglia. Evidently the local stimuli which are important in operation of the foot are entirely within the pedal nervous system. However, if the cerebral ganglion is destroyed, the muscle tone of *Aplysia* rises and parapodial activity increases. The

ganglia, bring the visceral ganglia forward. This results in the short-looped euthyneurous arrangement, as seen here in *Limnaea*. F-G. Scheme of the arrangement of the nervous system before and after torsion. Twisting occurs between the pleural and parietal ganglia, bringing the right parietal above and the left parietal below. It results in the pretorsion right visceral nerve cord lying above and the pretorsion left visceral nerve cord below the digestive tract. (A, after Hesse. B, after Pierce, in Brown. C, after Cooke. D and E, after Spengel, from Pelseneer, in Lankester.) *Eye:* 1, epidermis; 2, cornea; 3, lens; 4, hyaline secretion; 5, retina; 6, optic nerve. *Nervous system:* 7, buccal ganglion; 8, cerebral ganglion; 9, pedal ganglion; 10, pleural ganglion; 11, parietal ganglion; 12, visceral ganglion; 13, osphradial ganglion; 14, genital ganglion; 15, pedal nerve cord; 16, pallial nerve; 17, visceral nerve cord. *Other parts:* 18, proboscis; 19, esophagus; 20, salivary gland; 21, salivary duct; 22, esophageal gland; 23, gill.

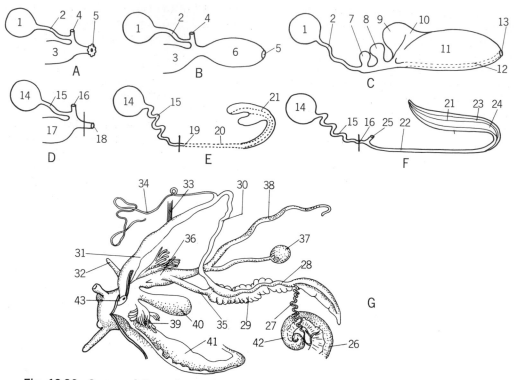

Fig. 13.30. Gastropod Reproductive Systems. In the female prosobranchs, the reproductive system varies from a simple system composed of the gonoduct proper and parts of the nephridium to a complex system which includes glands and other parts derived from the wall of the mantle cavity. At A a primitive system, as found in *Gibbula* and *Monodonta* is shown. The oviduct joins the renopericardial canal, and ova are discharged through the nephridiopore. A somewhat more complex system is seen at B, illustrating the condition in *Calliostoma*. A urogenital papilla extends into the mantle cavity with the nephridiopore it its tip. The mantle or pallial part of the oviduct has become very complex in *Potamopyrgous*, as seen in C, with the appearance of organs for sperm storage, and secretion of albumen and a capsule. The same general tendencies are seen in males. The primitive relationships, as seen in *Calliostoma*, are shown at D. Only the internal duct systems are present, and sperm are discharged through the nephridiopore. *Calyptraea* males (B) have a penis developed on the body surface, and sperm reach it by way of a groove which passes across the mantle cavity and along the penial surface. The roofing over of this groove provides the pallial portion of the sperm duct system. A more complex hermaphroditic system is shown at G, as found in a typical pulmonate, *Helix*. (A-F, after Fretter and Graham. G, somewhat modified, after Cooke.) *Female system:* 1, ovary; 2, original oviduct; 3, right kidney; 4, renopericardial canal; 5, nephridiopore; 6, urogenital papilla; 7, seminal receptacle; 8, bursa; 9, albumin gland; 10, mucous gland; 11, capsule gland and brood pouch; 12, ventral channel; 13, female gonopore. *Male system:* 14, testis; 15, internal sperm duct (original gonoduct); 16, renopericardial canal; 17, right kidney; 18, nephridiopore; 19, nephridial sperm duct; 20, seminal groove; 21, penis; 22, pallial sperm duct; 23, penial sperm duct; 24, prostate gland; 25, opening to mantle cavity. *Hermaphroditic system:* 26, ovotestis; 27, hermaphroditic duct; 28, male part of hermaphroditic duct; 29, female part of hermaphroditic duct; 30, sperm duct; 31, penis sac; 32, penis; 33, penial retractor; 34, flagellum; 35, oviduct; 36, vagina; 37, seminal receptacle; 38, caecum; 39, accessory glands; 40, dart sac. *Other parts:* 41, crop; 42, liver; 43, retracted eye.

518

cerebral ganglia evidently exercise an inhibitory effect on the pedal ganglia. Foot potentials of *Helix* also indicate an inhibitory effect of the cerebral ganglia on the pedal ganglion motor neurons. The cerebropedal connectives thus maintain relationships between the policy decision regions of the cerebral ganglia and the motor centers in the pedal ganglia.

Stimuli from the main sense organs, tentacles, tentacular eyes, and statocysts pour into the cerebral ganglia, which appear to be the over-all coordinating centers. Motor innervation of the mantle is largely from the pleural ganglion, although the parietal is also involved. Sensory stimuli also appear to enter the pleural and parietal ganglia, although distinct osphradial ganglia, associated with the visceral nerve, are often present.

The sympathetic or stomatogastric nervous system centers in the buccal ganglia and serves the main visceral organs, heart, kidney, and reproductive organs.

Reproductive System. Most prosobranchs are dioecious, but sexual dimorphism is rarely very conspicuous. Males are sometimes smaller than females, and may have other peculiarities. All gastropods have a single gonad, usually located high in the visceral mass or at the apex. Gametes of archeogastropods are usually discharged into a short gonoduct that opens into the right nephridium by one or several pores. The gametes depart through the right nephridiopore, and fertilization is external. Two factors are important in further differentiation of the prosobranch genital system. The right nephridium is reduced, the vestiges becoming incorporated in the gonoduct system, and mating occurs, involving the differentiation of parts used for copulation. As the right nephridium is reduced, its nephrostome and the upper part of the tubule become a canal and pore opening into the pericardial cavity, the gonopericardial canal. A part of the gonoduct is derived from the rest of the nephridium, ending at the old nephridio-pore. All of the organs utilized for copulation, and some of the glandular parts of the gonoduct are beyond the nephridial part of the gonoduct. This part of the gonoduct is termed the pallial gonoduct, and is at first no more than a groove across the mantle, later closing over and becoming a tube.

The male system is the simpler (Fig. 13.30D-F). Sperm may be stored before mating in the convoluted gonoduct, derived from the nephridial gonoduct. In many prosobranchs, the gonopore occurs at the end of this part of the gonoduct, although a penis is present, separated by some distance from the gonopore. In this case, a ciliated groove connects the gonopore and the penis, along which sperm pass at the time of mating. More commonly, however, the groove is roofed over to form a pallial gonoduct, and the penis is hollow instead of grooved.

The female system is derived in a similar manner, but the gonopore usually lies near the opening of the mantle cavity, and the last part of the oviduct is a pallial canal. The original oviduct is a short, upper region, usually convoluted. Beyond this is a short nephridial region, which may be connected to the pericardial cavity by a gonopericardial canal. The pallial oviduct contains the conspicuous glandular regions responsible for the secretion of the albumen and the capsules that cover the ovum. The albumen gland is smaller and more proximally located. A diverticulum, the seminal receptacle, usually lies near the albumin gland. In many cases, a copulatory bursa located just beyond the capsule gland first receives the sperm at mating. In this case the sperm later migrate to the seminal receptacle for storage.

Opisthobranchs and pulmonates are hermaphroditic. The male and female systems are complex, with functional regions that are about the same as in the more highly differentiated prosobranch systems. Although the animals are hermaphroditic they have only one gonad, which produces both sperm and ova. It opens into a hermaphroditic duct, usually divided by longitudinal folds into one channel for the sperm and another for the ova. The hermaphroditic duct ends in a hermaphroditic pore, near the mantle cavity entrance on the right side of the body. The penis does not lie near the hermaphroditic pore, and a ciliated channel conveys the sperm over the body surface to the anteriorly placed penis. This arrangement is seen in *Aplysia*, and many other opisthobranchs. As in the prosobranchs, the ciliated channel tends to become roofed over, forming a definite pallial duct. As a result, there are two gonopores, a female gonopore at the old hermaphroditic pore, and a male gonopore associated with the penis. This arrangement is common in nudibranchs and aquatic pulmonates. The next step is the extension of the female gonoduct onto the pallial region. In some nudibranchs it lies near the penis. In terrestrial pulmonates, the secondary relationship of the male and female gonopores becomes more intimate. The end of the male and female ducts open into a common genital antrum, which opens through a common gonopore. This common gonopore is at some distance from the site of the hermaphroditic pore of the more primitive opisthobranchs, for the lower part of both male and female tracts is pallial. In *Helix* (Fig. 13.30G) the upper part of the reproductive system is functionally, but not morphologically, divided into male and female channels. The lower part, beyond the old hermaphroditic pore, contains separate male and female duct systems, with associated glands.

A further complication is seen in some nudibranchs. A special copulatory pore provides an entrance into the copulatory bursa. The bursa is connected to the oviduct by an internal passageway. In such gastropods, there are three genital pores, a male gonopore associated with the penis, a female gonopore through which the ova emerge, and a copulatory pore through which sperm enter at mating.

In adapting to life in a variety of habitats, gastropods have developed many different reproductive habits and varied devices to protect the ova during early development under diverse conditions. The majority of these devices involve specializations of accessory organs associated with the female system, used to fabricate egg cases that will float or can be attached to objects. Cross-breeding is ensured in various ways in hermaphroditic species. *Helix*, for example, performs a curious prenuptial ceremony. The two animals approach with the genital atria everted. Each fires a calcareous dart, produced in a specialized dart sac associated with the reproductive tract. The dart penetrates deeply into the internal organs. After this sadistic performance, copulation and mutual exchange of sperm occurs.

Development. Early development follows the general molluscan plan, but may be considerably modified in ova with a considerable amount of yolk. The ova of archeogastropods are not enclosed in capsules, and develop into typical free-swimming trochophores. All other gastropod ova hatch at a later stage. Prosobranchs and opisthobranchs usually hatch as free-swimming larvae, somewhat more advanced than trochophores. This larval stage is known as a veliger. Pulmonates go a step further, retaining the veliger larva within the egg membranes, and hatching as diminutive snails. The trochophore larvae that are retained within the egg membranes are sometimes reduced, but are as a general rule well formed.

The transformation of a trochophore into a veliger involves considerable differentiation of parts, and some changes in basic organization (Fig. 13.31). The blastopore closes, a stomodaeum forms, makes connections with the primitive gut, and begins to differentiate into buccal structures. The prototroch grows and gradually shifts to a more dorsal position, eventually forming a large, bilobed, funnel-like velum, with prominently ciliated margins. Meanwhile, a shell gland appears on the posterodorsal surface and starts to secrete the larval shell. At first the shell gland is a posterodorsal cap, but it grows at the margins, eventually enclosing the whole visceral mass, and establishes the mantle. A larval mantle cavity, containing the anus, takes shape. The body projects ventrally from the mantle as a foot primordium, just ventral to the stomodaeum. A pair of eyes develop above the mouth at the center of the velum, and eventually come to lie at the base of the primordia of the cephalic tentacles. Statocysts lateral to the foot are formed. While these changes are taking place, the nutritive material from the ovum is concentrated in a nutritive sac at the apex of the visceral mass. The digestive gland comes to occupy this position during later development. The body is enveloped by the growing mantle, and the internal organs grow rapidly on the dorsal side. This brings the anus forward, toward the aperture of the larval shell, and gives the digestive tract its characteristic, sharply U-shaped form. It is at about this time that torsion occurs.

Most molluscs pass through a veliger larva stage. The most unusual feature of the gastropod veliger is torsion, the details of which need not be described again. The veliger larvae of the most highly modified gastropods show considerable recapitulation, strengthening the evidence of relationship between the various groups. Even in limpets with a cup-shaped shell, the larval shell coils in the veliger stage. Nudibranchs and pteropods which have no shell as adults pass through veliger stages in which a larval shell and operculum are present.

Some of the structures formed during embryonic development are temporary, giving way to entirely different adult parts. In some cases, these may give evidence of relationship to members of lower phyla. An example may be the ectodermal invaginations which develop into larval nephridia, later to be replaced by the adult nephridia. On the other hand, some of these structures are best understood as devices contributing to the immediate needs of the young organism. An example is the circulation of blood through the larval sinus system, long before a definitive heart is formed.

As development continues, the foot grows larger and the velum becomes relatively smaller. In many species, the late veliger is able to swim with the velar cilia, and to creep about with the foot. Eventually the velum is wholly resorbed, and the young snail becomes a juvenile, assuming an essentially adult way of life.

Some prosobranchs (e.g. *Vivipara*, *Campeloma*, some *Littorina*) and some pulmonates (e.g. *Achatina*, *Stenogyra*, and some *Helix*) retain the developing ova in the lower part of the oviduct. All early development is internal, and the young snails are fully formed when they emerge from the parent.

Class Pelecypoda

Pelecypods are bivalved molluscs: clams, mussels, oysters, and scallops. A number of them are commercially important shellfish, and all commercial pearls are obtained from pelecypods. Their shells are used to make buttons and other small pearly objects. Odd, highly modified pelecypods known as shipworms are important pests, burrowing into and destroying wooden pilings and other structures in harbors throughout the world, causing millions of dollars of damage every year.

There are only a few really aberrant and bizarre pelecypods. The first impression is that they are relatively homogeneous as a group. Nevertheless, they occur widely in marine habitats, from the upper part of the littoral zone to depths of almost 5000 m., and several families have established

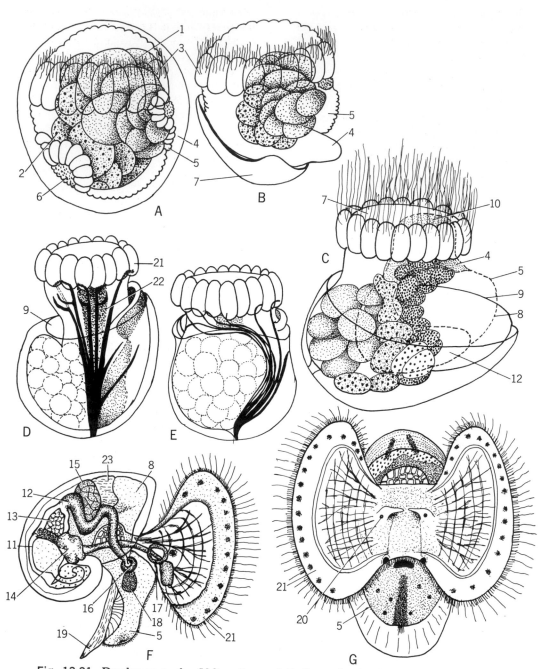

Fig. 13.31. Development of a Veliger Larva. **A-E.** Stages in the development of *Haliotus tuberculata*. The young trochophore just before hatching is shown at **A.** The blastopore is closed, and a stomodaeum is present. The foot and shell gland have begun to form. In **B** and **C,** the further development of the prototroch into the velum can be seen. The young shell begins to form, and mantle folds enclosing a mantle cavity appear. Subsequently six larval

themselves in ponds and fresh-water streams. Most of them plow through sand or mud with the aid of their wedge-shaped foot, feeding on organic detritus or plankton stirred up around them. A few burrow into wood or rocks or live permanently attached to rocks or other submerged objects. Nearly all of them are dependent on and specialized for ciliary feeding, a factor which has probably discouraged a more extensive adaptive radiation.

Pelecypods are simply organized (Fig. 13.15B). The visceral mass is laterally compressed, and a blade-like foot hangs below it. The mantle is in the form of two large folds, enclosing a huge mantle cavity and secreting a bivalved shell. The two valves meet at a dorsal hinge and are usually nearly symmetrical. A gill hangs from the mantle-cavity roof on each side of the body. The head is rudimentary, but a pair of labial palps flank the mouth. The body is typically symmetrical about a plane passing between the two valves, but the symmetry is sometimes spoiled by inequalities of the two valves.

The most primitive modern pelecypods belong to the Protobranchia. A typical ctenidium with flat gill filaments on each side of a central axis is found on each side of the body. In *Yoldia* (Fig. 13.32A), the axis is a muscular membrane containing the incurrent and excurrent blood vessels. As blood enters the gills, the supporting membrane relaxes, and the gills move downward in the mantle cavity. Water flows over the face of the gill filaments. The muscular membrane is then contracted, lifting the gill, forcing water into the excurrent channel above the

membrane, while blood departs from the filaments. While the muscular respiratory movements aid in ventilating the gill surfaces, cilia are more important. Powerful lateral cilia generate currents carrying water up over the gill filaments to the excurrent channel (Fig. 13.32B). Most clams burrow in soft bottoms, and protection against fouling of the gill surfaces by small particles is important. Hypobranchial glands in the mantle surface, just lateral to the gill suspensor, secrete mucus, in which particles are caught. They are swept away by small frontal cilia. Patches of interlocking cilia hold the ctenidium in place and help to support the individual filaments. Medial interlocking cilia behind the foot connect the right and left gills.

How could animals like these have evolved from the ancestral molluscan stocks? Yonge (1941) suggests that the pelecypod ancestors had a ventral mouth and lived on hard bottoms, like the hypothetical mollusc previously described. Adaptation to a burrowing life on soft bottoms involved the lateral compression and accompanying deepening of the body. However, as the body deepened, the mouth would be raised above the surface. Development and lengthening of the labial palps, Yonge thinks, served to compensate for the deepening body by maintaining contact between the mouth and the detritus-covered bottom. Primitive protobranchs have such an apparatus. A pair of palps encloses the mouth. Each palp is equipped with a long, slender palp proboscis (Fig. 13.32C). When the animal is feeding, the proboscides are thrust

retractor muscles develop, as seen at D and E. Contraction of the larval retractor muscles is responsible for torsion. At E, 90° of torsion has occurred. F and G. Side and front views of the veliger of *Crepidula fornicata*, showing the organization of the veliger. Note the bilobed form of the velum in front view. (A-E, after Crofts. F-G, after Werner.) 1, endoderm; 2, mesoderm; 3, prototroch; 4, stomodaeum; 5, foot; 6, shell gland; 7, shell; 8, mantle; 9, mantle cavity; 10, foregut; 11, stomach; 12, hindgut; 13, style sac; 14, digestive gland; 15, kidney; 16, statocyst; 17, cerebral ganglion; 18, pedal ganglion; 19, operculum; 20, tentacle; 21, velum; 22, retractor muscles; 23, larval heart.

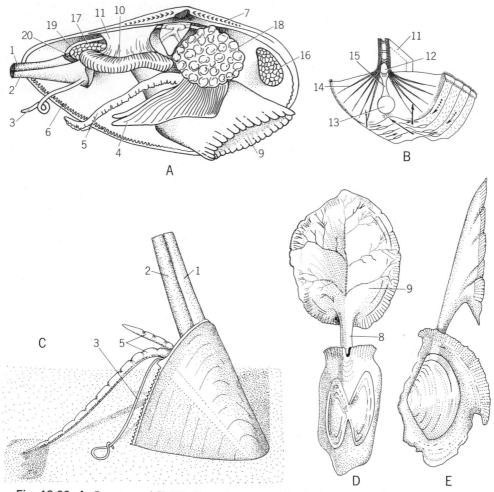

Fig. 13.32. **A.** Structure of *Yoldia limatula*, a protobranch clam. **B.** Scheme of protobranch gill. Notice the respiratory currents (dark arrows) and cleansing currents (dotted arrows). **C.** A feeding *Yoldia*. The foot is thrust deep into the sand, and the siphons elevated. One of the palp appendages is in contact with the surface of the sand. Particles of detritus move along the groove in the palp appendage to the mouth. **D and E.** Dorsal and side views of *Entovalva semperi*. Note the relatively small size of the shell in comparison with the mantle, and the distal expansion of the foot. A foot with a plantar surface like this is thrust into the sand or mud, expanded, and foot retractor muscles contracted to pull the shell forward. The foot is then contracted and thrust forward again. (A, after Pierce, in Brown. B, after Yonge. C, after Drew, D and E, after Ohshima, from Franc, in Grassé.) **1**, excurrent siphon; **2**, incurrent siphon; **3**, siphonal tentacle; **4**, labial palp; **5**, palp appendage; **6**, edge of mantle; **7**, hinge tooth; **8**, foot; **9**, plantar surface of foot; **10**, gill; **11**, suspensor ligament; **12**, afferent vessel; **13**, efferent vessel; **14**, gill support; **15**, exhalant passage; **16**, anterior adductor vessel; **17**, posterior adductor muscle; **18**, gonad; **19**, intestine; **20**, anus.

out of the shell and feel about in the mud or sand. Particles are carried upward toward the mouth along a ciliated groove, eventually reaching the palp lamellae on each side of the mouth. A ridged and ciliated sorting field on each lamella grades out the large particles, which pass to the mantle and are ejected with sediment from the gills. Small particles are diverted to a deep, ciliated oral groove, along which they move to the mouth.

Clams belonging to the orders Filibranchia and Eulamellibranchia have no palp proboscides. In these orders, the gills have undergone a profound change in structure, becoming organs used for filter-feeding as well as for respiration. The gills are very large, often extending the whole length of the mantle cavity, and each gill filament is greatly lengthened (Fig. 13.33 I-K). In most cases, the filaments bend back on themselves, so the whole gill is W-shaped in cross section. Efferent blood vessels lie at the bottom of the central axis in protobranchs, but as the filaments lengthen they divide and come to lie at the tip of the ascending arm of the filament, on each side of the axis. The original ctenidium is thus changed into two demibranchs, each demibranch consisting of the descending and ascending arms of one row of filaments.

Characteristic folding patterns are seen in the gills of various genera or families of filibranchs and eulamellibranchs. Some of the ark shells, for example, have an inner demibranch with only a descending arm, and some jingle shells have only descending arms on each demibranch. These are detailed variations on the same theme, however, and may be left to the specialists.

Although filibranchs and eulamellibranchs have gills with filaments similarly lengthened and folded, the gill structure provides the major distinction between them. It is evident that as the gill filaments draw out into long, recurved strands, they become mechanically weak. Some sort of

strengthening is necessary if the gill is to retain any real integrity as a whole organ. Longitudinal strengthening is needed to hold the individual filaments of the series together, and transverse strengthening, to hold the ascending and descending arms together. In both filibranchs and eulamellibranchs, tissue connections between the ascending and descending arms of a demibranch strengthen the gill transversely. Filibranchs use interlocking cilia to hold the adjacent filaments together, in this resembling the protobranchs (Fig. 13.33 B). Eulamellibranchs have tissue connections between the filaments (Fig. 13.33A). Connections between the ascending and descending arms of a demibranch are known as interlamellar junctions. They do not interfere with the flow of water over the faces of the gill filaments, although they prevent the ascending and descending arms from falling apart. In some of the filibranchs these connections are relatively simple, consisting of connective tissue only. In others, and in eulamellibranchs, blood vessels may pass through the interlamellar junctions. Tissue connections between adjacent filaments, characteristic only of eulamellibranchs, are known as interfilamental junctions. These connections interfere, to some extent, with the passage of water over the gill filaments. In some eulamellibranchs, the interfilamental junctions are sparse, but in many, the adjacent filaments are connected by large interfilamental junctions, leaving only small openings through which water can enter the space between filaments. These openings, known as ostia, open into inner spaces, bounded by interfilamental and interlamellar junctions, known as water tubes. In these cases, water enters the gills from the mantle cavity, passing through the ostia into the water tubes. The water passes upward in the water tubes to the exhalant space at the top of the gill. The large surface area exposed makes respiratory transfer a simple matter. The circulation of water through the gill is

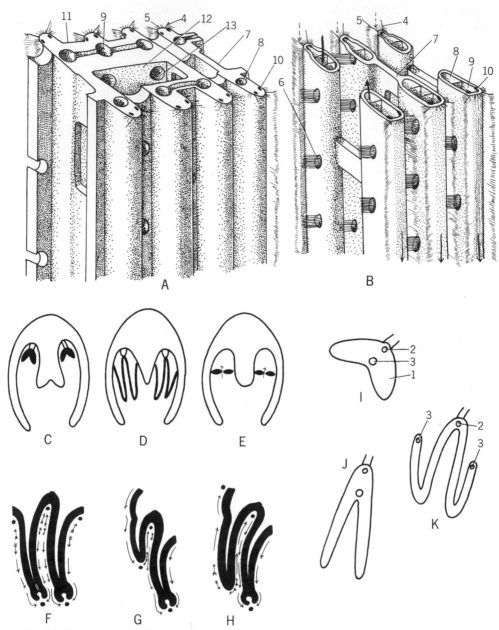

Fig. 13.33. Pelecypod Gills. Protobranchs have a pair of typical ctenidia (I, C) with broad, flat filaments and an axis containing the afferent and efferent blood vessels. Conversion of the filibranch and eulamellibranch gills into a filter-feeding apparatus involved lengthening the filaments (J, K), and reflecting them to permit further lengthening. As the filaments lengthened, the efferent blood vessel came to be located at the tip of the filament. As a result, they have a pair of demibranchs on each side of the body (D), with each demibranch composed of a descending lamella on the axis side and an ascending lamella on the outer side of the gill.

primarily caused by lateral cilia, as in protobranchs.

Delicate frontal cilia cleanse the surface of protobranch gill filaments. These small cilia have been used to build a food-collecting and sorting device in filibranchs and eulamellibranchs. They draw small particles over the gill surface, delivering them to ciliated food grooves. The particles move along the food grooves to the palps, where they are sorted, and particles of acceptable size are conveyed to the mouth. Most eulamellibranchs have two food grooves, one just below the afferent blood vessel at the gill axis, and one at the point where ascending and descending arms of the inner gill filaments meet, but a number of other patterns occur. *Pinna* and *Mytilus* have five food grooves, one at each junction of ascending and descending arms, one at the gill axis, and one at each junction of ascending arms and mantle cavity.

Septibranchs have evolved along an entirely independent line. They have no gill filaments, and respiratory exchange occurs at the surface of the mantle cavity

(Fig. 13.33E). The gill base of protobranchs is muscular. In septibranchs, only the muscular gill base persists. It forms a perforated muscular septum, which contracts rhythmically to pump water into the exhalant channel above it. Septibranchs, without gills or labial palps with proboscides, obtain their food in a different manner. The water is pulled into the mantle cavity with considerable force, and worms as well as small crustaceans and other animals are drawn into the mantle cavity. The large palps grasp these and pop them into the mouth.

CLASSIFICATION

Order Protobranchia. The most primitive modern pelecypods, characterized by simple, ctenida-like gills, not reflected, and not used for feeding; hypobranchial glands at the outer surface of each gill; foot with a ventral plantar surface; large palps, modified for feeding, and typically with long palp proboscides. Examples: *Solenomya*, *Nucula*, *Yoldia* (Fig. 13.32A); *Malletia*.

Septibranchs (E) solved their feeding problems in another manner, converting the axis of the gill and its supporting membrane into a muscular pump which pulls water through the mantle chamber and ejects it from the excurrent passageways above. Respiratory exchange occurs in the vascular mantle wall. The long, slender filaments are mechanically weak, and devices to strengthen the demibranchs appeared. Filibranchs have interlamellar junctions made of tissue, which connect the ascending and descending lamellae of a demibranch (B), and eulamellibranchs have added interfilamental junctions composed of tissue that connect adjacent filaments (A). The interfilamental junctions partially close the face of the demibranch, leaving ostia for the entrance of water into the water channels within. Adjacent filaments of filibranchs are more weakly attached by interlocking cilia. Powerful lateral cilia generate the currents which move water between the gill filaments, while delicate frontal cilia, used to cleanse particles from the surface of protobranch gills, move food particles along the surface of the gill filaments. At certain points, feeding currents convey the particles longitudinally, from filament to filament, eventually bringing them to the palps. These points are indicated by the dark dots in Figs. F-H. The position of the feeding currents and the direction of movement of particles over the filaments varies considerably in different groups of clams. *Lutraria* has two equal demibranchs and five feeding currents. The outer demibranch is slightly shorter in unionids (H) and there are only three feeding currents. In *Venus* the outer demibranch is still shorter, and while there are three feeding currents, they are differently located. Many other patterns of folding and patterns of ciliary currents have been described. (F-H, after Atkins.)
1, gill filament; 2, afferent blood vessel; 3, efferent blood vessel; 4, lateral cilia; 5, frontal cilia; 6, interlocking cilia; 7, interlamellar junction; 8, afferent blood vessel; 9, efferent blood vessel; 10, skeletal rods; 11, interfilamental junction; 12, water tube within eulamellibranch demibranch; 13, ostium.

A

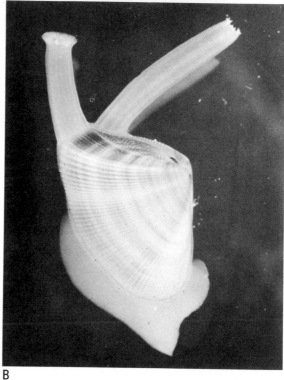

B

Fig. 13.34. Some Representative Pelecypods. **A.** Shell of *Tridacna*, the giant clam. *Tridacna* from the Great Barrier Reef may weigh several hundred pounds. **B.** *Donax denticulatus*, with foot and siphons extended. These small, very active, surf clams sometimes occur in large numbers in sand disturbed by breaking waves. **C.** Shell of *Spondylus*, a spiny oyster, one of the

C

D

showiest pelecypods. The spiny projections are probably protective devices. D. A boring clam, *Botula californiensis*. (B, courtesy of the Smithsonian Institution. C, courtesy of General Biological Supply Co.)

Order Filibranchia. Pelecypods with reflected gills, used for feeding; adjacent gill filaments connected by tufts of interlocking cilia; without interfilamental junctions; without hypobranchial glands; foot usually equipped with a byssal gland; palps small and lamellar. Examples: *Anomia* (jingle shells); *Arca* (ark shells); *Mytilus* and *Modiolus* (common mussels); *Pecten* (scallops).

Order Eulamellibranchia. Gills composed of filaments reflected as in filibranchs, but with adjacent filaments joined by interfilamental junctions through which blood vessels pass; no hypobranchial glands; gonads with gonopores; usually with two adductor muscles and with the mantle margins joined at one or two sutures. Examples: *Ostrea* (oysters); *Cardium* (cockles), *Unio, Sphaeridium, Quadrula* (fresh-water clams); *Ensis, Tagellus* (razor clams); *Venus* (hard-shell clam); *Mya* (soft-shell clam); *Teredo* (shipworm); *Petricola* (boring clam).

Order Septibranchia. Pelecypods with gills replaced by muscular septa used to pump water through the mantle cavity; mantle with two sutures and two siphons; a long slender foot without a well-developed byssal gland. Examples: *Poromya; Cuspidaria.*

ANATOMY AND PHYSIOLOGY

Shell and Mantle Cavity. The shell begins to form during the veliger larva stage. The two mantle folds secrete two tiny valves, composed of conchiolin and meeting in a narrow ligament, also formed of conchiolin. New material is added at the margins of the two valves, producing a series of concentric growth rings. As the veliger settles to the bottom, the mantle folds continue to add material at the shell margins, but more rapidly on the ventral side. As a result, the original larval shell is displaced dorsally, forming an elevation, the umbo. Generally the umbo is directed anteriorly, and the right and left valves can be easily distinguished.

The mantle is pressed against the inner surface of the valves. It ends in three folds, the outer of which secretes the new shell (Fig. 13.2B). Periostracum forms at the inner margin, calcareous material of the prismatic layer at the outer border, and the nacreous material on the whole mantle surface, thickening the shell as it ages.

No calcareous material is added to the valve margin at the hinge line, and a hinge ligament composed of conchiolin is secreted instead. The ligament binds the two valves together, and forms a spring that opens the shell, serving as antagonist to the adductor muscles that pull the two valves together (Fig. 13.35A-C). In most pelecypods, the articulation between the valves is ventral to the ligament, and the ligament is stretched when the adductor muscles close the valves. When the muscles relax the ligament opens the valves. In other pelecypods, a different mechanical principle is used. The conchiolin of the hinge is laid down as an elastic resilium, which extends between the margins of the valves. The resilium is compressed as the adductor muscles close the valves, and springs the valves open when the adductor muscles relax.

The hinge line is also known as the cardinal margin of the shell. Various kinds of adaptations of the cardinal margin are seen, most of which strengthen the articulation between the two valves. These take the form of interdigitating sculpturing that serves to prevent slippage. The projections are known as teeth, and the depressions as dental sockets (Fig. 13.35D). The articulating dentition is extremely varied, and is an important factor in the identification of shells.

Wherever muscles attach to the valves, the orderly secretion of the nacreous layer by the mantle is disturbed. As a result, muscle scars are formed (Fig. 13.35F-H). The most prominent muscle scars are caused by the large adductor muscles that close the valves. The number and position of the adductor-muscle scars

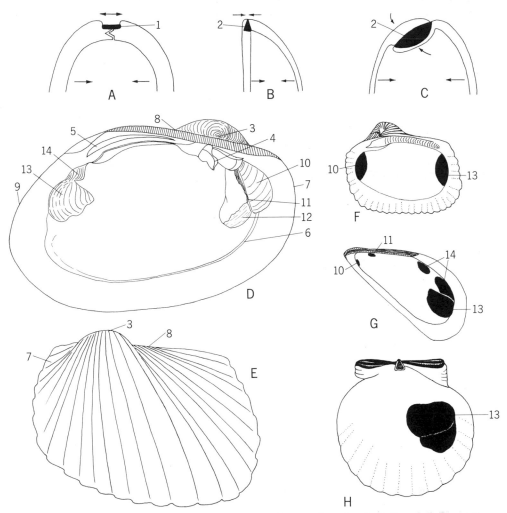

Fig. 13.35. Pelecypod Shells. A-C. Arrangements for opening the shell. In most clams the elastic hinge ligament is stretched when the adductor muscles close the shell, as in **A**. When the muscles relax, the hinge pulls the shell open. In some pelecypods, however, the conchiolin is built into an elastic resilium, which is compressed when the adductor muscles close the shell, as in **B** and **C**. The resilium springs back into shape when the muscles relax, opening the shell valves. **D** and **E**. General features of a pelecypod shell. **F-H**. Muscle arrangements. Some clams have approximately equal anterior and posterior adductor muscles, and they are said to be isomyarian, as in **F**. Others have an anisomyarian shell, with unequal anterior and posterior adductors, as in **G**. Still others have but a single adductor, and are said to be monomyarian, as in **H**. (A-C, after Shrock and Twenhofel. D, after Turner, from Clench, in Edmondson.) 1, hinge ligament; 2, resilium; 3, beak or umbo; 4, pseudocardinal teeth; 5, lateral teeth; 6, pallial line; 7, anterior end; 8, cardinal margin of shell; 9, posterior margin of shell; 10, anterior adductor scar; 11, anterior retractor scar; 12, foot protractor scar; 13, posterior adductor scar; 14, posterior retractor scar.

are important in classification, and have been used to separate pelecypods into different groups. They have proved to be inadequate characteristics for the designation of larger pelecypod groups, but are nevertheless valuable in taxonomy. Many pelecypods have two adductor muscles, with two adductor-muscle scars, one anterior and one posterior. This arrangement is termed diyarian. Other pelecypods have only a posterior adductor, which generally has moved to a fairly central position, and are said to be monomyarian. In some diyarian species, the posterior and anterior adductor muscles are of about equal size and importance. These are termed isomyarian, and typically have the anterior adductor placed above and in front of the mouth and the posterior adductor below and anterior to the anus. Other pelecypods have a small anterior adductor; in these the posterior adductor tends to take a more central position. They are said to be anisomyarian.

Other muscles also leave scars. The inner lobe of the mantle contains the orbicular muscle, which attaches to the shell in a scar known as the pallial line. The margin of the mantle is sealed to the shell along this line, preventing the entrance of particles into the space between the mantle and inner shell surface. When particles gain entrance into this space, they interfere with normal nacre deposition, and may serve as the nuclei of pearl formation. In many clams, the right and left mantle folds are united, defining siphons. Special parts of the orbicularis muscle serve as siphon retractors. These cause an identation of the pallial line, known as the pallial sinus. The size of the pallial sinus roughly corresponds to the size of the siphon, except in a few species which cannot retract the siphon into the shell.

Foot muscles also cause scars. A pair of anterior retractors attach to the shell just behind the anterior adductors, and a pair of posterior retractors attach in front of, and often a little above, the posterior adductors. A pair of anterior foot protractors attach near the anterior adductors, and usually ventral to the retractors. A median foot elevator is also present in some pelecypods.

It is evident that the size, shape, and hinge arrangements, the form, position, and number of muscle scars, and the relative size of the pallial sinus provide clues to a fairly comprehensive picture of a pelecypod. Clues of this kind are particularly valuable to the paleontologist, who must deduce from the hard parts available to him something of the habits of the animal and the structure of the soft parts of the body.

On the whole, pelecypod shells are less impressive than gastropod shells. Some are beautifully colored, however, and there is a great variety of external sculpturing. The shell provides enough clues to permit identification of most species on shell characteristics alone. Many pelecypod families or genera have shells with a characteristic form. The fluted scallop shells are familiar to nearly everyone. The elongated razor clams, the heavy, indented ark shells, the heart-shaped cockle shells, the delicate jingle shells, and the asymmetrical oyster shells are equally distinctive. The smallest clams are the fresh-water sphaerids; some species are smaller than large ostracods. The largest clam, *Tridacna*, may reach 500 pounds. A few unusual shell types are different enough to attract attention. Spiny oysters have long, spiny projections on the shells, for example, and the flattened, asymmetrical *Myadora* shells seem scarcely to leave room for an animal within.

The flow of water through the mantle cavity is one of the most critical factors in pelecypod survival. As water enters and leaves, it brings oxygen and food and wafts away wastes and carbon dioxide. It is not surprising that pelecypods have developed adaptations to make the entry and departure of water more orderly, nor that the more primitive protobranchs and filibranchs include a number of species with-

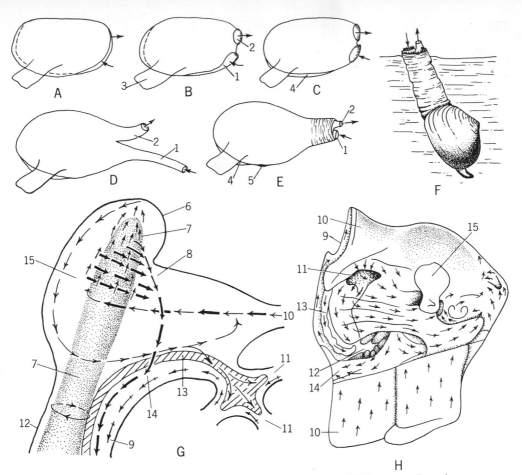

Fig. 13.36. A-E. Mantle openings and siphons in pelecypods. While some clams have mantles with completely free borders, as in **A**, there is a strong tendency to define more clearly the incurrent and excurrent channels by partial union of the mantle margins. The initial joining of the two mantle folds is between the incurrent and excurrent openings, as in **B**, with the mantle borders otherwise completely free. The second joining occurs below the incurrent siphon, separating a pedal opening from the two completely defined siphonal apertures, as in **C**. By a more posterior closure behind the foot, and more intimate joining of the mantle in the region of the siphons, well-developed protruding siphons can be formed, as in **D**. In some cases, the incurrent and excurrent siphons are surrounded by a muscular sheath. Especially with reduction of the foot and development of habits of attachment with byssal threads, a fourth mantle opening for the byssal threads is sometimes found (as in **E**). **F.** A siphonate pelecypod of burrowing habit. The long siphons, enclosed in a muscular sheath, are extended to the surface of the mud. **G.** Movement of particles and rotation of the crystalline style of a pelecypod, *Glossus humanus*. The thin arrows show the movement of fine particles and the heavy arrows the movement of coarse particles. The fine particles move into the digestive gland for further treatment and absorption, while waste particles and coarse particles eventually continue into the intestine. The rejected small particles are indicated by barred arrows. **H.** Stomach of oyster, showing ciliary currents. (A-E, after Lang, with some modifications. F, after Turner, from Shrock and Twenhofel. G, after Owen. H, after Yonge.) 1, incurrent siphon; 2, excurrent siphon; 3, foot; 4, pedal opening; 5, byssal opening; 6, dorsal hood; 7, style; 8, style sac; 9, midgut; 10, esophagus; 11, ducts to digestive gland; 12, caecum; 13, groove from caecum to midgut; 14, ciliated tract to caecum; 15, gastric shield.

533

out any adaptations for this purpose. The primitive condition, seen in some proto-branchs and filibranchs, is for the two mantle folds to be wholly free. In most pelecypods, however, the right and left mantle folds have fused in one or several places, defining passageways through which water enters or leaves (Fig. 13.36A-E). The mantle folds of many eulamellibranchs are united posteriorly, defining a ventral opening for the foot and an exhalant opening for water. The exhalant opening of many fresh-water unionids is subdivided into a more dorsal anal opening and a more ventral opening for water. Some proto-branchs and septibranchs and many eu-lamellibranchs as well have mantle folds joined in a second place, near the first but somewhat forward. This arrangement leaves three openings, a dorsal and posterior exhalant opening, a ventral and posterior inhalant opening, and a more ventral pedal opening for the foot. A few pelecy-pods, especially those with the foot far foward or rudimentary, have a fourth open-ing between the pedal and inhalant open-ing through which water may enter or leave. The mantle folds may be feebly or tightly joined, depending on the species. In many cases, the united mantle folds extend out from the shell, forming inhalant and exhalant siphons. The siphons are ex-tremely valuable to species that bury them-selves deeply in the mud, and in such cases are often very long.

Digestive System. Except for the septi-branchs, the pelecypods are all ciliary feeders. Fine particles are delivered to the mouth by ciliary currents passing along the palp proboscides or the gills, while coarse particles are rejected by sorting areas on the palps. The buccal region, so important in the food-gathering of most molluscs, has lost its function in pelecy-pods. The buccal cavity is usually much reduced, although a small one is found in *Nucula*, a relatively primitive pelecypod; *Nucula* also has a small pair of salivary glands. A radula is never present, and the mouth leads directly into a short esophagus that carries food to the stomach by ciliary currents.

The protobranch palps do not sort food as effectively as the gills of filibranchs and eulamellibranchs. The stomach retains a primitive character, somewhat resembling the stomach of *Diodora*. Food enters a ventral ciliated groove, and is carried into a ventral caecum. It passes the pores for the digestive glands on the way, and small par-ticles enter the digestive gland where they are digested intracellularly. Larger particles pass through the caecum and are entangled in a mucous style, protruding from a large style sac. The style rotates counterclock-wise, propelled by the style-sac cilia. Par-ticles at the upper end of the style are ground against the heavily chitinized gas-tric shield and girdle, attached to the dorsal wall of the stomach. Detached particles pass over a ciliated sorting field, and may enter the digestive glands for intracellular digestion, or be rejected and expelled along a ciliated groove to the intestine.

Improvements of the ciliary feeding system were centered in modifications of the filibranch and eulamellibranch gills, previously described. The gill cilia trap only fine particles. In these pelecypods the gastric shield is much reduced and the girdle is missing. The mucous style is re-placed by a crystalline style, containing amylase in a protein matrix. It is rotated briskly, with the upper part rubbing against the reduced gastric shield (Fig. 13.36G). The amylase is released and carbohydrate digestion begins in the stomach. The partly digested particles pass over a sorting area, eventually entering the digestive glands, where intracellular digestion of protein occurs. At least some of the eu-lamellibranchs complete carbohydrate di-gestion and carry on fat digestion intra-cellularly.

Septibranchs have evolved along differ-ent lines, pumping larger food organisms into the mantle cavity and capturing them with the large palps. They have a very heavily chitinized stomach, which serves as an effective crushing mill. The style is greatly reduced, and is thought to serve primarily to lubricate the food particles with slime, thus protecting the stomach lining.

Larval pelecypods, like gastropods, have asymmetrical digestive glands, the left one being the larger. The glands are nearly symmetrical in adults, however. Originally, each digestive gland opened into the stomach by way of a single pore, but the pores are usually subdivided in modern species. *Mytilus*, for example, has a dozen openings into its digestive glands. The digestive glands of all pelecypods are important in intracellular digestion. In at least some cases enzymes for extracellular digestion are also released. The digestive glands of

the wood-boring *Teredo* secrete cellulase and hemicellulase, used in the digestion of wood. Cathepsin and trypsin-like proteases have been recovered from the digestive glands of some pelecypods, and an active lipase is commonly found. Apparently the crystalline style is the only source of amylase for extracellular digestion, however.

The intestine is usually long. It passes through from one to many initial coils, then curves dorsally and eventually enters the pericardial cavity (Fig. 13.37). Here it turns posteriorly, running immediately above or below the heart in some cases, but usually passing directly through the heart. It continues posteriorly, ending in an anus situated close to the exhalant opening. A typhlosole-like dorsal ridge

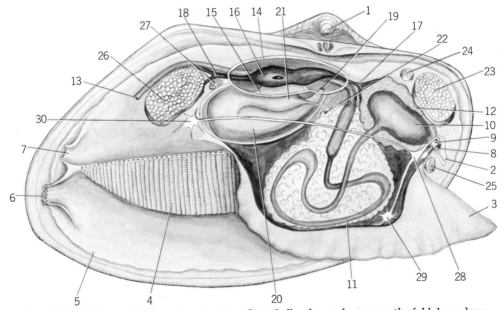

Fig. 13.37. Scheme of Clam Organization. One shell valve and one mantle fold have been removed, and the muscles have been clipped. *External features:* 1, umbo; 2, labial palp; 3, foot; 4, gill; 5, mantle; 6, incurrent siphon; 7, excurrent siphon. *Digestive system:* 8, mouth; 9, esophagus; 10, stomach; 11, intestine; 12, digestive gland; 13, anus. *Circulatory system:* 14, pericardial cavity; 15, auricle; 16, ventricle; 17, anterior aorta; 18, posterior aorta. *Excretory system:* 19, renopericardial pore (nephrostome); 20, glandular nephridium; 21, bladder of nephridium; 22, nephridiopore. *Muscles:* 23, anterior adductor; 24, anterior foot retractor; 25, foot protractor; 26, posterior adductor; 27, posterior foot retractor. *Nervous system:* 28, cerebropleural ganglion; 29, pedal ganglion; 30, visceral ganglion.

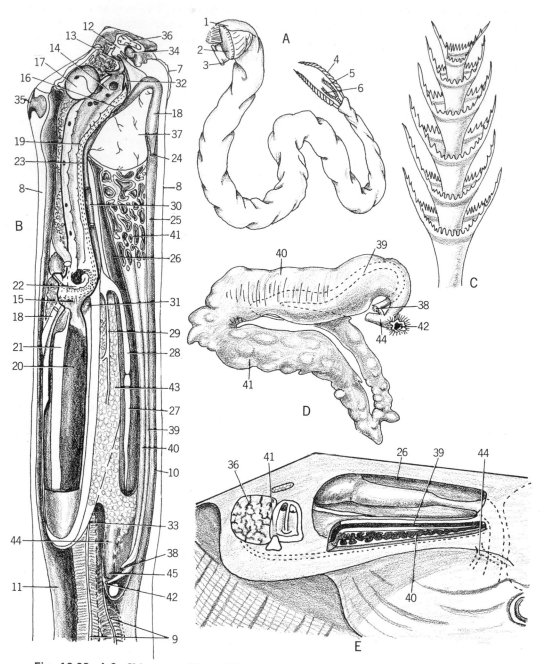

Fig. 13.38. A-C. Shipworms. The highly destructive shipworms are worm-like pelecypods, greatly modified for burrowing. The bivalve shell is very small, and is used as a rasp during burrowing. The mantle cavity is elongated, ending in incurrent and excurrent siphons at the posterior end of the body. Special parts, the pallets, are used to push the particles of wood out of the burrow. They consist of an axial stalk and a series of conical, calcareous parts,

increases the surface of the last part of the intestine, but does not appear to participate in digestion or absorption. The principal function of the intestine is feces formation, achieved by mucous secretion and water absorption.

Respiration. Gill currents and respiratory currents have been described, as has gill modification associated with feeding. The great enlargement of the gills of filibranchs and eulamellibranchs has provided a considerable respiratory reserve. Generally only about 10 per cent of the dissolved oxygen is removed from water passing over the gills. In intertidal clams, exposed to air during low tide, the reserve is somewhat less. *Mya*, for example, removes 25 per cent of the oxygen from water passing over its gills for a time immediately after low tide. The low percentages of oxygen removed do not mean that the gills are ineffective. Other molluscs remove 40 to 80 per cent of the available oxygen from water circulating over their gills, and there is no reason to suppose that clam gills are less effective. The critical oxygen tensions also give evidence of a great respiratory reserve. Oysters, for example, have a critical oxygen tension of 30 mm. Hg, considerably below critical oxygen tensions of *Helix* or squids.

Excretion. All pelecypods have a pair of metanephridia. The nephrostomes are reduced to renopericardial pores and wastes are removed from the blood primarily by the nephridial walls. The nephridiopores open into the mantle cavity, near the exhalant opening. Protobranchs have the most primitive nephridia. The tubule is U-shaped, and the two arms are similar. In less primitive and larger pelecypods, the nephridial surface is markedly amplified. The proximal tubule is highly folded and glandular, sometimes becoming a spongy, tubular mass. The distal tubule tends to be dilated near the nephridiopore, forming a bladder. The pelecypod nephridium is intimately associated with the circulatory system. This trend reaches its peak in the septibranchs, where the nephridia hang from the walls of the pallial sinus, completely bathed in blood. Although the wall of the proximal tubule is the site of greatest excretory activity, brownish cells form pericardial glands on the heart or pericardial wall. These cells appear to be nephrocytes, and it is assumed that the wastes they concentrate enter the nephridium by way of the renopericardial pore.

Marine pelecypods are predominantly ammonotelic. Under conditions of osmotic stress, as in fresh-water *Unio* and in intertidal species like *Mya* and *Mytilus*, ammonia excretion is sharply reduced. Unlike

forming the blade. A, *Bankia*, removed from its burrow. B, scheme of the organization of *Teredo navalis*, a common shipworm. C, a pallet. D. The left kidney of *Nuculana*, showing its regional differentiation and its relation to the gonoduct. E. Detail of the region of heart and kidney of *Anadonta*. (A and C, after Turner, from Shrock and Twenhofel. B, after Lazier. D, after Stempell. E, after Fernau, from Franc, in Grassé.) *External features:* 1, cephalic shield; 2, shell; 3, foot; 4, pallet; 5, exhalant siphon; 6, inhalant siphon; 7, dorsal mantle fold; 8, mantle; 9, gill; 10, suprabranchial cavity; 11, infrabranchial cavity. *Digestive system:* 12, mouth; 13, esophagus; 14, anterior stomach; 15, posterior stomach; 16, gastric shield; 17, style sac; 18, intestine; 19, gastric typhlosole; 20, caecum; 21, caecal typhlosole; 22, intestinal typhlosole; 23, ciliated ridge; 24, anus; 25, anal canal, an extension of the suprabranchial cavity. *Circulatory system:* 26, pericardial cavity, which continues posteriorly after bifurcating near origin of auricles; 27, auricle; 28, ventricle; 29, anterior aorta; 30, posterior aorta; 31, caecal artery; 32, supra-esophogeal artery; 33, afferent branchial vessel. *Muscles:* 34, dorsal pivot for shell; 35, ventral pivot for shell; 36, anterior adductor; 37, posterior adductor. *Excretory system:* 38, renopericardial pore; 39, proximal arm of nephridium; 40, distal arm of nephridium; 41, glandular nephridium; 42, nephridiopore. *Reproductive system:* 43, ovary; 44, gonoduct; 45, gonopore.

gastropods, pelecypods never form large amounts of uric acid. When ammonia excretion is cut down, nitrogen is excreted as amino acid or in other forms.

Circulatory System. Protobranch gills are relatively short and lie toward the back of the mantle cavity. They have a circulatory system like that of the hypothetical molluscan ancestor. The two auricles arise at the end of the efferent branchial vessels. Long and slender near the gill, they expand as they approach the ventricle. The ventricle lies in a dorsal pericardial cavity and forces blood into a single, anteriorly directed aorta (Fig. 13.38B). The aorta gives rise to a mantle artery, which supplies blood to the mantle tissues, and to a visceral artery, which supplies blood to the lacunae around the viscera. A pedal artery taking blood to the foot arises from the visceral artery. A system of sinuses collects blood from the viscera, mantle, and foot. The blood passes by the nephridia, entering a pallial sinus, from which afferent branchial vessels arise.

Modifications of the primitive arrangement are associated with several evolutionary trends affecting other parts of the pelecypod body. The much larger, longer gills of the filibranchs and eulamellibranchs do not have a posterior efferent artery to the auricle. The heart is more anteriorly placed, and blood enters the auricles at about the middle of the gill. With this change in position, the auricle also changes in shape. It is now wide at its junction with the gill vein and narrows as it approaches the ventricle. The development of strong posterior siphons favors the development of a posterior aorta, arising from the ventricle and carrying blood to the siphon and posterior part of the mantle cavity. In *Nucula* and some protobranchs, the posterior aorta is very small, but in most eulamellibranchs it is as large and important as the anterior aorta. The development of the glandular nephridium is accompanied by changes in the circulatory system which bring more blood to the nephridium and in some cases set up a more or less independent kidney arc. In *Anadonta*, for example, some of the blood returns to the heart from the kidney without having passed through the gills (Fig. 13.40). The mantle surface is very large, and blood circulated through the mantle is aerated. In a number of pelecypods, blood returning to the heart from the mantle is sent back to the heart, by way of the nephridium, without entering the gill vessels.

During active movement, the foot tissues are gorged with blood, producing a turgor pressure that is important in locomotion. The foot of sessile or swimming pelecypods is small, and pedal circulation is relatively insignificant, but the large foot of most pelecypods contains a considerable part of the blood. In these forms, a large pedal sinus at the tip of the foot drains into the median ventral sinus immediately above it. The opening between the two sinuses is guarded by Keber's valve. The valve is closed during movement, holding blood in the foot. Various other devices are used to maintain blood pressure in the foot. These include aortic enlargements, booster hearts, and compensation chambers, and occur sporadically in different pelecypod groups. Where siphons are very large, engorgement with blood is a factor in their movement also. In some cases, aortic enlargements on the posterior aorta are found.

Locomotion. The foot is used for locomotion in most pelecypods. In a number of protobranchs, the foot retains a plantar surface (Fig. 13.32D,E). The plantar surface is withdrawn as the foot is thrust forward, but is expanded when the foot is fully extended. The foot muscles are then contracted, pulling the animal forward. The anterior tip is then constricted, and the foot thrust forward again. Most pelecypods have no true plantar surface, but the foot dilates distally when it is extended. Distal enlargements of the foot and expansion of the plantar surface de-

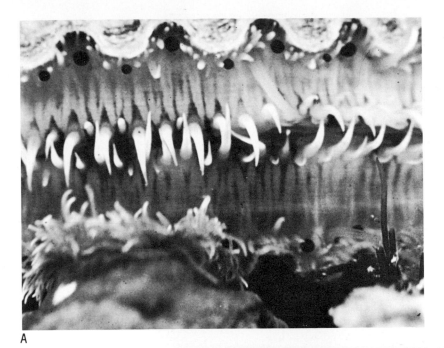

A

B

Fig. 13.39 A. The edge of the mantle of *Pecten*, a scallop. Notice eyes and tactile processes. The border of the mantle is typically supplied with sense organs in the more motile pelecypods, with especially strong development in swimming forms. B. Shell of the common mussel, *Mytilus*, showing many byssal threads. Many pelecypods attach themselves by byssal threads secreted by byssal glands in the foot. The foot of these species is considerably reduced. (Courtesy of General Biological Co.)

pends on the engorgement of the foot with blood as well as on contraction of foot muscles. In some cases, pelecypods have developed specialized foot movements. *Cardium*, for example, achieves a sort of jumping movement by sudden foot contractions that push it backward forcibly.

A number of pelecypods are sessile. Oysters are permanently attached by one shell valve, and many pelecypods attach themselves to objects by tough byssal threads, secreted by byssal glands in the foot. The secretion of the byssal thread by *Mytilus* has been described. The foot is extended, and a thread is attached. As the foot is retracted, the thread is spun out, its substance hardening on contact with the water. Thread after thread is spun, the foot moving from place to place. Jingle shells are unusual in having byssal threads that

pass through an opening in the right shell valve. Generally, the byssal threads extend through the pedal opening between mantle folds. As sessile pelecypods do not move about, it is not surprising to find that the foot is greatly reduced. Shipworms (Fig. 13.38A-C) burrow in wood, and some pelecypods burrow into rocks. The foot is not used for this purpose; the shell valves are modified and serve as rasps. Burrowing pelecypods have a much reduced foot.

Scallops swim awkwardly, propelled by jets of water ejected by sudden clapping movements of the shell valves. Water is forced out at both ends of the hinge, pushing the animal toward the ventral margin. Scallops can, however, reverse the direction of movement by expelling water ventrally. *Lima* is a swimming clam, which moves in much the same manner. Swimming pelecypods have reduced the foot markedly in

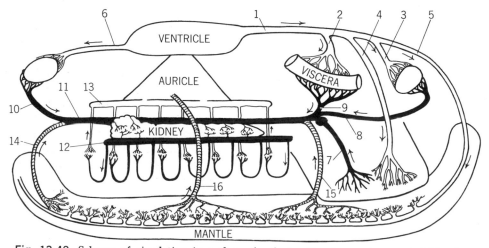

Fig. 13.40. Scheme of circulation in a clam, *Anadonta*. Vessels carrying aerated blood are shown in outline and those carrying blood that has lost oxygen to tissues are solid. Notice that the blood which passes through the mantle is at least partially aerated, and some returns directly to the auricle, while other blood returns through the kidney and gills. The extent to which mantle circulation is separate from circulation through the kidney and gills varies considerably in different pelecypods. 1, anterior aorta; 2, main visceral artery; 3, artery to anterior adductor and viscera; 4, pedal artery; 5, circumpallial artery; 6, posterior aorta; 7, pedal vein, guarded by Keber's valve at the top; 8, cephalic vein; 9, main visceral vein; 10, posterior vein; 11, venous sinus, giving rise to vessels in the kidney; 12, afferent branchial vessel; 13, efferent branchial vessel, opening into the auricle; 14, posterior mantle vessel; 15, anterior mantle vessel; 16, middle mantle vessel.

adapting to their unusual method of locomotion.

Neurosensory Apparatus. Pelecypods
have very poor sense organs, as befits quiet
animals. The close relationship between
the development of the sense organs and
movement is shown clearly, for the more
mobile species have somewhat better sense
organs.

The sense of touch is important, even
in sedentary animals. Tactile cells are
abundant in exposed parts of the body,
and are concentrated on the mantle border,
especially near the inhalant and exhalant
openings. Swimming pelecypods have definite sensory papillae or sensory tentacles
on the mantle border. Some of the pelecypods have sensory tentacles associated
with the siphons, also, as in the case of
Cardium.

A sensory patch, sometimes pigmented,
often lies near the gill attachment. It resembles an osphradium, but is innervated
from a ganglion connected to the cerebral
ganglion, so the question of homology with
the gastropod osphradia is uncertain. There
is some question, also, about its function,
for it is located in the exhalant channel
instead of the inhalant channel.

Nearly all pelecypods have a pair of
statocysts, close to or imbedded in the
pedal ganglia. In protobranchs, the statocysts are deep pits, open to the outside by
pores on the sides of the foot. Open statocysts are also found in some filibranchs
(e.g. *Mytilus*). Eulamellibranchs and septi-
branches have closed statocysts. Two types
of statoliths occur in the statocysts. A
single large statolith is often present, while
in other cases there are many small ones.
In a few cases, a large one and small ones
occur together. Although the statocysts are
gravity-detectors, organs of this kind can
be used for detecting vibrations. There is
some evidence that pelecypod statocysts are
sometimes used for this purpose, but more
work must be done before this can be established for certain.

Larval pelecypods have ocelli, but the
eyes are almost always lost during metamorphosis. They persist as cephalic eyes
in the Mytilidae, but as they are inside of
the shell they are of doubtful value. In
other pelecypods light reception has become a function of the mantle border. The
mantle photoreceptors are simple pigmented cells in some cases, but in some
pelecypods fairly complex ocelli are found.
Generally, the photosensitive elements are
concentrated in the region of the siphons.
A simple type of compound eye is formed
in the Areidae by clusters of pigmented
cells. The shallow-water scallops sometimes have complexly organized eyes (Fig.
13.39B) along the mantle border. *Cardium*
has equally complex eyes located on the
sensory tentacles of the siphon.

The simplicity of the pelecypod nervous
system is undoubtedly associated with their
sedentary habits and relatively undeveloped sensory apparatus. The most primitive arrangements are seen in the protobranchs. Here a neural triangle, composed
of cerebral, pleural, and pedal ganglia, with
pleuropedal and cerebropedal connectives,
lies on each side of the body. The cerebral
and pleural ganglia are partly united, so
the cerebropleural connectives are absent
although the ganglia are functionally connected. Commissures connect the two cerebral and two pedal ganglia. A pair of
visceral nerves arises from the pleural
ganglia, ending in visceral ganglia that are
connected by a commissure. The arrangement is essentially like that of gastropods,
but with no evidence of torsion, and with
the parietal ganglion omitted. In all other
pelecypods, the cerebral and pleural ganglia
have united to form a single ganglion, and
a single pair of connectives passes to the
pedal ganglia (Fig. 13.41). There are no
buccal ganglia, although a buccal connective often passes between the cerebral
ganglia on the two sides of the animal.
The sympathetic nerves arise from the visceral nerves or the cerebral ganglion.

Little is known of nervous function in
pelecypods. Stimulation of one nerve leads

to changes in the impulses in other nerves, indicating that feedback mechanisms are operating and that the nervous system acts as an integrated whole. Control over some specific functions is vested in specific ganglia, however. *Mytilus,* for example, loses its ability to open and close the shell in response to changes in water salinity when

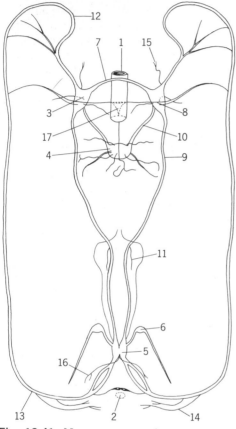

Fig. 13.41. Nervous system of a razor clam, *Tagelus,* seen from dorsal side. (After Stempell, from Franc, in Grassé.) **1,** esophagus; **2,** anus; **3,** cerebropleural ganglion; **4,** pedal ganglion; **5,** visceral ganglion; **6,** osphradial ganglion; **7,** cerebral commissure; **8,** buccal commissure; **9,** cerebropleuralvisceral connective; **10,** cerebropleuralpedal connective; **11,** renal nerve; **12,** anterior pallial nerve; **13,** posterior pallial nerve; **14,** nerve to siphon; **15,** nerve to anterior adductor; **16,** nerve to posterior adductor; **17,** stomatogastric nerve.

the visceral ganglia are removed, and the pedal ganglia are required for creeping movements and the spinning of byssal threads.

Reproduction. The reproductive system of pelecypods is very simple. Most of the pelecypods are dioecious, with a pair of gonads opening into a pair of gonoducts. In the more primitive pelecypods, the gonoducts join the nephridia on each side of the body. The point of junction of gonoduct and nephridium varies greatly. It is near the renopericardial pore in some protobranchs and near the nephridiopore in some filibranchs. The relationship of nephridium and gonoduct is lost in eulamellibranchs and some filibranchs. They have a complete gonoduct on each side of the body, ending in gonopores located near the nephridiopores. Hermaphroditism has apparently appeared independently in several groups of pelecypods, for the arrangements differ markedly. Some hermaphroditic species have a single gonad that produces both ova and sperm and opens by way of a single gonoduct. At the other extreme are species with testis and ovary completely separated, and separate gonoducts and gonopores for each. A variety of intermediate arrangements is known.

Development. Pelecypods give a good illustration of the principle that more primitive groups follow a more primitive course of development, and that larger, yolkier eggs, and eggs that are brooded, undergo modified development. In some of the protobranchs the velum is reflected, forming rows of ciliated test cells (Fig. 13.42A). The larva resembles an amphineuran larva or the larva of *Dentalium.* The test cells are suddenly shed. The abrupt dispersal of the test is reflected in the habit of pelecypods generally to cast off the velar cells as metamorphosis begins. Without the velum, the larva has no means of locomotion and settles to the bottom. It is at this time that sessile forms like the oyster attach to objects.

The pelecypod veliger has several peculiarities. Its basic organization is similar to the gastropod veliger, but the velum is circular in contrast to the bilobed velum characteristic of gastropods. The apical tufts of cilia are often fused to form a conspicuous "flagellum." The larval foot is invaginated at the larval byssal gland, even in species which have no adult byssal threads. The larval byssal thread is used in a variety of ways. It sometimes attaches the young to the maternal gills, and sometimes makes a temporary attachment to pebbles or sand. Gill formation follows a regular pattern. The most anterior gill filament appears first and the others appear in sequence. The larval gills, unlike the adult gills, are never reflected. Folding occurs during the growth and metamorphosis of the juvenile clams. As torsion does not occur, the veliger retains its bilateral symmetry (Fig. 13.42B,D); the shell is laid down originally in a bivalved form.

Fresh-water sphaerids and unionids incubate the young in the gills. The velum is greatly reduced, and the shell valves develop quickly. Sphaerids develop directly into juveniles when they emerge from the parent. Unionids, however, are released as glochidia (Fig. 13.42C), small shelled larvae that are obligatory parasites. Some swim about by clapping the shell valves together, while others lie in wait on the bottom with the valves open wide. Within a few days they must attach to the gills, fins, or body surface of a fish. The shell valves are clamped together on the host tissue, in some cases with the aid of a glochidial hook on the shell valves. Host epidermis grows around them, and they continue development in the resulting cyst. Phagocytic mantle cells feed on the host tissues. After from two to six weeks, the young clams break out of the cyst and fall to the bottom. They attach themselves temporarily with a byssus and become juveniles. Most species require several years to reach maturity.

Class Scaphopoda—Tusk Shells

Scaphopods are distinctive creatures with a shell in the form of a tapered tube, usually slightly curved, and open at both ends. About 200 species have been described. They burrow in sand or mud, with the larger, anterior end down and the other end thrust slightly above the bottom (Fig. 13.43A). Water enters and leaves through the posterior aperture, and the foot is thrust from the anterior aperture during burrowing. Some scaphopods live in shallow water, but most live at moderate depths. A few occur 5000 m. or more below the surface.

Eggs are released singly, and pass through trochophore and veliger stages. The symmetrical veliger is pelecypod-like, and forms a mantle and shell gland early in development. The mantle grows rapidly, and soon unites along the ventral margin, forming a tube around the body. Thereafter the shell is tubular, and the body lengthens as it grows. The general body organization is rather like that of a clam, with the mantle and shell sealed ventrally except at the anterior and posterior ends.

The relationship of scaphopods to other molluscs is not very clear. They most resemble pelecypods during early development, and like pelecypods, the adults have reduced heads. They may be a very early, divergent stem from primitive pelecypods, but if so have developed traits that are very unlike modern pelecypods. A well-developed buccal mass containing a radula with five teeth in each transverse row sets them off from modern pelecypods. There are no gills in the mantle cavity, and there is no heart, circulation occurring in a series of open sinuses. If they had pelecypod ancestors, it must have been at a time before pelecypods had lost their radula.

The long, slender foot is thrust forward during burrowing. It ends in a discoid tip or in lateral processes that can be ex-

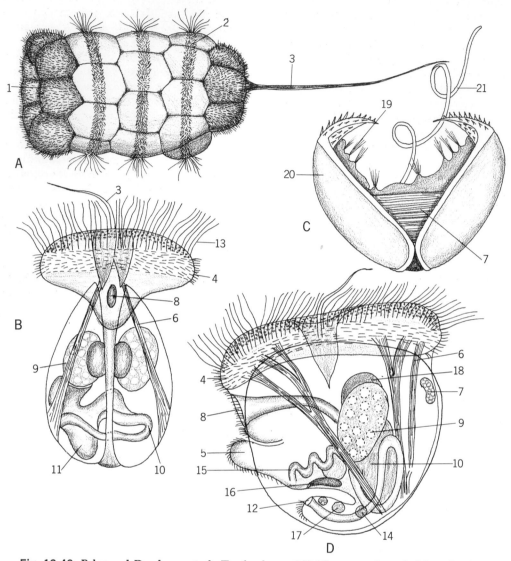

Fig. 13.42. Pelecypod Development. **A.** Trochophore of *Yoldia*, a protobranch. Note the five rows of ciliated test cells, which strip away suddenly during development, as in the Aplacophora. **B** and **D.** Two views of a pelecypod veliger. The veliger remains symmetrical, as torsion does not occur in pelecypods, and the conspicuous bilobed form of the velum, so common in gastropods, is not apparent. **C.** A glochidium of a fresh-water clam, *Anadonta*. Glochidia pass through a period of parasitism on fish gills. The larval thread protrudes from the shell and probably aids in attaching to the host fish. The larval shell bears hooks which clamp on the gill filaments of the host fish. (A, after Drew. B and D, after Meisenheimer. C, after Pennak.) **1**, blastopore; **2**, test cell; **3**, apical tuft; **4**, velum; **5**, foot; **6**, retractor muscle; **7**, adductor muscle; **8**, mouth; **9**, digestive gland; **10**, midgut; **11**, caecum; **12**, anus; **13**, prototroch; **14**, heart; **15**, gonad; **16**, pedal gland; **17**, visceral ganglion; **18**, pedal ganglion; **19**, sensory hair; **20**, valve; **21**, larval thread.

panded to form an anchor. The strong foot retractors pull the shell up toward the anchored foot.

The head is shaped like a proboscis, and is equipped with long, slender, capitate tentacles known as captacula. The captacula are prehensile and function as food gatherers, feeling about in the mud, and being retracted to carry food to the mouth. The spacious buccal cavity contains a radula used in swallowing and in food fragmentation. The esophagus produces a pair of pouches. The rather small stomach gives off a caecum, into which the digestive glands open. The large digestive glands branch out into the mantle. A coiled intestine opens through a ventral anus; the feces are carried out of the mantle cavity with the respiratory currents.

Scaphopods do not have a well-organized flow of water through the mantle cavity.

Cilia draw water into the mantle cavity, and when it is fully charged, sudden muscular contractions discharge the mantle contents.

There is no heart or pericardial cavity, and the paired nephridia, of course, have no nephrostomes. The nephridia are saccate, with much-folded walls. The nephridiopores are located on each side of the anus.

Little is known of scaphopod physiology. A subradular organ in the buccal cavity is thought to be chemoreceptive. The captacula are important tactile organs, and probably receive stimuli that mediate burrowing movements. Otherwise the only special sense organs are statocysts, located in the foot near the pedal ganglia. The nervous system is organized like that of protobranch pelecypods, but with the addition of a buccal ganglion on each side of

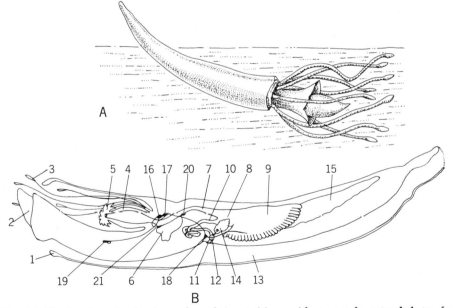

Fig. 13.43. Scaphopods. A. A scaphopod in position, with captacula extended to feed. B. Scheme of organization of *Dentalium*. (B, after Pelseneer, in Lankester.) 1, mantle; 2, foot; 3, captacula; 4, proboscis; 5, mouth; 6, radular sac; 7, esophagus; 8, stomach; 9, digestive gland; 10, intestine; 11 anus; 12, anal gland; 13, mantle cavity; 14, nephridium; 15, gonad; 16, cerebral ganglion; 17, pleural ganglion; 18, visceral ganglion; 19, pedal ganglion; 20, stomatogastric ganglion; 21, labial ganglion and commissure.

the buccal mass. The buccal ganglia are connected to the cerebral ganglia by connectives, and to each other by a commissure.

Sexes are separate. The single, median gonad is long, extending from an anterior gonoduct to the posterior tip of the body. The gonoduct is connected to the right nephridium, thus resembling the gonoduct of aspidobranch gastropods.

Class Cephalopoda—Squids, Octopi, and Nautilus

From the standpoint of complexity of structure and behavior, cephalopods stand at the apex of invertebrate evolutionary development. Some fossil and modern cephalopods are tiny creatures, 2 to 3 cm. long, but *Architeuthis*, the giant squid, may reach 18 m. or more in length, and giant conical shells from the Ordovician were 4½ m. long and 30 cm. wide at the aperture of the shell. The largest coiled shell, *Pachydiscus seppenradensis*, is from the Cretaceous and reaches 2.5 m. in diameter.

Cephalopods first appeared in the upper Cambrian. Three major groups can be recognized, the nautiloids, represented today by a single species, *Nautilus*; the ammonoids, now wholly extinct, and the coleoids, which include the modern squids, cuttlefish, and octopi. Although only *Nautilus* remains today, the nautiloids were very successful, reaching their peak during the Ordovician and Silurian periods, about 400 to 500 million years ago. Ammonoids reached their peak during the Mesozoic, about 200 million years ago. Coleoids did not appear until near the end of the Paleozoic. As they have reduced shells, their fossil record is quite incomplete. They may be near their peak today, or, perhaps have not yet reached it. All modern cephalopods are marine animals, and fossil findings suggest that this has always been so. They are widely distributed today,

occurring from the littoral zone to great depths.

The visceral hump of cephalopods, like gastropods, became very high. The first cephalopods had conical shells. Plane spirals appeared early, and some conical spirals appeared, but these were never abundant. Cephalopods are characterized by a whorl of tentacles around the margin of the head, and by a funnel, known as the hyponome, derived from the foot. The hyponome opens into the mantle cavity. Water is ejected from the mantle cavity through the hyponome, propelling the organism. The cephalopods are the most mobile of all molluscs, an important factor in directing the course of their evolutionary development. The head is highly developed, the sense organs are among the best to be found in animals, and the brain has an advanced structure. The nautiloids and ammonoids are characterized by an external shell. A cord of tissue, the siphon, extends to the tip of the shell, but the main mass of the body is withdrawn from the apex as the animal grows and more shell is secreted. At intervals, septa are formed, dividing the shell cavity into a series of chambers (camera). The last, large, living chamber houses the main mass of the body. Gas is secreted into the chambers of the shell, counterbalancing its weight, and so aiding in locomotion and floating.

Modern cephalopods are usually divided into two subclasses, Dibranchiata, characterized by a single pair of gills and an internal shell, and Tetrabranchiata, characterized by two pairs of gills and an external shell. *Nautilus* is the only living tetrabranch. Paleontologists do not have enough information about the soft parts of extinct cephalopods to feel safe in dividing them on the basis of gill number, although it is possible that the extinct forms may have had two pairs of gills, like *Nautilus*. They classify the cephalopods into three subclasses, Nautiloidea, Ammonoidea, and Coleoidea, on the basis of shell characters. As this system separates the tetrabranch *Nautilus* from other forms, and as there are so many more extinct than modern cephalopods, it seems best to follow the palaeontological classification.

CLASSIFICATION

Subclass Nautiloidea. Cephalopods with coiled or straight external shells, divided into chambers by straight septa that meet the shell in simple sutures. At least 14 orders are recognized, of which only Nautilida is recent. Example: *Nautilus* (Fig. 13.44A).

Subclass Ammonoidea. Cephalopods with coiled external shells, divided into chambers by variously shaped septa meeting the shell in complex sutures; typically with external sculpturing of the shell. About 5000 species have been described, but orders have not been agreed upon. Examples: *Idoceras* (Fig. 13.44B); *Baculites* (Fig. 13.44C).

Subclass Coleoidea. Cephalopods with a single pair of gills, and with an internal shell, considerably reduced, or without a shell.

Order Belemnoidea. Extinct coleoids with an internal shell having a well-developed apical part, the rostrum, a dorsal, plate-like pro-ostracum, and a chambered phragmacone. Example: *Belemnoteuthis* (Fig. 13.44E).

Order Sepioidea. Coleoids with a shell having a reduced rostrum, a modified pro-ostracum, and a rudimentary phragmacone; with ten tentacles and a well-developed coelom; with the fourth pair of tentacles specialized and equipped with a special pit into which they can be retracted. Examples: *Sepia* (Fig. 13.44F); *Spirula* (Fig. 13.44D).

Order Teuthoidea Coleoids without a rostrum and with the phragmacone rudimentary or missing; pro-ostracum modified to form a pen-shaped gladius; with ten arms; the fourth arms may be modified, but are never withdrawn into special pits. This order is divided into the *oegopsids*, usually without specialized fourth arms, and without a cornea in the eye (Example, *Architeuthis*, the giant squid, Fig. 13.45A), and the *myopsids*, with greatly lengthened fourth arms and a cornea (Example, *Loligo*, the common squid, Fig. 13.45B).

Order Octopoda. Coleoids with eight tentacles and a reduced coelom; with a shortened, rounded body, and usually without a vestige of the shell. Example: *Octopus* (Fig. 13.45C-E).

CEPHALOPOD ANATOMY AND PHYSIOLOGY

External Form. Cephalopod evolution has resulted in the complete shifting of the functional axes of the body. With the elongation of the visceral hump, and with the development of the hyponome or funnel, used for jet propulsion, from the posterior end of the foot, the primitive ventral surface was changed to the functional anterior end. The apex of the visceral hump, primitively the dorsal surface, has become the posterior end of the body. The funnel marks the primitively posterior end of the animal, but is functionally ventral. In discussing the cephalopods, functional rather than morphological axes will be used; head and tentacles will be considered anterior, and the funnel ventral.

During development the head and foot of cephalopods become indistinguishably merged. A circumoral ring, generally considered to be at least partly derivative of the foot, surrounds the head. From this ring the arms or tentacles develop. *Nautilus* has over 90 tentacles; sepioids and teuthoids, ten; and octopoids, eight. The funnel or hyponome, also derived from the foot, is attached to the ventral head surface. It is apparently homologous to the epipodia of some gastropods. In *Nautilus* it is composed of two separate folds, but in other cephalopods has become a single structure. An unusual feature of the *Nautilus* head is the muscular dorsal hood,

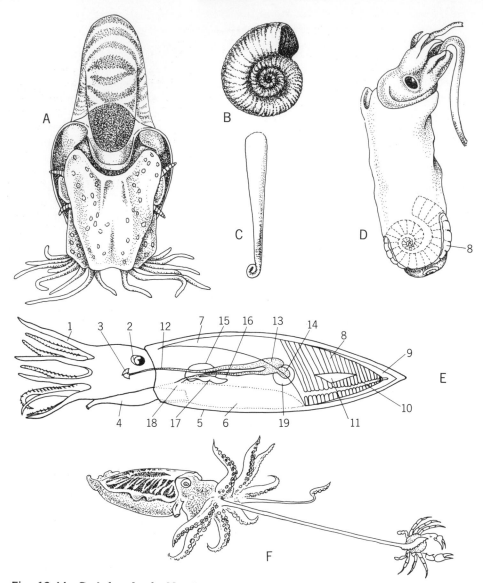

Fig. 13.44. Cephalopods. **A.** *Nautilus*, as it appears when creeping. *Nautilus* is the only living representative of the Nautiloidea, which differ from the ammonoids in having simple sutures where the septa dividing the shell into chambers meet the outer shell. **B.** *Idoceras*, a coiled ammonoid from the Jurassic. **C.** *Baculites*, a coleoid from the upper Cretaceous. Coleoids have a single pair of gills and an internal shell. The shell is well developed in the Belemnoidea, to which *Belemnoteuthis* (**E**) belongs. Impressions like these make it possible, in some instances, to get a fairly detailed idea of internal organization. **F.** *Sepia*, a cuttlefish, representing the Sepioidea. The sepioids have ten arms and a moderately reduced internal shell. **D.** *Spirula*, another sepoid with a small, coiled internal shell. (A, after Willey, from Pelseneer, in Lankester. B, after Imlay. C, after Reeside. E, after Roger. F, after Boulenger. D, after Owen and Adams, from Cooke.) 1, arm; 2, eye; 3, mandible; 4, funnel or hyponome; 5, mantle; 6, mantle cavity; 7, proostracum of shell; 8, phragmacone of shell; 9, rostrum of shell; 10, siphuncle; 11, fin, 12, esophagus; 13, stomach; 14, caecum; 15, digestive gland; 16, intestine; 17, ink sac; 18, anus; 19, gonad.

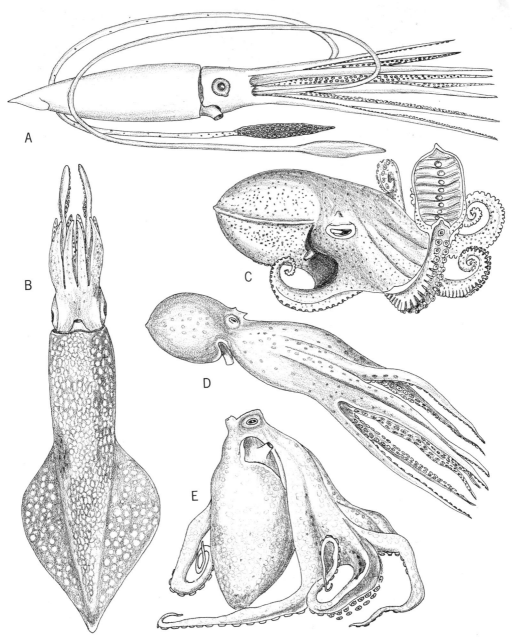

Fig. 13.45. A. *Architeuthis*, the giant squid. *Architeuthis* is a coleoid belonging to the order Teuthoidea, characterized by ten arms, a shell with no rostrum and either without or with a much-reduced phragmacone, and with a pen-shaped gladius formed from the proostracum. The giant squid is an oegopsid teuthoid, without a cornea and without specialized fourth arms. B. *Loligo*, the common squid, a myopsid teuthoid with elongated fourth arms and a cornea over the eye. C. *Octopus lentus*, a member of the Octopoda, characterized by eight arms, no shell, and a short, rounded body. The hectocotyl arm is turned up, showing the arrangement for carrying spermatophores. D and E. Resting and swimming positions of *Octopus vulgaris*. (A and C, after Verrill. D and E, after Merculiano, from Cooke.)

549

which serves as an operculum when the animal withdraws into the shell. One of the most prominent features of the head is the pair of large eyes, located on the lateral or dorsolateral surfaces.

The mantle invests the body. The *Nautilus* mantle lines the living chamber of the shell and extends through the septa as a siphon, reaching the last chamber at the apex. The tough, muscular coleoid mantle is external, and contains the reduced shell. The mantle of squids projects forward as a collar, which surrounds the head and funnel, leaving a clear path for water to enter the mantle cavity. The mantle of octopi, however, adheres to the dorsal and lateral surfaces of the head, considerably reducing the opening to the mantle cavity.

Shell. Nautiloids and ammonoids have an external, chambered shell. The protoconch or embryonic shell, lies at the apex. It is present or absent in fossil species, but is lacking in adult *Nautilus*. The upper part of the shell is divided into camera or chambers by perforated partitions (Fig. 13.46A). The chambered section of the shell is known as the phragmacone. The final large chamber is the living chamber, in which the body lies. A ventral notch, the hyponomic sinus, often marks the aperature, providing space for the funnel.

The first nautiloids had a straight conical shell, like the first gastropods. The shells of many fossil nautiloids are slightly curved, while others are loosely or tightly coiled. Some have exogastric shells, with the ventral surface convex, while others have endogastric shells, with the dorsal surface convex (Fig. 13.46B-E). Ammonoids appeared after the nautiloids, and originally had coiled shells. Secondarily straightened shells are not uncommon, however. The outstanding difference between the ammonoids and the nautiloids is the nature of the septa. Ammonoid septa are wrinkled and meet the shell in sinuous sutures, while the smooth nautiloid septa meet the shell in straight sutures (Fig. 13.46F,G).

Coleoids capitalized to a greater extent on the increased capacity for movement provided by the hyponome. Cephalopods are carnivorous animals, using the tentacles for food capture. While some carnivores are successful in ambushing or trapping prey, most carnivores pursue prey. Coleoids evidently followed an evolutionary line which increased their mobility and in this way contributed to success in food capture. In any case, shell reduction with increased mobility prevailed. The earliest coleoids retained the maximal shell protection with a minimal weight. *Belemnoteuthis* (Fig. 13.44E) shows the primitive organization of body and shell. A thickened guard, the rostrum, forms the apex of the shell, and a plate-like pro-ostracum covers the dorsal surface. A straight-shelled cephalopod could evolve such an internal shell by the addition of a rostral sheath around the phragmacone, and extending the anterior, dorsal margin of the aperture to form a pro-ostracum. All modern coleoids can be derived from an ancestral stock of the *Belemnoteuthis* type (Fig. 13.47). Loss of the pro-ostracum, followed by coiling and eventually loss of the rostrum, and coiling of the phragmacone leads to sepiods of the *Spirula* type. Conversion of the pro-ostracum into a covering for the phragmacone, reduction of the rostrum, and slanting of the septa would lead to forms like modern *Sepia*. Reduction of the rostrum, loss of the phragmacone, and conversion of the pro-ostracum into a conchiolin pen or gladius would lead to such teuthoids as *Loligo*. Total loss of the shell would lead to octopods.

Locomotion. Cephalopods swim by ejecting a jet of water through the funnel. *Loligo* pumps water in and out of the mantle cavity by alternate contractions of antagonistic circular and longitudinal muscles in the mantle. When the circular muscles relax and longitudinal muscles contract, the collar flares out and water enters through the space between the mantle and the head. Contraction of the

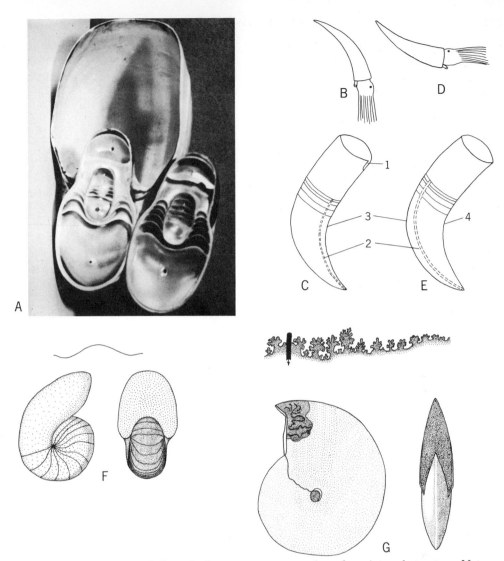

Fig. 13.46. **A.** *Nautilus* shell, with the upper part removed to show internal structure. Note the large living chamber, and many small chambers within. New septa are formed as the animal grows. An extension of the digestive gland, the siphon, passes through the siphuncle, which pierces each septum. Gas is secreted into the shell chambers, adding to the buoyancy of the animal and making it more mobile. **B-D.** Exogastric and endogastric shells. Many fossil cephalopods had straight shells, while others had curved or spirally coiled shells. Shells may be curved so that the funnel is on the concave or the convex side. When the funnel is on the concave side, a hyponomic sinus may mark the margin of the shell on this side, and the siphuncle lies near the concave side, as in B and C. These shells are endogastric. In exogastric shells, the relations are reversed (D, E). **F.** Two views of a Cretaceous *Nautilus*, and an outline of the complete suture. Note the simplicity of the sutural form. **G.** Two views of the shell, and an outline of part of the suture of *Placenticeras*, a Cretaceous ammonoid. Note the complexity of the sutural outline, characteristic of the ammonoids. (B-E, after Shrock and Twenhofel. F, after Sharpe. G, after Meek.) **1,** hyponomic sinus; **2,** siphuncle; **3,** ventral side; **4,** dorsal side.

circular muscles forces the collar against the head, so that the emerging water must pass through the funnel. The funnel can be aimed forward or back, so squids can swim in either direction. Fins on the mantle undulate gently when the squid is hovering, but make powerful movements during rapid swimming. They are, however, more important as stabilizers than as propellors. Squids swim gracefully and are able to achieve speeds that compare favorably with the most active fishes.

The details of swimming movements differ in other cephalopod groups, but all are essentially similar. *Nautilus* forces water out of the mantle cavity by retracting the body and contracting the funnel musculature. Octopi can also swim by ejecting water through the funnel, but have assumed a benthic life and usually creep about, using the suction cups on the arms for attachment as they pull themselves along. They can move with considerable speed, even on land. Some octopi are espe-

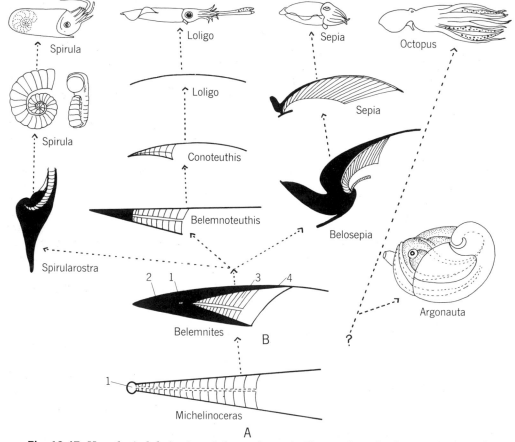

Fig. 13.47. Hypothetical derivation of the modern coleoid types from fossil types. Presumably a straight-shelled ancestral form enclosed the shell in the mantle (**A**), leading to the differentiation of the rostrum, phragmacone, and proostracum of the shell, as in *Belemnoteuthis* (**B**). Total reduction of shell leads to the Octopoda, although *Argonauta* has developed a calcareous egg case which resembles a shell. Different lines of shell reduction lead toward the modern *Spirula*, with the phragmacone retained; *Loligo*, with a gladius and no phragmacone; and *Sepia*, with remnants of both rostrum and phragmacone. (After Shrock and Twenhofel.)

cially modified for swimming, and have webs between the tentacles (Fig. 13.48A).

Chromatophores. Special pigment cells, known as chromatophores, are found in the mantle epithelium of coleoids. Each contains a single pigment, yellow, red, brown, or blue, as the case may be. Different species have different combinations of colors, in different proportions. The chromatophores have an elastic cell membrane. A circlet of smooth muscle cells attaches to the cell membrane. Contraction of the muscle cells stretches the cell and expands the pigment spot, while relaxation of the muscles and recoil of the stretched cell membrane contract the pigment spot (Fig. 13.49A,B). A number of other kinds of animals have pigment cells that can expand or contract, but most of them work slowly. The muscled chromatophores of cephalopods work with surprising speed. The chromatophores of a hovering *Loligo* blink on and off like lights in an electric sign, giving a beautiful display. The chromatophores are controlled by inhibitory and excitatory fibers. Inhibition is a cerebral function, apparently depending on a special color center located in the central ganglia. Stimuli pass through motor centers in the subesophageal ganglia on their way to the chromatophores. Substances in the blood, however, also affect the chromatophores. Tyramine acts like adrenalin, causing chromatophore expansion and a darker color. Betaine acts like acetylcholine, stimulating the inhibitory center and leading to the relaxation of the muscles, chromatophore retraction and lighter color. The humoral controls vested in the blood are not species specific. Blood transfusions between dark and light species cause a color change.

The presence of chromatophores permits color changes for background matching. Normal postural reflexes keep the ventral surface lighter than the dorsal surface, providing camouflage during swimming. Impairment of the optic nerves reduces, but does not stop, chromatophore changes and

prevents background matching. If the suckers on the tentacles are removed the animal becomes lighter. General stimulation and excitability increase chromatophore activity, producing responses that have an emotional quality.

Food Capture and Digestion. The arms are used for capturing prey. They are complexly muscled and under delicate control. *Nautilus* arms have no suckers, but are made adhesive by secretions. Coleoids have muscular suction cups on the inner surfaces of the arms. The suction cups are extremely variable in structure. Some are set on stalks, some have horny rims, and some have a hook that helps to attach the arms to the prey. The suction cups are quite powerful. Even the tough skin of a whale will show the marks made by the suckers of a giant squid. Other molluscs, crustaceans, and fish are the principal prey of cephalopods, the exact nature of the diet depending on the size and habits of the species.

The prey is brought to the mouth and attacked with the heavily muscled, horny, beak-like jaws. *Loligo* can take a clean bite out of a captured fish. Poison glands open into the buccal cavity near the subradular organ. Some of the cephalopod toxins are extremely effective. Crustaceans die almost instantaneously when bitten by octopi, and the bite of an octopus has been known to cause human death.

The buccal cavity contains a radula, typically with five teeth in each transverse row. Most cephalopods have two pairs of salivary glands. The anterior pair secretes mucus, possibly accompanied by some digestive enzymes. The posterior pair are the poison glands. *Nautilus*, however, has only the anterior pair.

The esophagus is muscular, and peristaltic contractions are used for swallowing. The esophagus may be a simple tube, but it is sometimes dilated to form a crop near the distal end, as in *Nautilus* and in octopi.

The esophagus opens into a stomach, to which a blind sac, the caecum, is attached

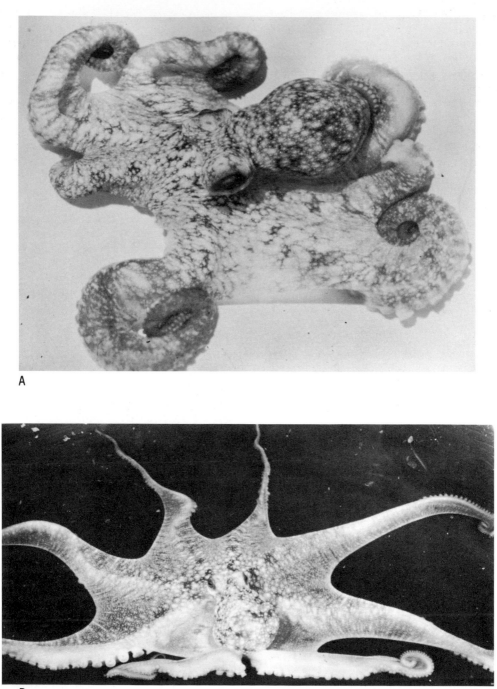

A

B

Fig. 13.48. Two views of *Octopus briareus*, a swimming octopus. Webs at the base of the tentacles aid in swimming. (Courtesy of the Smithsonian Institution.)

(Fig. 13.50). The caecum is a simple sac in *Loligo*, but in many cephalopods it is spiraled. The large digestive gland opens into the upper caecum by paired ducts. The structure of the digestive gland varies considerably in different cephalopods, but in all cases they are highly differentiated. *Sepia* has a pair of digestive glands, but in other cephalopods the two members of the pair are united to form a single organ. The digestive gland is composed of a larger,

more compact "hepatic" region and of a smaller, more follicular "pancreatic" region, and is sometimes called the hepatopancreas. In squids the two regions have become separated into distinct organs. The terms "hepatic" and "pancreatic" should be used with some care, as they do not imply functions entirely comparable to the functions of the vertebrate liver and pancreas. Proteases, peptidases, and lipases have been recovered from both hepatic and

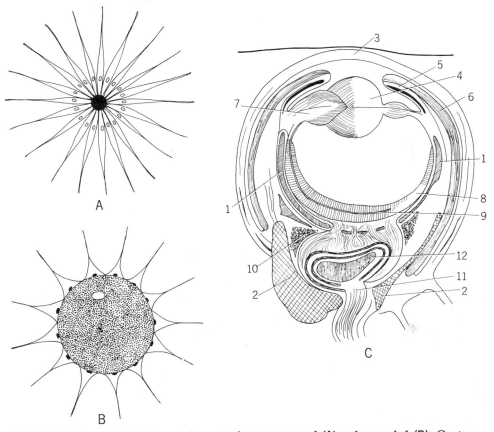

Fig. 13.49. A and B. Cephalopod chromatophores contracted (A) and expanded (B). Contraction of the radially arranged mucle fibers expands the chromatophore, causing expansion of the pigmented area and a darker color. C. Scheme of eye of *Sepia*. Note the strong convergence between the eye of cephalopods and vertebrates. (A and B, after Bozler, from Prosser *et al*. C, after Henson, from Pelseneer, in Lankester.) 1, cartilaginous capsule; 2, cephalic cartilage; 3, cornea; 4, lens; 5, iris containing cartilaginous support; 6, reflecting, pigmented layer; 7, ciliary body; 8, retina; 9, retinal pigment layer; 10, white body; 11, optic nerve; 12, optic ganglion.

pancreatic regions of *Sepia*, but the enzymes from the two regions differ biochemically. The hepatic region secretes only when the stomach contains food, but the pancreatic region secretes continuously, the

enzymes being stored in the caecum. Digestion begins in the stomach, and the partly digested food moves into the caecum. Here digestion is completed, and a major part of absorption also occurs. Spirally arranged, ciliated platelets form a sorting area, which diverts larger particles and returns them to the stomach. Food residues pass through a straight or coiled intestine. Here some food absorption takes place, and feces are formed.

A remarkable peculiarity of the coleoid digestive system is the specialization of the rectal gland into an ink gland and ink sac. The ink, known as sepia, has long been used as an artist's pigment. It usually consists primarily of melanin. However, some abyssal cephalopods secrete a luminescent ink. The ink apparatus is a protective device. When the animal is disturbed, it can eject a cloud of ink from its anus, escaping behind its protective screen.

Respiration. Respiratory exchange occurs at the surface of the folded, highly vascular gills. Ciliary currents, so important in gill ventilation in other molluscs, is of no consequence in cephalopods, for the muscular movements used in filling and emptying the mantle cavity suffice. The gills are evi-

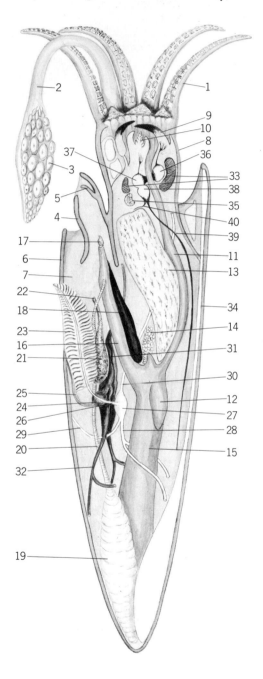

Fig. 13.50. Scheme of organization of *Loligo* (largely after Schechter). *External features:* 1, arm; 2, tentacle; 3, sucker; 4, hyponome (funnel); 5, valve; 6, mantle; 7, mantle cavity; 8, head. *Digestive system:* 9, jaw; 10, radula; 11, esophagus; 12, stomach; 13, hepatic portion of digestive gland; 14, pancreatic portion of digestive gland; 15, caecum; 16, intestine; 17, anus; 18, ink sac. *Urogenital system:* 19, gonad; 20, gonoduct; 21, nephridium; 22, nephridiopore. *Circulatory system:* 23, gill; 24, branchial heart; 25, efferent branchial vessel; 26, afferent branchial vessel; 27, systemic heart; 28, posterior aorta; 29, mantle artery; 30, anterior aorta; 31, anterior vena cava; 32, left posterior vena cava. *Shell and skeleton:* 33, cephalic cartilages; 34, gladius (pen). *Neurosensory apparatus:* 35, statocyst; 36, cerebral ganglion; 37, pedal ganglion; 38, visceral ganglion; 39, pleural nerve; 40, visceral nerve.

dently modified ctenidia, with a central axis containing the main afferent and efferent blood vessels, and flattened gill filaments containing capillary beds.

Nautilus, with two pairs of gills, is a representative of the most primitive cephalopod subclass. Are two pairs of gills primitive for the cephalopods? No other living cephalopod shows any evidences of a second pair of gills. Yonge (1947) has suggested that the dibranchiate line of cephalopods leading to the modern coleoids has always been present, and the four gills of *Nautilus* are a secondary development, perhaps a response to increased body size. Certainly larger species than *Nautilus* get along with a single pair of gills today, and if this is the case, addition of more gills probably occurred sporadically among ancient cephalopods. The fact that the number of pairs of gills is increased in the Amphineura indicates that this capacity exists in molluscs. Perhaps enough impressions of the soft parts of fossil forms will eventually be obtained to provide a good answer to the question.

Coelom and Nephridia. Cephalopods have a relatively spacious coelom, but it retains a molluscan character. A flattened pericardial cavity is partly separated from the larger perivisceral coelom by a perforated or incomplete septum. Lateral extensions of the pericardial cavity of sepioids and teuthoids enclose the accessory hearts at the bases of the gills, but in octopi the pericardial cavity extends only to the base of the accessory hearts. The perivisceral coelom is generally restricted to the visceral hump, but in some squids it extends far forward over the pericardial cavity, becoming very large. The larger coelom is in part the result of a reduction of the haemocoel lacunae, for in cephalopods the blood circulates, to a great extent, in arteries, veins, and capillary beds.

Nautilus differs from other cephalopods in having two pairs of nephridia. Is this duplication primitive or a secondary development? As with the duplication of gills,

there is insufficient evidence to be sure. The existence of several pairs of nephridia in *Neopilina* suggests that the first molluscs may have tended rather more toward metamerism than has generally been thought, and if this tendency proves to be primitive rather than secondary in *Neopilina*, it may mean that the first cephalopods had two or more pairs of nephridia and gills. The *Nautilus* nephridia have lost all relationship with the pericardial cavity. The nephrostomes, however, do not wholly disappear. They develop into two openings that connect the pericardial cavity with the mantle cavity.

Other cephalopods have typical molluscan nephridia, with nephridiopores opening into the mantle cavity, and renopericardial pores, representing vestigial nephrostomes associated with the pericardial cavity. Pericardial glands in the pericardial cavity may accumulate some wastes, but most wastes reach the nephridia through the circulatory system. A copious flow of blood reaches the much-folded, glandular nephridium through a large nephridial vein. The two nephridia unite at the midline. Here a diverticulum associated with the pancreas arises. Apparently the excretory surface is further amplified by pancreatic participation in excretion.

Circulation. Cephalopods have an advanced circulatory system, with a relatively complex organization. It differs from the circulatory system of other molluscs in having a much more extensive set of arteries and veins, and in having a number of capillary beds in place of the more open haemocoelic lacunae characteristic of most molluscs. Nevertheless, the basic pattern of blood-flow follows the typical molluscan plan (Fig. 13.51). Each gill drains into an auricle, so *Nautilus* has four auricles and other cephalopods two. An aorta carries blood from the ventricle, giving off branches to the viscera and continuing to the head, where branches to the cephalic organs and tentacles arise. Blood returns from the capillary beds through a complex venous system. Abdominal veins return blood from the viscera; pallial veins, from the mantle; and an anterior vena cava, from the head. All of these drain into the efferent branchial vessels, equipped with booster hearts that drive the blood into the gills. Blood returns to the auricles by way of efferent branchial veins.

Neurosensory Apparatus. Active life and a high grade of organization usually go with a well-developed set of sense organs and a centralized nervous system. Cephalopods are no exceptions.

Most of the sense organs are essentially like those of other molluscs, although some are somewhat more advanced. Tactile cells are found in the epidermis, and are concentrated in the tentacles and other points of high sensitivity. Tactile reception is particularly important in the suction cups of

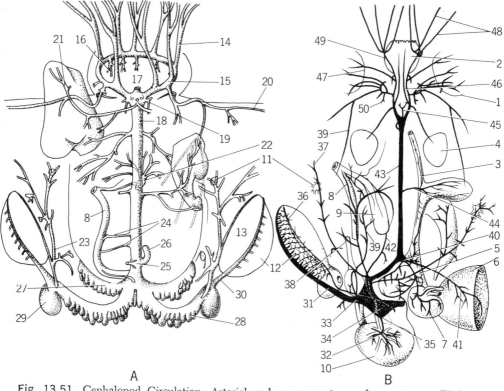

A   B

Fig. 13.51. Cephalopod Circulation. Arterial and venous systems of an octopus, *Eledone*. (After Isgrove.) *Landmark organs:* 1, eye; 2, buccal mass; 3, esophagus; 4, salivary gland; 5, stomach; 6, digestive gland (liver); 7, spiral caecum; 8, intestine; 9, ink sac; 10, gonad; 11, stellate ganglion; 12, gill; 13, branchial gland. *Veins:* 14, veins from tentacles; 15, cephalic vein; 16, superficial cephalic branches; 17, venous sinus; 18, anterior vena cava; 19, orbital vein; 20, mantle vein; 21, vein from siphon; 22, hepatic vein; 23, pallial vein; 24, intestinal veins; 25, septal vein; 26, abdominal vein; 27, lateral vena cava; 28, venous appendages; 29, branchial heart; 30, afferent branchial vein; 31, efferent branchial vein; 32, genital vein. *Heart and arteries:* 33, auricle; 34, ventricle; 35, genital artery; 36, branchial artery; 37, pallial artery; 38, septal artery; 39, artery to visceral envelope; 40, visceral artery; 41, hepatic artery; 42, artery to ink sac; 43, anterior aorta; 44, esophageal artery; 45, nuchal artery; 46, pharyngeal artery; 47, orbital artery; 48, arteries to arms; 49, cephalic artery; 50, artery to siphon.

the coleoid tentacles. *Nautilus* has a pair of osphradia near the gills, and the tentacles immediately in front of and behind the eyes are specialized for chemoreception. A pair of chemoreceptive pits near the eyes are often found in coleoids, and some of the teuthoids have rhinophores. Cephalopods generally have a pair of statocysts, near the pedal ganglia in *Nautilus,* but otherwise imbedded in the cephalic cartilages.

The eyes are the most remarkable sense organs. *Nautilus* has a relatively simple eye, with a large pigment cup and no cornea, lens, or other refractive parts. Other cephalopods have eyes of more advanced structure, and the best eyes are remarkably like vertebrate eyes, fully capable of forming a good image. The similarity of cephalopod eyes to vertebrate eyes is striking. Similar parts, used in similar ways, have evolved, although the cephalopod eye is derived wholly from the surface ectoderm, while much of the vertebrate eye arises from the embryonic neural tube. It is a remarkable instance of convergent evolution.

Sepia and *Loligo* eyes are among the best cephalopod eyes (Fig. 13.49C). A transparent cornea covers the lens, which is held in place by suspensors containing ciliary muscles. An adjustable pupil is centered in a pigmented iris. Pigmented and retinal layers line the optic cup. A capsule protecting the eye is formed from the cephalic cartilages. Special eye muscles attach to the cartilages and the external eye surface, making some eye movement possible. An eye of this type differs from a vertebrate eye primarily in its derivation, in having the retinal rods facing the open cup, and in having a large optic ganglion immediately below the retina.

The cephalopods have the most highly developed nervous systems to be found in invertebrates, and correspondingly complex behavior patterns. Masses comparable to the cerebral, pedal, pleural, and visceral ganglia can be recognized, but the ganglia

have lost their integrity as individual ganglia. They have been subdivided and assembled into a circumenteric nerve center, functionally a complex brain (Fig. 13.52A). A cortex of neurons covers a deeper neuropile, in which a number of organized tracts and pathways can be recognized. Definite centers control specific activities. Responses are partially prepackaged by virtue of specific neuronal linkages, but associational centers provide for discrimination and learning.

The subesophageal part of the brain consists of the paired pedal, pleural, and visceral ganglia and their subdivisions. The right and left sides have been partially fused, to form a symmetrical lobed mass. The branchial and infundibular ganglia are derived from the pedal ganglia. The pleural and visceral ganglia have united to form a single mass, usually termed the visceral ganglion. Nerves to the arms, funnel, mantle, and viscera arise from the subesophageal region, and centers for the control of a number of activities lie in this part of the brain. Among these are centers for the control of eye muscles, the iris and pupil, chromatophore activity, inhalant and exhalant respiratory movements, arm movements, movements of the mantle and fins, and the activity of various visceral organs.

The supra-esophageal region consists primarily of the cerebral ganglia and their subdivisions. However, a pair of nerves pass to the buccal complex, consisting of a circumenteric nerve ring formed by connected pairs of superior and inferior buccal ganglia. Sometimes the superior buccal ganglia are partly fused with the cerebral ganglia. While the subesophageal region is predominantly a motor center, the supra-esophageal region is predominantly composed of relay centers for the reception of sensory stimuli. Optic and olfactory nerves enter here, and sensory centers evoking specific responses to specific sensory stimuli are also built into this part of the brain. The cerebral region also contains

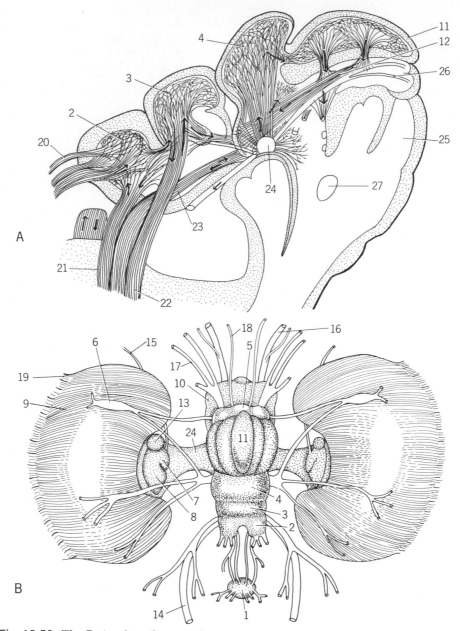

Fig. 13.52. The Brain of an Octopus. A. Dorsal view. B. Section through the vertical lobe region. Notice the complex organization, with cortex, tracts, and subdivision of the lobes. (After Boycott and Young, from Young.) 1, inferior buccal lobe; 2, superior buccal lobe; 3, inferior frontal lobe; 4, superior frontal lobe; 5, posterior basal lobe; 6, posterior superior ophthalmic ganglion; 7, olfactory lobe; 8, peduncle lobe; 9, optic lobe; 10, subesophageal lobe; 11, vertical lobe; 12, subvertical lobe; 13, optic gland; 14, first brachial nerve; 15, olfactory nerve; 16, pallial nerve; 17, retractor nerve of head; 18, symphathetic nerve; 19, optic nerve; 20, buccal nerve; 21, brachiobuccal tract; 22, brachio-inferior frontal tract; 23, brachio-cerebral tract; 24, optic tract; 25, dorsal basal lobe; 26, center for optic gland; 27, optic commissure.

an associative region. No responses are evoked when this part of the brain is stimulated, but its removal prevents the development of conditioned behavior in *Octopus* and it must be considered the functional equivalent of the associative regions of the vertebrate cerebrum. While many motor activities depend on subesophageal centers, motor centers that evoke the movement of large muscle groups are also found in the cerebral region.

The lobus magnocellularis contains giant neurons. It receives stimuli from sensory neurons, which activate the giant neurons. Each giant cell crosses to the other side and synapses in the visceral ganglion with giant neurons of the second order. The second-order giant neurons pass along the pallial nerves to the stellate ganglia, where they synapse with third-order giant neurons, whose axons innervate the mantle muscles. Squid giant neurons have been popular material for the study of neuron physiology. Much of this work has produced fascinating data, but the results are more important for physiological theory than for invertebrate zoology and must be left for the physiologists. The giant-neuron system transmits critical stimuli rapidly, evoking prepackaged startle reactions. More delicate controls are provided by smaller axons that run parallel to the giant fibers.

Cephalopods are among the few invertebrates to have cartilage tissue. This is composed of cartilage cells, located in lacunae surrounded by matrix material. Cephalopod cartilage closely resembles the cartilage of vertebrates, but differs in having adjacent cells connected by intracellular bridges that pass through the matrix. The cartilage is used to support the mantle margin, the fins, and to form a skull-like capsule around the brain. It is functionally like the cranium of vertebrates, as it provides a protective covering for the brain and also provides sites for muscle attachment.

Reproduction. The unpaired gonads lie in the wall of the coelom at the posterior tip of the body. Sexes are nearly always separate. Males are usually smaller than females, and sometimes show other evidences of sexual dimorphism. Gametes break out of the gonads, entering the coelom, to be picked up by the gonoducts.

Female octopi and many teuthoids have symmetrical gonoducts, which arise side by side and pass to the posterior end of the mantle cavity. *Nautilus* has a vestigial left and functional right oviduct. In other cephalopods the right oviduct is missing and the left is functional.

Several glands are associated with the oviduct. An oviducal gland secretes the inner albuminous or capsular covering of the egg. Where the oviduct courses over the mantle wall, nidamental glands may be found. These secrete gelatinous material around the eggs, or, in some cases, material that hardens on contact with water and is used to stick the eggs to objects.

In *Nautilus* the left sperm duct is rudimentary, while in other cephalopds the right sperm duct is missing. Sperm are temporarily stockpiled in seminal vesicles near the upper end of the sperm duct. Here they form masses, enclosed in a complex spermatophore (Fig. 13.53). Secretions from the prostate gland enter the seminal vesicle and are used as cement to hold the sperm together. The fully formed spermatophores pass into a distal, dilated part of the sperm duct (Needham's sac), where they are stored until the time of mating.

Nautilus males have four arms that are permanently modified for copulation, but most cephalopod males have a single specialized arm when sexually mature. The specialized arm varies considerably in form and in the way in which it is used. The most highly specialized copulatory arms are seen in *Argonauta* and some octopi. The modified end of the arm is detached during mating, and remains in the female mantle cavity. The copulatory arm was correctly understood by Aristotle, but was completely misinterpreted by zoologists of the last century. Cuvier described it as a

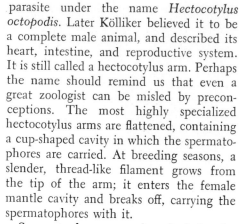

parasite under the name *Hectocotylus octopodis*. Later Kölliker believed it to be a complete male animal, and described its heart, intestine, and reproductive system. It is still called a hectocotylus arm. Perhaps the name should remind us that even a great zoologist can be misled by preconceptions. The most highly specialized hectocotylus arms are flattened, containing a cup-shaped cavity in which the spermatophores are carried. At breeding seasons, a slender, thread-like filament grows from the tip of the arm; it enters the female mantle cavity and breaks off, carrying the spermatophores with it.

Spermatophores are deposited in the mantle cavity or elsewhere on the body surface, depending on the species. *Nautilus* and squid spermatophores are attached to the head region, or inserted into a seminal receptacle near the mouth.

When the spermatophore cap is loosened, the ejaculatory organ is extruded, releasing the sperm. Eggs are fertilized as they emerge from the oviduct, before the secretions from the nidamental gland have hardened. Egg masses or single eggs are attached to stones or other objects as a general rule, but some pelagic species have floating eggs. Octopi often tend the eggs, ventilating them with jets of water from the funnel, cleaning them as well as keeping them surrounded by fresh water. The most unusual system is employed by the female *Argonauta*. She has a pair of highly modified dorsal tentacles, which secrete a thin, gently fluted shell into which the eggs are placed for brooding. This is not a true shell, falling better into the category of a highly modified capsule. The female carries the nursery throughout the period of egg development, retiring into it when disturbed, and males sometimes occupy the shell with the female and ova.

Development. The ova contain a great deal of yolk, derived from follicle cells. A germinal disc free of yolk occurs at the animal pole. The germinal disc undergoes

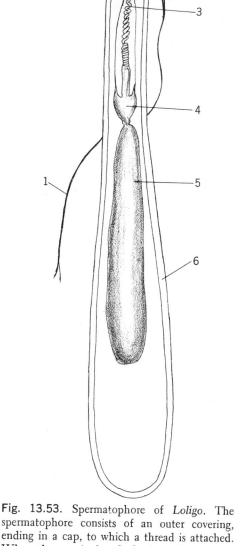

Fig. 13.53. Spermatophore of *Loligo*. The spermatophore consists of an outer covering, ending in a cap, to which a thread is attached. When the cap is detached, the coiled ejaculatory organ everts, pulling the mass of cement at its base and the large sperm mass with it. The sperm mass is thus cemented in place. 1, thread; 2, cap; 3, ejaculatory duct; 4, cement; 5, sperm mass; 6, base of spermatophore.

meroblastic cleavage, forming a discoid blastula. A layer of cells grows down from the margins of the germinal disc, turning under to form endoderm. Mesoderm forms from the posterior ends of the germinal disc, forming two crescentic strands of cells. The buccal cavity, radula, and associated parts rise from a stomodaeum, and the end of the rectum from a proctodaeum. Ectodermal fields corresponding to the ganglia give rise to the nervous system. Development is so greatly modified that relationships to other molluscs cannot be determined by embryonic stages.

Molluscan Affinities

The first molluscs probably lived well before the beginning of the Cambrian. Their relationship to annelids cannot be seriously doubted, for similarities in cleavage and in the trochophore larvae are too detailed to be considered convergent. There seem to be equally good reasons for thinking that both are derivatives of some flatworm stock, which became coelomate and established an early protostome stock that gave rise to all of the higher invertebrates on the protostome line.

The major question is at what time the molluscan and annelid stocks diverged. Had the main protostome line become metameric before the molluscs separated off or did metamerism develop on the annelid line after the molluscs had become distinct? The complete lack of evidence of metamerism in larval molluscs seems to indicate that the molluscs were primitively non-metameric. The eight plates of the chitons may appear to suggest an external metamerism, and the occurrence of muscles in series associated with the plates strengthens this appearance. However, there is no internal evidence of coelomic compartments associated with the shell valves, and internal organs are not metamerically arranged. The main weight of the evidence would, therefore, point to a molluscan origin prior to the appearance of metamerism.

The discovery of *Neopilina*, however, opens up new possibilities. The *Neopilina* shell is not divided, but there is a definitely metameric character to the internal organization. The internal metamerism does not appear to involve the coelom in quite the same way that it does in annelids, but nevertheless, it cannot be considered as a response to superficial segmentation of the body, as the series of muscles in a chiton can. Is *Neopilina* an independent molluscan venture into the field of metamerism, or does it retain traces of a metamerism present in ancestral stocks? It is too soon to draw any definite conclusions. Certainly, the development of *Neopilina* must be followed before it can be concluded that the earliest molluscan stocks were metameric. For all of the larvae of a phylum to lose all traces of a primitive metamerism in their development would be a remarkable phenomenon, and no known molluscan larvae preserve traces of metameric development. Several times in the past, aberrant forms, unlike the majority of the members of a phylum, have been used as "missing links." The highly flattened ctenophores, for example, have been used as ancestral stocks for the derivation of flatworms. By and large, as more evidence accumulates, schemes of phylogeny based on these unusual forms have tended to become less tenable. Whether this will be the case with *Neopilina* remains to be seen. Certainly it is a most interesting mollusc, and zoologists are waiting to find out more about it.

Relationships within the phylum are rather obscure. All of the major groups of molluscs were established early, perhaps in pre-Cambrian times. Some interesting similarities can be seen in pelecypods and scaphopods, but no forms transitional between the two groups are known. Similarities between the shells of early gastropods and nautiloids do not necessarily indicate relationship; they are probably convergent. Until more information is available, the classes cannot be assembled into definite adaptive lines.

References

Abbott, R. T. 1954. *American Sea Shells*. Van Nostrand, New York.

Atkins, D. 1936. On the ciliary mechanisms and interrelationships of lamellibranchs. III. *Quart. Jour. Micr. Sci.* 315: 375.

Bailey, K., and B. D. Warboys. 1960. The lamellibranch crystalline style. *Biochem. Jour.* 76: 487.

Baker, F. C. 1898. The Mollusca of the Chicago area. The Pelecypoda. *Bull. Nat. Hist. Surv. Chicago Acad. Sci.* 3: 1.

———. 1928. The Fresh Water Mollusca of Wisconsin. I. Gastropoda. II. Pelecypoda. *Bull. Wisc. Geol. Nat. Hist. Surv.* 70: 1.

———. 1939. Fieldbook of Illinois land snails. *Nat. Hist. Surv. Ill. Manual* 2.

Ball, G. H. 1922. Variation in fresh-water mussels. *Ecol.* 3: 93.

Barnes, G. 1955. The behavior of *Anadonta cygnea* and its neurophysiological basis. *Jour. Exp. Biol.* 32: 158.

Baylor, E. R. 1959. The response of snails to polarized light. *Jour. Exp. Biol.* 36: 369.

Berry, Q. 1928. Cephalopod adaptations. *Quart. Rev. Biol.* 3:92. (G)

Bidder, A. M. 1950. The digestive mechanisms of European squids. *Quart. Jour. Micr. Sci.* 91: 1.

Boycott, A. E. 1936. The habitats of fresh-water Mollusca in Britain. *Jour. Anim. Ecol.* 5: 116. (E)

Cheatum, E. P. 1934. Limnological investigations on respiration, annual migratory cycle, and other related phenomena in fresh-water pulmonate snails. *Trans. Am. Micr. Soc.* 53: 348.

Clench, W. J. 1946. The poison cone shell. *Occ. Pap. on Mollusks, Harvard U.* 1: 49.

Coe, W. R. 1936. Sexual phases in *Crepidula*. *Jour. Exp. Zool.* 72: 455.

Crofts, D. 1937. The development of *Haliotus tuberculata*. *Phil. Trans. Roy. Soc.* 125: 711.

———. 1955. Muscle morphogenesis in primitive mollusks and its relation to torsion. *Proc. Zool. Soc. London* 125: 711.

Dawson, J. 1911. The biology of *Physa*. *Behav. Monogr.* 1: 1.

Dean, B. 1941. Studies on the living *Nautilus*. *Amer. Nat.* 35: 819.

Duncan, C. J. 1959. The life cycle and ecology of the freshwater snail *Physa fontinalis*. *Jour. Anim. Ecol.* 28: 97.

———. 1960. The evolution of the pulmonate genital system. *Proc. Zool. Soc. London.* 134: 601.

Fretter, V. 1937. The structure and function of the alimentary canal of some species of Polyplacophora. *Trans. Roy. Soc. Edinburgh* 59: 119.

———. 1946. The genital ducts of *Theodoxus*, *Lamellaria* and *Trivia*, and a discussion of their evolution in prosobranchs. *Jour. Mar. Biol. Assoc.* 26: 312.

———, and A. Graham. 1961. *British Prosobranchs*. Ray Soc., London. (!)

Galli, D. R., and A. C. Giese. 1959. Carbohydrate digestion in a herbivorous snail, *Tegula funebralis*. *Jour. Exp. Zool.* 140: 415.

George, W. C., and H. J. Ferguson. The blood of gastropod molluscs. *Jour. Morph.* 86: 315.

Graham, A. 1949. The molluscan stomach. *Trans. Roy. Soc. Edinburgh* 61: 737.

———. 1953. Form and function in the molluscs. *Proc. Linn. Soc.* 164: 213. (G)

Hedgpeth, J. W. 1954. A problem in oyster taxonomy. *Syst. Zool.* 3: 21.

Howes, N., and G. P. Wells. 1934. The water relations of snails and slugs. *Jour. Exp. Biol.* 11: 344.

Hoyle, G. 1957. *Comparative physiology of the nervous control of muscular contraction*. Cambridge Univ. Press, Cambridge, Eng. (G)

Kawai, K. 1959. The cytochrome system in marine lamellibranch tissues. *Biol. Bull.* 117: 125.

Kerkut, G. A., and Laverack, M. S. 1957. The respiration of *Helix pomata*, a balance sheet. *Jour. Exp. Biol.* 34: 97.

Korringa, P. 1952. Recent advances in oyster biology. *Quart. Rev. Biol.* 27: 266, 339.

Krijgsman, B. J., and G. A. Divaris. 1955. Contractile and pacemaker mechanisms of the heart of molluscs. *Biol. Rev.* 30: 1.

Lemche, J. 1959. Molluscan phylogeny in light of *Neopilina*. *Proc. 15th Int. Congr. Zool. London* 15: 380. (G)

Martin, A. W., *et al*. The blood volume of some representative molluscs. *Jour. Exp. Biol.* 35: 260.

Morton, J. E. 1958. *Molluscs*. Hutchinson, London.

———. 1960. The functions of the gut in ciliary feeders. *Biol. Rev.* 35: 92. (G)

Nakazima, M. 1956. On the structure and function of the midgut gland of Mollusca, with a general consideration of the feeding habits and systematic relations. *Jap. Jour. Zool.* 2: 469.

Nelson, T. C. 1918. On the origin, nature, and function of the crystalline style of lamellibranchs. *Jour. Morph.* 31: 53.

Peterson, R. P. 1959. The anatomy and histology of the reproductive system of *Octopus bimaculoides. Jour. Morph.* 104: 61.

Pilsbry, H. A. 1939–46. Land Mollusca of North America. *Acad. Nat. Sci. Phila. Monogr.* 3: 1. (F)

Raven, Ch. 1958. *Morphogenesis: The Analysis of Molluscan Development*. Pergamon, New York. (!)

Schinedwolf, O. 1934. Concerning the evolution of the Cephalopoda. *Biol. Rev.* 9: 458. (G)

Sollas, I. B. 1907. The molluscan radula, its chemical composition and some points in its development. *Quart. Jour. Micr. Sci.* 51: 115.

Van Cleave, H. J. 1940. Ten years of observation on a fresh-water mussel population. *Ecol.* 21: 363.

Van der Schalie, H. 1940. Aestivation of freshwater mussels. *Nautilus* 53: 137.

Walker, B. 1918. A synopsis of the classification of the freshwater Mollusca of North America, north of Mexico, and a catologue of the more recently described species. *Mus. Zool. Univ. Mich. Misc. Publ.* 6: 1.

Welsh, J. H. 1956. Cardioregulators of *Cyprina* and *Buccinum. Jour. Mar. Biol. Ass.* 35: 193.

Yoneda, M. 1960. Force exerted by a single cilium of *Mytilus edulis. Jour. Exp. Biol.* 37: 461.

Yonge, C. M. 1932. The crystalline style of the Mollusca. *Sci. Prog.* 26: 643.

———. 1939. On the mantle cavity and its contained organs in the Loricata. *Quart. Jour. Micr. Sci.* 323: 367. (G)

———. 1947. The pallial organs in the aspidobranch gastropods and their evolution throughout the Mollusca. *Phil. Trans. Roy. Soc.* 232: 443. (G)

Young, J. Z. 1961. Learning and discrimination in the octopus. *Biol. Rev.* 36: 32.

14
Phylum Annelida

The ancient protostome stock from which the molluscs arose also gave rise to the annelids, establishing the obviously metameric protostome line, the annelid arthropod superphylum, which includes the greater part of all known animal species. We cannot specify which of the flatworm stocks produced the main protostome stem forms. They must have been characterized by endolecithal ova that underwent spiral, determinate cleavage and a larva of the trochophore type; they must have been at least moderately cephalized; and they must have developed an anus and a coelom early in their history. Details are unknown, for fossil findings do not go back far enough, especially for soft-bodied animals. The earliest fossil annelids are already differentiated into well-established groups. A number of suggestions about the early history of the annelids have been made. These differ markedly, depending on the views of the origin of the coelom and metamerism that are held.

If one subscribes to the gonocoel theory of coelomic origin (p. 310), it is reasonable to suppose that the coelom and internal metamerism arose simultaneously. If, on the other hand, the coelom first arose as spaces in the mesoderm, early stem forms may have become coelomate first, and segmented later, and an independent explanation of the origin of metamerism must be sought.

In the absence of critical fossil evidence, it is necessary to make comparisons of the organization of adults, especially of those which appear to preserve primitive characteristics, and of developing embryos. What kinds of evidence, pro and con, can one find for the simultaneous development of coelom and metamerism? Is the evidence adequate to justify strong convictions? There is considerable difference of opinion on both counts.

Embryonic development, especially similarities in the pattern of cleavage and the remarkable similarities in the destiny of specific blastomeres, leaves no room for serious doubts about the close relationship of annelids and molluscs. Slight differences in cleavage patterns resulting in the formation of the interradial molluscan cross and the radial annelid cross do not materially affect the kinds of parts derived from the blastomeres of the various quartets produced during spiral cleavage. The annelid and molluscan crosses nevertheless serve as embryonic evidences of an early separation of the spirally cleaving ancestral stocks into two distinct lines, one leading to the annelids and one to the molluscs. The unsegmented sipunculids (Chapter XV) have an annelid cross, and presumably have diverged from the annelid stem at a later time than molluscs, although they are not segmented. This may be an indication that they arose from the annelid stem before it had become segmented, although after molluscs had diverged from it. On the other hand, there remains the possibility that both molluscs and sipunculids have suppressed, even during development, all traces of a metamerism that they once possessed. The latter possibility, however, seems somewhat less probable.

In the metameric coelomates, the coelom appears as a series of spaces in the mesoderm. In molluscs it appears as a space in the mesoderm, without evidence of coelomic compartments in series. A search for good evidence that the one space of molluscs and the series of spaces in annelids either are or are not remnants of a primitive pair or series of pairs of gonads is needed if the gonocoel theory is to be accepted or criticized. Some pieces of evidence could be used to support either point of view, so differences of opinion can be supported. Ultimately it comes to deciding what kinds of evidence are most convincing. An examination of the gonad structure of flatworms and annelids, particularly, shows an interesting and unexpected situation. Flatworms have rather highly organized gonads, while annelids usually have gonads of simple construction, really patches of germinal cells in the coelomic wall, and the final stages of germ-cell maturation occur in the coelom or in coelomic sacs rather than the gonads. Goodrich (1947), particularly, developed the idea that the gonoducts of annelids are coelomoducts; that is, are mesodermal ducts which connect the coelomic cavity with the exterior, and that these coelomoducts are the old gonoducts of animals of the flatworm grade of organization. When taken with the rather ill-developed gonads of annelids, the argument for the derivation of a coelom from the gonads can be made a strong one. On the other hand, it appears that not all of the gonoducts are mesodermal in origin, and another embryological fact greatly weakens Goodrich's arguments. The germ cells are generally differentiated from the somatic cells early in protostome development. During embryonic development, these cells do not, in any way, participate in the formation of the coelom. They are often formed at some distance from their eventual position in the animal, and migrate to the gonad at a later time. The actual mechanics of the formation of a series of coelomic compartments during embryonic development do not very strongly support the thesis that they are vestiges of old gonads, or that the molluscan embryos are, in fact, suppressing a metamerism they once possessed. Perhaps the only acceptable conclusion that can now be drawn is that even if the coelom is derived from gonadal cavities, so much larval evolution has occurred since the event that we will probably never be sure of it.

The alternative idea is that the coelom first arose as spaces in the mesoderm during evolutionary development as it does during embryonic development. In this case, molluscs and sipunculids may have diverged from an early unsegmented but coelomate protostome stock which became metameric in lines leading toward the annelids and arthropods. How can the metameric organization be explained if this has happened? Two suggestions have been made. The fission theory supposes that worms forming a chain of zooids by transverse fission became segmented by subordination of the component zooids, somewhat as in cestodes. The principal objection to the fission theory is that metameric organisms form new segments serially at the posterior tip of the body. The segments thus occur in a regular series, with the oldest ones in front. The worms that form chains of zooids do not ordinarily work in this fashion. Each zooid tends to divide, so no such regular distribution of zooids by age occurs in the chain. It must be admitted, however, that where processes that originally occurred in adults are incorporated into embryonic development, they often become more regular. Furthermore, there are cases of rhythmic growth in which a series of individuals are produced from a growing budding zone, producing chains of animals showing a regular age distribution. Hyman (1951) makes an alternative suggestion, which may be considered the pseudosegmentation theory. Serially arranged plates and muscles sometimes develop in the body wall of elongated organisms, as in some of the pseudocoelomates. Pseudosegmentation of this type could be the first step in the development of metamerism. Parts other than body-wall parts also become serially repeated, as in many flatworms, where gonads, accessory nephridiopores, and other internal parts form a regular series. This hypothesis presents a neater but not necessarily truer picture of the appearance of metamerism in the early protostome coelomates. It would account for the pseudometamerism of the chitons in the absence of coelomic metamerism, and permit a view of metameric evolution from a non-colonial stock of protostomes. Perhaps someone will be able to present really critical evidence permitting a final decision between the various possibilities, but at present the phylogenetic discussions are really speculations.

Whatever happened during the earliest stages of annelid evolution, and however annelids may be related to other phyla, one of the most important steps in the evolution of the animal kingdom occurred when a stem of segmented, coelomate animals with a straight digestive tube appeared. Out of this stem two of the largest and most important invertebrate phyla, the Annelida and Arthropoda, eventually developed.

Annelids are soft-bodied and have not left a continuous fossil record. What material is available shows that the major groups of annelids must have been established early in the Paleozoic. Two major annelid lines developed, the Polychaeta and the Clitellata. The polychaete line is characterized by: 1) paired muscular extensions of the body wall, known as parapodia, and 2) separate sexes with many segmentally arranged gonads. The parapodia are composed of a dorsal lobe, the notopodium, and a ventral lobe, the neuropodium (Fig. 14.2D). They contain skeletal supports, the acicula, and are equipped with bristles, known as setae, with tactile organs, and in many cases, with gills. The Clitellata are characterized by 1) the absence of parapodia; 2) a hermaphroditic reproductive system, usually concentrated in a few somites; and 3) a glandular clitellum, actually a modified part of the body wall, used to secrete a cocoon around the ova.

Two features, the coelom and metamerism, greatly influence the fundamental body plan of annelids (Fig. 14.1). The coelom arises as a pair of spaces in the mesoderm of each body segment. They enlarge to form a pair of large coelomic compartments in each somite. The coelomic compartments are true peritoneal cavities, lined wholly with peritoneal tissue. The parietal peritoneum lines the body wall, the visceral peritoneum covers the gut and internal organs, and the right and left coelomic compartments meet in a dorsal and ventral mesentery on the midline above and below the digestive tube. The coelomic compartments of adjacent segments meet to form the septa. The septa and mesenteries are formed of two leaves of peritoneum. Septa are usually invaded by muscle tissue, and both septa and mesenteries may be partly open, permitting communication between the various coelomic compartments in adult animals.

Metamerism affects all of the organ systems, except the usually straight, tubular digestive tube, and even here paired series of glands sometimes appear on the gut wall. The major longitudinal blood vessels extend the length of the body above and below the digestive tube, but give rise to segmentally arranged lateral branches in each segment. Each segment contains a pair of nephridia, primitively, although the nephridia of some somites may be suppressed in adults. The nephridia are typically true metanephridia, with an open nephrostome in the segment immediately in front of the segment containing the body of the nephridial tube. The first part of the nephridial tubule passes through the septum in front, and the nephridium ends

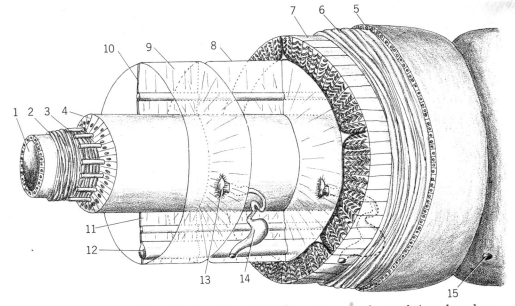

Fig. 14.1. Scheme of Organization of Annelid Somites. Successive layers of tissue have been removed to show their relationships, and cellular detail has been omitted in the peritoneum and mesenteries. The body is a tube within a tube, with a coelomic cavity separating inner and outer tubes. The coelom arises as bilateral spaces, a pair for each somite. As the spaces expand, their peritoneal lining is pushed against the body wall, where it forms the parietal peritoneum, and against the gut wall, where it forms the visceral peritoneum, and is pushed together at the midline to form the two-leaved dorsal and ventral mesenteries. The peritoneum of adjacent somites is pushed together to form the two-layered septa. In most annelids, much of the dorsal mesentery and a part of the ventral mesentery are lost during later development, and in some cases some of the septa are also lost. Paired excretory tubules, the metanephridia, occur in the coelomic compartments. Each opens into the coelomic compartment in front of it by a nephrostome, and to the exterior by a nephridiopore. The main blood vessels are a dorsal vessel in the dorsal mesentery and a ventral vessel in the ventral mesentery. The nerve cord may be in the body wall, or in the ventral mesentery, as shown here. *Gut wall:* 1, mucosa, derived from the endoderm; 2, circular viseral muscle; 3, longitudinal visceral muscle; 4, visceral peritoneum, often modified, as shown here, into large chlorogogue cells. *Body wall:* 5, epidermis, derived from ectoderm; 6, circular somatic muscle; 7, longitudinal somatic muscle; 8, parietal peritoneum. *Coelom:* 9, coelomic compartment; 10, dorsal mesentery containing dorsal blood vessel; 11, ventral mesentery, containing ventral blood vessel; 12, nerve cord; 13, nephrostome; 14, nephridium; 15, nephridiopore.

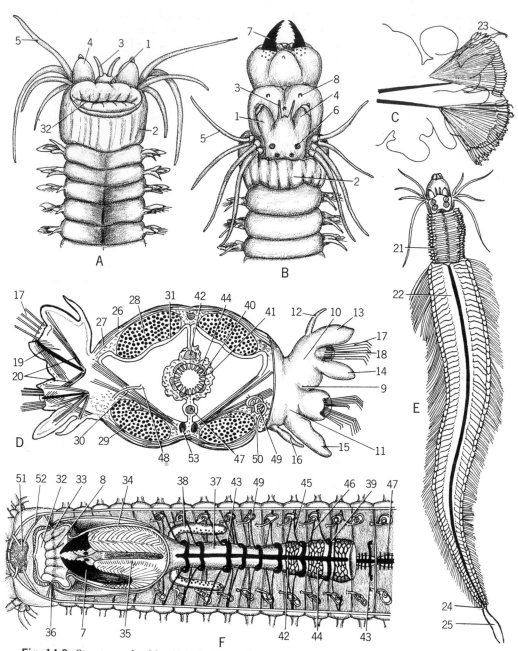

Fig. 14.2. Structure of a Nereid Polychaete. **A** and **B.** Ventral and dorsal views of *Neanthes virens*, with proboscis withdrawn in ventral view, and proboscis partly extended in dorsal view. **C.** Form of the parapodium of the heteronereis of *Perinereis cultrifera*, with a few of the nereid setae not yet shed. **D.** Scheme of cross section of a nereid, showing the parapodial structure on the left. The parapodium on the right shows the form of the normal parapodium of *Perinereis cultrifera*, before metamorphosis into a heteronereid. **E.** The male heteronereid

in a nephridiopore. Segmental ganglia and segmental nerves give the nervous system a metameric character. External rings, parapodia, and setae give the external surface a metameric character.

The most outstanding annelid characteristic include:

1. bilateral symmetry;

2. metameric organization;

3. body wall composed of an outer epidermis, and segmentally arranged outer circular and inner longitudinal muscle layers, and lined with parietal peritoneum; a cuticle secreted by the epidermis usually present;

4. metamerically arranged, chitinous setae usually present, secreted by epidermal follicles;

5. a head of variable complexity, formed of a preoral segment, the prostomium, and a peristomium containing the mouth;

6. a closed circulatory system, typically with a dorsal vessel in which blood flows anteriorly and a ventral vessel in which it flows posteriorly; blood often with a respiratory pigment dissolved in the plasma;

7. coelom a schizocoel, generally spacious, and divided into segmental compartments;

8. primitively with one pair of nephridia in all but the first and last somites;

9. a circumenteric nerve ring, containing dorsal cerebral ganglia, subpharyngeal ganglion, and connectives, and a ventral, double nerve cord with paired segmental ganglia and commissural connections;

10. spiral, determinate cleavage, and primitively, a trochophore larva.

Classification

Class Polychaeta. Predominantly marine annelids, usually with paired appendages known as parapodia, from which chitinous setae project; usually strongly cephalized, with specialized head appendages; almost universally with separate sexes and with many gonads, segmentally arranged; without a glandular clitellum for secretion of a cocoon.

Subclass Errantia. Polychaetes with the body not divided into distinctive regions; with all somites similar and provided with nephridia and gills, except those at the anterior and posterior extremities; head usually with a distinct prostomium bearing lateral appendages; with well-developed parapodia supported by skeletal rods

of *Nereis irrorata*. When sexually mature, the posterior region develops into an epitoke, with modified parapodia. F. Internal structure of a nereid. (C, after Bouchot-Boutin and Bobin. E, after Rullier, from Clark. D and F, composite.) *External features:* 1, prostomium; 2, peristomium; 3, prostomial tentacle; 4, prostomial palp; 5, peristomial cirrus; 6, eye; 7, jaw; 8, denticle; 9, parapodium, *divided into:* 10, notopodium and 11, neuropodium; 12, dorsal cirrus; 13, dorsal gill blade (ligula) of notopodium; 14, ventral gill blade of notopodium; 15, ventral gill blade of neuropodium; 16, ventral cirrus; 17, cluster of setae; 18, setigerous lobe of notopodium; 19, aciculum; 20, muscles moving the aciculum and so manipulating the setae; 21, unmodified anterior region (atoke); 22, modified posterior region (epitoke); 23, nereid seta being shed; 24, pygidium, the last somite; 25, pygidial tentacle. *Body wall:* 26, epidermis; 27, circular muscle; 28, dorsal longitudinal muscle tract; 29, ventral longitudinal muscle tract; 30, transverse muscles, operating parapodia; 31, parietal peritoneum. *Digestive tract:* 32, mouth; 33, buccal cavity; 34, pharynx; 35, proboscis, withdrawn into pharynx; 36, diaphragm; 37, esophagus; 38, esophageal caecum; 39, midgut (intestine); 40, intestinal mucosa; 41, visceral peritoneum (chlorogogue). *Circulatory system:* 42, dorsal vessel; 43, lateral vessel; 44, intestinal plexus; 45, afferent parapodial vessel; 46, efferent vessel from body wall; 47, ventral vessel. *Nephridial system:* 48, nephrostome; 49, nephridium; 50, nephridiopore. *Nervous system:* 51, cerebral ganglion; 52, nerves to prostomial and peristomial sense organs; 53, nerve cord.

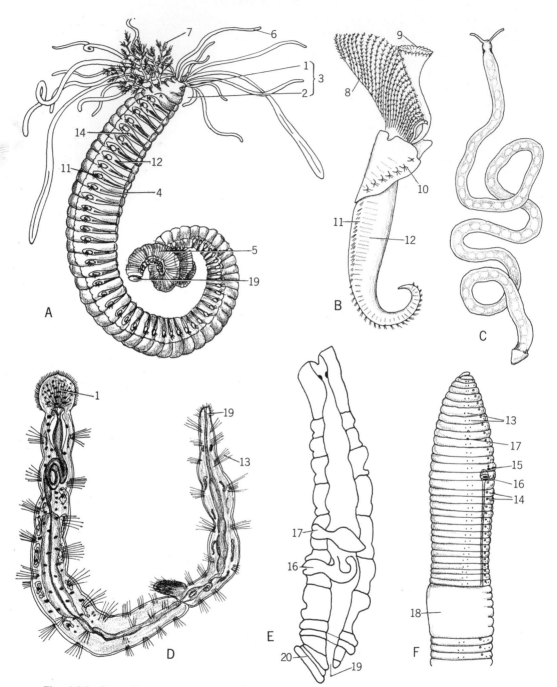

Fig. 14.3. Some Representative Annelids. **A.** *Amphitrite ornata*, a polychaete belonging to the subclass Sedentaria. They are typically provided with several body regions, and have a prostomium and reduced parapodia. **B.** *Serpula vermicularis*, removed from its tube. *Serpula* is another member of the Sedentaria, with a crown of brachioles used in respiration and feeding,

known as acicula; generally with a protrusible pharynx equipped with chitinous jaws; crawling, swimming, and burrowing forms, a few living in tubes. Example: *Neanthes* (Fig. 14.2)

Subclass Sedentaria. Microphagous polychaetes with a body usually divided into distinctive, specialized regions; nephridia usually found only in the anterior somites; with a relatively small prostomium and few or no head appendages other than gills; parapodia reduced and without acicula; a pharynx that is not protrusible and has no jaws; usually living in tubes. Example: *Amphitrite* (Fig. 14.3A).

Subclass Archiannelida. A small group of reduced polychaetes of diverse origin, with a ciliated epidermis, no parapodia, and septa reduced or missing; segments few or indistinct; with larvae linking them with other polychaetes. Example: *Polygordius* (Fig. 14.3C)

Class Oligochaeta. Predominantly freshwater and terrestrial annelids, without parapodia and with relatively few setae; a small head without cephalic appendages; hermaphroditic, with testes anterior to the ovaries and with only one or two pairs of male and female gonads located in a few genital somites; with a complex gonoduct system and seminal receptacles; with a glandular clitellum used to secrete a co-coon; development direct, without larval stages.

Order Plesiopora. Mostly aquatic, minute oligochaetes with seminal receptacles near the genital segments, and with the male gonopores in the segment behind the one containing the testes. Example: *Aeolosoma* (Fig. 14.3D).

Order Prosopora. Aquatic oligochaetes with male gonopores in the somite containing the testes or, when two pairs of testes are present, in the second male somite. Example: *Cambarincola* (Fig. 14.3E).

Order Opisthopora. Mostly terrestrial oligochaetes with relatively long male gonoducts and with gonopores some distance behind the male somites. Example: *Lumbricus* (Fig. 14.3F).

Class Hirudinea. Leeches. Typically dorsoventrally flattened annelids, with 32 somites and a prostomium; superficial annuli dividing somites into from two to 14 rings; mouth in an anterior sucker composed of the prostomium and first two somites and with a posterior sucker, typically containing the last seven somites; coelom generally reduced to a system of sinuses; a complex hermaphroditic reproductive system and a clitellum; development direct, without larval stages.

Order Acanthobdellida. A primitive order, transitional between leeches and oli-

and the body more highly specialized into regions than in *Amphitrite*. C. *Polygordius neapolitanus*, a member of the subclass Archiannelida, characterized by the absence of parapodia, lack of septa, and general body reduction. D. *Aeolosoma hemprichi*, an oligochaete belonging to the Plesiopora, characterized by minute size, aquatic habits, and a male gonopore in the somite immediately behind the one containing the testes. E. *Cambarincola elevata*, an oligochaete parasitizing crayfish. *Cambarincola* is a member of the Prosopora, characterized by male gonopores in the somite containing the testes, and of the family *Branchiobdellidae*, which have many superficial resemblances to leeches. F. Anterior end of *Lumbricus terrestris*, an oligochaete belonging to the Opisthopora, characterized by long male gonoducts and male gonopores well behind the somite containing the testes. (A, after Brown. B, after Eales. C, after Fraipont. D, after Lankester, from Beddard. E, after Goodnight, in Edmondson.) 1, prostomium; 2, peristomium; 3, cephalic region; 4, thoracic region; 5, abdominal region; 6, tentacles, probably derived from the prostomial palps; 7, gills, probably derived from dorsal cirri of the notopodia; 8, crown of brachioles used in respiration and food capture; 9, operculum; 10, thoracic membrane; 11, notopodium; 12, neuropodium; 13, setae; 14, nephridiopore; 15, female gonopore; 16, male gonopore; 17, pore for the seminal receptacles; 18, clitellum; 19, anus; 20, posterior sucker.

gochaetes, erected for the Russian genus *Acanthobdella*, parasitic on salmon, and probably an independently evolved group. *Acanthobdella* is characterized by 29 somites and a prostomium, has no anterior sucker, and has a posterior sucker containing only four somites; coelom spacious; setae present on anterior somites. Example: *Acanthobdella* (Fig. 14.12A).

Order Rhynchobdellida. Leeches with an eversible pharynx, without jaws, and with colorless blood that does not circulate in coelomic sinuses; somites usually with three external rings. Example: *Glossiphonia* (Fig. 14.11B).

Order Gnathobdellida. Leeches without an eversible pharynx and with three toothed jaws; with red blood circulating in a coelomic sinus system. Example: *Hirudo* (Fig. 14.11C).

Order Pharyngobdellida. Leeches resembling the gnathobdellids, but without teeth. Example: *Haemopis*.

Class Polychaeta

Nearly all of the 3500 species of polychaetes are marine. They are especially abundant from low tide line to about 50 m., but many live in the intertidal zone and some have been found at depths of over 5000 m. Polychaetes are diversified and play a variety of roles in marine ecosystems. Some burrow in the bottom; some crowd into crevices in or under rocks and shells or live in the tubes on houses of other animals; some build tubes in the bottom material or on the surface of submerged objects. They are often extremely abundant; thousands of polychaetes may live in a single square meter of a mud flat. When numerous they are important elements of the food chain. Some are primary or intermediate consumers, while others convert organic debris into protoplasm, gathering small particles with a ciliary-mucous feeding apparatus or swallowing quantities of mud. They are preyed upon by hydroids, flat-worms, other annelids, crustaceans, echinoderms, or fishes.

It is particularly interesting to study the external form of polychaetes. Through all of the permutations of external structure suited to diverse living quarters and diverse habits, the fundamental organization of the animal is preserved, and homologous parts of the parapodia or the head are made suitable for different functions by small changes. Two great groups of polychaetes are recognized, the Errantia and the Sedentaria, based on adaptations to a more active or a more sedentary life. The division is not a sharp one, and should not be construed as separating two discrete lines of evolutionary descent. It is rather the recognition of the complex of evolutionary consequences of adaptation to a more active life, or to a tube-dwelling, inactive life. The active forms retain a more primitive form, but tend to develop better sense organs, a more definite head, and more highly developed parapodia. Sedentary forms, most of which remain permanently in tubes, have entirely different ecological and physiological problems. It is, however, misleading to suppose that polychaetes actually fall into two sharply separate ways of life. Errant polychaetes form tubes, although they rarely remain in them permanently, and some sedentary polychaetes burrow in soft bottoms and build no tubes. The most important factors in molding external form have been the dwelling places and food habits. Tube-dwelling habits, burrowing without tube formation, ectoparasitic habits, and free and active locomotion have had important effects on form. Predaceous feeding, mud-eating, and ciliary-mucous feeding systems have also been important in determining the course of evolutionary changes in form. Different combinations of feeding habits and dwelling places have made for diversification and resulted in species withdrawing from competition from each other.

External Form and Habits. The primitive polychaete organization is best reflected in the simpler errant species; most of its features can be seen in *Neanthes* (Fig. 14.2). The head is composed of a preoral piece, the prostomium, which projects forward over the mouth, and the peristomium, a modified somite containing the mouth. The rest of the segments are similar. All bear a parapodium, composed of a basal part, a dorsal part (notopodium) and a ventral part (neuropodium). A skeletal rod, the aciculum, supports each lobe, ending in depressions containing epidermal follicles that secrete setae. Muscles move the acicula, and as they move they extend or retract the setae. A great many of the specific adaptations fitting polychaetes for different ways of life have involved modifications in the head and parapodial structure, and these parts are valuable in taxonomic work.

Probably the first annelid head was composed only of the prostomium, and all of the body somites were essentially alike. The prostomium contains the cerebral ganglia and is equipped with prostomial eyes, a pair of ventral palps, and one or more pairs of dorsal tentacles. It is a common tendency for arthropods to add somites to the posterior end of the head as cephalization becomes more pronounced, and it is probable that the addition of the peristomium to the annelid head is essentially the same kind of phenomenon, although the peristomium is always somewhat different than other somites because it contains the mouth. Even today, however, some polychaetes,

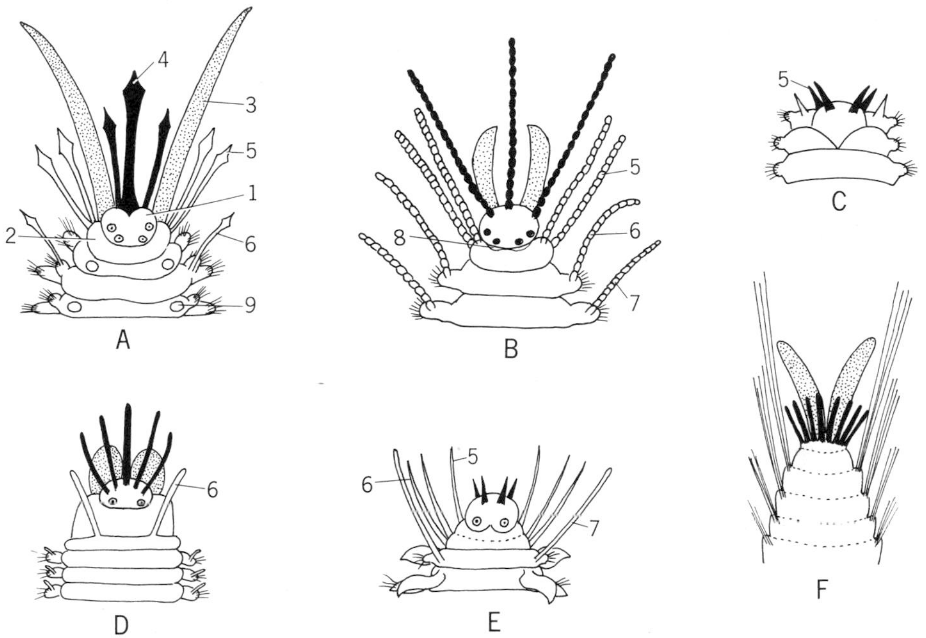

Fig. 14.4. Polychaete Heads (schematic). Notice that the head region is differentiated by tactile organs associated with the prostomium, peristomium, and in some cases, with the second or third somites. A. A polynoid. B. A syllid. C. *Nephthys*, a nephthyd. D. *Eunice*, a eunicid. E. *Phyllodoce*, a phyllodocid. F. *Trophonia*, a chloraemid. For ease of comparison, the prostomial palps are stippled, the prostomial tentacles shown in black, and the peristomial or notopodial cirri are left white. (All after Benham.) 1, prostomium; 2, peristomium; 3, prostomial palp; 4, prostomial tentacle; 5, peristomial cirrus; 6, cirrus of second somite; 7, cirrus of third somite; 8, nuchal organ; 9, point of attachment of scale (elytra).

like *Aphrodite* and *Nephthys* (Fig. 14.4), have a peristomium which has a pair of parapodia and setae, although they are somewhat modified. Most of the active, errant polychaetes have a peristomium derived from a single, modified somite which has neither parapodia nor setae, but a few have added a second somite to the peristomium, like *Phyllodoce*, and the second somite is also without parapodia. Parts of the parapodia of somites behind the peristomium may be modified so that they serve as parts of a specialized front end, whether one wishes to consider them as a part of the head or not. The third segment of *Phyllodoce* has long, peristomial cirri resembling the cirri of the peristomial region, and the hesionids have the first four body segments modified in this manner. The relative sizes and numbers of the sensory appendages of the head and first few somites are characteristic of the various families of polychaetes.

Active, errant polychaetes have strong, prominent parapodia, either elongated and leg-like or flat and paddle-like. Modifications of parapodial form are important in taxonomy, and reflect the habits of the various species (Fig. 14.5). The *Neanthes* parapodium shows the basic form (Fig. 14.2D). The dorsal lobe, the notopodium, bears a tentacle-like dorsal cirrus, and the ventral lobe, the neuropodium, bears a similar ventral cirrus. Vascular, flattened blades are attached to the notopodium and neuropodium. These are the gills. Modifications of parapodial structure involve changes in the number and type of setae, the form and position of the gills, the number of acicula, the relative development of the notopodium and neuropodium, and sometimes by unusual modifications that set a group apart. A flat plate, the elytra, takes the place of the dorsal cirrus in *Aphrodite*, for example, and in the scale worms generally (Figs. 14.6B; 14.7A). The scales are used to generate respiratory currents. *Aphrodite*, the beautifully iridescent sea mouse, also

has remarkable modifications of the setae. The notopodium produces two kinds of setae: lateral, finer, iridescent setae, and stiffer, dorsal setae. A felted mass of fine chitinous filaments covers the dorsal surface, hiding the elytra. The setae, in combination with the short, stout body form, make the name sea mouse appropriate.

Most of the active, predaceous, errant polychaetes live under rocks, in crevices, among seaweeds, corals, and other colonial animals, or emerge from burrows to feed. Swimming is not a very important part of their lives, and the parapodia are relatively short. The pelagic polychaetes, however, have very prominent parapodia, like *Tomopterus* (Fig. 14.6A), or may have natatory setae on the parapodia. An eversible pharynx is characteristic of the predaceous errant polychaetes. It is operated by a hydraulic system formed of the body-wall muscles and coelomic fluid. Contraction of the circular muscles compresses the coelomic fluid and shoots the proboscis out, sometimes so rapidly and powerfully that an audible pop is sounded. The proboscis jaws are inverted when the proboscis is withdrawn, and are positioned for use by proboscis extrusion (Fig. 10.2F). Most polychaetes have a single pair of jaws, but some have a single stylet-like tooth, and others have one lower and several upper jaws. Small denticles sometimes stud the proboscis surface. The form of the jaws or other proboscis armament is important in taxonomy, and varies considerably with the kind of food taken. When food is engaged by the extruded proboscis, retractor muscles haul it back and the food is swallowed. Nearly all errants with an eversible proboscis feed on living or dead animal tissue, but a few use the proboscis to crop tissues from seaweeds.

Nearly all of the Errantia move, to some extent, through the upper strata of the bottom. Some are active burrowers, and these tend to have smaller parapodia, like *Glycera*. Some of the burrowing poly-chaetes are Sedentaria, but these, unlike *Glycera*, are mud-eaters and swallow much of the mud and sand moved during bur-rowing. *Arenicola*, the common lugworm, is a good example (Fig. 14.6D). *Arenicola* is one of the few Sedentaria with an eversible proboscis. It is thrust into the sand, and mucous secretions glue finer particles to the proboscis surface while larger particles are thrust aside. The detritus-laden proboscis is retracted and adherent particles are swallowed. Burrow-ing mud-eaters like *Arenicola* do not form tubes, for they must keep moving to ob-tain food. They must swallow a great deal of material to obtain adequate food sup-plies. Large species of *Arenicola* reach a foot or more in length and burrow through the upper 50 to 60 cm. of the ocean floor.

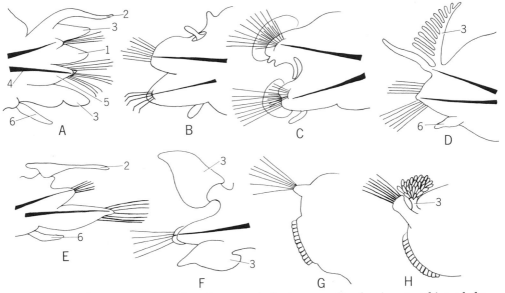

Fig. 14.5. Schematic representation of some polychaete parapodia, showing something of the variability found in different groups. The parapodial form is varied by the position and general shape of the gills, the size and development of the neuropodium and notopodium, and the number and arrangement of the setae. In errant polychaetes, one or two acicula are present, while in sedentary polychaetes the acicula are missing and the neuropodium and notopodium are usually poorly developed. Detailed differences in shape are seen within families, but each family has a basic arrangement of parapodial parts that is characteristic. In A a nereid para-podium is shown, with about equal development of the notopodium and neuropodium, and with the dorsal and ventral cirri distinct. A glycerid is shown in B, without conspicuous gill blades, and with relatively small cirri. A nephthyd is shown in C, with about equally developed notopodium and neuropodium, although differently formed than in nereids. In D a eunicid is shown. Here the notopodial setae are gone, and the gill is filamentous. A polynoid is shown in E. These are the scale worms, which have a scale, the elytra, attached to a flattened surface, which has developed from the dorsal cirrus. In F a phyllodocid is shown. The notopodium is nearly absent, except for the gill blade which has developed from it. A sabellid is shown in G. There are no acicula, and the neuropodium consists of a group of very short setae. An arenicolid is shown in H. Here the notopodium is rather like the sabellid notopodium, but also gives rise to a filamentous gill. (From various sources.) 1, notopodium; 2, dorsal cirrus; 3, gill; 4, aciculum; 5, neuropodium; 6, ventral cirrus.

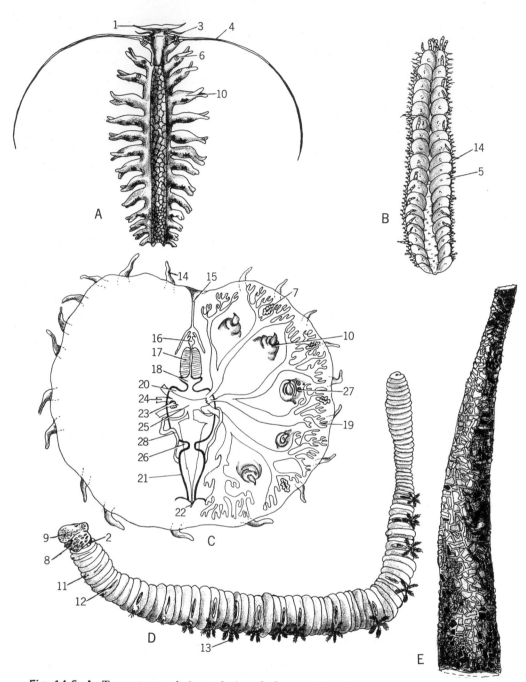

Fig. 14.6. A. *Tomopterus rolasi*, a pelagic polychaete with well-developed sense organs and long parapodia without setae. B. *Halosydna brevisetosa*, a scale worm, with elytra attached to the notopodia. The scales are tilted to maintain a respiratory current, fanning the water toward the posterior end. C. *Myzostomum antarcticum*, a myzostomid. These highly specialized polychaetes live as commensals or parasites on the surface of crinoids and other echinoderms. Note

Where they are abundant, they do a tremendous amount of work and keep the ocean floor in constant circulation. A burrowing *Arenicola* swallows every five seconds or so for a minute or two, and then rests for a few minutes. It works for from five to eight hours a day, with occasional long rests of an hour or so. Davidson calculated that where *Arenicola* is abundant, some 1900 tons of sand are brought to the surface per acre per year. All of the material in the upper 50 to 60 cm. of the bottom is worked through by *Arenicola* once in about two years, making them among the most influential geological agents in littoral regions.

Most of the Sedentaria are permanent tube-dwellers. Many feed on detritus, gathered by straight or branched filamentous processes, built of specialized prostomial palps or tentacles or of peristomial cirri. The feeding apparatus is usually thrust into the upper parts of the bottom material. Particles are caught in mucus and move up ciliated grooves to the mouth. A number of terebellids feed in this manner (Fig. 14.3A). As the tentacles move about, and as new material is delivered by water currents, they need not move about like the burrowing species. Those that feed farther below the surface do move around, as new material does not accumulate so rapidly. They either form no tubes or build unattached tubes that can be moved about, like *Pectinaria* (Fig. 14.6E). Annelids of this type usually have some system for sorting out the particles that are picked up; some use the rejected particles for building the tube.

Not all of the permanent tube-dwellers feed on detritus, however. Some lift the food-gathering equipment above the bottom, trapping planktonic organisms as they move past. Among these are some of the most beautiful of the polychaetes. Serpulids and sabellids are sometimes called the feather-duster worms for the crown of feathery tentacles extending above the tube (Fig. 14.7B). Although the processes undoubtedly serve as a respiratory surface, they are not true gills, and are known as radioles. The ciliated, feathery processes are equipped with a mucous-ciliary apparatus for the capture of food and its conveyance to the mouth.

Polychaete tubes vary greatly in form, composition, and location. Some tubes are built of mucus, and are little more than a consolidation of the particles of which the bottom is made. Others are built of onuphin, conchiolin, or other organic compounds that harden on contact with water to make tough, membranous tubes. The serpulids build calcareous tubes on an onuphin or mucous base, and large aggregations of the tubes form soft, rocky masses. Still others build tubes of consolidated sand grains or other particles. They may be straight, irregularly curved, U-shaped, or spiraled, and may be branched or unbranched. Each type of tube reflects some peculiarity of physiology, habits, or both, and some types are especially suitable to a particular kind of

the gut diverticula, used for food distribution. D, *Arenicola*, a lug worm. These sedentary polychaetes burrow in the sand, feeding on detritus. The number of external rings does not correspond to the number of somites. E. Tube of *Pectinaria*, a sedentary polychaete that builds a tube of small sand particles, glued together with mucoid secretions. (A, after Greef. B, after Ricketts and Calvin. C, after Stummer-Traunfels, in Kükenthal and Krumbach. E, after M'Intosh, from Benham.) *External features:* 1, prostomium; 2, peristomium; 3, anterior prostomial process; 4, posterior prostomial process; 5, elytra attached to notopodia; 6, rosette organ, a dermal eye; 7, eye; 8, buccal papillae; 9, protruded pharynx; 10, parapodium; 11, notopodium; 12, neuropodium; 13, gill; 14, cirrus. *Internal organs:* 15, mouth; 16, proboscis, withdrawn; 17, proboscis bulb; 18, esophagus; 19, gut diverticula; 20, stomach; 21, hindgut; 22, cloacal pore; 23, ovary; 24, uterine diverticula; 25, uterus; 26, oviduct; 27, penis; 28, nephridium.

A

B

C

Fig. 14.7. Some Representative Polychaetes. A and C, dorsal and ventral views of *Aphrodite*, the sea mouse. B. *Hermodice*, a polychaete with conspicuous branched parapodial gills and thick tufts of parapodial setae. D. *Sabellastarte magnifica*, a sedentary polychaete with conspicuous radioles. E. Another sedentary polychaete, *Spirobranchus giganteus*. The tubicolous

D

E

sedentary polychaetes have food-gathering devices which are extended from the tube, and include some of the most strikingly beautiful animals. (A and C, courtesy of General Biological Supply Co. B, D, and E, courtesy of the Smithsonian Institution.)

environment. The calcareous serpulid tubes are usually found on rocks or molluscan shells, and the tiny, spiral tubes of *Spirorbis* are often seen on seaweeds. Soft membranous tubes are especially suitable for fitting into crevices or attaching to seaweeds.

The relationship of the worm to its tube is a very intimate one, and the animals adapt in a variety of ways to the special self-made environment in which they live. As adaptation has been taking place for very long periods, nearly every body system can be affected in one way or another. *Chaetopterus* (Fig. 14.8) is a good example of the sort of intensive adaptation to tubicolous life that is seen in so many polychaetes. Its bizarre body seems senselessly distorted unless its precise adaptation to its tube is taken into account. The fourteenth to sixteenth parapodia are large fans that move back and forth rhythmically, sweeping a flow of water through the U-shaped tube. The twelfth notopodia are drawn out to form two wings. In position, they make a partial partition across the tube, leaving a small aperture through which all of the water must pass. The wings secrete abundant mucus, which moves down into the aperture. As water is formed, more mucus is secreted and moves into place. The sheet of mucus billows out to form a mucous sac, which lengthens until it reaches a ciliated cupule midway between the wings and the fans. All of the water must pass through the mucous sac, leaving its burden of particles behind. When full, the sac is wrapped up to form a pellet in the cupule. Cilia in a special groove carry the pellet forward to the mouth for swallowing.

Locomotion. Polychaetes swim, creep about over the surface of algae, rocks, and other objects or through the soft bottom material, and move about in their tubes. Errantia are predominantly creeping organisms, but are usually able to swim. Sedentaria are usually restricted to movements that extend the body away from and withdraw it into the tube.

Creeping is by no means as simple as it looks. To creep effectively calls for close cooperation of the body-wall musculature and the parapodia. Consider the mechanical problems in any one body segment. The parapodia move alternately, with the right one making a forward, recovery stroke while the left makes a backward, effective stroke. It is not, however, a simple problem of alternate movements on the two sides of the body. When a parapodium completes its recovery stroke, muscles moving the aciculum are contracted and it is forced outward, extending the setae. This increases the resistance to movement through the water, and also tends to engage the bottom. As the effective stroke ends, the acicula are withdrawn, which withdraws the setae for the recovery stroke, and the parapodium is lifted slightly, disengaging it from the bottom. These coordinated movements will produce a forward thrust with each parapodial "step," but the worm as a whole will get nowhere unless the parapodia of its many somites are working in a coordinated fashion. Coordination of the various segments is achieved by activation waves, which start at the posterior end of the body. The activation waves are initiated on the two sides of the body alternately, and move forward alternately on the two sides. Each activation wave affects about four to eight parapodia, and they are so timed that when the first group of parapodia complete the effective stroke, the next complete the recovery stroke. The alternating activation waves coordinate the body longitudinally and evoke the necessary stimuli to make the alternating parapodial movements. Forward impetus, however, comes mainly from body movements. Alternate contraction and relaxation of the longitudinal muscles on opposite sides of the body produce undulatory movements. These are so timed that the contraction wave affecting a group of segments coincides with the effective parapodial strokes. As a result, longitudinal muscles are contracting and pulling the body forward while the setae are engaged in the substrate. Movement of this kind is widespread in Errantia, and is effective for swimming as well as creeping. The rhythmic, muscular contractions are largely dependent on prepackaged intersegmental reflexes, but movements are also under the direct control of the central nervous system.

Polychaetes can suddenly withdraw into their tubes or make sudden contractions of the whole body. Stimuli for such movements result from a giant fiber system in the nerve cord. These "startle" movements are especially rapid in tubicolous species, which have very strong longitudinal muscles. They are an important part of the behavioral equipment of errant polychaetes as well.

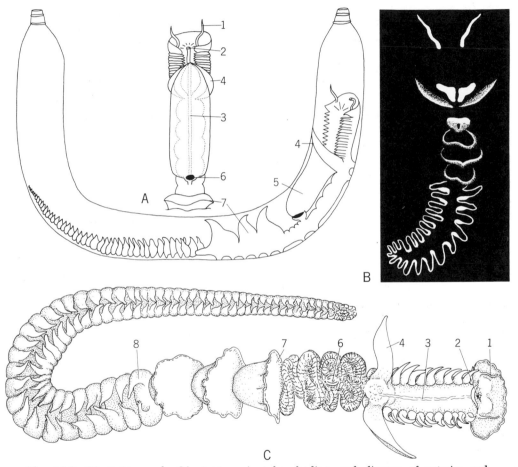

Fig. 14.8. *Chaetopterus*. A. *Chaetopterus* in tube, feeding, and diagram of anterior end. B. *Chaetopterus* luminescence. C. *Chaetopterus* removed from its tube. (A, after MacGinitie from the MacGinities. B, after Panceri, from Benham.) 1, peristomial cirrus; 2, mouth; 3, ciliated groove; 4, wing or aliform notopodium; 5, mucous bag, secreted by the wings and used for straining food; 6, ciliated food cup, into which the food bag extends; 7, fans, used to set up currents in the tube; 8, unmodified parapodium.

Tubicolous polychaetes may use parapodia to produce water currents in the tube, but these are relatively unimportant and the parapodia are usually much reduced. The setae, however, retain importance, for they engage the tube wall and help to withdraw or extend the body. They also make it more difficult to pull the worm out of its home. The setae often are hooked or have terminal structures that make them more effective. Setal shape is of value in taxonomy of some groups.

Burrowing polychaetes also tend to have reduced parapodia, but some, like *Aphrodite*, have large parapodia and use them as shovels. Coordination of the movements for burrowing pose entirely different problems than for creeping. In creepers, the right and left longitudinal muscles are antagonists and cause an undulating movement. In burrowing forms, however, the circular and longitudinal muscles are antagonists. Relaxation of the longitudinal muscles of a segment and contraction of the circular muscles applies pressure to the coelomic fluid and causes the segment to elongate. When the circular muscles relax and the longitudinal muscles contract, the segment shortens. Each segment is a diminutive hydraulic system; muscle contractions change its form but not its volume, and it increases or decreases in diameter to compensate for changes in length. Longitudinal muscles on both sides contract simultaneously rather than alternately. Forward progression, however, depends on traction provided by the setae. The setae are brought against the substrate in short, stout, contracted segments, and lose contact in long, slender, elongated segments. The elongated segments thus thrust forward while the contracted segments serve as anchors, preventing backward movement.

The most highly modified polychaetes are the myzostomes (Fig. 14.7C), which live as ectoparasites on crinoids, brittle stars, and asteroids. Some make limited movements, while others are permanently attached. Each parapodium ends in two modified setae, one a hook and the other a guard, providing excellent anchorage.

The Oligochaeta

Most of the 2500 species of oligochaetes live in the soil, but some live in freshwater environments and a few are marine animals. Terrestrial earthworms live in moist soil almost everywhere, but are especially characteristic of good soil in temperate regions. The aquatic species are also widespread, and a few have become parasitic on aquatic animals.

External Form. Oligochaetes are far less diverse than polychaetes externally. They have no parapodia and relatively few, inconspicuous setae. The greatly reduced head has no sensory appendages in the majority of species. As a result they are externally simplified, with relatively few features that can reflect adaptation. The terrestrial earthworms are larger than aquatic species. Some species become very large; *Megascolides australis*, an Australian species, reaches lengths of over 3 m. Some of the aquatic species are barely visible to the naked eye.

Burrowing polychaetes tend to adapt by reduction of the head and parapodia. Oligochaetes have carried these trends to greater extremes. The head is scarcely a true head, for there are no sensory appendages and the prostomial eyes generally found in polychaetes have disappeared. The prostomium is a tiny flap, sometimes united with the peristomium (Fig. 14.9). The peristomium has no setae, but in other respects closely resembles the body segments. The only vestiges of the parapodia are the setae. Setae occur in four groups on the sides of the somites, a dorsolateral and ventrolateral group on each side. Many species, like *Lumbricus*, have two setae in each of these groups, a total of eight per somite. The dorsolateral fields of setae are undoubtedly the vestige of the notopodium, while the ventrolateral fields are a vestige of the neuropodium.

The body somites differ slightly in size because of tapering, but with few visible evidences of specialization. The setal shapes are characteristic of species. Generally the terrestrial species have sigma-shaped setae, often with a swelling (nodulus) at the middle (Fig. 14.10E). Each seta projects from the secretory follicle in which it forms, and is manipulated by protractor and retractor muscles. Some of the burrowing earthworms have more than eight setae per somite. *Megascolex*, for example, has eight setae on anterior somites but the number rises posteriorly, and *Perichaeta* has many setae in each segment, arranged in a continuous row around the middle of the somite.

A system of dorsal pores connects each coelomic compartment with the exterior in most of the burrowing earthworms. Coelomic fluid can be extruded through the dorsal pores. Giant earthworms can squirt coelomic fluid several centimeters. The value of this arrangement is not very clear. The fluid may moisten the body surface, but numerous epidermal mucous glands are also present. Where it can be squirted out, it may startle predators. Neither function seems adequate to account for the wide distribution of dorsal pores in terrestrial oligochaetes, however. One suggestion is that the fluid may harden to form consolidated walls in chambers used for estivation or hibernation.

Genital pores occur in specific somites, differing with the species. They are useful in identification of earthworms. The genital pores will be discussed later with the reproductive system. The glandular clitellum is characteristic of adult animals. It is a girdle that wholly or partly encircles several somites, and secretes the wall of the cocoon as well as helping to form slime tubes during copulation.

Modified setae in the clitellar region are not uncommon.

Oligochaetes have no external structures that can be adapted for food-getting. Food is obtained by pumping movements of the pharynx that draw in humus or bits of dried vegetation, or the pharynx is extruded somewhat to pick up particles. All of the terrestrial oligochaetes are herbivorous detritus-eaters. Darwin pointed out the vast quantities of soil that earthworms move. In the area he studied, about 18 tons of soil are brought to the surface by earthworms per acre per year. A slow circulation of the upper layers of the soil results from the activities of earthworms and other burrowing animals, and is an important factor in determing the zonation and mixing of the soil strata.

Aquatic oligochaetes are somewhat more diversified in external appearance, but are far less striking than the polychaetes. They are smaller than the terrestrial forms, and although they are benthic organisms they are more mobile than the land species as a rule. They tend to

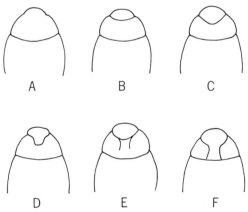

Fig. 14.9. The prostomium and peristomium of earthworms may be united or separate, and the prostomium may extend back toward the first somite. The various arrangements are taxonomically useful. A. Zygolobous. B. Prolobous. C. Proepilobous. D. Epilobous. E. Pro- and epilobous. F. Tanylobous. (After Michaelsen, in Kükenthal and Krumbach.)

have better-developed sense organs and the setae are more highly developed. They creep about on the bottom or on submerged plants and sometimes form soft mucous tubes on leaves or other objects. Some burrow in the soft bottom mud, and a few are ectoparasites.

None have a conspicuous head, but some have a large prostomium. *Stylaria* has an elongated prostomium, used as a delicately mobile tactile organ (Fig. 14.10G). *Stylaria*, *Nais*, and a few others have eyes. The peristomium has no setae, and sometimes the setae are modified or are missing in several anterior somites. These, however, are never incorporated into a definite head.

Setal structure is quite variable (Fig. 14.10). Slender, flexible hair setae increase surface resistance and are useful in swimming. Stiffer needle setae provide traction against the bottom or the walls of burrows or tubes. The setae occur in dorsolateral and ventrolateral tufts, preserving the traditional notopodial and neuropodial positions. In many cases the dorsal and ventral setae of a somite are different. As a rule, the dorsal setae are hair-like and the ventral setae needle-like.

Some of the aquatic oligochaetes have gills. The most remarkable gills are seen in *Branchiura* (Fig. 14.10I), where long, digitate, dorsal and ventral projections extend from the body surface. *Dero* has four ciliated body projections at the posterior end which serve as gills, and *Aulophorus* has three. These worms extend the pos-

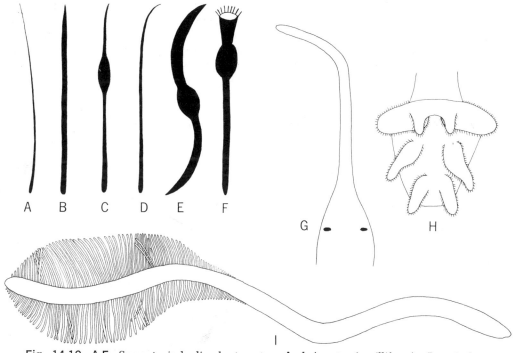

Fig. 14.10. A-F. Some typical oligochaete setae. A, hair seta (capilliform). B, aciculate. C, aciculate with nodulus. D, uncinate. E, sigmoid, with nodulus. F, pectinate. G. Anterior end of *Stylaria fossularis*, with the prostomium extended forward as a proboscis and with a pair of eyes. H. Posterior end of *Dero digitata*, showing the ciliated gills. I. Side view of *Branchiura sowerbyi*, showing the dorsal and ventral gills. (G and I, after Pennak. H, after Bousefield, from Goodnight in Edmondson.)

terior end of the body from their tubes for respiratory exchange, and the surface cilia ventilate the gills. Body movements are also used to ventilate respiratory surfaces.

Most of the aquatic oligochaetes have a thin, inconspicuous clitellum. Many of the smaller species reproduce primarily by transverse fission, and in some cases chains of individuals are formed. The reproductive organs are often immature most of the year, and reproduction occurs only by fission.

Detritus and algae, especially diatoms, are the principal foods. Extrusion of the pharynx exposes an adhesive region, coated with mucus. Particles adhere to it, and are swallowed when the pharynx is retracted. The burrowing species swallow quantities of mud, digesting out the organic material and casting the remainder at the end of the burrow. Like polychaetes and earthworms, they contribute to the circulation of the bottom material. Tiny *Chaetogaster*, less than a millimeter long, is an exception. It feeds on microcrustaceans, other worms, and insect larvae of appropriate size.

The most highly specialized oligochaetes are the branchiobdellids, which live on the gills or body surface of crayfish. They are considerably modified, in many ways resembling leeches. Probably leeches arose from oligochaetes by following an adaptive line that was not unlike that followed by the branchiobdellids. Branchiobdellids have a constant number of somites, 15 or 16 as the case may be. The first four somites are fused together to form a cylindrical head. Finger-like projections and a sucker occur on the head. A pair of strong, chitinous jaws in the buccal cavity are used for feeding. The trunk consists of 11 segments. Finger-like appendages are often found on the trunk somites, and in *Cambarincola* (Fig. 14.3E) a flange-like frill is found on the dorsal surface of each. Not much is known of the physiology of branchiobdellids, but

it is evident that their bodies are highly specialized for an epizoic life.

Class Hirudinea

Leeches make up a relatively homogeneous group of highly specialized annelids. About 300 species have been described, predominantly from fresh-water habitats. A few, however, are marine, and some have adapted to terrestrial life in warm, moist regions. Leeches have a clitellum and a hermaphroditic reproductive system that resembles the reproductive system of oligochaetes in some ways. They are thought to have arisen from an oligochaete stock that adapted to ectoparasitic life, rather like the branchiobdellids. *Acanthobdella* is far more oligochaete-like than other leeches. It has undoubtedly developed from an independent stock, and serves to exemplify the general features of leeches as they may have been in ancient times. It differs in so many particulars that it has been excluded from the following discussion of external form.

Leeches are far more diversified in their habits than most people realize. They are not true parasites, but are rather to be considered predaceous animals, many of which take blood meals from vertebrates or invertebrates. Some live more or less permanently on a single animal and so verge on true ectoparasitism. Others make only infrequent visits to the prey for a blood meal, and still others are ordinary predators or scavengers.

External Form. Leeches are usually flattened dorsoventrally and taper fore and aft. Many are broad and leaf-like, while others look like plump worms. Most fall into a size range between 20 to 25 and 50 to 60 mm., but a few species are less than 10 mm. long, and the largest leeches are said to reach nearly 0.5 m. when creeping.

Except for *Acanthobdella*, leeches have a remarkably constant metameric organi-

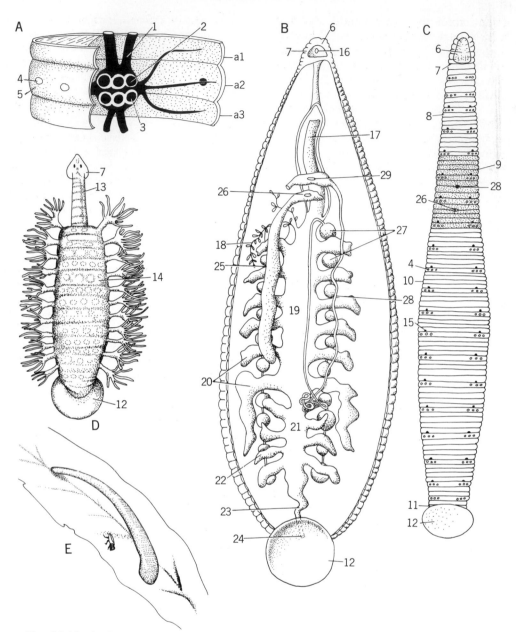

Fig. 14.11. A. A primitive leech segment, with three annuli. The middle annulus is the sensory annulus, bearing the sense organs. Notice the six masses of neurons associated with the ganglion. B. Internal organization of *Glossiphonia complanata*, a pharyngobdellid leech. C. Ventral view of *Hirudo medicinalis*, a gnathobdellid leech. D. *Ozobranchus jantzeanus*, a piscicolid leech with lateral gill filaments. The body of piscicolid leeches is divided into a head region, a trachelosome, and a urosome. E. *Haemadipsa*, a haemadipsid leech attached to a leaf, waiting for an appropriate host. (A, after Mann, from Avel, in Grassé. B, after Harding. C, after Mann. D, after Oka. E, after Scriban and Autrum, from Mann.) *Somite structure:*

zation, indicating close relationship and a high level of specialization. The body is formed of 34 somites (33 by one method of counting). The major body divisions contain the same somites in all leeches: the head (I-VI); preclitellar region (VII-IX); clitellum (X-XIII); postclitellar region or trunk (XIV-XXIV); anal region (XXV-XXVII); and posterior sucker (XXVIII-XXXIV). They seem to have more somites, however, for each is subdivided into annuli by transverse grooves (Fig. 14.11A). The number of primary somites can be determined by counting the ganglia on the nerve cord or by counting the lateral nerves. Comparative studies indicate that three annuli occur in the primitive somite. Some leech somites remain undivided, however, and some have only two annuli; presumably as a result of suppression of one or two annuli. Many leeches have more numerous annuli formed by subdivision of the original three. To make it easier to describe annulation, a system for the designation of annuli has been devised. The three annuli of a primitive segment are designated a_1, a_2, and a_3, with a_1 the most anterior annulus. If each annulus of the primitive somite were subdivided, there would be six annuli and they would be designated b_1-b_6. Subdivisions of the third order produce annuli c_1-c_{12}; of the fourth order d_1-d_{24}. Most leeches have only a and b divisions; very few have d divisions. Generally, the three primitive annuli are differently subdivided in the same somite when more than three annuli are present. Annulus a_2 is the sensory annulus, as it bears the sense organs and contains the main branch of the lateral nerve. Piscicolid leeches (Fig.

14.11D) are differently divided. The body is composed of a head, a trachelosome made up of the preclitellum and clitellum, and a urosome, extending to the posterior sucker. A definite collar at the posterior end of the clitellum may sharply define the body regions. Somites X-XIII still make up the clitellum, however, and the basic features of the metameric organization remain unchanged.

Leeches are well supplied with sense organs. Eyes of varying complexity, papillae, and tubercles are distributed over the body. Stripes of pigment or irregular patches of color are not uncommon, and in many cases, metamerically arranged pigment spots are placed in a definite relationship to the sense organs. The simplest ocelli contain a single photoreceptor cell surrounded by pigment. Such unicellular photoreceptors, and other sensory cells, may occur anywhere on the body surface. The more complex sense organs, however, are associated with the sensory annulus. The number, disposition, and kind of sense organs present are important in taxonomy, as is the annulation pattern seen in the various somites.

Leeches are distinctly cephalized. The anterior sucker may be very prominent or may consist of little more than thickened lips around the mouth. Rhynchobdellid leeches have a protrusible proboscis, and the oral sucker lies behind the mouth, but the mouth is centered in the oral sucker of gnathobdellids and pharyngobdellids. The compound eyes also lie on the head. Their position, number, and form are important in identification of species.

Most leeches respire through the body

1, nerve cord; 2, ganglion; 3, mass of parikaryons on ganglion; 4, sense organ; 5, sensory annulus. *External features:* 6, anterior sucker; 7, head; 8, preclitellar region; 9, clitellum; 10, trunk; 11, anal region; 12, posterior sucker; 13, trachelosome; 14, urosome; 15, nephridiopore. *Digestive tract:* 16, proboscis pore in anterior sucker; 17, proboscis; 18, salivary gland; 19, crop; 20, crop diverticula; 21, intestine; 22, intestinal diverticulum; 23, rectum; 24, anus. *Reproductive system:* 25, ovisac containing ovary; 26, female gonopore; 27, testis; 28, sperm duct; 29, male gonopore.

surface generally, but a few have definite gills. The gills are usually simple, vascular vesicles on the sides of the body, but some have plumose gills (Fig. 14.11D).

The posterior end of the body is formed of seven compacted somites, with no trace of external divisions. The nerve ganglia serving them are lumped together in a single mass. The last of these somites is the pygidium, which normally contains the anus in annelids. A few leeches have the anus located in the posterior sucker, no doubt associated with the pygidium, but in most cases the old anus is closed off and a new dorsal anus just anterior to the posterior sucker replaces it. The posterior sucker is a powerful suction cup, useful in locomotion as well as for attachment during feeding.

Acanthobdella is a most interesting leech from a evolutionary standpoint. Its external form reveals its distinctiveness from other leeches and shows some oligochaete-like traits. The body contains only 27 somites and four of these are united to form the posterior sucker. There is no trace of an anterior sucker. The first five somites have setae, wholly lacking in all other leeches. The absence of an oral sucker, the simple posterior sucker, and the presence of setae are all primitive traits. Branchiobdellid oligochaetes have some leech-like traits; and *Acanthobdella*, with its oligochaete-like characteristics, emphasizes the probable relationship of leeches to oligochaetes. While it is improbable that branchiobdellids or *Acanthobdella* are directly related to the stem forms between oligochaetes and leeches, they do show that the oligochaetes tend to become leech-like when they assume ectoparasitic habits and that the most primitive leech has traits that are far more oligochaete-like than the more highly evolved leeches.

Habits. Rhynchobdellid leeches have a probosics and no jaws. These structural peculiarities are correlated with their habits, which differ somewhat from those of other leeches. Rhynchobdellids fall naturally into two groups, the glossiphonids and the piscicolids. Glossiphonids are flattened, fresh-water leeches with an inconspicuous anterior sucker. Most of them are predators or scavengers, moving about actively in search of worms or other small invertebrates. Prey is caught with the proboscis. Some feed on snails and live in or on snail shells, and some take blood meals from cold-blooded vertebrates. *Glossiphonia* (Fig. 14.11B) is a good example. Piscicolids (Fig. 14.11D) are the fish leeches. Most of them live as ectoparasites on fresh-water fishes and crustacea, but a few occur on marine elasmobranchs. Most of the piscicolids leave the host to breed and attach their egg capsules to submerged objects, but some attach the egg capsules directly to the host animal. They have no jaws, and the method used to penetrate the host skin remains a mystery. Piscicolids are usually long and cylindrical and have a conspicuous anterior sucker, used for holding on.

Gnathobdellids have no proboscis and three toothed jaws surround the mouth. The family Hirudidae includes the more familiar forms. *Hirudo medicinalis* (Fig. 14.11C), long used for blood-letting, is probably most often studied as an example of leech structure. *Hirudo*, like most of the members of its family, lives in relatively shallow water in temperate or subtropical regions. When it feeds, the jaws make a small, triangular incision. Saliva, containing an anticoagulant, hirudin, is applied to the wound. The muscular pharynx pumps blood into the stomach. As a rule, the hirudids visit animals to take blood meals infrequently. Some, however, enter the upper respiratory tract of cattle and horses as they drink, causing respiratory difficulties and secondary infections. The family Haemadipsidae includes the tropical land leeches with blood-sucking habits. They live on the ground in moist places, and some climb up on shrubs or other plants to wait for the arrival of a bird or mammal on which they can feed (Fig. 14.11E).

Some of the hirudids have quite small jaws and do not ordinarily depend on blood meals. They attack their prey, usually small worms or other invertebrates, and swallow it whole. The pharyngobdellids have no jaws and feed in the same manner. Probably all hirudids and pharyngobdellids will take a blood meal when a bleeding wound is available, however. In some species this tendency is stronger than in others.

Locomotion. Terrestrial leeches creep by attaching the posterior sucker, extending the body, attaching the anterior sucker, and pulling the posterior end forward. This inching along is essentially like the locomotion of earthworms, except that the body as a whole extends and contracts alternately, behaving like a single segment of an oligochaete. Evidently the nature of the built-in intersegmental reflexes have been modified to bring about simultaneous contractions of the longitudinal muscles of all somites together.

Aquatic leeches can creep in the same manner, but some can also swim gracefully, with undulatory movements of the body. The undulatory movements are similar to those of other annelids, involving the alternate contractions of the longitudinal muscles on the two sides of the body, so that they work as antagonists and with small groups of somites acting in unison. Movements of this type depend on activation waves of a type not required for creeping. Terrestrial leeches cannot swim, and drop to the bottom of a pond to creep out to the shore. Some of the aquatic leeches are also limited to creeping movements. As in other annelids, the activation waves responsible for undulatory movements are affected by, but are not dependent on, the brain. Removal of the brain and the compound ganglion at the base of the posterior sucker does not destroy the ability to swim.

Anatomy and Physiology of Annelids

The Body Wall. The annelid body wall consists of layers of cuticle, epidermis (also termed hypodermis, as it is covered by a thin cuticle), a very thin to moderate layer of connective tissue forming a dermis, circular muscle, longitudinal muscle, and parietal peritoneum.

The cuticle is a non-chitinous, albuminoid material, somewhat variable in thickness but generally very thin and flexible. The scale-worms (Fig. 14.6B) mold the cuticle into a strong protective plate on the dorsal side of each elytra. Slime and other secretions from the epidermis must pass through the cuticle to reach the surface; the cuticle contains pores for this purpose. Some oligochaetes and polychaetes have a striated cuticle. When the striations are sufficiently delicate, they confer iridescence to the body surface. *Lumbricus* is slightly iridescent, but in no way compares to some of the polychaetes, with brilliant, iridescent blue and green hues resulting from cuticular striation. *Aphrodite*'s dorsal covering of felted filaments has been mentioned previously. The filaments are striated and brilliantly iridescent. Many of the polychaetes use surface cilia in some regions for food-getting or to generate respiratory currents. In these regions the cuticle is reduced. The ancestral stocks from which the annelids arose were probably equipped with surface cilia, like the modern flatworms. The development of a cuticle accompanied by reduction of the surface cilia was undoubtedly an important progressive trait, producing selective pressures that favored the further development of the body-wall musculature and, indirectly, of the other body systems.

The epidermis consists of a single layer of epithelium, usually columnar, but varying in height in different regions of the body. An interesting feature of the anne-

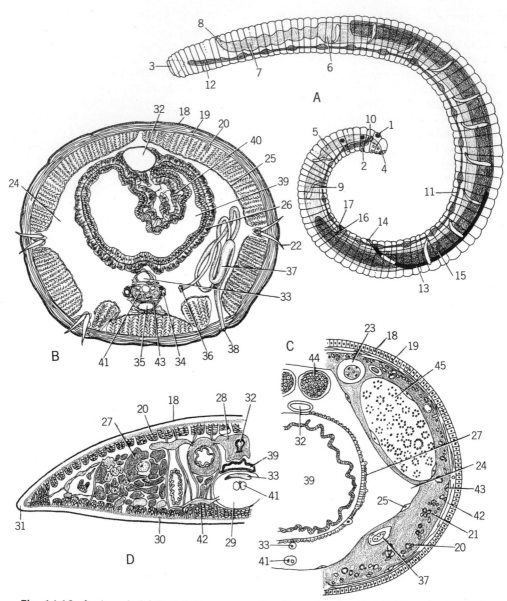

Fig. 14.12. A. *Acanthobdella peledina*, representing the order Acanthobdellidea characterized by a posterior sucker of only four somites, the presence of setae, and other primitive leech traits. B. Transverse section through *Lumbricus terrestris*, showing the basic organization of oligochaetes. C. Transverse section through *Acanthobdella*. Note the open coelom, closed in part in other leeches by the accumulation of botryoidal tissue. D. Transverse section through a glossiphonid leech, *Placobdella*. In the glossiphonids, the coelom is reduced to narrow passages in the botryoidal tissue. (A and C, after Livanoff. D, after Scriban, from Avel, in Grassé. B, composite.) *Acanthobdella, External features:* 1, eye; 2, setae; 3, posterior sucker. *Digestive tract:* 4, mouth; 5, esophagus; 6, middle intestine; 7, posterior intestine; 8, anus. *Excretory system:* 9, nephridium. *Nervous system:* 10, brain; 11, nerve cord and ganglia; 12, anal nerve

lid epidermis is the scarcity of mitotic figures. Many sections can be examined without finding a mitotic spindle. In the epidermis of *Lumbricus,* as of other annelids, a scattered population of basal cells can be seen. There is some evidence that these cells arise from the mesodermal tissues below and migrate out to the epidermis, replacing moribund epidermis cells as required. A similar migration of deep cells out into the epidermis is seen in a budding *Aeolosoma.* If this is generally true, it would mean that in an adult annelid most if not all of the epidermis would actually be composed of cells of mesodermal origin. A variety of unicellular gland cells are interspersed among the columnar cells. Mucus is produced by unicellular goblets, which become the predominant cell in regions of high mucous production. The product of the other kinds of gland cells are usually of unknown chemical composition and often of unknown function. Terrestrial oligochaetes have albuminous gland cells that contain finely dispersed secretions, closely resembling some of the gland cells of polychaetes, but the role played by the secretions is not certain in either type of annelid. Many of the polychaetes secrete mucus containing luminescent material (Fig. 14.8B), produced in special epidermal gland cells. Some of the gland cells become very large and are deeply insunk. The clitellar epidermis of both leeches and oligochaetes is profoundly modified, with insunk gland cells extending into the deeper layers of the body wall (Fig. 14.13).

The bright pigments of polychaetes and leeches are epidermal. The pigmented cells of polychaetes are often taller than the surrounding cells, forming low pigmented elevations. The pigments produced by annelids are quite diverse. Many have been named, but there is little information about their chemical nature. In some cases nitrogenous wastes appear to be used in pigment formation, providing an effective and unusual adjunct to more ordinary methods of excretion. Most of the oligochaetes are unpigmented, but *Aeolosoma* has brightly colored oil droplets in its epidermal cells.

The dermis is more delicate in small species than in large, and in polychaetes and oligochaetes than in leeches. In small polychaetes it is little more than a basement membrane. In large leeches it is an extensive layer, containing the tips of the dorsoventral muscle strands. In some of the oligochaetes, fibrils from the epidermal cells penetrate the basement membrane and pass through the dermis, attaching directly to the circular muscle. This arrangement is reminiscent of the epidermal fibers used to strengthen muscle attachments in many arthropods.

Nature is a ruthless logician where adaptational changes are concerned, using the device of differential survival to sort out the ill-organized and unsuitable combinations. A better understanding of the totality of the life process is gained by observing adaptive trends, for these trends are the result of convergent or parallel evolutionary patterns, of similar adaptational responses to similar problems

center. *Reproductive system:* 13, ovary; 14, female gonopore; 15, seminal vesicle; 16, male gonoduct; 17, male gonopore. *Sections: Body wall:* 18, epidermis; 19, circular somatic muscle; 20, longitudinal somatic muscle; 21, mesenchyme; 22, seta; 23, giant gland cell. *Coelom:* 24, coelomic cavity; 25, parietal peritoneum; 26, visceral peritoneum (chlorogogue); 27, botryoidal tissue; 28, dorsal lacuna; 29, ventral lacuna; 30, hypodermal lacuna; 31, lateral lacuna. *Circulatory system:* 32, dorsal vessel; 33, ventral vessel; 34, lateral neural vessel; 35, subneural vessel. *Excretory system:* 36, nephrostome; 37, nephridium; 38, nephridiopore. *Digestive system:* 39, intestine; 40, typhlosole. *Nervous system:* 41, nerve cord; 42, lateral nerve; 43, neuron. *Reproductive system:* 44, ovary; 45, seminal vesicle.

arising from similar habitats or similar activities. Adaptation to any kind of activity is a complex event, for every species adapts as a whole living system of inter-

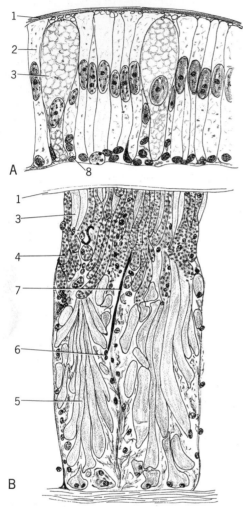

Fig. 14.13. Epidermis of *Lumbricus terrestris*. A. Section through epidermis of an unspecialized somite. B. Section through epidermis of the clitellum. Notice the specialized gland cells and increased thickness of epidermis. (B, after Grove.) 1, cuticle; 2, epithelial cells; 3, mucous gland cells; 4, coarsely glandular clitellar gland cells; 5, finely granular clitellar gland cells; 6, connective tissue; 7, blood vessel; 8, basal cells, thought to replace epithelial cells.

dependent and cooperating parts, with modifications of any one part or function evoking suitable compensatory or synergistic changes in another part or function. Some of the correlations between the amount and kind of movement and the external form have been mentioned. The kind of movement also affects the patterns of neuronal firing, or, to be more precise, a particular type of movement, whether it be creeping, swimming, or burrowing, cannot be accomplished effectively unless appropriate nervous activities are an integral part of the organism's equipment. Differences in the development of the body-wall musculature become sensible when viewed in the same light.

Annelids invariably have an outer layer of circular muscle and an inner layer of longitudinal muscle in the body wall, but the two layers differ greatly in relative development in different annelids. Most polychaetes have a delicate layer of circular muscle and relatively powerful longitudinal muscles. The longitudinal muscles are especially strong in tubicolous species. This is sensible and logical, for their most rapid and powerful movements are for withdrawal into their tubes. As a rule, polychaete longitudinal muscles are arranged in a set of four strong longitudinal muscle bands, two dorsolateral and two ventrolateral (Fig. 14.2D). Both creeping and swimming movements depend on the antagonistic contractions of the longitudinal muscles of the two sides of the body. The circular muscles are not very important, for the use of the coelomic fluid and body wall as a hydraulic system is not consequential in locomotion. In burrowing forms, and especially in oligochaetes, a relatively even development of circular and longitudinal muscles is seen. The terrestrial oligochaetes have an almost continuous sheath of longitudinal muscle, separated into seven strips by narrow interruptions at the middorsal line, at the level of the setal groups, and at points about midway between the ventral setae and midventral line, where the nephridiopores open (Fig. 14.12B). In their movements, the circular and longitudinal muscles are antagonists, and the body-wall and coelomic compartments serve as a series of dimunitive hydraulic systems in movement. Although some leeches can swim by undulatory movements, the characteristic leech locomotion involves the whole body. All forward thrust depends on the use of the circular muscles of the body as a whole, and it is not surprising to find the circular muscle layer of leeches better developed than in oligochaetes of comparable size. When the whole body moves as a unit rather than in small sections, muscles more complicated than simple circular and longitudinal layers are needed to provide reasonable control. Leeches have a layer of diagonal muscles between the circular and longitudinal layers, and slips of muscles pass through the leech body, forming dorso-ventral bundles or bundles that take a somewhat oblique course through the body.

Annelid muscles vary considerably in detailed structure. The muscle fibers of *Nereis* and *Lumbricus* are rather ribbon-shaped (Fig. 14.14B). *Lumbricus* muscle fibers are about 20 μ wide, 2.5 μ thick, and 2-3 μ long and contain peripheral fibrils arranged in a right-hand spiral at a 10° angle to the fiber axis when extended and at a 30° angle when 50 per cent contracted. Layers of sarcoplasm separate the fibrils. Nuclei are difficult to demonstrate and the muscle units are probably not true cells. The spiraled muscle fibrils contain thick and thin filaments that spiral when contracted. *Hirudo* muscle is differently constructed (Fig. 14.4A). The muscle fibers are round in cross section and contain a clear region of sarcoplasm containing nuclei at the center. The muscle fibrils form a continuous layer around the periphery of the muscle fiber. Not enough is known about the significance of detailed differences in the ultrastructure of muscle fibers, and more

work on the structure of annelid muscle would be profitable. Earthworm and polychaete muscles with spiral fibrils bear considerable resemblance to the fast muscles of molluscs, but the extent and significance of this similarity have not yet been determined.

The muscles of most annelids are ill-suited to some kinds of physiological analysis because of the difficulty of getting individual fibers, and information on muscle physiology is rather scant. The muscles of *Neanthes* contain both large and small filaments, and show both fast and slow responses to nerve stimulation, in this resembling the muscles of some molluscs. Presumably this indicates a double innervation, but details remain undescribed. Leech muscle, on the other hand, shows only the slow response. Perhaps the most outstanding peculiarity of annelid muscle is the diversity of phosphagens that have been recovered from them. Several different phosphagens are sometimes found in the same species, and several phosphagens have been found only in annelids. Some of the polychaete muscles contain creatine, which is especially characteristic of vertebrates. This is, probably, no more than an interesting case of biochemical convergence.

The Digestive System. Annelids have a tubular digestive system with an anterior mouth and posterior anus. The gut is usually straight, although some part of it is spiraled or coiled in a few exceptional species. The relatively extensive foregut is derived from the stomodaeum and lined with epidermis, some of which secretes cuticle. The midgut is relatively long, and the hindgut is very short. The hindgut is lined with epidermis from the proctodaeum.

As in most animals with a tubular digestive tract, functionally specialized regions are usually found. These regions vary somewhat with the feeding habits of the species. In general, the major regions are the buccal cavity, pharynx, and esophagus,

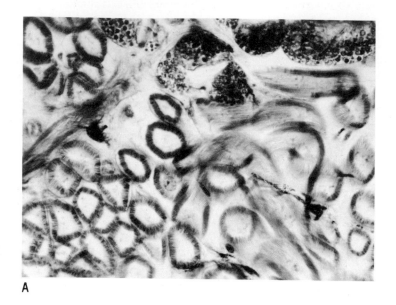

A

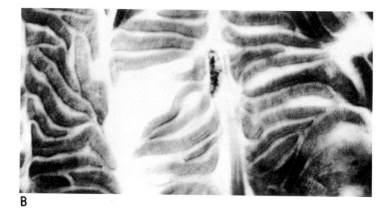

B

Fig. 14.14. **A.** Muscle fibers of a leech, *Hirudo*. **B.** Muscle fibers of an earthworm, *Lumbricus*. The myofibrils of leech and oligochaete muscles are differently arranged. The myofibrils of the leech muscle are arranged in a peripheral layer, surrounding a central region of clear sarcoplasm. The earthworm muscle fiber contains no clear region of sarcoplasm, and the lamelliform myofibrils are densely packed throughout the muscle fiber. (From Andrew.)

596

derived from the stomodaeum; the stomach and intestine derived from the midgut; and a short, terminal part of the intestine derived from the hindgut.

Annelids are quite diversified in their eating habits, but this has not had drastic effects on the general structure of the digestive tract. Among the polychaetes there are mud-eaters like *Arenicola*; microphagous filter-feeders, like *Amphitrite*; microphagous plankton-feeders, like the sabellids; and predaceous species, like *Neanthes*. The oligochaetes are predominantly detritus eaters when aquatic and eat soil or particles of vegetation when terrestrial. Leeches include blood-suckers and carnivores.

Foregut. The principal internal parts associated with food-getting are the buccal cavity and pharynx. These parts clearly reflect the kind of feeding in the majority of cases.

Predaceous polychaetes have a proboscis, equipped with cuticular jaws, denticles, or teeth. It is everted suddenly to grasp and tear food, and pulls the prey back into the mouth for swallowing. The sclerotized parts of the proboscis vary considerably in different groups of polychaetes. For example, *Glycera* has four jaws but no denticles, and *Neanthes* has two jaws and denticles. The most complex arrangements are found in the Eunicidae. They have upper and lower jaws formed of a series of plates and diversely shaped teeth, held in a special sac. A few of the predaceous polychaetes have one or more sharp stylets used to stab the prey. *Autolytus* feeds on hydroids. It has a circlet of stylets used to pierce the unfortunate hydroid, while the main body of the pharynx remains within the worm, pumping out the soft tissues and the contents of the hydroid gastrovascular cavity.

The ciliary-mucous feeders usually have a small pharynx that cannot be everted, as do the sabellids. The pharyngeal walls are richly supplied with mucous glands. They are ciliated or have ciliated grooves used for swallowing mucous strings containing food. *Amphitrite* is a good example of this type of polychaete (Fig. 14.15B).

Arenicola is a good example of a mud-eating polychaete. The pharynx is protrusible but unarmed, and picks up particles on an adhesive glandular surface. The much smaller aquatic oligochaetes have a pharynx that works on the same principle. The pharynx is attached to the body wall by diagonally placed muscle fibers, used to extrude it for feeding. Some of the terrestrial oligochaetes feed in the same manner, but in most cases the pharynx is supplied with dilator muscles used to expand the pharynx and suck in particles of soil and bits of vegetation (Fig. 14.15A).

Some of the predaceous leeches have a proboscis used much like the proboscis of polychaetes for food capture. Others have a simple pharynx used for ordinary swallowing. Those that are adapted for taking blood meals use teeth on the walls of the buccal cavity to make an incision, and pump in the flowing blood with the pharynx.

Polychaetes have simple mucous glands associated with the pharynx, but oligochaetes and leeches usually have conspicuous pharyngeal glands. The function of the pharyngeal glands of the aquatic oligochaetes is not clear. They undoubtedly secrete mucus, but may also secrete some enzymes. Some of them have very large pharyngeal glands, presumably of considerable importance. In the amphibious enchytraeids, for example, they extend up on the adjacent septa. The terrestrial oligochaetes take dry food which cannot be swallowed until it is moistened. The pharynx wall of *Lumbricus* is heavily infiltrated with dark-staining gland cells that secrete mucus containing a protease. In some earthworms, modified nephridia empty into the pharyngeal region, helping to lubricate the food and secreting enzymes.

The pharyngeal glands of leeches secrete saliva containing an anticoagulant that keeps the blood flowing during feeding. The form of the pharyngeal glands varies

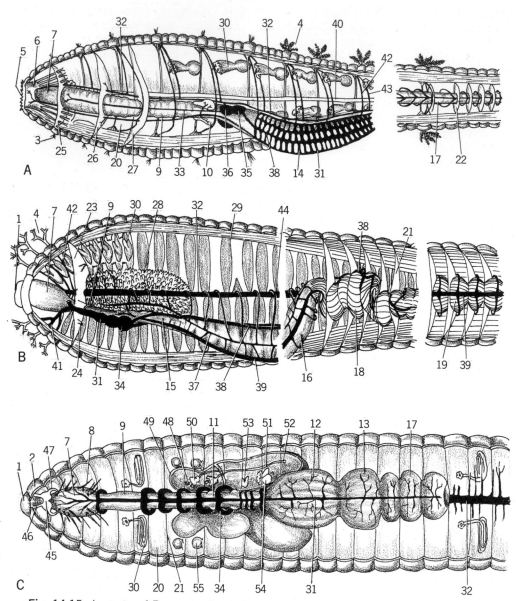

Fig. 14.15. Anatomy of Representative Annelids. **A.** *Arenicola.* **B.** *Amphitrite.* **C.** *Lumbricus.*
(A, after Ashworth. B, after Brown, somewhat modified, from Brown. C, composite.) *External
features:* 1, prostomium; 2, peristomium; 3, setae of notopodium; 4, gill. *Digestive tract:*
5, mouth; 6, buccal sheath; 7, pharynx; 8, pharyngeal dilator muscles and pharyngeal glands;
9, esophagus; 10, esophageal gland; 11, calciferous gland; 12, crop (proventriculus); 13, gizzard (ventriculus); 14, stomach; 15, anterior stomach; 16, posterior stomach; 17, intestine;
18, anterior intestine; 19, posterior intestine. *Coelom, septa, and body wall:* 20, coelom;
21, septum; 22, caudal septum; 23, diaphragm; 24, diaphragm sac; 25, first diaphragm;
26, second diaphragm; 27, third diaphragm; 28, ventral mucous gland; 29, oblique muscle.
Excretory system: 30, nephridium. *Circulatory system:* 31, dorsal vessel; 32, ventral vessel;

598

considerably. *Placobdella* has salivary glands composed of many scattered unicellular glands with minute ducts that join the dorsal longitudinal muscles, forming a strand on each side. The tracts enter the proboscis and continue through the proboscis muscle, opening through a pore at its tip.

The tubular esophagus is lined with cuticle or with ciliated epithelium. It carries food to the midgut, usually by peristalsis if there is no ciliary-mucous feeding system. Errant polychaetes with a very long proboscis often have an S-shaped esophagus, which straightens out only when the proboscis is extruded. Usually, however, the esophagus is a straight tube. Dilations of the esophagus provide special organs in many annelids. The esophagus may be dilated to form a thin-walled storage chamber, the crop or proventriculus, or to form a thick-walled, sclerotized grinding chamber, the gizzard or ventriculus.

The crop and gizzard are especially characteristic of the oligochaetes, although some polychaetes, the syllids, for example, have a gizzard. The occurrence of the crop and gizzard in the oligochaetes is subject to considerable variation. A crop may or may not be present, and some of the terrestrial oligochaetes have more than one. *Lumbricus* has a single crop and gizzard. The esophageal wall is lined with thin cuticle, continued without much change in the crop, but strengthened in the gizzard where it forms a protective lining for the muscular walls. The crop and gizzard of terrestrial oligochaetes have no characteristic position. The *Lumbricus* crop and gizzard, for example, lie at the distal end of the esophagus, while they are proximal in megascolecids. These appear to be superficial differences, for in any case the crop functions as an organ for temporary storage and preliminary moistening and softening, while the gizzard triturates the material in preparation for the final stages of digestion and absorption. The crop and gizzard are usually more than one somite long but where there are multiple gizzards, each occupies a single somite. Multiple gizzards are not uncommon; in eudrilids, for example, four to six gizzards are found. The so-called "crop" of leeches is typically a part of the midgut, and will be described with this part of the digestive tract.

Esophageal glands occur sporadically among polychaetes, are absent in aquatic oligochaetes, and are found in terrestrial oligochaetes. The oligochaete esophageal glands are composed of epithelial plates or tubes in intimate contact with blood sinuses and often contain tiny calcite crystals. Ingested soil contains a considerable quantity of calcium and other inorganic ions, some of which can unbalance the body fluids from a physiological point of view. These ions appear to be controlled, in part, by the action of the esophageal glands, more commonly called calciferous glands. The calcite crystals formed there pass unchanged through the gut and emerge with the feces.

Midgut. Carnivorous, herbivorous, and detritus-eating habits have relatively little to do with differences in the midgut of annelids. Leeches, however, do have a distinctive midgut, associated with their adaptation for blood-sucking. Apparently the food reaching the midgut has undergone sufficient preliminary processing to minimize the importance of its original nature. Diversity centers about alternative

33, lateral esophageal vessel; 34, heart; 35, auricle; 36, ventricle; 37, lateral gastric vessel; 38, subintestinal vessel; 39, dorsal gut sinus; 40, lateral neural vessel; 41, afferent branchial vessel; 42, efferent branchial vessel; 43, lateral vessel; 44, ventral ring vessel. *Nervous system:* 45, cerebral ganglion; 46, prostomial nerve; 47, circumenteric connective. *Reproductive system:* 48, testis; 49, seminal vesicle; 50, seminal funnel; 51, sperm duct; 52, male gonopore; 53, ovary; 54, oviduct; 55, seminal receptacle.

systems of dealing with similar physiological problems.

The simplest possible kind of midgut is a straight tube, with no specialized regions. A midgut of this kind is seen in many polychaetes, in earthworms, and in most aquatic oligochaetes. It is termed the intestine or stomach-intestine, and is the site of the greater part of digestion and absorption of foods. Annelid digestion is at least predominantly extracellular.

The annelid intestinal wall is composed of a layer of visceral peritoneum on the outer surface, followed by layers of longitudinal muscle, circular muscle, and mucosa (Fig. 14.1). The mucosa consists of a single layer of epithelium resting on a delicate submucosa of loose connective tissue containing blood sinuses or capillaries. The mucosa is typically ciliated, and in many polychaetes contains a ciliated groove that runs the whole length of the intestine. The cilia stir up the intestinal contents, thus hastening absorption, and in species with a delicate musculature are of importance in conducting food through the tube. Generally, however, peristaltic waves move along the intestine and are the main means of forcing food along. Peristalsis also mixes digestive secretions with the food substances and brings new material in contact with the absorptive cells.

The capacity for digestion and absorption is partly determined by the area available for secretion and absorption. The shape of most annelids precludes the amplification of intestinal surface by lengthening and coiling of the gut, but the anterior intestine of *Amphitrite* is slightly coiled, and some of the most highly modified Sedentaria have a coiled intestine (Fig. 14.16C). The most common method of surface amplification is provided by longitudinal ridges, perhaps evolutionarily related to the factors which produce ciliated grooves in the digestive tracts of organisms which feed on small particles. Any part of the intestinal wall of polychaetes may be folded, and the same was probably true of primitive oligochaetes as well. Modern earthworms, however, have a single dorsal ridge or, if several are present, have a larger dorsal ridge, known as the typhlosole. It appears near the beginning of the intestine and continues to the last few segments of the body. Some of the earthworms have a simple typhlosole, with only the mucosa entering into the fold, but in *Lumbricus* (Fig. 14.12B) the muscle and peritoneal layers are involved in the folding of the wall. Other methods of surface amplification are seen in the midgut of some oligochaetes and polychaetes. *Aphrodite*, for example, has lateral diverticula in each somite, which add to absorptive surface and also contribute to food distribution. Only fluid and small, partly digested particles find their way into the diverticula. Preliminary digestion takes place in the intestine proper, and the final stages of digestion and absorption occur in the diverticula. This pattern of midgut amplification is, of course, similar to that seen in molluscs, where large digestive glands are characteristic derivatives of the midgut.

As organisms evolve into more complex creatures, sequentialism becomes a more significant feature of the digestive process. Although more quantitative histology is needed to make generalization profitable, it is evident that histologically differentiated regions occur in the midgut of many polychaetes. Three histologically differentiated regions can be recognized in *Clymenella*, for example. This trend culminates in the formation of a definite stomach. *Arenicola* (Fig. 14.15A) has a stomach with a highly glandular mucosa. The intestinal mucosa contains very few gland cells. Evidently there has been some separation of the digestive and absorptive functions. *Amphitrite* (Fig. 14.15B) has a stomach divided into two regions. The anterior stomach is glandular and the posterior stomach has heavily muscled walls protected by a firm lining secreted by special cells. The posterior stomach is a gastric gizzard, where both chemical and mechanical trituration of the foods occur. Some of the aquatic oligochaetes also have a stomach between the esophagus and intestine, but the details of histological differentiation in these regions are not known.

The leech midgut is highly specialized (Fig. 14.11B). It is made up of two regions, here called the crop and intestine. The crop is sometimes termed the stomach. Neither term is really apt, for it functions as a crop where food is stored, but it is derived from the midgut rather than the foregut. The crop may be a simple tube or be equipped with lateral diverticula (caeca). In predaceous species the crop is without caeca or has relatively few, while in bloodsucking species there are many large caeca. Some of the blood-sucking rhynchobdellids have as many as 14 pairs of caeca. Hirudids have fewer, but can nevertheless store a

large quantity of blood. A feeding leech may take as much as four times its weight in blood. Water and chlorides are removed from the blood as it enters the crop and nephridia excrete copiously during feeding. Condensation continues for a time, but the blood cells remain unchanged for long periods of time, up to 18 months in some cases. Where meals are taken at relatively long intervals (*Hirudo medicinalis*, for example, can survive from 18 to 24 months without feeding) some arrangement for slow digestion is needed. It appears that leeches may have adapted to this problem by greatly reducing their capacity for enzyme formation. Even the predaceous leeches appear to lack the enzymes needed to start protein digestion, and blood-sucking leeches produce even less in the way of enzymes than predaceous leeches. A bac-

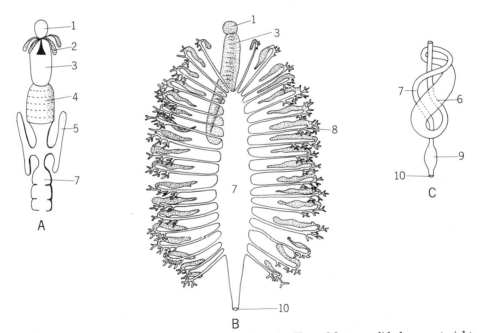

Fig. 14.16. Surface Amplification in Polychaete Digestive Tract. Most annelids have a straight digestive tract, but diverticula and lengthening with concomitant coiling are sometimes seen. A. Anterior end of digestive tract of a syllid (schematic). B. Digestive tract of *Aphrodite*. C. Digestive tract of *Petta*. (A, after Benham. B, after Gegenbauer and C, after Wirén, from Benham.) 1, buccal region; 2, salivary glands; 3, pharynx; 4, gizzard; 5, esophageal diverticula; 6, stomach; 7, intestine; 8, intestinal caecum; 9, rectum; 10, anus.

terium, *Pseudomonas hirudinis,* isolated from the leech gut, causes a very slow breakdown of blood constituents and eliminates *Staphylococcus* when it is present. It may prove to be responsible for the breakdown of blood constituents. Food breaks down and is absorbed rapidly as it enters the intestine, which is generally short but has caeca in some of the bloodsucking species. The intestine opens into a short hindgut or rectum which discharges wastes through the anus.

Proteases, amylases, and lipases have been recovered from annelids, but the sites of production of specific enzymes are not determined. More information is required before it is profitable to speculate on the significance of the results obtained so far.

Hindgut. Most of the annelids have no conspicuous hindgut. The intestine may change character slightly as it approaches the anus, but only leeches can be said to have a rectum. The anus is primitively situated in the last somite, but in most leeches has been moved outside of the posterior sucker that contains the last somite.

Defecation becomes a problem for an animal that lives in a burrow or tube, and habits or structures to prevent fouling the home are important. Most burrowers come to the mouth of the burrow to defecate, even when the burrow is U-shaped, in which case the feces are piled at the back door. Earthworms, *Arenicola,* and some of the tube-dwellers behave in this fashion. Some species with tubes open at both ends maintain respiratory currents in the tube which waft away the feces. Sabellids and serpulids, however, have a special ciliated groove, used to convey the fecal pellets up to the tube mouth.

Coelom and Circulation. A metameric coelom, divided into compartments by septa at the somite boundaries, is characteristic of annelids. It is a true coelom, completely lined with peritoneum. Parietal peritoneum covers the body wall; visceral peritoneum covers the viscera, and septal peritoneum covers the faces of the septa.

The right and left coelomic compartments begin as independent cavities and meet in the dorsal and ventral mesenteries in the midline. Each mesentery is composed of two leaves of peritoneum. The basic plan is thus a series of pairs of coelomic compartments, one for each somite, but the coelom is never quite like this in adults. The ventral and dorsal mesenteries are somewhat incomplete, and septa are often suppressed to produce large coelomic spaces that extend through several body segments.

A nearly primitive arrangement is seen in many oligochaetes. *Lumbricus,* for example, has a complete series of septa dividing the coelom into metameric compartments. The dorsal mesentery, however, persists only at the septum and the ventral mesentery does not reach the body wall (Fig. 14.12B), so right and left coelomic spaces are joined in each somite. On the other hand, most leeches have no septa whatsoever, and the coelom has become a circulatory system in some.

What factors have been important in directing the course of coelomic adaptation? The coelomic fluid is important in the transportation of substances within the body. This function is best served by the longitudinal linkage of coelomic compartments. An opening for the nerve cord in each septum provides this link. The coelomic fluid also acts as a hydraulic skeleton and is an important factor in locomotion and in extrusion of the pharynx. This function is best served by coelomic compartmentalization. A compromise is reached in *Lumbricus* and a number of other annelids, where the opening around the nerve cord in each septum is guarded by a sphincter. A large number of the differences seen in the coelom of various annelids are comprehensible when the problems of internal transport and hydraulic mechanics are taken into account.

The placement and form of the septa are often related to body movements or the movement of parts. Many oligochaetes and polychaetes have cupped or slanted septa which move the coelomic fluid, or the parts to which the septa are attached, when the septal muscles are contracted. The *Lumbricus* pharynx, for example, can be partly protruded by the contraction of strongly slanted septa attached to it. Septa are usually suppressed at the anterior end of polychaetes, converting the coelom into a hydraulic compartment used to evert the proboscis or extend the hollow tentacles. The septum immediately behind these hydraulic compartments is heavily muscled and is termed a diaphragm. In some polychaetes, *Arenicola*, for example, several such diaphragms are present (Fig. 14.15A).

Acanthobdella is the only leech with a coelom divided by septa. In all other leeches the coelom is reduced and septa are missing. The inch-worm gait of leeches has favored septal reduction, for the body extends as a whole rather than as a series of compartments and a single coelomic chamber suffices for movement.

Many of the annelids are moderately large and would be physiologically inefficient without provisions for internal transport. The body wall is not extremely thick and the gut wall is also relatively thin. Body construction favors the use of coelomic fluid as a transporting medium. As it happens, annelids have a double transport system, the coelom and the circulatory system. The coelomic fluid and blood share the responsibility for the transport of food, wastes, and respiratory gases, but to different degrees and in different ways in different annelids. The coelom and circulatory system are competitors, so to speak, and the development of one is often accompanied by the reduction of the other.

The gut and nephridia are bathed in coelomic fluid and it is highly probable that the coelomic fluid of the annelid ancestral stocks was primarily responsible for the transport of foods and wastes, at least within somites. The primitive circulatory system probably consisted of a system of sinuses around the gut as in modern *Aeolosoma* (Fig. 14.17A). A circulatory system of this type is primarily responsible for longitudinal transport, bringing food forward from the absorptive regions of the gut. Ancestral annelids were probably small forms, able to get along without respiratory pigments. Syllid, chaetopterid, and phyllodicid polychaetes have no respiratory pigments, and small aquatic annelids, like *Aeolosoma*, many naids, and even the amphibious enchytraeids have no respiratory pigment. The variety of respiratory pigments found in annelids also supports the idea that the primitive forms did not have any, and the pigments present in modern forms developed independently in different groups.

Primitively, a pair of nephridia lie in each somite, and wastes reach the nephridia by way of the coelomic fluid. As the circulatory system becomes more highly organized, the nephridia come to be supplied with blood vessels. With the development of a vascular bed around the nephridium, the waste materials can arrive as well by way of the blood as by the coelomic fluid. The nephridia never lose their contact with the coelomic fluid, however, and a nephrostome remains as evidence of the importance of coelomic transport of wastes. However, with the development of nephridial circulation, longitudinal transportation of wastes is greatly improved, permitting the reduction of nephridia in some somites, or permitting the nephridia to assume other functions than elimination of wastes. Generally speaking, oligochaetes and errant polychaetes retain nephridia in nearly all somites. Tubicolous polychaetes tend to eliminate the posterior nephridia, this trend culminating in forms like the sabellids, which have a single pair of nephridia that empty near the opening of the tube. Coelomic fluid in the posterior parts of the coelom is thus isolated from the nephridia, favoring the increased importance of circulatory-system waste transport.

Respiratory transport may be assumed by the blood, the coelomic fluid, or both. It is especially in respiratory transport that the competition of coelomic and blood systems appears. Some of the smaller annelids have no respiratory pigment in either the coelomic fluid or the blood. In the greater part of the annelids, the blood contains the respiratory pigment and the coelomic fluid has none. In a few worms, *Terebella lapidarius* and *Travisia forbesii* for example, the coelomic fluid contains haemoglobin in haemocytes and the blood contains haemoglobin dissolved in the plasma. Generally, however, when the coelomic fluid contains a respiratory pigment, the circulatory system is reduced or disappears entirely. This has occurred in the Glyceridae, Capitellidae, and in some species of *Polycirrus*. In these forms the circulation of the coelomic fluid is enhanced by tracts of peritoneal cilia.

Apparently the size and habits of polychaetes make a respiratory pigment useful but not essential. A number of polychaetes of moderate size have none. Among these, the establishment of a good circulation of coelomic fluid tends to be accompanied by the reduction of the circulatory system. *Aphrodite*, for example, has a coelomic circulation powered by tracts of cilia and a reduced circulatory system, although neither blood nor coelomic fluid contains haemoglobin.

Most commonly in both polychaetes and oligochaetes, the blood contains a respiratory pigment dissolved in the plasma, and is primarily responsible for respiratory transport, while the coelomic fluid remains important in the transport of foods and wastes. A variety of respiratory pigments occur in polychaetes. These often show through the body wall or tint the gills and tentacles, adding to their colorful appearance. Haemoglobin is the most common pigment, occurring in a variety of species. The green blood of sabellids, serpulids, and chlorhaemids is colored by chlorocruorin, an iron pigment with properties like haemoglobin. A few serpulids have both haemoglobin and chlorocruorin. *Magelona* blood is given a rose-madder color by cor-

puscles containing haemerythrin. In all of these the circulatory system is well developed. Oligochaetes and leeches are less variable; only haemoglobin has been reported from them.

The circulatory systems of oligochaetes and polychaetes have similar designs. There are two longitudinal vessels, a dorsal vessel above the gut and a ventral vessel below it. Blood flows forward in the dorsal vessel and back in the ventral vessel. This longitudinal flow delivers food from the sinuses and capillaries of the midgut to the anterior parts of the body. Large size, greater complexity, and greater activity favors the development of additional lateral circulatory arcs. The most important of these is a subcutaneous plexus in the body wall, used for respiratory exchange and useful for the delivery of food and removal of wastes from the body-wall tissues. Subsidiary circulatory arcs serve the parapodia of errant polychaetes, and smaller, but functionally important arcs develop to serve the nephridia. Details differ greatly, but the general course of lateral circulation is similar in most species. Blood flows outward from the ventral vessel through paired afferent segmental vessels in each somite. They give rise to nephridial vessels, to branches reaching the body wall, and in polychaetes to branches for the parapodia. Efferent segmental vessels return the blood to the dorsal vessel (Fig. 14.17B). As blood flows through the intestinal wall from the dorsal to the ventral vessel a complete lateral circulation is established, permitting the cycling of blood within a somite. The intestinal circulation passes in the other direction in earthworms, entering the gut wall from the ventral vessel.

Additional longitudinal vessels are found associated with the nerve cord in many annelids, as in *Lumbricus* (Fig. 14.18). In *Lumbricus* some freshly aerated blood is routed into vessels around the nerve cord, on its way to afferent segmentals (parietal vessels) which empty into the dorsal vessel. *Arenicola* has a supraneural vessel connected with the ventral vessel. Additional longitudinal vessels appear in the typhlosole of terrestrial oligochaetes and special subintestinal and lateral intestinal vessels sometimes occur in polychaetes.

With specialization of the body parts, the circulatory arcs are modified. These modifications are especially abundant in polychaetes, which differ so markedly in the number and position of the nephridia, the subdivisions of the digestive tube, and the number and position of the gills. The blood vessels generally change in front of the midgut, or, where the midgut is specialized to form several chambers, in front of the intestine. In many cases, simple loops connect the dorsal and ventral vessels, and the lateral circulatory arcs to the body wall are considerably changed.

The most primitive method of blood propulsion is blood-vessel contraction. Annelids generally retain a primitive, diffuse

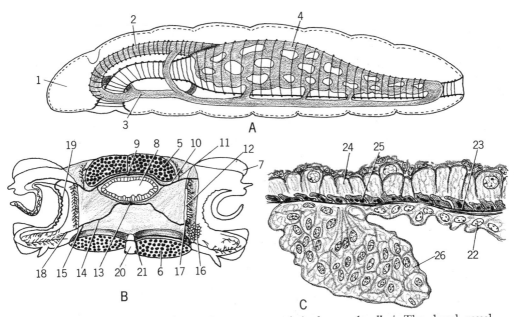

Fig. 14.17. A. Scheme of the circulatory system of *Aeolosoma headleyi*. The dorsal vessel carries blood forward from the intestinal sinus, and the ventral vessel carries blood back and up to the intestinal sinus. Vessels around the foregut connect the dorsal and ventral vessels. Presumably this pattern is not far removed from the primitive annelid organization. B. Schematic view of the lateral circulation in the middle of the body of *Nephthys californiensis*. Blood passes to the parapodium for aeration from the subintestinal vessel and returns to the dorsal vessel. A complete circulation can be set up within a single somite by way of the circumintestinal connectives. C. Section through the wall of the heart of *Allobophora*, including a part of one of the valves that prevent backflow. Circular muscles with fibrillar bases lie outside of the intima. (A, after Marcus, from Avel, in Grassé. B, after Clark. C, after Dahlgren and Kepner.) *Aeolosoma*: 1, prostomium; 2, dorsal vessel; 3, ventral vessel; 4, intestinal sinus. *Nephthys*: 5, dorsal longitudinal muscle; 6, ventral longitudinal muscle; 7, parapodium; 8, intestine; 9, dorsal vessel; 10, dorsal intersegmental; 11, dorsal muscle branch; 12, intersegmental connective; 13, subintestinal vessel; 14, subintestinal segmental vessel; 15, nephridial branch; 16, ovarian branch; 17, transseptal branch from posterior segment; 18, deep interramal branch; 19, dorsal interramal branch; 20, ventral nerve; 21, neural vessel. *Blood vessel:* 22, intima; 23, cuticular base of intima; 24, muscle cell; 25, basal fibers of muscle cell; 26, valve composed of intima cells.

propulsion mechanism, but show some tendencies toward centralization in more highly specialized groups. The dorsal blood vessel is the most important contractile vessel, but other vessels may be contractile and contribute significantly to blood-flow. Lateral vessels, esophageal vessels, and to a lesser extent, nephridial vessels are sometimes contractile. None of the annelids have a definite heart, although dilations of the dorsal vessel are sometimes called heart bodies. Some terebellids have a heart body (Fig. 14.15B), but it is a spongy non-pulsating organ of unknown function. Pulsating chambers occur in a few species, as in *Chaetopterus* and *Arenicola* (Fig. 14.15A), but these are never the sole pulsating parts and cannot be considered as true hearts. Oligochaetes have pulsating esophageal vessels connecting the dorsal and ventral vessels. These are sometimes

termed hearts or aortic arches, but the dorsal vessel is also contractile and is at least as important in blood propulsion. The number of pairs of pulsating vessels in the esophagus region varies considerably in oligochaetes. Aquatic oligochaetes usually have a single pair, and in *Lumbricus* five pairs are found.

Annelids have a primitively organized circulatory system, but the blood vessels have well-developed walls. Pulsating vessels have a thick endothelium (Fig. 14.17C). The wall is strengthened by a strong basement membrane around which a layer of circular muscles lies. In non-pulsating vessels, wall cells replace the circular muscles, although some retain a few muscle fibers, perhaps used for vasoconstriction. Capillaries are composed of endothelium only. Although annelids are said to have a closed circulatory system, the system of intestinal

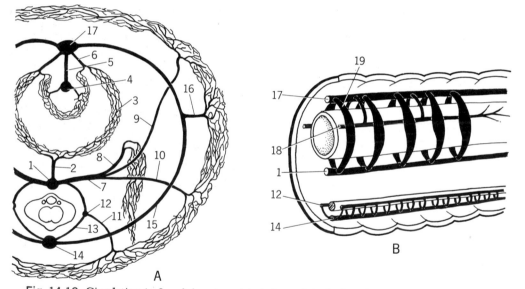

Fig. 14.18. Circulation in *Lumbricus terrestris* (schematic). A. Circulatory connections within a somite. B. Relationship of vessels in esophageal region. 1, ventral vessel; 2, intestinal afferent; 3, intestinal sinus; 4, typhlosolar vessel; 5, typhlosolar connectives; 6, efferent intestinals; 7, lateral segmental vessel; 8, nephridial branch; 9, dorsal branch to body wall; 10, ventral branch to body wall; 11, somatic efferent to lateral neural vessel; 12, lateral neural vessel; 13, connective between lateral neural and subneural; 14, subneural vessel; 15, parietal vessel; 16, dorsal efferent from body wall to parietal; 17, dorsal vessel; 18, intestinotegumentary vessel; 19, hearts (circumenteric segmentals).

sinuses does not have a complete endothelial lining. In larger species with well-developed circulatory systems, the dorsal vessel has a system of valves, derived from the endothelium, preventing backflow, and where other pulsating vessels are present, they, too, may contain valves.

Molluscs have myogenic hearts, while arthropods have myogenic and neurogenic hearts. Annelids are closely related to both, and it is of interest to determine how pulsations are initiated in annelid hearts. So far the results have been problematic. Heart ganglion cells have been found in *Arenicola* and *Lumbricus*, but not in *Neanthes*. In some instances, the stretching of a vessel by the contained blood is an important factor in stimulating its contraction. Generally neurogenic hearts show fast oscillatory electrocardiograph waves, while myogenic hearts show slow waves. In *Arenicola* both kinds of waves are seen. More work is needed in this area before satisfactory generalizations can be made.

However the pulsations originate, peristaltic waves sweep forward every 2 to 3 seconds in *Lumbricus,* at a rate of about 25 mm./sec. These are in no way coordinated with the contraction of the "hearts," which beat independently, with no common rhythm, although the two members of a pair usually contract together. *Arenicola* has a "heart" on each side of the esophagus. Blood passes forward in the dorsal vessel, through a plexus on the stomach wall to the lateral gastric vessels, and into the pulsating chambers. The lateral gastric vessels and the "hearts" beat at different rates. Evidently no over-all coordination of pulsating parts is achieved in annelids as a general rule. Each part appears to be on its own in an essentially anarchical organization. This, like the widespread dispersion of pulsating regions, is a primitive characteristic of the annelid circulatory system.

Little is known about annelid blood pressures. Pressures of 1.1 to 7.2 mm. Hg pressure have been recorded in a resting *Neanthes* and of 17.6 mm. Hg in active animals. Pressure during activity is enhanced by increased coelomic pressure, which reaches about 11 mm. Hg.

Leeches have not been mentioned with the polychaetes and oligochaetes because they have followed an entirely different evolutionary line. *Acanthobdella* has a typical annelid coelom, divided into compartments by septa, but somewhat reduced by encroachment of the parenchymal tissue and muscles on the cavity (Fig. 14.12C). The coelom of rhynchobdellids, however, is greatly reduced. Muscles pass through the coelomic region and pigmented botryoidal tissue has completely filled the coelom in some regions (Fig. 14.12D). Narrow spaces in the botryoidal tissue form a capillary plexus, roughly analogous to the lymphatic system of vertebrates. The botryoidal tissue also divides the coelomic remnants into a system of passageways, together forming a coelomic sinus system. Dorsal and ventral coelomic sinuses contain the dorsal blood vessel and ventral nerve and vessel respectively (Fig. 14.19A). Intermediate sinuses connect the dorsal and ventral sinuses with the lateral coelomic sinuses at the body margin. A system of subepidermal lacunae connects with the lateral sinuses. It is evident, on morphological grounds, that the coelom must be a significant factor in internal transport.

The rhynchobdellids also have a circulatory system that is not much different from that of other annelids (Fig. 14.19D). Blood flows forward in a dorsal vessel above the gut and back in a ventral vessel below the gut. A system of looped vessels in the posterior sucker connects the dorsal and ventral vessels. Three commissural vessels, rather like those seen in oligochaetes but much elongated, connect the dorsal and ventral vessels in the esophageal region. Looped vessels for the anterior sucker arise from the anterior commissural vessel, and the most posterior one loops far back in the body.

Although some of the rhynchobdellids are quite active and relatively large, they usually have no respiratory pigment. Presumably the combination of a circulatory system and a circulating coelomic fluid compensates for the lack. The botryoidal capillaries, coelomic sinuses, and blood vessels do not constitute three discrete systems. Injection experiments have shown that all three intercommunicate, forming a to some extent unified transport system.

Pharyngobdellids and gnathobdellids have lost the original circulatory system entirely, replacing it by further development of the coelomic sinus system. In adapting to assume the full responsibility for internal transport, however, the coelomic sinus system has lost all resemblance to a coelom and become a veritable circulatory system, and the coelomic fluid has become blood-like. The coelomic fluid contains haemoglobin dissolved in the plasma, while other annelids carry any respiratory pigments present in the coelomic fluid in haemocytes. The simple walls of the rhynchobdellid coelomic sinuses are replaced by more complex walls, resembling those of blood vessels, and the subepidermal lacunar system is replaced by an extensive capillary bed. *Hirudo* and some other leeches retain dorsal and ventral coelomic sinuses, while others have lost them entirely. In any event, the lateral sinuses are more important. They converge at the anterior and posterior ends of the body and give rise to segmental connections with the subepidermal plexus and with the median sinuses, if they are present. Plexi extend to and around the nephridia, gonads, and other body parts, as in ordinary circulatory systems. The two lateral sinuses serve as tubular "coelomic hearts," pumping the coelomic fluid around the circuit. Piscicolids serve to bridge partially the gap between the glossiphonids and the pharyngobdellids. They are equipped with a series of special pumping chambers associated with the lateral sinuses (Fig. 14.19B,C), although they retain a circulatory system.

The replacement of the primitive circulatory system with a substitute coelomic circulatory system illustrates the general competition between the coelomic fluid and blood in internal transport, seen on a lesser scale in polychaetes. The development of one at the expense of the other is a common annelid phenomenon. As a rule, unless the circulatory system of larger annelids contains a respiratory pigment it is at least somewhat reduced, although the limitation of longitudinal transport by septa dividing the coelom encourages its retention. The coelom is retained, even if the blood contains a respiratory pigment, probably because of its importance as a hydraulic skeleton and for the mechanics of locomotion. The different kind of locomotion emphasized in leeches and the disappearance of septa made it possible for the coelom to take over completely the functions of the circulatory system. The tendency for one or the other system to predominate suggests that it is more efficient to have one circulating fluid than two. Among annelids, the most simply organized of the coelomate protostomes, the blood and coelomic fluid compete, with the issue in doubt and the victory going sometimes to one and sometimes to the other. However, as the body wall became heavy and muscular, the coelomic transport system was doomed to fail, and the circulatory system predominates in molluscs, arthropods, and chordates.

Respiration. Respiratory exchange takes place at the body surface. Many annelids have a smooth body surface, and it is tempting to think of them as being without respiratory adaptations. Respiratory exchange, however, is facilitated in a number of ways, including: 1) amplification of the body surface to form gills; 2) ventilation of the surface by respiratory currents of one kind or another, making the available surface more efficient; 3) regulation of respiratory movements under conditions of respiratory stress; 4) use of respiratory pigments; and 5) increased vascularization of tissues near the respiratory surface, facilitating removal of the absorbed oxygen and increasing the favorable concentration gradient. In this broader sense, all annelids probably have some kind of respiratory adaptations.

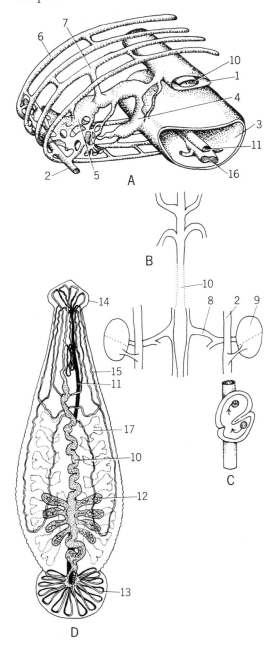

The smallest oligochaetes and polychaetes have no circulatory system or have one that does not serve the body wall. In larger forms, either blood or coelomic fluid is circulated through a subepidermal plexus where respiratory exchange can occur rapidly and the absorbed oxygen be removed quickly while carbon dioxide is delivered constantly for elimination. A few of the polychaetes have coelomic subepidermal capillaries, but this is uncommon except in leeches.

Surface amplification for respiratory exchange is not profitable unless the body surface is vascularized. Even when a sub-

FIG. 14.19. Leech Coelom and Circulation. **A.** The coelomic sinus system of a glossiphonid. Development of the botryoidal tissue has reduced the coelom to canals around the dorsal and ventral blood vessels, and a system of lacunae responsible for much of internal transport. **B.** Pulsating vesicle system in piscicolids. These leeches have pulsating vesicles associated with the lateral coelomic sinuses. Coelomic fluid flows into them from the dorsal sinus, and is discharged into the lateral sinuses. **C.** Pulsating vesicles of *Piscicola*, opened to show valvular openings which regulate direction of flow. **D.** Scheme of circulatory system of the rhynchobdellid, *Hemiclepsis*. The original circulatory system is retained in these leeches. Vascular caeca from the dorsal vessel extend over the digestive system diverticula, and looped blood vessels connect the dorsal and ventral vessels. (A and D, after Oka, from Beddard. B, after Autrum. C, after Selensky, from Scriban and Autrum, in Kükenthal and Krumbach.) *Coelomic sinus and lacunar system:* 1, dorsal coelomic sinus; 2, lateral coelomic sinus; 3, ventral coelomic sinus; 4, vestiges of the medial coelomic sinus; 5, intercalary lacuna; 6, hypodermal lacuna; 7, lacuna to the hypodermal lacunae; 8, transverse communicating lacuna; 9, pulsating vesicle. *Circulatory system:* 10, dorsal blood vessel; 11, ventral blood vessel; 12, lateral caecum of dorsal vessel; 13, looped vessels to posterior sucker; 14, looped vessels to anterior sucker; 15, elongated perienteric commissural vessels. *Other parts:* 16, nerve cord; 17, crop diverticula.

epidermal plexus is present, surface amplification is not likely to occur unless respiratory stress is strong enough to favor gill development. Some of the largest annelids have no gills. Leeches are almost universally without gills, although gills are found in some piscicolids. This does not mean that other kinds of annelids suffer no respiratory stress, however, for there is evidence that leeches tolerate anaerobiosis rather better than most animals. Gills are most common in polychaetes, but their occurrence is not clearly linked with body size. The activity of species and differences in the oxygen tension of the habitat are more important than size, as is the effectiveness of the system used for respiratory transport.

Errant polychaete gills are usually modifications of the dorsal or ventral cirri of the parapodia. Most of them have dorsal gills, but some have gills on both notopodium and neuropodium, and a few have only ventral gills. The parapodial gills may be flat plates or filiform; filiform gills are often branched or plumose. They are always highly vascular, and sometimes contrast with the body in color because of the haemoglobin or chlorocruorin in them. Notopodial gills also occur in Sedentaria, but they are usually found on only a few of the anterior somites, as in *Arenicola* (Fig. 14.20A). Prostomial and peristomial gills are more common, and are derived from various cephalic parts. The gills of chlorhaemids arise from the prostomial tentacles. *Amphitrite* gills are probably derived from the prostomial palps. The common occurrence of gills among Sedentaria is undoubtedly associated with the low oxygen tensions in the tube, which reduces the value of the general body surface for respiration.

Very few oligochaetes have gills of any kind, even when very large. The West African Yoruba worm, *Alma*, has a pair of retractile processes that were once thought to be gills (Fig. 14.20B), but they contain parts of the reproductive system and probably have nothing to do with respiration. Gills are found among small, aquatic oligochaetes, however, and usually at the posterior tip of the body, as in *Dero* (Fig. 14.10H).

Ventilation of the respiratory surfaces by ciliary currents or muscular movements can compensate for the lack of gills or make gills more efficient. Many polychaetes have dorsal cilia and cilia on the parapodial gill surfaces. Ciliary currents usually flow toward the posterior end of the body over the dorsal surface and to or from the gills to the main current. Ciliary tracts on the body of Sedentaria usually keep water flowing through the tube and aid somewhat in respiratory exchange. Nereids and glycerids have no body cilia, but use undulatory movements of the body to ventilate the surface. Highly specialized respiratory currents are characteristic of the scale-worms. Ciliary tracts bring water up between the parapodia and to a main stream which flows back under the elytra. *Aphrodite* has lost its external gills, but a similar current is produced by tilting the elytra in regular sequence, beginning at the anterior end. As in molluscs, the principle of counterflow usually operates, as the respiratory currents flow back over the dorsal surface, in the direction opposite to blood-flow.

Aquatic oligochaetes usually thrust the posterior end of the body from their burrows, and have posterior gills when gills are present. Tubificids usually have no gills, but the posterior tip of the body is waved rhythmically to ventilate the surface. When oxygen tension falls, they lift the tail end of the body higher and increase the frequency of ventilating movements. Leeches also move the body rhythmically to ventilate the surface and change the rate of movements with increased temperatures or other factors producing respiratory stress.

Respiratory pigments differ markedly in their properties. Some become saturated with oxygen at low oxygen tensions while others require relatively high oxygen tensions. The percentage of saturation may fall rapidly or slowly with falling oxygen tensions. In a habitat with relatively high oxygen tensions a respiratory pigment may be saturated with oxygen at all times, so playing no part in respiratory transport unless the oxygen tension falls drastically, while in another case, the respiratory pigments may account for a considerable part of oxygen transport.

Annelids are so diverse that it is reasonable to expect that respiratory pigments may be used in a variety of ways. On purely morphological grounds, it would be reasonable to suppose that the annelids with parts adapted for respiratory exchange and with capillary beds in these parts, at least, would carry a considerable part of their oxygen with respiratory pigments. What evidence is available indicates that

this is the case, but also shows that annelids can carry a considerable amount of oxygen without respiratory pigments and have a good ability to tailor their activity to match the amount of oxygen present. Exposure to carbon monoxide prevents oxygen transport by haemoglobin but does not affect the transport of oxygen dissolved in blood plasma or coelomic fluid. *Lumbricus* oxygen consumption falls with exposure to carbon monoxide at high but not at low oxygen tensions. This unexpected result appears to indicate that the earthworm adjusts its metabolism downward when oxygen is in short supply and uses its haemoglobin for transport primarily when oxygen tensions are high. *Tubifex* haemoglobin carries only a third of the oxygen used at high oxygen tensions and the percentage falls at lower oxygen tensions, and in several species of leeches the same kind

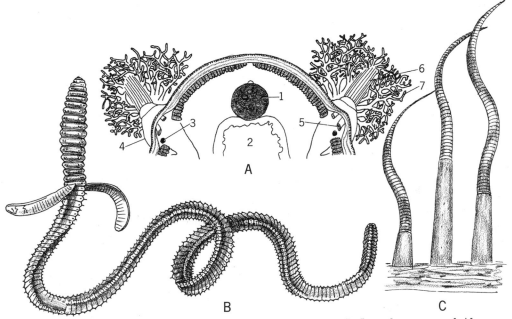

Fig. 14.20. A. Gills of *Arenicola*, derived from the notopodium. B. Lateral processes of *Alma*, an oligochaete, once thought to be gills. C. Tubificids extending the posterior end of the body from their tube. The body surface is aerated by spiral waving movements of the tail, and increased oxygen uptake is promoted by extending more of the body from the burrow. (A, after Wells. B, after Beddard.) 1, dorsal vessel; 2, intestine; 3, notopodial longitudinal vein; 4, notopodium; 5, notopodial retractor muscle; 6, bundle of setae; 7, gill.

of results have been obtained. Apparently the ability of an earthworm to reduce the importance of haemoglobin transport at lower oxygen tensions is fairly widespread among annelids. Exactly opposed results are obtained with *Nereis diversicolor*. At high oxygen tensions, the haemoglobin carries about 50 per cent of the oxygen used, while at low oxygen tensions, blockage of haemoglobin with carbon monoxide destroys all oxygen consumption. Evidently the haemoglobin of *Nereis* is especially important in transport when oxygen tensions are low and depends more on dissolved oxygen with increased oxygen tensions. The properties of chlorocruorin from sabellids and serpulids indicate that it can load up with oxygen at tensions normally present at the gills, and unload at tensions normally found in the body tissues. It is undoubtedly an important factor in normal internal transport of oxygen.

Excretion. The primitive annelid somite contains a pair of coelomic compartments, each open to the exterior by way of two ducts (Fig. 14.21). According to the gonocoel theory of coelomic origin, one of these ducts is a coelomoduct derived from the primitive gonoduct when the gonad lumen became the coelomic compartment. The term coelomoduct is reserved for a mesodermal duct that grows outward from the coelom to pierce the body wall and connects the coelom with the exterior. The second duct is the nephridium. There is considerable difference of opinion about the origin of the annelid nephridium. It arises from a nephridium mother cell during development, and the origin of the cell varies or is in doubt. If it is a mesodermal derivative, the nephridium is also a coelomoduct, but if it is an ectodermal derivative, it must grow in from the exterior and be an independent kind of duct. The nephridial mother cell has been described as arising from both ectoderm and mesoderm in different annelids, and the issue remains in doubt. The final answers will not prove or disprove the gonocoel theory,

but it is generally agreed that the persuasiveness of the gonocoel theory would be enhanced if the nephridium is not a coelomoduct. Goodrich (1947), an important proponent of the gonocoel theory, has studied the relationship of the nephridia and coelomoducts in various polychaetes.

A few annelids have a protonephridium, with the tubule closed off from the coelom by terminal solenocytes (Fig. 14.21F). In some of these the gonoduct is wholly separate from the nephridium. In other cases the protonephridium has united with the gonoduct to form a protonephromixium. A number of polychaetes have nephridia of this kind. The gametes enter through the gonoduct funnel and wastes through the tubule walls, but both pass through the lower part of the compound tubule.

The capitellids have a metanephridium, open to the coelom by way of a ciliated nephrostome, and a completely distinct gonoduct used for the discharge of gametes. The metanephridium and coelomoduct tend to unite, however, and various kinds of metanephromixia have been described, differing in the extent of union. In all, a double ciliated opening occurs, one the nephrostome and the other a gonostome.

In still other polychaetes a single duct is present, showing no obvious evidence of a compound origin. It is difficult to quarrel with Goodrich's (1947) interpretation that these represent the ultimate outcome of the union of nephridium and gonoduct, however. Goodrich calls these nephromixia. *Arenicola* provides a good example. The intimacy of the union between the nephridium and gonoduct is not perfectly correlated with the primitiveness of polychaetes in other matters, but this is not surprising in view of the long history of polychaetes.

Among Sedentaria the nephridia undergo further specialization. A few of the anterior nephridia are enlarged and serve primarily for excretion, while the many smaller nephridia in the posterior parts of the body are used primarily for the discharge of gametes.

All of the oligochaetes have metanephridia, and as the gonads lie in a few genital somites and have a distinct set of gonoducts, the nephridia are not used for the discharge of gametes. The primitive arrangement in oligochaetes has a pair of metanephridia in each somite. Each nephridium is made up of a preseptal nephrostome and a complex, postseptal tubule that ends in a nephridiopore, as in *Lumbricus* (Fig. 14.23A). This type of nephridium may be termed an exonephric holonephrid-

ium, as the tubule opens to the outside (exonephric) and is not divided to form smaller nephridia (holonephridium). The nephridial surface of some oligochaetes is amplified by subdivision of the nephridia in each somite into many nephridia, known as meronephridia. In megascolecids the strand of embryonic tissue from which the nephridium arises divides into a series of loops, each of which becomes an indepedent nephridium. Meronephridia vary considerably in form. Many are equipped with a preseptal nephrostome, and are essentially like the holonephridia, although they never have a bladder region. Others

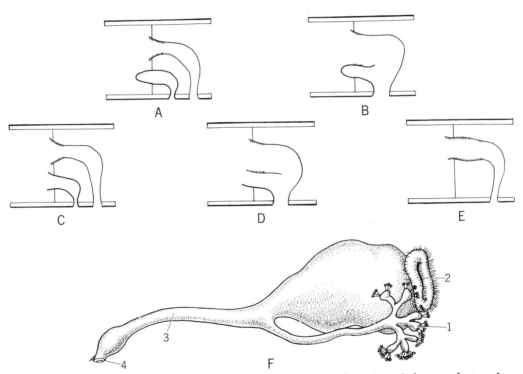

Fig. 14.21. Annelid Nephridia. **A-E.** Hypothetical stages in the union of the gonoduct and nephridium. **A,** Primitive condition, with separate protonephridium and gonoduct with ciliated funnel, as in *Vanadis*. **B,** Protonephridium united with the gonoduct, as in *Phyllodoce*. This arrangement is known as a protonephromixium. **C,** Completely separate metanephridium and gonoduct, as in *Notomastus*. **D,** United metanephridium and gonoduct, as in *Hesione*. This arrangement is a metanephromixium. **E,** Completely united nephridium and gonoduct, as in *Arenicola*. This arrangement is termed a mixonephrium. **F.** A protonephromixium of *Alciopa*. (After Goodrich.) **1,** solenocytes of protonephridium; **2,** opening of gonoduct; **3,** nephridial tubule; **4,** nephridiopore.

are closed, without a nephrostome, and lie wholly within a single somite. Some open into the gut instead of the outside and are said to be enteronephric. Enteronephridia that open into the pharynx or esophagus are thought to have a digestive function, but those that open into the lower part of the intestine probably excrete wastes that are further concentrated in the gut by water reabsorption. *Pheretima*, which has all of its somites behind the fifteenth equipped with enteronephric nephridia, has a higher resistance to drying than most oligochaetes. In a number of genera, several kinds of nephridia are found in a single organism (Fig. 14.22C).

Annelid protonephridia are essentially like the protonephridia of other animals. The tubule does not branch, but ends in a cluster of solenocytes known as the glomerulus. Each solenocyte contains a flagellum, which functions like the cilia in a flame bulb. Presumably the tubule walls are the primary site of excretion, as in the flame-cell systems of flatworms.

Coelomic fluid enters the nephrostome of open metanephridia and is processed as it passes through the tubule, eventually becoming urine. Differences between coelomic fluid and urine reveal something of what goes on in the tubule. Depending on the conditions to which the animal is adapted, the main changes of the fluid are: 1) changes in the water content, as urine becomes either hypotonic or hypertonic to the coelomic fluid, depending on whether water must be excreted or retained to preserve the osmotic balance; 2) changes in the salt concentration, as salts are excreted or retained; 3) changes in the concentration of the nitrogenous wastes; and 4) changes in the sugar content or concentrations of other organic compounds that may be useful to the organism.

Water regulation is less critical in marine than in fresh-water and terrestrial species. Littoral marine species, however, may encounter considerable dilution of sea water in estuaries, and their distribution may be partly determined by their ability to cope with a more dilute medium. The properties of the body wall are also important in water regulation.

Some annelids are osmotic conformers, adjusting their salt content to that of the environment. *Arenicola*, for example, has blood with a freezing point identical to that of the surrounding water in a range of $-0.29°$ to $-1.72°$ C. It evidently has a high tolerance for the dilution of its body fluids.

The most detailed information about polychaetes is available for nereids. *Perinereis cultrifera* is an osmotic conformer, very much like *Arenicola*. Its sac-like nephridia provide little surface (Fig. 14.22B). The body fluid of *Nereis diversicolor* becomes somewhat diluted, but remains hypertonic in diluted sea water. Its nephridia are long and convoluted (Fig. 14.22A). There is some evidence indicating that this species excretes water by forming urine more dilute than its body fluids, either by reabsorbing salts at the nephridial surface or by actively discharging water. In any case the body wall also helps in water regulation, for it is less permeable to water in dilute media and actively absorbs chlorine in a hypotonic medium. The ability of nephridia to regulate the osmotic properties of the urine probably depend in part on the length of the tubule, whether water or salts are being reabsorbed.

Polychaetes tend to have rather simple nephridia, consisting of a large, often frilled nephrostome, an excretory tube of varied length, and a terminal bladder. The tube and bladder of shorter nephridia may be combined to form an excretory sac. Oligochaetes have more complex nephridia, probably in response to the greater osmotic stresses they encounter. The nephridium is divided into a series of histologically distinct regions in both aquatic and terrestrial species (Fig. 14.23B-E). The functional significance of histological specializations is not very well understood, and little is known of the urine of aquatic oligochaetes. In earthworms the urine concentration changes as it moves down the tubule, indicating that materials are being absorbed or eliminated. The greatest changes in chloride content occur near the nephridiopore, where the wide part of the

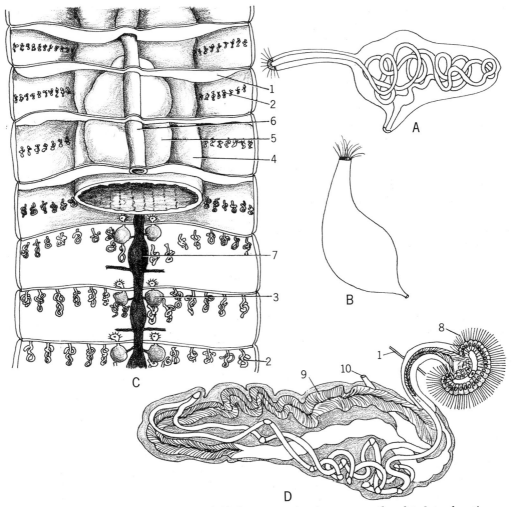

Fig. 14.22. Annelid Nephridia. Nephridial structure is often apparently related to function differences. *Nereis diversicolor* has rather complex nephridia (A), and can live in brackish water. It is capable of some osmoregulation. *Perinereis cultrifera* has very simple nephridia (B) and cannot regulate its water content in dilute sea water. Some oligochaetes, during development, derive many small meronephridia from the original pair of nephridia in each segment. The meronephridia may be open or closed. The distribution of open and closed meronephridia in part of a *Eutyphoeus* is shown at C, and the detailed structure of an open meronephridium at D. (A and B, after Jurgens, from Prosser *et al.* C and D, from Bahl.) 1, septum; 2, closed meronephridia; 3, open meronephridia; 4, intestine; 5, digestive gland; 6, dorsal blood vessel; 7, ventral nerve cord; 8, nephrostome; 9, ciliated tract in middle canal; 10, terminal nephridial canal.

tubule is located (Fig. 14.23E). An extensive recovery of salts from the urine is indicated by comparisons of the freezing point of coelomic fluid and urine. Earthworms kept in tap water have a coelomic fluid with a freezing point of $-0.31°$, while the urine has a freezing point of $-0.06°$. The chloride content of the urine is only about a thirteenth that of the coelomic fluid. Similar values are quoted for *Pheretima*. The low salt content of earthworm urine does not mean that water reabsorption is unimportant, however. Both water and salts are reabsorbed in the long, narrow tube, but in such proportions that the over-all osmotic properties of the fluid remain about constant. The salt is probably reabsorbed as a means of recovering the water. In the wide tube, more salts than water are reabsorbed, and the osmotic concentration falls rapidly. While more information is available about the movement of chlorides than of other substances, it is evident that useful compounds disappear from the fluid in the nephridium as it passes down the tubule. Glucose and amino acids are wholly reabsorbed from the nephridium of *Pheretima* during urine formation. Where the coelomic fluid participates in the transport of food, and this is certainly widespread among annelids, some such mechanism can be expected to develop.

Some of the visceral peritoneum of oligochaetes and polychaetes is histologically differentiated as yellowish to brownish chlorogogue cells. They occur on the surface of the midgut, in patches on the nephridia and esophagus, or as small deposits on the major blood vessels. Deamination of protein compounds occurs here; some foods are stored; and some nitrogenous waste materials are formed. Chlorogogue cells release ammonia and urea. They become detached and float in the coelomic fluid as amoeboid eleocytes. Bits of the chlorogogue cells may be budded off, to enter the nephrostome, and, in some cases at least, whole coelomic corpuscles

may enter the nephridium, bringing a load of nitrogenous compounds. They may also be deposited as yellow bodies in the body wall or pass completely out of the body. The chlorogogue cells are also important in food transport, collecting about the ova and nourishing them during maturation. They are, in many respects, a rough equivalent of the vertebrate liver cells.

Leech nephridia have not been mentioned, because they are so unlike those of the oligochaetes and polychaetes. This is to be expected, of course, for the reduction of the coelom and its conversion into a circulatory system makes the traditional metanephridial system with an open nephrostome inefficient or physiologically unsuitable. The rhynchobdellid nephridia are least modified (Fig. 14.24A). A nephrostome opens into the median ventral coelomic sinus and is connected by a short ciliated tube to a thin-walled sac, the capsule. The capsule is filled with phagocytic cells, often crowded together and with tiny ducts between them. The capsule is a characteristic addition to the leech nephridium, and is found in the nephridia of the gnathobdellids and pharyngobdellids as well. In the hirudids the capsule is large and has multiple funnels, while in the pharyngobdellids, each nephridium is supplied with two capsules and two funnels (Fig. 14.24B,C). Openings to the capsule, however, are not entirely homologous with the old nephrostome, for in some cases the vestige of the nephrostome is found in ciliated bodies in the lining of the coelomic sinuses. Unfortunately there is little known about the details of leech excretion. They have no single cell comparable to the chlorogogue cells of other annelids, but the botryoidal cells take up injected particles in *Hirudo*, and probably partially correspond to the chlorogogue cells. Amoeboid corpuscles in the coelomic fluid are also phagocytic and play an important role in excretion, although the details are not understood. In any case, the phagocytic cells which fill the open capsule of the

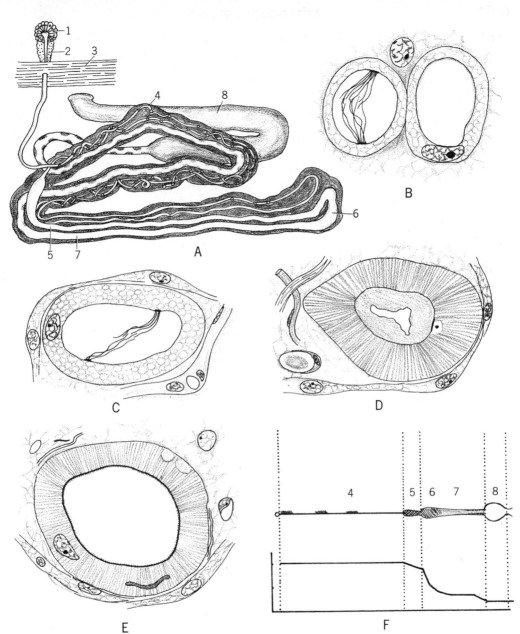

Fig. 14.23. Nephridium of *Lumbricus terrestris*. **A.** Somewhat simplified scheme of *Lumbricus* nephridium. Note the great length and extensive regionalization, associated with adaptation to a terrestrial habit. **B-E.** Sections through parts of the *Lumbricus* nephridium at different regions. **B,** narrow tube; **C,** brown, middle tube; **D,** ampulla; **E,** below ampulla. Note the considerable difference in histological structure of different regions. **F.** Osmotic concentration of urine in various parts of the *Lumbricus* nephridium, in percent concentration of salt in Ringer's fluid. (**A,** after Benham from Michaelson, in Kükenthal and Krumbach. **B-E,** after Dahlgren and Kepner. **F,** after Ramsay.) **1,** nephrostome; **2,** preseptal tube; **3,** septum; **4,** narrow tube; **5,** middle tube; **6,** ampulla; **7,** wide tube; **8,** muscular tube.

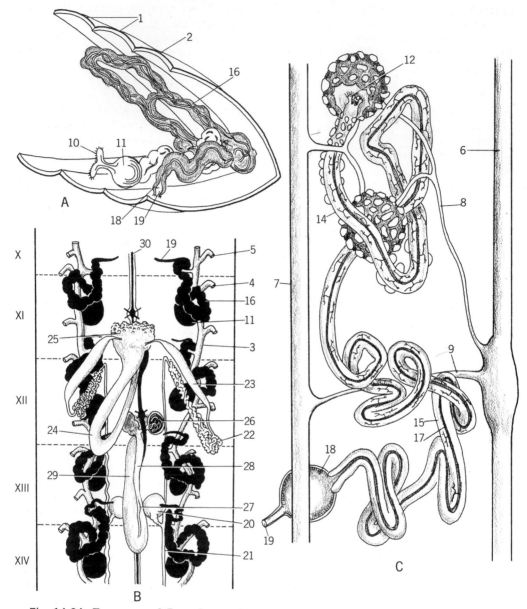

Fig. 14.24. Excretory and Reproductive Organs of Leeches. **A.** Nephridium of a glossiphonid in place. Note the ciliated nephrostome leading to the coelomic capsule. **B.** Nephridial
and reproductive system of *Haemopis*. **C.** Anastomosing nephridia of *Erpobdella*. Note the
disappearance of the nephrostome with the conversion of the coelom into a circulatory system.
(**A**, after Oka. **B**, after Mann. **C**, after Graf, from Harant and Grassé, in Grassé.) **1,** rings of
anterior somite; **2,** rings of posterior somite. *Coelomic sinuses and lacunae;* **3,** lateral coelomic
lacuna; **4,** dorsal coelomic lacuna; **5,** lateral branch from the lateral coelomic lacuna; **6,** ventral
coelomic vessel; **7,** lateral coelomic vessel; **8,** nephridial vessel; **9,** commissural vessel. *Nephridial system:* **10,** nephrostome; **11,** nephridial coelomic capsule; **12,** ciliated coelomic branches

rhynchobdellid leeches appear to accumulate particles of material which are passed down into the nephridial tubule. It seems probable that primitively the capsule was a chamber in which corpuscles could accumulate, for the capsule is not walled off from the tubule in the most primitive rhynchobdellids. However, it is closed off in others, and in these cases it is not easy to understand how the capsules function. In the hirudids, the cilia associated with the capsule beat outward, and it seems likely that as the coelom became a circulatory system, the capsule lost its original function and assumed a new one, the production of corpuscles. There is evidence that suggests that the material in the corpuscles of the more advanced leeches never enters the nephridium, but is permanently stored in the botryoidal tissue. However the leech capsule works, it is evident that much of the waste material that emerges from the nephridium must pass through the tubule walls.

Beyond the capsule the nephridium becomes a cord of cells containing a tortuous and usually branched, non-ciliated intracellular duct. A short terminal section of the nephridium is formed of invaginated epidermal cells, and serves as a bladder.

Annelids are ammonotelic, like other aquatic invertebrates. *Hirudo* excretes about three-fourths of its nitrogen as ammonia and similar values have been obtained for *Aphrodite*. Significant amounts of other nitrogen compounds are also eliminated: some urea, some amino acid, some purines, as well as unidentified compounds. It should be emphasized, however, that where a significant amount of nitrogenous material is permanently accumulated in the body tissues, the determination of the compounds released gives a very incomplete picture of excretory physiology. Not enough is known of the metabolic pathways utilized in excretory physiology, but the ornithine cycle is known to operate in some annelids. There is some evidence to indicate that leeches depend on bacteria for the production of ammonia from urea. When kept free of bacteria by antibiotics the ammonia content of the urine falls.

Adaptation to land life is accompanied by changes in excretory patterns, although earthworms excrete a considerable amount of ammonia. *Pheretima*, for example, excretes about half of its nitrogen as ammonia. Earthworms have the ability to change the excretory product with changes in the availability of water. When they are submerged in water, they are ammonotelic. When held in moist air, the urea content of the urine rises to 50 per cent or more. Starvation also modifies the excretory physiology. Well-fed *Lumbricus* excrete large quantities of ammonia, while starved ones switch to urea. *Eisenia*, on the other hand, works in the opposite direction, with urea output rising in well-fed organisms. It is probable that these differences are associated with the way in which acids are neutralized in the gut cavity. Ammonia is used for this purpose in *Lumbricus*, while *Eisenia* depends on carbonates and other compounds. Although many of the details of annelid excretion remain unknown, it is evident that the biochemical organization, like the morphological organization, has become complex. Various kinds of feedback mechanisms must be operating to permit modification of excretory physiology in response to dietary or environmental changes.

of capsule; 13, botryoidal cells of capsule; 14, afferent glandular nephridial canal; 15, efferent glandular nephridial canal; 16, glandular nephridium; 17, intracellular nephridial canal of glandular nephridium; 18, bladder; 19, nephridiopore. *Male reproductive system:* 20, testes; 21, sperm duct; 22, epididymis; 23, ejaculatory duct; 24, penis sac; 25, prostate gland. *Female reproductive system:* 26, ovary; 27, oviduct; 28, albumin gland; 29, vagina. *Nervous system:* 30, nerve cord in ventral sinus.

Neurosensory Apparatus

Sense Organs. The sensory equipment of annelids is interesting in the sense that an evolutionary reverse in trends occurred. Polychaetes, especially the errant species, have a well-developed sensory apparatus, but the oligochaetes, adapted to burrowing in the soil, have poorly developed sense organs. Leeches, which arose from oligochaetes, assumed an active, predatory way of life, and have good sense organs. However, as they came from a stock of animals which had reduced sense organs, a new set developed, confirming the general rule in evolutionary mechanics that a part, once lost, cannot be regained.

Two kinds of light receptors occur in annelids, cephalic eyes associated with the prostomium, and dermal eyes, which may appear at various points on the body surface. Prostomial eyes are characteristic of errant polychaetes and are rarely seen in any other group of annelids. They range from simple, converse pigment-cup ocelli to relatively advanced eyes. The simplest eyes have a cuticular cornea and characteristic neurosensory cells that extend as glassy rods above the pigment layer of the cup. As a general rule, however, the prostomial eyes have a cuticular lens (Fig. 14.25A,B). Most of the Errantia have one or two pairs of eyes, but some have as many as five pairs. Simple pigment-cup ocelli are also found in some naids, but otherwise this type of eye occurs only in polychaetes.

Polychaetes also have photoreceptor cells scattered in the epidermis. These sometimes aggregate to form eyes at various points on the body surface. *Polyophthalmus*, for example, has eye-spots on each somite, and many tubicolous species have eyes-spots on the tentacles or radioles that extend out of the tube. Even when conspicuous, these eyes are not built like prostomial eyes. They are essentially clusters of photosensitive cells, each of which contains an intracellular lens with an intra-cellular retina made of a tangle of nerve fibers below it.

Terrestrial oligochaetes have similar epidermal photoreceptor cells. They tend to be somewhat concentrated on the prostomium and the first and last few somites. It has been shown that sensitivity to light is highest in regions with the largest number of photoreceptor cells.

Leeches arose from oligochaete stocks that must have had no prostomial eyes, and have evolved cephalic and dermal eyes independently, using the epidermal photoreceptors for the purpose. Dermal eyes are clusters of photoreceptor cells (Fig. 14.25C). The sensillae are compound sense organs found on the sensory annuli, containing photoreceptors as well as other kinds of receptors. The large cephalic eyes are clusters of photoreceptors surrounded by a sheath of pigment (Fig. 14.25D). Leech eyes may be inverse or converse, and vary considerably in structural detail.

Very few annelids have specialized gravity receptors. A pair of open pits containing various foreign objects, such as diatoms, sand grains, and the like, are found in arenicolids. Sabellids and terebellids also have statocysts. These are burrowing forms, which probably depend more than most species on being able to distinguish between up and down, and which cannot depend on contact with the substrate for the purpose. *Arenicola* burrows downward, head first, and will slant its burrow if placed in a slanted tank. The sabellid *Branchioma* orients itself to burrow backward instead of forward, but also appears to depend on statocysts for orientation. The burrowing oligochaetes do not have statocysts, and it is not clear how they orient themselves, at least when in their burrows. Perhaps factors other than gravity are used. All of the annelids will right themselves when overturned. These righting reflexes apparently depend on epidermal, tactile stimuli.

The sense of touch is important in the life of annelids. Many are strongly thigmotactic, as might be expected in burrowing and tubicolous species, and in forms that creep under rocks or other objects. Touch reception appears to center in the nerve endings and general neurosensory cells of the epidermis. These are concentrated in the tactile processes on the body of polychaetes, especially the palps, parapodial cirri, and the prostomial and peristomial tentacles. As in other animals, most of the bristles are touch receptors. The setae of polychaetes and oligochaetes are important tactile organs. Some of the oligochaetes have special sensory hairs, especially at the anterior end of the body.

Ciliated nuchal organs are found on the heads of predaceous and burrowing polychaetes. They vary considerably in form, but are evidently homologous, for all are associated with the posterior part of the cerebral ganglia. Nuchal organs are plaques of ciliated, sensory epithelium, sometimes invaginated as pits, and often interspersed with gland cells, histologically resembling the chemoreceptors of flatworms. They probably work in much the same way. Capitellids have unusual nuchal organs, set on protrusible stalks, somewhat resembling the rhinophores of some molluscs. The nuchal organs are the only chemoreceptors to be positively identified in annelids. *Slavina*, an aquatic oligochaete, has sensory tubercles made up of a cluster of sensory cells, which may be chemoreceptive. Other

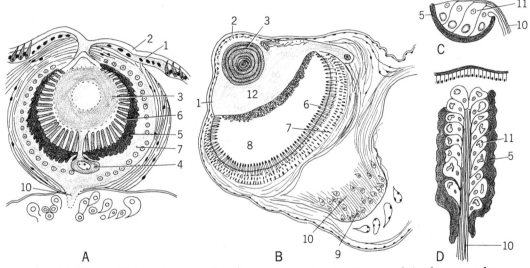

Fig. 14.25. Annelid Visual Organs. Polychaete eyes are pigment cup eyes of simple or complex structure, developing from sensory epithelium in the epidermis. Oligochaetes are generally without eyes, but have photosensory cells scattered in the epidermis. Leeches, derived from oligochaetes, have further developed the individual photosensory cells and clustered them to form inverse or converse eyes on an entirely different nature than polychaete eyes. A. The eye of *Phyllodoce*, a polychaete. It is a fairly complex pigment cup eye, with special cells for lens secretion and differentiated sensory rods. B. The eye of *Vanadis*, another polychaete. The structure is considerably more complex, and chambers containing a vitreous and an aqueous body are present. C. A glossiphonid eye, showing inverse construction, and photosensory cells containing intracellular lenses. D. A converse pigment cup eye from a hirudid leech. (A, B, C, and D, from Hesse.) 1, epidermis; 2, cuticle; 3, lens; 4, secretory cells; 5, pigment; 6, retinal rod; 7, sensory cell; 8, aqueous body; 9, ganglion cell; 10, optic nerve; 11, epidermal cell containing intracellular lens; 12, vitreous body.

such cell clusters have been described, but their functions have not been demonstrated. There is evidence that the sensillae of leeches include chemoreceptive cells. Some of the terrestrial oligochaetes have a pair of water-sensitive receptors which permit orientation toward a more moist environment.

Although annelid chemoreceptors are not very well known, studies of behavior indicate a high sensitivity to chemical stimuli. Predaceous annelids usually recognize the presence and direction of prey. Leeches orient and move toward body fluids from prey animals, although *Piscicola*, which lives in turbulent water where chemoreception would be relatively inefficient, appears to lack this ability. Chemoreception without contact with material, however, is widespread among annelids. Contact chemoreception also occurs. Leeches respond strongly to surfaces coated with body fluids of normal prey, and other annelids avoid certain kinds of chemicals. Gustatory organs are also present, probably in the buccal cavity. Leeches stop feeding when sufficient quantities of quinine, salt, or sugar are added to the food, and earthworms can distinguish between and show preference for different foods.

Nervous System. The simplest annelid nervous systems show strong similarities to the arrangements in flatworms. A subepidermal plexus is in contact with the epidermis. It is thickened to form a pair of ventral nerve cords, connected in each somite by commissures. At the junction of the nerve cords and commissures, ganglia occur. At the anterior end of the body a circumenteric nerve ring is formed of a pair of dorsal cerebral ganglia connected by a cerebral commissure, and a pair of connectives which join the first ganglia on the ventral nerve cords. The cerebral ganglia lie in the prostomium of polychaetes and give rise to nerves to the prostomial sense organs (Fig. 14.26A). This type of nervous system is seen in archiannelids, some other small polychaetes, and in *Aeolosoma*. Annelids with a nervous system of this kind are not necessarily primitive; some are certainly somewhat reduced and simplified. Nevertheless, they probably reveal something of the form of the ancestral annelid nervous organization.

The general lines of improvement lead to a more compact and better-protected nervous system. As in other phyla, the nervous system has tended to move inward to a more protected position (Fig. 14.26 F-H). The nervous system retains its subepidermal position in some polychaetes, like *Clymenella*, but in the majority it lies in the muscle layer of the body wall. It is sometimes in the muscle layer of oligochaetes, but in larger species it has moved into the coelom, as in *Lumbricus*. Muscle cells are incorporated in the sheath of the nerve cord, however, preserving a record of its past intramuscular position. The nerve cord of leeches lies within the coelomic sinuses (Fig. 14.12D).

The originally paired ganglia in each somite tend to assume a more medial position and eventually to unite (Fig. 14.26A-C). The ganglia are still paired in some tubicolous polychaetes, notably the sabellids and serpulids. In other polychaetes the ganglia have united to form a single, median mass, which, however, preserves histological evidence of its double origin. *Aeolosoma* retains double ganglia and a double nerve cord, but other oligochaetes have united ganglia. The first ventral ganglion is the subpharyngeal ganglion, and is distinctly larger than the others in nearly all cases. It is physiologically dominant over the rest of the ventral ganglia, although subsidiary to the cerebral ganglia in the chain of command.

The double nerve trunks tend to unite as a simple, median nerve cord, but not as quickly as the ganglia. Phyllodocid polychaetes have a double nerve cord between the united ganglia, for example. The two nerve cords of *Amphitrite* lie side by side, enclosed in a single connective-tissue sheath. In *Arenicola* the two cords have united, but remain histologically double, with a double neuropile. Nearly all of the oligochaetes, like *Arenicola*, have a single nerve cord with paired neuropiles. Many of the leeches retain a double nerve cord between the median ganglia. *Hirudo* and the gossiphonids have a single nerve cord, but it, too, is histologically double.

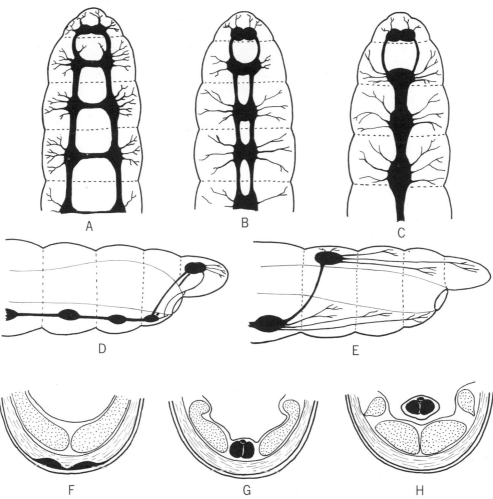

Fig. 14.26. Several evolutionary tendencies are observed in annelid nervous systems. The primitive arrangement, shown at **A**, has the brain in the prostomium, and a double ventral nerve cord. A ganglionic swelling is located on each nerve trunk in each somite. Commissures connect the ganglia in each somite. The paired nerve cords tend to assume a more medial position, resulting in the union of the paired ganglia (**B**) and eventually the enclosure of the two nerve cords in a single sheath (**C**). In polychaetes, the brain remains in the prostomium. In oligochaetes and leeches, however, the brain tends to move posteriorly (**D**, **E**). As the brain becomes more posterior, elongated nerves extend forward to the sense organs and muscles of the more anterior somites. Primitively, the nerve cord is subepidermal in position (**F**). As in other phyla, the nerve cord tends to migrate inward, lying first in the muscle layer of the body wall (**G**), and eventually coming to lie in the coelom (**H**).

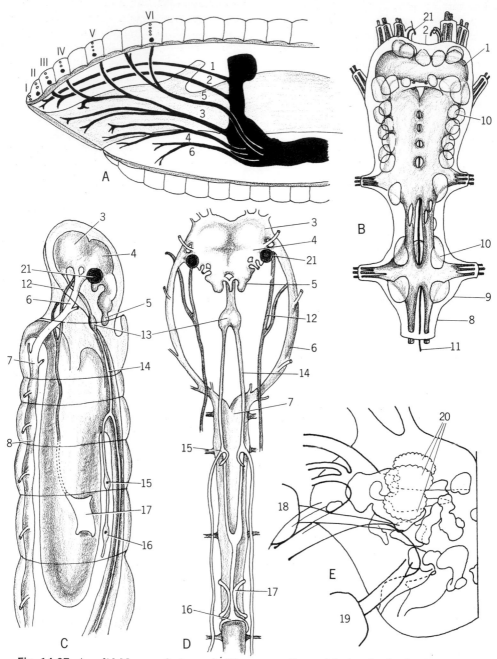

Fig. 14.27. Annelid Nervous Systems. **A.** The nerve collar and brain of a leech, showing the relationship of the nerves to the sensory annuli of the head region. Nerves are numbered inside of the body, and the somite numbers are shown in Roman numerals on the outside of the body wall. The backward movement of the brain and connectives in leeches has gone farther than in other annelids, probably in connection with the development of an oral sucker.

The cerebral ganglia retain their primitive position in the prostomium in polychaetes, but tend to migrate backward in the oligochaetes and leeches, accompanied by the connectives and the subpharyngeal ganglion. Among the oligochaetes, only the aeolosomatids have the cerebral ganglia in the prostomium. In all others the cerebral ganglia are more posteriorly located, generally, as in *Lumbricus*, in the third somite. In leeches with an anterior sucker the cerebral ganglia are still more posteriorly placed. As the brain moves back, the prostomial nerves are necessarily lengthened, as are the peristomial nerves from the subpharyngeal ganglion.

Superficial follicles of perikaryons lie on the surface of the ventral ganglia of leeches. Six such follicles, arranged in two rows of three, are associated with each ganglion (Fig. 14.11A). As the cerebral ganglia move posteriorly, the anterior ganglia of the ventral chain unite with the subpharyngeal ganglion. The follicles of perikaryons remain discrete, however, and the number of fused ganglia can be determined by counting them. Typically, six ganglia unite to form the compound subpharyngeal ganglion of leeches (Fig. 14. 27B). Leeches have some other peculiarities. The ganglia for the seven crowded somites in the posterior sucker also unite to form a compound ganglion. One of the annuli in each somite contains a subepidermal nerve ring associated with the sense organs. This is typically the sensory annulus. The nerve rings for adjacent somites are connected by longitudinal association neurones.

The general trends of evolutionary change in the annelid nervous system have involved the inward movement of the central nervous system and centralization. Centralization is achieved by the union of the originally paired ganglia and nerve trunks on the midline, and by the development of dominance in the cerebral and subpharyngeal ganglia. In arthropods, union of ganglia in different somites leads to still further nervous centralization. This occurs in leeches, but it probably does not signify quite the same thing as in arthropods. The crowding of somites in the regions of the suckers is probably more important than centralization in bringing about the union of leech ganglia.

The cerebral ganglia are closely associated with the prostomial sense organs. The errant polychaetes have well-developed heads and prostomial sense organs, while oligochaetes have reduced heads, and leeches, although well cephalized, have a less diversified set of sense organs than the

B. Brain region of a leech, *Branchellion*, from dorsal view. Note the follicles of neurons that remain discrete on the surface of the compound subesophageal ganglion. As there are three pairs of follicles for each segmental ganglion, counting the number of follicles makes it possible to determine how many ganglia are united to form a compound ganglion. C and D. Scheme of central nervous system of *Eunice*, in dorsal and side views, showing the relationship of the sympathetic or stomatogastric nervous system to the brain. E. Section through part of brain of *Nereis*, showing the nerves arising from the brain and some of the nuclei in the brain. Holmgren was able to identify 15 pairs of nerves and 23 pairs of nuclei in the *Nereis* brain. The nuclei shown with scalloped edges are the three centers of the corpus pedunculatum, the principal nuclei associated with the eyes. (A, after Mann. B, after François, from Harant and Grassé. C and D, after Heider. E, after Holmgren, from Fauvel, in Grassé.) 1, cerebral ganglion; 2, cerebral commissure; 3, forebrain; 4, midbrain; 5, hindbrain; 6, circumenteric connective; 7, subesophageal ganglion; 8, nerve cord; 9, segmental ganglion; 10, follicle of neurons; 11, nerve of Faivre; 12, sympathetic (stomatogastric) nerve to pharynx; 13, supraesophageal sympathetic ganglion; 14, supraesophageal sympathetic nerve; 15, infraesophageal sympathetic ganglion; 16, terminal sympathetic ganglion; 17, X-organ; 18, anterior eye; 19, posterior eye; 20, parts of corpus pedunculatum; 21, nuchal organ.

polychaetes. The errant polychaetes, primitive in many other respects, have the most highly evolved brains. The cerebral ganglia are differentiated into a number of functionally discrete lobes or centers, each associated with a special part or function (Fig. 14.27E). The development of specific centers and tracts is by no means as extensive as in the brain of cephalopods, but it is nonetheless important. It sets a pattern for the brain development in the annelid-arthropod stem, and this pattern has been remarkably stable. Although the Sedentaria and Oligochaetes have fewer cephalic sense organs, their brain retains the basic organization developed in errant polychaetes, and a strong similarity of many centers in the brains or arthropods and polychaetes provides strong evidence of their evolutionary relationship.

In the annelid brain, a cortex of small associational neurons relays sensory stimuli to motor centers, evoking responses that are predominantly prepackaged. The cerebral ganglia are not merely relay centers, however. True policy decisions, involving inhibition as well as the evocation of activity, are made here. The subpharyngeal ganglion, on the other hand, gains dominance as the primary motor center, subservient to the cerebral ganglia but dominating over the other ventral ganglia.

Removal of parts of the nervous system and observation of behavioral lesions show the extent to which the cerebral and subpharyngeal ganglia dominate activity. An earthworm normally turns away from light shone upon it from the side. If the ventral nerve cord is cut, however, the segments anterior to the cut turn away from light and those behind the cut turn toward the light. It is evident that in the intact worm, behavior follows the pattern laid down by the anterior ganglia, actually diametrically opposed to the patterns which the ventral ganglia dictate. A simple mechanism may account for this. There are more photoreceptors in the prostomium and anterior somites than in other parts of the body. Tracts from the prostomium and anterior somites cross over from one side to the other in the brain. With strong light intensities, these prevail and the animal is photonegative. With weak intensities the balance tends to fall the other way and the worm may respond positively. In this instance, the number and placement of the sense organs may directly influence the development of dominance.

The rather poorly developed oligochaete brain is not critically important, however. When the brain is removed, an earthworm is hyperactive but can still crawl, right itself, eat, copulate, and burrow slowly. Evidently most of the essentials of oligochaete life can go on without a brain. The more complex polychaete brain is more important to behavior. Removal of the brain destroys the ability to feed and burrow as well as most sensitivity to light and chemicals. The decerebrate polychaete is hyperactive, as are decerebrate leeches. Evidently the cerebral ganglia exercise an inhibitory influence on the motor centers of the subpharyngeal ganglion. Removal of the subpharyngeal ganglion has more drastic consequences than removal of the brain, for it effectively removes the influences of the cerebral ganglia as well. Nereids, for example, are almost motionless when it has been removed.

The ganglia on the nerve cords are not well marked in the more primitive nervous systems. Indeed, the ganglia of most polychaetes and oligochaetes have no sharp limits. Adaptation sometimes has lead to further decentralization. In *Arenicola* the neurons have spread throughout the nerve cord, and ganglionic thickenings cannot be identified. In leeches, on the other hand, the ganglia are sharply defined and the nerve cords slender. Something of the same kind is seen in the circumenteric ring. In some annelids, notably the errant polychaetes, the brain is quite large and distinct, but in leeches the cerebral ganglia are small and the connectives large, so the brain and connectives together form a nerve collar.

A giant fiber system is often found in animals. It is used for rapid conduction and evokes fast startle contractions. Most annelids have a giant fiber system, but the details differ greatly in different annelid groups. *Aphrodite* and the chaetopterids have no giant fiber system. Other polychaetes have giant fiber systems with from one to many fibers (Fig. 14.28). The giant fiber system is more stable in terrestrial oligochaetes. Most of the earthworms, like *Lumbricus*, have five giant fibers, a large middorsal fiber, a pair of dorsolateral fibers, and a pair of much smaller ventral fibers. Two general types of giant fibers can be distinguished. Some are no more than hugely overgrown neurons, arising from a single cell. Others are formed by the end-to-end connection of large neurons in each somite, which are converted into metameric conduction units of essentially non-cellular form. In the earthworm, each unit meets the next in a slanting septum formed of vesiculated double membranes. Impulses move across the septa without synaptic delay, and although the giant fibers are polarized in the animal, they can conduct stimuli in either direction with equal rapidity under experimental conditions.

The rate at which impulses move along an axon is a function of its cross-sectional area. The obvious advantage of giant fibers is rapid conduction. The fast neurons of vertebrates are myelinated, and giant fibers lack the conspicuous myelin sheath characteristic of fast neurons, although electron micrographs reveal a thin myelination in some. In any case, their large size makes up for whatever they lack in myelin. The large median giant fiber of *Lumbricus* conducts stimuli up to 45 m./sec., which compares favorably with the smaller fast fibers of cold-blooded vertebrates. The value of the giant fibers is emphasized by comparative conduction rates. The median giant fiber of *Lumbricus* carries impulses about 1600 times as fast as the small neurons. Their length is a further advantage, as they can conduct an impulse the whole length of an animal without synaptic delays. In each somite, branches from the giant fibers extend out to the musculature (Fig. 14.28G). Earthworm giant fibers have been described best. The median fibers have anterior sensory connections and conduct impulses back to the muscles. The lateral fibers are connected transversely in each somite. They have sensory connections at the rear and conduct stimuli forward.

Peripheral nerves arise from the brain, circumenteric connectives, and the ventral ganglia. The number of nerves per somite varies. Polychaetes have from two to five pairs in each somite; aquatic oligochaetes usually have four pairs; terrestrial oligochaetes have three, and leeches have two or three. The lateral nerves contain both sensory and motor fibers, and, in at least some cases, innervate definitely delimited portions of a somite. In *Erpobdella*, for example, the anterior pair of nerves innervate the dorsal, and the posterior pair the ventral part of the somite. The anterior, middle, and posterior pairs of nerves in each somite of *Lumbricus* innervate longitudinal bands of sensory cells in their own and adjacent somites. Primitively, the polychaetes had a series of ganglia associated with the peripheral nervous system. At the base of each parapodium a pedal ganglion occurred on the lateral nerve. A longitudinal nerve connected the pedal ganglia on each side of the body. This primitive arrangement has been reduced in modern polychaetes. Some have retained the pedal ganglia but lost the lateral longitudinal nerves, while others have lost the pedal ganglia as well.

Polychaetes with an eversible pharynx have one or two pairs of motor nerves extending to the pharynx region, forming the stomatogastric nervous system (Fig. 14.27C,D). These nerves arise from the brain, the circumenteric connectives, or

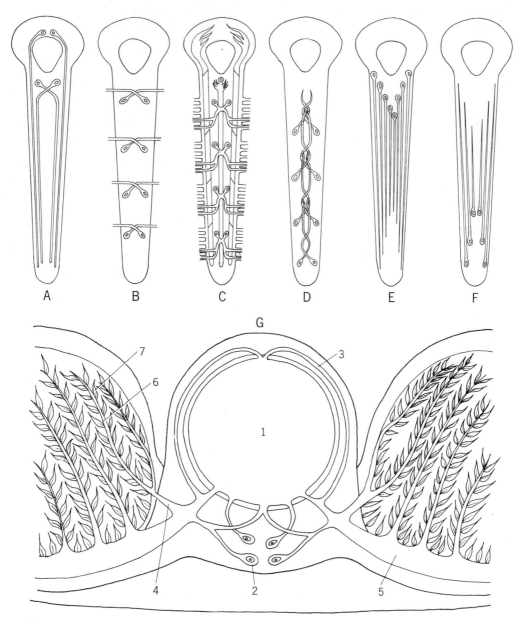

Fig. 14.28. Annelid Giant Fibers. Giant fibers are important for rapid conduction of impulses, and are especially responsible for quick, startle reactions. They are extremely variable among annelids. Giant fiber cells may occur in the brain or the ganglia of the ventral nerve cord, and may decuss or may remain on the side of their origin. In some cases, smaller neurons unite to form giant fibers with oblique interruptions, where multiple synapses occur, as in *Neanthes* (E), and *Lumbricus*. A. Giant fibers of *Sigalion*, made up of unicellular giant fibers from the brain and the anterior region of the nerve cord. B. Intersegmental giant fibers of *Lepidasthenia*, which decussate and pass to the body wall in each segment. C and E. Giant fiber system of

both, and often are associated with a series of small ganglia. An enteric nervous system provides motor control over the gut in *Lumbricus*, and presumably in most other oligochaetes. It may be derived from the stomatogastric system of polychaetes, as it arises as a pair of nerves from the circumenteric connectives. The nerves are ganglionated and may be responsible for the control of secretion as well as muscular activity. Some kind of nervous control of secretion is indicated, for stimulation of the ventral nerve cord evokes secretion by the digestive glands.

The importance of reflexes within and between somites in the control of body movements has been mentioned in connection with locomotion. There is no general annelid pattern, for the annelids move in different ways. Intrasegmental reflexes between circular and longitudinal muscles or between opposing sets of longitudinal muscles can ensure that antagonistic muscle systems are not contracted simultaneously during movement, and intersegmental reflexes can ensure the smooth passage of an activation wave along the body. All of these are routed through the ventral nerve cord and involve neurons specially placed and precisely formed for the kind of coordinating job they do. Most of these reflexes are triggered by muscular tensions resulting from the contraction of muscles in the body wall, constituting a complex feedback system that will sustain creeping or swimming movements.

Reproduction

Although the annelids are relatively highly organized, they have not wholly lost the capacity for asexual reproduction. This capacity is best developed in aquatic oligochaetes and certain of the polychaetes. Naids and aeolosomatids reproduce almost wholly by budding, and sexual reproduction is rarely seen. Budding occurs in a definite somite in any one worm, but the somite may differ among members of the same species. A budding zone appears, from which new posterior somites for the front animal and new anterior somites for the back one develop (Fig. 14.29D). The old segments behind the budding zone become the more anterior somites of the new worm. In some species the posterior animal develops a budding zone before separating from the anterior animal, and chains of zooids develop.

Spontaneous fragmentation of the body, followed by regeneration of the missing parts, is a common method of asexual reproduction in some polychaete groups. Syllids and sabellids have this habit. In many syllids, the points of breakage are predetermined, and can be recognized by peculiarities in the septa between the somites where separation will occur. In such species, fragmentation and regeneration have become highly organized and each fragment can develop a new anterior and posterior end. Regenerating annelid

Neanthes. In the nerve cord there are a pair of lateral fibers and a median giant fiber (E), the latter associated with one or more cells in the subesophageal ganglion, and the former of multicellular origin. The lateral fibers are associated with giant fibers which anastomose and arise from a pair of giant fiber cells in each segmental ganglion (C), and there is also a system of smaller giant fibers which decussate and extend through two somites (D). Their arrangement provides for side transmission as well as longitudinal transmission. F and G. Giant fiber system of *Halla*, consisting of anteroposterior and posteroanterior fibers in the nerve cord. H. Cross section of the nerve cord, giant fiber, and branches of *Myxicola*. (A, after Rhode. B, after Haller. C-E, based on Hamaker and on Stough. F and G, based on Ashworth. H, after Nicol, from Nicol.) 1, giant fiber; 2, giant fiber cells; 3, dorsal branch; 4, lateral branch; 5, peripheral branch; 6, branch to muscle; 7, longitudinal muscle.

fragments are fascinating objects for study. Two basic patterns of regeneration occur. In some cases the original somites grow smaller as new somites arise, and so come to be normal parts of the new organism. The details of the use of the parent somites and the mechanisms which operate as it dwindles to match the size of the new somites are not yet understood. In other cases the original somites remain large. A slender head and tail regenerate at each surface. These break off; the head end grows a new tail, and the tail end grows a new head. In *Dodececaria* a second, and sometimes a third, set of anterior and posterior ends develop before the original somites are exhausted. The spontaneously formed fragments may be quite numerous; some species of *Dodececaria* and *Ctenodrilus* produce some single somite fragments. Many species which do not reproduce by fragmentation have high powers of regeneration after experimental fragmentation. As a rule, polychaetes with specialized body regions do not regenerate as well as those without specialized regions, but there are exceptions. *Chaetopterus*, for example, can produce new individuals from any of several of the highly specialized anterior somites (Fig. 14.29A). Berrill (1961) has a fascinating review of regeneration experiments with polychaetes and oligochaetes.

Polychaetes have a very simple reproductive system. Sexes are nearly always separate. The reproductive cells arise from definite, small regions of the peritoneum, placed differently in different species. As cells proliferate, they become detached and float in the coelom, where both maturation divisions usually occur. When the animal is sexually ripe, the coelom is filled with gametes. Ova are brightly colored, and often show through the thin body wall. Ova and sperm are shed into the water, the gametes emerging through separate gonoducts in a few, but generally passing out by way of the nephromixia. Fertilization is external, and development

usually occurs in the open sea. A few brood young in their tubes. Scale-worms brood young in the respiratory channel beneath the elytra. But these are the exceptions rather than the rule.

As a general rule, errant polychaetes produce gametes in most of the body somites. This is probably a primitive trait. When the body becomes specialized into several regions the number of genital somites is reduced. In most tubicolous species, gametes are produced only in the more posterior, abdominal somites and the abdominal nephridia function as gonoducts. As a general rule polychaetes have many genital somites, but the number is sharply reduced in some. *Arenicola* has only six genital somites, and *Trophonius* has but one.

Nereids, syllids, and eunicids live throughout most of the year as sexually unripe animals, known as atokes. As the breeding season approaches, sexually ripe forms known as epitokes are produced by the atokes. At some sort of a signal the epitokes arise to the surface by the millions, swim about excitedly for a night, and as the morning sun strikes, shed their gametes. Fish congregate to feed on the swarming worms, and birds gather to take their share of worms or fish, as the case may be. Man, too, may await swarming time for capturing the fish or worms. *Eunice viridis* epitokes were highly prized as food, baked or eaten raw, by the Samoans. Several interesting biological problems are presented by swarming and the phenomenon of epitoky. How, and under what influence, do the atokes produce the epitokes? How is the activity of millions of worms so perfectly coordinated that all mature and swarm together?

Atokes produce epitokes by direct transformation or by budding. *Nereis* atokes become epitokes by transformation. The body becomes larger, the eyes enlarge, the parapodia change form, and the cephalic appendages are reduced (Fig. 14.2C,F). The adult, sexually unripe atoke metamor-

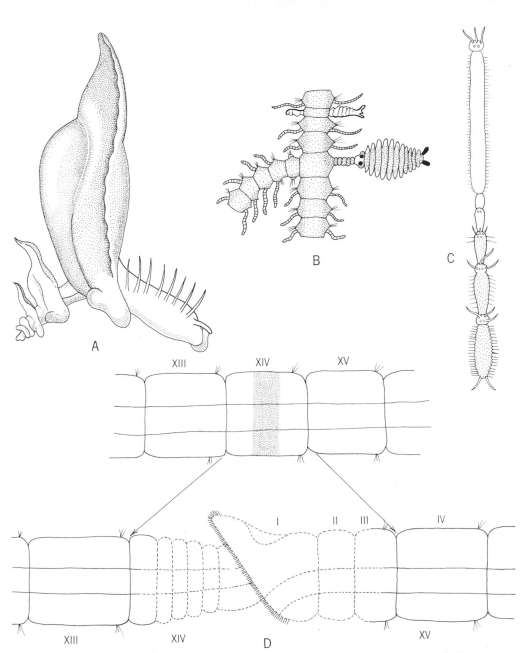

Fig. 14.29. **A.** Anterior and posterior regeneration from the single fan segment of *Chaetop-terus*. **B.** *Syllis*, at the point of a branch in the body, and with a chain of reproductive individuals budding off of the parapodia. **C.** A chain of zooids of *Autolytus*. Note the growth zone from which the epitokes are formed. **D.** Budding zone of *Aeolosoma*. A definite somite serves as a growth zone, where a new posterior end and a new anterior end for the young individual forms. (**A**, after Berrill. **B**, after MacIntosh, from Hegner. **C**, after Malaquin, from Benham. **D**, after Marcus, from Pennak.)

phoses into a sexually ripe adult, the epitoke. The transformation is a profound one, changing the *Nereis* into a freely swimming, pelagic animal. The parapodial setae are adapted for swimming, and a number of the other traits resemble those seen in pelagic polychaetes.

Some polychaete atokes develop a budding zone, not unlike the budding zone of some aquatic oligochaetes. This method probably developed from the habit, still followed by some polychaetes, of transforming the posterior somites into an epitoke, which breaks away from the parent atoke as a new head develops for it. The parent atoke then develops a new growth zone at its posterior end and adds new somites, which in their turn will mature to form a new epitoke. This scheme of epitoke production is further developed in *Autolytus*. The first epitoke arises by transformation of the posterior somites and the development of a head. Before the epitoke is released, however, the growth zone, now a budding zone, proliferates to lay down a number of epitokes (Fig. 14.29C). In the resulting chain of zooids the most posterior epitoke is the eldest and has been formed by direct transformation of the posterior somites. *Trypanosyllis* shows still further specialization for epitoke production. The budding zone protrudes as a stolon, from which a number of epitokes develop. An unusual method of epitoke production is seen in *Syllis ramosus*. Multiple budding zones develop at the sides of the body, from which epitokes arise. The young epitokes develop secondary buds of their own, so a single atoke can produce a large number of epitokes (Fig. 14.29B). The varied methods used to produce epitokes suggest an evolutionary trend toward the production of numerous epitokes. This is probably related to the relatively low probability of completion of the life cycle. Epitokes are greedily eaten by various animals at the time of swarming, and polychaete larvae are fair game for the myriads of ocean plankton-eaters. There can be no doubt that epitoky materially increases the reproductive potential of a species, especially when it is coupled with multiple budding.

Swarming is often under precise control, and the date or even the hour of swarming can be predicted with considerable accuracy. As a rule, epitokes swarm at some definite lunar period and at some definite season. Swarming is not controlled by any single factor, for such environmental factors as light can sometimes suppress it. It is known that neurosecretions are involved in the production of at least some epitokes, and they are very probably involved in epitoke behavior. The transformation of a *Nereis* atoke into an epitoke is similar in nature, though different in detail, to the assumption of breeding plumage by birds or the development of breeding ornamentation by fish. In these cases, hormonal secretions which are evoked by such environmental factors as increased or decreased length of day have proved to be a common cause. The removal of the brain of a young *Nereis* induces epitoky, and the grafting of a young brain into an adult *Nereis* suppresses epitoky. Evidently neurosecretions fit into the picture of epitoke production in some manner.

Nearly all of the polychaetes have separate sexes, but a few sabellids and hesionids are hermaphroditic. The hermaphroditic species usually produce ova in the more anterior abdominal somites and sperm in the more posterior ones, but some produce both sperm and ova in the same somite. It is not known what determines whether a young germ cell will become an ovum or a sperm.

Aeolosomatids are like polychaetes, forming gametes in many somites and using nephridia for the release of gametes. All other oligochaetes have a very few genital somites, served by a specialized set of gonoducts. The placement of the genital organs and arrangement of the gonoducts are variable, and important in classification and taxonomy.

Aquatic oligochaetes typically have one pair of testes and one pair of ovaries located in the anterior half of the body. The testes and ovaries are little more discrete than in polychaetes, being essentially thickenings of the peritoneum. The young germ cells are released and mature in the coelom (Fig. 14.30F). The segment containing the testes contains a sperm sac or seminal vesicle, actually a portion of the coelom specialized for the reception of the developing sperm. In some of the aquatic oligochaetes the sperm sacs are elongated, occupying several somites, and in the tubificids a second sperm sac extends forward from the anterior septum of the male somite. The gonoduct ends in an open seminal funnel, located in the sperm sac, and the short male gonoduct opens through a male pore in the somite just behind the one containing the testes. Prostatic gland cells usually surround a part of the gonoduct. The function of the prostatic secretion is unknown. The ovaries lie in the somite immediately behind the male genital somite. They release ovocytes which mature in an ovisac, comparable to the sperm sac. The short female gonoduct opens into the ovisac and leads to the genital pore in the somite immediately behind the ovaries.

The terrestrial oligochaetes live in an entirely different kind of habitat and are much larger than aquatic oligochaetes, but their reproductive system differs only in details from the pattern seen in water forms. They generally have two pairs of testes instead of one, with each pair in a different somite. The sperm ducts are long, opening several somites behind the two containing the testes. In *Lumbricus* (Fig. 14.30A) a third pair of sperm sacs is present, extending forward from the anterior septum of the anterior male somite, and the two sperm ducts unite to form a common sperm duct on each side. These open four somites behind the one with the posterior testes. The ovisac is very small and is missing in some earthworms.

Two pairs of seminal receptacles are present instead of the single pair found in aquatic oligochaetes. Differences such as these are important to taxonomists but do not change the major aspects of reproductive behavior.

Embellishments and refinements are found sporadically in one or another group of earthworms. Prominent glandular regions in the vicinity of the male gonopores are often seen. The scattered prostatic gland cells are sometimes gathered together to form a discrete multicellular gland. Minor modifications of the pattern of the sperm-duct system are common enough. Specialized setae are often found around the male gonopores, the openings of the seminal receptacles, or on the clitellum; these help to attach copulating worms more firmly. In a few cases the gonopore is raised on a sucker-like pad, and sometimes the terminal part can be everted as a penis. These are simple improvements, however, and do not affect the basic nature of the copulatory and reproductive behavior.

Sperm is exchanged mutually when two oligochaetes copulate. The two worms often appose the male gonopores and the pores of the seminal receptacles. Sperm from each worm move into the seminal vesicles, and the two animals disengage and move apart. In other species the pores are not apposed, and in this case external grooves which lead to the seminal receptacles are usually present, as in *Lumbricus*. Rich mucous secretions help to hold the animals together during copulation, and may also help to guide the sperm along the sperm grooves.

Egg-laying need not occur immediately after mating. Although the oligochaetes mate, fertilization actually occurs externally. At the time of egg-laying, the clitellum secretes a tough, membranous girdle. The worm backs out of the girdle, and gametes enter as it passes the female genital pores and the pores of the seminal receptacles. The two ends snap together as it

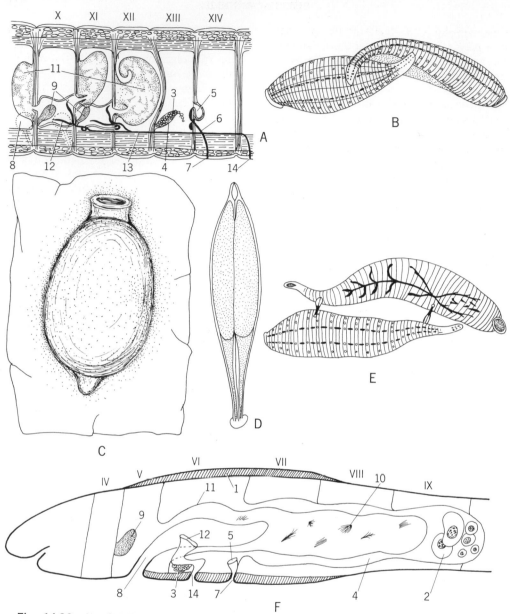

Fig. 14.30. Annelid Reproduction. **A.** Scheme of the reproductive organs of *Lumbricus terrestris* as seen in longitudinal section. **C.** A cocoon of *Stylaria*, an aquatic oligochaete. **D.** The spermatophore of a glossiphonid leech. **B** and **E.** Copulation of *Glossiphonia*. The two leeches attach by means of the ventral suckers. As they separate, each implants a spermatophore on the partner. **F.** Diagram of the structure of the reproductive organs of a typical naidid. (**A**, after Hesse, from Stephenson. **B, D, E**, after Brumpt, from Harant and Grassé, in Grassé. **C**, after Pennak. **F**, after Stephenson, from Pennak.) 1, clitellum; 2, ovum; 3, ovary; 4, ovisac; 5, ostium of oviduct; 6, oviduct; 7, female gonopore; 8, seminal receptacle; 9, testes; 10, clusters of developing sperm; 11, seminal vesicle (sperm sac); 12, seminal funnel; 13, sperm duct; 14, male gonopore.

slips over the head, enclosing the gametes in a relatively impervious cocoon. Aquatic species usually attach the cocoon to objects (Fig. 14.30C), while terrestrial species leave them free in the soil. Each cocoon contains a number of ova, but usually only one or two worms emerge.

As leeches evolved from oligochaetes, the reproductive system was profoundly altered. Probably the reduction of the coelom was one of the important factors in evoking the changes. Leeches have a single pair of ovaries, placed far forward between the anterior pair of testes (Fig. 14.24B). The ovaries are not simple, but include the specialized peritoneum that forms the reproductive cells and a reduced ovisac, a vestige of the coelom. A short oviduct, possibly a modified coelomoduct, leads from each ovary. The two oviducts unite and a short vagina leads to the median female gonopore.

The male system is more complex. The testes occur in pairs, one pair to a somite. *Hirudo* has ten pairs, but some leeches have as few as four pairs. The testes are built like the ovaries, consisting of the proliferative peritoneum enclosed in a reduced sperm sac. Each testis opens into a sperm ductule which joins a longitudinal sperm duct on each side of the body. The sperm ducts are also vestiges of the coelom. In front of the most anterior testes the sperm ducts are dilated to form seminal vesicles. The two seminal vesicles unite to form a median antrum, which is often complex, especially in the gnathobdellids, where a part of the antrum can be everted as a penis. The muscular antrum of the rhynchobdellids and pharyngobdellids cannot be everted, but serves as a chamber for the formation of the spermatophores. The single male gonopore lies just anterior to the female gonopore.

Leech spermatophores (Fig. 14.30D) are double, consisting of a mass of sperm derived from each of two seminal vesicles that is enclosed by a tough membrane secreted by the antrum wall. During copulation the sharp point of the spermatophore is driven into the body of the mate, in some cases into a target area especially adapted for the reception of the spermatophores. The spermatophore discharges the sperm into the underlying tissues. Sperm find their way to the ovaries. In some leeches a special vector tissue has appeared, which conducts the sperm to the ovaries.

Gnathobdellids have no spermatophores, and the penis is everted into the female gonopore. Sperm are discharged into the vagina, where they are stored.

Leeches have a clitellum and secrete cocoons, like oligochaetes. Glossiphonid cocoons, however, are very delicate and are attached to the ventral surface of the body. The young already have a posterior sucker when they emerge and attach to the ventral surface of the parent, where they continue their development. The parent leech remains rather quiet while brooding the young, cupping the body around them, but if the oxygen level falls, the leech moves rhythmically to aerate them.

Development

Polychaetes undergo spiral determinate cleavage, closely resembling molluscan and flatworm embryos (p. 311). After gastrulation a trochophore larva develops which corresponds to the trochophore stage of molluscs. (Fig. 14.31A). The trochophore has a girdle of cilia, the prototroch; an apical sensory plate with an apical tuft of cilia; a posterior circlet of cilia, the telotroch; and in some cases an extra band of cilia betwen the prototroch and telotroch, the metatroch. The curved gut opens at a mouth located just below the prototroch, and at an anus which is encircled by the telotroch. The mouth arises from the anterior margin of the blastopore, and the anus from a proctodaeum that appears near the closed-over posterior margin of the blastopore. The part of the larva between the apical tuft and a point somewhat below the mouth will develop into the head of the young animal. When it is present, the line of the metatroch lies near the posterior margin of the future head. The telotroch and anus will develop into the final somite of the body, the pygidium. All of the trunk arises from the short, tapered region between. During metamorphosis, this part of the larva grows very rapidly; it may be termed the growth zone.

The growth zone grows steadily and rapidly. As it lengthens, the anterior part is cut off as the first postcephalic somite. It continues to grow, and the second somite forms behind the first. The rhythmic production of new somites follows a regular pattern. Apparently new tissue from the growth zone undergoes some maturation process, probably an early stage of differentiation, that triggers the division of the somite from the growth zone (Fig. 14.31B,C).

Setal sacs and setae differentiate in the new somites. A girdle of cilia around each somite often persists throughout the planktonic phase of larval life. Blastomere 4d has, at an earlier stage, divided into two mesoblasts, the mother cells of the mesoderm. Each of the mesoblasts has divided repeatedly, establishing a pair of mesodermal bands that extend into the growth zone. As the somites form, paired spaces appear in the mesodermal rudiment of the somite, eventually enlarging to form the right and left coelomic compartments of the segment. All of the ectodermal covering of the trunk arises from the second quartet of micromeres. Blastomeres 2a–2c give rise to the lateral dorsal ectoderm and to some other parts, including the stomodaeum. Cell 2d proliferates to form a ventral plate of ectodermal cells, from which the ventral nerve cord and ganglia arise.

The brain develops from the apical sensory plate. The part of the larva around the plate develops into the prostomium, and grows tentacles and palps on each side at this time. In *Polygordius*, the prostomial region is separated from the rest of the body by a large part of the trochophore. As growth continues, this part of the trochophore collapses, partly as a result of the contraction of larval muscle strands, bringing the prostomium back to the developing trunk. The peristomium develops from the collapsed part of the trochophore, which contains the mouth and through which the connectives to the subpharyngeal ganglion pass. In many polychaetes the subpharyngeal ganglion lies in the peristomium. In this case the adult peristomium is formed by the union of the first trunk somite and the peristomial region of the trochophore. This is the case with *Nereis*, for example, As development continues, the larva settles to the bottom and takes up its normal way of life. Not all polychaetes pass through all of the stages mentioned. As in other animals, larval life may be shortened by a delayed emergence from the protection of the egg membranes. Where this happens the trochophore larva is often somewhat modified.

The primitive scheme of annelid development thus involves a ciliated larval stage. It is obvious that a drastic change is required to develop an embryo which can survive in a terrestrial habitat. Oligochaetes do not pass through a larval stage, nor is there any vestige of a trochophore-like stage of embryonic development. The eggs are larger, containing a considerable quantity of yolk, and the cleavage pattern is greatly disturbed. Some traces of spiral cleavage remain, and cleavage proves to be determinate, but the derivation of the body parts from the quartets of micromeres so characteristic of polychaetes and primitive molluscs is changed. A mesoblast cell is formed but it does not arise from blastomere 4d.

The blastula gastrulates by invagina-

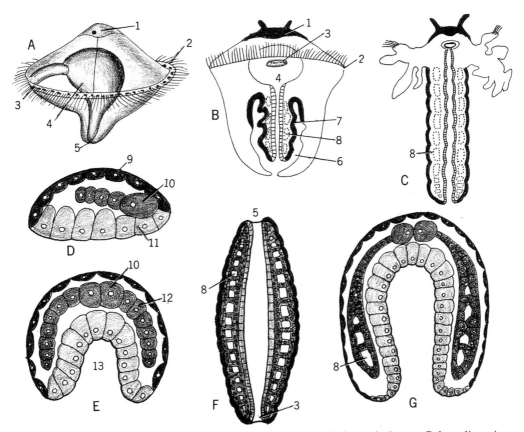

Fig. 14.31. Annelid Development. **A-C.** Development of the polychaete, *Polygordius*. A normal trochophore **(A)** is formed, which undergoes metamorphosis **(B** and **C)** to become worm-like. The prostomium develops from the region of the apical plate. The body segments develop from a growth zone which appears just in front of the telotroch, with the pygidium forming first. The remainder of the trochophore largely degenerates, leaving the peristomium behind it. **D-F.** Development of *Lumbricus*. After unequal but total cleavage, a coeloblastula develops. As it gastrulates by invagination **(D, E)**, mesodermal cells are produced from the mesoblast cell, which move into the old blastocoel. As the embryo elongates, the mesodermal bands on each side of the body keep pace with the growth **(G)**; segmentally arranged spaces appear in the mesoderm, and develop into the coelomic compartments **(F)**. The mouth develops from the blastopore, and the anus erupts at the other end. Septa arise from the tissue between the coelomic compartments, and the dorsal and ventral mesenteries from the walls of the paired coelomic compartments as they meet above and below the gut. Ectoderm is shaded dark, endoderm light, and mesoderm intermediate. (A, after Fraipont. B and C after Harant and Grassé, from Harant and Grassé, in Grassé. D-G, after Sedgewick and Wilson, from Hegner.) 1, apical plate; 2, prototroch; 3, mouth; 4, midgut; 5, anus; 6, amniotic cavity; 7, metasome forming somites; 8, developing coelomic compartment; 9, ectoderm; 10, mesoblast cell; 11, endoderm; 12, mesodermal band; 13, primitive gut.

tion, with the mesoblast cell moving into the blastocoel and later dividing to form the characteristic mesodermal bands at the sides of the archenteron (Fig. 14.31D-G). The embryo elongates and the mesodermal cells continue to proliferate. Coelomic spaces appear on each side of each somite and expand to establish the coelomic compartments, the septa, and the mesenteries. The mouth develops from the blastopore and the anus eventually breaks through at the opposite end. With some modifications, leeches follow an essentially similar pattern of direct development.

Affinities of Annelids

Similarities in the early development of annelids, flatworms, and molluscs emphasize their close relationship. A number of similarities, some undoubtedly superficial, can be seen between annelids and various kinds of flatworms. A number of flatworms and nemertines have an eversible proboscis, like the errant polychaetes. Some of them show a distinct tendency toward a pre-metameric arrangement of gonads, of parts of the protonephridial system, of intestinal diverticula, and of other parts in nemertines. The circulatory system of the nemertine worms may have been derived from an ancestral design that also gave rise to the annelid-molluscan type of circulatory system. At the present time, no one stock of flatworms or nemertines can be designated as the one that must have given rise to annelid ancestors.

Within the phylum, it is evident that the polychaetes are the most primitive. The reproductive system is very simply organized, and the animal undergoes a primitive type of embryonic development which is modified in the other classes. It is also clear that the errant polychaetes preserve more of the primitive characteristics than the sedentary polychaetes. They have a degree of cephalization that is consonant with their level of organization, and there is every reason to suppose that the assumption of sedentary habits would evoke the kinds of retrogressive changes in head organization that are seen among sedentary forms. It is not possible, however, to designate any one of the errant stocks alive today as the obvious primitive group from which all of the remaining types could be derived. Certainly the modern polychaetes have all had a very long history of being polychaetes, and none can be considered truly primitive except in respect to some specific traits or body parts.

While there can be little question that some polychaete stock was ancestral to the oligochaetes, it is not possible to choose any one of the modern forms as a model for the oligochaete ancestor. It is very likely that the polychaetes that gave rise to oligochaetes were hermaphroditic, like some modern polychaetes, and probably had a tendency toward the reduction of the number of genital somites, like *Arenicola*. It is possible to construct a hypothetical scheme deriving the simpler aquatic oligochaetes or the larger, burrowing, land oligochaetes from polychaetes, and both schemes have been advocated. Again, there are more questions than answers.

That leeches have arisen from oligochaetes is scarcely to be doubted in view of the similarities in their reproductive habits and the common occurrence of a clitellum. Transitional forms in the sense that they are intermediate in character are seen in *Acanthobdella* and the branchiobdellids. Undoubtedly some group of epizoic oligochaetes, differentiating along lines somewhat parallel to those seen in branchiobdellids, established the hirudinean stem. While *Acanthobdella* may be truly primitive, preserving the organizational features of this early hirudinean stem, is not impossible but seems improbable in view of the differences in number of somites in the body, a remarkably constant feature of both branchiobdellids and of the other hirudineans. The same line of reasoning makes it improbable that the rhynchobdellids, although quite unlike the gnathobdellids and pharyngobdellids, are a wholly independent stem. That two stocks should come to have bodies composed of the same number of somites, with a clitellum occupying the same somites, is asking too much of coincidence. There seems little doubt, however, that the early main ancestral stock from which the three major leech groups arose must have diverged very soon into a rhynchobdellid line and another which gave rise to the other two orders.

References

Allen, M. J. 1959. Embryological development of the polychaetous annelid, *Diopatra cuprea*. *Biol. Bull.* 116: 339.

Arbit, J. 1957. Diurnal cycles and learning in earthworms. *Sci.* 126: 654.

Bahl, K. N. 1947. Excretion in the Oligochaeta. *Biol. Rev.* 22: 109.

Beddard, E. F. 1895. *A Monograph of the Order Oligochaeta*. Clarendon Press, Oxford.

Berrill, N. J. 1952. Regeneration and budding in worms. *Biol. Rev.* 27: 401.

Bullock, T. H. 1945. Functional organization of the giant fibre system of *Lumbricus*. *Jour. Neurophys.* 8: 55.

Chapman, G. and G. Newell. 1947. The role of the body fluids in relation to movement in the soft-bodied invertebrates. *Proc. Roy. Soc. London* 134: 431.

Clark, L. B., and W. N. Hess. 1940. Swarming of the Atlantic palolo worm, *Leodice fucata*. *Tortugas Lab. Papers* 33: 21.

Clark, R. B. 1961. The origin and formation of the heteronereis. *Biol. Rev.* 36: 199.

Cohen, S., and H. Lewis. 1949. The nitrogen metabolism of the earthworm. *J. Biol. Chem.* 180: 79.

Dales, R. P. 1957. Some quantitative aspects of feeding in sabellid and serpulid fanworms. *Jour. Mar. Biol. Ass.* 36: 309.

Dausend, K. 1931. Über die Atmung der Tubifiziden. *Ztschr. vergl. Phys.* 14: 557.

Galloway, T. W. 1911. The common freshwater Oligochaeta of the U.S. *Trans. Am. Micr. Soc.* 30: 285. (F)

Gee, W. 1912. The behaviour of leeches with especial reference to its modifiability. *Univ. Calif. Publ. Zool.* 2: 197.

Goodnight, C. J. 1940. The Branchiobdellidae (Oligochaeta) of North American crayfishes. *Ill. Biol. Monogr.* 17: 1. (F)

——, and E. S. Goodrich. 1945. The study of nephridia and genital ducts since 1895. *Quart. Jour. Micr. Sci.* 86: 113. (G, B)

Gray, J. 1939. The kinetics of locomotion of *Nereis diversicolor*. *Jour. Exp. Biol.* 16: 9. (G)

——, and H. W. Lissman. 1938. Locomotory reflexes in the earthworm. *Jour. Exp. Biol.* 15: 506. (G)

——, et al. 1938. The mechanism of locomotion in the leech. *Jour. Exp. Biol.* 15: 408. (G)

Hartman, O. 1936. New species of polychaetous annelids of the family Nereidae from California. *Proc. U.S. Nat. Mus.* 83: 467.

——. 1945. The marine annelids of North Carolina. *Duke. U. Mar. Sta. Bull.* 2: 1. (F)

——. 1951–59. Literature of the polychaetous Annelids. *Allan Hancock Found. Publ. Occas. Pap.* No. 23.

Hedley, R. H. 1956. Studies on serpulid tube formation. *Quart. Jour. Micr. Sci.* 97: 411.

Heidermanns, C. 1937. Excretion und Excretstoffwechsel der Wirbellosen. *Tab. Biol.* 14: 209.

Hess, W. N. 1925. Reactions to light in the earthworm *Lumbricus terrestris*. *Jour. Morph. Physiol.* 39: 515.

——. 1925a. Nervous system of the earthworm, *Lumbricus terrestris*. *Jour. Morph. Phys.* 40: 235.

Izuka, A. 1912. The errantiate Polychaeta of Japan. *Jour. Coll. Sci. Imp. Univ. Tokyo* 30: 1.

Johnson, H. P. 1903. Fresh-water nereids from the Pacific Coast and Hawaii, with remarks on fresh-water Polychaeta in general. *Mark. Anniv. Vol.* 205.

Jones, J. D. 1955. Observations on the respiratory physiology and haemoglobin of the polychaete genus *Nephthys*. *Jour. Exp. Biol.* 32: 110.

Kiyoshi, H. 1959. The fine structure of the giant fibres of the earthworm. *Jour. Biochem. Biophys. Cytol.* 6: 61.

Krishnan, G. 1952. On the nephridia of Nereidae in relation to habitat. *Proc. Nat. Inst. Sci. India* 18: 241.

Krivanek, J. O. 1956. Habit formation in the earthworm, *Lumbricus terrestris*. *Phys. Zool.* 29: 241.

MacGinitie, G. E. 1939. The method of feeding of *Chaetopterus*. *Biol. Bull.* 77: 115.

Mann, K. H. 1953. The segmentation of leeches. *Biol. Rev.* 28: 1.

———. 1962. *Leeches (Hirudinea), Their Structure, Physiology, Ecology, and Embryology*. Pergamon, New York. (!)

Manwell, C. 1960. Comparative physiology of blood pigments. *Ann. Rev. Physiol.* 22: 191.

Marcus, E. 1958. On the evolution of the animal phyla. *Quart. Rev. Biol.* 33: 24.

Meyer, M. C. 1940. A revision of the leeches (Piscicolidae) living on fresh-water fishes of North America. *Trans. Am. Micr. Soc.* 59: 354.

Miller, J. A. 1929. The leeches of Ohio. *Cont. Franz Theodore Stone Lab.* 2: 1.

———. 1937. A study of the leeches of Michigan, with key to orders, suborders and species. *Ohio Jour. Sci.* 37: 85.

Moment, G. B. 1953. On the way a common earthworm, *Eisenia foetida*, grows in length. *J. Morph.* 93: 489.

Moore, J. P. 1898. The Hirudinea of Illinois. *Bull. Ill. State Lab. Nat. Hist.* 5: 479.

Needham, A. E. 1958. Pattern of nitrogenous excretion during regeneration in oligochaetes. *Jour. Exp. Zool.* 138: 369.

Newell, G. 1950. Role of coelomic fluid in the movements of earthworms. *Jour. Exp. Biol.* 27: 110.

Oka, A. 1894. Beitrage zur Anatomie der *Clepsine*. *Ztschr. wiss. Zool.* 58: 79.

Ramsay, J. 1949. The site of formation of hypotonic urine in the nephridium of *Lumbricus*. *Jour. Exp. Biol.* 26: 65.

Reynoldson, T. B. 1947. An ecological study of the enchytraeid worm population of sewage bacteria beds. *Jour. An. Ecol.* 16: 26.

Roots, B. I. 1960. Some observations on the chlorogogenous tissue of earthworms. *Biochim. Biophys. Acta* 2: 381.

Schoumkine, O. B. 1953. Embryonic development of *Hirudo*. *Trud. Inst. Morf. Zhiv.* 8: 216.

Sedgewick, A. 1884. On the origin of metameric segmentation and some other morphological questions. *Quart. Jour. Micr. Sci.* 24: 43.

Smith, R. I. 1958. Reproductive patterns in nereid polychaetes. *Syst. Zool.* 7: 60.

Stephenson, J. 1930. *The Oligochaeta*. Clarendon Press, Oxford. (!)

Tucker, D. S. 1958. The distribution of some freshwater invertebrates in ponds in relation to annual fluctuations in the chemical composition of the water. *Jour. An. Ecol.* 27: 105.

Welch, P. S. 1920. The genera of the Enchytraeidae (Oligochaeta). *Trans. Am. Micr. Soc.* 39: 25. (F)

Wilson, D. M. 1960. Nervous control of movements in annelids. *Jour. Exp. Biol.* 37: 46.

Wilson, E. B. 1892. Cell lineage of *Nereis*. *Jour. Morph.* 6: 361.

15

The Minor Coelomate Protostomes

With the appearance of a coelom, a great evolutionary flow began among the protostomes. Dividing into three great channels, this flow established the three great protostome phyla, Mollusca, Annelida, and Arthropoda. These three channels, however, did not carry all of the adaptive currents which the coelomate protostomes generated. Some of the less successful lines may never be recovered from ancient rocks, but a few have continued on, never abundant but still somehow surviving in spite of the growing competition from the more successful. The minor groups of coelomate protostomes are, by and large, unimportant from the standpoint of man's economic welfare or the great ecological systems established in the seas or on land. Yet they are worthy of close attention from the theoretical biologist, for they have developed from the annelid-arthropod stem at different times and reveal something, however dimly, about the nature of that stem at different points in its history. Unfortunately, not enough attention has been given to some of these groups, and it is safe to say that none of them has told us all it can about the historical development of life on the protostome road.

Phylum Sipunculida

Although there are only about 250 species of sipunculids, they are widespread marine animals, centering in the littoral zone of warmer seas, but extending into polar waters and reaching abyssal depths. The relatively few species and wide geographical distribution indicates that they are not very sensitive to the forces which create new species, at least as they are today. Sipunculids are sedentary creatures, burrowing in the sand or mud and occupying any protected niche of appropriate size, whether a rocky crevice, a convenient niche among corals, an annelid tube, or a molluscan shell. One minute species lives in foraminiferan shells. They range from about 2 mm. to over half a meter in length.

The outstanding sipunculid characteristics are the following:

1. bilaterally symmetrical, unsegmented coelomate structure;

2. body divided into an anterior introvert containing the mouth and a plumper trunk;

3. one pair of nephridia, or a single nephridium;

4. absence of a circulatory and respiratory system;

5. a dorsal brain, a circumenteric nerve ring, and an unsegmented ventral nerve cord;

6. separate sexes, with simple gonads derived from the peritoneum and gametes maturing in the coelom, discharged through the nephridia;

7. spiral cleavage, a trochophore larva, and schizocoelous coelomic development, as in other protostomes.

Sipunculids have a very simple external form. The long or short introvert ends in an anterior oral disc, bordered by tentacles of variable number, size, and complexity. A smooth zone, the collar, may be found immediately behind the tentacles. Minute spines or hooks and sensory or glandular papillae stud the surface of the introvert. Not uncommonly, a calcareous shield is found at the upper end of the trunk in species living in coral rocks, and in one genus a posterior shield also occurs (Fig. 15.1A). The trunk has no hooks or spines, but usually has sensory and glandular papillae. The circular and longitudinal muscles of *Sipunculus* can be seen through the body wall, giving it a gridded appearance. The conspicuous anus is usually found at the anterior end of the trunk or on the introvert, marking the middorsal line. On the other side of the body, at about the same level, a pair of ventral nephridiopores is usually found.

The body wall is composed of layers of cuticle, epidermis, dermis, circular muscle, sometimes a layer of diagonal muscle, longitudinal muscle, and peritoneum. The layers vary in thickness and complexity with the size and habits of the species. Introvert retractor muscles (Fig. 15.1D) merge with the longitudinal muscle layers of the body

wall and insert at the anterior tip of the introvert, on the upper end of the esophagus.

The coelom is spacious and undivided; only vestiges of mesenteries are present. The coelom and body wall act as a hydraulic system to operate the introvert. Contraction of the body wall musculature raises coelomic pressure and everts the introvert, to be pulled back by the introvert retractor muscles. Burrowing sipunculids thrust the introvert forward in the mud, dilate it at the tip, and then retract it, pulling the body forward.

It would be awkward if the tentacles could be manipulated only at the same time as the introvert. Unlike many animals with oral tentacles and a coelom, the coelom does not extend out into the tentacles. Instead, a separate hydraulic system for the operation of the tentacles is used. One or two tentacular canals extend into each tentacle and open into a ring canal around the upper end of the esophagus. One or two compensation sacs arise from the ring canal. Muscles in the compensation sac contract to extend the tentacles. When the tentacles contract, fluid is forced back into the compensation sacs. Ciliated tracts on the lining cells of the tentacular canals are sometimes found, and presumably cause a circulation of the fluid in the system. The ring canal, compensation sacs, and tentacular canals are remarkably like the ambulacral system of the echinoderms. Differences in larval development and in the organization of the rest of the body leave no doubt that the similarities are entirely convergent, representing a similar but independent solution of similar problems in each group.

The tentacles are sometimes used as a ciliary-mucous feeding system, but are too small to be adequate in most species. Sipunculids eat sand and mud, and subsist on whatever food material they may yield. Diatoms, protozoans, larvae, and small particles of organic detritus provide most of their nourishment. *Golfingia procera*, however, pierces the body wall of *Aphrodite* with its introvert and sucks in the body fluid and soft tissues.

The large mouth opens into a short, muscular pharynx, or leads directly into the slender esophagus. The posterior end of the esophagus of *Golfingia* has several longitudinal ridges, and is sometimes called a stomach. The ascending arm of the gut is a coiled intestine, which straightens and continues as the rectum. In some species a blind sac, the rectal diverticulum, extends from the rectum, and digitate or branching rectal glands may be found near the anus.

Little is known about digestion. The intestine has a conspicuous ciliated groove which aids in moving food along. Digestion and absorption appear to center in the descending arm of the gut, and the ascending arm is probably concerned primarily with feces formation. Food is stored in the intestinal wall as lipids, ribonucleids, and carbohydrates.

Glucose has been recovered from the coelomic fluid, which must play an important role in internal transport. Coelomic channels extend into the body wall of many species (Fig. 15.1E). Several kinds of amoebocytes and corpuscles containing a respiratory pigment, haemerythrin, float in the coelomic fluid. Haemerythrin also occurs in the fluid of the tentacular canals, and in some species the properties of the haemerythrin in the two systems differ. According to Manwell (1958), this has a curious effect in *Dendrostomum* and *Siphonosoma*. The coelomic fluid of *Dendrostomum* has a higher affinity for oxygen than the tentacular fluid; in this case the tentacles pick up oxygen and transfer it to the coelomic fluid. *Siphonosoma* coelomic fluid has a lower affinity for oxygen than the tentacular fluid. It does not respire through the tentacles, and transfers oxygen from the coelomic to the tentacular fluid.

Chlorogogue tissue, presumably with functions like annelid chlorogogue, arises from the peritoneum on the intestine. Some sipunculids have curious peritoneal structures known as coelomic urns (Fig. 15.1F). They appear as elevations of the peritoneum, containing a ciliated cell. In some species they remain attached to the peritoneum, but in others the urns break away and swim about actively in the coelom. Particles adhere to them and are eventually converted into brown bodies or discharged through the nephridia.

Most species have a pair of large, saccate, brownish metanephridia, with open nephrostomes and nephridiopores. Some species have lost the nephridium on one side. The brownish glandular walls probably excrete nitrogenous wastes into the tubule. Sipunculids are ammonotelic, with up to 90 per cent of the nitrogenous wastes being released as ammonia. When put in hypotonic media, they can expel salt through the intestine and nephridia, thus regaining normal body volume. There is some evidence that they can also expel water.

Sipunculids have surprisingly varied sense organs. Scattered neurosensory cells, papillate sensory buds, and protrusible ciliated pits are commonly found on the body surface or tentacles. A ciliated region, the nuchal organ, on the dorsal edge of the oral disc is probably a chemoreceptor. In some species, a deep ciliated pit, the cerebral organ, extends back to the brain where it expands as a flattened sac. It is thought to be sensory. A number of sipunculids have almost tubular pigment-cup ocelli imbedded in the brain. Filamentous and leaf-like processes from the brain surface extend into the coelom, and may provide information about coelomic conditions.

The nervous system is rather like that of an annelid, but the only ganglia are the cerebral ganglia, and the lateral nerves show no sign of a metameric distribution. They may be opposite, alternate, or arise in a completely irregular manner. Nerves

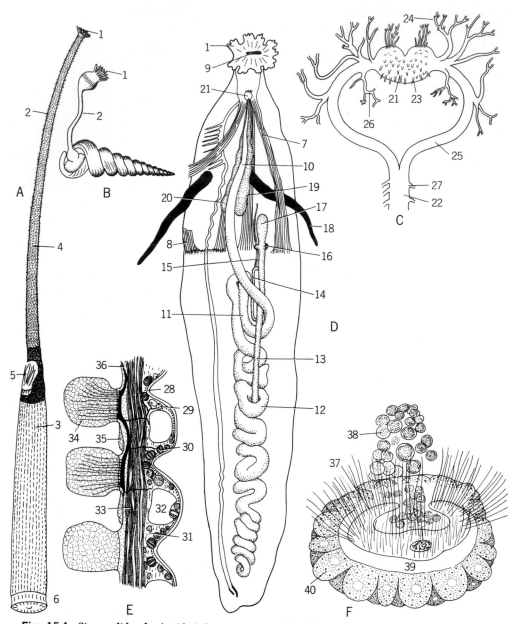

Fig. 15.1. Sipunculids. **A.** *Aspidosiphon*, a sipunculid with an anterior shield dorsal to the base of the introvert, and a posterior shield. **B.** *Phascolion*, at home in a snail shell. **C.** The central nervous system of *Golfingia gouldi*. Notice the lack of segmentation in nerves from the nerve cord. **D.** Dissection of *Sipunculus nudus*, a sipunculid with four equal retractors. **E.** Transverse section through the wall of *Sipunculus*. Coelomic canals near the body surface permit respiratory exchange. **F.** A free coelomic urn of *Phascolosoma*, with attached debris. (**A,** after Hyman. **B,** after Théel. **C,** after Andrews. **D** and **E,** after Metalnikoff. **F,** after Salinsky.) *External features:* **1,** tentacles; **2,** introvert; **3,** trunk; **4,** circlets of spines; **5,** anterior

644

to the retractor muscles usually arise from the circumenteric ring. There is evidence that the sipunculid brain, like that of annelids, exercises an inhibitory effect on other parts of the motor nervous system.

The gonads are peritoneal outgrowths, located at the junctions of the retractor muscles and the body wall. The germ cells are immature when they are released and ripen in the coelom. Sexes appear to be separate in all sipunculids.

Gametes are released into the water and fertilization is external. *Golfingia* fills its nephridia with sea water and accumulates gametes in them when it is ready to spawn. Evidently some kind of sorting device excludes the immature reproductive cells. The males discharge sperm first. The touch of spermatic fluid induces the females to eject ova.

Cleavage follows the annelid pattern, although the micromeres are somewhat larger. During cleavage an annelid cross is formed. A typical trochophore larva is formed, and elongates as it metamorphoses into a juvenile. At no time is there evidence of metamerism in the developing larva. It is interesting that the *Golfingia* metanephridia appear to arise from an ectodermal invagination and a mesodermal, peritoneal primordium that produces the nephrostome. In *Sipunculus*, on the other hand, the whole nephridium arises from mesodermal cells. Where two such closely related members of a small phylum disagree, one wonders how much dependence can be placed on the embryonic origin of nephridia as a means of determining the probability of any concept of coelomic origin.

Phylum Echiuroidea

Echiuroidea is a small phylum of annelid-like, marine worms with a remarkable proboscis. The proboscis has greatly influenced their way of life and so played a big part in moulding the evolutionary trends that have affected the adaptation of other body parts. Most echiuroids retreat from the world, dwelling in burrows and crevices and thrusting the proboscis out as a periscope and food-finder. They show considerable diversity in spite of an over-all sameness. *Urechis* and *Echiurus* build U-shaped mucous tubes in soft bottoms. Others live among rocks in convenient crevices or live in the shells or tests of other animals. *Thalassema melitta* when young enters the tests of sand dollars and grows too large to emerge, but lives well enough in its self-chosen cage with the help of its proboscis. Most echiuroids are sedentary, but some will move about considerably in captivity. *Bonellia minor*, when first put in an aquarium, probes about inquisitively with its sensitive proboscis, and when an acceptable nook is found, attaches it, pulling the body into the space, proboscis first. It turns about and extends the proboscis once more, exploring the neighborhood before it begins to feed. The *Bonellia* proboscis is a remarkable instrument. *B. viridis* has a proboscis that is only about 7 cm. long when contracted, but can be extended to as much as 1.5 m. When fully extended it is an almost transparent thread.

shield; 6, posterior shield. *Muscles:* 7, dorsal retractor; 8, ventral retractor. *Digestive tract:* 9, mouth; 10, esophagus; 11, proximal intestine loop; 12, intestinal coil; 13, rectum; 14, rectal diverticulum; 15, spindle muscle; 16, rectal gland; 17, anus. *Nephridial system:* 18 nephridium. *Introvert system:* 19, dorsal compensation sac; 20, ventral compensation sac. *Nervous system:* 21, brain; 22, ventral nerve cord; 23, pappuli from processes; 24, tentacular nerves; 25, circumenteric connective; 26, pharyngeal nerve; 27, lateral nerve. *Histology:* 28, cuticle; 29, epidermis; 30, epidermal gland; 31, dermis; 32, longitudinal coelomic canal; 33, circular muscle; 34, longitudinal muscle; 35, diagonal muscle; 36, nerve. *Coelomic urn:* 37, ciliated cell; 38, debris accumulated by ciliated cells; 39, urn cavity; 40, chlorogogue cell.

The most outstanding characteristics of echiuroids are the following:

1. bilaterally symmetrical, coelomate construction;

2. body divided into a plumper trunk and an extensible, grooved proboscis, corresponding to the annelid prostomium;

3. a convoluted digestive tube, opening at a mouth situated at the base of the proboscis, and a posterior anus;

4. one to many nephridia, with nephrostomes and nephridiopores;

5. a simple circulatory system, with dorsal and ventral vessels;

6. a circumenteric nerve ring and ventral nerve cord, subepidermal in position, with no definite brain or ventral ganglia;

7. separate sexes, with reproductive cells arising from modified peritoneum, maturing in the coelom, and escaping by way of the nephridia;

8. spiral cleavage and a trochophore larva; embryo passing through a transient segmented stage, but with all traces of metamerism lost during later development.

The proboscis is extremely sensitive to touch and is probably a center for chemoreception. It secretes a mucous cover on which organisms and small particles stick, to be conveyed to the mouth by a ciliated groove and by muscular movements of the proboscis itself. *Urechis* (Fig. 15.2C,D) has evolved a different method of feeding, capitalizing on its U-shaped tube in much the same manner as *Chaetopterus*. The proboscis secretes a mucous funnel which is attached to the proboscis base and the wall of the tube. Peristaltic movements of the body wall pump water through the tube, pulling it through the mucous funnel. When filled, the funnel is wrapped up and swallowed. The funnel is a remarkably effective strainer, for the openings in it measure only about 40 Å.

The mouth opens into a short buccal tube, leading to an often large pharynx (Fig. 15.2B). The esophagus is a narrow tube, often coiled, which leads to the midgut. A muscular gizzard and saccate stomach sometimes lie between the esophagus and intestine. The long intestine is irregularly coiled, and is attached to the body wall by muscular mesenterial strands. The intestinal musculature is delicate, and food moves along a ciliated groove. A narrow ciliated tube, the siphon, parallels the intestine for some distance and then rejoins it. Its precise function is unknown, but it evidently serves as a shunt for some of the intestinal contents. It may keep the concentration of enzymes high in the main intestinal channel by conducting water to the lower intestine. The intestine straightens and continues as a short rectum, from which a pair of diverticula, the rectal sacs, protrude. The rectal sacs are simple or branched, but in either case are open to the coelom through ciliated funnels. Their exact function is uncertain; they have been thought to serve as accessory nephridial organs, to provide control over coelomic pressure, and to be used in respiration.

The spacious coelom is undivided. The coelomic fluid contains amoebocytes and haemocytes in which haemoglobin is retained. The haemoglobin appears to serve primarily for oxygen storage, to provide against periods of low oxygen availability, such as when the tide is out. It can hold enough oxygen to maintain metabolism for some time at the reduced rates characteristic of *Urechis* at ebb tide. Anal pumping has been described in *Urechis*. Rhythmic peristaltic movements pass coelomic fluid over the rectal wall, indicating that respiratory exchange must be taking place.

Echiuroid nephridia are much like the nephridia of sipunculids. They vary greatly in number. *Bonellia* has but one, while *Ikeda* has over a hundred pairs. Most species, however, have from one to three pairs of nephridia. Brownish inclusions in the glandular part of the nephridial tube probably mean that this region is an active one for nitrogenous excretion.

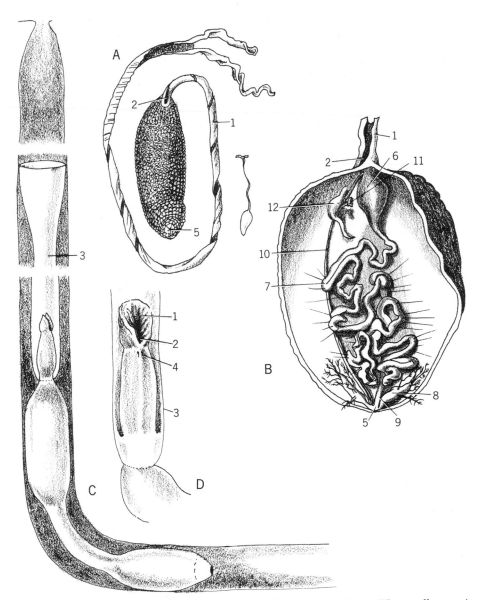

Fig. 15.2. Echiuroids. A. *Bonellia viridis* and *B. fuliginosa*, natural size. The smaller species is more naturally arranged. B. Dissection of a female *B. viridis*, opened laterally. C and D, *Urechis caupo*, in its tube, with a mucous funnel in position. (A and B, after Shipley. C and D, after Fisher and MacGinitie, from the MacGinities.) *External features:* 1, proboscis; 2, mouth; 3, slime tube; 4, ventral hooks; 5, anus. *Digestive system:* 6, pharynx; 7, intestine; 8, anal sac; 9, rectum. *Nervous system:* 10, nerve cord, accompanied by ventral vessel. *Nephridial system:* 11, nephrostome; 12, nephridium.

The circulatory system is simple and the blood is without a respiratory pigment. In this the echiuroids resemble annelids which have a respiratory pigment in the coelomic fluid. A ventral vessel runs above the nerve cord. Blood passes to the dorsal vessel through contractile circumintestinal and circumesophageal vessels, varying in number with the species. The dorsal vessel arises at the junction of the most posterior circumintestinal vessels and runs forward to the anterior tip of the proboscis. Here it divides to form right and left branches, which pass along the proboscis margins and join together behind the mouth to form the ventral vessel.

The body wall is composed of the same layers that occur in the sipunculid body wall. Various glandular cells and sensory papillae are scattered over the body surface. A pair of ventral setal sacs contains the roots of the two hooked setae.

The sedentary life of the echiuroids is reflected in the simplicity of the neurosensory equipment. There are no special sense organs, unless the proboscis be considered one. The simple nervous system is built on the annelid pattern, but contains no ganglia. The circumenteric ring is drawn out into a long loop, which follows the proboscis margin and connects with a ventral nerve cord that has no ganglionic swellings.

The character of the reproductive system emphasizes the relationship of annelids, sipunculids, and echiuroids. Sexes are separate, and the gonads are specialized regions of the ventral mesentery. Gametes are shed into the coelom before they reach maturity. After they have ripened, they escape through the nephridia.

Fertilization usually occurs in the ocean, but *Bonellia* has worked out other arrangements. *Bonellia* females are very large, and the males are very small. Any isolated larva develops into a female. A larva that develops near or in contact with

a female becomes a male. Its development is retarded and it remains a small, ciliated organism with many juvenile characteristics. It may cling to the proboscis of the female for a time, but eventually enters the female mouth and takes up residence in a fold of the nephridium, living the rest of its life as an internal parasite. This method of sex determination occurs in *Haemingia* also, and in these genera the ova are fertilized in the nephridia and remain there during early development.

The zygote undergoes spiral cleavage and develops into a trochophore. The next steps in development parallel those of the polychaetes. Coelomic compartments appear in the bands of mesoderm, and a series of segmentally arranged thickenings appear in the ventral plate, as if segmental ganglia were to form. In some cases, segmental furrows, segmentally arranged ciliary bands, or segmentally arranged pigmented regions appear. About 10 to 15 of these larval somites appear, after which all are suppressed and the adult becomes unsegmented and without ganglia. Embryonic development thus provides clear evidence that the echiuroids have arisen from a segmented, annelidlike ancestral stem.

Phylum Tardigrada—Water Bears

About a dozen or so of the 350 species of tardigrades are marine, living in beach sand. Some of the rest live in fresh-water habitats, in bottom detritus or attached to fresh-water plants, but the majority are semi-aquatic, living on mosses, lichens, and liverworts. These live under remarkable conditions. Most of their lives are spent in a dessicated anabiotic state. In this condition they look like shriveled mummies, but they are nevertheless metabolizing slowly. As soon as water becomes available, they become plump and active. The capacity to resist dessication by entering a state of suspended activity is shared with some of the rotifers. Spallanzani studied the resistance of tardigrades to drying nearly 200 years ago, but a number of physiological problems must still be solved before the anabiotic state can be explained. Anabiotic tardigrades are quite resistant to low temperatures and to chemicals. In this state they can pass through unfavorable periods of the year, and some may be disseminated by air currents while dessicated. Some of the aquatic tardigrades can enter anabiosis when dessicated, but others secrete a thick-walled cyst inside of the cuticle.

Tardigrades are sometimes classified with the arthropods, but they have a number of characteristics that make their recognition as a separate phylum preferable. Among their outstanding peculiarities are:

1. a minute, bilaterally symmetrical body with four body somites, each with a pair of stumpy appendages ending in secreted claws;

2. a cuticular exoskeleton, sometimes divided into segmentally arranged plates, that is molted during growth;

3. no circulatory or respiratory system

4. a large, dorsal brain, circumenteric connectives, and subpharyngeal ganglion in the head and paired nerve trunks containing metameric ganglia in the body;

5. sexes separate, but with females predominating; some species without males;

6. development direct, the embryo forming five coelomic spaces which later deteriorate, the posterior coelomic compartment persisting as the lumen of gonad and gonoduct;

7. growth of post-embryonic stages without cell divisions, and possible cell constancy;

8. the adult body cavity derived from the blastocoel, and therefore a pseudocoel.

Tardigrades have an odd combination of traits, shared by such diverse groups as deuterostomes, pseudocoelomates, and coelomate protostomes. Cell constancy and a pseudocoelom derived from the blastocoel, as well as anabiosis, gives tardigrades some similarities to the pseudocoelomates. The mesoderm arises from outpocketings of the gut, as in enterocoels, but the coelomic compartments are formed as in protostomes. The appendages are under the body, as in arthropods, but lack the jointed form characteristic of arthropods. The habit of molting is shared with arthropods, but the exoskeleton is not chitinous. With this unusual combination of traits, tardigrades are worthy of considerably more attention than they have attracted.

Tardigrades are minute animals, ranging from about 50 μ to a millimeter in length. Sensory cirri occur at the sides of the head of mesotardigrades and heterotardigrades, but are lacking in eutardigrades. A pair of red or black cup-shaped ocelli are usually imbedded in the lateral lobes of the brain. The edge of the mouth is strengthened by one or more rings of thickened cuticle, and the dorsal cuticle is folded to form rings, typically two to a somite. Scuteschniscids, however, have dorsal, metameric plates of thickened cuticle (Fig. 15.3E). The short legs sometimes have single or two double claws formed anew at each molt.

Tardigrades take no solid food. They pierce plant cells and suck in the protoplasm, using a complex feeding apparatus with sharp stylets. The mouth opens into a short buccal cavity, stiffened by cuticular rings. This is followed by a long, cuticularized buccal tube, sometimes called the tubular pharynx. A pair of sharp stylets lie beside the buccal tube. At the junction of the buccal cavity and buccal tube, two slots, the stylet sheaths, introduce the stylets to the buccal cavity. Muscles protrude the stylets for feeding and retract them after use (Fig. 15.3B). The buccal tube opens into a heavily muscled sucking pharynx. In the pharynx wall are six cuticular pieces, the macroplacoids, to which muscles attach. Histologically, the tardigrade pharynx resembles the pharynx of a nematode, for it has a triangular lumen and radial muscles. Food passes from the pharynx to the midgut, which is divided into an esophagus and a stomach. The short hindgut opens through a ventral anus, located between the third and fourth pairs of legs. Little is known of digestive physiology, and the precise functions of the glands associated with the digestive tract have not been determined. Unicellular glands are found around the mouth. A pair of stylet glands open into the buccal cavity. They secrete new stylets before a molt, but whether they have other functions is unknown. Some zoologists have believed they have an excretory function, and they are often termed salivary glands. A few tardigrades attack small animals with the stylets, and some may be true carnivores, but the great majority are herbivores.

Tardigrades have no respiratory organs, and are quite sensitive to low oxygen tensions. When deprived of oxygen, they enter into a state of asphyxy, becoming motionless and swollen. They can survive several days in this state, recuperating promptly when given oxygen. They must have a very limited ability to carry on anaerobic respiration or to dispose of the end products which are formed during anaerobic oxidation.

The methods used for excretion are not understood. Some of the wastes are deposited in the cuticle and shed at molting. Three glands attach to the gut at the union of midgut and hindgut. The Malpighian tubules of arthropods join the gut at this point, and the glands are often called Malpighian tubules, although they have not been shown to be excretory. The intestine itself may also participate in excretion and osmoregulation, as it does in many animals. There is evidently some mechanism for controlling the salt and water content of the body, for tardigrades tolerate different salinities remarkably well.

An extensive cavity occupies the space around the muscle fibers and between the internal organs and the epidermis. This cavity is, on the basis of its origin, a pseudocoel, but is sometimes termed the haemocoel. It contains a perivisceral fluid in which a large population of cells is suspended. The chemical nature of the perivisceral fluid is not known, and the functions of the cells have not been worked out. The cells may be centers for the storage and transport of food. Undoubtedly the perivisceral fluid serves for internal transport of substances, but the small size of tardigrades makes transport a relatively minor problem.

Tardigrades are clumsy animals. Even the aquatic tardigrades cannot swim, but creep awkwardly over plants or on the bottom, using the claws to cling to surfaces. The muscles are strands made up of only one or a few cells. Despite the simplicity of the muscular system, it shows some important progressive features that are especially characteristic of arthropods. The muscle fibers are attached to the exoskeleton. They have definite origins, insertions, and actions. The worm-like invertebrates generally depend on layers of muscles in the body wall, and even in the parapodia of the polychaetes there is no use of an exoskeleton in this manner. With the musculature of the body wall dispersed to form slips passing from one part of the exoskeleton to another, the body wall itself is greatly simplified. The tardigrade body is arched by the contraction of the longitudinal muscles. Five to six muscle fibers from the dorsal or ventral exoskeletal surfaces enter the legs from various angles, providing five or six directions of movement (Fig. 15.3C). Movements are clumsy because of the severe limitations imposed by the few muscle strands running into each leg, but the control of movement requires an independent stimulus for each muscle strand in each leg. The surprisingly complex nervous system is probably a response to the requirements imposed by the nature of the muscular system.

The nervous system is typical of the annelid-arthropod stem. The complex brain is dorsal, and is composed of three median lobes and a pair of large, lateral lobes. Connectives attach the brain to the double ventral nerve cord, along which median segmental ganglia occur.

Animals encased in a strong, cuticular exoskeleton find it difficult to grow. As soft tissues increase they must crowd into the space provided by the unyielding exoskeletal casing. The solution to the problem has been found independently in animals belonging to several phyla. The cuticular covering is periodically shed, and a new, larger covering is secreted. This process is known as molting. The actual shedding of the cuticle is the molt, or ecdysis, and the period between molts is an instar. A complex physiological system for the control of molting has developed in arthropods, but little is known of the molting physiology of the tardigrades. They prepare for a molt by shedding the hard parts of the buccal apparatus and growing new ones, and by secreting new claws for the legs. When ready to molt, the soft tissues draw away from the old cuticle, which then splits at the anterior end. The animal squirms out of its old exoskeleton and develops a new one very quickly. Most of the tardigrades molt from four to six times, becoming sexually mature after the second or third molt. Molting is also evoked by unfavorable conditions, and in some of the aquatic species is associated with breeding.

A simple testis or ovary lies in the midline above the intestine (Fig. 15.3A). In males a pair of sperm ducts passes around the rectum and opens through a median gonopore on the ventral surface, just in front of the anus. The single oviduct of eutardigrades passes to a similarly placed female gonopore, but in the heterotardi-grades the oviduct opens into the rectum. In these tardigrades, a diverticulum of the rectum serves as a seminal receptacle.

As a rule, the females of aquatic species molt just before depositing eggs. The males inject sperm through the anus or gonopore of the old cuticle before the female emerges, and the eggs are fertilized in the space between the old cuticle and the body surface of the female. When the female leaves the shed cuticle, it serves as an egg case, within which development occurs.

Semi-aquatic species must be ready to become anabiotic at any time, and do not usually combine breeding and molting. The males inject sperm into the anus or the female gonopore and the eggs are fertilized internally. Some species produce a single egg and others as many as thirty, but most species produce from two to six. Eggs not retained in the old cuticle are usually stuck to objects by adhesive secretions.

Males are relatively scarce, and it is not improbable that many of the ova develop parthenogenetically. Some species produce two kinds of ova, one with thin shells and one with thick shells. These are rather like the summer and winter eggs of rotifers, and also resemble rotifer eggs in the more rapid development of thin-shelled ones. The factors which determine whether thin- or thick-shelled eggs are produced, and the role of the two kinds of eggs in the life cycle as a whole, are not presently clear.

Phylum Onychophora

About 70 species of onychophorans are alive today. They are an ancient group, as a few fortunate finds of Cambrian fossil species indicate. The fossil onychophorans were marine, but surprisingly like the modern species nevertheless. They probably adapted to life along the shorelines and spread to humid land environments.

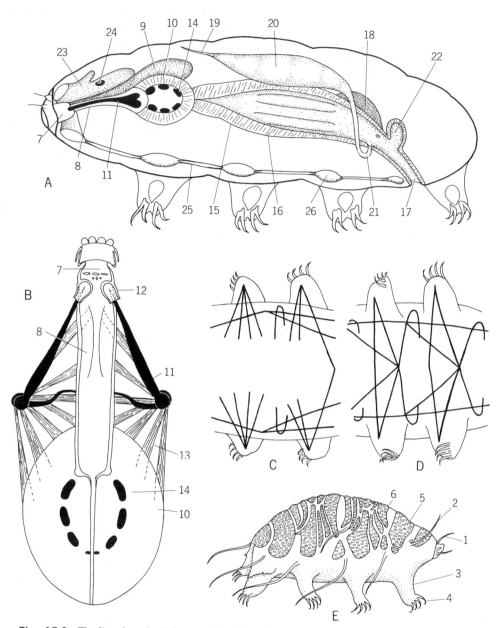

Fig. 15.3. Tardigrades. **A.** Scheme of tardigrade organization. **B.** Scheme of the buccal apparatus of a tardigrade, with the stylets withdrawn. **C** and **D.** Dorsal and ventral views of the musculature of the middle somites of a tradigrade. The anterior end is to the left. The longitudinal muscle strands arch the body, and the strands that extend at various angles into the leg give control over the direction of the leg movements. **E.** a tardigrade with metameric dorsal plates, *Echiniscus scrofa.* (A, composite. B, C, D after Pennak. E, after Richter, from Kükenthal and Krumbach.) *External features:* **1,** cirrus; **2,** lateral filament; **3,** leg; **4,** claw; **5,** tergal plate; **6,** intertergal plate. *Digestive system:* **7,** buccal cavity; **8,** tubular pharynx;

They were probably widespread at one time, and are now hanging on in a few restricted localities. Their present distribution would support this view, for they occur sporadically and discontinuously in tropical to subtropical regions and in wet temperate regions of the southern hemisphere. Few animals are more interesting to zoologists, for they have a curious blend of annelid and arthropod characteristics. They have been called the missing link between the Annelida and Arthropoda, but while they hardly qualify for this, they certainly help us to understand the nature of the ancient annelid-arthropod stem creatures at an interesting time in their development.

The onychophoran head is composed of three somites. The first pair of appendages are the antennae (Fig. 15.4). They are mobile but not retractile, and each has an eye at its base. Small peribuccal lobes surround the mouth, hiding the three jaws. One jaw is middorsal and the other two are lateral. The lateral jaws are vestiges of a head appendage, arising from small papillae on the embryonic second head somite. The jaws, themselves, appear to be the modified claws of this appendage. Oral papillae flank the mouth. They are a poorly developed, specialized pair of appendages on the third head somite. The head structure is unlike that of any arthropod, but nevertheless has an arthropod character, for arthropod cephalization is achieved by the incorporation of somites with specialized appendages into the head.

The only real evidence of segmentation externally is provided by the paired appendages. The thin, flexible cuticle is not depressed to form external rings, like annelids, nor is it strong enough to form segmental plates, as in arthropods. The body surface is studded with minute, scaled tubercles, some of which are equipped with sensory bristles. There are from 14 to 43 pairs of stumpy legs, each ending in two claws and a ventral pad that serves as a wearing surface. At the base of each leg are small nephridiopores, and nearby are prominences with the pores for the crural glands at their apex. The anus is posterior and ventral, and the gonopore lies directly in front of it.

The Onychophora live in inconspicuous places, under leaves, beneath logs, or along the margins of bodies of water. They creep about, with the body undulating as they walk. The legs swing back and forth with each step, somewhat coordinated but without the regularity of such animals as millipedes or centipedes (Fig. 15.5B). Evidently their intersegmental reflexes are not so highly organized as in the polychaetes or the arthropods.

Digestive System. They feed on animal and plant material, with animal food probably predominating in most species. They capture food and defend themselves by ejecting a stream of non-toxic, sticky material from the oral papillae. They are probably the champion spitters of the animal kingdom, gram for gram, for they achieve distances of up to 0.5 m. Strong contractions of the body wall propel the slime, formed by a pair of large adhesive glands in the lateral haemocoel spaces (Fig. 15.6A). The soft prebuccal lobes are pressed against the food. The jaws tear at it while the pharynx sucks in particles and juices. The space between the prebuccal lobes and the jaws is the vestibule or prebuccal cavity, comparable to the preoral cavity of insects and other arthropods. The true mouth is bounded by the jaws. The dorsal jaw is moistened by secretions from a pair of salivary glands, derived from the nephridia of the third

9, salivary gland; 10, sucking pharynx; 11, stylet; 12, stylet sheath; 13, stylet muscles; 14, macroplacoid; 15, esophagus; 16, midgut; 17, rectum; 18, Malpighian tubule. *Reproductive system:* 19, suspensory ligament; 20, ovary; 21, oviduct; 22, seminal receptacle. *Nervous system:* 23, brain; 24, ocellus; 25, nerve cord; 26, segmental ganglion.

Fig. 15.4. The Head of an Onychophoran. Notice the antennae and the oral papillae. The body appendages are leglike, in this resembling the appendages of arthropods, but are not jointed. (Courtesy of Ward's Natural Science Establishment, Inc., Rochester, New York.)

654

cephalic somite. The chitin-lined foregut is divided into a dilated pharynx and a narrow esophagus. The somewhat dilated midgut fills much of the perivisceral cavity. The very short hindgut opens at the anus.

Respiration. Onychophorans are adapted to air-breathing, with a tracheal system resembling that of terrestrial arthropods. There is no reason to think that tracheate arthropods inherited their trachea system from onychophorans; the two systems are in all probability convergent. Nevertheless, the tracheal system is another of the traits that make onychophorans so arthropod-like and demonstrate that they arose from stocks with very similar potentialities.

Many small openings, known as spiracles, occur on the body surface. Each leads to a short tracheal pit, or atrium, which penetrates the epidermis and ends in the muscular layer (Fig. 15.6D). It is lined with a delicate cuticle, and from it a tuft of tracheal tubes arises. The tracheae generally do not branch, going directly to the organ they serve. In some species, spiral chitinous strands support the walls of the tracheae, as in insects.

The tracheae are adequate for respiratory exchange, but are father of one of the important physiological weaknesses of the Onychophora. Well-adapted tracheate arthropods can open and close the spiracles, and so minimize the water loss that accompanies respiratory exchange. Onychophora lack this capacity. Although their cuticle is more impermeable to water than the cuticle of earthworms, they lose twice as much water through the body surface, and 80 times as much as cockroaches. This weakness has been an important factor in restricting them to humid habitats. Even here, they are predominantly nocturnal, forced to assume water-conserving habits in lieu of water-conserving structural features.

Excretion. Each somite except the first two has a pair of nephridia, but the first pair has been converted into salivary glands. The coelom of Onychophora has been reduced, and, as in the leeches, each

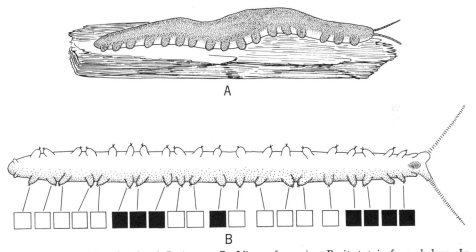

Fig. 15.5. A. Habit sketch of *Peripatus.* **B.** View of moving *Peripatopsis* from below. In somites corresponding to the blackened squares, the paired legs are moving together, while in the remaining segments, the paired legs are moving in opposite directions. Evidently the onychophorans lack the highly organized locomotor reflexes characteristic of arthropods, and of errant polychaetes. (**A**, after Sedgewick. **B**, after R. F. Lawrence.)

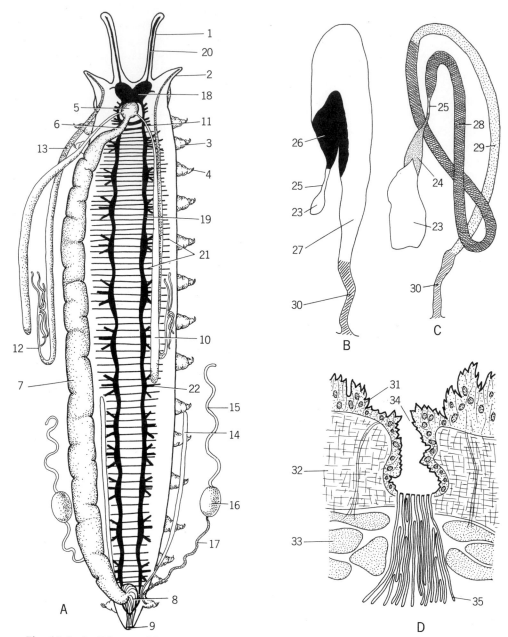

Fig. 15.6. A. Scheme of Internal Organization of an Onychophoran. B and C. Scheme of organization of the slime gland (B), compared with that of a nephridium from the anterior body somites. D. Section through a stigma, showing the origin of tracheal tubes. Note that tubules occur in a tuft, and do not branch. (A, composite. B and C, after Gabe. D, after Pflugpfelder.) *External features:* 1, tentacle; 2, oral papilla; 3, leg; 4, tarsal claws. *Digestive system:* 5, pharynx; 6, esophagus; 7, midgut; 8, rectum; 9, anus; 10, salivary gland; 11, salivary duct. *Glands:* 12, slime gland; 13, slime duct; 14, crural gland of last leg. *Reproductive*

nephridium opens into a sac-like coelomic vestige (Fig. 15.6C). A ciliated tubule opens into this space, and is followed by a coiled canal. The nephridium ends in an ectodermal bladder and nephridipore. Little is known of excretory physiology, but what is known indicates that they are predominantly uricotelic. If this proves to be generally true, the onychophorans have achieved an excretory pattern suitable for land organisms.

Body Wall and Coelom. The body wall is composed of layers of cuticle, epidermis, dermis, and circular, diagonal, and longitudinal muscle; it has no peritoneal lining, however. A conspicuous coelom is formed during embryonic development, for each mesodermal somite contains a coelomic compartment. These divide into dorsal and ventral parts (Fig. 15.7A-C). Then ventral compartments move out into the base of the appendage, giving rise to the coelomic sacs associated with the nephridia. The dorsal compartments move up to the middorsal line, and the anterior ones eventually disappear, leaving only a tubular heart behind them, while the posterior ones contribute to the formation of the gonad.

Meanwhile, the space between the body wall and the gut is partitioned to form the various haemocoel sinuses. A dorsal partition cuts off the pericardial sinus in which the heart lies. Below the dorsal diaphragm is the much larger perivisceral sinus in which the gut and other organs lie. A ventral diaphragm partially separates a ventral sinus from the perivisceral sinus. Muscles associated with the appendages cut off the lateral sinuses. None of the partitions are complete, and blood flows freely from one compartment of the haemocoel to another.

Circulation. The heart is a contractile tube, open to the pericardial cavity by segmentally arranged openings called ostia. Heart pulsations force the blood forward and down into the perivisceral sinus. Body movements as well as heart movements help to circulate the blood. The heart, ostia, and the system of haemocoelic sinuses closely resemble the similar parts of arthropods, although the system is less highly organized than in the majority of arthropod groups.

Neurosensory Apparatus. The principal sense organs are the antennae. They are richly supplied with tactile endings, and have a direct, pigment-cup ocellus at their bases. A chitinous lens occupies the opening of the cup. Water is exceedingly critical for onychophorans, and they have hygroreceptors on both antennae and the body surface, permitting orientation to water vapor.

The nervous system is well centralized. The dorsal brain is connected to the paired ventral nerve cords by circumenteric connectives. Transverse commissures connect the two nerve cords, but ganglionic enlargements of the nerve cords are inconspicuous. The jaws are innervated from the circumenteric connectives, and nerves to the digestive tube arise from the posterior end of the brain. Lateral nerves pass to the body wall and leg muscles.

Reproduction. Female onychophorans are somewhat larger than males, and in some species have more somites. The female reproductive system consists of an irregular mass of peritoneal tissue, the ovary, served by a pair of recurved oviducts, derived from the coelom and perhaps to be considered highly modified nephridia (Fig. 15.8A). Near each ovary

system: 15, testis; 16, seminal vesicle; 17, sperm duct. *Nervous system:* 18, brain; 19, ventral nerve cord; 20, antennal nerve; 21, commissural nerve; 22, peripheral nerves. *Nephridia:* 23, coelomic sac; 24, nephrostome; 25, neck gland; 26, mucous region; 27, serous region; 28, ciliated region; 29, striated region; 30, excretory duct. *Histology:* 31, cuticle and epidermis; 32, dermis; 33, muscle; 34, stigma; 35, tracheal tube.

the gonoduct is expanded as a seminal receptacle. Except for some oviparous Australian species, the eggs develop in the dilated, main part of the oviduct, the

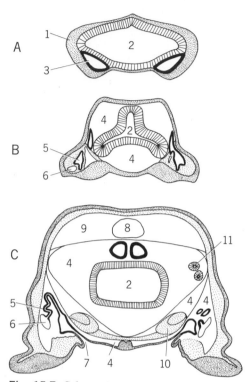

Fig. 15.7. Schematic transverse sections, showing the changes in the relationships of the coelom during the development of an onycophoran. At an early stage of development (A), the small paired coelomic compartments lie on each side of the primitive streak, between the ectoderm (stippled) and the endoderm (white). During later development the ectoderm and endoderm separate, leaving large haemocoelic spaces, and the coelom divides into dorsal and ventral parts (B). By the time of birth the haemocoel has become subdivided, and the ventral part of the coelom has developed into the nephridia (C). (After Sedgewick.) 1, ectoderm; 2, gut cavity; 3, mesoblast and coelom of somites; 4, haemocoel primordium; 5, nephridial part of coelom; 6, coelomic sac of nephridium; 7, nephridiopore; 8, cardiac region of haemocoel; 9, pericardial region of haemocoel; 10, nerve cord; 11, slime gland.

uterus. The right and left uteri join near the gonopore.

The male system is no less complex (Fig. 15.8B) and has a similar origin. The generally tubular testes open into a seminal vesicle, the first, dilated part of the sperm ducts. The right and left sperm ducts unite to form a common sperm duct, which may contain a compartment where spermatophores are formed. Apparently the spermatophores may be inserted in the gonopore or on the body surface, depending on the species, but mating is not a common occurrence and has not been observed directly. The sperm make their way to the seminal receptacle for storage.

Embryonic development follows the arthropod pattern. The rather large ova cleave superficially, and a slit-shaped blastopore develops, below which the endoderm cells lie (Fig. 15.8C,D). Mesodermal bands develop on each side of the blastopore, forming a prominence, the primitive streak, from which the mesodermal somites develop. The two most anterior somites unite in front of the mouth. The blastopore elongates and the anterior part forms the mouth while the posterior part forms the anus. Ectodermal cells turn in at the mouth and anus to form the stomodaeum and proctodaeum. The chitinous pieces of the foregut and the chitinous lining of the foregut and hindgut thus arise from ectoderm, as is the general rule in invertebrates.

Phylum Pentastomida

The pentastomids are a group of about 60 species of parasites of uncertain affinities. They are evidently closely related to the arthropods, and are sometimes classified with the Acarina because the larva bears some resemblance to certain mite larvae. The larva is nearly as much like a tardigrade, however, and some prefer to consider the pentastomids as very

early derivatives of the arthropod ancestral stocks. As they are parasites of vertebrates, it is probable that their simplicity
is secondary and that they are of relatively

recent origin. They are so simplified, however, that to include them with the arthropods tends to destroy the homogeneity of
the phylum and to make it very difficult

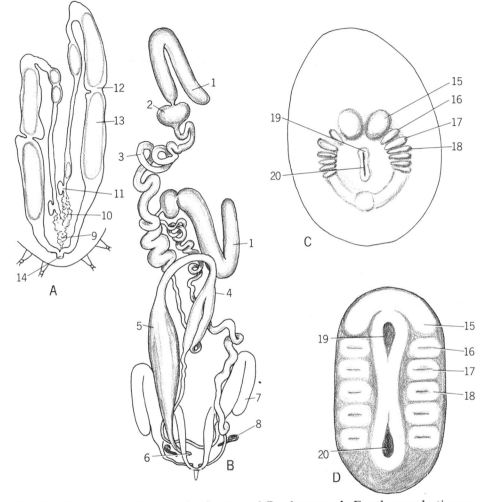

Fig. 15.8. Onycophoran Reproductive System and Development. A. Female reproductive system of *Eoperipatus*. B. Male reproductive system of *Peripatoides*. C. Young embryo of *Peripatopsis*. The blastopore is elongating at this time, and somites are developing from the
mesodermal bands on each side. The large yolk mass is below. D. Somewhat later stage of
Peripatopsis, showing only the germinal region. The blastopore is further elongated, and mouth
and anus are distinct. (A, after Gravier and Fage. B and C, after Bouvier. D, after Sedgewick, from Zacher, in Kükenthal and Krumbach.) *Male reproductive system:* 1, testis;
2, seminal vesicle; 3, sperm ductule; 4, common sperm duct; 5, sac for spermatophore
formation; 6, gonopore; 7, anal gland; 8, crural gland. *Female reproductive system:* 9, ovary;
10, egg receptacle; 11, seminal receptacle; 12, uterus; 13, embryo; 14, gonopore. *Embryo:*
15, primordium of antenna; 16, mandible; 17, oral papilla; 18, first leg; 19, mouth; 20, anus.

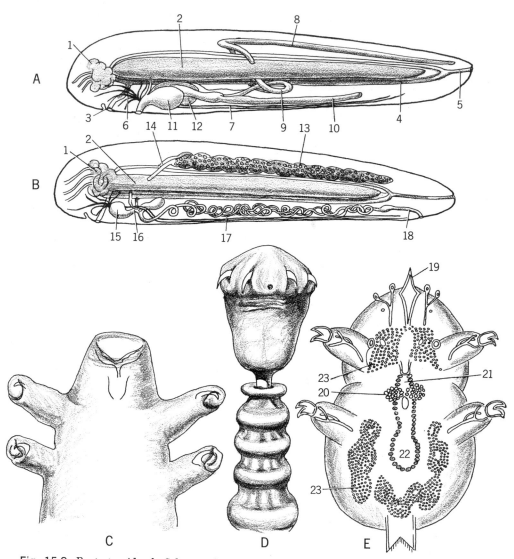

Fig. 15.9. Pentastomids. A. Scheme of organization of female *Porocephalus*. B. Male *Poro-cephalus*. C. Anterior end of *Cephalobaena*, showing the hooked leg and proboscis. D. Anterior end of *Armillifer*, which has lost all traces of legs except for the hooks. E. Larva of *Porocephalus*. (A and B, after Spencer. E, after Stiles, from Shipley. C, after Heymons, in Kükenthal and Krumbach.) *Glands:* 1, cephalic gland; 2, hook gland. *Digestive tract:* 3, foregut; 4, midgut; 5, hindgut. *Nervous system:* 6, circumenteric nerve ring; 7, nerve cord. *Male reproductive system:* 8, testis; 9, seminal vesicle; 10, ejaculatory duct; 11, cirrus sac; 12, sac for the dilator rod. *Female reproductive system:* 13, ovary; 14, oviduct; 15, seminal receptacle; 16, accessory gland; 17, uterus; 18, vagina. *Larva:* 19, penetration organ; 20, ventral ganglion; 21, mouth; 22, gut; 23, gland cells.

to characterize. It seems best, therefore, to treat them as a separate phylum of relatively recent origin, perhaps derived from an early acarine stem, although the evidence for the latter is relatively superficial. They have become so modified for parasitism that it is difficult to do more than guess at the nature of the free-living ancestral stem forms from which they arose.

Pentastomids live as respiratory parasites of amniotes, and especially of tropical reptiles. They also occur in birds and mammals, and extend into Europe, but have not been reported from North America.

The worm-like body varies from about 2 to 15 cm. in length. Two pairs of hooked appendages, or the hooks only, are found at the anterior end (Fig. 15.9C,D). The mouth usually lies on a fifth prominence; the name pentastomid is derived from the five anterior prominences. The claws are used to attach to the nasal passages or lungs of the host.

The anterior end of the worm is the cephalothorax or prosoma, and the ringed, posterior part is the abdomen or opisthosoma. The hooks wound the soft tissues of the respiratory tract, and blood is sucked into the digestive tract. The hooks are secreted by hook glands. Large frontal glands, which may secrete an anticoagulant, join the hook glands (Fig. 15.10A,B). Blood from the sucking pharynx moves into the large midgut. A short hindgut opens through a terminal anus.

There are no circulatory, respiratory, or excretory organs. The nervous system is simplified, but of the general type seen in the annelid-arthropod stem. A large, ventral ganglion is composed of three segmental ganglia. A circumenteric ring attaches to the ventral ganglion. It is a simple ring, without a dorsal ganglion. Nerves pass to the legs or hook musculature, and to the body wall of the cephalothorax. A long pair of nerves passes back to the abdomen on the ventral side.

As is typical of parasites, the reproductive organs are large and relatively complex (Fig. 15.9A,B). The reproductive potential is enormous. A single female *Waddycephalus* may contain a half a million fertilized ova in its uterus. The males are smaller than the females, and more restless, moving about in the host in search of a mate. The eggs are fertilized internally, and ova are stockpiled in the uterus for some time, probably to mature. They emerge with the secretions of the respiratory tract.

When ova are eaten by an appropriate intermediate host they hatch and release a migatory larva that pierces the stomach wall and encysts in the host tissues. Some of the larvae prefer vital organs and cause illness or death of heavily infected hosts. The larva is a curious little creature, with two pairs of legs and a superficial resemblance to a four-legged tardigrade or mite larva (Fig. 15.9E). When the intermediate host is eaten by a suitable final host, the larvae mature. They migrate to the respiratory tract by way of the esophagus and trachea if they live in the lung, or by way of the esophagus and pharynx if they live in the nasal passages. After several months they are mature and begin to release ova. The details of the life cycles are not very well known, and intermediate hosts are, for the most part, unidentified. All of the life cycles so far worked out involve an intermediate host. It appears that the intermediate hosts are usually vertebrates that occur in the food chain of the final hosts.

References

Andrews, A. 1933. *Peripatus* in Jamaica. *Quart. Rev. Biol.* 8: 155.

Arvy, L., and M. Gabe. 1952. Particularities histochimiques du tube digestif de *Phascolion strombi*. *Bull Lab. Mar. Din.* fasc. 36.

Baldwin, E., and W. Yudkin. 1950. The annelid phosphagen, with a note on the phosphagen in Echinodermata and Protochordata. *Proc. Roy. Soc. London* 135: 614.

Bues, C. T. 1923. The geographic distribution of the Onychophora. *Amer. Nat.* 57: 210.

Heinis, F. 1910. Systematik und Biologie der Moosbewohnen den Rhizopoden, Rotatorien und Tardigraden. *Arch. f. Hydrobiol.* 5: 89. (E)

Manton, S. M. 1937. The feeding, digestion, excretion and food storage of *Peripatopsis*. Phil. *Trans.* 227: 411.

————. 1950. The locomotion of *Peripatus*. *Jour. Linn. Soc. Zool.* 41: 529.

Marcus, E. 1928. Zur vergleichenden Anatomie und Histologie der Tardigraden. *Zool. Jahrb. Abt. Allg. Zool.* 45: 99.

————. 1929. Zur Embryologie der Tardigraden. *Zool. Jahrb. Abt. Anat.* 50: 333.

Morrison, P. R. 1946. Water loss and oxygen consumption by *Peripatus*. *Biol. Bull.* 91: 181. (G)

Robertson, J. 1953. Further studies on ionic regulation in marine invertebrates. *Jour. Exp. Biol.* 30: 277.

Sedgewick, A. 1888. A monograph on the genus *Peripatus*. *Quart. Jour. Micr. Soc.* 28: 431.

Thulin, G. 1928. Über die Phylogenie und das system der Tardigraden. *Hereditas.* 11: 207.

Uexküll, J. v. 1903. Die biologische Bauplan von *Sipunculus*. *Ztschr. Biol.* 44.

Zuckerkandl, E. 1950. Coelomic pressures in *Sipunculus nudus*. *Biol. Bull.* 98: 161.

16
Some General Arthropod Characteristics

No other phylum of animals rivals the arthropods insofar as successful living is concerned. Much of their success can be traced to a remarkable flexibility. Successive waves of adaptive radiation have established the primary groups and repeatedly differentiated the secondary groups. Even some of the smaller groups of arthropods have become adapted to remarkably diversified habitats, evolving patterns of living that have very little in common. Parasitic habits have appeared in group after group, and, more remarkably, a number of the aquatic groups have invaded land independently with varying degrees of success, while a number of the terrestrial groups have successfully adapted to living in the water for all or a part of their lives. As a result of this remarkably adaptive plasticity the arthropods have spread to all parts of the earth's land or water formations where temperatures rise above freezing for a long enough time to permit breeding. Three principal divisions of arthropods became established, the Trilobita, the Chelicerata, and the Mandibulata. Trilobites are now extinct, but were extremely successful inhabitants of the ancient seas. Today, the chelicerates and mandibulates make up somewhere between a half and three-fourths of the living animal species.

The outstanding arthropod characteristics are the following:

1. They are bilaterally symmetrical, segmented protostomes, primitively equipped with a pair of appendages attached to each body segment. The appendages are often reduced or lost in some of the body segments, however.

2. Although all of the post-oral appendages were similar in primitive forms, modern arthropods have appendages that have been specialized for specific functions. Much of arthropod evolution is reflected in the specialization of the appendages, and the nature of the appendages is an important factor in classification.

3. The surface of the body and the appendages is covered by a continuous cuticle of complex structure. In most cases the cuticle forms a series of heavy, skeletal plates or rings, connected by thinner, flexible articular membranes, permitting freedom of movement.

4. The cuticle is turned in at the stomodaeum and proctodaeum to form chitin-

663

ous linings of the foregut and hindgut. These linings are molted with the surface cuticle during growth.

5. Paired, segmental, coelomic compartments appear during development, but are greatly reduced with the development of the haemocoel.

6. A contractile heart, derived from a dorsal blood vessel, lies in a dorsal pericardial sinus. Blood enters the heart through pairs of apertures known as ostia.

7. The metameric nephridial system typical of annelids has disappeared with the coelom, although some arthropods have retained some modified nephridia as excretory organs, and the gonoducts may be considered as highly modified nephridia.

8. The nervous system is built on the annelid plan, with a double nerve trunk and primitively with segmental ganglia. The brain, however, is more highly differentiated.

9. Cilia are completely missing and all movements of the organism or its body parts are dependent upon muscle. With the appearance of an exoskeleton to which muscles can be attached, the muscular system becomes very complex.

10. The eggs are richly supplied with yolk, and few show traces of spiral cleavage or a mesoderm stem cell. However, mesodermal bands resembling those formed in a trochophore larva, in which coelomic compartments appear, are formed during early development. The body forms from a primitive streak that serves as the growth center of the embryo.

A list of attributes of this kind does little to reveal the reasons for the success of arthropods, but no doubt the important factors are included in it. Certainly no single factor can be taken as the primary reason for the adaptability of arthropods. The level of organization, together with the combination of traits they possessed, provided an organic system capable of myriads of minor changes that could slightly change the capacities of the organisms without preventing survival.

The origins of this extremely important group of animals are problematic, for a number of ideas have been expressed and no one of them is at this time so clearly preferable that it can be given unqualified support. One of the possibilities is outlined below. After considering the characteristics of the various arthropod groups, it will be more profitable to compare the different ideas about arthropod evolution. References to several articles that discuss the origin of arthropods are included in the bibliography at the end of the chapter.

The first protostomes were acoelomate flatworms. As the flatworm stocks established themselves and capitalized on their bilateral symmetry, becoming more freely motile, a tendency toward cephalization appeared. This tendency has had a profound effect upon the evolutionary development of protostomes, generally, for nearly all of them are strongly cephalized. The deuterostomes, on the other hand, were rather poorly cephalized, living predominantly as sessile or sedentary animals, until the establishment of a bilaterally symmetrical, active stock leading toward the vertebrates.

Still another important protostome characteristic appeared with the flatworms. A series of spiral cleavages that established quartets of micromeres with definite roles to play in the formation of the adult became established as a fundamental trait. The pattern of determinate, spiral cleavage left a strong imprint on most of the groups arising from the early flatworm stocks. Some modified it greatly, like the modern flatworms with ectolecithal ova, and some appear to have deserted it entirely. Nevertheless, spiral determinate cleavage appears as a primitive characteristic of most of the groups that have arisen from the main protostome line.

Some of the early stem forms on the main protostome line remained at the flatworm level of organization, differentiating into the various types of flatworms seen today. Others diverged, establishing other adaptive lines, progressive or retrogressive as the case may have been. In the foreseeable future we will probably not be able to do more than speculate on possibilities. Although some of the main lines of development appear to be fairly well established, the detailed determination of the characteristics and sources of the ancestral stocks is uncertain.

Some early flatworm stock, possibly before all of the traits associated with modern flatworms had appeared, followed an adaptive line in which two factors were particularly important in determining the directions of change. One was the formation of an anus and the conversion of the gastrovascular cavity into a one-way street. Full realization of the advantages of a tubular gut depends on freeing the gut wall for peristaltic movements, and on the development of a system for internal transport to replace the distributing diverticula of the gastrovascular cavity. In one group of creatures, the gut wall was freed, and internal transport was solved, by the reduction of the parenchymal tissue that connected the gut and body wall in flatworms, resulting in a pseudocoel filled with perivisceral fluid. The organisms which followed this line also reduced or lost their body ciliation in favor of the elaboration of a protective, cuticular covering. Several ancestral stocks, derived from flatworms, may have followed this general line of adaptation, but if so it would be most difficult to demonstrate it. The modern pseudocoelomates belonging to the superphylum Aschelminthes are the terminal twigs of this adaptive line or lines, and are today a loosely coherent group of organisms in which it is difficult or impossible to distinguish between similarities resulting from convergent evolution and those derived from common ancestral stocks. Most of them have remained minute, and none of the moderately large

forms with reasonably strong musculature evolved patterns of living in which active, progressive movements were important. There was no pressure favoring the further development of cephalization, and in many instances cephalization rather dwindled than increased.

Out of some other, and probably more advanced, flatworm stock, intestinal motility was achieved by the development of a coelom, a peritoneal cavity lined with mesodermal tissue. No one can be sure how the coelom arose. It may have come from the lumen of the gonads, as some have thought, or have been a specialization in the development of the parenchyma, leaving a space useful for internal transport. It may have been spaces associated with the storage of waste products. However the coelom may have arisen, its appearance led to the most important series of progressive changes among animal stocks, from which all of the remaining animal stocks emerged.

It appears that the coelomate protostomes diverged along two major lines, one leading toward sedentary habits and one retaining an actively motile life. The origin of the more sedentary line is a real mystery, for they are today so modified that even the embryological evidence is somewhat dubious. Their sedentary habits center about the development of a ciliary-mucous feeding organ, the lophophore. While a few were burrowing forms, the majority have developed a protective case and sessile habits. The phoronids appear to show some vestiges of a trochophore stage in their life cycle, but the lophophorates as a whole have lost the spiral, determinate cleavage and typical cell-lineage pattern of the main protostome stem. Coelom formation is also a curiously varied process among the various lophophorate groups. In some, a coelom appears as a space in the mesoderm, following the schizocoelous pattern, but in others, the coelom arises as outpocketings of the archenteron in the enterocoelous fashion. It is possible that the lophophorates mark the point at which the main line of the protostomes and deuterostomes separated. In any event, the sedentary habits of the lophophorates were associated with a retreat from cephalization and a reduction of the muscular system to gear suitable for operating the lophophore and taking full advantage of the protective casing for the body.

The active stem of protostomes have followed two main lines of adaptation. In one, culminating in the molluscs, segmentation did not appear or was suppressed, while along the other, segmentation became an essential and important feature of the body organization, and many of the adaptive changes involved specialization of the segments of the organism. Were the first molluscans segmented? Did the coelom and segmentation develop at about the same time, or were the two events independent? A long period of dispute and speculation has never produced a scheme that could satisfy everyone. Proponents of the gonocoel theory of coelomic origin are especially inclined to link the appearance of the coelom and metamerism. This theory was once the predominant theory, but has recently come in for some severe criticism. Its strong points are the undeniable relationship of reproductive cells and the peritoneum in many of the phyla, and its convenient explanation of the coelomoduct system of annelids. However, the lophophorates show no evidence of metamerism, although some of them appear to use a protostome-like technique to grow a coelom during development, and the molluscs have very few traits which support the idea that they were once segmented. Some of the parts of chitons are metamerically arranged, particularly the musculature, and especially in relation to the linear series of valves. The recently found *Neopilina* is the strongest evidence of metamerism among molluscs, and in this form the coelom as well as the body-wall musculature is involved in the metamerism. The many primitive features of *Neopilina* help to make it persuasive to many as reflecting the basic organization of a segmented molluscan ancestor. Against this point of view, however, is the view that if one accepts *Neopilina* as primitively segmented, one must also assume that all of the thousands of molluscan species have suppressed all evidences of metamerism during embryonic development, even when, as in the chitons, some of the body-wall musculature is to assume a metameric character in adults. This is a rather large pill to swallow, and it may turn out that *Neopilina* has a metamerism that has developed independently within the molluscan phylum, perhaps following along lines of body-wall pseudo-segmentation related to polyplacophoran ancestral stocks. This idea would be more persuasive if *Neopilina* had a segmented shell. Until the embryonic origin of *Neopilina*'s metamerism has been described we must withhold judgment, with the uncomfortable feeling that however it comes out something rather improbable must be incorporated into our hypotheses. This is unsettling, for one thing stands out in the speculations about evolutionary adaptation. As a general rule, the main lines of evolutionary change are very logical and comprehensible, following trends that are suitable for creatures insofar as their organizational level and habits are concerned. Evolutionary speculations based on peculiar species of a phylum have tended to become less acceptable as time passes, and for the purposes of schematic representation, the view has been used that molluscs as a group arose before the segmental pattern of the other protostomes appeared (Fig. 16.1).

If segmentation and the origin of the coelom were independent events, it is probable that the minor groups of coelomate protostomes diverged from the main stem at different points. The sipunculids show no evidences of metamerism in embryonic development or in adult structure, and may be worm-like animals that, like molluscs, arose from the protostome stem before metamerism appeared, but enough later to account for the appearance of an annelid cross during development. Alternatively, they may have suppressed metamerism wholly, as the molluscs may have done, in which case the point of divergence may have been later. The echiuroids have suppressed metamerism in the adult but preserve traces of metamerism in the metamorphosing larva. They certainly represent another worm-like group, presumably of more recent origin than the sipunculids.

This leaves the main annelid-arthropod stem, the most important of the invertebrate stems in numbers of species and ecological influence. There is every reason to believe that the early stem forms were essentially like polychaetes. The errant forms have a degree of cephalization suitable for organisms at their level of organization, and the relatively simple form and lack of regional specialization of the appendages are also suitable for primitive organisms. There is no reason to suppose that the first polychaetes were like modern species, but certainly they must have exhibited some of the primitive traits now seen in one or another group of errant polychaetes in various body systems.

From the ancestral polychaetes, the modern polychaetes, both errant and sedentary, have evolved. From some burrowing polychaete stock the oligochaetes stemmed, and these themselves, after consolidating their type of reproductive system and losing their cephalic sense organs, gave rise to the leeches. The annelids are a large and successful phylum, but far less so than either the molluscs or the arthropods. The difference in the successfulness of the two metameric lines requires some explanation. It rests, probably, on new potentialities that appeared among arthropods rather than on a lack of viability of the annelid organization.

There is little doubt that the first protoarthropod stem was a derivative of the main protostome line when the protostomes had characteristics that were poly-chaete-like. Some would consider the protoarthropods as derivatives of the polychaetes directly, while others prefer to derive them from the stem from which polychaetes also arose. This is more a question of semantics than a matter of biological importance, for there is every reason to suppose that the first protoarthropods were derived from a stem with the brain in a prostomium, with a pair of sensory appendages associated with the prostomium, and with a brain having an essentially polychaete structure. It is probable that the most important feature of these first arthropods was a heavy rather than a thin cuticle, for this would explain many of the progressive features of the arthropods as a whole. The cuticle was not a continuous, box-like covering, or else the arthropods might have had the same kind of success story as molluscs. It was probably thickened in some regions and flexible in others, providing flexibility as well as protection and support. The segmented exoskeleton must have been metameric in its organization, employing the same system used in joints between somites to provide flexibility in the appendages. The jointed exoskeleton was a far more important progressive step than appears at the surface. Such an exoskeleton provides suitable sites for the origin and insertion of specialized muscles. An explosive adaptive trend apparently resulted. The muscle layers characteristic of the worm-like animals dispersed, to be replaced by specific muscle slips, crossing specific joints and providing specific movements. The specificity of muscle action is meaningless unless there is a delicacy of nervous control consonant with the new potentialities for movement. The jointed exoskeleton thus served as a tremendous stimulus to adaptive forces improving and specializing the muscular and nervous systems, with a corresponding favorable effect on the sensory apparatus. To a very considerable extent, molluscs were forced to choose a satisfactory compromise between motility and protection. The arthropods

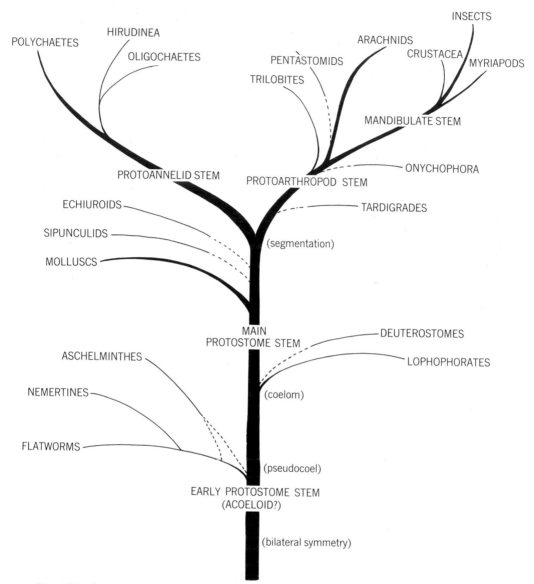

Fig. 16.1. One view of the phylogeny of the protostome stem. Assuming that the acoel type of organization is primitive in the protostomes, the early protostome stem established the flatworm stock, from which nemertines eventually differentiated. The relationships of the aschelminths remain uncertain. In any case, whether in a protostome stem that was more advanced than flatworms or in the flatworm stem, a pseudocoel appeared, which with other aschelminth traits served to distinguish them from other protostomes. Along the main line of protostome descent the appearance of a coelom followed. The lophophorates separated as a special line with the development of the lophophore, and the main protostome stem gave rise to the three great groups of higher invertebrates. It seems probable that molluscs were primitively unsegmented, despite the recently found monoplacophoran *Neopilina*, and that the segmentation characteristic of the annelid-arthropod stem appeared after molluscs had diverged from the

did not sacrifice mobility for defense. The protective layer had become an essential part of the locomotor system, and, if anything, they are more mobile than other organisms in their size range. The combination appears to have been irresistible, for from Cambrian times on a rich fossil fauna records the continual success of one or another group of arthropods.

The first arthropods were marine, and modern arthropods remain extremely important members of marine communities. The heavy cuticle, however, proved suitable for preventing excessive evaporation as well as mechanical protection, and arthropods have continually invaded land habitats. In many cases, this invasion was fantastically successful, and arthropods have become the most influential of terrestrial invertebrates. In many of the regions in which modern agricultural methods are used, the ecologically dominant animals, exclusive of man, are arthropods. The lack of serious competition in their size range gave the arthropods a relatively free hand. The colonization of land sparked a series of adaptive radiations leading to different methods of coping with the problems of land life.

One of the important problems to be solved is whether there were one or several protoarthropod lines. Considerable disagreement has developed on this point, for reasons that will become more clear as the various arthropod groups are studied. One popular view sees the protoarthropod

stem as diverging into three main lines, here recognized as subphyla. Two of these lines were extensively subdivided early, perhaps during the Cambrian. All of the major groups, fossil and modern, had been established by the middle of the Paleozoic.

The first and most primitive line to appear was the Trilobita. The trilobites were well differentiated at the beginning of the Cambrian and so must have had an extensive pre-Cambrian history. On this point there is general agreement. Opinions differ about the relationship of the other two lines to the trilobites, however. Störmer (1949) suggested that the arachnid stem arose directly from the trilobites, while others have preferred to derive the arachnids from the same protoarthropod stem that gave rise to the trilobites. According to this view, the protoarthropods, after giving rise to trilobites, differentiated along two lines, one leading to the modern chelicerates, and the other to the modern mandibulates (Fig. 16.1).

The cuticle, claws, haemocoel, and trachea of the Onychophora, to mention only a few traits, are far more arthropod-like than annelid-like. However, the worm-like body and the exoskeleton, which is not heavy enough to require joints in the appendages, are more annelid-like. The first Onychophora appear to have been marine animals, and it is probable that they arose from some polychaete stock, later developing the trachea. The outstanding point in

main line. The time of origin of the echiurids and sipunculids is uncertain although both have traits indicating a closer relationship to annelids than to molluscs. The protoannelid stem gave rise to the polychaetes, from which the oligochaete stem arose. Leeches arose from the oligochaetes. The protoarthropod stem gave off trilobites very early. On this point there is general agreement. The relationship of tardigrades and onychophora to the protoarthropod stem is more uncertain. The onychophora presumably diverged while the protoarthropods were essentially wormlike, although the jaw structure suggests mandibulate relationships, and adaptive radiation of the appendages of onychophorans is somewhat more advanced than in trilobites. In any case and with uncertain relationships to the trilobites, the main arthropod line diverged into an arachnid stem without mandibles, and a mandibulate stem, from which the Crustacea, insects, and myriapods differentiated. An alternative scheme would see the Crustacea as much older than would be suggested by this arrangement, and have the mandibulates diphyletic. Critical evidence in support of the various views is not yet available.

their evolutionary line was the specialization of head appendages and incorporation of them into the mouth structure. While many polychaetes have specialized the cephalic appendages or some of the parapodial parts to aid in feeding, the onychophoran head appendages are considerably more arthropod-like than anything found in annelids. As a matter of fact, they are in some ways more advanced than those of the trilobites, although in other ways more primitive.

The three arthropod stems have had different histories. Trilobites declined suddenly during the late Silurian and Devonian; by the Mesozoic they had disappeared. They may have succumbed to strong enemy pressure from the newly developed marine vertebrates and cephalopods. The chelicerate stem branched off along three main lines. The marine Merostomata enjoyed early success, but declined during the Ordovician and today are represented by a few species of horseshoe crabs. Another marine group, the Pycnogonida, or sea spiders, has left an inadequate record to permit our knowing much about its fossil history. About 400 species are known today. The third group, the Arachnida, includes terrestrial forms, and has been highly successful, differentiating into such groups as the spiders, mites, ticks, and scorpions. The mandibulate stem has followed two main lines, an aquatic line which has been very successful, the Crustacea, and a terrestrial line which has been even more successful, differentiating into the centipedes, millipedes, and insects.

Subphylum Trilobita

Whole trilobites are rarely found. Most of them have been preserved with the dorsal side up, probably because they were heavily armored above and tended to decompose when upside down. The trilobite exoskeleton was predominantly chitinous, but was strengthened in some regions by

calcium carbonate. Most of the trilobites were 5 to 7 cm. long, but extremes of about 1 and 67.5 cm. have been reported. Trilobites are so named because the body is divided into three divisions, an anterior prosoma (head, cephalon), a middle thorax (trunk), and a posterior pygidium (Fig. 16.2A). The head is covered by a single, roughly semicircular, dorsal shield. The thorax is segmented, with separate skeletal plates for the various somites. The pygidium is also segmented in the more primitive species, but in more advanced forms is covered by a single dorsal plate, formed by the union of the dorsal plates of the component somites.

The trilobite head has complex markings. A pair of dorsal furrows divides the head into the lateral cheeks or genae and a central, raised region, the glabella. Transverse furrows divide the glabella into three to five lobes. A facial sulcus crosses the cheeks, separating the medial fixed cheeks from the lateral free cheeks. The facial sulcus bounds the cranidium, made up of the glabella and fixed cheeks. A palpebral lobe lies near the eye at the margin of each free cheek. Most of the trilobites had a pair of large, compound eyes rather like the eyes of Crustacea. At the margin of the head shield, the thickened border is turned under to form the anterior and lateral doublures.

The appendages can be seen in ventral view (Fig. 16.2B). A pair of slender ringed antennae are preoral, and may be considered homologous to the antennae of insects and the antennules of Crustacea. The head also bears four pairs of legs, whose structure will be considered later. A median lobe, the labrum, or hypostome, lies over the mouth, and a smaller plate, the metasome, lies behind the mouth. The front part of the head, bearing the antennae, is the acron; the remainder of the head consists of four cephalic somites, bearing the four cephalic appendages. Störmer (1949) considers the acron an unsegmented piece, corresponding directly to the polychaete prostomium, while others have thought it includes a second, abortive segment. The two views lead to different ideas about the homologies of the head appendages of trilobites, chelicerates, and mandibulates. For a general understanding of the arthropods, however, exact homologies are relatively unimportant, for all arthropod groups amply illustrate the formation of a head by the union of primitive trunk segments and the preoral acron. Enough plasticity is characteristic of the appendages to make it quite conceivable that an appendage of any given form in one group is homologous to an appendage of any given form in another group. The detailed correspondances will continue to be of high interest among those who specialize in arthropods, of course, for they have much to do with views of the relationships of different groups.

The thorax is covered by a series of overlapping dorsal plates. Fossils are often curled up, suggesting that trilobites were quite flexible in life. Probably curling up the body protected the relatively soft under surface. Each dorsal plate is a single piece, but is divided into regions by furrows. The axial furrow defines a median axis, corresponding to the glabella of the head, and a pair of lateral pleura, corresponding to the genae of the head. Each pleuron is divided into anterior and posterior lobes, and is sometimes divided into inner and lateral parts by a pleural furrow. The pleura are folded under to form the lateral doublure, which extends to the bases of the legs.

The pygidium contains from two to 27 somites, united in most cases by a solid dorsal shield. Axial and pleural furrows may continue into the pygidium, defining regions corresponding to the axis and pleura, and lateral pleural regions. The last segment contains the anus and corresponds to the telson of Crustacea. The somites and appendages of the pygidium are usually somewhat reduced, but the basic form of the appendages remains unaltered.

A doublure like that seen in the head and thorax is present in the pygidium.

A great deal of discussion has centered on the trilobite legs, and considerable difference of opinion still exists. The legs are attached to the ventral surface below the axial furrow by a basal piece, to which a slender dorsal and heavier ventral branch are attached. The ringed dorsal branch bears filaments that were probably gills. The jointed ventral branch ends in several claws or hooks.

Even a superficial comparison of the legs of a trilobite, a terrestrial arthropod, and a crustacean raises problems (Fig. 16.2C-E). Terrestrial arthropods have uniramous legs, while Crustacea have biramous (Y-shaped) legs composed of a basal piece, the protopodite, and two branches, an outer exopodite and an inner endopodite. A dorsally placed epipodite, bearing gill filaments, may also be present, attached to the protopodite. The trilobite leg has been interpreted in two ways. If the gill-bearing arm is an exopodite, the remaining arm can be considered the endopodite. Störmer (1949), however, considers the gill-bearing branch an epipodite, which means that the main branch of the appendage can be homologized with a uniramous leg or a crustacean leg in which the exopodite is missing. In any case, the gill-bearing branch of the trilobite leg arises from the coxopodite, in this sense differing from the exopodite in crustaceans, which joins the basipodite segment of the protopodite.

The segments of the appendages have, unfortunately, been given two sets of names, one that is most commonly employed for the crustacean leg, and one that is used for the legs of spiders, insects, and other terrestrial arthropods. Each segment is a podite, and the terms used for Crustacea incorporate podite with the root which designates the specific segment. The podites can be homologized (Table 16.1), but the literature on arthropods employs both sets of terms.

Little is known of the internal anatomy

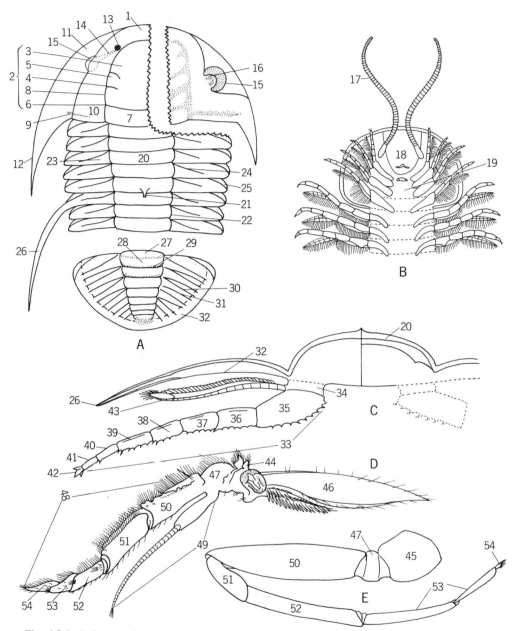

Fig. 16.2. Trilobites. A. Diagram showing the basic organization and terminology of trilobites. On the right half of the head, the typical proparian form is shown, with the facial suture cutting the lateral margin of the head and the fixed cheek carrying the genal spine. On the left half of the head, the typical opisthoparian form is shown, with the facial suture cutting the posterior margin, and the genal spine on the free cheek. B. Ventral surface of a trilobite, showing the resemblance of the head appendages, except for the antennae, to the trunk appendages. C. Schematic cross section of a trilobite, showing the relationship of body and appendage. D and E. Appendages of a crustacean (D) and a spider (E) for comparison with

Table 16.1. Podites of arthropod appendages

TERRESTRIAL MANDIBULATE	AQUATIC MANDIBULATE	CHELICERATE
(Centipede)	(Crustacean)	(Spider)
Coxa	Coxopodite	Coxa
First trochanter	Basipodite	Trochanter [1]
Second trochanter [2]	Ischiopodite	Femur
(prefemur)		. . . . . .
Femur	Meropodite	Patella
. . . . . .	. . . . . .	. . . . . .
Tibia	Carpopodite	Tibia
Tarsus [3]	Propodite	Tarsus [1]
Pretarsus [4]	Dactylopodite	Pretarsus

Although the terms used are simple enough, determination of homologies is not so easy. The position of the knee bend (shown by dotted lines) and the musculature suggests that the femur of chelicerates and terrestrial mandibulates is homologous to the meropodite of aquatic mandibulates. In this case, the patella, which lies between the double knee bend of chelicerates, is an extra piece, not found in mandibulates.

[1] Sometimes divided into two pieces.
[2] Missing in insects, as a rule.
[3] Commonly divided into two to many pieces.
[4] Missing in most insects.

of trilobites, but guesses based on similarities of their body regions to the regions of modern arthropods can lead to a reasonable, if hypothetical, reconstruction of their body plan. There is good evidence that the organs lay in the axis, while the pleura were little more than lateral hoods over the appendages. Evidences have been found of a dorsal circulatory system, resembling that of modern arthropods, but otherwise it has been necessary to hypothesize inner structure. It is generally assumed

the trilobite appendage. Crustacea are mandibulates, with biramous appendages, and spiders are chelicerates with uniramous appendages. The main branch of the leg is the telopodite. In crustaceans this is the inner endopodite, and a second branch, the exopodite, arises from the basal protopodite. The outer branch of the trilobite appendage fastens at a different point on the telepodite and is considered a pre-epipodite. It is general practice with Crustacea to combine the suffix podite to the term designating the various leg segments. The various segments of the telepodite are thought to be homologous, however, as indicated below. (A and C, after Whittington. B, after Beecher, from Woods.) *Features of the cephalon:* 1, preglabellar region; 2, glabella (axis of head); 3, frontal lobe; 4, lateral glabellar furrow; 5, lateral glabellar lobe; 6, occipital furrow; 7, occipital ring; 8, axial furrow; 9, facial suture; 10, fixed cheek; 11, free cheek; 12, genal spine; 13, anterior pit; 14, eye ridge; 15, eye lobe; 16, palpebral lobe; 17, antennule; 18, hypostome; 19, metastome. *Features of thorax:* 20, axis of thorax; 21, axial spine; 22, axial furrow; 23, pleural band of pleuron; 24, pleural furrow; 25, facet; 26, pleural spine. *Features of pygidium:* 27, articulating half-ring; 28, axial ring; 29, ring furrow; 30, pleural furrow; 31, interpleural groove; 32, doublure. *Appendages of trilobite, as named by Störmer:* 33, telopodite; 34, precoxa; 35, coxa; 36, trochanter; 37, prefemur; 38, femur; 39, patella; 40, tibia; 41, tarsus; 42, pretarsus; 43, pre-epipodite. *Crustacean and spider appendages* (showing homologous terminology; terms applied to legs of terrestrial arthropods are shown in parentheses): The crustacean limb base is the protopodite 44, consisting of 45, coxopodite (coxa), to which the 46, epipodite is attached, and a 47, basipodite (trochanter), to which the 48, endopodite and the 49, exopodite are attached. The endopodite is the telopodite, and is made up of 50, ischiopopodite (femur), 51, meropodite (patella), 52, carpopodite (tibia), 53, propodite (tarsus) and 54, dactylopodite (pretarsus).

to have been very much like that of modern arthropods.

Arthropod Origins

With this information about trilobites, it is easier to appreciate some of the problems surrounding the origin of arthropods. There can be little doubt that the trilobites are very primitive arthropods, with a close relationship to the polychaetes. Their lack of specialized head appendages, except for the antennae on the acron, is certainly a primitive characteristic. Yet the polychaetes have a biramous appendage, with a definite neuropodium and notopodium. If the trilobites have gills on an epipodite, it is not difficult to see how this might have originated from the dorsal cirrus of a notopodium, which so often forms the gills of polychaetes. If the rest of the notopodium were lost and the neuropodium were transformed into the main branch of the trilobite leg, an appendage of the trilobite type could be derived from a leg of the parapodium type. But if this is the case, and if the trilobites were the first arthropods, it is difficult to explain the biramous appendage of Crustacea. Certainly the principle that a part once lost is not regenerated during evolutionary change would suggest that the crustaceans could not have developed from trilobites. It would be more convenient if the trilobite leg were biramous, but Störmer (1949) makes a strong case for the epipodite nature of the gill-bearing branch of the trilobite leg. If the Crustacea could not have arisen from the trilobites, the only alternative is to suppose that they arose independently, from a different stem, and the arthropods, in this case, are at least a diphyletic group. To make matters more complex, the Onychophora have antennae corresponding to the antennules of Crustacea and the antennae of insects. The oral papillae on the next somite may be considered homologous to the crustacean second antennae and to the missing appendage in the insect head. In this case the onychophoran jaws occur in the same somite as the jaws of the insects and Crustacea. They have uniramous legs, also, and one cannot discount the possibility that the myriapods arose independently from a stock that also gave rise to the onychophorans. If the biramous legs of Crustacea indicate an independent origin, and the myriapods and eventually the insects arose from a stem related to the onychophorans, the Mandibulata would themselves be diphyletic. In short, there are many possibilities, and one must choose the point of view which seems most persuasive to him, not as a definitely proven thing, but as the best of several possibilities. Is it likely that three completely independent lines would have evolved legs with such detailed correspondences in their segments? Do the partly reduced oral papillae of the onychophorans partly bridge the gap between the segment bearing the second antennae of crustaceans and the segment in the insect head lacking an appendage? If so, how can one account for the biramous legs of Crustacea? Questions like these pile up rapidly, and any choice one may make carries with it some undesirable features.

The scheme shown in Fig. 16.1 rather begs some of the questions. One of the things that one sometimes forgets is that if in Cambrian times a zoologist were classifying animals, he would assemble them into phyla and classes very much as he would today. When we speak of, or visualize, an ancestral stem form, we tend to think of a species rather than an order or class of animals, but in the real world, no doubt, the groups which were so important as a source of progressive species were probably fairly large and fairly diversified. As time passes and these stocks become more diversified, it becomes necessary to consider them as belonging to two or more groups. This really implies that the two adaptive lines of development have brought not one but many species to the point where they are best placed in a new taxonomic group. From the standpoint that a single key species was ancestral to the arthropods, it is highly improbable that they are a monophyletic group. From the standpoint that there was at one time a protoarthropod stem from which all of the arthropods appeared, it is probable that arthropods are monophyletic. The main line of coelomate, segmented protostomes probably diverged first into a stem with more lateral parapodia, which then assumed the characteristics of a protoannelid line, and eventually developed into the modern polychaetes. The protoarthropod line probably had more ventral appendages and divided early into a line with softer cuticle and unsegmented legs, which then differentiated into the Onychophora, and into a stock with firm cuticle; from this stock the trilobites probably arose, and a third line which, like the Onychophora, were developing a consolidated head in which jaws were differentiated from the leg bases of a pair of head appendages, and in which the appendages immediately behind the jaws had a strong tendency to be specialized for feeding. From this last line, in due time, an aquatic line with biramous appendages and a terrestrial line with uniramous appendages eventually became distinct, becoming the modern crustaceans and myriapods. It was probably very early in the development of the trilobite line that species with reduced antennae appeared, in which chelicera tended to develop from the first pair of head appendages, and from which the modern chelicerates developed. The pentastomids may be an offshoot of the arachnid side of the chelicerate line.

Several systems of arthropod classification have been devised, reflecting different views of the relationships of the early ancestral stocks. The system used here recognizes three subphyla, each considered as a separate and major branch of the phylum. *Subphylum Trilobita*. Trilobites. Wholly extinct arthropods with a head or cephalon composed of a preoral somite with antennae, and four postoral somites bearing unmodified appendages like those of the trunk; body divided into three parts, a cephalon, thorax, and pygidium.

Subphylum Chelicerata. Chelicerates. Arthropods without antennae, the corresponding part of the brain being reduced; head without appendages in the preoral part, and with three postoral somites, the first bearing pincer-like chelicerae, the next reduced, and the third with unmodified appendages or with pedipalps; uniramous walking legs on the thoracic somites; abdomen without appendages or with highly modified appendages.

Subphylum Mandibulata. Mandibulates. Arthropods with a head consisting of a preoral somite bearing antennae and with four postoral somites, the first with or without antennules, the second with mandibles, and the third and fourth typically with food-handling appendages known as maxillae; thorax with uniramous or biramous appendages, some of which may be associated with the mouth-parts; abdomen not divided from the thorax and bearing appendages, or distinct from the thorax and with or without appendages.

The Exoskeleton

A single glance is usually enough to see that an animal is an arthropod. The jointed exoskeleton covering the body and legs is unique. It has had an important unifying influence on the phylum as a whole, for it tends to confer similar potentialities and pose similar problems to all arthropods. The most important common potentialities grow out of the adequate protection it affords without causing a loss of mobility, the effectiveness of the appendages when they are specialized for specific tasks, and the great stimulus it provides for the development of muscles, nervous system, and sense organs. Some disadvantages have partly compensated for the advantages. The firm exoskeleton imposes limitations on growth and restricts the passage of materials in or out at the body surface, as well as making it difficult to receive stimuli from the environment. The limitations imposed by the exoskeleton have been overcome in rather similar manners by various types of arthropods. The development of molting habits has overcome the restrictions imposed on growth. The reduced capacity for surface respiration and excretion has favored the development of effective respiratory organs, even in small arthropods, and also the development of effective excretory organs. The presence of a firm outer casing has tended to favor the development of rather similar sense organs in all of the arthropods.

Minute details of exoskeletal anatomy and musculature cannot be discussed in a volume devoted to all invertebrates; only the most basic can be emphasized. The student who wishes to pursue this area further is referred to Snodgrass's excellent *A Textbook of Arthropod Anatomy*. It is important to grasp the basic principles, for they help us to understand arthropods and to see some of the factors that have affected the adaptational lines they have followed.

With the development of the exoskeleton, the body wall is profoundly changed (Fig. 16.3C). It contains only the cuticle, the epidermis that secretes it, and a basement membrane, sometimes somewhat amplified by a discontinuous dermis composed of connective tissue. The circular, diagonal, and longitudinal muscle layers found in the body wall of typical coelomates have been dispersed to form the specific musculature that manipulates the various joints of the body. The peritoneum does not form an inner layer, for the coelom is reduced and a large haemocoel fills the space within the body wall.

Three distinct layers can be recognized in the cuticle. A thin outermost layer of tanned proteins, waxes, and other fatty compounds makes up the epicuticle. Beneath it is the procuticle, made up of two layers, an outer exocuticle, often pigmented and impregnated with the sub-

stances found in the epicuticle, and an inner endocuticle. It is the exocuticle that is thickened to form the skeletal plates or sclerites. The endocuticle is a continuous layer, sometimes thinner in some areas, and particularly important in the flexible membranes between the skeletal plates. Both layers of the procuticle are laminated and contain a good deal of chitin, an aminopolysaccharide. In some groups, especially among the Crustacea, the skeleton is impregnated with calcium salts. The thickened sclerites need not be richer in chitin than the other parts of the cuticle. Insect sclerites, for example, contain more carbohydrate and less chitin than the rest of the cuticle. The waxy compounds of the epicuticle and exocuticle are very important, for they reduce water loss in terrestrial forms. If the waxes are removed, water loss increases rapidly. It also increases at temperatures above the melting point of the waxes of the exoskeleton. Because of asymmetry of water movement, a sheet of tanned gelatin which is waxed on one side will absorb water from the atmosphere. This principle explains the way some insects and arachnids absorb water from the air, using layers of wax and tanned protein in the exoskeleton. It also explains the method by which tick egg cases are prevented from drying. A waxy compound is secreted by the organ of Gené and used to wax the surface of the egg when it is laid. Without the waxy layer, the eggs quickly shrivel and die.

The capacity of the epidermis to secrete cuticle is important to other functions than protection. Wherever the epidermis is turned in during development, it carries with it the capacity for cuticle formation. The epidermal lining of the proctodaeum and stomodaeum secretes the cuticular lining of the foregut and hindgut. The tracheal system of the terrestrial mandibulates is lined with epidermis, which secretes a lining cuticle, thickened at various points for support. Spiral cuticular ridges, the taenidia, are found in the walls of the trachea, preventing their collapse. At the point where two skeletal plates meet, and especially in the vicinity of flexible joints, the epidermis is invaginated. Here it secretes internal ridges, plates, or spikes of cuticle, known as apodemes (Fig. 16.3A-C). The arthropods have an endoskeleton composed of apodemes, of varying degrees of complexity. Muscle attachment to the apodemes increases the flexibility of the leverage system, and plays an especially important role in arthropods with very thin, flexible, external exoskeleton.

Mobility of the body and its parts is maintained by specializations of the exoskeleton at the points where two sclerites

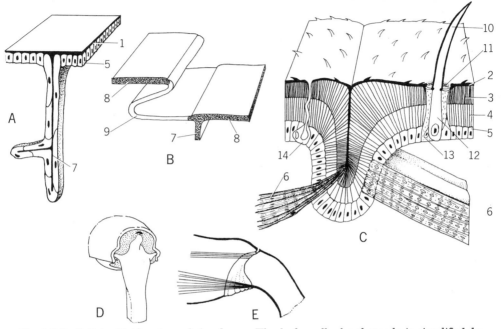

Fig. 16.3. Cuticle, Epidermis, and Apodemes. The body wall of arthropods is simplified by the disappearance of the coelomic cavity, and the division of the muscles into slips for moving specific joints. It consists of the epidermis and the cuticle, with associated glands, bristles, and other superficial structures. The muscles attach to the epidermis, often modified at the point of muscle attachment, or extend through the epidermis to attach to the cuticle directly. The heavy cuticle extends inwards (A) to provide spines or shelves for muscle attachment. These endoskeletal parts are the apodemes. The surface cuticle is often between body segments, forming a flexible articulating membrane (B), permitting movement. Similar articulating membranes occur at the joints of the appendages and at the base of movable spines or bristles. The relatively impervious cuticle is interrupted at glands and at sense organs, as seen in C. Movable joints of appendages are usually equipped with condyles, at which movement occurs. In monocondylic joints (D), the single condyle is located opposite a wide, flexible articulating membrane, and free movement is restricted to one plane. In dicondylic joints (E), the two condyles fit into corresponding depressions in the next segment, permitting freer movement of the joint. (D and E, after Snodgrass.) *Body wall:* 1, cuticle; 2, epicuticle; 3, exocuticle; 4, endocuticle; 5, epidermis (hypodermis); 6, muscle; 7, apodeme. *Special parts:* 8, skeletal plate; 9, articular membrane between segments; 10, sensory seta; 11, alveolus (setal socket); 12, trichogen cell, which secretes seta; 13, tormogen cell, which secretes the socket; 14, gland cell.

or cuticular rings covering adjacent podites meet. Immovable sutures occur in the head region and at other points. Here the epidermis often invaginates during development and forms apodemes. Movable sutures in the body wall usually involve two adaptations. The sclerites overlap, thus providing protection, and the cuticle between the sclerites is folded under (Fig. 16.3B). The folded-in cuticle is thin and flexible, providing a good deal of movement. At joints of the appendages, a somewhat different problem is encountered. If the joint were a simple infolding of more delicate, flexible cuticle, the weak cuticle would necessarily bear the full weight of the body or full thrust of the leg. The joint is strengthened by gliding surfaces or condyles, built of the hardened exoskeletal material. Opposing the condyle or surrounding it, the more flexible articular membrane connects the remaining surfaces of the two skeletal parts. Among insects, legs may have either one or two condyles at the joints (Fig. 16.3D,E). The form and positioning of the condyles, of course, determine the relative freedom and direction of movement.

The Musculature

The tremendous development of the musculature associated with the development of a jointed exoskeleton has been mentioned previously. There are a great many joints in the body and its appendages, and each joint calls for its set of specialized muscle fibers. The body musculature, in particular, can become very complex (Fig. 16.4B). Most arthropods are small animals, and a muscle contains relatively few individual muscle fibers. The nervous system contains a limited number of neurons. The kind of muscle that has been so suitable for vertebrates is not suitable for arthropods generally. Both muscle fiber and neuron have been histologically and physiologically adapted along lines appropriate

to operating a mechanically complex musculature with a minimum of neurons and muscle fibers. As a result of this adaptation, principles which apply to vertebrate muscles often do not apply to arthropod muscle. In vertebrate muscle, the power resulting from fiber contraction is dependent on the number of fibers stimulated, each fiber obeying an "all-or-none law" and contracting maximally or not at all. In vertebrates, the speed of contraction is dependent on the intrinsic qualities of the muscle fiber itself rather than on the kind of stimulus delivered to it. In arthropods, on the other hand, a single axon may innervate several muscle fibers, and a single muscle fiber may receive stimuli from several different kinds of axons. In at least some cases, the same motor end plate serves more than one kind of axon (Fig. 16.4A). As a result, a single arthropod muscle fiber may contract more or less rapidly and more or less powerfully, depending on the kind of stimulus it receives.

The primitive arrangement seems to have consisted of a fast and a slow axon to each muscle fiber, but triple and even quintuple innervations of fibers have been described. A large axon delivers a stimulus that evokes a rapid, high-tension contraction, nearly as powerful as tetanic contraction. An intermediate axon evokes a slower response, which builds up rapidly on repetition and follows a different fatigue pattern. A third, and usually the smallest, axon, suppresses contraction, but does not necessarily prevent facilitation. As a result, an extra impulse from other fibers can evoke a sudden large response when the small axon is operating. The inhibitory stimuli have rather more effect on the slow than on the fast contractions. Equipment of this kind is not used in a simple manner with the large or the intermediate axon evoking contractions independently. The two kinds of axons co-operate. A series of slow impulses augmented by a single fast stimulus can sustain a high-tension contraction, for example, permitting a holding response. Not nearly enough is known of arthropod nerve and muscle physiology. Certainly it is clear from our present knowledge that arthropods are capable of a wide range of responses, in this sense rivaling the much larger vertebrates, but achieve the responses in an entirely different way. The combination of electron microscopy with the physiological study of tissues is opening up a new and fascinating field of study, in which the suitability of the form and chemical composition of tissues is being related to the conditions under which tissues function. Arthropod muscle is one of the most interesting materials for this new approach to evolutionary adaptation.

It is not uncommon for arthropods to have some highly specialized muscles with unusual structural or physiological quali-

ties. Muscles used in flight and in sound production are good examples. The physiological problems associated with flight muscles are very interesting. Generally speaking, a muscle responds to a single stimulus by a single contraction. When stimuli are delivered repetitively, a point is reached when the contractions fuse into a sustained contraction. As a general rule, the faster a muscle fiber contracts, the higher the rate of stimulus repetition it can tolerate before contractions become fused. Many insects must move their wings very rapidly in flight, and the problem centers around developing a set of muscles that can be successfully used for flight, contracting with sufficient speed without going into fused contraction. Some insects have very fast muscle fibers that can make a distinct contraction to a very rapid set of

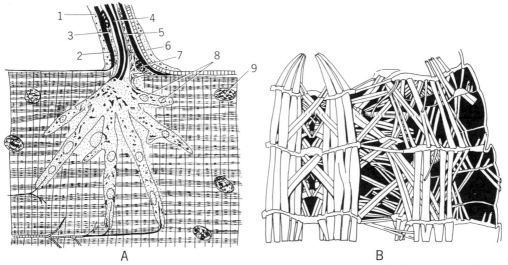

A   B

Fig. 16.4. The development of a jointed exoskeleton provides a great stimulus to the evolutionary development of the muscular system. Small muscle slips which provide specific movements for specific body parts develop, resulting in remarkable complexity, even in small organisms. The ventral muscles and muscles of the right half of the mesothorax and metathorax of a caterpillar (B) serve as an example. In small animals with such muscular complexity, innervation of muscles is different than in vertebrates. At A is shown the end plate of a muscle in the leg of a locust. It is served by both fast and slow neurons, and the specific activity of the muscle is the result of the combined stimuli delivered by the two kinds of neurons. (A, after Hoyle, in Scheer. B, after Snodgrass.) 1, fatty envelope; 2, neural lamella; 3, cellular layer of sheath; 4, fast axon; 5, slow axon; 6, trachea; 7, nucleus of sheath cell; 8, end plates; 9, nucleus of muscle.

nerve stimuli. They have flight muscles that contract with each wing movement and receive a stimulus for each contraction. Wing movements up to 20 to 40 per second can be maintained by this direct system. However, some insect flight, and all kinds of sound production, involves muscle contractions at frequencies far higher than this, frequencies at which only fused contractions are possible when separate stimuli are delivered to the muscle. It is clear that in this case the fiber must contract several times for each nerve stimulus. This is achieved by skeletal arrangements which stretch the muscle by recoil after the muscle has exerted its pull. The muscle contracts a second time, not because it has received a new nerve impulse, but because it has been stretched by the recoil mechanism. In systems of this kind, the frequency of muscle contraction, and of wing movements, is determined by the nature of the recoil system, and nerves are used only to keep the muscle in an active state. In some other cases, repeated oscillatory contractions result from a single stimulus. More work is needed to analyze the various types of mechanisms involved in the control of the very fast arthropod muscles used for oscillatory contractions.

Molting

Thinner, more flexible parts of the cuticle are folded in at each joint. These folds can be somewhat stretched by the growth of tissues beneath the exoskeleton, but this permits only a very moderate amount of growth at the most. Only by shedding the exoskeleton can the epidermis be relieved of external pressure so that the growing tissues can expand. After the old cuticle is shed, a new exoskeleton is secreted, larger than the last and providing some room for further growth. The young arthropod grows to fit its new case, as a small boy grows to fill the clothes which were bought when a little too large for him. The shed-

ding of the cuticle is know as molt or ecdysis. The periods between molts are known as instars.

Embryonic growth of arthropods, as of other animals, is a precisely controlled affair, following a predetermined course. The more gradual change of the juvenile organism into an adult is no less controlled, although one may not be so aware of it. In arthropods, this phase of growth is complicated by the problem of molting, but tends, nonetheless, to become organized. The method used is to develop a pattern of definite molts and instars, with each instar representing a definite stage with a characteristic form and size. Irregularities may result from unusual environmental conditions, but within the extremes normally encountered by the developing young, the number of molts between hatching and the attainment of adult form is often constant within a species, or sometimes constant for all members of a family or order. In this case, each instar may be considered as a stage or stadium of development, and the gradual development of the adult form can be followed from stadium to stadium. Among the common changes that occur in the form of young organisms at molts are the addition of body segments or of pairs of appendages. In some cases, a remarkable transformation of the body structure occurs at molt, and the molt may be termed a metamorphic molt. A good example is the molt at the end of the pupa stage of some insects, in which a wingless larva is changed to a winged adult.

Molts are recurrent crises in the lives of arthropods. Until the new skeleton hardens, the protective case is weak, and without the hardened skeletal plates, movement is often restricted. In many arthropods special behavior patterns appear at molt, which tend to minimize the dangers of the molting period. They may seek a secluded spot for molting, build a protective molting web, retire into burrows, or have special mechanisms to speed skeletal hardening. In any event, molting remains an especially dangerous time in the life cycle.

Molt is far more than a simple splitting of the cuticle and the secretion of a new one. Arthropod life consists of alternating periods of premolt, molt, postmolt, and intermolt. Some of the arthropods escape into a permanent intermolt when they are adult; this period is known as anecdysis. Others, however, never achieve stability, molting at intervals throughout adult life.

The physiology of most of the body parts is affected by premolt. Glycogen reserves are built up. Some crustaceans resorb minerals from the old exoskeleton and store them, thus hastening skeletal hardening after molt. The epidermis secretes an enzyme that softens the cuticle at its base. It pulls away from the epidermal cells, stimulating the formation of a new epicuticle (Fig. 16.5). The epicuticle is impervious to the molting enzyme. Beneath its protective wall, new cuticle develops. At the end of premolt the old cuticle splits. The soft body within swells and emerges. Various tactics are used to keep the body at a maximum volume while the new skeleton hardens. Insects inflate the crop with air, and sometimes other body parts are inflated. The Crustacea imbibe water. The tissues grow rapidly, and the new cuticle hardens during the short postmolt period. At this time the stored mineral resources of Crustacea are rapidly exhausted, for they are deposited in the hardening cuticle. After postmolt, the animal may enter intermolt, but full intermolt probably occurs only in adults. The rapidly molting juveniles must have, at the best, a very short period of stability.

Molting is a complex event from the physiological point of view, and it is clear that some kind of physiological controls are required. In insects and decapod crustaceans, molting is under the control of hormonal mechanisms. Presumably, similar kinds of controls operate in other arthropods. Neurosecretory cells in the eye-

stalks of decapods occur in the X-organs of the medulla terminalis, and in the sensory papillae (Fig. 16.6A). These end in the sinus glands, made up of the hormone-filled terminations of the neurosecretory cells. A pair of glands in the maxillary or second antennal somites, the Y-organs, are controlled by secretions from the X-organs. The Y-organs also secrete hor-

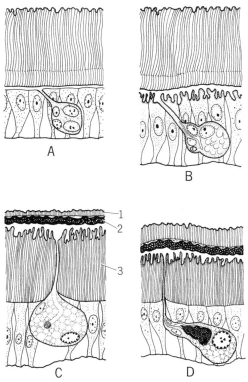

Fig. 16.5. Four stages in the molting of the hemipteran *Rhodnius*. At A, the old cuticle is beginning to separate from the epidermis, and new dermal glands are appearing. At B, three days later in the process, the dermal gland is enlarged and the first evidence of the digestion of the old cuticle is seen. Three days later, at C, the old cuticle is largely digested, the new cuticle is almost fully formed, and the dermal gland cell is very large. One day before C, as seen at D, the dermal cells are full of secretion, as the cuticle is being laid down. (After Wigglesworth.) 1, old cuticle; 2, digesting cuticle; 3, new cuticle.

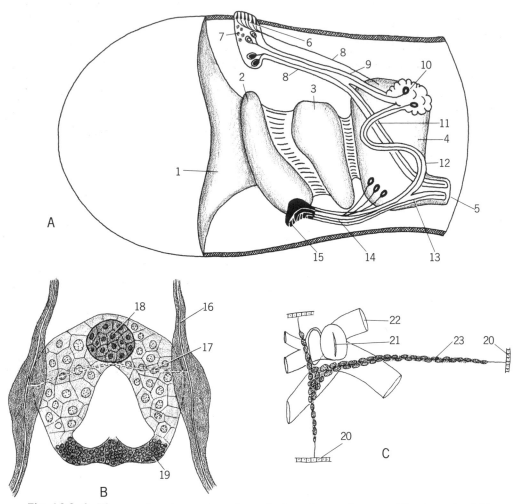

Fig. 16.6. **A.** The neurosecretory system of a natant crustacean, *Lysmata*. The sinus gland-X-organ system inhibits the molting cycle. **B.** Semischematic figure of the ring gland of a mature *Drosophila* larva, showing the corpus allatum and corpus cardiacum. **C.** The prothoracic gland of a late caterpillar of *Prodenia*. In insects the control of molt and metamorphosis is linked with the corpora allata, which produce a juvenile hormone, and the corpora cardiaca, which stimulate the prothoracic glands to form ecdysones, responsible for molting. (**A,** after Carlisle and Knowles. **B, C,** after Bodenstein.) *Sinus gland-X-organ system:* **1,** lamina ganglionaris; **2,** medulla externa; **3,** medulla interna; **4,** medulla terminalis; **5,** peduncle of optic lobe; **6,** sensory pore; **7,** sensory papilla of X-organ; **8,** sensory nerve; **9,** X-organ connective; **10,** medulla terminalis ganglionic X-organ; **11,** brain-X-organ tract; **12,,** sinus gland-X-organ-tract; **13,** brain-sinus gland tract; **14,** common sinus gland tract; **15,** sinus gland. *Ring gland:* **16,** lateral tracheal trunk; **17,** transverse tracheal trunk; **18,** corpus allatum; **19,** corpus cardiacum and hypocerebral ganglion. *Prothoracic gland:* **20,** epidermis; **21,** spiracle; **22,** trachea; **23,** gland cells.

mones which stimulate molt. Removal of the Y-organs prevents molting, and implantation of new Y-organs restores the ability to molt. Y-organ secretions trigger the premolt changes, but once premolt begins, the process goes on to completion, even though the Y-organs are removed. The X-organ and sinus gland, on the other hand, inhibit molting. When the eye-stalks which contain the X-organs and sinus glands, are removed, molting is accelerated. Implantation of sinus glands into animals whose eye-stalks have been removed retards molting. Apparently the sinus gland liberates molt-inhibiting hormones during postmolt and intermolt. Under appropriate internal or external conditions, the sinus gland secretion disappears, and the Y-organ, freed from restraint, secretes the molt-initiating hormone.

As a general rule, insects do not resemble the parents when they hatch. Some are rather like the adults, however, and undergo a series of gradual changes during development. These are said to be paurometabolic. In other cases, the insects hatch as larvae, without wings and quite unlike the adults. Although changes occur with each molt, they retain juvenile traits throughout the early instars and undergo one profound, metamorphic molt associated with a quiescent period known as the pupation period. These are termed holometabolic. In still other insects, especially those with aquatic larvae and winged adults, wing buds are present during the aquatic instars and undergo some development, but the last molt is more thoroughly metamorphic than is the case with most paurometabolic insects. These are said to be hemimetabolic. It is clear from the varied patterns of development that molt and metamorphosis, in one pattern or another, are closely associated in insects, and that the methods of integration of the two differ markedly in different kinds of insects.

In insects, molting and metamorphosis are integrated by an endocrine mechanism somewhat similar, but different in detail, to that seen in decapods. Neurosecretory cells of the brain end in the corpora cardiaca. When a molt-initiating stimulus affects the organism, the corpora cardiaca release the brain hormone. The brain hormone activates the prothoracic glands, which liberate a hormone known as ecdysone. Ecdysone evokes an increase in the epidermal mitochondria and endoplasmic reticulum, an elevation of protein and RNA content, and initiates premolt. A juvenile hormone is produced by small glands associated with the stomodaeal nervous system, the corpora allata. The juvenile hormone prevents metamorphic molts. There is good evidence of the functions of the various hormonal factors. When corpora allata are introduced into immature insects, metamorphosis is delayed, while removal of the corpora allata results in the development of adult-like insects at early instars. Insects that are deprived of the brain hormone do not molt. They will molt, however, under the influence of ecdysone. These hormones are not species-specific, but like vertebrate hormones act generally on all members of the group. It is evident that there are other controlling factors, but these are not yet understood.

The sensitivity of body tissues to the hormones changes during differentiation. Probably the different patterns of development seen in various insect orders depend at least in part, on the ways that the molting and juvenile hormones are released, and particularly on the pattern of corpora allata secretion, and on the sensitiveness of the tissues to the hormones (Fig. 16.7). Where the juvenile hormone is produced in large quantities during early instars, or where the tissues are highly sensitive to it, metamorphic changes are largely postponed until a metamorphic molt associated with pupation occurs. Where the amounts of juvenile hormone gradually change during development, or where the sensitivity of the tissue to the juvenile hormone gradually changes, a gradual metamorphosis takes place.

Arthropod Development

Arthropod development is highly modified, partly because of the large, yolky eggs, and partly because, as end twigs of the annelid-arthropod stem, they are furthest removed from the ancestral stocks. That their development follows a pattern established in the protostome stem in protoannelid times is best shown by the fact that the more highly specialized annelids tend to deviate

from the primitive annelid type of development in the same ways, though they are not as greatly modified as arthropods.

A few arthropods have small eggs that undergo holoblastic cleavage. In some of these, traces of spiral cleavage have been reported. Most arthropods, however, produce ova that are rich in yolk and in which cleavage patterns are greatly modified. Insects provide a good example of arthropod development in its more modified form. The zygote nucleus divides repeatedly to produce a number of cleavage cells in the yolk mass (Fig. 16.8A-C). These arrange themselves in an external layer, forming a blastoderm. A few yolk cells are usually

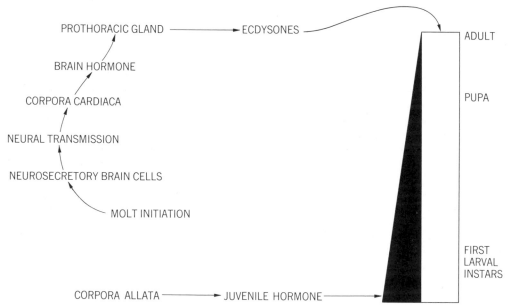

Fig. 16.7. Control of Molting and Metamorphosis in Insects. Insects pass through a series of molts. In many insects, each molt is accompanied by some change in form, and a gradual metamorphosis occurs. In others, most of metamorphosis occurs in a single, special molt, taking place during pupation. Whatever internal or external factors are responsible for initiating molt result in evoking activity in neurosecretory cells, whose secretion is released in the corpora cardiaca as the brain hormone. This activates the prothoracic glands, which liberate ecdysones responsible for triggering the molt. The corpora allata produce a juvenile hormone, which inhibits metamorphosis. The rate of metamorphosis is associated with the relative concentration of the juvenile hormone present during molt and postmolt stages. A gradual reduction of juvenile hormone occurs during gradual metamorphosis. Presumably, more sudden changes in the quantity of juvenile hormone are associated with the metamorphic molts of the higher insects.

left within the yolk mass, and in some cases, germ cells can be recognized at a region near the posterior end of the embryo. The embryo is, at this stage, a coeloblastula with the central cavity completely filled with yolk. The yolk is not divided into separate yolk cells, but is rather an undivided mass of material containing some nuclei.

Details of germ-layer formation vary considerably in different kinds of insects. Germ-layer formation is preceded by the appearance of a germ band or primitive streak on the ventral side of the embryo (Fig. 16.8D). In many insects, the embryo comes to lie in an amniotic cavity, formed by the growth of amniotic folds toward the midline on the ventral side of the egg (Fig. 16.8E). The amniotic folds gradually enclose the embryo while it gastrulates. In such cases, the remaining blastoderm becomes a squamous area immediately within the egg membranes. Gastrulation involves the involution or inturning of some of the cells of the germ band (Fig. 16.8F). The cells that are turned under are mesoderm and endoderm, but they cannot at first be distinguished. The blastopore is never open. It corresponds to the long, median part of the germ band where involution occurs (Fig. 16.8G).

The mesoderm forms a strip of cells beneath the germ band ectoderm, on each side of the midline. Paired coelomic cavities appear in the mesodermal bands (Fig. 16.8G). Meanwhile, the nervous ectoderm separates off as a double primordium, from which the nerve cord and ganglia develop. The first endodermal cells are scattered through the yolk, phagocytizing and digesting it. Eventually new endoderm is developed from three endodermal rudiments, one at the site of the future proctodaeum, one at the future stomodaeum, and one below the germ band mesoderm. These primordia eventually surround the remaining yolk, forming the midgut (Fig. 16.8H).

The generalized relationship of arthropod coelomic compartments to the embryonic segments is shown in Fig. 16.9A. The eyes as well as the first antennae and preantennae develop in the broad, anterior part of the embryo, corresponding to the acron of trilobites. New somites are added at the posterior end of the embryo, immediately in front of the last segment or pygidium, as in the case in annelids.

Trilobite larvae appear to have followed this general course of development. The youngest larvae were composed of the acron and of the first four postoral segments. The pygidium formed very early. Once it was present, new segments were added between the pygidium and the next most anterior segment (Fig. 16.9B-D). The first four postoral segments were incorporated into the cephalon of adults.

After hatching, the young arthropod follows the general rules seen in embryos. If all of the body segments are not present at hatching, new segments are added in front of the last segment, at molts. Development in which new somites are added to the body during developmental molts is called anamorphic. It is common in many groups of arthropods.

At the time of hatching, the young animal emerges as a larva in the great majority of cases. Larval forms vary greatly in different arthropod groups. Horseshoe crabs have a curious trilobite larva (Fig. 16.9F), named for its superficial resemblance to a trilobite. A number of somites and appendages must be added before the trilobite larva becomes an adult. The sea spiders, or pycnogonids, have only three pairs of appendages when they hatch, and add others during molts. Most of the arachnids are anamorphic. Mites and ticks hatch with three pairs of legs and add a fourth pair at the first molt. The details of insect development vary greatly. A few of the most primitive insects have anamorphic development, adding segments during molts after hatching. Generally, however, the insect has a full set of body segments at the time of hatching, al-

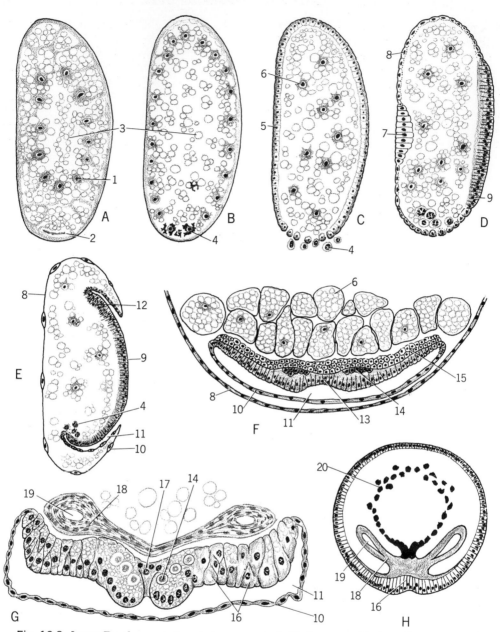

Fig. 16.8. Insect Development. Insects have a centrolecithal ovum, with the yolk concentrated in the center of ovum. The first cleavage divisions produce a group of cleavage nuclei **(A)**, which migrate to a more superficial position **(B)**. Germ cells are differentiated early, at one pole of the developing embryo. While a few cleavage nuclei remain in the yolk, most become incorporated in a continuous blastoderm which surrounds the yolk mass **(C)**. The blastoderm thickens on the dorsal side to form the dorsal organ, subsequently absorbed by the yolk, and on the ventral side to form the germ band **(D)**. The remaining blastoderm cells flatten out to form a thin membrane, the serosa. In many insects, the head and tail ends of the germ band in-

though it does not have an adult form. If it changes gradually to resemble the adult, the juvenile stages are called nymphs. The aquatic nymphs are usually referred to as naiads, and must undergo a somewhat more extensive metamorphosis at the last molt, when they leave the water and become land animals. When the young insect is wingless and must undergo pupation to assume the adult form, the juvenile stages are called larvae. In general, the most primitive insects resemble the parents most at hatching, while the most highly evolved insects are holometabolic, passing through larval, pupal, and adult stages.

Among Crustacea, the characteristic first larva is the nauplius. It has only three pairs of appendages, the first two being the two pairs of antennae, and the third the mandibles (Fig. 16.9E). New somites

Summary Table 16.2. Body and appendages of arthropod subclasses

TAGMA		TRILOBITA		CHELICERATA		MANDIBULATA	
		Somites	Appendages	Somites	Appendages	Somites	Appendages
Head	Preoral (acron)	Antennae		Preoral	None	Preoral	First antennae
	H-I	Unmodified leg		H-I	Chelicerae	H-I	Second antennae or none
	H-II	"	"	H-II	None	H-II	Mandibles
	H-III	"	"	H-III	Pedipalps or legs	H-III	First maxillae
	H-IV	"	"			H-IV	Second maxillae or legs or none
Trunk	Many, similar	"	"	Many, differentiated into prosoma and opisthosoma	Walking legs, respiratory appendages, gonopods, spinnerets	Many, usually divided into shorter or longer thorax and abdomen	Walking legs on thorax when present; abdomen with or without appendages, specialized for various functions
	Last joined as pygidium of various lengths						
	Telson			Telson or reduced		Telson or reduced	

vaginate, and amniotic folds of serosa grow up over the germ band, forming an amniotic cavity (E). When amniotic cavity formation is completed a double membrane covers the germ band, the outer being the serosa, and the inner layer, continuous with the margin of the germ band, being the amnion (F). The germ band at this time is double, the outer layer being the ectoderm and marked by a medial neural groove. The inner layer arises as a result of invagination along the midline, at the point where the neural groove eventually appears. A medial strip of mesoderm and the two mesodermal bands in which the somite cavities appear (G) arise from the inner layer. Presumably the invaginating inner layer represents the mesoderm, and with the closure of the blastopore (the space at the center of the invaginating cells), the primary endodermal lining of the primitive gut disintegrates (H). Actually, certain yolk cells just below the mesoderm of the inner layer and at the future stomodaeum and proctodaeum serve as sources for the secondary and permanent endoderm formed later in development. (A-G, after Johannsen and Butt. H, after Snodgrass.) 1, cleavage cell; 2, oösome; 3, yolk; 4, germ cell; 5, blastoderm; 6, yolk cell; 7, dorsal organ; 8, serosa; 9, germ band; 10, amnion; 11, amniotic cavity; 12, head organ; 13, neural groove; 14, neuroblasts; 15, inner layer of blastoderm; 16, ectoderm; 17, median nerve strand; 18, mesoderm; 19, coelomic cavity; 20, endoderm from yolk cells disintegrating.

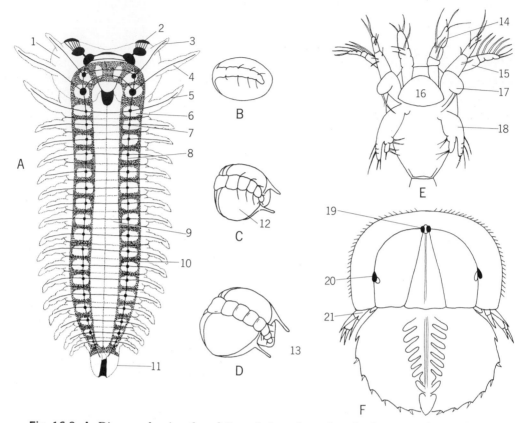

Fig. 16.9. A. Diagram showing the relation of the arthropod coelomic sacs to the ganglia of the central nervous system and the associated appendages. Snodgrass considers the preoral appendages to be different in character from those of the remainder of the body, corresponding to the prostomial appendages of polychaetes. B-D. Trilobite protaspis larvae, showing stages in early development. The youngest larva (B) contains the unsegmented part of the head, or acron, and the four somites which will be incorporated into the cephalon. At the posterior end of these somites is a bud serving as a growth zone, from which the protopygidium develops (C). New somites form from the subterminal growth zone between the pygidial and cephalic somites. E. The characteristic larva of microscopic Crustacea, known as the nauplius. It has three pairs of appendages, the two antennae and the mandibles. At this stage of development the mandibles are used for locomotion. F. A trilobite larva of *Limulus*. The resemblance to trilobites may be partly superficial, although it is possible that chelicerates arose from trilobite ancestors. (A, after Snodgrass from Johanssen and Butts. B-D after Störmer from Whittington. E, after Calman. F, after Kingsley. Takano, from Shipley). *Arthropod organization*: 1, acron; 2, eye; 3, preantenna; 4, antenna; 5, second antenna; 6, coelomic cavity; 7, ganglion; 8, connective between ganglia; 9, commissure between ganglia 10, mesoderm; 11, telson. *Protaspis larva*: 12, acron; 13, protopygidium. *Nauplius*: 14, first antenna; 15, second antenna; 16, labrum; 17, gnathobase; 18, mandible. *Limulus larva*: 19, median eye; 20, lateral eye; 21, last walking leg.

688

and appendages are added with each molt. Crustacea which have passed beyond the nauplius stage but are not yet adults are usually called metanauplii or zoaea, although special larval stages occur in a number of crustacean groups. Details of crustacean development will be discussed subsequently.

References

GENERAL

Birch, L. C., and D. P. Clark. 1953. Forest soil as an ecological community with special reference to the fauna. *Quart. Rev. Biol.* 28: 13.

Butt, F. H. 1960. Head development in the arthropods. *Biol. Rev.* 35: 43. (G)

Crampton, G. C. 1928. The evolution of the head region in lower arthropods and its bearing upon the origin and relationships or the arthropodan groups. *Canad. Ent.* 40: 284. (G)

Edney, E. B. 1957. *The Water Relations of Terrestrial Arthropods.* Cambridge Univ. Press, Cambridge, Eng. (G)

Ewing, H. E. 1928. The legs and leg-bearing segments of some primitive arthropod groups, with notes on leg-segmentation in the Arachnida. *Smithsonian Misc. Coll.* 80. No. 11.

Fichter, E. 1954. An ecological study of invertebrates of grassland and deciduous shrub savanna in eastern Nebraska. *Amer. Midl. Nat.* 51: 321.

Henry, L. M. 1948. The nervous system and the segmentation of the head in the Annulata. *Microentom.* 13: 1.

Jacot, A. P. 1940. The fauna of the soil. *Quart. Rev. Biol.* 15: 28.

Kevan, D. K. (ed.). 1955. *Soil Zoology.* Duckworth, London.

Krijgsman, B. J. 1952. Contractile and pacemaker mechanisms in the heart of arthropods. *Biol. Rev.* 27: 320.

Lawrence, R. F. 1953. *The Biology of the Cryptic Fauna of Forests.* Balkema, Amsterdam. (G)

Lees, A. D. 1956. *The Physiology of Diapause in Arthropods.* Cambridge Univ. Press, Cambridge, Eng.

Macan, T. T., and E. B. Worthington. 1951. *Life in Lakes and Rivers.* Collins, London.

Manton, S. M. 1949. The early embryonic stages of *Peripatopsis* and some general considerations concerning the morphology and phylogeny of the arthropods. *Phil. Trans.* 223: 483. (G)

———. 1953. Locomotory habits and the evolution of the larger arthropodan groups. *Symp. Soc. Exp. Biol.* 7: 339.

———. 1958. Habits of life and design of body in arthropods. *Jour. Linn. Soc. Zool.* 44: 58. (G)

———. 1960. Concerning head development in arthropods. *Biol. Rev.* 35: 265.

Pearse, A. S. 1950. *The Emigrations of Animals from the Sea.* Dryden, New York.

Richards, G. 1951. *The Integument of Arthropods.* Univ. Minn., Minneapolis.

Snodgrass, R. E. 1938. Evolution of the Annelida, Onychophora, and Arthropoda. *Smithson. Misc. Coll.* 97: 1. (G)

———. 1951. *Comparative Studies on the Head of the Mandibulate Arthropods.* Cornell Univ., Ithaca, N.Y. (G)

———. 1952. *Arthropod Anatomy.* Cornell Univ., Ithaca. (!)

Störmer, L. 1933. Are the trilobites related to the arachnids? *Amer. Jour. Sci.* 26: 147.

Tiegs, O. W., and S. M. Manton. 1958. The evolution of the arthropods. *Biol. Rev.* 33: 255. (G)

TRILOBITA

Garstang, W. 1940. Störmer on the appendages of the trilobites. *Ann. Mag. Nat. Hist.* 6: 59.

Raymond, P. E. 1920. The appendages, anatomy, and relationships of trilobites. *Mem. Conn. Acad. Arts and Sci.* 7: 1.

Störmer, L. 1939. Studies on trilobite morphology. I. *Norsk. Geol. Tidssk.* 19: 143.

———. 1942. Studies on trilobite morphology. II. *Norsk. Geol. Tidssk.* 21: 49.

Whittington, H. B. 1957. The ontogeny of trilobites. *Biol. Rev.* 32: 421.

17
The Chelicerates

Everyone is familiar with some of the chelicerates. Spiders, scorpions, and ticks are, perhaps, the most familiar chelicerates, although some of the mites are familiar enough, if generally unseen. The chigger bites that irritate the skin so severely are caused by an arachnid, and the red spider that destroys gardens and crops is also a mite. A number of the other mites are destructive to crops before or after harvest. Those who live in coastal areas may be familiar with the horseshoe crabs, which are not truly crabs but belong to Merostomata, one of the chelicerate classes.

Although a smaller subphylum than Mandibulata, Chelicerata is nevertheless a very large subclass containing thousands of species, many of which are important to man from an economic point of view. Two outstanding traits of the chelicerates set them apart from other arthropods. They have no antennae, and the first pair of appendages are pincer-like chelicerae. They often have silk glands, although this is especially characteristic of the arachnids. The body of chelicerates is divided into two regions, or tagmata. The anterior tagma is the prosoma, made up of the head, mouthparts, and somites bearing the walk-

ing legs. The posterior tagma is the opisthosoma, which has reduced or modified appendages. The prosoma and opisthosoma are sometimes called the cephalothorax and abdomen, respectively, but they do not correspond exactly with the parts of mandibulates which are termed head, thorax, and abdomen. The most outstanding features of the chelicerates are the following:

1. The prosoma is never divided into separate head and thorax regions.

2. Antennae are missing, and the deutocerebrum, the second part of the brain, which contains the brain centers for the antennae of other arthropods, is also reduced.

3. The first pair of appendages are pincer-like chelicerae, formed by a postoral somite, and moving forward during development.

4. The second pair of appendages are pedipalps, sometimes leg-like and sensory, but sometimes chelate and prehensile.

5. The next four somites usually complete the prosoma. Each somite bears a pair of walking legs.

6. The opisthosoma contains up to a maximum of 13 somites and a telson.

Summary Table 17.1. Chelicerate classes

	MEROSTOMATA	PYCNOGONIDA	ARACHNIDA
Prosoma	Continuous dorsal carapace	Large, jointed prosoma	Single or double carapace
Prosomal appendages	Chelicerae and five or six pairs of moderately modified appendages	Chelicerae, pedipalps, ovigerous legs, and 4–6 pairs of walking legs	Chelicerae, pedipalps or legs, four pairs of walking legs
Opisthosoma	12–18 somites plus a telson	Greatly reduced	11–13 somites, with an additional telson in some
Opisthosomal appendages	genital operculum and appendages modified as book gills	none	vestiges associated with book lungs; special sensory appendages; spinnerets

Summary Table 17.2. Arachnid orders

ORDER	PROSOMA	CHELICERAE	PEDIPALPS	OPISTHOSOMA	RESPIRATORY ORGAN
Palpigradida	2 parts with separate carapaces	Strong, with unique sternal plate	leg-like	11 segments, with long, jointed postabdomen	none
Uropygida	carapace in 1 or 2 pieces	2 segments, with fang	chelate, prehensile	mesosoma of 8 and metasoma of 3 somites, with long or short postabdomen	book lungs opening in 2 pairs of opisthosomal spiracles
Ricinuleida	single carapace, with hood in front	2 segments	chelate	12 united somites, with pedicel and terminal anal tubercle	prosomal spiracles and unbranched tracheae
Scorpionida	single carapace	3 segments, strong	powerful, chelate	mesosoma of 7 and metasoma of 5 somites, with telson containing sting	4 pairs of opisthosomal book lungs
Pseudoscorpionida	single carapace	2 segments and silk glands	strong, with poison glands	12 segments, broad, and flat	2 pairs of spiracles and tracheal system
Solpugida	carapace in 2 pieces	powerful, with 2 segments	leg like	10 segments, no pedicel	1 prosomal and 2 opisthosomal pairs of spiracles and tracheae
Aranaea	single carapace	2 segments, with poison glands	leg-like, modified for copulation in males.	12 united segments, with pedicel, modified appendages as spinnerets	2 opisthosomal spiracles and book lungs or tracheae
Opiliones	single carapace	3 segments	leg-like, but may be chelate	9 somites, without a pedicel	1 pair of spiracles and a tracheal system
Acarina	single carapace	chelate or piercing	chelate or leg-like	segmentation obscure	with or without spiracles and tracheae

Summary Table 17.3. Some arachnid organs

	COXAL GLANDS		MALPHIGHIAN TUBULES	NUMBER OF OSTIA	SOMITE OF BOOK LUNGS	SOMITE OF TRACHEAL SPIRACLES
	INTERNAL POSITION	LOCATION OF PORE				
Palpigradida	2	Palpi	—		4,5,6 or none	
Uropygida	3,5	Leg 1	+	9	9,10	
Amblypigida	3	Leg 1	+	9?	9,10	
Ricinuleida		Legs 1,2	+			3rd coxa
Scorpionida	5,6	Leg 3	+	7	10,11,12,13	
Pseudo-scorpionida	Abd.	Leg 3	—	1		9,10
Solpugida	2	Palps	+	8		4,9,10,11
Araneae	3 or 3,5	Palps	+	3	9,10	9,10
Opiliones	3	Between legs 3,4	?	3		8
Acarina	1–4 pairs	varied	±	—		variable

Opisthosomal appendages are always reduced or highly modified.

7. The first opisthosomal somite is the pregenital segment, which is reduced or modified in some manner.

8. The second opisthosomal somite is the genital segment, which contains the gonopores.

9. Several succeeding opisthosomal somites may bear appendages modified for respiration and converted into book gills or book lungs. These are replaced by tracheae in some arachnids.

10. Excretory organs may be highly modified nephridia known as coxal glands, or may be Malpighian tubules, attached to the digestive tube at the junction of midgut and hindgut.

The chelicerates are divided into three classes, all of which include some modern species. Merostomata, however, is represented by only a few modern species and is predominantly made up of fossil species. Except for the merostomates, the chelicerates have not fossilized well, so a continuous fossil history is not available. All of the classes probably have a long history, however. The merostomates appeared in the Cambrian or Ordovician. Some of the arachnid groups appeared during the Silurian, and since the end of the Devonian, the arachnids have been fairly well differentiated into groups. Pycnogonids also go back at least to Devonian times. The major groups and their principal characteristics are given below. The orders marked by an asterisk are discussed only in the classification section.

Class Merostomata. Chelicerates with the prosoma covered by a continuous dorsal carapace; five or six opisthosomal somites bear flattened appendages associated with respiration; a long pointed telson at the posterior end; a pair of compound and a pair of simple eyes.

Subclass Xiphosura. Horseshoe crabs. Merostomates with an essentially semicircular prosoma; four- to six-segmented walking legs; six pairs of book gills on the opisthosoma. Two subgroups are recognized, the Limulada with the opisthosomal somites covered by an unsegmented dorsal shield, and the Synziophosura, with the opisthosomal shield segmented. Examples: *Xiphosura* (Fig. 17.1A); *Koenigiella* (Fig. 17.1B).

Subclass Eurypterida. Giant water scorpions. Wholly extinct merostomates with a body more elongated than in xiphosurans; opisthosoma divided into an often broad, anterior mesosoma of six somites and a posterior, narrower metasoma of six segments, often resulting in a scorpion-like body contour; mesosomal segments with discrete sternal sclerites on the ventral surface, and metasomal sclerites with complete skeletal rings; with chelicerae and five pairs of legs, usually of different sizes and sometimes some modified as paddles for swimming; last leg with nine podites; five pairs of plate-like appendages on the anterior opisthosomal somites are probably modified for respiration; telson sometimes flattened, but often scorpion-like. Examples: *Eurypterus* (Fig. 17.1C); *Pterygotus* (Fig. 17.1D).

Class Pycnogonida. Sea Spiders. Marine chelicerates with a large prosoma and a greatly reduced opisthosoma; mouth near the end of a proboscis; four simple eyes; sometimes with five or six pairs of legs on the prosoma, but typically with four pairs; without either excretory or respiratory organs. Examples: *Pycnogonum, Nymphon* (Fig. 17.1E).

Class Arachnida. Arachnids. Predominantly terrestrial chelicerates; with adaptations for air-breathing, usually in the form of book lungs or tracheae; prosoma with a pair of chelicerae, pedipalps, and four pairs of walking legs. Many orders are recognized, some wholly extinct, and several of the modern orders are small and but little known.

*Order Palpigradida. Palpigrades. A small order of minute, primitive arachnids, living in soil or under objects in warmer lands. Prosoma divided into two parts with separate carapaces; chelicerae well-developed and with a sternal plate, unique among arachnids; pedipalps used as walking legs and first pair of legs carried forward and used as sensory appendages; opisthosoma of 11 segments, ending in a long, jointed postabdomen; with a pair of coxal glands; without respiratory organs. Example: *Koenenia* (Fig. 17.2B,C).

*Order Uropygida. Whip scorpions. About a hundred species of tropical, or subtropical, nocturnal arachnids, typically living in the ground stratum among leaves and detritus, represented in North America by *Mastigoprocteus giganteus* (Fig. 17.2D), about 13 cm. long. The prosoma is covered by a single or double carapace. Two-jointed chelicerae end in a hook or fang. Pedipalps are jawed and prehensile. A pair of eyes are usually present. The elongated first pair of legs are sensory appendages, with many terminal segments. The opisthosoma contains eight broad anterior somites and three posterior, narrower somites, ending in a long or short, jointed postabdomen. Two pairs of book lungs open on the third and fourth opisthosomal somites. A pair of coxal glands open behind the first pair of legs, and Malpighian tubules are also present. A pair of large anal glands discharge formic or acetic acid for defense.

*Order Ricinuleida. Ricinuleids. Rare tropical to subtropical arachnids living in the ground stratum in humid surroundings. A single carapace covers the prosoma. The chelicerae have two segments and pedipalps end in small pincers. The third legs of males are modified as copulatory organs. The prosoma and opisthosoma are separated by a narrow pedicel. The opisthosoma is formed of twelve united somites, and ends in an anus on a short tubercle. Spiracles at the sides of the prosoma open into tufts of tiny, unbranched tracheal tubules. Malpighian tubules and a pair of coxal glands are present. The most outstanding trait is the hinged plate (hood), which is attached at the front of the carapace and folds down to cover the mouth and chelicerae when the organism is not feeding. Example: *Ricinoides* (Fig. 17.3C,D).

Order Scorpionida. Scorpions. Arachnids with the prosoma covered by a single carapace and with the opisthosoma di-

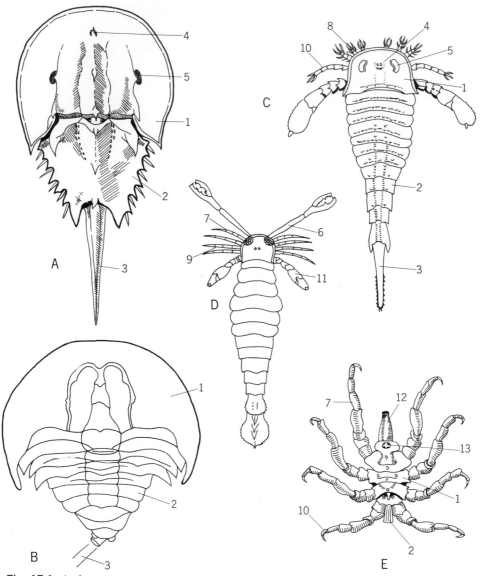

Fig. 17.1. A characteristic feature of arthropods is the specialization of somites, often accompanied with a partial union of groups of somites, to form definite body regions or tagmata. Another feature is the specialization of appendages, often leading to drastic modifications of their structure, as special functions are assumed. Much of arthropod classification depends on the set of appendages and the body tagmatization. Chelicerates all have chelate first appendages, known as chelicerae, and lack mandibles. Class Merostomata (A-D) is characterized by a prosoma covered by a single carapace, and to which the walking legs are attached. The opisthosoma has flattened respiratory appendages (not shown) and ends in a usually spine-like telson. The pycnogonids (E) or sea spiders have a ridiculously small opisthosoma which hangs like a tiny appendage on the large and obviously segmented prosoma. *Nymphon* (E) has four pairs of legs, like most pycnogonids, but some pycnogonids have five or six pairs of legs. The

694

vided into a mesosoma of seven broad somites and a metasoma of five narrower somites, ending in a telson modified as a poison gland and sting; prosoma with a pair of powerful three-jointed chelicerae and large, chelate pedipalps; four pairs of walking legs with nine podites, two of which are tarsi; a pair of modified, comb-like appendages (pectines) on the 2nd opisthosomal somite; a medial triad and two lateral groups of eyes; four pairs of opisthosomal book lungs; one pair of coxal glands and Malpighian tubules. Example: *Chactas* (Fig. 17.3B).

Order Pseudoscorpionida. Pseudoscorpions. Minute arachnids with a dorsal carapace covering the prosoma and with a broad, flattened opisthosoma; prosoma with two-jointed chelicerae containing silk glands and powerful pedipalps containing poison glands; walking legs with five to seven podites; eyeless or with one to two pairs of eyes; two pairs of spiracles opening into a tracheal system; a pair of coxal glands opening on the third pair of legs. Example: *Chelifer* (Fig. 17.3E).

Order Solpugida. Sun Spiders. Arachnids with a prosoma covered by a carapace of anterior and posterior plates, and with a ten-segmented opisthosoma; prosoma with two-jointed, powerful chelicerae, a pair of leg-like adhesive pedipalps, and four pairs of walking legs with five to seven podites; a pair of eyes on the anterior carapace; a tracheal system open through one pair of prosomal and two pairs of opisthosomal spiracles; one pair of coxal glands and Malpighian tubules. Example: *Galeodes* (Fig. 17.3F).

Order Aranaea. Spiders. Arachnids with a prosoma covered by a single carapace and with an opisthosoma of twelve united segments attached to the prosoma by a narrow pedicel; prosoma with two-jointed chelicerae containing poison glands, leg-like pedipalps used for food handling and modified as copulatory organs in males, and four pairs of walking legs with seven podites; up to eight eyes, differently located on the prosoma; with book lungs, tracheae, or both; with one to two pairs of coxal glands and Malpighian tubles. Example: *Lycosa* (Fig. 17.16A).

Order Opiliones. Daddy longlegs or harvestmen. Arachnids with an undivided prosoma broadly attached to a nine-segmented opisthosoma; chelicerae three-jointed; pedipalps long, leg-like, and sometimes chelate with a chewing plate at the base; walking legs very long, with multiple tarsal segments; base of first walking leg modified to form a chewing plate; a pair of eyes on prosoma; usually with a single pair of spiracles opening to a tracheal system in first opisthosomal somite; a pair of coxal glands opening between the third and fourth legs. Example: *Leiobunum* (Fig. 17.4C,D).

large proboscis with a terminal mouth is characteristic of the group. Merostomates are divided into two subclasses, Xiphosura, the horseshoe crabs (A, B), and Eurypterida (C, D), the giant water scorpions. Eurypterids are wholly extinct, but a few species of horseshoe crabs are still living. The broad, crescentic prosoma of the Xiphosura is characteristic. *Koenigiella* (B) is a member of the wholly extinct Synziophosura, with an opisthosoma on which the sutures between somites can be seen. *Xiphosura* (A) is a living representative of the Limulada, with the dorsal surface of the opisthosoma covered by a continuous plate, hinged to the telson. The eurypterids had a narrow prosoma, and the segmented opisthosoma was divided into a broader, anterior mesosoma and a narrower, posterior metasoma, giving them a scorpion-like body outline. Their appendages were quite variable, the chelicerae sometimes being very long, and many having one or more (most commonly the last) pairs of walking legs modified into paddles for swimming. (A, C, D, and E, after Snodgrass. B, after Eller.) 1, prosoma; 2, opisthosoma; 3, tail spine (telson); 4, median (dorsal) eye; 5, compound lateral eye; 6, chelicera; 7, first walking leg; 8, second walking leg; 9, third walking leg; 10, fourth walking leg; 11, fifth walking leg; 12, proboscis; 13, dorsal ocelli.

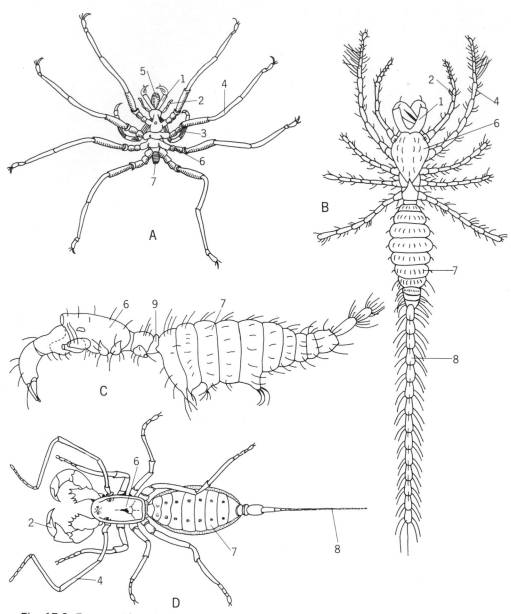

Fig. 17.2. Pycnogonids and Arachnids. **A.** A female *Nymphon hirsites*, with five pairs of legs. The diminutive first pair are the ovigerous legs, on which males carry eggs. **B** and **C**. *Koenenia*, a palpigrade. **B**, dorsal view; **C**, lateral view with legs removed. Palpigrades have a prosoma divided into two sections, each with separate carapace. The chelicera are well developed, and the next pair of appendages (pedipalps) look like and are used as walking legs. The first pair of legs, however, are longer, and are carried forward as sensory appendages. The long opisthosoma is followed by a long, jointed postabdomen. **D.** *Mastigoprocteus*, a uropygid. The uropygids have a single or double prosomal carapace, and an opisthosoma with eight broader somites making up a mesosoma, and three narrower ones forming the metasoma. A long

696

Order Acarina. Ticks and mites. Arachnids with a single prosomal carapace and a broad junction between the prosoma and opisthosoma; opisthosomal somites united; prosoma with chelicerae modified for piercing or chelate, leg-like or chelate pedipalps, and four pairs of legs with a variable number of podites; spiracles and tracheae sometimes present; one to four pairs of coxal glands, or Malpighian tubles, or both. Example: *Dermacentor* (Fig. 17.4A).

Class Merostomata

The five existing species of horseshoe crabs are the last leaves on the merostomate tree. They look like archaic creatures, deservedly, for animals like them rubbed elbows with trilobites. Many of the ancient merostomates were large and had heavy exoskeletons, and thus fossilized well. Although they probably appear to have been more common than they actually were, there is no reason to doubt that they were relatively abundant throughout the later Ordovician and Silurian days. *Limulus*, one of the modern genera, first appeared about 200 million years ago, during the Triassic. In a sense the horseshoe crabs are living fossils, thus deserving of the extensive study that they have received.

Xiphosura polyphemus, the American species, reaches a length of about 0.6m. The prosoma is circular in front and covered by a solid carapace. At the margins the dorsal covering is turned under to form a conspicuous doublure (Fig. 17.5). The opisthosoma is also covered by a dorsal shield. It is hinged to the prosoma and to the long, spiky telson. The prosoma bears seven pairs of appendages on its ventral side. The first pair are the chelicerae, pincer-like appendages used to partially macerate the food. The next four pairs are leg-like and end in small pincers or chelae. The next pair, also leg-like, end in curious leaf-like tips used to sweep away mud that clings to the body surface during burrowing. The seventh pair of appendages are attached to the pregenital somite, which is generally reduced. They are very small, modified appendages known as chilaria. The lack of any significant difference between the second pair of appendages, which in the majority of chelicerates are modified appendages known as pedipalps, and the third pair of appendages, which in most chelicerates are the first walking legs, is a primitive characteristic. Generally, the head region is enlarged by the addition of segments to its posterior end, usually with the accompanying specialization of the appendages of the added segments, most often as mouthparts.

The prosomal appendages function to some extent in locomotion but are particularly important in capturing prey. Horseshoe crabs feed on worms, especially nereids, in the soft bottoms that they most commonly prefer. The prey is caught by the chelicerae while *Xiphosura* burrows in the mud. The first four pairs of walking legs have projections known as gnathobases on the inner side of the basal podites. These are used to break the prey into particles that can be swallowed.

Six pairs of flap-like appendages are found on the opisthosoma. Although they have lost all resemblance to ordinary legs, they are undoubtedly highly modified appendages. The first pair form a flattened operculum, used to cover most of the posterior appendages. The gonopores are found in the operculum. The rest of the

postabdomen is attached. The chelicerae are large, and the pedipalps are chelate and prehensile. (A and D, after Snodgrass. B and C, after Kraepelin, from Savory.) 1, chelicera; 2, pedipalp; 3, ovigerous leg; 4, walking leg; 5, proboscis; 6, prosoma; 7, opisthosoma; 8, postabdomen; 9, pedicel.

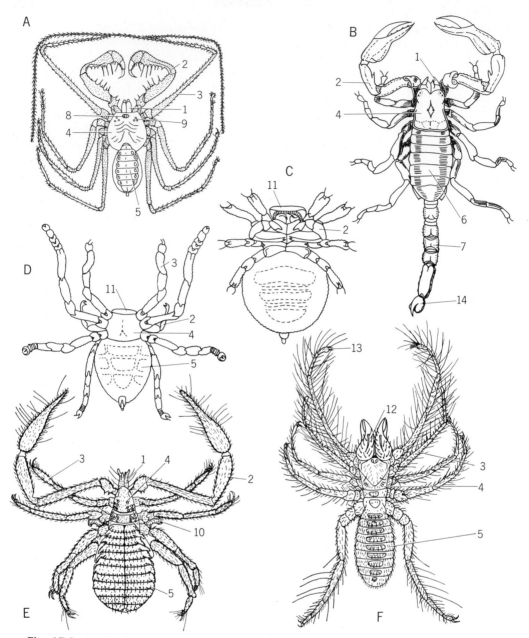

Fig. 17.3. Arachnids. **A.** *Stygopharynus*, an amblypygid. Amblypygids are arachnids without
a postabdomen, and with a single narrow segment at the rear of the opisthosoma, but otherwise much like whip scorpions. **B.** *Chactas*, a scorpion. Scorpions have a prosoma with a
single carapace, an opisthosoma with a broader mesosoma of seven somites and narrow metasoma of five somites, and a telson modified to form a sting. The pedipalps are large and
have conspicuous chelae. **C** and **D.** *Ricinoides*, a ricinuleid. C, ventral view. D, dorsal view;
the prosoma has a single carapace, and males have modified third legs. A narrow pedicel connects the prosoma and opisthosoma. A hood at the front of the carapace covers the mouth

opisthosomal appendages have gill plates on their posterior surface. The gill plates are fitted together, rather like the leaves of a book, and are sometimes termed book gills. The tail spine, or telson, starts just behind the anus. It is probably not homologous to the telson found in other arthropods, where it is the final somite containing the anus. The telson is used to right the body when it is overturned, and pushes the body forward during burrowing. A strong hinge attaches the telson to the opisthosoma.

A horseshoe crab looks ungainly. It creeps about slowly and awkwardly and swims very poorly, using the flattened opisthosomal appendages as paddles. One might expect, however, that any creature constructed on such an ancient pattern must be beautifully adapted to some kind of environment. In the case of horseshoe crabs this environment is soft mud or sand. The sharpened margin of the carapace makes an excellent shovel edge, and with the aid of the legs and telson which thrust it forward against relatively high resistance, it gets about very handily in the soft-bottom material.

Digestion. The mouth opens into the foregut, lined with cuticle continuous with exoskeleton. A narrow, tubular esophagus leads forward and upward, expanding into a thin-walled, distensible crop, which opens into a heavy-walled, sclerotized gizzard. The opening of the gizzard into the midgut is guarded by a conical valve. The cuticular lining of the valve is folded, and strains out large particles of food. The midgut consists of a small stomach, and a relatively wide intestine. Large digestive glands open into the stomach through pores on each side of the stomach. The hindgut is a short rectum (Fig. 17.6A).

The lack of jaws has undoubtedly had an important part to play in determining the course of foregut evolution. Food is not ground up by the chelicerae and gnathobases at the base of the legs. Large pieces of food material are often swallowed. These pieces are mashed in the gizzard. The hardened gizzard walls protect the lining cells and aid in the trituration of food. Any material that cannot be ground up in the gizzard cannot pass the valve to the midgut, and must be regurgitated.

Food entering the stomach undergoes a preliminary digestion caused by trypsin and alkaline lipase. The partly digested food enters the digestive glands, where the final phases of protein digestion and much of absorption take place. Food residues returned to the stomach pass into the intestine. In the last part of the intestine, mucous fecal pellets are formed.

Circulation. Horseshoe crabs have a typical arthropod heart, derived from a dorsal blood vessel like that of annelids, which carries blood forward. The arthropod heart is especially modified to serve a circulatory system in which much of circulation takes place in open, haemocoelic sinuses. As a rule, a high development of the arterial or venous systems is not a progressive trait in arthropods, al-

and chelicerae. E. *Chelifer*, a pseudoscorpion. These tiny arachnids have a single carapace over the prosoma, and a broad, flat opisthosoma. The chelicerae contain silk glands and the powerful pedipalps contain poison glands. F. *Galeodes*, a solpugid. The solpugids are relatively large arachnids with two dorsal plates covering the prosoma. The huge chelicerae contain no poison glands, but are remarkably powerful. The leg-like pedipalps are adhesive, and are used in climbing and in handling food. (A, E, and F, after Savory. C and D, after Hansen and Sorensen, from Savory. B, after Snodgrass.) 1, chelicera; 2, pedipalp; 3, walking leg; 4, prosoma; 5, opisthosoma; 6, mesosoma; 7, metasoma; 8, median (indirect) eye; 9, lateral (direct) eye; 10, lateral genital sac; 11, cucullus or hood; 12, flagellum of chelicera; 13, sucker on pedipalp; 14, sting.

though in larger species a fairly complex system of blood vessels is often retained. The relatively complex system of arteries and veins of horseshoe crabs is undoubtedly a reflection of their relatively large size and of their primitiveness.

The heart is a long, tubular structure, held in the pericardial sinus by a system of nine pairs of suspensory ligaments. No veins return blood to the heart. Blood returns into the pericardial sinus, and the heart is bathed by blood. Blood enters the heart by way of ostia, a series of paired openings through the heart wall. Each

ostium is guarded by a valve, preventing the exit of blood when the heart is contracting. The long, tubular form of the heart and the large number (eight pairs) of ostia are primitive characteristics. In some arthropods the heart has lost its similarity to a blood vessel and is relatively short, with one or a few pairs of ostia. Blood enters the pericardial sinus during diastole and flows through the ostia into the heart lumen. A long pacemaker ganglion on the dorsal side of the heart intiates the beat. Inhibitory nerves from the brain pass to the pacemaker

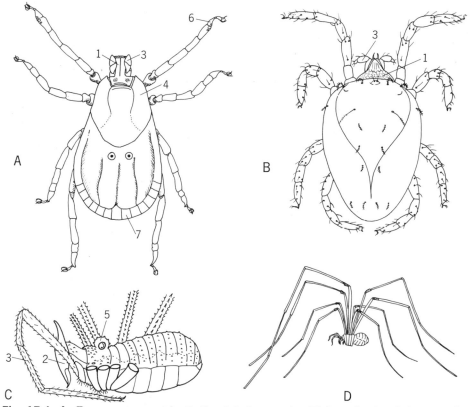

Fig. 17.4. **A.** *Dermacentor*, a tick. **B.** *Penthalodes*, a mite. Ticks and mites belong to the order Acarina, and are widespread and important arachnids. The capitulum, formed by the head and mouth parts, is characteristic of the Acarina. **C** and **D.** Body and over-all view of a harvestman. The opiliones can be recognized by the lack of a pedicel and the long, slender legs. The dorsal tubercle containing the eyes is also characteristic. (A, after Snodgrass. B, after Baker and Wharton. C, after Roewer, from Savory.) **1**, capitulum; **2**, chelicera; **3**, pedipalp; **4**, dorsal shield; **5**, dorsal tubercle; **6**, tarsal sense organ; **7**, festoon.

ganglion. During systole the ostial valves close and blood is forced into the arteries. Blood entering the heart has returned from the gills and is freshly aerated, so the heart is an arterial heart. At the end of systole, the backflow of blood is prevented by the closure of semilunar valves at the arterial bases.

The arterial system is complex. Four pairs of lateral arteries pass from the heart to a pair of collateral arteries which tend to run parallel to the heart (Fig. 17.6B). The collateral arteries serve as feeder vessels for several circulatory arcs. From the front of the heart a pair of aortae and a median frontal artery arise. These are feeder vessels for cephalic arteries and, as the aortae combine and turn backward below the gut, for the circulatory arcs arising from the ventral vessel.

Four pairs of intestinal arteries arise from the collateral arteries, and convey blood to the midgut. The collateral arteries also give rise to fourteen pairs of lateral arteries, which twig out to the tissues in their region and extend to a system of marginal arteries at the edge of the prosoma and opisthosoma. The two collateral arteries unite behind the heart to form the superior abdominal artery, which runs to the telson and gives rise to a pair of lateral arteries that extend to the posterior marginal arteries of the opisthosoma. The anterior marginal artery runs along the prosomal margin and supplies blood to the eye and digestive gland. The system of arteries arising from the collateral arteries is a predominantly dorsal arterial network and is strongly metameric in its organization.

The frontal artery supplies blood to the foregut, and branches each way to anastomose with the anterior marginals.

The paired aortae curve down and back, giving off branches to the foregut. They join near the mouth, forming a vascular ring around the base of the esophagus. Most of the ventral arteries arise from this ring. The relationship of the nervous system and ventral arterial system is inter-

esting. The brain lies within a vascular ring, and most of the major nerves run within arteries. A similar arrangement seen in many arachnids gives evidence of the relationship of the merostomates to the arachnids. A large ventral artery encloses the nerve cord and runs caudad, sending a branch up to the superior abdominal artery and ending near the origin of the nerves to the telson. The ventral

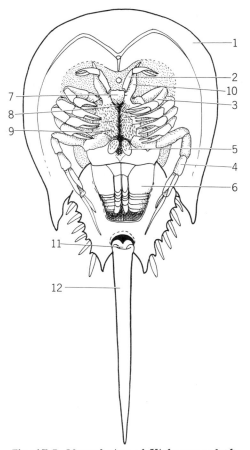

Fig. 17.5. Ventral view of *Xiphosura polyphemus*, a horseshoe crab, showing the prosomal and opisthosomal appendages. (After Snodgrass.) 1, doublure; 2, chelicera; 3, first walking leg; 4, fifth walking leg; 5, chilaria; 6, opisthosomal appendages; 7, epistome; 8, mouth; 9, endites (gnathobases of walking legs); 10, coxa of first walking leg; 11, anus; 12, tail spine.

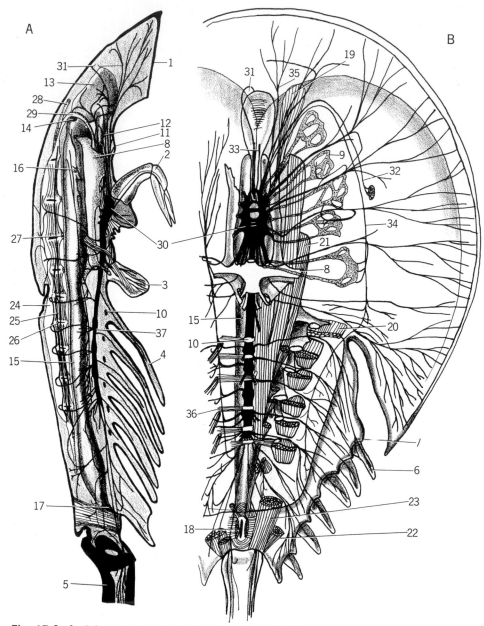

Fig. 17.6. **A.** Schematic longitudinal section through *Xiphosura*, showing internal organization. **B.** Scheme of internal organization of *Xiphosura*, as seen in ventral view. (After Patten
and Redenbaugh, from Shipley.) *External features:* 1, cephalic doublure; 2, chelicera;
3, chilarium; 4, genital operculum (first opisthosomal appendage); 5, tail spine; 6, lateral
spines of opisthosoma; 7, lateral projections of opisthosoma. *Skeleton:* 8, endosternite;
9, endocoxite; 10, opisthosomatic endochondrite. *Digestive system:* 11, mouth; 12, esophagus;
13, proventriculus; 14, pyloric valve; 15, intestine; 16, opening of digestive gland; 17, anal

artery supplies blood to the midgut and ventral tissues generally. A number of vessels to ventral prosomal parts arise from the vascular ring. Nerves lie in these arteries.

At the ends of the finest arterial twigs, the blood enters haemocoelic lacunae, where most of the exchange between blood and tissues occur. All of these empty into lateral and dorsal collecting vessels, which unite with a main ventral collecting vessel on each side of the body. An afferent branchial vessel to each gill arises from the ventral collecting vessel. Efferent branchial vessels return aerated blood into a branchiopericardial vessel that conveys the blood to the pericardial sinus.

The blood contains a respiratory pigment, haemocyanin, and has an oxygen-carrying capacity about a fourth as high as most fishes. The haemocyanin is dissolved in the plasma.

Respiration. The heavy arthropod exoskeleton interferes with surface respiratory exchange and favors the development of special respiratory surfaces. The book gills of *Xiphosura* are interesting, for they resemble the book lungs of many terrestrial arachnids.

Each book gill is made up of a hundred or so thin "leaves" with stiffened outer margins and a delicate cuticle (Fig. 17.7A). Arthropods have no cilia, and ventilation of the respiratory surfaces must be achieved without dependence on ciliary currents. Rhythmic movements of the opisthosomal appendages circulate water over the gill surface, and also serve to drive blood into the leaves of the gill with each forward movement and drain blood from the leaves with each backward movement.

This arrangement serves the same purpose as the booster hearts of many molluscs and annelids.

Excretion. Xiphosura has a system of coxal glands. Four pairs of red glands lie at the bases of the walking legs. The glands contain a tangle of fine ducts which merge to form a single duct. These ducts converge on each side in an excretory sac derived from the coelom. A coiled tubule arises from the excretory sac (Fig. 17.7B). The tubule is dilated terminally as a bladder. Urine is discharged from an excretory pore at the base of the fifth legs. The coxal glands are thought to be highly modified derivatives of the nephridia. As the arthropod coelom is greatly reduced, the kind of nephridial system that suffices for the annelids cannot be used. Probably some of the same factors that lead to modifications of the leech nephridia in conjunction with coelom reduction were also operating in arthropods.

Details of excretory physiology are unknown. It is known that the digestive glands excrete excess calcium into the gut, and it is probable that the gut wall also has a secondary excretory function.

Nervous System. Although horseshoe crabs are primitive in some respects, they have a highly centralized nervous system, considerably more advanced than that of many arthropods. The primitive nervous system must have been much like that of polychaetes, with a series of segmental ganglia associated with the nerve cord. A greater degree of centralization can be achieved by the union of ganglia to make compound structures, or by the suppression of some of the ganglia and enlargement of others. Arthropods have used both systems. In *Xiphosura*, all of the pro-

sphincter; 18, anus. *Muscles:* 19, tergoplastral muscle; 20, external branchial muscle; 21, branchiothoracic muscle; 22, extensor of telson; 23, flexor of telson. *Circulatory system:* 24, pericardial cavity; 25, heart; 26, ostium; 27, anterior end of lateral artery; 28, frontal artery; 29, aortic arch. *Nervous system:* 30, brain; 31, nerve to median eye; 32, nerve to lateral eye; 33, olfactory nerve; 34, lateral nerve I; 35, lateral nerve II; 36, lateral sympathetic nerve; 37, ventral nerve cord in ventral sinus.

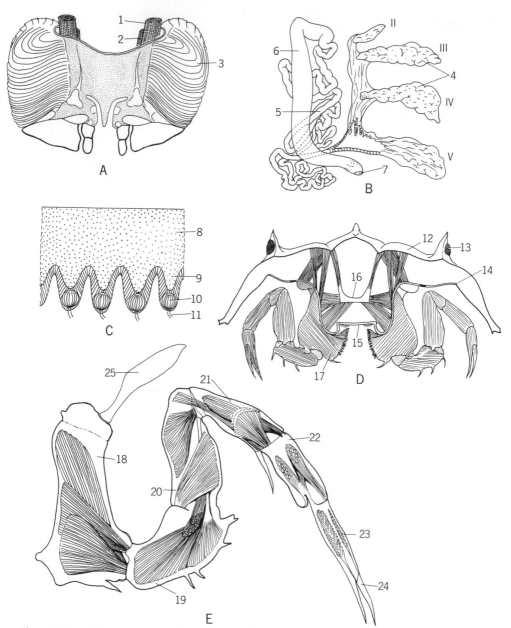

Fig. 17.7. **A.** Posterior view of second opisthosomal appendages, showing arrangement of the gill plates. **B.** Coxal glands of a horseshoe crab. The coxal glands are compound, formed from organs in four somites, all opening through a single duct and pore. **C.** Scheme of structure of a part of the compound eye of a horseshoe crab. Note the continuous cuticle and separate ommatidia, each with its own nerve. **D.** Scheme of cross section of *Xiphosura*, showing the relationship of skeletal regions and appendages. **E.** The last leg of *Xiphosura*, showing podites and muscular arrangement. (A, D, and E, after Snodgrass. C, after Lankester and Bourne, from Snodgrass. B, after Patten and Hazen, from Gehardt, in Kükenthal and

somal ganglia are united with the brain and circumenteric connectives to form a complex nerve collar. The collar lies in the vascular ring and gives rise to a double nerve cord located in the ventral vessel. Five opisthosomal ganglia lie on the ventral nerve cord, indicating some centralization of the opisthosomal nervous system as well as the prosomal nervous system. A sympathetic (stomodaeal, stomatogastric) nervous system provides nervous control of the heart and digestive tract. Lateral longitudinal nerves parallel the nerve cord, and give rise to nerves to the heart ganglion, augmenting or depressing heartbeat. Nerves arise from the nerve collar to the sense organs, prosomal appendages, and segmental musculature, and from the opisthosomal nerve cord to the musculature of the opisthosoma.

It is evident that the nervous system is far more complex in *Xiphosura* than in polychaetes. The musculature is far more complex, and the sense organs at least as highly advanced and in some instances considerably more so. A part of the nervous complexity is the consequence of the simultaneous improvement of the musculature and motor nervous system, and the development of sense organs and the sensory nervous system. There is, no doubt, an important gain in feedback controls over physiological processes and in the kinesthetic feedback which is so important in locomotion, but these are not very well analyzed in *Xiphosura*.

Sense Organs. With the development of a heavy cuticle, the simple surface sensory cells become outmoded. Receptive cells must either be lifted, like periscopes extending from the heavy hull of a submarine, or be supplied with some kind of instruments that will transmit the energies striking the relatively impervious surface to the sensitive endings. By and large, sense organ development in arthropods has followed the line of obtaining the maximum of information with the minimum of exposure. The exoskeletal surface is not interrupted, although it may be attenuated at the sense organs. A variety of bristles extend from the surface. Many of these are sensory. Most of the kinds of sense organs typical of arthropods are known better in other groups and will be discussed elsewhere (pp. 738, 894). The horseshoe crabs are sensitive to chemicals and to tactile stimuli and have well-developed eyes.

Some of the annelids have compound photoreceptors, formed of clusters of sensory cells. The same tendency, in arthropods, has led to the development of compound eyes. *Xiphosura* has three pairs of eyes, a pair of larval eyes that degenerate during development; a pair of median, pigment-cup ocelli, with cuticular lenses and corneas, known as the median eyes; and a pair of compound lateral eyes. The structure of the lateral eyes is particularly interesting. Each visual component of the eye is an ommatidium, formed by 10 to 15 photosensitive cells surrounding a central rhabdome. The rhabdome is formed by the union of the photoreceptive rhabdomeres present in the component retinula cells. When light strikes the rhabdome it evokes an impulse in a ganglion cell associated with the rhabdome. This is an interesting development, for in general the neurosensory cells of invertebrates are receptors and transmitters of stimuli. The

Krumbach.) *Opisthosomatic appendage:* 1, promotor muscle; 2, remotor muscle, which with the promotor muscle moves appendages to ventilate the respiratory surfaces; 3, leaves of book gill. *Coxal glands* (Roman numerals designate body somite in which the glands lie): 4, coxal gland; 5, convoluted tubule; 6, bladder; 7, excretory pore. *Eye:* 8, cornea; 9, lens; 10, ommatidium; 11, nerve fiber. *Cross section:* 12, carapace; 13, eye; 14, doublure; 15, venter; 16, endosternum; 17, endite of leg. *Leg:* 18, coxa; 19, trochanter; 20, femur; 21, patella; 22, tibia; 23, tarsus; 24, pretarsus; 25, epipodite.

sensory neuron associated with the ommatidium is structurally independent of the receptor. Each of the ommatidia is an independent unit and serves as the source of an independent nerve impulse. The compound eye of *Xiphosura* is made up of a number of ommatidia, each with an independent lens (Fig. 17.7C).

The larval eyes originally lie at a point immediately in front of the bases of the chelicerae. At this point, peculiar papillate sense organs are found in the adult. They are innervated from centers in the brain associated with the compound eyes. Spiny taste receptors are found on the gnathobases of the legs, and sensory bristles can be seen on the gill blades. At various points tactile bristles and pores thought to have a sensory function have been described, but a full analysis of sensory reception has not yet been made.

Skeleton and Musculature. As the cuticle of arthropods becomes hardened to form a heavy exoskeleton, four skeletal regions tend to form in each somite. The dorsal surface of the somite is covered by a sclerite known as the tergum, the ventral surface by a sclerite known as the sternum, and the two lateral surfaces by a pair of sclerites known as the pleura. Not all of these sclerites are formed in all arthropods. Sometimes they are all fused into a skeletal ring for each somite. In other cases the plates are fused longitudinally to form compound plates over whole tagmata, as in *Xiphosura*. In still other cases, the plates are divided into smaller, subsidiary sclerites.

A cross section of *Xiphosura* shows the basic arrangement of skeletal and muscular parts. The carapace is formed by the united terga of the prosomal somites (Fig. 17.7 D), and is doubled under to form the doublure, so that part of ventral exoskeleton is formed from the dorsal skeletal plates. At the margin of the doublure, the exoskeleton becomes membranous and curves downward. This is the pleural region, which is largely without skeletal plates in *Xiphosura*. Five much reduced and modified pleura

are found on each side of the body, however. The ventral exoskeleton is more flexible than the dorsal, and is separated from the dorsal exoskeleton by the membranous pleural regions.

Xiphosura has an endoskeleton independent of the apodemes that may be present at sutures between plates. An endosternum, composed of cartilage-like tissue, is swung from the carapace by muscles and provides sites for the attachment of body musculature and muscles reaching the leg bases.

The leg musculature of *Xiphosura* is typical of that of arthropods in general, although details differ considerably in different groups. The musculature is arranged to exploit the possibilities of the jointed skeleton (Fig. 17.7E). The coxal podite is attached to membranous, flexible cuticle, and is moved by nine muscles attached to its margin, five from the carapace and four from the endosternum. The large number of muscle strands at the leg base provide relatively delicate control of the leg movements. The musculature of the leg itself is relatively simple. Each joint of the leg is typically a hinge joint, permitting movement in one plane only. In a mechanism of this kind, the required musculature is a set of flexors and extensors for each of the various joints between podites. Legs which terminate in chelae are equipped with tarsi that project forward as immovable fingers, and are opposed to movable fingers formed of the pretarsi. At these joints the flexor and extensor muscles become levators and depressors of the pretarsal finger of the pincer. Leg muscles are relatively stable and are sometimes useful in determining the homologies of leg podites when two legs with differing numbers of podites are being compared.

Reproductive System. The reproductive organs are quite similar in males and females. A median gonad is formed of loosely organized masses of follicles, in which the sperm or ova are produced. The gonad extends forward into the prosoma, where it tends to become tangled with the digestive gland, and back into the opisthosoma, where it lies below the intestine. In each sex, paired gonoducts arise from the gonad, and lead to paired gonopores located on the operculum, formed by the first pair of opisthosomal appendages.

The female builds nests in the sand for the eggs, or attaches them to the opisthosomal appendages. The male clings to the female and releases sperm over the eggs as they are put into place. The eggs are then enclosed in a leathery capsule which eventually breaks away.

The egg undergoes holoblastic cleavage and eventually becomes a stereoblastula. The gastrula stage is also solid, as is typical of arthropods generally. The mesoderm is arranged in two growth centers, one forming the first four prosomal somites, and the other the last three prosomal and the opisthosomal somites. The young eventually emerge as trilobite larvae (Fig. 17.8B). The larvae are active creatures, clambering about on the bottom and sometimes burrowing in the mud. The telson gradually develops during the early molts.

Other Xiphosura. Xiphosurids appeared first in the upper Silurian. Among the more primitive xiphosurids the dorsal skeleton of the opisthosoma is composed of separate, segmental plates. *Limulus* appeared first in the Triassic and is one of the oldest living animal genera. A considerable number of other kinds of fossil Limulada, with fused opisthosomal tergites, has been described.

There is some question about how closely the xiphosurids and trilobites are related. The similarity of the trilobite larva to trilobites may be superficial. However, the two growth centers of the xiphosurid embryo play the same role as the acron and pygidial growth center of trilobites, and the Eurypterida, which are also merostomates, have similar growth centers appearing during development. It is certainly not impossible that the fossil merostomates were related to the trilobites more closely

than either were related to the first mandibulates.

Eurypterida. Eurypterids were once very prominent but are now extinct. They appeared first in marine habitats, but moved into fresh-water, and, perhaps, to terrestrial environments. They are among the largest arthropods that have ever lived and include the largest arthropod species known. *Pterygotus* reached almost 3 m., and some other eurypterids were nearly as large. Because of their large size they are sometimes called the Gigantostraea. The

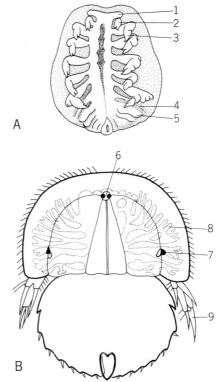

Fig. 17.8. Development of Horseshoe Crab. A. An embryo, with developing appendages. B. A trilobite larva. (A, after Iwanoff. B, after Kingsley and Takano, from Shipley.) 1, cephalic lobe; 2, primordium of chelicera; 3, primordium of first leg; 4, primordium of chilarium; 5, primordium of first opisthosomatic appendage; 6, middle eye; 7, lateral eye; 8, margin of digestive gland; 9, tip of last walking leg.

first eurypterids appeared in the lower Ordovician, and the last ones were found in the Permian.

Eurypterids had a superficial resemblance to scorpions (Fig. 17.1C,D). The opisthosoma was divided into a broader mesosoma and narrower metasoma. The telson was sometimes sharp and recurved, bearing a close resemblance to the sting of a scorpion, and sometimes flattened, as if for swimming. The prosoma bore a pair of chelicerae and five pairs of legs, modified for creeping or swimming.

An interesting eurypterid feature was the flat, gill-like appendages on the ventral surface of the opisthosoma, concealed by extensions of the skeletal plates. These concealed gills may be a step toward the formation of the book lungs of terrestrial arachnids, and some have thought eurypterids are the ancestral stock from which scorpions arose. This, however, is far from certain. The earliest eurypterids were considerably less scorpion-like than the later ones, and by the time that they had become so similar to scorpions, scorpions had already appeared. Furthermore, it is not now so universally believed that scorpions are the most primitive of arachnids. In any case, the similarity of the concealed book gills of the eurypterids and the book lungs of scorpions either indicates a very strong convergent trend or is true evidence of relationship.

Class Pycnogonida

If one were asked to design a Thing from Outer Space, one might do worse than take a pycnogonid as his model. These weird-looking arthropods seem to be all legs, as their alternative name, Pantopoda, suggests. Their brain structure clearly places them among the chelicerates, but they are as unconventional about internal anatomy as about external appearance, and it is impossible to guess how they are related to the other chelicerates. They have special-

ized along lines that would appear to be unrewarding, but they are far from uncommon among the bryozoan and hydroid colonies upon which they feed. They are found in tropical and in polar seas, and in both shallow and deep waters. Most of them are only a few millimeters long, but the largest have a leg spread of over 0.4 m.

The pycnogonid body is almost gone, and the little that is left is almost wholly prosoma (Fig. 17.1E; 17.2A). The opisthosoma is reduced to a tiny, unsegmented protuberance with the anus at its tip. The prosoma is unconventionally formed. The mouth is at the end of a proboscis, sometimes nearly as long as the body. The remainder of the head has four pairs of appendages, chelicerae, palps, and two pairs of legs. The anterior legs are slender ovigerous legs, on which males bear clusters of eggs at breeding time (Fig. 17.9B). The rest of the prosoma is segmented, and usually contains three segments, each with a pair of walking legs, but in some species one or two additional segments and pairs of legs are present. The additional segments appear sporadically, with no obvious relationship to the characters used to divide the pycnogonids into subsidiary groups. The legs are unusual in having an extra podite. The addition of legs, somites, and podites to the usual complement is a great burden to students of comparative arthropod anatomy, and considerably complicates the matter of determining homologies.

The chelicerae have three segments and are fairly standard. The palps are reminiscent of the pedipalps of arachnids; they are sometimes missing and have a variable number of segments when present. The ovigerous legs differ with the species, and appear to be reduced walking legs. The normal walking legs or pereiopods have nine segments, the tarsal segment being divided into two pieces. They are like arachnids in having a patella that is carried horizontally, or, as Snodgrass (1952) puts it, a double knee. The most unusual feature of the leg is the independent musculature of the two tarsal segments of the ovigerous legs, found nowhere else among arthropods.

Pycnogonids creep about over the surface of colonial hydroids and bryozoa. A part of a zooid is grasped by the chelicerae and sucked into the mouth. Sometimes the chelicerae clip off fragments, but this is usually unnecessary. The muscular proboscis contains the pharynx, which has a hardened lining. The sucking movements of the proboscis fragment soft food par-

ticles as they are swallowed, and bristles at the end of the pharynx strain out all but the finest particles. Food passes through a narrow esophagus into the midgut. Digestion and absorption of food occurs in the midgut. Branches of the midgut extend out into the appendages, reaching almost to the tips. Intracellular digestion occurs in the mucosal lining of the midgut and its branches. Pycnogonids are unique in many ways, but in no point are they more so than in the method of intracellular diges-

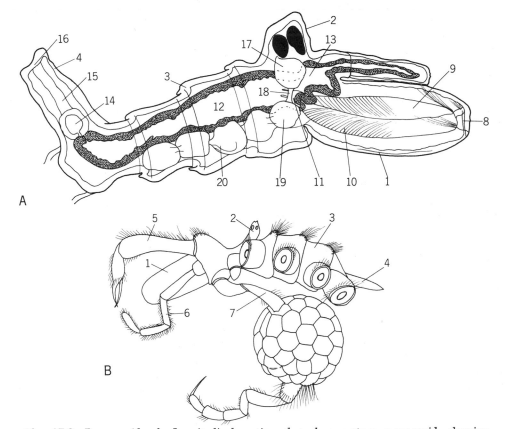

Fig. 17.9. Pycnogonids. A. Longitudinal section through a mature pycnogonid, showing scheme of organization. B. Lateral view of a male pycnogonid, with all but the ovigerous legs removed. (A, after Dohrn. B, after Sars, from Helfer, in Kükenthal and Krumbach.) *External features:* 1, proboscis; 2, dorsal tubercle, containing ocelli; 3, prosoma; 4, opisthosoma; 5, chelicera; 6, pedipalp; 7, ovigerous leg carrying egg mass. *Digestive system:* 8, mouth; 9, proboscis cavity; 10, straining bristles; 11, esophagus; 12, midgut; 13, anterior caecum; 14, hindgut; 15, rectum; 16, anus. *Nervous system:* 17, cerebral ganglion; 18, circumenteric connective; 19, subesophageal ganglion; 20, nerve cord and segmental ganglion.

tion. Certain of the mucosal cells take up food material until they are gorged with food. They strip away from the mucosa and float freely in the cavity of the midgut. Other mucosal cells absorb food from them until, with the food exhausted, the floating cells are eliminated from the anus.

Internal anatomy is very simple, for there is no excretory system or respiratory system, and the circulatory system is not complex. A transverse membrane separates the dorsal pericardial sinus from the rest of the haemocoel. The heart lies in the pericardial sinus. Blood enters the heart through paired ostia and is driven forward to enter the perivisceral cavity anteriorly. It flows back in the perivisceral sinus and into the appendages. Blood returns to the pericardial sinus through openings in the transverse membrane separating the two sinuses.

Little is known of pycnogonid sense organs. Four inverse pigment-cup ocelli are found on the posterior end of the cephalon, directly over the brain. The brain is composed of a protocerebrum and tritocerebrum, without a deutocerebrum, as is characteristic of chelicerates generally. The archicerebrum of polychaetes contains centers associated with the eyes and prostomial palps, and the first nerves to a body appendage arise from the first ganglion on the nerve cord (Fig. 17.10). In mandibulates, the archicerebrum is somewhat more complex, having divided into a protocerebrum associated with the optic nerves and a deutocerebrum associated with the antennal nerves. A third part of the brain, the tritocerebrum, is associated with the nerves to the second antennae of Crustacea. Chelicerates have no deutocerebrum. Apparently the parts which correspond to the first antennae are missing, and the portion of the brain associated with these appendages has been reduced. The chelicerae are innervated from the tritocerebrum, and so appear to correspond to the second antennae of crustaceans.

The proboscis contains a dorsal, gangli-onated nerve from the brain, and a pair of ventrolateral nerves from the subesophageal ganglion. An anterior ring ganglion passes around the proboscis, and additional nerve rings occur at intervals. The nerve cord is double. It arises at the subesophageal ganglion and has four ganglia on it. Nerves to the opisthosoma arise from the end of the nerve cord.

Sexes are separate, and females have reduced ovigerous legs. The gonads are U-shaped and branch out into the legs, opening through gonopores on the coxal leg podites. Some males have gonopores on the last pair of legs only, but most males and all females have gonopores on several or all pairs of legs. In females the eggs are stored in the femurs of legs with gonopores.

Males shed sperm on the eggs as they leave the female. The eggs are deposited directly on the ovigerous legs of the male, or the male gathers them together. The eggs are cemented to bristles on the legs and the leg is bent back like a hook while carrying the eggs. The young may remain attached to the male parent for a time after hatching, or they may scatter at once to become internal or external parasites on hydroids.

Development follows the general arthropod pattern. The zygote undergoes holoblastic cleavage, equal or grossly unequal, depending on the amount of yolk in the egg. Mesodermal bands form on the surface of the solid gastrula. The appendages develop from the mesodermal bands, the chelicerae first and the remainder in regular sequence, from front to back. The young usually have three pairs of appendages at hatching and acquire additional appendages with succeeding molts. The larvae develop cheliceral glands that secrete an adhesive used for attachment to the male parent or to hydroids.

Pycnogonids are queer animals, with queer habits. They are certainly chelicerates, and appear superficially to be more like the arachnids than the merostomates. They are so highly modified, however, that it is not possible to define their relationship to the other members of the subphylum. The larva is peculiar, and is in a sense highly specialized because of its habit of attachment to the hydroids or male parent. Yet, in many ways the larva is one of the most primitive of arthropod larvae. Some have felt that the larva relates pycnogonids to the protoarthropod stem and that they are derivatives of the chelicerate stem near its point of origin. Be that as it may, the pycnogonids are very interesting creatures and deserve rather more attention than

they have had from both physiological and evolutionary points of view.

Class Arachnida

Arachnids are the most successful chelicerates today, and even so may not have reached their peak. Well over 50,000 species have been described. An intensive study of the mites has just begun and the number of species will certainly go far beyond the present count. Arachnids com-

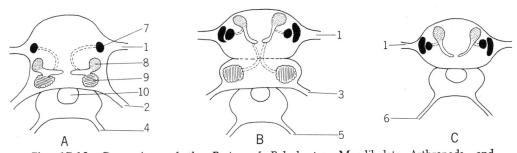

Fig. 17.10. Comparison of the Brains of Polychaetes, Mandibulate Arthropods, and Chelicerates (schematic.) In polychaetes (A) the brain is located in the prostomium, and the first trunk appendages are innervated from the subesophageal ganglion. The brain gives rise to an optic nerve, associated with optic nuclei (black) and the corpora pedunculata (stippled), and to a palp nerve, associated with a palp nucleus (striated). In mandibulate arthropods (B) the brain is composed of a protocerebrum, deutocerebrum, and tritocerebrum. In all mandibulates the protocerebrum contains the corpora pedunculata and optic centers, and gives off the optic nerve. In Crustacea the deutocerebrum contains nuclei associated with the first antennae and gives off nerves to the first antennae. It seems clear that the protocerebrum and deutocerebrum correspond to the brain of polychaetes. In insects, the tritocerebrum is small, while in the Crustacea the tritocerebrum is larger and is associated with the second antennae. It appears evident that the antennae of insects correspond to the first antennae of Crustacea, and that the tritocerebrum is a new part of the brain, derived from the subesophageal ganglion of polychaete-like ancestors. As the addition of posterior somites to the head is the general method of head development in arthropods, this appears a reasonable interpretation of the evidence. In chelicerate arthropods (C) the protocerebrum corresponds to the protocerebrum of mandibulates and gives off the optic nerves. There is no appendage corresponding to the first antennae of Crustacea and the antennae of insects, and the deutocerebrum has wholly disappeared. The tritocerebrum corresponds to the tritocerebrum of the mandibulate arthropods, and gives off nerves to the chelicerae, which must therefore correspond to the second antennae of Crustacea and the reduced somite in the insect head. Precise head homologies, however, are made more complex than this account would suggest because of the possibility of some segments and their appendages having degenerated and disappeared, leaving no corresponding brain regions. (After Hanström.) 1, optic nerve; 2, nerve to palp; 3, nerve to first antenna; 4, nerve to first appendage of trunk; 5, nerve to second antenna; 6, nerve to chelicera; 7, optic ganglion; 8, pedunculate body; 9, ganglion for palp or antenna; 10, opening for digestive tube.

pensate for their small size by large numbers, and are ecologically important in most terrestrial environments. Arachnids make up 18 per cent of the arthropod macrofauna of Illinois deciduous and Utah coniferous forests, and are predominant in the mesofauna of the soil. About 20,000 mites per cubic meter are reported from soil 10 to 20 cm. below the surface in tropical and temperate forests; over 160,-000 mites per cubic meter have been found in disturbed grassland soil in England.

Arachnids were the first arthropods to invade terrestrial habitats. The oldest arachnid fossils are Silurian scorpions, but by the end of the Palaeozoic, a number of arachnid orders had appeared, including the Opiliones, Acarina, Araneae, Uropygi, Ricinulei, and Solpugida. Fossil records are scanty, however, for most arachnids live under conditions that are not conducive to fossilization.

EXTERNAL FORM AND HABITS

The large number of orders reveals an extensive adaptive radiation of arachnids, followed by secondary waves of radiation in the larger groups. The smaller orders, Palpigradi, Uropygi, Amblypygi, and Ricinulei (p. 691) are predominantly inhabitants of the upper soil and surface litter in warm temperate to tropical lands. Small terrestrial animals have a relatively great body surface, at which loss of water can occur, and the majority of the more minute arachnids are limited to humid habitats. Larger arachnids are more common in cooler and in drier places. The great majority of arachnids are carnivorous. Prey is killed and held by chelae on the chelicerae or pedipalps, and food is reduced to fine particles before it is swallowed.

Scorpionida. Scorpions prefer tropical and subtropical climates, but some species occur in temperate regions. They live at the ground level, hiding in crevices or under things and emerging at night to feed.

Some species require a humid environment, but others have adapted to arid habitats.

The scorpion body is composed of a prosoma covered by a solid carapace, and an opisthosoma with separate somites. The opisthosoma is made up of a broader mesosoma (preabdomen) of seven somites and a narrow metasoma (postabdomen) of five somites, and it ends in a sting (Fig. 17.3B). Several pairs of lateral eyes are found on the carapace margin, and a pair of median eyes on the dorsal surface.

The exoskeleton is primitive in the sense that discrete pleural sclerites do not occur. The fused terga forming the carapace make up most of the prosomal exoskeleton (Fig. 17.11B,C). The prosomal cuticle folds down at the carapace margin as a narrow pleural membrane, and the appendage bases occupy the whole lower surface of the prosoma except for a narrow sternum. Each mesosomal somite is covered by a dorsal tergum and a ventral sternum, connected by the membranous pleural membrane on each side. The tergal and sternal sclerites are united to form complete skeletal rings in the metasoma.

At the anterior end of the body the carapace is turned under as a doublure, covering the bases of the chelicerae. The membranous undersurface is thickened to form a large, median labrum between the bases of the pedipalps and a horizontal plate, the epistome, immediately behind (Fig. 17.21A). The prosoma is made up of six postoral somites, each of which bears a pair of appendages. The first pair of appendages are the short, powerful chelicerae, made up of three segments. The next pair are pedipalps, which end in strong chelae (Fig. 17.11D), and have the pretarsus reduced to a terminal claw or else entirely missing. The walking legs have eight podites, two of which are tarsal segments.

The first opisthosomal somite is the pregenital somite, and since this is lost during development, the metasoma begins with somite VIII. A genital operculum covering

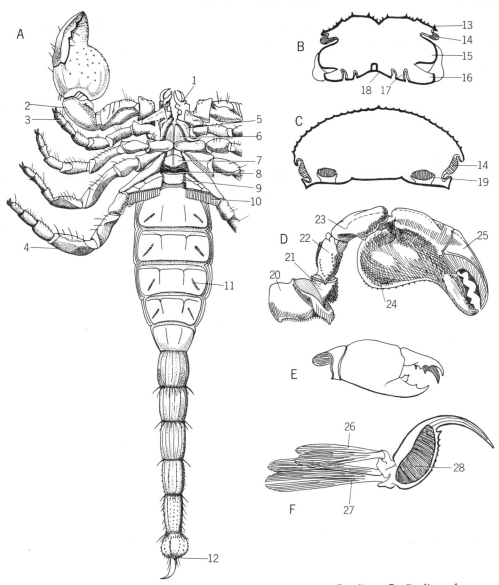

Fig. 17.11. Scorpion Anatomy. A. Ventral view of a scorpion, *Pandinus*. B. Outline of cross section through scorpion prosoma, showing relationship of the exoskeletal regions. C. Similar cross section through the mesosomal region of a scorpion. D. Pedipalp of *Pandinus*. E. Chelicera of *Centruroides*. F. Scheme of section through scorpion sting, showing musculature. (A, after Demoli and Versluys, from Kästner, in Kükenthal and Krumbach. B-D, after Snodgrass. E, composite based on Snodgrass.) *External features*: 1, chelicera; 2, pedipalp; 3, first walking leg; 4, fourth walking leg; 5, coxal endite (gnathobase) of first walking leg; 6, coxal endite of a second walking leg; 7, genital operculum of first opisthosomal appendage; 8, gonopore; 9, sternite of somite IX; 10, pecten; 11, spiracle; 12, sting. *Cross sections*: 13, carapace; 14, pleural fold; 15, coxa IV; 16, coxa V; 17, coxa VI; 18, sternum; 19, book lung. *Podites*: 20, coxa; 21, trochanter; 22, femur; 23, patella; 24, tibia; 25, tarsus. *Sting*: 26, flexor of sting; 27, extensor of sting; 28, muscles around the poison glands.

the gonopore is found on the genital somite. It is a remnant of a pair of appendages. The sternum of somite IX is narrow, and is flanked by a pair of pectines, comblike sensory appendages. The next four sterna are broad, flat plates, perforated by pairs of spiracles opening into the book lungs, which are also considered to be vestiges of appendages.

The rest of the somites have no appendages. The last metasomal somite contains the anus. The sting may be a somite also, for it arises from an embryonic primordium with a ganglion. A pair of poison glands make the sting a formidable weapon. A muscular sheath covers the poison glands, forcing the poison through the paired poison ducts to a terminal pore in the barb (Fig. 17.11F). Two pairs of muscles from the last somite extend to the base of the sting. Scorpions carry the sting aloft and ready, curving the postabdomen up and forward. The ventral pair of muscles thrust the sting upward and into the prey, while the dorsal pair retract the sting. The scorpion poison is a neurotoxin, highly effective against the organisms on which it feeds, killing them immediately. The sting of most scorpions is painful but not dangerous to man, but there are some exceptions. The most dangerous is *Androctonus australis* from the Sahara, which causes death in about seven hours if the victim is not treated with antitoxin. A number of deaths in Mexico have been attributed to scorpion stings. The primary cause of death is respiratory and cardiac failure.

Most scorpions prey primarily on other arthropods, especially on the larger insects. Prey is caught by the powerful pedipalp chelae and torn up by the chelicerae, sometimes with the aid of the coxal endites on the first legs. Relatively quiescent prey may not be stung, but struggling prey is quickly overpowered by stinging. Scorpions are nocturnal animals and cannot use the eyes for recognition of prey. So little is known of sense organ physiology that the way food organisms are identified and located remains unknown.

Pseudoscorpionida. Pseudoscorpions are relatively common at the ground level in all but the most arid climatic regions. They live quiet lives in the surface litter, among grasses or mosses, or under stones. As they are only 1 to 8 mm. long, they are often overlooked. Some live in ant or termite nests, and a few live in trees. *Garypus* is found on sandy beaches in the intertidal zone, hiding under stones. *Chelifer cancroides* lives with man in his houses and outbuildings, feeding on mites or other small arthropods.

Pseudoscorpions have a superficial resemblance to scorpions, for they have large pedipalps and a broad opisthosoma, but they lack the narrower metasoma and sting at the posterior end of the body. The prosoma has six segments and the same set of appendages as scorpions, but these are suited for different purposes. One or two pairs of laterally placed, indirect eyes may be present on the unsegmented carapace of the prosoma.

Although arachnids have no jaws the esophagus is very narrow, and only very small food particles can be swallowed. Different kinds of arachnids solve this problem in different ways. The chelicerae of pseudoscorpions are equipped with comblike serrules and a field of bristles that are used to clean the mouth after eating and to strain out particles too large to swallow (Fig. 17.12A). A common but not universal capacity of arachnids is the ability to secrete silk. They differ considerably among themselves about where silk glands should be located. In pseudoscorpions the prosomal silk glands open through pores on the movable finger of the chelicera or on a spinneret or galea located on it. Silk is spun by attaching the spinneret to a surface and drawing the chelicera away. Pseudoscorpions use the silk to build nests for hibernation or into which they can retreat during molting. Although they are not given to long treks, they are not homebodies, and a new nest is built for each molt. The females also build a nest in which the young are brooded. The chelate pedipalps (Fig. 17.12B) resemble the pedipalps of scorpions superficially. They are especially important as tactile organs, but often contain poison glands with ducts opening on one or both jaws of the chelae.

The feeding habits of pseudoscorpions are rather like those of true scorpions, but on a diminutive scale. The prey are usually minute arthropods, such as psocids, collembola, and small dipterans, although species that live with ants attack the ants, often in small groups. Prey is caught in the pedipalps, and stung into submission if necessary. The chelicerae are thrust into the body of the prey, at the articular membranes between joints if the surface exoskeleton is too strong to pierce. Body fluids are sucked in, and enzymes are added to the tissues to soften them before they are ingested.

Solpugidae. Solpugids or sun spiders are characteristic of hot deserts, where they hide in burrows or crevices until night, when they come out to feed. They are formidable-looking creatures that reach up to about 7 cm. long.

The prosoma is covered by a double carapace, with a pair of eyes on the anterior piece (Fig. 17.3F). The opisthosoma is composed of ten segments and is broadly united to the prosoma, without a narrow pedicel.

The outstanding feature of the solpugids is the huge, three-segmented chelicerae, used to kill prey and tear it apart. The huge pincers can bite viciously, and in areas where they are common the solpugids are much feared. No poison glands have been located in the chelicerae, although bites are slow to heal in some instances. Some human deaths have been attributed to the bites of solpugids, but the general opinion is that the deaths were the result of secondary infections. The chelicerae are formidable weapons, and can kill scorpions so rapidly that they have no chance to sting. The prey is held crosswise in the chelicerae and pulped by lateral and vertical movements of the pincers. The macerated prey

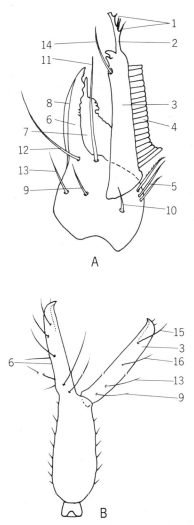

A

B

Fig. 17.12. A. Chelicera of *Lamprochernes*, a pseudoscorpion. B. End of pedipalp of a pseudoscorpion, *Chelifer cancroides*. (After Hoff.) 1, rami; 2, galea (spinneret); 3, movable finger; 4, exterior serrule; 5, flagellum; 6, fixed finger; 7, interior serrule; 8, exterior lamina; 9, basal seta; 10, external seta; 11, interior seta; 12, laminal seta; 13, subbasal seta; 14, apical seta; 15, terminal seta; 16, subterminal seta.

is held against the mouth, and the softened parts are sucked in.

The second pair of appendages are the pedipalps, which are long and leg-like and have adhesive pads sometimes used to aid in the capture of food. They are highly mobile appendages and serve as shields in combat as well as for tactile purposes. The four pairs of legs are long, and most solpugids are very fast runners. A pair of spiracles opens behind the coxae of the second legs, and two or three pairs open on the ventral side of the abdomen.

Araneae. Spiders are the best known of the arachnids, and they are common nearly everywhere. They are extremely successful small carnivores, and play an important role in the ecological balances of their communities, serving as checks against some insect species. Unable to fly, the spiders are somewhat more restricted than insects, but they have nevertheless adapted to a wide range of habitats, living in the surface litter, in trees, and in herbaceous plants. Some trap their prey, others pounce on the prey or wait for food organisms in ambush.

Spiders have a prosoma covered by a single dorsal carapace, typically bearing two rows of four eyes. The number and arrangement of the eyes are taxonomically important. The ventral surface of the prosoma is covered by a large sternum, formed by the fused sclerites of somites III-IV, and a small sternal plate of somite III, the labium, which serves as an underlip. The spider labium is not homologous with the labium of insects, although similarly named. The rest of the prosomal wall is membranous, except in spiders which have a narrow lateral plate, probably formed by fused pleura, immediately above the bases of the legs. A hard plate, the epistome, lies behind the pedipalp coxae in a few spiders. A flap-like fold of cuticle in front of the mouth forms a large labrum or rostrum. It contains muscles and a pair of glands of uncertain function.

The prosoma and opisthosoma are attached by a very slender pedicel, through which the gut, aorta, tracheae, and nerve trunks pass. As a general rule, the opisthosoma is oval to globose, but in some cases it is bizarrely shaped. In some of the more primitive spiders, 12 discrete opisthosomal terga can be recognized, but the exoskeleton is usually fused into a continuous dorsal covering. The pedicel is the first opisthosomal somite. Behind the pedicel, a transverse furrow crosses the ventral surface of the opisthosoma (Fig. 17.13A). This is the epigastric furrow. The gonopore lies immediately in front of it, and in most females a heavy plate, the epigynum, lies in front of the gonopore. Openings to the seminal receptacle pierce the epigynum, and the spiracles which open into the anterior pair of book lungs lie at the edge of the epigastric furrow. In primitive spiders. a second pair of spiracles that open into a second pair of book lungs lie immediately behind the first pair. In most spiders, however, the second pair of spiracles open into a tracheal system, and are united to form a single spiracle in front of the spinnerets. The anterior spiracles lie in somite VIII and the posterior pair in somite IX, but as somite IX includes the whole ventral surface from the epigastric furrow to the spinnerets, the spiracles can move over a large area without losing connection with their somite (Fig. 17.3C). Six spinnerets are usually associated with somites X and XI. A small anal lobe represents the ventral side of somite XVIII, and the ventral parts of somites XII-XVII are crowded together in the short space between the spinnerets and the anal lobe.

As in other arachnids, spiders have six pairs of prosomal appendages, a pair of chelicerae, a pair of pedipalps, and four pairs of walking legs. The two-segmented chelicerae arise from a postoral somite during development, but move forward and come to lie above the mouth in adults. The second cheliceral segment is the fang, which contains the pore for the poison gland. The large poison glands often extend deep into the prosoma. They are homologous to the silk glands of pseudoscorpions, and in one spider the glands are double, with one half secreting poison and the other half silk.

The fangs are flexed and extended by powerful muscles. As a rule they are not strong enough to penetrate human skin, but some species can and do bite humans. The black widow (*Latrodectus*) produces a powerful neurotoxin that can cause great pain, nausea, convulsive muscular contractions, and death by respiratory failure. The bites of some spiders cause a local necrosis of tissues, apparently as a result of a necrotoxin or a haemolysin, and are very slow to heal.

The pedipalps are leg-like and are often carried forward as sensory appendages. A few species, however, use the pedipalps as legs and carry the first walking legs forward as antennae. The base of the pedipalp is an accessory mouth part. The coxae carry dense brushes of bristles, used to strain out particles too large to swallow. The so-called salivary glands are also found in the pedipalps. Despite the name of these glands, the function of the secretion is unknown. The pedipalps of males are enlarged at the tip to form copulatory organs. Some of the pedipalps are equipped with extremely complex copulatory arrangements, and in any event, the form of the male pedipalp is valuable for species identification. The pretarsus, and sometimes the tarsus, is enlarged (Fig. 17.14A). The pretarsus is modified to form a basal bulb and a spirally coiled embolus in which the seminal vesicle is located. The articular membrane between the pretarsus and the tarsus may be swollen to form a chamber, the haematodocha, that erects the embolus when it is gorged with blood, preparing it to be thrust into the female gonopore. In *Erigone* the tarsus is also highly modified, forming a cup-like cymbium which, with an accessory arm, the paracymbium, encloses the haematodocha.

The walking legs contain seven true podites, but the last one, the pretarsus, is

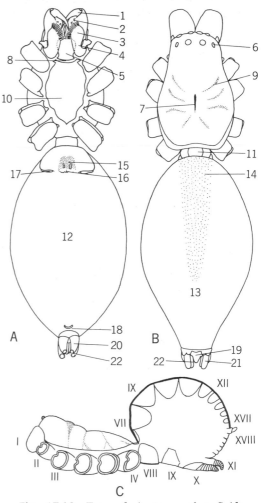

Fig. 17.13. External Anatomy of a Spider. A. Ventral view. B. Dorsal view. C. Scheme of longitudinal section, showing relationships of segments. Numbers of segments are shown in Roman numerals. (A and B, after the Kastons. C, after Bristowe and Millot.) 1, fang; 2, retromarginal cheliceral teeth; 3, scopula of maxilla; 4, endite of pedipalp; 5, labium; 6, eyes; 7, thoracic groove; 8, cervical groove; 9, radial furrow; 10, sternum; 11, larum of pedicel; 12, venter of opisthosoma; 13, dorsum of opisthosoma; 14, cardiac region; 15, epigynum; 16, epigastric furrow; 17, lung slit (anterior spiracle); 18, posterior spiracle; 19, anal tubercle; 20, anterior spinnerets; 21, posterior spinnerets; 22, median spinnerets.

usually obscured by the hairy tarsus, and the tarsus is divided into two pieces, a basitarsus or metatarsus, and a telotarsus or tarsus. Muscles attach to the coxal border and to the carapace and endosternum, giving considerable delicacy of control over the coxal movements. Intrinsic leg muscles move the leg at the various joints. The leg muscles are relatively complex; each tarantula leg has 31 muscles. Most of the muscles are flexors, however, and the extension of the legs is caused in part by changes in blood pressure.

Spiders are extremely diversified in their habits, but in almost all the ability to spin

silk is an important factor in their lives. Spider silk is a scleroprotein that hardens as it is pulled out and comes in contact with air. It may be tough and elastic or sticky, and strands of different sizes and qualities are produced by different spinnerets.

Embyronic development shows that two pairs of spinnerets are derived from the appendages of somites X and XI, while the remainder of the spinning apparatus arises from two pairs of outgrowths on the ventral body wall. The course of development of the spinnerets differs in different species, so the number of spin-

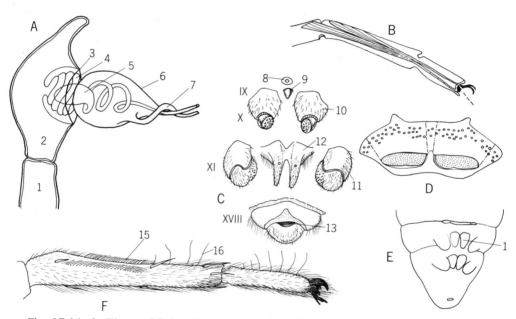

Fig. 17.14. **A.** The modified pedipalp of a male spider, used in transferring sperm to the female. Male pedipalps are extremely variable, and important in classification. **B.** The first and second tarsi of a spider leg. Note that the muscles and tendons to the pretarsus pass through the two tarsi. **C.** Spinnerets of *Argiope*. Roman numerals indicate somite numbers. Most spiders with three pairs of spinnerets have a median colulus, the remnant of the anterior median pair of spinnerets. **D.** The cribellum of *Filistata*. In cribellate spiders, the cribellum replaces the colulus. **E.** End of the abdomen of the embryo of *Filistata*, showing the primordia of the spinnerets. The cribellum arises from the median, anterior spinnerets. **F.** Calamistrum of *Amaurobius*. The calamistrum is used in web-spinning. (A, after Warburton. B and C, after Snodgrass. D and E, after Montgomery. F, after the Kastons.) 1, tibia; 2, tarsus; 3, alveolus; 4, haematodocha; 5, seminal receptacle; 6, bulb; 7, embolus; 8, spiracle; 9, colulus; 10, anterior spinnerets; 11, median spinnerets; 12, posterior spinnerets; 13, anus; 14, cribellum; 15, calamistrum; 16, trichobothria.

nerets is variable. The spinnerets derived from the appendages are more laterally placed; the pair associated with somite X are the anterior spinnerets and the pair on somite XI are the posterior spinnerets. As a general rule the ventral parts of these somites are so crowded together that the spinnerets lie very close to the anus. A pair of median spinnerets derived from the abdominal body wall of somite XI usually lie between the bases of the posterior spinnerets, and a small colulus, the vestige of the body-wall primordia on the tenth somite, lies between the bases of the anterior spinnerets. In some spiders the colulus is replaced by a porous plate, the cribellum (Fig. 17.14D,E). Sticky silk is spun from the cribellar pores and is combed out by one or two rows of spines on the first tarsal piece of the most posterior pair of legs. The comb is known as the calamistrum, and is found only in cribellate spiders (Fig. 17.14F).

Each spinneret is a compound spinning organ, made up of a number of small spinning tubes, known as fusules, and larger spinning tubes known as spigots. The number and pattern of fusules and spigots vary considerably in different species. In general, small silk glands are associated with the fusules and cribellum and each pore is associated with a single gland. The spigots serve fewer and much larger silk glands. Apparently there has been considerable independent adaptation of the silk glands in different spider groups, and attempts to classify the types of silk glands have not been wholly satisfactory. Threads of silk differ markedly in their properties. Some are relatively thick, others are quite thin. Sticky strands are especially used for the capture of prey. Spider silk is remarkable for its strength and elasticity. A thread 0.1 mm. in diameter will support a weight of 80 grams and will stretch up to 20 per cent before breaking.

Silk is used for a variety of purposes. Some spiders spin tiny sperm webs, on which sperm is discharged. The seminal vesicles of the pedipalps are charged by dipping the tips into the suspended sperm on the sperm webs. Silk is used to build a cocoon for the eggs and to suspend the cocoons from or attach them tightly to surfaces. One of the most remarkable uses of silk is for the construction of gossamer threads. Many young spiderlings clamber up on grasses or other plants when they emerge from the cocoon. When they reach the uppermost point, they spin strands of silk so light that they float the young animal on gentle air currents. Aerial rafting is common in several spider families and plays an important role in dissemination. It is particularly important for carnivorous animals to spread out, avoiding high population densities in small localities. Spiders cannot fly, and the ability to float about on silk is a remarkably effective method of getting about. Spiders were certainly among the first, if not the first, to reach Krakatoa after the great volcanic eruption had destroyed animal life there. The most common and best-known use of silk is for the spinning of webs.

Mygalomorphae are medium to large spiders that burrow in the ground or produce sheet-like or funnel-shaped webs. Among them are the tarantulas and the trap-door spiders, which form a hinged door for the burrow (Fig. 17.15E). In many families of spiders a rather flattened or irregular web is built, but in some cases the web has a characteristic and precise form. The irregular or flattened webs of the Dictynidae and Aglenidae contain a funnel-shaped hole into which the spider retreats (Fig. 17.15C). Argiopidae are orb-weavers, producing a beautifully regular web of radiating strands and a spiraled strand woven among them. The web of the orb-weavers makes an effective trap (Fig. 17.15D). There are many ground spiders. Lycosids or wolf spiders are large, active species that spin no web but sometimes line a nest with silk. Attids are jumping spiders that live on the ground or on plants. They, too, make no web but make

Fig. 17.15. Uses of Silk. A. A spider preparing to float on silk strands. B. A silken snare. Irregular snares of this type are formed by several groups of spiders. C. A tubular home. Such tubular hiding places may be combined with snares, or be formed without snares. D. An orb

web. The beautiful web of the orb weavers is an effective snare. **E.** Tunnel and trap door of a trap door spider. **F.** Egg sac. (**A**, from McCook. **B-F**, courtesy of American Museum of Natural History.)

silk-lined nests. Thomisids or crab spiders make no web. They are commonly found on flowers or on leaves of herbaceous plants, beautifully camouflaged and lying in wait for unsuspecting insects that visit the plants. In general, spiders that do not spin a web set a dragline that protects them if they slip.

Opiliones. The harvestmen or daddy longlegs are familiar to all, but few laymen distinguish them from spiders. They are most common in reasonably humid, temperate to tropical forests, where they are abundant among litter on the forest floor and on or around fallen logs. The most common species are from 4 to 10 mm. long, discounting the legs. The common *Leiobunum vittatum* has a maximal leg spread of about 9 cm., but some tropical forms are about twice as large.

A single glance suffices to distinguish between a long-legged spider and a harvestman, for a harvestman has no pedicel. The prosoma is covered by a single carapace, and joins the opisthosoma in a broad union. A dorsal tubercle with an eye on each side lies on the middle of the carapace (Fig. 17.4C). Near the base of each pedipalp is a small pore which leads to the repugnatorial, or stink glands. These give off an offensive secretion when the animal is disturbed. In some species the secretion is odorless but repels attackers because of its unpleasant taste, while in other species the secretion has a nauseating odor. The opisthosoma contains nine or ten somites, usually so completely fused as to be indistinct. The sterna of the first and second opisthosomal somites are joined to form a genital operculum in which the gonopores are located. The third opisthosomal sternum contains a pair of spiracles opening into the tracheal system.

Opiliones have the usual set of prosomal appendages. The chelicerae are small, and the long, leg-like pedipalps end in small chelae. The four pairs of long legs are striking primarily because of their great length. As is generally true of arthropods,

the leg is lengthened partly by the lengthening of the podites and partly by the presence of many tarsal pieces.

Opiliones are voracious creatures, feeding on arthropods of suitable size and in some instances attacking terrestrial snails. They will feed on dead organisms, and some feed on bits of fruit or vegetation. Food is grasped by the pedipalp chelae and is broken up by the chelicerae and endites on the coxae of the pedipalps and first two pairs of walking legs. Opiliones take a more varied diet and swallow larger particles than most arachnids.

Acarina. The Acarina were rather neglected, except for the species that are economically important to man, but in recent years the area of acarology has been a particularly active one. Acarines are a remarkably successful group of mostly minute arachnids, and they have adapted along a number of independent lines. The acarines are probably a polyphyletic group, including several independent groups of arachnids that have undergone convergent evolution. They occupy extremely diverse habitats. Some live in plant galls; some live in or on birds or mammals; some contaminate grain or other products; and many live in mosses or surface litter or the upper levels of the soil. Some have become aquatic, and live in salt or fresh water.

Ticks are the largest acarines. They have no clearly defined prosoma and opisthosoma, for the whole dorsal surface is united. Some female ticks have a dorsal shield, but this is not a prosomal carapace. The anterior end of the body is a head-like capitulum, or gnathosoma, thrust into the animal from which a blood meal is taken. Three arbitrary divisions of the acarine body can be recognized, a propodosoma, metapodosoma, and opisthosoma (Fig. 17.17A), but they are not evolutionarily significant and are merely useful for purposes of description. The specialization of the tick body is best seen from below (Fig. 17.17B). The gonopore is far forward, lying between the second and third

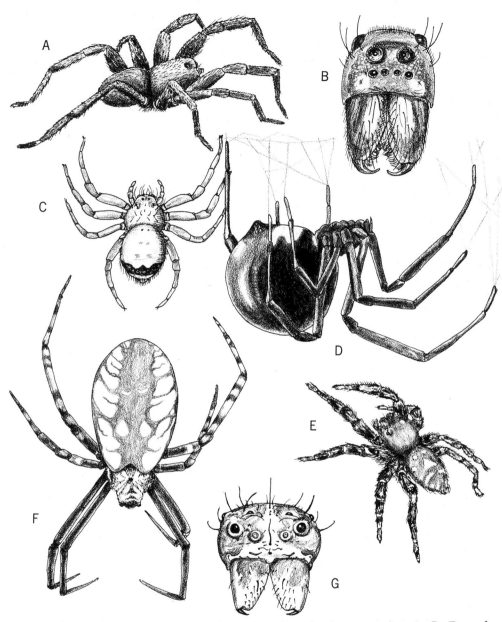

Fig. 17.16. Some Representative Spiders. **A.** A wolf spider, *Lycosa carolinensis*. **B.** Face of a *Lycosa*. **C.** One of the crab spiders, *Synema*. **D.** The black widow spider, *Latrodectus mactans*. **E.** One of the salticid jumping spiders, *Phidippus*. **F.** The common garden spider, *Argiope aurantia*, perhaps the best-known orb-weaver. **G.** The face of a thomisid spider, *Xysticus*. (A and D, after the Kastons. B and G, after Bristowe.)

pairs of legs, and the anus lies in the middle of the ventral surface. The primitive ventral surface has been crowded together and moved anteriorly, especially at the midline.

Ticks have very few external features. They have no eyes, but a pair of circular sense organs are found on the middorsal surface, and a pair of lateral spiracular plates contain the spiracles. All acarines have a capitulum, but the details vary considerably in different groups. The capitulum is a sclerotized, compound part, formed of the mouth parts and the first two pairs of prosomal appendages (Fig. 17.17 C-E). The base of the capitulum is attached at a notch in the body. In ticks, the rostrum is formed of cylindrical extensions of the basis, containing the slender chelicerae, and of a ventral, concave hypostome. The basis is formed of the cheliceral sheaths. In most ticks the hypostome is studded with teeth, which aid in attachment during feeding. These parts surround the prebuccal cavity. The mouth lies at the base of the hypostome and is equipped with a slender stylet, derived from the labrum immediately above it. The palps are modified pedipalps and are attached to the base of the capitulum. A wound is made with the chelicerae, and the rostrum is thrust into it. The palps

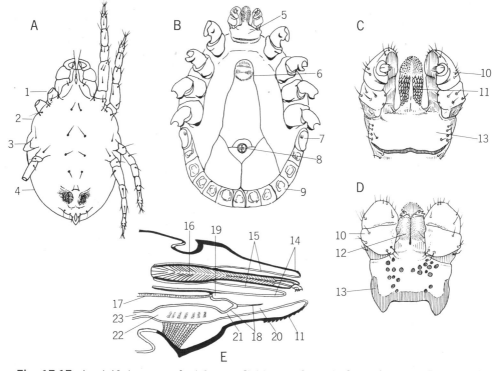

Fig. 17.17. Acarinid Anatomy. A. Arbitrary divisions and terminology of a mite. B. Ventral view of a tick, *Haemaphysalis aponommoides*. C and D. Ventral and dorsal views of the capitulum of a tick. E. Scheme of longitudinal section through the capitulum of a tick. (A, after Vizthum, from Baker and Wharton. B-D, after Hoogstraal. E, after Snodgrass.) 1, gnathosoma; 2, propodosoma; 3, metapodosoma; 4, opisthosoma; 5, capitulum; 6, gonopore; 7, spiracle; 8, anus; 9, festoon; 10, palp; 11, hypostome; 12, cheliceral sheath; 13, basis of capitulum; 14, outer cheliceral sheath; 15, inner cheliceral sheath; 16, chelicera; 17, epistome; 18, labrum; 19, salivary pocket; 20, food canal; 21, mouth; 22, pharynx; 23, esophagus.

spread to the side as the rostrum enters. During feeding, the hypostome armature engages with the soft tissues, holding the capitulum in place.

Ticks have legs with eight podites. The tarsus is divided into two pieces, and there is a second trochanter between the femur and the first trochanter. Mites generally have six-segmented legs.

Mites live in so many different habitats and have such varied habits that they have become very diversified in appearance. Most of them show few superficial resemblances to ticks. Some of the most highly modified mites are the worm-like *Demodex* (Fig. 17.18A), the mange mite, which lives in the hair follicles and sebaceous glands, and *Eriophyes* (Fig. 17.18B), which causes galls on various plants. Feather mites (Fig. 17.18C) live on the surfaces of birds and are modified for clinging; some are fantastically shaped. The Tetranychidae (Fig. 17.18E) include the spider mites, or red spiders, which are so destructive to many crops. They use the needle-like chelicerae to pierce plant tissues, sucking in the cell contents. They spin silk from oral silk glands, and use a tarsal comb to walk over and manipulate the silken strands. Fresh-water mites (Fig. 17.18F) are often brightly colored, and have spherical to oral bodies. They usually have prominent swimming hairs, or natatory setae, on the legs, which increase surface resistance and make the legs effective paddles. Some of these are huge, by mite standards, reaching lengths up to 7 mm. or so. A few have become parasitic on clams or other aquatic molluscs. *Trombicula* (Fig. 17.18D) is a good example of a mite with a parasitic larval stage. Eggs are laid on the ground, and the young larvae creep onto the surface of a convenient vertebrate host. They secrete saliva into a minute wound on the skin. Enzymes digest away a minute crater, the stylostome, in the skin. The crater is filled with partially digested tissues on which the chigger feeds. When the animal has completed its larval development, it leaves the host and takes up life as an adult.

DIGESTION

Despite differences in the size, general appearance, habitats, and eating habits of arachnids, the organization of the digestive tract remains remarkably stable. It is a curious fact that the arachnids, which have no jaws, have developed other methods of triturating the food before swallowing, and actually swallow more finely divided food particles than any other large arthropod group. The methods used to reduce the food particles to swallowing size vary somewhat in different groups, but undoubtedly adaptation to feeding without jaws has had the effect of producing convergent tendencies in the various arachnid groups.

Most of the arachnids are carnivores which capture the prey with chelicerae or pedipalps. Food is held in front of the mouth, and the process of ingestion is slow. It is broken into small fragments by the chelicerae, sometimes with the aid of endites on the pedipalps or leg coxae, but generally salivary secretions are poured on the food, predigesting and softening it for swallowing. Undoubtedly the slow ingestion process has favored the development of venom glands to immobilize the prey. Venom glands appear at various places in the body—in the posterior sting of scorpions, in the chelicerae of spiders, or in the pedipalps of pseudoscorpions. It is evident that venom glands have developed independently in different arachnid groups.

Secretions used for the predigestion of food are supplied by glands from different parts of the body as well. Salivary glands are found in the chelicerae or pedipalps of some arachnids, but others regurgitate digestive juices secreted by glandular diverticula of the midgut. Several interesting points grow out of the nature of the secretory activities of arachnids. The development of glands in different parts of the body for the formation of enzymes,

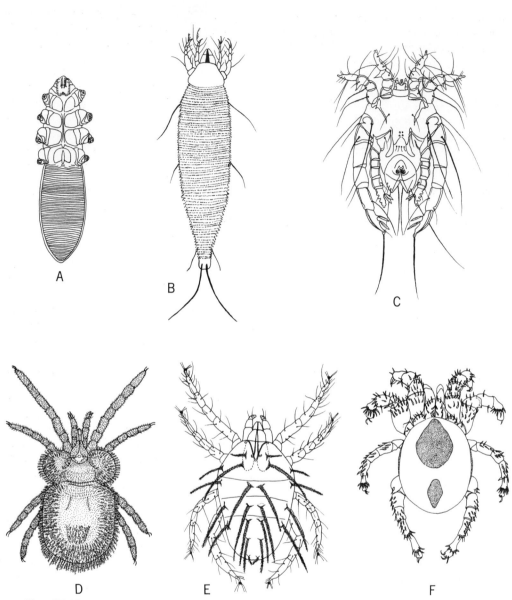

Fig. 17.18. Some Representative Mites. **A.** *Demodex muscardini*, female. Democids are parasitic mites found in the skin of various kinds of mammals. **B.** *Eriophyes pyri*, the pear leaf blister mite. Eriophyids cause galls, blisters, and other disturbances in many important domestic plants. **C.** A feather mite, *Megninia columbae*. Feather mites are often fantastically modified through specializations fitting them for their unusual habitat. **D.** *Trombicula alfreddugési*, a chigger. Chiggers are common pests in many parts of the United States. **E.** A spider mite, *Metatetranychus ulmi*. Spider mites are economically important pests affecting many species of domestic plants. **F.** A water mite, *Tyrrelia*. (A and C, after Hirst. E, after Baker and Wharton, from Baker and Wharton. B, after Essig. F, after Newell, in Edmondson.)

726

silk, or venom speaks for convergent evolutionary trends growing out of adaptation leading to independent but similar solutions to similar problems. Underlying this, however, is the utilization of homologous glands for different functions in different groups of animals. Cheliceral and pedipalp glands may be used to secrete venom, silk, or enzymes, as the case may be. Originally similar parts have thus specialized along different lines even though convergent evolution was at the same time tending to produce similar kinds of secretions in different parts of the body.

A variety of minor variations is seen. Some spiders wrap their prey in silk before feeding on it. Some mites pierce plant tissues and pour enzymes into them instead of capturing prey. Ticks take blood meals. Harvestmen are predominantly carnivores, but will take plant food or feed on dead animals. They are all minor variations on the same theme, however, and all arachnids take in small particles or fluid food. The esophagus is narrow and could be fouled easily, and a variety of straining devices have been developed. Rows or fields of bristles on one of the first two pairs of appendages or in the buccal cavity are found in nearly all arachnids, and some have specialized bristles used for cleaning the mouth parts or the buccal cavity.

Nearly all of the arachnids depend on a pumping system to handle the fluid food. The pumping chamber is usually a part of the foregut and lies between the nerve ring and the mouth. The pharyngeal pump of a scorpion illustrates the basic design. The mouth leads into a chamber, infolded dorsally and here strengthened by an elastic rod. Compressor muscles cover the wall of the pharynx, and dilator muscles attach the body wall to the dorsal and lateral walls of the pharynx. Compressor and dilator muscles work in antagonism, pulling the food into the pharynx and forcing it down into the midgut. Pseudoscorpions have a valve and straining device at the entrance to the esophagus, beyond the pharyngeal

pump. The back part of the pharynx is lined with stiff bristles, and a conical, chitinous valve is located at the esophagus entrance.

Spiders are exceptional in having the pump located beyond the nerve ring instead of in front of it (Fig. 17.19). The mouth opens into a slender esophagus that extends to the middle of the prosoma. Here it expands suddenly to form a chitinized sucking stomach, located immediately above the endosternum. Dilator muscles extend from the endosternum to the ventral wall of the sucking stomach, and from the dorsal wall to the carapace. The dorsal muscles attach to a heavy chitinous plate. The intrinsic muscles of the wall are constrictors. The development of a chitinous lining or of chitinous plates in the sucking stomach are, of course, an important factor in improving its performance. Although it is usually termed a sucking stomach, the spider pumping apparatus is a part of the foregut.

The usually partly digested, liquid food enters the midgut, where digestion is completed and absorption occurs. As a general rule the sucking pharynx opens into an esophagus which passes through the nerve ring and opens into the midgut, but in spiders the sucking stomach opens directly into the midgut. The arachnid midgut is always equipped with some kind of diverticula, and in a number of arachnids large digestive glands, sometimes termed the liver or hepatopancreas, are found. In the majority of arachnids the greatly amplified secretory surface of the midgut diverticula is important in producing enzymes used for preliminary digestion.

Scorpions have a midgut with six pairs of diverticula (Fig. 17.20B). One of the pairs of diverticula is located in the prosoma. These diverticula serve as salivary glands. The remaining diverticula are located in the mesosoma. They are greatly folded and branched, and are gathered together into a general mesosomal mass by connective tissue. The midgut continues through the metasoma to the short hindgut without any conspicuous dilations or other modifications. The lining of the midgut is entirely unlike the lining of the foregut or hindgut. There is no chitinous lining, and the cells are tall and columnar. The change in the nature of the lining between the epidermally lined foregut and hindgut and the endodermally lined midgut·is consistent throughout the arachnids, although details vary somewhat.

Solpugids have no pedicel, but an internal diaphragm separates the prosoma and opisthosoma. The midgut is tubular, without conspicuous dilations, but is constricted at the diaphragm. At the front of the opisthosomal midgut, two long, tubular diverticula arise. Innumerable small branches cover the surface of the main diverticula. Near the union of the midgut and hindgut a sac-like stercoral pocket arises. The stercoral pocket is used for the concentration of nitrogenous wastes, and will be discussed in conjunction with excretion.

Despite their small size, the pseudoscorpions have a very complex midgut. There are two five-lobed lateral diverticula, two median ventral diverticula, and a pair of large, dorsal digestive glands. The functions of the various kinds of diverticula are as yet uncertain. Behind the fourth opisthosomal somite the midgut narrows sharply At the junction of the midgut and hindgut, a stercoral pocket is found.

The broad midgut of the harvestmen is completely surrounded by diverticula. Clusters of small caeca cover the narrower anterior part of the midgut, and two large caeca parallel the midgut, giving rise to secondary branches which extend throughout the opisthosoma. Branched pairs of lateral diverticula add to the confusion. Seven ventral diverticula, different in appearance, are thought to correspond to the digestive glands of other arachnids.

As might be expected from their diverse feeding habits, the acarines vary enor-

mously in the detailed structure of the digestive tube. The most complicated arrangements are seen in ticks (Fig. 17.20A). The esophagus is S-shaped and opens into a four-lobed stomach, with thin, extensible walls. When gorged with blood, the walls dilate greatly. The lining cells put out pseudopodia and ingest blood cells, which are digested intracellularly. A large rectal sac apparently corresponds to the stercoral sac of other arachnids.

The spider midgut is composed of a dilated, prosomal stomach, a constricted tube that passes through the pedicel, and an opisthosomal stomach (Fig. 17.19). A narrow intestine continues to the stercoral pocket at the junction of the midgut and hindgut. The sucking stomach, actually a part of the foregut, opens immediately into the prosomal stomach, from which a pair of prosomal diverticula arise. These extend forward, around the dorsal dilator muscles, and may join anteriorly. From each of the prosomal diverticula, four branches arise, passing to the bases of the legs. The branches of the prosomal diverticula vary greatly in complexity. In some instances they branch out into the appendages or into the head. Beyond the pedicel the midgut expands again as an opisthosomal stomach. The opisthosomal diverticula branch complexly, forming the digestive glands. In all probability, however, the spider digestive glands are not true glands. The lining cells appear to be simple continuations of the lining of the opisthosomal stomach, and are probably absorptive rather than digestive in function.

In summary, the outstanding developments of the arachnid midgut include arrangements to handle liquid food, partially shared with the foregut, and extensive surface amplification of the midgut lining. There is good evidence that the increase of surface is in part associated with the production of enzymes used for digestion, and in part associated with the absorption of food. The lining of the midgut may participate in intracellular digestion, but the extent to which arachnids depend on intracellular methods of digestion and absorption is as yet uncertain. They may be used more extensively than has generally been thought. In one group or another, the diverticula arising from the midgut are differentiated into two or more types. In very few cases is there real information about the functional significance of these differentiated parts. Even the enzymes used by arachnids in digestion are not very well known. Proteinases, lipases, and amylases have been recovered from the scorpion, but there is no significant information about

where they are formed and where they act during digestion.

RESPIRATION

Long ago, the land was nearly free of animal life, and any group of animals that could make the change from aquatic to land life could escape the intense competition characteristic of water habitats and exploit a new, relatively untouched territory. Despite the powerful forces favoring the change, very few groups of animals have succeeded in invading land, for aquatic organisms emigrating to land face many problems. Arachnids are among the suc-

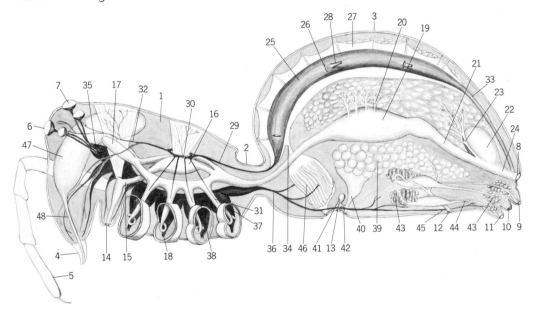

Fig. 17.19. Anatomy of a Spider. *External features:* 1, prosoma; 2, pedicel; 3, opisthosoma; 4, chelicera; 5, pedipalp; 6, anterior row of eyes; 7, posterior row of eyes; 8, anus; 9, posterior spinnerets; 10, median spinnerets; 11, anterior spinnerets; 12, posterior spiracle; 13, seminal receptacle aperture; 14, mouth. *Digestive system:* 15, esophagus; 16, sucking stomach; 17, prosomal midgut diverticula; 18, prosomal caeca; 19, opisthosomal stomach; 20, digestive glands; 21, intestine; 22, stercoral pocket; 23, Malpighian tubules; 24, hindgut. *Circulatory system:* 25, heart; 26, ostium; 27, pericardial cavity; 28, lateral artery; 29, anterior aorta; 30, arterial circle; 31, leg artery; 32, cephalic artery; 33, posterior aorta; 34, efferent vessel from book lung. *Nervous system:* 35, brain; 36, prosomal ventral ganglion; 37, leg ganglion; 38, posterior nerve. *Reproductive system:* 39, ovary; 40, oviduct; 41, seminal receptacle; 42, gonopore. *Other parts:* 43, silk gland; 44, silk duct; 45, trachea; 46, book lung; 47, poison gland; 48, poison duct.

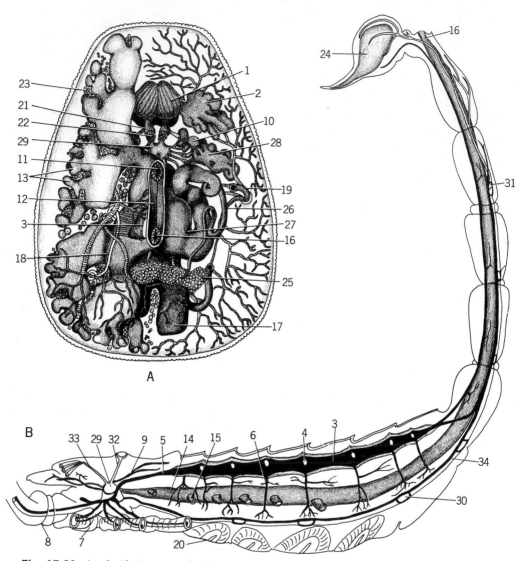

Fig. 17.20. Arachnid Anatomy. A. The anatomy of a tick. B. The anatomy of a scorpion. (A, after Hegner, Root, and Augustine. B, after Kaestner, in Kükenthal and Krumbach.) 1, Gené's organ; 2, glandular part of Gené's organ. *Circulatory system:* 3, heart; 4, ostium; 5, aorta; 6, lateral artery; 7, base of leg, containing artery and nerve; 8, base of pedipalp containing artery and nerve; 9, supracerebral artery. *Digestive system:* 10, salivary gland; 11, esophagus; 12, stomach; 13, alimentary caeca; 14, midgut; 15, digestive gland; 16, rectum; 17, rectal sac. *Excretory system:* 18, Malpighian tubule. *Respiratory system:* 19, trachea; 20, spiracle of anterior book lung. *Chelicerae and muscles:* 21, chelicera; 22, cheliceral muscle; 23, dorsoventral body muscles; 24, poison gland. *Reproductive system:* 25, ovary; 26, oviduct; 27, uterus; 28, accessory genital gland. *Nervous system:* 29, brain; 30, segmental ganglion; 31, ganglion for segments 18 and 19; 32, nerve to median eye; 33, nerve to lateral eye; 34, nerve cord.

cessful few, and the way they have managed the change is of considerable interest.

One of the critical problems in changing from water to land is respiration. The simplest kind of vascularized surface is an adequate aquatic respiratory organ, for dessication is not a problem. Some sort of control over the loss of water at the body surface is a general requirement for terrestrial animals, and the mechanisms that prevent surface evaporation are generally antagonistic to surface respiration. The new land animal faces a difficult choice. Shall it retain surface respiration and run the risk of drying out, or shall it close off the surface transfer of gases and run the chance of suffocation? As it can afford neither of these choices, the really successful land animal develops an internal respiratory organ, where respiratory transfer can be conducted over surfaces suitable for gaseous transfer, and water loss can be minimized. Yet nature is never so simple that it can be so easily predicted. There are exceptions, and these are often related to a secondary factor, that of body size. The smaller the organism, the greater its surface relative to its internal volume. If the metabolic rates and oxygen requirements of the tissues remain the same, the smaller organism need not take in so much oxygen per unit of body surface and may, even when the body surface is protected by a covering, find the unmodified body surface adequate for its needs. On the other hand a larger organism may get along reasonably well in moister terrestrial habitats with a body surface that is not very well protected against water loss. The exoskeleton of arthropods appears to have developed first in aquatic organisms, providing protection and sites for muscle attachment. The arthropods were, as a result, unusually well suited for the adaptive leap required for successful invasion of the land. The relatively impervious exoskeleton favored the adaptation of respiratory surfaces in water habitats and provided a covering that would tend to protect the new land animal from water loss. The principal problem was one either of developing suitable internal respiratory organs from the ones already available or of developing new ones.

Book lungs are the primitive arachnid respiratory organs. They bear a close resemblance to the book gills of the merostomates like *Xiphosura*, and the eurypterids appear to have had similar plates enclosed in ventral pockets on the opisthosoma. One of the more popular ideas has been that the eurypterids gave rise to scorpions, which modified the book gills into book lungs. There are disadvantages to this idea. The leaves of book gills are evaginations, while the leaves of book lungs are invaginations of the body surface. However, book lungs, like book gills, are associated with opisthosomatic appendages, representing the last vestiges of legs that are otherwise abortive during development. If book lungs did not arise from book gills, the two must have developed in a similar manner from similar parts of ancestral creatures that were very similar. As the arachnids became arachnids by making the shift to land life, so to speak, some originally aquatic respiratory organ must have been modified to form book lungs.

Each book lung is a packet of hollow, flat plates through which air circulates (Fig. 17.21B-D). Blood flows over the outer surface of the leaves, delivering carbon dioxide and absorbing oxygen. The book lungs arise as ectodermal invaginations on the ventral surface, and have a remarkably stable organization in divergent arachnid groups. The external opening, or spiracle, leads to a chamber, the atrium, in which the leaves occur. The atrial walls are flexible except at the dorsal surface, where the folding to form the leaves occurs. Firm cuticular bars cross the dorsal wall between adjacent leaves, preventing their collapse and bounding the haemocoelic

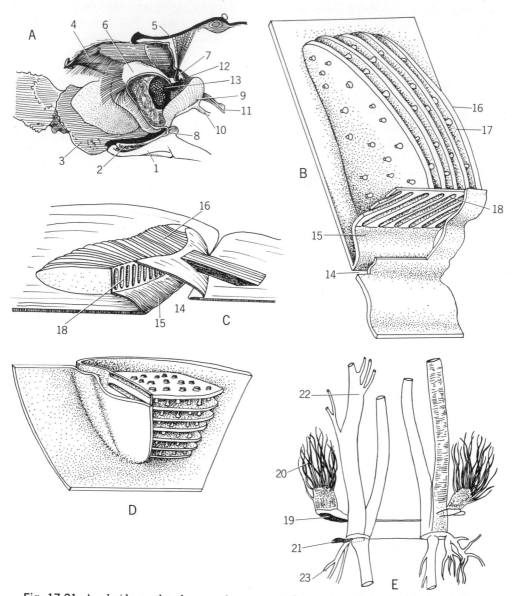

Fig. 17.21. Arachnids, as they have no jaws, can at the most crush food with the chelicera and pedipalp chelae. The pharynx and esophagus are narrow, and food is partially digested by enzymes extruded from the mouth, often in a preoral cavity bounded by the coxae of the head appendages and the modified surface of the head, as in a scorpion (A). Others are modified to suck fluid food from plants or animals. A large number of arachnids are equipped with book lungs. The book lungs are remarkably similar in otherwise widely divergent arachnids, as can be seen by comparing the book lungs of a scorpion (B), a uropygid (C), and a spider (D). The spiracle opens into an atrium. The hollow leaves of the book lung contain the respiratory surfaces, and blood circulates between the leaves of the lung. Spiders may have one pair of book lungs and a tracheal system associated with the posterior spiracles, or may have

752

sinus around them. The delicate cuticular covering of the leaves provides little resistance to respiratory exchange. Book lungs are found in the more primitive arachnids, such as uropygids, amblypygids, and scorpions, and in some spiders. There is little reason to doubt, considering their occurrence in such divergent groups, that the first arachnids had book lungs as respiratory organs.

Two lines of improvement are seen in organisms with book lungs, one leading to control of the spiracle and the other to muscular movements that ventilate the lung. Neither of these appear to be critical problems in the organisms, for the body is small and a relatively large surface area is exposed in the book lung. Apparently ventilating movements are not usually required, and diffusion suffices for respiratory exchange at an adequate rate. The effectiveness of the book lungs is shown by removal of the book lungs of scorpions. This reduces respiratory exchange to zero, indicating that the general body surface plays no part in respiratory exchange. Some scorpions have muscles that can expand the spiracles and atrium, and some spiders have similar muscles. These appear to be brought into play only at periods of great activity. They are probably more closely associated with water economy than with respiratory efficiency. It is clear that the smaller the spiracles, the less the loss of water at the book lung. Methods which permit the dilation of spiracles and expansion of the atrium also permit the reduction in size of the spiracle to a size that is normally adequate for moderate activity.

A number of arachnids use respiratory tubules known as tracheae for respiratory exchange. Arachnid tracheal systems are considerably more diversified than book lungs, and have probably developed independently in several arachnid lines.

All tracheal systems are formed by ectodermal invaginations, and typically open through spiracles located just behind the coxae of an appendage. The spiracle opens into a vestibule or atrium with a relatively thick cuticular lining. A system of internal tracheal tubes arises from the vestibule (Fig. 17.21E). Two types of tracheal systems can be distinguished. In some cases the tracheae are used to oxygenate the blood, and respiratory transport is cared for by the body fluids. In other cases the tracheal tubes extend to the body tissues themselves, serving as capillaries for respiratory transport.

Tracheae used to oxygenate blood hang down in a dense cluster into a haemocoel sinus. They are sometimes referred to as tracheal lungs, an apt term, as they are very like book lungs with tubular rather than lamellar respiratory surfaces. They are undoubtedly derived from book lungs. Tracheal lungs are found only in spiders, and especially in spiders with posterior book lungs.

Tracheae that carry oxygen directly to the tissues are much more common. They are found in spiders, pseudoscorpions, solpugids, harvestmen, and acarines. The simplest tracheal systems consist of simple tufts of unbranched tracheae associated with each spiracle, differing from tracheal lungs only in that the tracheal

a pair of tracheal lungs in addition to the branching tracheal system. A tracheal lung (E) consists of a tuft of tracheal tubules which are surrounded by a blood sinus. (A, after Snodgrass. B and C, after Kästner. D, after Gerhardt and Kästner. E, after Bertkau, from Gerhardt and Kästner, in Kükenthal and Krumbach.) *External features:* 1, coxal endite of second leg; 2, coxal endite of first leg; 3, coxa of pedipalp; 4, chelicera; 5, carapace; 6, labrum; 7, epistome; 8, mouth. *Internal parts:* 9, pharynx; 10, esophagus; 11, apodeme from epistome; 12, dorsal dilator muscle; 13, transverse muscle of labrum. *Book lungs:* 14, spiracle; 15, atrium; 16, lamella of lung; 17, pulmonary sinus of haemocoel; 18, opening into the lumina of lamellae. *Tracheal system:* 19, anterior spiracle; 20, tuft of trachea forming tracheal lung; 21, posterior spiracle; 22, longitudinal tracheal trunk; 23, tributary trachea extending to tissues.

tubules extend to the tissues instead of hanging in the haemocoel. Two main lines of progressive changes lead off from such primitive systems. The first and most common line of improvement involves the formation of a system of branching rather than unbranched tracheae. The total cross-sectional area of a system of unbranched tracheal tubules is limited by the size of the vestibule, but is not so limited in a branched system. Furthermore, the main tubes of a branched system can be much larger, favoring more rapid movement of air in the tracheal system. The second line of improvement leads to the longitudinal linkage of the tracheal systems associated with different spiracles, as well as the commissural linkage of pairs of tracheae on the same somite. In primitive systems, the tracheae associated with each spiracle are wholly independent, functioning as an isolated unit. As cross and longitudinal connections are made, the respiratory system emerges as an integrated whole, with many new possibilities. No one part of the body is dependent on the proper functioning of the spiracle in its immediate vicinity, so the margin of safety is increased. The flow of air through the tracheal system can be more highly organized, through the development of physiological devices of one kind or another. Alternate opening and closing of spiracles can be used to maintain a definite flow of air through the trachea in a given direction, and some spiracles can be used as incurrent and others as excurrent openings. As a general rule, arachnids appear to have progressed less far in the exploitation of linked tracheae than insects, but more work is needed along these lines.

As a rule, the simpler tracheal systems are found in smaller arachnids. Pseudoscorpions have two pairs of tracheal spiracles. The tracheae from the anterior pair extend forward and those from the posterior pair extend backward. They appear to be independent. Mites that have tracheal systems have very simple ones, but the somewhat larger ticks have tracheal tubes that branch extensively, passing to all parts of the body (Fig. 17.20A).

The respiratory organs of spiders are particularly interesting. Some spiders have two pairs of book lungs; others have one pair of book lungs and one pair of tracheal tubes; and still others have two pairs of tracheal tubes. Some spiders have tracheal lungs, while others have extensively branched tracheal systems. In all cases, the spiracles are associated with somites VIII and IX. It is tempting to conclude that the tracheae arose from the book lungs, probably by way of tracheal lungs as an intermediate step, and it would be convenient if this could be shown to be true. However, not all students of spiders have agreed, and it may turn out that the tracheae are independent developments. In the embryo the rudiments of the book lungs do not appear to be identical with those of the tracheal spiracles, and while early development is by no means an infallible guide to the recognition of homologies, the differences that have been described indicate that no firm conclusions about the homology of tracheal and book lung systems are justified.

The most highly developed tracheal systems among arachnids are found in the harvestmen and solpugids. Opiliones have large longitudinal tracheae that pass forward into the prosoma from spiracles at the base of the last legs, sending branches to the legs and prosomal parts (Fig. 17.23B). Tracheae in the opisthosomal region are much less well developed. In solpugids one pair of prosomal and two pairs of opisthosomal spiracles are connected by a main longitudinal tracheal tube on each side of the body. Small branches from the tracheal trunks extend to all parts of the body.

EXCRETION

Two entirely different kinds of excretory organs are found in arachnids, coxal glands and Malpighian tubules. There can be no real doubt that the coxal glands are the more primitive. They are highly modified nephridia, resembling the coxal glands of *Xiphosura*, and are in general more suitable for aquatic excretion than excretion under terrestrial conditions. Malpighian tubules, on the other hand, are characteristic of terrestrial arthropods generally, occurring in insects and myriapods as well as some arachnids.

Arachnid coxal glands are similar to the coxal glands of *Xiphosura*, although not united longitudinally. The sacculus is a derivative of the coelom. It is connected to a tortuous tubule which forms the labyrinth, and where nitrogenous material appears to be added to the tubule contents. The labyrinth is followed by a straight tube which extends to the excretory pore. Additional regions are not uncommonly seen. A dilated part of the tubule between the labyrinth and the straight tube is often present, serving as a bladder. In some cases a labyrinth sac lies between the sacculus and the labyrinth. The detailed form of the coxal glands and the somites in which they are found vary considerably from arachnid group to group, but there is ample reason to consider them all as modifications of the same basic design.

Malpighian tubules are blind tubules attached near the union of the midgut and hindgut. As a general rule, the Malpighian tubules of arachnids are branched and become more or less tangled with the diverticula of the midgut. In a number of arachnids, a stercoral sac arises from the gut near the point where the Malpighian tubules enter, or the Malpighian tubules are attached directly to the stercoral sac.

Unfortunately, the details of arachnid excretion are only partly known. At least some of the arachnids excrete most of their nitrogenous wastes in the form of guanin. Guanin compounds have a real advantage for terrestrial animals, for their solubility changes very markedly with the *p*H of the medium in which they are held. In an acid medium, they precipitate out, forming insoluble crystals. Water can be reabsorbed from the crystalline guanin, which can then be excreted in a solid form. Malpighian tubules and the stercoral sac appear to be devices which are especially suited for guanin excretion. In spiders, for example, the midgut walls contain a number of guanin cells which empty guanin into the lumen of the gut. These crystals may or may not go into solution in the midgut, but in any case they are crystallized out by the acid contents of the stercoral sac, preparing the way for water reabsorption before the guanates are eliminated. Guanin compounds are also picked up by the Malpighian tubules, and emptied into the stercoral sac or into the gut near the stercoral sac. The contents of the Malpighian tubules are acid at the time of their discharge into the digestive tube, but the stercoral sac undoubtedly aids in keeping the gut contents acid enough to prevent the guanin compounds from going into solution. The movement of nitrogenous wastes to the Malpighian tubules is not yet described. Certain cells in the prosoma of spiders and some other arachnids are athrocytic, but it is not clear how materials taken up by these cells are delivered to the Malpighian tubules. Presumably the nitrogen compounds are transported in a more soluble form, or the body fluids are alkaline enough to permit the movement of guanates in solution. It is probable that the cells of the Malpighian tubules can convert nitrogenous wastes of other kinds into guanin compounds.

CIRCULATION

The arachnid circulatory system shows the usual arthropod design. A dorsal, tubular heart lies in a pericardial sinus, into which blood returns on its way to the heart. Blood enters the heart through paired ostia, and is driven through an arterial system into a haemocoelic sinus system. Blood from the haemocoelic sinuses drains into an

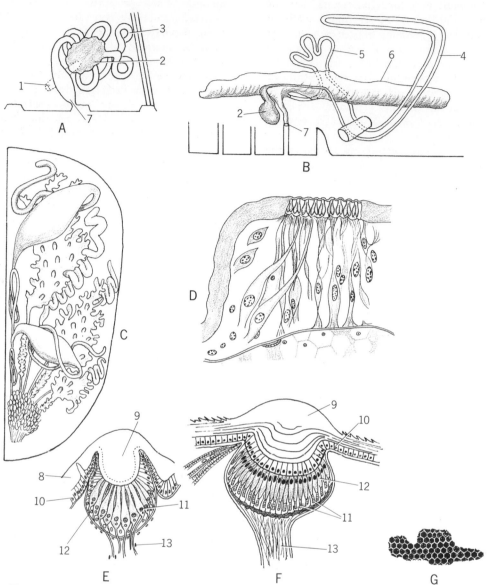

Fig. 17.22. Some Arachnid Organs. The primitive excretory organs appear to be the coxal glands, which occur in many kinds of arachnids. Although somewhat variable in form, they consist primarily of a sacculus and a convoluted tubule or labyrinth, of variable complexity. The terminal straight tube is often dilated as a bladder. Scorpions have fairly primitive coxal glands, of the type shown at **A**. The more highly specialized coxal gland of a harvestman is shown at **B**.   **C**. The silk glands of *Aranea*. *Aranea* is typical in having several kinds of silk glands, morphologically distinct and producing silk of varying properties. **D**. A lyriform organ of a spider. These are characteristic spider sense organs, whose function may be chemorecep- tion. Although basically like some of the insect sense organs, they are morphologically distinct. **E and F**. Some arachnid eyes are direct, with the retinal rods or rhabdomes extending toward

efferent sinus system that returns it to the pericardial sinus. Where the blood is responsible for transporting oxygen, the returning blood is routed past the book lungs or the tracheal lungs.

Arachnids have had a long history, and while several adaptive trends can be recognized in the circulatory system they must be interpreted with considerable caution. As a general rule, the more primitive arachnids tend to have elongated hearts with many ostia, while the more specialized ones tend to have shorter hearts with fewer ostia. The arterial system tends to be somewhat more highly developed in primitive than in more highly specialized groups. Many of the arachnids are quite small, however, and small size tends to favor reduction of the circulatory system. It is not always easy to separate simplicity resulting from the reduction of the circulatory system from simplicity resulting from tendencies to shorten the heart or to depend more fully on a haemocoelic sinus system than upon arteries.

The scorpion circulatory system is relatively primitive (Fig. 17.20B). The heart is long and tubular, and has seven pairs of ostia, each associated with a segment of the heart from which a pair of lateral arteries arise. A posterior aorta runs back into the metasoma and an anterior aorta runs forward into the prosoma. As in *Xiphosura*, there is an intimate relationship between the prosomal branches of the anterior aorta and the nerves, and some of the nerves lie within arteries. A supraneural artery, also known as a ventral artery, runs immediately above the nerve cord and extends far back into the metasoma. As in the merostomates, the ventral circulation is largely established by branches from the anterior aorta, while lateral branches are associated with the more dorsal body parts.

Spider hearts are shorter tubes, with three pairs of ostia and three pairs of lateral arteries that ramify to the tissues of the opisthosoma (Fig. 17.19). The anterior aorta passes through the pedicel, curves downward near the pumping stomach, and gives rise to a number of arteries to the legs and anterior appendages. Spiders have no ventral vessel, and the nervous and arterial systems are not so intimately associated as in scorpions. However, a system of ventral sinuses collects the blood from the tissues and returns it to the lungs, from which it passes through a pair of pulmonary veins to the pericardial sinus.

The circulatory system varies considerably in the other arachnid groups. The primitive Urpoygi have hearts with nine pairs of ostia. Solpugids, though not otherwise so primitive, have a long heart with eight pairs of ostia. Most of the tracheate arachnids are small, and it is difficult to determine whether small size or tracheal

the lens. Other arachnid eyes are indirect, with the retinal rods extending away from the lens. Direct eyes in spiders are the anterior median pair, and arise from the first cephalic somite. The remaining six, derived from the second cephalic somite, are indirect. In all cases, however, the essential structure is similar. A typical arachnid direct eye is found in a scorpion (E). The indirect eye shown here (F) is from a spider, *Epeira*. In either type of eye, each rhabdome serves as a distinct receptor, and a mosaic image is formed. Even in an efficient spider eye, the number of rhabdomes present is too small to provide more than a sketchy image. The image of another spider, as seen when 8 cm. away from a good spider eye, is shown at G. (A, after Buxton. B, after Kästner, from Kästner, in Kükenthal and Krumbach. C, after Apstein, from Gerhardt and Kästner, in Kükenthal and Krumbach. D, after Kaston, from Bristowe. E, after Lankester and Bourne. F, after Grenacher, from Dahlgren and Kepner. G, after Homann, from Carter.) *Coxal glands:* 1, arterial branch from leg artery; 2, sacculus; 3, labyrinth; 4, opisthosomatic labyrinth; 5, prosomal labyrinth; 6, straight tube, modified as a bladder; 7, coxal pore. *Eye:* 8, cuticle; 9, lens; 10, epidermis; 11, retina; 12, rhabdomes; 13, optic nerve.

transport of oxygen is responsible for the reduction of the circulatory system. Pseudo-scorpions have quite small hearts with a single pair of ostia. In mites, circulatory reduction is more extensive, and a system of irregular haemocoelic sinuses without a heart suffices.

Little is known of the physiology of transport in arachnids. Haemocyanin has been found in the blood of some scorpions, but its role in respiratory transport remains obscure. It may, like the haemocyanin of some other arthropods, circulate at less than full saturation with oxygen.

SENSE ORGANS

The development of a firm exoskeleton poses problems in the area of sensory reception, but arthropods in general have made a virtue of necessity, using parts of the exoskeleton as instruments for deforming or otherwise applying a stimulus to sensory cells. It is by no means easy to determine the function of a part that appears, by its structure, to be a sense organ, and there are many devices of arachnids and other arthropods whose functions remain uncertain.

Perhaps the most outstanding feature of sense organ development among arthropods, and one which is apparently fully shared by the arachnids, is the differentiation of mechanoreceptors. In a very real sense, every hair or bristle that projects from the surface of an arachnid is a potential lever that can be used to deform a mechanoreceptor. Some of these projections are not sensory, for they lack receptor cells; but even these may communicate vibrations to the exoskeletal plate on which they lie and serve a secondary sensory function. It is easy to forget that the stimuli which pass to the central nervous system from the sense organs are not in themselves different, whether they stem from a mechanoreceptor or a chemoreceptor. It is the instrument used to evoke the stimulus—the sense organ—which is responsible for giving the incoming stimulus a specific meaning. The hairs and bristles that are used to convey a stimulus to receptor cells vary greatly. Some are short and stubby, while others are long, flexible filaments. Depending on the form of the hair or bristle, and the frequency with which the nerve fiber from the receptor cell can accept a new stimulus, the mechanoreceptors can provide surprisingly diverse bits of information about the environment. Simple tactile stimuli are important, of course, and provide information that helps in escaping enemies or capturing food, as well as helping to set up reflexes that are important in walking, running, fighting, or mating. The sagging of a long, slender hair can provide information about the direction of a gravitational field or, as it blows in the wind, give clues to the direction and strength of air currents. Filamentous receptors can also record vibrations, and so be used as sources of information about the texture of surfaces with which the receptor is in contact or the frequency and amplitude of vibrations in the sound range. They can describe the changing tensions in a spider's web and so give clues to the arrival of food, a mate, or other things that may affect the web. Every arachnid has not one but several of these filamentous mechanoreceptors, but there is a dearth of information about their specific functions. More is known of insect mechanoreceptors, and a discussion will be postponed for a time (see p. 894). It seems safe to conclude, however, that the general principles that operate in terrestrial mandibulates are no less applicable to arachnids.

Just as every bristle is a potential point of sensory reception, so is every pit or thin spot in the exoskeleton. A number of sense organs are small, depressed pits or slits with attenuated cuticle at the floor. The tarsal organs of spiders and the lyriform organs (Fig. 17.22D) of spiders and some other arachnids are examples. Pit-shaped receptors, like filamentous receptors, may be used for a variety of purposes.

They are particularly useful for recording exoskeletal tensions and for vibrations, but are also a common pattern for chemoreception. The lyriform organs of spiders serve as good examples. Each receptor is a narrow pit, covered by a delicate floor against which sensory endings project. Although well described from a structural point of view, their uses remain uncertain, and several functions have been ascribed to them. There is some evidence that they function in chemoreception, and some have considered them as hygroreceptors. On the other hand, there is some evidence that they are used to recognize vibrations in the web and evoke attack reactions when stimulated. It is not impossible that several kinds of lyriform organs, sensitive to different stimuli, exist, but when the experimenter is limited to trying to describe changes of behavior evoked by stimulation when specific sense organs are functional or inactivated, there is a considerable area left open for disagreement. In these circumstances, he must demonstrate that the methods of the experiment do not themselves affect behavior, and that behavior is not disturbed for indirect reasons when a sense organ is inactivated by some experimental technique. There is room for a great deal of careful experimentation and analysis in the field of arachnid sense organs.

Photoreception is better understood, and the eyes of arachnids fit nicely into the patterns seen in animals belonging to other phyla. Arachnid eyes are simple ocelli, with a circular lens filling much of the cavity of the pigment cup. The lens is a corneal lens, formed by corneagenous cells which are differentiated from the epidermis. Evidently there has been a good deal of independent eye evolution among arachnids. The corneagenous cells of scorpion eyes do not extend over the light-receptive retinular cells, but in spider eyes they form a layer over the retinula cells (Fig. 17.22E,F). As in *Xiphosura*, the retinula cells form clusters around a rhab-

dome, formed by the combined rhabdomeres from each retinula cell of the cluster. Each individual rhabdome serves as a source of light reception, and initiates a separate nerve stimulus. The quality of the image which is formed depends on the number of rhabdomes present in the ocellus. This number varies greatly in different arachnids, and even within the same group. Lycosid eyes, for example, may have from 100 to 4500 rhabdomes, depending on the position of the eye and the species. At the very best, arachnid eyes have very few rhabdomes compared with the number of rods or cones in a vertebrate eye, and the image is sketchy (Fig. 17.22G). In some arachnid eyes the rhabdomes are directed toward the lens, while in others the rhabdomes are directed away from the lens. The eyes may thus be considered as direct or converse, and indirect or inverse. As a general rule, the medial eyes are inverse and the remaining eyes are converse. An unusual feature of inverse spider eyes is the presence of intrinsic eye musculature, which can tilt the eye—thus directing it to different points without changing the position of the body—and change the focal depth by compressing the corneagenous cells below the lens. Spiders with eyes of this type are the only invertebrates which can be said to have definite eye muscles, save for the cephalopods, in which the eye musculature is sometimes quite complex. In arachnid eyes, a layer of cells forms behind the eye capsule. This postretinal layer forms the back of the eye, and is sometimes converted into a tapetum, a layer containing crystals that reflect light. The eyes of some spiders, for example, gleam when a beam of light strikes them as a result of the reflection of light by the tapetum.

THE NERVOUS SYSTEM

The primitive arthropod nervous system consists of a brain, a circumenteric nerve ring, and a nerve cord with a ganglion in each somite, but tendencies toward centralization of the nervous system result in modification of the primitive pattern. The chelicerate arthropods, like the mandibulate arthropods, have tended to concentrate ganglia, which move forward as they are incorporated in the general nerve mass, in front of the body. As a general rule, the chelicerates have gone rather further than most mandibulates in this process of concentration.

Scorpions have a relatively primitive nervous system. The nerve cord is a recognizable nerve trunk, and bears seven distinct ganglia (Fig. 17.20B). As there are fewer ganglia than body segments, however, it is evident that some centralization has occurred. As a general rule, most of the nervous tissue of arachnids is gathered together to form a nerve collar around the esophagus. Nerves to various parts of the body arise from the nerve collar (Fig. 17.23). Some of the arachnids retain a recognizable nerve cord, but in others no definite nerve cord is found. Where a nerve cord can be distinguished, one or several ganglia may be found associated with it. Uropygids, for example, have a posterior ganglion at the end of the nerve cord, associated with the operation of the tail filament. Solpugids have an abdominal ganglion which gives rise to nerves serving the alimentary tract. As a general rule, however, the nervous system is concentrated in the nerve collar and all peripheral nerves arise from the brain or nerve collar.

The brain proper is dorsal or anterior to the esophagus. It is made up of a protocerebrum, closely associated with the visual organs, and a tritocerebrum associated with the chelicerae. The complex mass of the rest of the nerve collar lies below the esophagus and contains the subesophageal ganglion united with all of the other ganglionic material that is retained. Arachnids, like all other chelicerates, are without a deutocerebrum (p. 710).

The relationship between brain regions and behavior has been partially described. The protocerebrum is associated with the optic nerves, but although arachnids usually have several pairs of eyes the visual sense is not the most important in determining behavior, and no more than 3 per cent of the brain is occupied by visual centers. In this arachnids contrast sharply with insects, in which a much larger part of the brain volume is turned over to visual centers. Two centers, the corpora pedunculata and the central body, are primarily responsible for integrating behavior. The corpora pedunculata are visual centers as well as integrating centers in arthropods, and they tend to become relatively larger in arachnids which are larger or more active. The central body appears to be most closely associated with behavior patterns that are generally considered to be instinctive, and also to be related to visual co-ordination.

As a general rule, arachnid behavior patterns are complex. They burrow, build nests, construct webs of varying complexity and precision of design, indulge in courtship rituals, and carry out a variety of complex activities. Arachnid behavior is far too extensive a topic to be discussed here, and for those who wish to study it further, some excellent books on arachnids are recommended at the end of this chapter. In general, two points become obvious when arachnid behavior is examined. The behavior patterns are meaningless unless carried out with some relation to the environmental factors. A complicated courtship ritual on the part of a male spider is nonsensical unless there is a female nearby. It is evident, therefore, that sensory stimuli pouring into the central nervous system from the many kinds of sense organs are utilized to evoke the complex behavior patterns exhibited under various kinds of conditions. In the second place, the forms of many kinds of activities are very strongly ritualized. Many of the complex responses to specific environmental conditions appear to be prepackaged responses, innate rather than learned, and predictable to a rather high degree. Arachnids have only a limited ability to do more than react in a predetermined way to the situations they are "built" to anticipate. Few areas in biology are more fascinating than the study of these complex behavioral adaptations, made possible, it is true, by advancing complexity of the nervous system, but nevertheless involving a minimum of learning and adjustment. The blind processes of environmental selection and gene survival select out and make innate a kind of biological forethought. Genetic changes, becoming operational through all the intricacy of embryonic development,

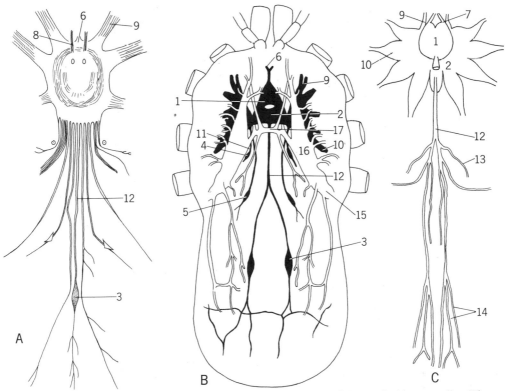

Fig. 17.23. The nervous system is very strongly concentrated in arachnids generally. The brain, connectives, and subesophageal ganglia are fused to form a complex nerve ring, as seen in a solfugid (A), a harvestman (B), and a spider (C). The prosomal nerve tissue is also concentrated, forming a massive prosomal ganglion, with extensions, in many cases, into the bases of the legs. The abdominal nervous system has no segmental ganglia in most arachnids, and in many instances no ganglia whatsoever. Nerves to the various body parts extend from the ganglionic mass in the prosoma. Harvestmen also have a fairly complex tracheal system, with longitudinal tracheal trunks which are expanded, and probably function in part like the air sacs of insects. (A, after Bernard. B, after Warburton, from Warburton. C, based on Kästner, in Kükenthal and Krumbach.) *Nervous system:* 1, brain; 2, prosomal ganglion; 3, abdominal ganglion; 4, genital ganglion; 5, visceral ganglion; 6, labral nerve; 7, optic nerve; 8, cheliceral nerve; 9, pedipalp nerve; 10, ganglion and nerve to leg; 11, lateral nerve; 12, abdominal nerve; 13, nerve to book lung; 14, nerves to spinnerets. *Tracheal system:* 15, spiracle; 16, prosomal longitudinal trunk; 17, commissural trachea.

result in predetermined neural pathways between predetermined neural relay centers, evoking prearranged responses. The phenomenon of behavioral adaptation deserves a great deal more thorough analysis than has so far been achieved.

REPRODUCTION

Some of the problems of adjusting to land life are more critical during the reproductive phase than in the adult phase. The danger of excessive water loss is more critical in ova or in juvenile stages than in mature stages, for smaller size means a greater surface-volume ratio, and young animals are less able to replace water that is lost. The development of resistant egg coverings is an important countermeasure used by terrestrial annelids and molluscs as well as arthropods. The formation of such coverings, however, requires the presence of accessory glands in the reproductive system, and a simple reproductive system of the kind seen in polychaetes is not adequate. The presence of egg coverings also favors the development of copulatory habits, for as a general rule an ovum must be fertilized before the resistant covering is applied. Habits of depositing eggs in humid parts of the environment or of building burrows or nests where some humidity control is possible may be added to the list of things favored by land life. Some of the arachnids have achieved the same end result by the development of parasitic larval stages that can obtain moisture as well as food from their hosts, and others have followed an alternative line of adaptation, leading to the internal development of the young.

The ciliated larvae of many aquatic animals can achieve independence at a very early stage of development. Usually the appearance of brooding habits is associated with an increase in the amount of yolk stored in the ovum and the reduction of larval stages. Land animals have no choice, and usually arise from stocks of aquatic animals that can produce eggs rich in yolk. Terrestrial larval stages, where they exist, are necessarily more advanced than simple aquatic larvae, for they must be able to cope with the more austere conditions of land life and cannot move about with cilia. Larger eggs, with more direct development and the omission of the earliest larval stages, are typical of land animals.

As a rule, successful terrestrial reproduction depends on modifications of the reproductive system to permit the production of eggs that are better protected against drying, or have more reserve food to permit longer development before hatching, or to provide a site for internal development of the young. Some land animals, however, have compensated for the lack of such adaptations by developing special behavior patterns, or by utilizing the functional potentialities of systems other than the reproductive system.

Spiders provide a good example of a group of terrestrial animals that have achieved solutions to the problems of land reproduction with the minimal differentiation of the reproductive system. Scorpions, on the other hand, have adapted to land reproduction by an extensive modification of the reproductive system.

Spiders have a pair of large ovaries, opening into oviducts that unite a short distance in front of the gonopore (Fig. 17.19). A pair of copulatory pores open into ducts that lead into one or more pairs of seminal receptacles. These are usually connected to the median oviduct, which is sometimes called the vagina. The male system is even more simple. The paired testes open into sperm ducts, which are coiled or convoluted and contain space for sperm storage. These unite before they open through the gonopore.

The simplicity of the reproductive system contrasts with the complexity of reproductive behavior. The structure of the modified male pedipalp has been described (p. 717). When sexually ripe, the male charges the pedipalp with sperm, dipping it into a drop of semen secreted on a tiny sperm web.

Male spiders make a number of different kinds of approaches to females. The female has formidable fangs and in some cases is perfectly willing to kill and eat the male. The male is well advised to make an approach that will give him the maximum chances of success.

The male *Tetragnatha* makes a direct approach. He has larger chelicerae than the female. The male wedges her fangs open with his so that she cannot bite, maintaining this hold throughout mating. When finished, he rapidly disengages and lowers himself to the ground on a thread of silk. Some of the other spider males are forceful. The male *Xysticus* fastens the female to the ground with silk before mating, for example. This is counterbalanced by the conduct of the female *Argiope*, which tries to wrap the male in silk during mating, and if the male is not strong and fast enough to escape, feeds on him afterwards. But the battle of the sexes is not always so fiercely fought. Some lycosid males present the female with a fly, wrapped in silk, and mate with her if she accepts. Others perform courtship dances, involving vibrations of the body or appendages (Fig. 17.25). The female may retreat, attack, or, if in the mood, signal her acceptance by similar vibrations. Vibration of the body or its parts plays an important role in courtship affairs generally. The male often vibrates the web of the female in a characteristic fashion, as one might knock on a lover's door, and in some cases the male has a stridulating organ that is brought into play during courtship.

However the preliminaries may be effected, the male gorges the haematodocha of the pedipalp with blood, erecting the embolus in readiness for mating. The embolus is inserted into the copulatory pores, and the seminal receptacles are filled with sperm.

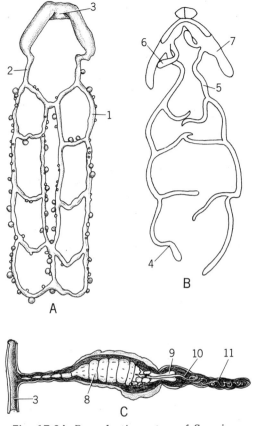

Fig. 17.24. Reproductive system of Scorpions. The female (A) and the male (B) systems are similar, with branching gonads and paired gonoducts. In ovoviviparous scorpions, the uterus gives rise to diverticula (C) in which embryos develop. A placental extension of the diverticulum extends to branches of the digestive gland. Food is processed in the coiled, tubular bottle, which ends in a teat. The embryonic chelicerae are permanently attached to the teat, and the embryo uses its sucking pharynx to nurse. (A and B, after Pawlowsky, from Kästner, in Kükenthal and Krumbach. C, after Vachon, from Cloudsley-Thompson.) 1, ovary; 2, oviduct; 3, uterus; 4, testis; 5, sperm duct; 6, seminal vesicle; 7, paraxial organ; 8, abdomen of embryo; 9, arm of chelicera; 10, teat; 11, bottle.

The female does not lay eggs immediately. When the eggs are ready they are deposited in masses on a silken film. Sperm from the seminal receptacles is poured over them, and a covering sheet is added. The whole mass is wrapped up in layers of silk to form a cocoon. Cocoons may be carried about, attached to leaves or under objects, hung on threads from leaves or twigs, or deposited in a nest or burrow. The silken cocoon protects the eggs from mechanical injury and from dessication, serving the same function as the heavy egg membranes secreted by the accessory glands in some animals or as the special brood chambers found in others.

Scorpion ovaries are composed of a series of tubules with cross connections between the main lateral tubes on each side (Fig. 17.24). A short oviduct leads from each ovary to the dilated seminal receptacles, located just within the gonoducts. A short genital atrium separates the gonopores and the seminal receptacles. The testes are built like the ovaries and open into a long sperm duct, with several accessory glands.

Scorpions carry on a long courtship dance (Fig. 17.25A). Eventually the male persuades the female to retire with him into a burrow or digs a special hole into which they retire. A true copulation occurs, with terminal parts of the male system serving as a penis. Not all scorpions work in this manner, however. In some cases the sperm are cemented together to form a spermatophore in a special chamber in the male system. During the courtship dance the male sticks the spermatophore into the ground and maneuvers the female over it. He presses her down on it so that the tip enters the genital atrium. However sperm transfer is effected, the sperm move up the female ducts, eventually reaching the seminal receptacles.

Development is internal. Some scorpions produce large, yolky eggs that develop in the oviducts. Others have small ova, with insufficient nourishment to carry the young creature through development. In these species, the young animal gets nourishment through a placenta-like arrangement (Fig. 17.24C). The oviduct puts out diverticula that extend to the nearest diverticula of the midgut and absorb nourishment for the embyro.

A variety of different solutions to the problems of mating and of development are seen in other kinds of arachnids. The pseudoscorpion male, like some scorpion males, thrusts a spermatophore into the ground and presses the female down upon it. The male harvestman is equipped with a very long penis that conducts sperm to the female, while the female has a long ovipositor that is used to scoop out a burrow for the eggs.

Most arachnids provide a certain amount of postnatal care for the young. This may involve little more than building a burrow or nest in which the young develop and guarding it for a time. A number of spiders guard the cocoon zealously throughout development and many others carry it until the young hatch (Fig. 17.26A). Pseudoscorpions usually retire to a silken nest for brooding the eggs. An incubation chamber is formed by the mother, attached to the gonopore, and the eggs are laid in the sac. The eggs hatch in a few days, and the larvae develop a sucking beak used to ingest a secretion produced by the female from the transformed ovaries. They grow enormously, and before they emerge from the incubation chamber, the mass of young in the brood pouch may be larger than the mother.

As a general rule the mother's duties are over when the young hatch, but in some cases the period of postnatal care continues for a time. Scorpions, wolf spiders, and some of the pseudoscorpions carry the young about for a time, and in some cases the young organisms have special structures to help them hang on. Some of the arachnids feed the young for a time (Fig. 17.26C), either with special secretions or with regurgitated food.

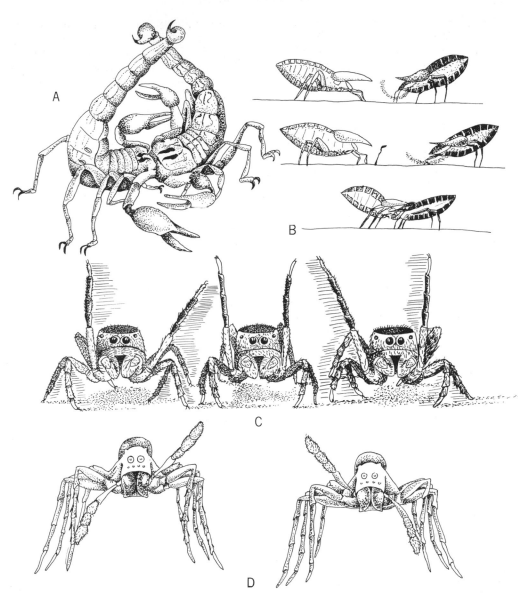

Fig. 17.25. Courtship and Mating. Many arachnids have most interesting courtship practices, and mating is accomplished in a variety of ways. Scorpions undergo a prolonged prenuptial dance (A) prior to a true copulation, or to the transfer of a spermatophore to the female orifice. Pseudoscorpions also undergo a prenuptial dance (B), during which the male produces a spermatophore that is thrust into the ground. The female advances and places the genital pore over the spermatophore. The mating behavior of spiders varies greatly. A common practice involves some sort of posturing by the male. The male *Attulus* (C) runs back and forth rapidly on three pairs of legs, facing the female, and swings the lifted fourth pair of legs back and forth until he is accepted by the female. Some lycosids (D) move the pedipalps up and down, like semaphores, to attract the female. (A and B, after Vachon, from Cloudsley-Thompson. C and D, after Bristowe.)

745

Arachnids have remarkably complex reproductive behavior, much of which tends to increase the chances of survival of the young. Descriptions of some of their behavior patterns make interesting reading. A monograph or book dealing with spiders or arachnids should be consulted for further details.

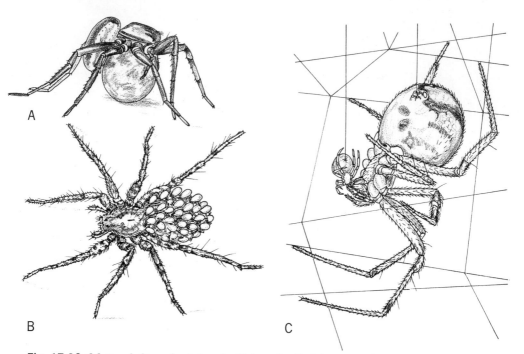

Fig. 17.26. Maternal Care. **A.** A female *Dolomedes fimbriatus* carrying an egg sac. A large number of female spiders carry the egg sac until the young emerge. **B.** A female *Lycosa*, covered with her young. Wolf spiders carry the young for about a week after they hatch, after which they are able to fend for themselves. **C.** A spider madonna and child. A female *Theridion* feeding a baby. She regurgitates food for her young for the first several days after they hatch. (After Bristowe.)

References

Alexander, A. J. 1959. Courtship and mating in the buthid scorpions. *Proc. Zool. Soc. London* 133: 145.

Baerg, W. 1958. *The Tarantula.* Univ. of Kansas Press, Lawrence, Kans.

Baker, E. W., and G. W. Wharton. 1952. *An Introduction to Acarology.* Macmillan, New York. (!)

Barrows, W. M. 1925. Modification and development of the arachnid palpal claw, with especial reference to spiders. *Ann. Ent. Soc. Amer.* 18: 483.

Bishop, S. C. 1949. The Phalangida of New York. *Proc. Rochester Acad. Sci.* 9: 159. (F)

Bristowe, W. S. 1939–41. *The Comity of Spiders.* Ray. Soc., London.

———. 1958. *The World of Spiders.* Collins, London. (G)

Buxton, B. H. 1913. Coxal glands of the arachnids. *Zool. Jahrb. Suppl.* 14: 231.

Clarke, J. M., and R. Ruedemann. 1912. The Eurypterida of New York, *N.Y. Stat. Mus. 65th Ann. Rep. Mem.* 14, Vol. 3, 4.

Cloudsley-Thompson, J. L. 1958. *Spiders, Scorpions, Centipedes, and Mites.* Pergamon, New York. (G)

Comstock, H., and W. Gertsch. 1948. *The Spider Book.* Cornell Univ., Ithaca, N.Y.

Cole, L. J. 1901. Notes on the habits of pycnogonids. *Biol. Bull.* 2: 195.

Davies, M. E., and E. B. Edney. 1952. The evaporation of water from spiders. *Jour. Exp. Biol.* 29: 571.

Demoll, R. 1914. Die Augen von *Limulus. Zool. Jahrb. Anat.* 38: 443.

Dohrn, A. 1881. Die Pantopoden des Golfes don Neapel und der angrenzenden Meeresabschnitte. *Fauna u. Flora. v. Golfes Neapel* 3.

Douglas, J. R. 1943. The internal anatomy of *Dermacentor andersoni* Stiles. *Univ. Calif. Publ. Ent.* 7: 207.

Ellis, C. H. 1944. The mechanism of extension in the legs of spiders. *Biol. Bull.* 86: 41.

Ewing, H. E. 1918. The life and behavior of the house spider. *Proc. Iowa Acad. Sci.* 25: 177.

Fraenkel, G. 1929. Atmungsmechanismus des Skorpions. *Ztschr. vergl. Physiol.* 11: 656.

Gertsch, J. W. 1949. *American Spiders.* Van Nostrand, New York.

Hedgepeth, J. W. 1947. On the evolutionary significance of the pycnogonids. *Smithson. Misc. Publ.* 106. No. 18. (G)

———. 1948. The pycnogonids of the Western North Atlantic and the Caribbean. *Proc. U.S. Nat. Mus.* 97: 157.

Hoff, C. C. 1949. The pseudoscorpions of Illinois. *Bull. Ill. Nat. Hist. Surv.* 24. (F)

Hoyle, G. 1958. Studies on neuromuscular transmission in *Limulus. Biol. Bull.* 115: 209.

Kaston, B. J., and E. Kaston. 1953. *How To Know the Spiders.* Brown, Dubuque, Ia.

Kingsley, J. S. 1892–3. The embryology of *Limulus. Jour. Morph.* 7: 35; 8: 195.

Lees, A. D. 1948. The sensory physiology of the sheep tick, *Ixodes ricinus* L. *Jour. Exp. Biol.* 25: 145.

Lowrie, D. C. 1948. The ecological succession of spiders in the Chicago area dunes. *Ecol.* 29: 334.

Montgomery, T. H. 1903. Studies on the habits of spiders, particularly those of the mating period. *Proc. Acad. Nat. Sci. Phila.* 55: 59.

Muna, M. H., and K. E. Muna. 1949. Studies on a population of prairie spiders. *Ecol.* 30: 485. (E).

Nørgaard, E. 1951. On the ecology of two lycosid spiders, *Pirata piraticus* and *Lycosa pullata* from a Danish sphagnum bog. *Oikos* 3: 1.

Pavlovsky, E. N., and E. J. Zarin. 1926. On the structure and ferments of the digestive organs of scorpions. *Quart. Jour. Micr. Sci.* 70: 221.

Petrunkewitch, A. 1912. The circulatory system and segmentation in arachnids. *Jour. Morph.* 36: 157.

———. 1933. An inquiry into the natural classification of spiders, based on a study of their internal anatomy. *Trans. Conn. Acad. Arts Sci.* 31: 299.

Pringle, J. W. S. 1955. The function of the lyriform organs of arachnids. *Jour. Exp. Biol.* 32: 270.

Purcell, W. F. 1910. The phylogeny of the tracheae in Araneae. *Quart. Jour. Micr. Sci.* 54: 519.

Savory, T. H. 1928. *The Biology of Spiders.* Sidgewick & Jackson, London.

Scheuring, L. 1914. Die Augen der Arachnoideen, II (Phalangida und Araneida). *Zool. Jahrb. Anat.* 8: 191.

Vachon, M. 1953. The biology of scorpions. *Endeavour* 12: 80.

Wesenberg-Lund, C. 1919. Contributions to the knowledge of the post-embryonal development of the Hydracarina. *Vidensk. Medd. Dansk. Naturhist. For.* 70: 5.

Wirén, E. 1918. Zur Morphologie und Phylogenie der Pantopoden. *Zool. Bidrag. Uppsala.* 6: 41.

Wolcott, R. H. 1905. A review of the genera of water mites. *Trans. Am. Micr. Soc.* 26: 161.

18

The Aquatic Mandibulates—Crustacea

The subclass Mandibulata includes most of the arthropods, in spite of the relatively high success of arachnids. Mandibulates are especially characterized by their head appendages. All have a pair of preoral antennae, which appear to be homologous with the antennae of trilobites, and which have no corresponding parts in the chelicerates. The second postantennal somite bears the pair of mandibles for which the mandibulates are named. The next two somites typically bear flattened mouthpart appendages known as maxillae, but in some of the most primitive mandibulates these may not be differentiated. The first postantennal somite is the basis for differentiating between the two main lines of mandibulates. A predominantly aquatic stem, the Crustacea, has a pair of second antennae on this somite. In the predominantly terrestrial stem, which includes the myriapods and the insects, this somite is reduced and has no appendages.

Crustacea are distinguished from the myriapods and insects by many more traits than the presence of a second pair of antennae. A striking difference is seen in leg structure. The appendages of crustaceans are biramous, consisting of a basal part, the protopodite, an inner arm, the endopodite, and an outer arm, the exopodite, while the appendages of the terrestrial mandibulates are uniramous, with no evidence, even during development, of an endopodite and exopodite. The major characteristics of the Crustacea are as follows:

1. They are predominantly aquatic, with gills for respiration.

2. They have five pairs of head appendages: first antennae or antennules; second antennae or antennae; mandibles; first maxillae or maxillules; and second maxillae or maxillae.

3. The body is divided into different tagmata in subsidiary groups, but usually has a recognizable head, thorax, and abdomen.

4. A posterior somite, the telson, contains the anus and bears no appendages.

5. They have a typical arthropod circulatory system with a heart having ostia, sometimes reduced in small forms.

6. The excretory system contains antennal glands or maxillary glands or both.

7. A median eye and usually a pair of lateral eyes are present.

Table 18.1. Comparison of mandibulates

	CRUSTACEA	CHILOPODA	DIPLOPODA	INSECTA
Tagmata	Head, thorax, and abdomen in most cases; head and thorax may be covered by a common carapace	Head, trunk	Head, trunk, with first few trunk somites bearing a single pair of legs and sometimes considered thoracic	Head, thorax, and abdomen
Head appendages	First antennae Second antennae Mandibles First maxillae Second maxillae in most	Antennae missing Mandibles First maxillae Second maxillae	Antennae missing Mandibles First maxillae Second maxillae, legs, or none	Antennae missing Mandibles First maxillae Second maxillae
Thorax	Variable number of segments	Not differentiated from trunk	Anterior trunk somites with single pair of legs	Three somites
Thoracic appendages	Typically differentiated into several types with different functions	Maxilliped with poison glands followed by pairs of similar legs, one pair to each somite; gonopods differentiated	First few "thoracic" somites with single pairs of legs	One pair of walking legs to each somite
Abdominal appendages	Reduced, or somewhat differentiated if present	Not distinct from thoracic appendates	Two pairs of similar legs to each diplosomite; only gonopods differentiated	Reduced or absent, except those modified for reproduction

8. Sexes are usually separate, with indirect development and, typically, a nauplius larva stage.

Introduction to Crustacea

Crustacea have not differentiated into as many species as insects or arachnids, for only about 26,000 species are known. They are extremely abundant, however, and many are relatively large. They are almost as influential in the sea as insects are on land. They are abundant in freshwater plankton; their disappearance would greatly disturb the natural balance of lakes and ponds. Only a few have ventured on land, however, and as these have tended to retain the physiological patterns of the aquatic species, they are found only in humid environments and have not been particularly successful. One might wish to make an exception, however, of the region just above high tide line, where a number of species live and are among the most important animal inhabitants.

The most careful studies have failed to bring general agreement about the homologies of the appendages of various kinds of arthropods. There is no space to discuss the various ideas and the kinds of evidence that has been brought to their support. There is a strong similarity of the trilobite acron and the polychaete prostomium. One might anticipate that there would be a good deal of convergence in anterior sensory appendages in different animal stocks, but similarities in the brain centers and innervation of the sensory appendages of the head strongly support the idea that the antennules of crustaceans correspond to the prostomial sense organs of polychaetes. There is every reason to suppose that polychaetes and arthropods arose from a common ancestral stem, whatever the details of relationship may be, and however the protoannelid and protoarthropod stocks may have been constructed at the time that they began to diverge.

Probably all of the postoral appendages were alike in ancestral stocks. This arrangement is retained in the more primitive polychaetes, but is lost in the more highly specialized Sedentaria. Probably the first arthropods, like the annelids, had a body composed of discrete segments. In some of the polychaetes the peristomium is a compound somite, but the annelids did not venture into the intimate union of somites to form special body regions. This tagmatization of the body is characteristic of arthropods. It shows up first in the addition of anterior somites to form a complex head. It has occurred to some extent in the Onychophora, but it is in the arthropods that the development of specialized body regions, the head and other tagmata, reaches its highest development.

Crustacea are ancient creatures, and there has been ample time for them to become highly specialized. Nevertheless, some quite primitive Crustacea appear to have survived, if our ideas about the nature of the early crustacean stocks are correct. In examining a number of different kinds of Crustacea, one can see evidences that some retain more and others less of the primitive traits, and it is well to watch for them and to note when several primitive traits tend to go together, and where combinations of primitive and advanced traits are found. In this way one can form an opinion of one's own about the persuasiveness of the various pictures of crustacean relationships that have been suggested.

As a general rule, the following are important factors in crustacean evolution and give clues to the relative primitiveness of crustacean stocks. (1) How many somites are a part of the functional head? For reasons of simplicity, it is conventional to consider the head as the part of the animal that bears the first five appendages, counting the first antennae as appendages. However, the animals have not read the books, and in some cases the first thoracic appendages function as mouth parts while in others the last head appendages are not differentiated from the thoracic appendages. An increase in the number of head somites and appendages, from a functional point of view, is considered evidence of more advanced structure. (2) How clearly is the body divided into definite regions? Tagmatization, the specialization of definite body regions, appears to have been an important adaptive trend among arthropods generally, and among crustaceans evidences of more advanced tagmatization may be taken as evidence of less primitive structure. In Crustacea, tagmatization has become involved with the development of a carapace. Something of the same kind is seen in arachnids, where the prosomal somites have a carapace formed by the fused terga of the region, and where in some instances the carapace is continuous, and in other instances is composed of two distinct plates. The crustacean carapace, however, is formed in an entirely different manner. A fold of the integument develops from the back part of the head, and comes to partly or wholly enclose the body. The exoskeleton of the carapace forms an important protective cover where it is well developed, and provides an enclosure in which water may be channeled over gills or toward the mouth. As the carapace encloses the thoracic somites, the head and thorax tend to be combined into a compound tagma, the cephalothorax. (3) Are the appendages similar or varied in form? The most primitive stocks tend to have appendages which are alike, while in the more advanced forms the appendages are specialized for specific uses, or may be reduced and wholly lost in some parts of the body. Perhaps in conjunction with the specialization of appendages and the loss of appendages in parts of the body, there is also a tendency for the body to become shorter in more advanced forms, at least insofar as the number of somites is concerned.

Except for the first antennae, crustacean appendages are basically biramous. Even in appendages which become uniramous in adults, the embryonic appendages are biramous. The appendage is Y-shaped, with the base of the Y attached to the somite. The basal piece is the protopodite, the inner branch the endopodite, and the outer branch the exopodite. Some crustacean appendages have a very delicate cuticular covering and are not further segmented, but in most cases the heavy exoskeleton of the appendage is broken down into a series of skeletal rings. The resulting leg segments, known as podites, may be homologized with the leg segments of uniramous appendages of arachnids and insects (Table 16.1).

Crustacean appendages are important tools and have undergone an extensive adaptive radiation, fitting them for a variety of special tasks, including sensory reception, chewing, food capture, food manipulation, swimming, walking, breathing, copulation, and brooding eggs. In many cases adaptation has profoundly altered the basic form of the appendage. The structure of crustacean appendages is an important factor in classification and taxonomy. One of the first things to do in identifying a crustacean is to examine its set of appendages. The functional flexibility of the appendage is increased by the addition of processes to one or another part of it. It is important to know the vocabulary associated with these processes. Medial processes are termed endites, while lateral processes are exites. Exites attached to the protopodite are calleded epipodites. In many cases a basal endite is used for handling or fragmentation of food. Such an endite is called a gnathobase. The adaptive radiation of crustacean appendages is nicely exemplified by the set of appendages seen in a crayfish or lobster (Fig. 18.1). It is particularly interesting, as all appendages, except for the first antennae, arise from similar embryonic primordia, and, presumably, from a series of similarly formed appendages in some ancient ancestral stock. One can homologize between the appendages of different somites of one organism, as one can homologize between the appendages of the same somite in different organisms. Homologies seen in a series of metameric parts of the same organism are termed serial homologies, and are an interesting phase of evolutionary study in metameric animal groups.

The crustacean cuticle is much like the cuticle of other arthropods, but is heavily calcified in larger species and usually contains appreciable amounts of calcium even in smaller forms. The epicuticle is double and is calcified, and the three-layered procuticle contains calcium in the upper two layers. The calcium helps to strengthen the cuticle and permits relatively rapid hardening of the cuticle after molting. The cuticle of many Crustacea contains pigments, usually deposited in the outer, vacuolated part of the procuticle.

Custacea resemble other arthropods in the general features of internal organization, but there are many differences in detail, related to the great diversity in size and habits. Crustacea have gills for respiration, associated with the appendages. Gills are sometimes mere flat blades on the appendages, and are sometimes filamentous. As a general rule they are associated with the thoracic appendages, but there are exceptions. The number and position of the gills are useful in classification and are valuable clues in identifying an unfamiliar organism.

Subclasses of Crustacea

Crustacean classification is necessarily complex. No less than eight subclasses can be distinguished, seven of which constitute the old group, Entomostraca, no

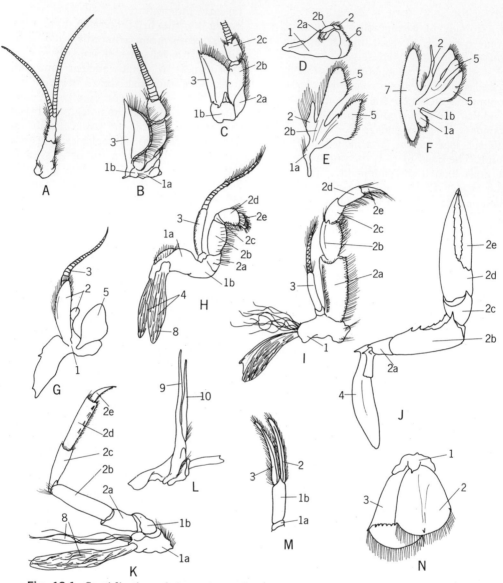

Fig. 18.1. Specialization of Appendages. Crustacea, like other arthropods, live in an exoskeletal box, and the movable appendages are important tools. The appendages are primitively biramous, composed of a basal part (protopodite) to which an outer branch (exopodite) and an inner branch (endopodite) are attached. Further lobes may be attached to the three parts. Epipodites are attached to the coxa (coxopodite) of the protopodite. The endopodite and exopodite are attached to the trochanter (basipodite) of the protopodite. Other podites may bear inwardly directed lobes (endites) or outwardly directed lobes (exites). While the most primitive crustaceans have similar appendages attached to nearly all of the trunk somites, evolutionary development has generally resulted in modification of particular appendages associated with their specialization for specific functions. This has resulted in similar embryonic rudiments becoming very diversified during later development. The basic format of the

752

longer considered valid. Entomostraca is still sometimes used as a general term for smaller types of Crustacea not belonging to the Malacostraca. It will be helpful to examine figures of representative species while reading about the major features of the various subclasses. Note that the characterization given below is the only one given in this book for the three starred subclasses.

Subclass Cephalocarida. A very primitive group of crustaceans recently discovered in Long Island Sound. Tiny, eyeless forms, about 3 mm. long, with two pairs of maxillae, the last pair resembling the trunk appendages. Trunk divided into an anterior thorax region with nine segments and a posterior abdominal region of ten segments. Appendages occur only on the thoracic segments. A pair of large caudal furca arises from the telson. Each trunk appendage has an external lobe, the pseudepipodite, which is unique. The triramous appendage is thought by some to be more primitive than the biramous appendages of other crustaceans. Cephalocarids are hermaphroditic, with gonopores on the ninth somite, and they pass through a metanauplius stage in development. Example: *Hutchinsoniella* (Fig. 18.2A).

Subclass Branchiopoda. Small, free-living, predominantly fresh-water Crustacea, with an elongated, segmented body and many appendages, or a short, compact body, obscurely segmented, and few appendages; usually with a dorsal carapace; compound eyes; mandibles with or without rudimentary palps; usually with four or more pairs of flattened, leaf-like appendages (phyllopodia) used for swimming, respiration, and filter feeding; sexes separate, but often reproducing by parthenogenesis through much of the year; development direct or through a nauplius stage.

Subclass Ostracoda. Small, free-living predominantly marine Crustacea with a short, compact, externally unsegmented body; a bivalved carapace closed by an adductor muscle; with or without compound eyes; mandibles with palps; leg-like second maxillae; only two pairs of slender trunk appendages; abdomen usually ending in a pair of claws known as the furca; sexes separate and parthenogenesis common; larvae hatch at nauplius stage or later.

Subclass Mystacocarida. A recently discovered, primitive group of small crustaceans living in the littoral zone in salt water; body divided into a head with the usual five pairs of appendages, thorax with maxillipeds and four pairs of appendages, and abdomen with appendages on the first four somites; with a median eye but no lateral eyes; with prominent cerci on the last somite; sexes separate; development through a metanauplius stage. Example: *Derocheilocaris* (Fig. 18.2B).

Subclass Copepoda. Small, free-living or parasitic, fresh-water or marine Crustacea; body divided into a head, thorax, and abdomen, but with one or two thoracic somites united with the head and variable abdominal segmentation; no compound

appendages is often so changed that homologies are difficult to work out. In a crayfish, the appendages are extremely diversified. The antennule (A) is probably derived from the prostomial tentacles of an ancestral stock which was polychaete-like, and cannot be homologized successfully with the other appendages. In the other appendages, the basic structure can be recognized by identification of the podites. A. Antennule. B and C. Dorsal and ventral view of antenna. D. Mandible. E. First maxilla. F. Second maxilla. G. First maxilliped. H. Second maxilliped. I. Third maxilliped. J. Cheliped. K. Fourth walking leg or pereiopod. L. First swimmeret of male, modified for copulation. M. Swimmeret. N. Uropod. 1, protopodite, composed of 1a, coxopodite and 1b, basipodite; 2, endopodite, composed of 2a, ischiopodite, 2b, meropodite, 2c, carpopodite, 2d, propodite, 2e, dactylopodite; 3, exopodite; 4, epipodite; 5, endite; 6, gnathal lobe of mandible; 7, scaphognathite (bailer), the epipodite of the second maxilla; 8, gill; 9, cannula; 10, accessory lobe of gonopod.

eye, but usually with a median eye; head with the usual five pairs of appendages; mandibles with or without palps; thorax with six pairs of appendages, but with the last two pairs modified and the last pair sometimes missing; with a caudal furca on the telson; sexes separate.

Subclass Branchiura. Fish lice. Highly modified Crustacea living on the gills or body surface of fresh-water and marine fishes; with the body flattened dorsoventrally and largely covered by a dorsal shield; head with a pair of compound eyes; head appendages much modified and reduced, but second maxillae large, equipped with claws, and used for attachment to the host; four thoracic somites with appendages; short abdomen bilobed; labrum and labium modified to form a sucking mouth; sexes separate and development usually direct. Example: *Argulus* (Fig. 18.2C).

Subclass Cirripedia. Barnacles. Marine Crustacea with sessile habits, living attached to objects or animals or as internal parasites; highly modified in association with their peculiar habits; body usually in a mantle cavity enclosed in a large carapace; without second antennae in the adult; first antennae reduced; no compound eyes; mandibles usually with palps; typically with six thoracic segments, each with a pair of appendages and a reduced abdomen ending in a furca; usually hermaphroditic; development through nauplius and cypris stages, the latter resembling an ostracod.

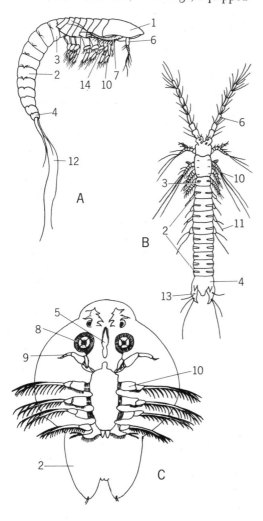

Fig. 18.2. Some Representative Crustacea. A. *Hutchinsoniella*, member of the primitive subclass Cephalocardia. Cephalocarids have second maxillae which resemble the trunk appendages, and ten abdominal somites without appendages. The trunk appendages bear unique pseudopipodites and the last abdominal segment has a large caudal furca. B. *Derocheilocaris*, a member of the primitive subclass, Mystacocarida. Mystacocarids have a head with the usual set of appendages, four thoracic segments with legs, and a long abdomen with appendages on the first four segments. Prominent cerci on the last abdominal segment form a caudal furca. C. *Argulus*, a member of the highly specialized subclass Branchiura. Branchiurans are fish lice, with flattened bodies suitable for clinging. The head appendages are reduced or adapted for clinging, and the labium and labrum are specialized to form a sucking proboscis. (A, after Waterman and Chace, from Waterman. B, after Noodt, from Green. C, after Cameron.) 1, carapace; 2, abdomen; 3, genital somite; 4, telson; 5, proboscis; 6, antennule; 7, antenna; 8, first maxilla; 9, second maxilla; 10, pereiopod; 11, pleopod; 12, caudal furca; 13, cercus; 14, pseudoepipodite.

Subclass Malacostraca. A diversified group of often large Crustacea, mostly marine, but including some fresh-water and terrestrial forms; body divided into head, thorax, and abdomen; head usually with stalked compound eyes; mandibles with or without palps; usually a carapace over the thorax; eight thoracic segments with the female gonopores on the sixth and the male gonopores on the eighth somite; sexes separate; development variable.

Subclass Branchiopoda

Branchiopods are among the most primitive of modern Crustacea, but the oldest fossil branchiopods appeared in the middle of the Paleozoic, and it is not surprising that highly specialized characteristics accompany the primitive traits. The most primitive features of the branchiopods are the many body segments, the series of similar appendages with a minimum of regional specialization, and a very primitive nervous system (p. 825). The body is much shortened in the Cladocera, however, and is modified in other groups as they have adapted to the carapace.

An unusual feature of the branchiopods is the soft, flattened type of trunk appendages characteristic of most of the groups. Covered with a delicate cuticle, they are flexible enough to move freely without segmentation. This type of appendage is known as phyllopodium, in contrast to the slender, jointed appendages of most Crustacea, known as stenopodia. Because of their appendages, branchipods are sometimes called phyllopods. It is not clear whether the phyllopodia are primitive or highly specialized. Those who believe the phyllopodia to be primitive point to their resemblance to parapodia and to the primitive nature of the branchiopods. However, other primitive Crustacea have stenopodia, and a good case can be made for thinking of stenopodia as the more primitive form of crustacean appendage.

The branchiopods include four distinctive types of organisms, arranged in three orders, with one order divided into two suborders. The form of the carapace is the most important distinguishing feature of the different groups.

CLASSIFICATION

Order Anostraca. Fairy shrimps. Branchiopods without a carapace; body elongated, with at least 20 somites and 11 to 19 pairs of trunk appendages; abdomen without appendages and ending in a short furca; stalked compound eyes. Example: *Artemia* (Fig. 18.3A).

Order Notostraca. Tadpole shrimps. Branchiopods with a low, oval carapace, notched at the rear, and covering the head and thorax; abdomen uncovered, ending in a long furca; up to 60 pairs of appendages; sessile compound eyes. Example: *Apus* (Fig. 18.3B).

Order Diplostraca. Branchiopods with a laterally compressed carapace, typically enclosing the trunk and appendages; large second antennae used in swimming; trunk appendages often considerably specialized; sessile compound eyes; abdomen variable in length and usually ending in a pair of claws.

Suborder Conchostraca. Clam shrimps. Carapace hinged and shell-like, with adductor muscle; not fused to the thorax but completely enclosing the body and head; 10 to 28 pairs of trunk appendages; generally with a nauplius larval stage in development. Example: *Cyzicus* (Fig. 18.3C).

Suborder Cladocera. Water fleas. Carapace without a hinge or adductor muscle, typically enclosing the thorax and abdomen but not the head; carapace usually attached to several thoracic segments; 4 to 6 pairs of thoracic appendages; a single, median compound eye; young develop in a brood sac beneath the carapace. Example: *Daphnia* (Fig. 18.3D).

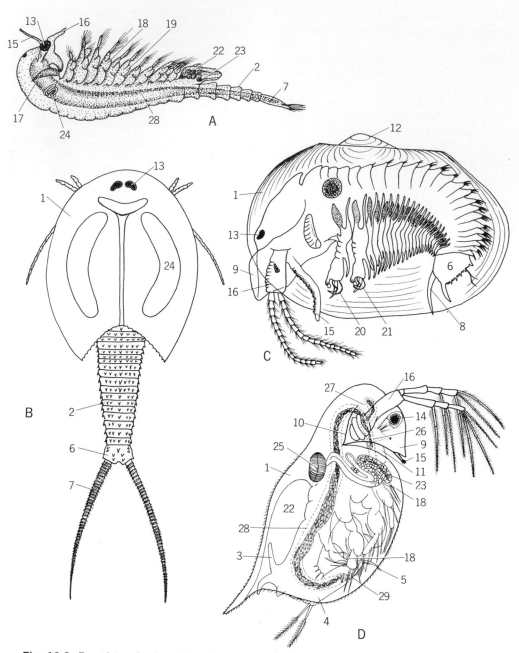

Fig. 18.3. Branchiopods. Branchiopods are divided into three orders, Anostraca, Notostraca, and Diplostraca. Anostraca, the fairy shrimps, have no carapace and typically, like *Artemia* shown at **A**, swim with the ventral surface up. The stalked compound eyes and abdomen without appendages are also characteristic of Anostraca. Notostraca, the tadpole shrimps, have a low, broad carapace not divided into valves or laterally compressed. *Apus*, shown at **B**, is a typical representative. The uncovered abdomen ending in a long caudal furca is characteristic.

EXTERNAL FORM AND HABITS

A few marine Cladocera are known, but nearly all of the branchiopods are freshwater animals. Except for the Cladocera, they are especially characteristic of small temporary ponds, so common over most of the temperate zone. As a general rule, fairy shrimps are sensitive to high temperatures, and usually disappear during late spring or summer. They are easy prey for carnivorous fish and insects, and occur predominantly in habitats without carnivores. They tolerate a wide range of pH and salinity, important for animals living in temporary ponds that change rapidly from week to week. *Artemia salina,* the brine shrimp, can excrete a hypertonic urine and tolerate extreme salinities. It lives in Great Salt Lake, for example. The Notostraca are also found in small freshwater pools in the western United States and arctic regions. They prefer alkaline water and are not disturbed by high turbidity. The Conchostraca live in small, temporary ponds, but prefer warmer water and tend to be abundant in late spring and summer. Cladocera are widespread, occuring in small, temporary ponds and in large lakes. A number of species are common among the emerging vegetation of the littoral zone, while others abound in the limnetic region. A few are adapted to bottom life, but most of them swim about jerkily in open water or among vegetation. They are less sensitive to temperature than most branchiopods, and occur throughout most of the year, although many species are characteristically abundant in one season.

Some branchiopods are cosmopolitan, while other are known only from restricted localities. All *Artemia,* for example, appear to belong to a single, highly variable species composed of a number of morphological and physiological strains. Some species of Cladocera have been reported on several continents. It is not unusual for survivors of once abundant groups to have a puzzling geographical distribution, and this may be a factor in the distribution of some branchiopods. Another factor may be their adaptation to life in temporary ponds. Temporary ponds are themselves capricious, varying from year to year, and it is not surprising that their characteristic inhabitants should appear and disappear suddenly.

The four major types of branchiopods are distinctive. Anostraca have no carapace, as their name suggests. The shield-like dorsal carapace of Notostraca is characteristic, and the bivalved shells of the Diplostraca are equally distinctive. Conchostraca are considerably larger than Cladocera, sometimes exceeding 10 mm. in length. The growth lines on the shells of most species, and the fact that the head is enclosed, give them the appearance of small, swimming clams. Cladocera have a single compound eye, and their transparent carapace does not enclose the head.

The Diplostraca are divided into two suborders, the Conchostraca or clam shrimps, and the Cladocera or water fleas. Both have laterally compressed carapaces which cover the abdomen. *Cyzicus,* shown at C, is a typical clam shrimp. The carapace is a bivalved shell, closed by an adductor muscle, and encloses the whole body, including the head. *Daphnia,* shown at D, is a typical water flea. The carapace is not hinged, and the head extends forward. The large antennae are used for swimming. (A, after Green. B, after Pennak. D, after Storch, from Pennak. C, after Mattox, in Edmondson.) 1, carapace; 2, abdomen; 3, abdominal processes; 4, postabdomen; 5, postabdominal claw; 6, telson; 7, caudal furca; 8, cercopod; 9, rostrum; 10, fornix; 11, labrum; 12, umbone; 13, paired compound eye; 14, median eye; 15, antennule; 16, antenna; 17, mandible; 18, thoracic appendage; 19, branchial lobe (exite); 20, first clasper; 21, second clasper; 22, brood pouch; 23, shell gland; 24, excretory organ; 25, heart; 26, esophagus; 27, hepatic caecum; 28, intestine; 29, anus.

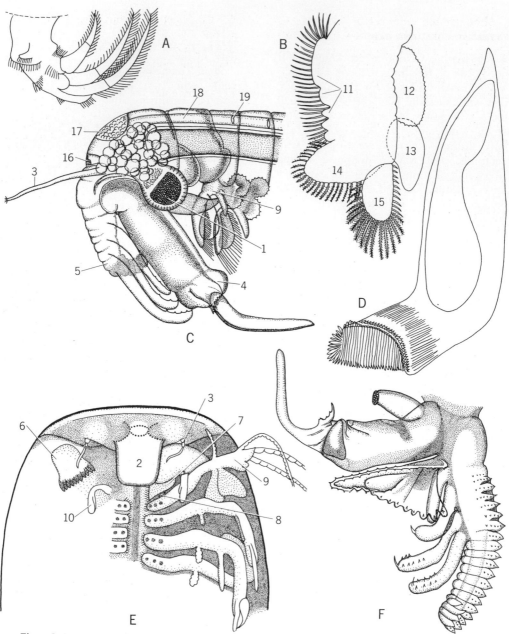

Fig. 18.4. Branchiopods. **A.** The maxilla of *Daphnia*. **B.** A trunk appendage of a fairy shrimp, *Branchinecta*. Appendages of this type, soft and flattened, without the joints so commonly seen in arthropod legs, are known as phyllopodia. A prominent exite serves as a gill lobe. **C.** Side view of the head of an anostracan, *Chirocephalus*. The specimen shown is a male, with greatly modified antennae, used as claspers. **D.** The mandible of a cladoceran, *Daphnia*. **E.** The ventral surface of the head of a notostracan, *Triops*. The antennae are much reduced and the thoracic appendages are all similar, with gnathobases used to push the food into the

Although the same set of five pairs of appendages are found on the head of all Crustacea, they vary markedly in form in different crustacean groups, as do other structures of the head region. Fairy shrimps have a large head with stalked compound eyes (Fig. 18.4C). The first antennae are small and inconspicuous, and the second antennae are large, inflated appendages, modified in males to serve as claspers. Antennal structure varies greatly in different species, and in some cases the antennae are fantastically developed, with appendages, tubercles, and other apparatus (Fig. 18.4F). The form of the male antennae is important in recognizing species. A small frontal organ lies above the median eye and is probably sensory in function. The mouth tends to be enclosed by an upper lip that hangs down in front and by a pair of mandibles and the two maxillae that lie on each side of it.

The notostracan head (Fig. 18.3B) is covered by the carapace on which two sessile compound eyes are set well behind the anterior margin. A frontal organ of varying size lies just behind the eyes. The appendages can be seen only from the ventral side (Fig. 18.4E). The small first antennae, also known as antennules, are located just behind a shallow doublure, and a large labrum hangs over the mouth. The second antennae are missing or greatly reduced, and the maxillae are small.

The head is quite different in the two suborders of the Diplostraca, although similar in the sense that the appendages of the body are enclosed by the shell and the antennae are developed as swimming organs. The carapace covers the head in the Conchostraca, while the head is free in the Cladocera. The front part of the conchostracan head is extended as a rostrum. The compound eyes are sessile and a small, ventral ocellus is also present. The antennules are small, but the large, biramous antennae have natatory setae that increase surface resistance and improve their performance as swimming organs. The protruding head of a cladoceran is often separated from the carapace by a groove, the cervical sinus. Clodocera have a large, median, compound eye and a tiny ocellus. (Fig. 18.3D). The small antennules end in one or more olfactory setae. The large, biramous antennae have natatory setae, which vary in different species and with their habits. Strong swimming, pelagic species have many plumose setae on the antennae. Species with fewer, bristle-like setae scramble about, sometimes pushing through the mud with the antennae and postabdomen. The head also bears a pair of powerful mandibles and a pair of tiny first maxillae (also called maxillules), and may have a pair of minute second maxillae. In some species, the second maxillae are missing. The head appendages are greatly modified, especially the mandibles, and it is not easy to recognize the parts of the appendage that are retained (Fig. 18.4B,D). In some Cladocera the carapace is stiffened by a ridge immediately above the base of the antennae, the fornix.

Body regions differ markedly in different branchiopod groups. Anostraca have 11 to 19 thoracic somites on which phyllopodia are attached, followed by two modified somites containing the reproductive

mouth. The mandible on the left is pulled back to show the grinding surface. **F.** The claspers of *Chirocephalus*, as they appear when unfurled. (A and D, after Lilljeborg, from Pennak. B, after Sars, from Calman, in Lankester. C and F, after Smith and Weldon. E, after Green.) 1, stalked compound eye; 2, labrum; 3, first antenna (antennule); 4, second antenna (antenna); 5, appendage of male second antenna; 6, mandible; 7, first maxilla; 8, second maxilla; 9, first thoracic leg; 10, tube containing opening of excretory organ; 11, endites; 12, proepipodite; 13, exite (gill); 14, endopodite; 15, exopodite (flabellum); 16, median eye; 17, frontal organ; 18, heart; 19, ostium.

organs. By custom the two genital somites are considered a part of the thorax. Seven limbless abdominal somites follow, and the telson is equipped with a furca composed of a pair of cercopods. Typical trunk appendages have a basal protopodite, an exopodite known as the flabellum, and an endopodite. One or two proepipodites are found on the lateral margin of the protopodite, followed by the epipodite, which serves as a gill blade. Five medial endites are found on the inner margin of the endopodite. The larger, basal one is the gnathobase, used for the manipulation of food. Setae and filaments on the endites, endopodite, and exopodite are used to strain out food particles as water flows over the appendages.

The Notostraca have external cuticular rings that do not correspond to the somites, a unique feature. Eleven rings encircle the thorax, and a variable number is found on the abdomen. The rings have no constant relationship to the placement of the appendages. The first two thoracic appendages have long setae, and are probably used as tactile sensory appendages (Fig. 18.4E). The appendages become progressively smaller at the rear, eventually becoming difficult to recognize. There are no appendages in the abdominal region. Although there are minor differences in lobulation, the thoracic appendages are essentially like the appendages of the anostracans. The telson bears a pair of ringed cercopods.

The conchostracan body is curved to fit the contour of the shell (Fig. 18.3C). The 10 to 28 pairs of trunk appendages diminish in size posteriorly, and one or two anterior pairs are modified as claspers in males. Although differing somewhat in detail, the appendages are phyllopodia, essentially like those of anostracans. The telson has a pair of dorsal ridges, between which a biramous filament arises, and ends in a pair of spiny cercopods.

Cladocera may be divided into two groups, the Haplopoda and the Eucladocera. Haplopods are elongated animals, up to 18 mm. long, with the body and legs outside of the carapace (Fig. 18.5B). The small carapace is used only as a brood chamber. The legs of haplopods are cylindrical instead of flattened and have no gill blades. Eucladocera have a shortened body, and trunk appendages have gill blades. One family, the Polyphemidae, resembles the haplopods somewhat, in not being enclosed by the carapace (Fig. 18.5A). Polyphemids differ from haplopods in having a larger carapace and gills on the thoracic appendages. The body, but not the head, of other Cladocera lies within the carapace, A space, the brood chamber, lies between the dorsal body surface and the carapace (Fig. 18.3D). They have five or six pairs of thoracic phyllopodia and a short abdominal region without appendages. The body ends in a recurved postabdomen or telson with two terminal claws and a pair of dorsal abdominal setae. Unlike most of the branchiopods, Cladocera usually have thoracic appendages that are markedly different from each other (Fig. 18.5C-G). Because of the shortening of the body and the differentiation of the thoracic appendages, the Cladocera are considerably less primitive that the other branchiopods.

The branchiopods are filter-feeders, and although details of the feeding currents may differ, all employ essentially similar tactics Movements of the thoracic appendages create water currents that ventilate the gill surfaces and deliver food, predominantly algae, to a food groove between the appendages. Although the main flow of water is backwards, propelling the animal forward, eddying currents at the bases of the appendages generate a small stream that flows forward in the food groove. Glands on the labrum secrete slime, in which particles are trapped. The gnathobases at the base of the appendages push the food forward, delivering it to the maxillae. The maxillae are used to shovel the food between the mandibles,

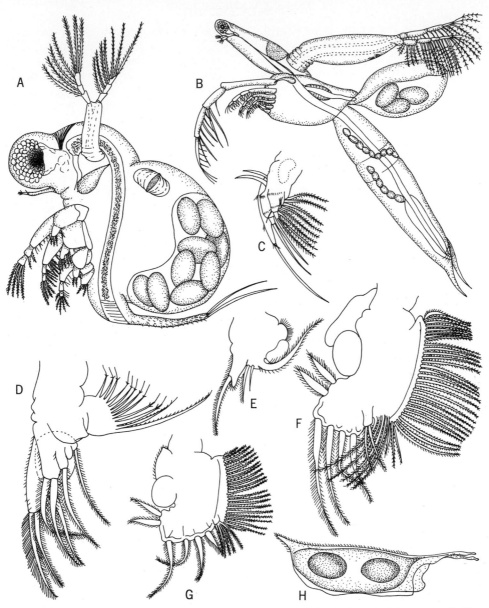

Fig. 18.5. Cladocera. B. *Leptodora kindtii*, an example of the haplopod cladocera, with the carapace not covering the body and legs. Instead of flattened phyllopodia, they have cylindrical stenopodia. A. *Polyphemus pediculus*, a eucladoceran that somewhat resembles a haplopod. Unlike haplopods, they have gills on the thoracic appendages, and the carapace is somewhat larger. C–G. Trunk appendages of a eucladoceran, *Daphnia*. There is little differentiation of thoracic appendages in most branchiopods, but the cladocera have morphologically diverse trunk appendages. C, first leg; D, second leg; F, third leg; G, fourth leg; E, fifth leg. H. A recently shed ephippium of *Daphnia*, containing two winter eggs. (A, composite. B and C, after Lilljeborg, from Calman, in Lankester. D–G, after Uéno, from Pennak. H, after Smith and Weldon.)

which grind it before it is swallowed. *Leptodora* and *Polyphemus* are exceptions. The cylindrical legs have no gills, and there are no respiratory currents like those in other branchiopods. Feeding is simple. Prey, largely Protozoa, rotifers, and tiny Crustacea, are grasped by the legs and held between the mandibles, which kill and crush the food organisms.

The appendages of the fairy shrimps and tadpole shrimps beat metachronously as they swim gracefully through the water, with obvious activation waves passing along the body in regular sequence. The speed of movement is adjusted by changes in the angle at which the exopodites are held, and to some extent by independent movements of the exopodites. Although they can swim in any orientation, the fairy shrimps normally swim with the ventral side uppermost, and the tadpole shrimp with the dorsal side up. Tadpole shrimps often scramble about awkwardly on the bottom or burrow in the mud.

Diplostraca are covered by a carapace, and the enlarged second antennae serve as paddles, propelling them through the water. Each stroke of the antennae produces a forward thrust, and they move rather jerkily and erratically, although some of the Cladocera achieve respectable speeds. The larger, heavier Conchostraca have relatively smaller antennae and so are weak swimmers. When disturbed, they close the shell by contracting the adductor muscle and sink to the bottom, looking like small clams with the foot retracted. When Cladocera are clinging to plants or in the mud, they may use the postabdomen to push the body along. Some of the benthonic species depend primarily on this type of locomotion.

Branchiopods generally have simple reproductive systems and complex reproductive habits. Sexes are separate, and paired gonads are found on each side of the abdomen. The relatively simple gonoducts usually open on the genital somites, but the sperm ducts of Cladocera open near the end of the postabdomen, while the oviducts open into the brood chamber.

Males clasp the females for mating, using special clasping appendages. Genital pores are opposed in Notostraca and Conchostraca, but the male fairy shrimps have a pair of penes, and the postabdomen is modified for copulation. All of the branchiopods brood the ova, but they use somewhat different techniques. Anostraca have an elongated brood sac attached to the ventral surface of the body (Fig. 18.3A). In the Notostraca the flabella of the eleventh trunk appendages are enlarged and, in conjunction with the gills, form a brood chamber. The Conchostraca use the space inside of the shell as a brood chamber, secreting a gelatinous material to hold the ova in place. The Cladocera, of course, have a built-in brood chamber between the carapace and the dorsal body surface.

In some species males have never been found, and parthenogenetic development is common in all. In a number of species the males appear capriciously, and the factors that favor male production are not described. A number of branchiopods form summer and winter eggs. The more resistant winter eggs are covered by a heavy, brownish membrane and are slower to develop. In some species the thickness of the egg membrane varies at different times, and the rate of development varies with the membrane; the thicker-walled ovum is undoubtedly associated with the temporary pond habitat, for it permits branchiopods to withstand winter cold and desiccation. As a rule, eggs with heavy membranes are highly resistant and develop only when conditions are favorable. The relationship of parthenogenesis and winter egg production is not clear. In some cases the heavy ova can be produced by either fertilized or parthenogenetic females.

The reproductive habits of the Cladocera are highly organized. Thin-walled ova are parthenogenetic, and under as yet unspecified conditions, males appear. Females able to copulate appear with them and produce winter eggs in the heavy-coated ephippium (Fig. 18.5H). A cladoceran population may contain parthenogenetic females producing thin-walled ova, "sexual" females producing ephippia, and males at the same time. Evidently the parthenogenetic females produce ova of three kinds, but the factors that control development and the production of the different kinds of eggs are not understood.

Cladocera tend to fall into three groups, species with a double population peak, one in the spring and one in the fall (dicyclic); species with a single population peak (monocyclic); and species that fluctuate little during the year (acyclic). Similar patterns of seasonal populations are sometimes seen in other branchiopods. The cycles are probably associated with temperature. Acyclic species are especially characteristic of cold waters with little seasonal temperature change. It is not yet clear to what extent the monocyclic and dicyclic peaks are dependent on food and other kinds of external factors, and to what extent they are related to internal changes in reproductive potential and activity. A number of the Cladocera, like some of the rotifers and Protozoa, gradually change in form as the season progresses (cyclomorphosis). These changes in form, obviously reflecting a response to some changing factors, may be in some way related to the changing patterns of sexual reproduction and to shifts in population peaks.

Subclass Ostracoda

About 2000 species of ostracods are known, of which about two-thirds are marine. Ostracods are small animals, with most of the species not far from a millimeter in length, but there are some fairly large species, and the largest ostracods attain a length of over 10 mm. Enclosed in a bivalved carapace, ostracods superficially resemble Conchostraca, but are smaller and have a much more highly specialized body. The trunk of the body is very short, and has lost its external segmentation. Some ostracods are excellent swimmers, but most of them live on or about the bottom and creep in the bottom mud or over the surface of plants. Some of them have become parasitic on aquatic animals. Most of them are filter feeders, but some are predaceous and others pick up particles of food from the bottom mud. They are widely distributed in fresh water and the seas. Although most species prefer shallow waters where vegetation is present, some species have been taken at depths of 2000 m.

Order Myodocarpa. Marine ostracods with second antennae having small, immobile exopodites and long endopodites with at least seven segments and with swimming setae.

Order Cladocopa. Marine ostracods with both the exopodites and the endopodites of the second antennae well developed and important in swimming.

Order Platycopa. Marine ostracods with flattened, leaf-like second antennae having well-developed exopodites and endopodites.

Order Podocopa. The largest ostracod order, including both marine and freshwater species. The second antennae have no exopodites or, at the most, minute ones, and the endopodites end in claws. Example: *Cypricercus* (Fig. 18.6A).

The two valves of the carapace are attached by a dorsal hinge of elastic, non-calcified cuticle. The adductor muscles stretch the hinge as they close the shell, and the hinge springs the valves apart when the muscles relax, somewhat as in clams. A notch in the carapace of the Myodocopa permits the extrusion of the second antennae while the carapace is closed. Bristles, pits, and other external markings are found on the carapace, but growth lines like those seen in many Conchostraca are absent. The carapace is often pigmented but is rarely brightly colored.

The large ostracod head is completely enclosed by the shell (Fig. 18.6A), and bears four pairs of appendages. There are two pairs of antennae, both well developed. A pair of mandibles flanks the mouth. The mandibles usually have a toothed cutting edge and a prominent three-segmented palp (Fig. 18.6B). There is a single pair of large maxillae, which have a conspicuous gill plate. Four basal processes are found on the maxillae, the largest serving as a palp. Ostracod eyes are extremely variable, Some ostracods are eyeless. Some have a median ocellus, derived from the eye of the nauplius larva. Others have a pair of ocelli, sometimes intimately united. Still others have a pair of compound eyes, somewhat like cladoceran eyes.

The trunk is short and not segmented externally. It bears no more than three pairs of appendages. The first pair of trunk appendages are thought by some to be second maxillae, and so to belong to the head. Each appendage is a small, flattened part with a single lobe, the gnathobase. In the male it has a palp and is used as a clasper. The next pair of appendages is leg-like and they usually end in a claw. The third pair of appendages is turned back and is often highly specialized, serving to clear mud away from the shell cavity (Fig. 18.6C). The abdomen is greatly reduced. It consists of paired caudal cerci, sometimes very long, forming a furca that usually ends in setae or claws. It is extruded from the shell to push the body forward through the mud.

Antennal modifications seen in the various orders are correlated with differences in habits. Species with long swimming setae are good swimmers. Species with few setae or bristles on the antennae are usually bottom-dwellers, using the abdomen to push themselves along. Cytherids have leg-like second antennae, used to capture food and to cling to vegetation. A few African and New Zealand ostracods live in wet forests in the upper layer of humus, burrowing with the aid of the first antennae, which are specialized to form stubby shovels.

The majority of ostracods are filter-feeders. Setae on the first pair of thoracic legs and the maxillae are used to filter out particles. Mucus from the labral glands mold food into masses that are shoved into the mouth by the maxillae and ground by the mandibles.

Ostracods are dioecious. Females have a pair of ovaries, which extend into the shell valves in Cypridae. The oviducts are usually paired and are dilated at some point to form a seminal receptacle. The female gonopores are located behind the last pair of trunk appendages. Males have a pair of testes, each consisting of four long tubules that extend into the shell valves. The testicular tubules unite in the body to form a sperm duct. A complex ejaculatory duct leads to a penis on each side of the body (Fig. 18.6D). The spermatozoa are very peculiar in form and are sometimes longer than the body. Details of the male system are quite varied and are useful in taxonomy.

Some ostracods reproduce only by parthenogenesis, and males do not appear to occur. In some species the males and females are about equally abundant. All gradations between these extremes are seen. According to Lowndes, the complex sexual apparatus of the males is a farce. He contends that the ova are never fertilized and that all ostracods reproduce by parthenogenesis, even though males are present and mating has occurred.

The ostracods are highly specialized and illustrate the major evolutionary trends seen in the Crustacea. The appendages are all different, each specialized in a different way for a different function. In different groups of ostracods the appendages are turned to different functions, another characteristic of a high degree of specialization. The number of appendages has been sharply reduced, and the body is short, with obscure segmentation. Ostra-

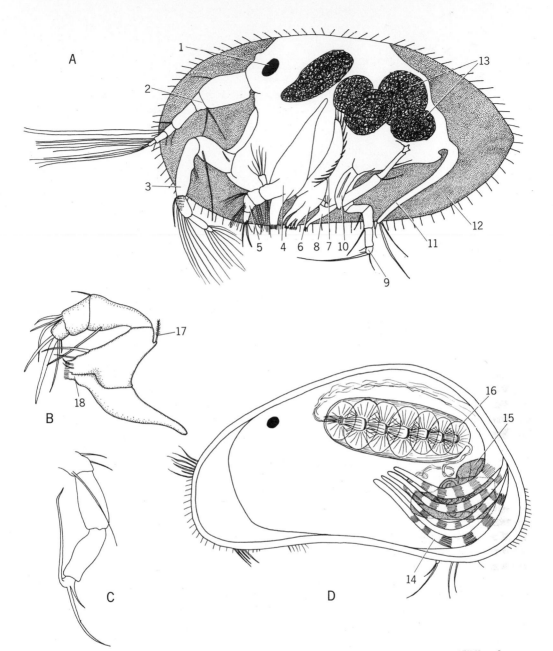

Fig. 18.6. Ostracods. **A.** External features of an ostracod, *Cypricercus*, with one shell valve removed. **B.** The mandible of an ostracod. Note the tiny exopodite. **C.** The third leg of an ostracod, *Cypridopsis*. This appendage is used to clean out material from the shell. **D.** The male reproductive system of an ostracod, *Candona*. (A and C, after Hoff. B, after Muller, from Calman, in Lankester. D, after Pennak.) 1, eye; 2, antennule; 3, antenna; 4, mandible; 5, mandibular palp; 6, maxilla; 7, gill blade; 8, first trunk appendage; 9, second trunk appendage; 10, third trunk appendage; 11, caudal ramus; 12, shell; 13, masses of food in gut; 14, testis; 15, penis; 16, ejaculatory duct; 17, exopodite; 18, gnathobase.

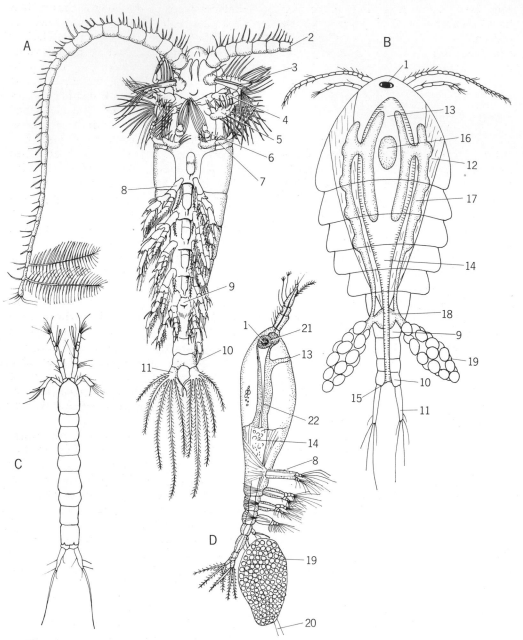

Fig. 18.7. Copepods. **A.** A calanoid copepod, *Calanus*. Calanoids are generally pelagic, and have very long antennae with many natatory setae. The hinge joint is between the fifth and sixth thoracic socites. **B.** Semischematic figure of *Cyclops*, a typical cyclopoid. Cyclopoids have a broad metasome and narrow urosome, the hinge is between the fourth and fifth thoracic segments, and the antennae are relatively short. They are moderately good swimmers. **C.** A harpacticoid copepod, *Parastenocaris*. Harpacticoids are poor swimmer, with very short antennae and with little difference in breadth of metasome and urosome. The hinge joint is

cods have had a long time to develop their peculiarities. The earliest known ostracods lived in the upper Cambrian, and more fossil than modern species have been described.

Subclass Copepoda

Copepods are the most successful of the entomostraca. They are abundant in marine and in fresh-water lentic habitats, and many are successful parasites. Free-living species are from about one to a few millimeters long. They make an important link in aquatic food chains, for they feed on microscopic organisms and are eaten by macroscopic carnivores. In many kinds of fresh-water habitats, especially, they are the most important group of organisms that do this, and their disappearance would greatly disturb the macroscopic consumers in the region. About 4500 modern species are known, but nothing is known of the geological history of copepods

Copepods are quite typical-looking Crustacea, with a head bearing five pairs of appendages, a thorax with paired appendages on each somite, and an abdomen without appendages. Appearances are deceiving, however, and the copepods are non-conformists, with the functional regions of the body not coinciding with the parts that make up the head, thorax, and abdomen of other crustaceans. They have a dorsal carapace, which covers not only the head somites but also the first one or two thoracic somites. The functional anterior piece of the body is thus neither head nor cephalothorax, but the head and the first thoracic somite or two. The last thoracic somite is the genital somite, which in many females is united with the first abdominal somite, so that the line between the thorax and abdomen is evidently an arbitrary one. The abdominal somites are covered by rings of cuticle. Two of the abdominal somites meet in a special, flexible joint, sometimes called the hinge joint. Difficulties in defining the head, thorax, and abdomen are partly overcome by speaking of the body as composed of an anterior metasome and a posterior urosome. Unfortunately, however, not everyone agrees about what the metasome and urosome are. Some arbitrarily define the urosome as the genital somite plus the abdomen. Others consider the urosome as the part of the body behind the hinge joint. In reading about copepods, it is important to discover how an author is using the terms metasome and urosome. Here the urosome is considered the part of the body behind the hinge joint. This seems the preferable usage as it reflects a functional division of the body.

Seven orders of copepods are recognized. In four of these the adults are free living or predominantly free living. The other orders contain species with parasitic adult stages, but in some cases only the females are parasitic.

Order Calanoida. Copepods with a broad metasome and narrow urosome, and the hinge joint between the fifth and sixth thoracic segments; females with long an-

between the fourth and fifth thoracic somites. D. A monstrilloid copepod, *Haemocera.* Larval monstrilloids are parasitic in polychaetes and adults are free-swimming but have no second antennae and mouthparts. (A, after Giesbrecht. B, after Bullough. C, after Pennak, in Pennak. D, after Malaquin.) *External features:* 1, median eye; 2, antennule; 3, antenna; 4, mandible; 5, first maxilla; 6, second maxilla; 7, maxilliped; 8, first thoracic leg (actually the second thoracic appendage as the maxillipeds are thoracic appendages); 9, first abdominal somite; 10, telson; 11, caudal ramus. *Internal parts:* 12, longitudinal muscle bands; 13, stomodaeum; 14, intestine; 15, anus; 16, ovary; 17, oviduct; 18, seminal receptacle; 19, ovisac; 20, genital seta; 21, brain; 22, nerve cord.

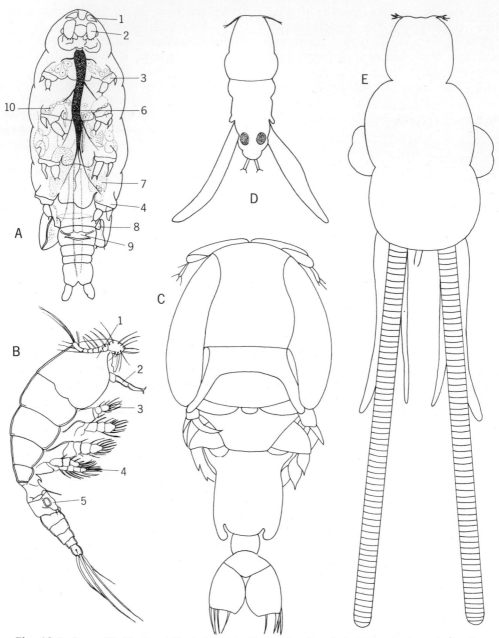

Fig. 18.8. Some Highly Specialized Parasitic Copepods. A and B. Ventral view of female and lateral view of male *Enterocola,* a notodelphyoid copepod. In these copepods the female is highly modified for clinging to host tunicates, while the males retain a relatively normal copepod appearance. C. *Parapandarus nodosus,* a caligoid copepod. The caligoids are generally ectoparasites of fishes, and have a greatly modified body. The head appendages, especially the second antennae, are prehensile. D and E. Male and female of *Lernanthropus,* a lernaeopodoid copepod. The lernaeopodoids are highly modified ectoparasites of fishes, and generally

tennae of 23 to 25 segments; fifth thoracic legs scarcely reduced and used in swimming; eggs carried in one or two ovisacs attached to the genital somite; predominantly marine and almost exclusively planktonic; never parasitic or commensal. A very large order with over 150 different genera. Example: *Calanus* (Fig. 18.7A).

Order Cyclopoida. Copepods with a broad metasome and narrow urosome, and with the hinge joint between the fourth and fifth thoracic segments; first antennae rather short, ending between the posterior end of the carapace and the urosome, and having from six to 17 segments; fifth pair of legs uniramous and vestigial, without an enlarged basal segment; eggs carried in two ovisacs attached to the sides of the genital somite; fresh-water and marine, predominantly littoral, and including some benthonic and a few planktonic species. Example: *Cyclops* (Fig. 18.7B).

Order Harpacticoida. Copepods with the metasome and urosome of approximately equal breadth, and with a shallow hinge joint between the fourth and fifth thoracic segments; first antennae very short, not longer than the carapace in females and with five to nine segments; right and left antennae of males prehensile; fifth thoracic legs reduced and with an inner expansion of the basal segment; usually a single ovisac carried medially on the genital somite; marine and fresh-water bottom dwellers, rarely commensal or parasitic. Example: *Parastenocaris* (Fig. 18.7C).

Order Monstrilloida. Marine copepods with the second antennae and mouth parts missing and the gut greatly reduced; larvae parasitic in polychaetes and adults free swimming. The two families differ in the position of the metasome-urosome junction. Example: *Haemocera* (Fig. 18.7D).

Order Notodelphyoida. Copepods parasitic in tunicates, with the females showing a variable degree of reduction of the appendages and corresponding loss of motility; in most females the hinge joint is between the fourth and fifth thoracic segments; females usually with a dorsal brood pouch. Example: *Enterocola* (Fig. 18.8A,B).

Order Caligoida. Copepods usually living as ectoparasites on marine or fresh-water fishes and with females showing varying degrees of modification; males considerably less modified than females; urosome often larger than the metasome; hinge joint between the third and fourth thoracic segments, but some females rigid; first antennae very short, with two segments, and second antennae prehensile; eggs carried in two long ovisacs. Example: *Parapandarus* (Fig. 18.8C).

Order Lernaeopodoida. Copepods ectoparasitic on fresh-water and marine fishes; highly modified for parasitism with loss of segmentation; male very small, attached to body of female; second maxillae specialized as a cylindrical attachment organ; thoracic appendages largely absent, especially in females; eggs in paired ovisacs, often very large. Example: *Lernanthropus* (Fig. 18.8D,E).

Copepods are particularly interesting because one can see several different evolutionary trends, and some of these have resulted in more or less parallel developments in species that are obviously not closely related. Three relatively sharp lines can be seen, one leading toward free-living habits, one toward parasitism in the larval stage, and one toward adult parasitism. Differences in the position of

have a rigid body. The tiny males cling to the body of the female. As is common in parasites, the reproductive potential is very great, and most parasitic copepods develop very large ovisacs. (A and B, after Canu. C, D, and E after Wilson.) 1, antennule; 2, antenna; 3, first thoracic leg; 4, fourth thoracic leg; 5, first abdominal somite; 6, nerve cord; 7, ovary; 8, oviducal gland; 9, vagina; 10, gland cell.

the hinge joint are of no great functional significance, but are useful with other traits to show that several different groups of copepods have been following adaptive lines leading in some of the same directions. The group of copepods that have been adapting to larval parasitism has culminated in free-living adults that do not feed but depend entirely on food reserves laid down during larval stages. As in nematomorphs, the non-feeding adults have come to be less and less important, until they are really little more than a migratory stage of the life cycle, and, as it happens, the stage when the ova are fertilized. Among the copepods which are parasitic as adults, a number of the kinds of adaptation customarily seen among parasites appear, but they have gone a good deal further in some groups than others. As a general rule, the females are far more highly modified than the males. Locomotor organs and, to a lesser extent, the mouthparts, are reduced, eliminated, or modified to attachment organs. This is a suitable development in parasites which do not move about as adults. Body flexibility, probably most useful in locomotion, is reduced. As in most parasites, the reproductive potential is high, and the ovisacs are often very large. Where parasites do not occur in large numbers in a host animal, there is a strong possibility that both sexes may not be present, or where the parasites have sacrificed mobility for attachment devices, they may be present but never come in contact. The less modified, more mobile males reduce this hazard as far as possible in this group of copepods.

Free-living copepods, on the other hand, have tended to develop along lines that suit them to a pelagic life or a benthonic life. The harpacticoids, with short antennae, are obviously less suited for active swimming than the calanoids, with very long antennae. The rather straight sides of the harpacticoids are suitable for creatures living in the shifting material of soft bottoms, while the highly developed swimming setae of calanoids help them to float when at rest and to swim when active. The cyclopoids have not committed themselves strongly to either way of life and remain to some extent intermediate in character as well as in habits.

In typical free-living copepods a single carapace covers the head and one or two thoracic somites. This region is sometimes called a cephalothorax, although not all of the thoracic somites are included. Copepods generally are characterized by a single median eye, derived from the larval nauplius eye.

The antennules are conspicuous, uniramous appendages of variable length (Fig. 18.9A-C). They are usually important for swimming and are also equipped with sensory hairs. The antennules of males are modified as claspers. Male calanoids have only the right antennule modified, while the male harpacticoids and cyclopoids have both antennules altered. The male antennules are bent more or less sharply and in extreme cases have a hinge joint.

The antennae are shorter than the antennules, and may be uniramous or biramous. In cyclopoids the exopodite is missing. As a rule the antennae are sensory, but they are prehensile in male harpacticoids and, of course, are often highly modified in parasites. The parasitic larvae of the monstrilloids use the second antennae as slender feeding processes, which absorb food from the polychaete host, and in Calgoida and Lernaeopodoida the antennae are used as attachment organs.

The mouth lies between upper and lower lips formed by protuberances of the head exoskeleton. The lips are fused together to form the sipho of some parasitic copepods, and in the adult monstrilloids the mouth and mouthparts are missing. The mandibles of typical copepods have a toothed gnathobase and are usually equipped with a tuft of bristles attached to the point where a mandibular palp is seen in some other crustaceans. The two pairs of maxillae are variable. They usually have definite gnathobases and are somewhat flattened. They may be uniramous or biramous (Fig. 18.9F). In parasitic copepods the maxillae are reduced or highly modified. In some of the lernaeopodoids the second maxillae have been altered to form attachment organs.

The first thoracic somite is covered by the carapace and is essentially an adjunct to the head. It is often attached to the head, and its appendages are accessory mouthparts, the maxillipeds. The maxillipeds are usually uniramous, and to some extent intermediate in structure between the maxillae and the other thoracic legs.

The next four pairs of thoracic appendages are essentially alike in structure. They are flattened and have marginal bristles, making them more effective paddles for swimming (Fig. 18.9D). In most copepods the fifth pair of thoracic legs is modified, but in female calanoids they are like the other thoracic legs. The fifth thoracic legs of male calanoids are modified for the transfer of spermatophores to the female and are asymmetrical (Fig. 18.9E). In cyclopoids and harpacticoids the fifth thoracic legs are modified in both males and females but are symmetrical in both sexes. Modification of the appendages of the pregenital

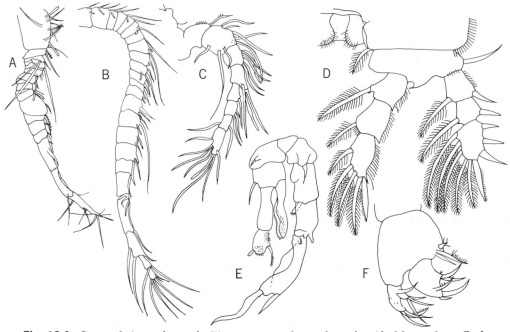

Fig. 18.9. Copepod Appendages. **A.** First antenna of a male cyclopoid, *Mesocyclops*. Both antennules of male cyclopoids and harpacticoids are jointed, while calanoids have only the right antennule jointed. The joint adapts the antennule for use during copulation. **B.** Right antennule of a calanoid, *Diaptomus*. The small, blunt projections extending from the antennules and antennae are aesthetasks, presumably sensory in function. **C.** Antenna of *Mesocyclops*. **D.** Typical swimming leg of *Cyclops*. **E.** Fifth leg of a male *Diaptomus*. This pair of legs is reduced or missing in both male and female cyclopoids and harpacticoids, but is prominent in calanoids. In male calanoids, the right and left fifth legs differ. **F.** Second maxilla of *Mesocyclops*. (A, C, F, D, after Gurney. B and E, after Wilson, in Edmonson.)

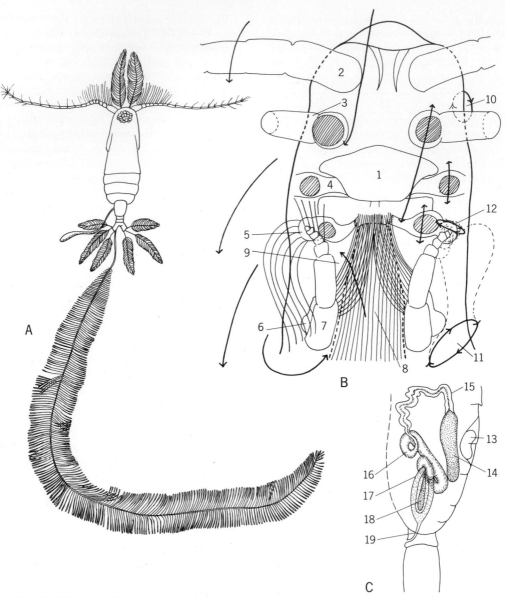

Fig. 18.10. **A.** A pelagic calanoid. The long, projecting setae increase water resistance, and are flotation devices. Many calanoids have remarkably developed setae. **B.** Swimming and feeding currents of *Calanus finmarchicus*. The one-ended arrows on the left side show water currents. The circular and two-ended arrows on the right describe movements of appendages. The water flows back at the front and sides of the animal as a result of swimming movements. It eddies around the maxillipeds and passes through the filter chamber, equipped with many filtering setae. Here food is removed, to be pushed forward between the mandibles. Feeding is, to some extent at least, automatic. **C.** Genital system of a male. (**A**, after Giesbrecht. **B** and **C**, after Marshall and Orr.) *External features:* 1, labrum; 2, antennule; 3, antenna; 4, mandible; 5, first maxilla; 6, second maxilla; 7, maxilliped; 8, filter chamber; 9, suction chamber;

somite is a common feature of many Crustacea. The seventh thoracic somite is the genital somite; by some it is considered the first abdominal somite. At the most it has rudimentary appendages, and in most females it is wholly legless.

The abdomen has up to six somites, all without appendages. At the posterior end of the body a pair of caudal rami form the furca. Pelagic copepods often have long plumose bristles on the furca and thoracic appendages, which help them to float. Some of the calanoids are fantastically ornamented with such natatory setae (Fig. 18.10A).

The planktonic copepods, especially the calanoids, are excellent swimmers. At times they move smoothly and at others make sudden jerky movements. Movements of the antennae and mouth parts are responsible for smooth swimming movements during feeding, and the sudden, jerky spurts result from powerful thrusts of the thoracic legs alternating with antennal movements. The mouthparts of cyclopoids contribute little to swimming, and they depend primarily on the antennae and thoracic legs. The harpacticoids are almost entirely benthonic and clamber about on the bottom or creep over the surface of aquatic plants.

The swimming copepods are filter-feeders. The antennae, mandibular palps, and first maxillae vibrate rapidly, causing swirling currents that pull food forward against the filtering setae of the second maxillae (Fig. 18.10B). As food moves up between the appendages. the gnathobases of the maxillipeds and maxillae are used to push it into the mouth. Most of the cyclopoids are active predators, catching prey with mouthparts or picking up particles of food from the bottom or from the surface of submerged plants.

The harpacticoids also use the mouthparts to pick up particles of food. Most copepods are predominantly herbivorous. Some are predators, but the important copepod role in aquatic communities is that of a primary consumer, cropping the microscopic plant life.

Female copepods have a relatively simple reproductive system. The one or two ovaries open into paired oviducts. When ova are released they pass into paired lateral diverticula from the oviduct, the uteri, where they grow and accumulate yolk (Fig. 18.7B). The oviducts continue to the gonopore, known as the vulva, on the genital somite. At the last molt a sac is formed on the genital somite. A short duct connects the sac to the oviduct. At mating time the sperm from the spermatophores move into the sac, which serves as a seminal receptacle. The ova are fertilized as they pass down the distal part of the oviduct after leaving the uteri. As they emerge they are accumulated in one or two ovisacs, attached below or at the sides of the genital somite.

Free-living male copepods usually have a single testis (Fig. 18.10C). The sperm ducts are paired in cyclopoids, but a single sperm duct is found in calanoids and harpacticoids. The end of the sperm duct is glandular and secretes the vehicle used to cement the sperm together to form a spermatophore. In the genital somite the sperm duct expands as a seminal vesicle, where the secretions harden around the sperm and the spermatophore assumes a form characteristic of the species.

At mating the male uses the modified antennae, and in some cases the fifth thoracic leg, to clasp the female. The spermatophore is transferred to the female by the thoracic appendages, where it is

10, path of rotation of the exopod on the antenna; 11, path of rotation of the tips of the setae on the first maxilla; 12, path of rotation of the tip of the maxilliped. *Internal parts:* 13, heart; 14, testis; 15, sperm duct; 16, seminal vesicle; 17, spermatophore sac; 18, spermatophore; 19, ejaculatory duct.

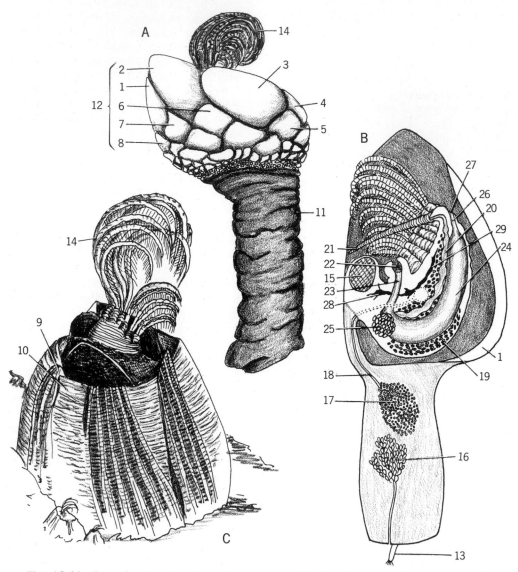

Fig. 18.11. Barnacles. A. A pedunculate barnacle, *Mitella*. The peduncle is the greatly
lengthened front of the head, and all of the important parts of the body are in the capitulum,
enclosed by the scales and plates of the carapace. **B.** Anatomy of a pedunculate barnacle. The
internal organization of *Balanus* is very similar. **C.** A sessile barnacle, *Balanus tintinnabulum*.
(B, composite. C, after Ricketts and Calvin.) *Plates:* **1,** carina; **2,** tergum; **3,** scutum; **4,** rostral;
5, rostrolateral; **6,** lateral; **7,** carinolateral; **8,** carinal; **9,** ala; **10,** radius. *External features:*
11, peduncle; **12,** capitulum; **13,** antennule; **14,** flagella of thoracic appendages; **15,** adductor
muscle; **16,** adhesive gland. *Reproductive system:* **17,** ovary; **18,** oviduct; **19,** testes; **20,** seminal vesicle; **21,** penis. *Digestive system:* **22,** mouth; **23,** esophagus; **24,** midgut; **25,** digestive
gland; **26,** rectum; **27,** anus. *Nervous system:* **28,** brain; **29,** nerve cord.

774

attached by cement, probably derived from the seminal vesicle wall. The sperm move into the seminal receptacles, where they may be stored for some time before the ova mature.

Subclass Cirripedia

All over the world barnacles attach by the millions to rocks, pilings, boats, and other objects in shallow waters and the intertidal zone. They do not limit themselves to inanimate substrates, for many are ectoparasitic on crustaceans, echinoderms, whales, turtles, and other marine animals. Adaptations for a sessile life and extensive exoskeletal modification make barnacles unlike other Crustacea. Barnacles have been extremely successful, for about 800 modern species are known, and in favorable habitats they are remarkably abundant, covering every available surface. They are economically important as fouling organisms, slowing boats down and fouling harbor installations. Because of the calcareous nature of their "shell," they were thought to be molluscs rather than crustaceans until 1830. The skeletal plates that make up the barnacle shell tend to scatter, and only about 200 fossil species are known. The first definitely identified species lived in the Silurian.

It is difficult to understand how barnacles started off on their peculiar line of adaptation, for they are unique creatures that attach themselves to objects with cement discharged near the antennules and stand on their heads throughout life. It is hard to visualize how this habit could have, at its inception, been so useful that it led to a line of intensive adaptation. Nevertheless, barnacles established themselves and followed two main lines of evolutionary development. Some of them have become pedunculate, with a long stalk, the peduncle, and a capitulum, consisting of the main mass of the body enclosed in a carapace (Fig. 18.11A).

The peduncle is actually a stalk formed by the drawn-out front part of the head. Other barnacles are sessile and have no stalk. In these forms the front of the head is modified to form a flattened, membranous or calcareous basis attached to the surface on which the barnacle lives.

Barnacles have become so highly modified that the terms dorsal and ventral have lost their significance. The barnacle carapace is a fleshy mantle, separated from the body by a mantle cavity except at the attachment point. The side where the body attaches to the mantle is termed rostral and the opposite is the carinal side. Actually the plane of symmetry passes from the middle of the carinal to the middle of the rostral side, so they may be considered as roughly corresponding to dorsal and ventral, although not from a functional point of view.

The barnacle body is greatly modified, and the body regions are unlike those of other Crustacea. The head is very large, and the abdomen is almost missing. The thoracic region bears six pairs of legs, which extend upward toward the opening in the carapace on the rostral side. Each leg is built of a basal piece and two slender, ringed cirri.

The most primitive fossil barnacles had an elongated body without a peduncle or capitulum, and were covered by a shell composed of many plates. A series of carinal plates covered the carinal surface, and an opposing series of rostral plates covered the rostral surface. Three rows of plates covered each side. Along the pedunculate line of development, the number of shell plates was reduced as the capitulum appeared. Thus in *Loricula* the lower part of the body is covered by plates very much like those of the primitive *Turrilepas*, but the plates at the distal end are enlarged, foreshadowing the capitulum (Fig. 18.12). In *Mitella* the skeletal plates are further reduced and the capitulum more highly developed. The capitulum is dominated by five

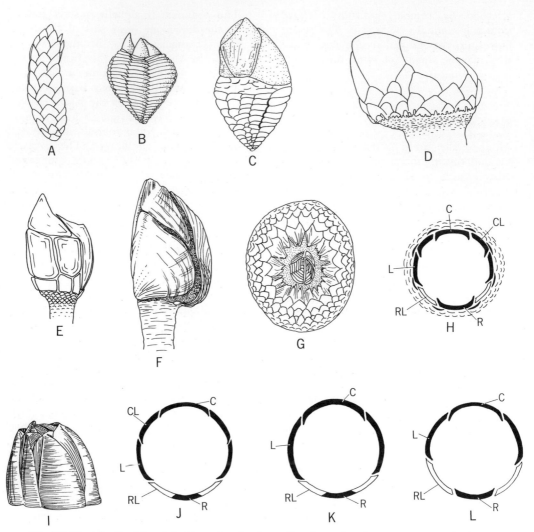

Fig. 18.12. Adaptive Trends in Barnacles. In the earliest barnacles, the upper part of the body was covered by distinctive plates, much like those seen in *Lepas* today, and the stalk or peduncle was not covered with lateral scales. However, an early trend toward armoring the developing peduncle developed, and in forms like *Turrilepas* (A) no well-developed capitulum can be recognized. The body is elongated, and unpaired rostral and carinal plates occur at the dorsal and ventral sides of the organism, while the sides of the body were covered with paired lateral plates, with paired carinolateral plates between the laterals and the carinals, and paired rostrolateral plates between the lateral and the rostrals. The main line of adaptation has resulted in the emergence of a definite peduncle and capitulum, with the capitular plates becoming more and more simplified, as seen in the series including *Stramentum* (B), *Archeolepas* (C), *Scalpellum* (D), *Mitella* (E), and *Lepas* (F). Something of the same tendency is seen in the sessile barnacles. They probably arose from pedunculate stocks which had eight large plates in the capitulum, and with small lateral scales on the peduncle. *Catophragmus* (G and H) has many tiny basal scales, and eight large plates, corresponding to the rostral, carinal, lateral, carinolateral, and rostrolateral plates seen in the older forms. Further develop-

major plates. A single, median carina covers the carinal surface. Each side of the capitulum is covered by two plates, a scutum on the rostral surface and a tergum between the scutum and carina. The aperture of the carapace is opposite the carina. Additional, smaller side plates may also be present. *Scapellum* and *Lepas* show the result of additional adaptation along this line, with the peduncle becoming wholly naked and the capitulum more definite. In *Lepas* only the five major capitular plates remain. In parasitic barnacles the skeletal plates are further reduced, until in forms like *Conchoderma* all of the skeletal plates are gone.

The sessile barnacles have followed a different adaptational line. The peduncle is reduced to a basis, but the peduncular plates are persistent, forming several whorls of tiny basal plates in the more primitive forms. Carinal, rostral, and three pairs of lateral plates can be recognized, and pairs of scutal and tergal plates form an operculum that can be opened or closed for feeding or protection. Further development along this line leads to the disappearance of the basal plates and the simplification and consolidation of the wall plates.

CLASSIFICATION

Order Thoracica. Barnacles with six pairs of thoracic appendages, ending in filamentous cirri; typically enclosed in a calcareous shell of discrete plates. Three suborders can be recognized. *Lepadomorpha*, the pedunculate barnacles, have the body divided into a peduncle and capitulum. Example: *Mitella* (Fig. 18.11A). *Verrucamorpha*, the asymmetrical sessile bar-

nacles, have a shell with a unique wall, formed of carina and rostrum on one side and the scutum and tergum on the other. The operculum is formed of the remaining scutum and tergum. Example: *Verruca* (Fig. 18.13A). *Balanomorpha*, the symmetrical sessile barnacles, have a shell composed of various combinations of rostral, carinal, and lateral plates, and the operculum is formed of paired scutal and tergal plates. Example: *Balanus* (Fig. 18.11C).

Order Acrothoracica. Boring barnacles. Barnacles without calcareous plates; with four pairs of thoracic appendages and with a space between the first and last three pairs; living in burrows cut into mollusc shells and corals. Example: *Alcippe* (Fig. 18.13B).

Order Ascothoracica. Naked barnacles with a mantle into which diverticula from the gut extend; thoracic appendages somewhat reduced; parasitic on corals and echinoderms. Example: *Laura* (Fig. 18.13C).

Order Rhizocephala. Naked barnacles without a digestive tube or appendages; usually with an extensive system of absorptive processes extending from the mantle into the host tissues. Parasitic in crustaceans and tunicates. Example: *Sacculina* (Fig. 18.13E).

Most barnacles are of moderate size, from about 1 to 5 cm. long, but a few are a good deal larger. *Balanus psittacus*, the largest sessile barnacle, reaches 2.2 cm. high and 8 cm. in diameter, and the pedunculate barnacle, *Lepas anatifera*, may have a peduncle 0.5 m. long and reach 0.75 m. over-all. Some of the burrowing barnacles, on the other hand, are only a few millimeters long.

ment led to loss of the basal scales, and the consolidation of the shell by the simplification of the walls. In *Balanus* (I and J) the rostrolateral plates (shown without shading) united with the rostrals to produce a wall of six plates. In *Tetraclita* (K) the wall is further simplified by the loss of the carinolateral plates. *Chthamalus* (L) has followed a different line of simplification. Although it has six plates in the wall, the rostrolaterals are distinct, and the carinolaterals have been omitted. (Adapted from various sources.)

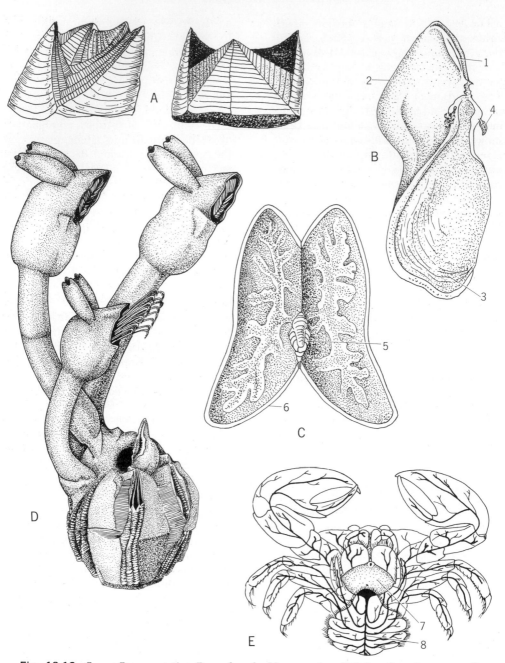

Fig. 18.13. Some Representative Barnacles. **A.** *Verruca spongicula*, a thoracian or sessile
barnacle belonging to the suborder Verrucamorpha, characterized by an asymmetrical shell,
formed of the carina and rostrum on one side and the tergum and scutum on the other. At
the left, the normal wall is shown; at the right, the wall with an immovable tergum and
scutum. **B.** *Alcippe*, one of the acrothoracic or boring barnacles. They bore into corals and
shells, and have lost the calcareous plates so characteristic of free-living and many parasitic

778

The forepart of the head is the most highly modified part of a greatly altered body, having become the membranous basis of sessile barnacles and the elongated peduncle of pedunculate barnacles. The anterior head appendages have been involved in the changes of the head. The antennules are degenerate in adults, and the antennae are wholly missing. Barnacles attach-themselves with cement formed in glands that open near the site of the antennules. The middle part of the head attaches the body to the mantle, and the mouthparts lie near this junction. The mouth lies behind a large labrum and is flanked by a pair of mandibles with setose palps. The first pair of maxillae are small, flap-like parts, and the second maxillae are fused medially to form a lower lip. The tendency of the second maxillae to fuse at the base to form a lower lip is a common one in mandibulates generally, although it does not happen in many crustacean groups. Parasitic barnacles are greatly changed as they adapt to parasitic conditions and, as in other parasitic Crustacea, the head appendages tend to be further reduced. Boring barnacles have a pair of antennae as adults, but it is not clear whether they are the first or second antennae.

The thoracic appendages are used only to kick food into the mouth and are quite different from the appendages of most Crustacea. The basal part is the protopodite, made up of the usual two podites. The exopodite and endopodite, however, are long, slender, flexible cirri, with many setae. The cirri are thrust through the aperture when the barnacle is feeding. They work busily, making an effective stroke downwards and toward the midline. Food organisms are caught on the cirral setae and shoved into the mouth by the maxillae. The anterior cirri of some barnacles have been altered to serve as filters, and the remaining cirri, in this case, generate water currents. Most barnacles feed on bits of organic matter and small plankton organisms, but large barnacles can eat sizable organisms, which are wrapped up in the cirri and brought individually into the range of the maxillae. The thoracic appendages of the boring barnacles and the parasitic barnacles are reduced to a greater or lesser degree. Parasitic barnacles absorb food from their hosts with absorptive processes of the mantle. *Laura* (Fig. 18.13C) has enormously developed mantle lobes containing branches of the digestive glands. Mantle papillae bring vascular

barnacles. The discus corresponds to the surface of the peduncle by which pedunculates attach. C. *Laura*, an ascothoracic barnacle. These naked barnacles are parasitic in echinoderms and corals. The huge mantle, containing the branches of the digestive gland, plays an absorptive role. The body of the barnacle is considerably reduced. D. Two whale barnacles. At the bottom is the cask-shaped acorn barnacle, *Coronula*, which attaches to the whale surface. Above are three rabbit-eared barnacles, *Conchoderma*, which attach to *Coronula*. *Conchoderma* is a pedunculate barnacle, modified for parisitism. Water enters through the aperture at the right, from which the flagella of the thoracic appendages extend, and departs through the unique ear-shaped funnels. *Conchoderma* orients itself so that the feeding aperture faces forward; the swimming movements of the host thus aid in feeding. E. A crab infected by *Sacculina*, a rhizocephalan barnacle. These parasitic barnacles live in crustacea and tunicates. Adults lose all resemblance to normal barnacles, becoming more or less saccate organisms with branching, absorptive processes that extend into the host tissue. The absorptive processes of *Sacculina* extend throughout the body of the parasitized animal. (A, after Gruvel. B, after Berndt, from Broch, in Kükenthal and Krumbach. C, after Lacaze-Duthiers from Calman, in Lankester. E, after the MacGinites.) 1, mantle opening; 2, capitulum; 3, discus; 4, attached male in cypris stage; 5, main body of animal; 6, mantle, opened to show branches of digestive gland and ovary; 7, body of parasite, hanging from ventral surface of the host; 8, nutritive processes, branching throughout body of host.

channels close to the host tissue, facilitating absorption. The most remarkable absorptive processes are found in the rhizocephalids. *Sacculina* (Fig. 18.13E) is a saccate parasite whose mantle develops extensive, root-like processes covering the host intestine and extending to all parts of its body.

Ectoparasitic barnacles have developed parts that are especially suited to their way of life. *Conchoderma auritum* is an interesting pedunculate barnacle that attaches to the acorn barnacle, *Cornula diadema* (Fig. 18.13D). The carapace plates of *Conchoderma* are small, and the mantle forms a hood-like covering around the operculum, drawn out into two funnels. Both barnacles live on whales, and *Conchoderma* attaches with the operculum toward the front end of the host. As is often the case with parasitic forms, the shape and orientation of the body is a means of avoiding hard work. As the whale swims, water currents flow into the mantle cavity of *Conchoderma*, who can afford to be lazy.

Barnacles are hermaphroditic, in this differing from the majority of Crustacea. This is probably an important part of adaptation to a sessile life, for the eggs of Crustacea have a heavy membranous covering, and fertilization is internal. Isolated barnacles can presumably reproduce after self-fertilization. The ovaries are found in the peduncle and sometimes extend into the mantle, as in *Laura* and *Entoconcha*. The oviducts are paired, and extend to the gonopores, situated near the first thoracic appendages. (Fig. 18.11B). The testes are also in the head region, but often extend into the thorax or the thoracic appendages. Sperm ductules unite to form a pair of sperm ducts, which join at the base of a long, slender penis, attached in front of the anus on the ventral side. Wherever barnacles are attached in dense aggregations, they outbreed, the long penis reaching out to neighboring animals.

Some of the pedunculate barnacles have developed another system to achieve cross-fertilization while living a sessile life. The males are dwarfed and live in the mantle cavity of the females. The dwarf males may be like diminutive females, or in some cases are extensively simplified, retaining a number of larval characteristics. In some of these species, the large barnacles have lost all traces of male organs, and so are structural as well as functional females.

Eggs are usually brooded in the mantle cavity, and hatch in the nauplius stage. The barnacle nauplius has a characteristic triangular carapace (Fig. 18.14A) and is equipped with the usual three pairs of appendages, antennules, antennae, and mandibles. After several molts it becomes a cypris larva, remarkably like an ostracod in general appearance (Fig. 18.14B). The cypris attaches with its antennules, and metamorphoses into an adult (Fig.18.14 C-E).

The most remarkable life cycles are seen in the rhizocephalids. The body of the adult rhizocephalid is more extensively affected by parasitic habits than is true of other parasitic barnacles, and the life cycle provides further evidence of a long history of parasitism and an intimate adaptation of all stages of the life cycle to the parasitic habit. A motile larval stage plays an important role in the dissemination of many parasites. The *Sacculina* cypris larva swims about for a time, eventually attaching to a suitable crab. It undergoes a dramatic metamorphosis, in which the whole trunk is discarded and a cuticular tube is formed, through which the remains of the larva gain entrance to the host body. The parasite is little more than a mass of undifferentiated cells at this stage. It migrates through the host haemocoel and attaches to the intestine. Root-like processes grow out, eventually extending to all parts of the body while the central mass below the intestine is developing into the mantle and visceral mass of the parasite. Some secretion produced by the *Sacculina* inhibits the formation of cuticle in its vicinity, and at the next host molt, the central mass pops out of the host body and hangs down from the external surface, thus becoming an ectoparasite, but with an extensive system of internal roots. For some reason, *Sacculina* inhibits the host reproductive system, causing the phenomenon of parasitic castration. The female crab takes on a more juvenile appearance when it molts, and the male becomes more female-like. If the *Sacculina* dies, a male crab may develop a hermaphroditic gland, producing both sperm and ova. Evidently the hormonal secretions of the parasite are enough like those of the host to scramble the physiology of the host animal.

The Malacostraca

About two-thirds of the species of Crustacea belong to the Malacostraca. Malacostraca are far more homogeneous than the

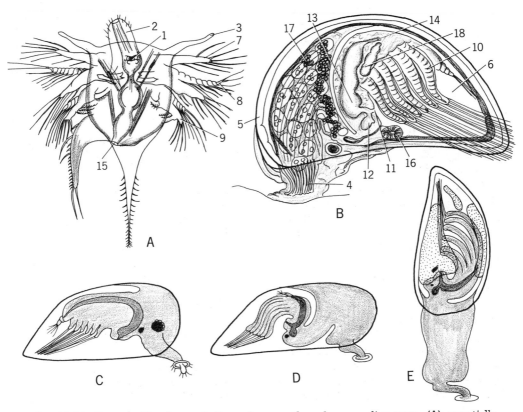

Fig. 18.14. Barnacle Development. Barnacles pass through a nauplius stage, (A) essentially like the nauplii of other crustacea. After the metanauplius stage, they metamorphose into a cypris larva (B), remarkably like an ostracod, at least from external appearances. The cypris larva develops adhesive glands, and grows a peduncle from the portion of the head adjacent to the antennules, eventually becoming an adult barnacle (C-E). (A, after Claus, from Calman, in Lankester. B, composite, based especially on Claus. C-E, after Korscheldt.) *External features:* 1, eye; 2, upper lip; 3, frontolateral horn; 4, developing peduncle; 5, shell; 6, mantle cavity; 7, antennule; 8, antenna; 9, mandible; 10, thoracic appendages. *Internal parts:* 11, mouth; 12, caecum of esophagus; 13, midgut; 14, rectum; 15, anus; 16, adductor muscle; 17, adhesive gland; 18, ganglion.

entomostraca, and the differences between the various groups are less obvious. They are rather bewildering at first. What does one look for to recognize the main types of malacostracans? Probably the best approach is to have a clear picture of the general features of the group, and then to note the modifications of the general pattern that is characteristic of the main groups. By concentrating in this way on the unique features of the different types of mala-costracans, it is relatively easy to recog-nize most of them.

The most important general features of Malacostraca are summarized in Fig. 18.15. The head and thorax are covered by a common carapace, which ends in an anterior rostrum. Stalked eyes, biramous antennules, and antennae with a scale-like exopodite are prominent features of the head. The thoracic legs are pereiopods, also called walking legs, but have exopo-dites that may help in swimming. The female gonopores are on the sixth tho-racic appendages, and the male gonopores are on the eighth thoracic appendages. There is a total of eight thoracic somites, and six abdominal somites. The first five

abdominal somites have pleopods, also called swimmerets, and the last bears a pair of uropods. The last somite is the telson, which has no appendages and, with the uropods, makes up the tail fan. This combination of characteristics is some-times known as the "caridoid facies" and has been considered as describing a hypo-thetical ancestral stock. There are severe difficulties with this idea, however, as a number of Malacostraca have features that appear to be more primitive than the car-dioid facies. Nevertheless, this combination of characteristics provides a good picture of generalized malacostracan structure.

Almost every feature of the general scheme is modified in one or another mala-costracan group. It will be helpful to anticipate some of the more common and important modifications so they can be noted as various groups are discussed. In examining a malacostracan, the main ques-tions that must be asked if it is to be identified are related to these alterations of basic form.

1. How is the carapace formed, and how intimate is the union of head and

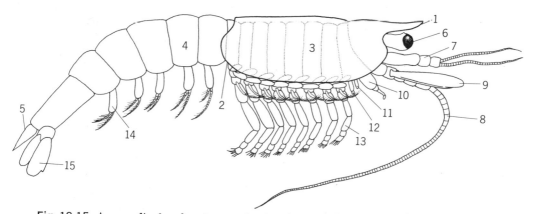

Fig. 18.15. A generalized malacostracan, showing the combination of traits sometimes termed the "caridoid facies." The caridoid facies summarize the more common attributes of Malacostraca, but cannot be considerd as describing an ancestral stock. (After Calman, in Lankester.) 1, rostrum; 2, carapace; 3, thoracic somite; 4, abdominal somite; 5, telson; 6, eye; 7, antennule; 8, antenna; 9, antennal scale; 10, mandible; 11, first maxilla; 12, second maxilla; 13, pereiopod; 14, pleopod; 15, uropod.

thoracic regions of the body? The carapace may not cover the whole thoracic region, and it may not be a single exoskeletal piece. There is a strong tendency for the thoracic segments to unite with the head. One or two of the thoracic somites may be united with the head even when a carapace is missing. As a part of this general tendency, the first thoracic appendages may be modified for food handling, serving as maxillipeds.

2. How have the thoracic appendages been adapted for specific functions? In addition to the tendency to alter the anterior thoracic appendages into maxillipeds, there is a tendency for one or two of the legs behind them to be raptorial legs, used for food capture. Raptorial legs are longer and more powerful than other thoracic legs and are modified for grasping. The most common type ends in powerful pincers, or chelae, as in crabs and lobsters. In this case the appendage is a cheliped. Some raptorial legs are subchelate, ending in a toothed or ridged podite that can be forcibly bent back against the preceding podites, closing as a jack-knife closes. Stomatopods have powerful subchelate raptorial legs that are said to chop a shrimp in two so effectively that the two halves fall in their relative positions as if chopped by a guillotine. A few raptorial legs end in other ways, with harpoon-like spines or stabbing blades. Thoracic legs can also be reduced, and in some groups the somites as well as the legs may be reduced.

3. What kind of gills are present, and where are they located? Gills are a characteristic feature of Crustacea generally, but the position and form of gills vary greatly. It is evident that oxygen levels tend to differ in different kinds of habitats, and especially in intertidal regions, where Crustacea face differing conditions at high and low tide. Larger and more active forms will require larger respiratory surfaces. In some groups the gills are blade-like processes on the appendages, while in others the gills are filamentous or branched. The gills are formed of epipodites, or of filaments of uncertain origin attached at the base or joints of legs. In the great majority of Malacostraca, the gills are attached to the thoracic legs, but in a few groups the gills are abdominal. As they occur in only a few groups, the presence of gills on the abdominal appendages is a rather critical diagnostic feature.

4. What provisions are made for brooding eggs? In some of the Malacostraca, medial plates are attached to the thoracic appendages. These are the oöstegites, and they form a brood chamber on the ventral surface. They are usually found only in females, but in some cases the males also have rudimentary oöstegites. Some Malacostraca brood eggs on the pleopods instead of the thoracic appendages, but this does not usually involve structural specialization of the pleopods.

5. What kinds of appendages occur on the abdominal somites? The pleopods may be relatively large or small. The first abdominal appendages are sometimes modified as gonopods, used for the transfer of sperm or spermatophores to the female. Pleopods may be used for walking or crawling, but they are typically swimming appendages and are equipped with natatory setae. The appendages on the somite next to the telson are particularly valuable. Most of the Malacostraca have a tail fan, composed of the flattened telson and the flattened uropods, but a few have elongated uropods. Elongated uropods are unusual enough to be a relatively critical characteristic.

The Malacostraca include the largest Crustacea and also some quite small ones. They are extremely abundant and very diversified in habits. Some of them are economically important. Lobsters, crabs, and shrimp are among the most valuable commercial shellfish, and others are significant elements of the food chain of economically important aquatic animals. The classification is necessarily complex. It should be noted that those groups marked with an asterisk are discussed only in the classification section.

CLASSIFICATION

Series Leptostraca, Superorder Phyllocarida, *Order Nebaliacea*. The Nebaliacea includes seven species of small, marine malacostracans found in bottom mud among seaweeds in littoral, marine habitats. These primitive malacostracans are unique in having seven abdominal somites, six with appendages, and a telson with caudal rami forming a conspicuous caudal furca. The antennules are equipped with a conspicuous movable scale, and the antennae have a very long flagellum, longer in the male. The strong mandibles have large palps, and the first maxillae typically have a long, slender palp that extends up under the carapace. The second maxillae are not modified as mouthparts and resemble the thoracic legs. The head is covered by a hinged rostral plate, and bears a pair of stalked eyes, sometimes rudimentary. The head, thorax, and first abdominal somites are enclosed in a bivalved carapace which can be closed by an adductor muscle. The eight pairs of thoracic legs are phyllopod-like. All are similar and are used to generate filter-feeding currents. Food collects in a ventral groove between the appendages and moves forward into the mouth. The first four pairs of abdominal appendages are pleopods, used for swimming, and the last two pairs are reduced. Respiratory exchange occurs at the inner surface of the carapace, and at the large, flattened epipodites and exopodites of the thoracic legs. The long heart has seven pairs of ostia, the last above the sixth thoracic legs. Vestigial antennal and maxillary glands are present, and pairs of glands at the bases of the thoracic legs are thought to be excretory. Eggs are brooded in a chamber between the thoracic legs of the female, and they pass through nauplius and metanauplius stages before hatching. At hatching, the juveniles resemble the parent but have a small carapace. Example: *Nebalia* (Fig. 18.16A-C).

Series Eumalacostraca. Malacostracans, typically with six abdominal somites, the last with a pair of appendages; a telson without furcal rami; never with a carapace having an adductor muscle; typically with specialized thoracic appendages.

Superorder Syncarida (Order Anaspidacea). A small group of primitive freshwater malacostracans, found in caves and mountain pools, ranging from about 0.5 mm. to 5.0 cm. in length. The protocephalon, bearing the eyes and two pairs of antennae, is covered by a separate plate ending in a short rostrum. A compound head plate covers the last three head somites, which carry the last three head appendages. In all other malacostracans the protocephalon is joined to the last three head somites. The first antennae are biramous and have a long flagellum. The second antennae are usually equipped with a long flagellum and a movable scale. The mandibles have a large palp, and the two pairs of maxillae are setose and flattened. The first thoracic legs are maxillipeds and have a distinct gnathobase. The remaining seven pairs of thoracic legs are pereiopods and usually have branchial epipodites, as well as exopodites that generate respiratory currents. The five pairs of abdominal pleopods are powerful swimming organs. Flattened uropods occur on the sixth abdominal somite and with the telson form a tail fan. The first two pairs of pleopods are modified as male copulatory organs. Sperm are transferred to a seminal receptacle on the ventral side of the last thoracic somite of the female. Eggs are not brooded and develop without free larval stages. Example: *Anaspides* (Fig. 18.16D,E).

Superorder Hoplocarida (Order Stomatopoda). Mantis shrimps. Large (up to 30 cm.) malacostracans with the head ending anteriorly in two movable pieces, one carrying the eyes and the other the first antennae; a carapace over the remaining head somites and the first thoracic somites, but leaving at least four thoracic somites free; first five pairs of thoracic legs subchelate, and the second pair enlarged as raptorial legs; the last three thoracic appendages simple and elongated; five pairs of flattened abdominal appendages with gills, and a pair of uropods; uropods and telson form a tail fan; male gonoduct at the tip of a long penis at the base of the eighth thoracic leg; with a prolonged period of larval development and a complex metamorphosis. Example: *Squilla* (Fig. 18.16F).

Superorder Peracarida. Malacostraca without a carapace or with a carapace leaving at least four thoracic somites free; first thoracic somite fused with the head; oöstegites on some or all of the thoracic legs form a brood pouch in the female; eggs develop in the brood pouch and hatch at a late stage.

Order Mysidacea. Opossum shrimps. Elongated, shrimp-like Peracarida with a transparent carapace over most of the thorax; eyes stalked or absent; first thoracic and sometimes the second thoracic appendage modified as maxillipeds; the remaining thoracic appendages with swimming setae; abdominal pleopods often reduced; uropods on last abdominal somite which, with the telson, form a tail fan; all appendages present in the young at hatching. Example: *Mysis* (Fig. 18.17A).

* *Order Cumacea.* Exclusively marine Peracarida, living in burrows or mucous tubes in bottom mud of littoral to deep waters. They are usually tiny, only a few millimeters long, but deep sea and arctic species reach a maximum length of about 3.5 cm. The greatly inflated carapace contains a gill cavity and covers the first three to four thoracic somites. The slender abdomen usually lacks pleopods in females and has two to five pleopods in males. The slender, filiform uropods do not form a tail fan with the telson. Rows of bristles on the uropods are used to clean off the an-

terior appendages. Respiratory and feeding currents are combined. Water is drawn in by movements of the second maxillae and maxillipeds and is discharged anteriorly after circulating over the gills and passing through the filtering setae on the maxillae. Some species also scrape food from sand grains picked up by the three pairs of maxillipeds. The antennules have very small or no inner flagella. Females have vestigial antennae and males have large antennae, modified as claspers or with long flagella. The mandibles have no palps. The first three pairs of thoracic legs are modified as maxillipeds, and the next four have oöstegites. The fourth thoracic legs are raptorial or prehensile. The fifth thoracic legs are often reduced, and the sixth to eighth are used for digging. Some species leave their burrow and swarm at the surface, possibly mating at this time. Eggs develop in the brood chamber and hatch with the last thoracic legs incomplete. Example: *Diastylis* (Fig. 18.17E).

* *Order Tanaidacea.* Usually tiny (1 to 2 mm., but up to 12 mm.), almost exclusively marine peracaridans with a flattened body, somewhat resembling isopods. They live in burrows or mucous tubes in the bottom mud, preferring littoral regions, but reaching depths of 4000 m. The carapace covers the first two thoracic somites and encloses a small, vascularized gill chamber on each side, which is ventilated by fanning movements of the exopodites of the thoracic legs. The remaining six thoracic somites are free, and are followed by a short abdomen with crowded somites. Although some females have no pleopods, five pairs of pleopods are usually present. The last abdominal somite is fused with the telson and has slender, filiform uropods. The first thoracic legs are maxillipeds, with flattened epipodites that extend into the branchial cavity. The second thoracic legs are large, chelate, raptorial legs. The third thoracic legs are sometimes specialized for burrowing, but in most cases the third to eighth thoracic legs are all similar pereiopods.

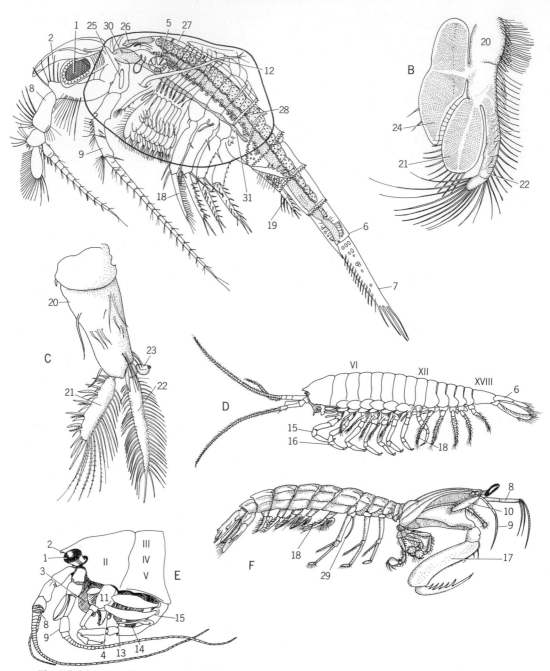

Fig. 18.16. Some Representative Malacostraca. Malacostraca are divided into a large number of larger and smaller groups. The series Leptostraca is exemplified by *Nebalia*, the only genus of the superorder Phyllocarida, shown in **A-C.** Series Leptostraca is characterized by seven abdominal somites and the presence of a caudal furca, while the series Eumalacostraca is characterized by the absence of a caudal furca, and the general occurrence of six abdominal

Females have oöstegites on the sixth or the second through the sixth thoracic legs, forming a marsupium. Setae on the second maxillae or maxillipeds are sometimes used for filter-feeding. Excretion is by maxillary glands, sometimes with the aid of vestigial antennal glands. Eggs are brooded in the marsupium and hatch with the last thoracic legs and pleopods undeveloped. Example: *Apseudes* (Fig. 18.17B).

Order Isopoda. Dorsoventrally flattened peracarids with the first and rarely the second thoracic somite joined to the head, but without a carapace; abdominal somites often partially joined; last abdominal somite generally joined to the telson and with biramous sensory uropods; sessile or immovable eyes; eight pairs of uniramous thoracic legs, the first pair modified as maxillipeds and the rest similar or variously modified; second and third thoracic legs often modified as chelate gnathopods, used for food handling; six pairs of typically biramous pleopods bearing gills; the second and sometimes the first pleopods usually modified in males; oöstegites on some thoracic legs of the females; eggs usually brooded in the brood chamber, and hatching with the last pair of thoracic legs undeveloped. Example: *Asellus* (Fig. 18.17D).

Order Amphipoda. Usually bilaterally flattened peracarids with the first, and rarely the second, thoracic somite joined to the head but without a carapace; abdominal somites not fused, and the last not usually joined to the telson; first thoracic legs modified as maxillipeds and joined basally to form a ventral plate; second and third thoracic legs often modified as gnathopods, and the remaining five pairs usually present and used as pereiopods; females usually with oöstegites on the third through the sixth thoracic legs, and with lamellar or branched gills on some of the thoracic coxopodites; usually with six pairs of pleopods, the first three larger and natatory and the last three alike and termed uropods; eggs carried in a brood chamber and hatched at an advanced stage, with all of the appendages present but the last not fully formed. Example: *Gammarus* (Fig. 18.17C).

Superorder Eucarida. Malacostracans with all of the thoracic terga incorporated in the carapace; stalked eyes; thoracic legs

somites. The flattened, phyllopod-like thoracic appendages (B) of *Nebalia* are characteristic, and justify the name Phyllocarida. A pleopod is shown at C. The bivalved carapace, with an adductor muscle, is also characteristic of *Nebalia*. It shows its primitive character in having all of the thoracic appendages alike, and, in fact, the second maxilla are very like the thoracic appendages. *Anaspides*, shown at D, is a primitive eumalacostracan of the order Anaspidacea. As in other eumalacostraca, the thoracic appendages are somewhat specialized, although only the first pair are modified as maxillipeds. The head of *Anaspides*, shown at E, is unique. The protocephalon, bearing the two pairs of antennae and eyes, is covered by a separate plate, while the next three somites, which carry the mandibles and two pairs of maxillae, are covered by a second plate. The somite numbers corresponding to the head plates are shown in Roman numerals. *Squilla*, shown at F, is a eumalacostracan belonging to the order Stomatopoda. The stomatopods are hoplocarids. The part of the head containing the eyes and the part carrying the antennules are movable pieces. The remainder of the head and the front part of the thorax are covered by a carapace. The very large raptorial legs on the second thoracic segment are characteristic. (A-C, after Claus. D and E, after Snodgrass. F, after Calman, in Lankester.) *External features:* 1, eye; 2, rostrum; 3, protocephalon; 4, paragnath, a lobe from the sternal plate of the maxillary somite; 5, adductor muscle; 6, telson; 7, caudal ramus. *Appendages:* 8, antennule; 9, antenna; 10, antennal scale; 11, mandible; 12, palp of first maxilla; 13, first maxilla; 14, second maxilla; 15, maxilliped; 16, first pereiopod; 17, raptorial limb (second pereiopod); 18, first pleopod; 19, sixth pleopod; 20, protopodite; 21, exopodite; 22, endopodite; 23, internal appendix; 24, epipodite. *Internal parts:* 25, antennal gland; 26, liver diverticulum; 27, heart; 28, ovary; 29, penis; 30, brain; 31, nerve cord.

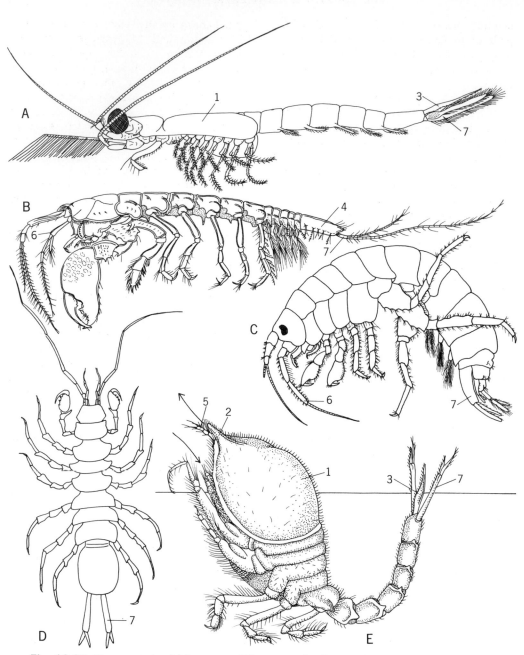

Fig. 18.17. Representative Malacostraca. The superorder Peracarida includes the eumalacos-traca with a short carapace leaving at least four thoracic somites free or lacking a carapace. The first thoracic somite is fused with the head, and shelf-like oöstegites on at least some of the thoracic legs of the females form a brood pouch in which the young develop. *Mysis*, shown at A, is a peracarid belonging to the order Mysidacea. They have a transparent carapace, and one or two pairs of maxillipeds. The brood pouch can be seen under the thorax. *Apseudes*, shown at B, is a member of the order Tanaidacea. The short carapace covers only

bending between the fourth and fifth podites; no oöstegites; eggs carried on pleopods; usually with a complex metamorphosis involving several advanced, postlarval stages.

* *Order Euphausiacea.* A group of small (1 to 6 cm.) eucarids, differing from decapods in having biramous thoracic appendages. They are pelagic marine animals, occurring from the surface to depths of over 3500 m. They often swarm in large numbers, and several species are important elements of whale diets. Some are transparent and others a vivid red; nearly all are luminescent. The long, biramous antennules are sometimes modified in males. The antennae have large scales. The mandible usually has a palp, and the two pairs of maxillae are small and flattened. The first thoracic appendages are not maxillipeds; all are similar and all are equipped with natatory setae. Each thoracic leg bears a gill formed from a usually branched epipodite. There is no branchial chamber beneath the carapace and the gills are exposed. The setose thoracic legs are usually used to strain out food organisms. A few are predaceous, and have the second or third thoracic legs modified by harpoon-like spines or chelae to form a raptorial leg. The last 1 to 2 pairs of thoracic legs are often reduced or vestigial. The large pleopods have natatory setae and the first two

pairs are modified for copulation in males. The telson and the flattened, biramous uropods form a tail fan. Spermatophores are formed in the dilated, terminal part of the sperm ducts. Ova may be carried for a time in a basket formed by the setae on the thoracic legs or cemented to the lower surface of the thorax. They hatch as nauplii and pass through several larval stages. Example: *Meganyctiphanes* (Fig. 18.18).

Order Decapoda. The major group of malacostracans, including the shrimp, lobsters, crayfish, crabs, and other large crustaceans. The first pereiopods are usually large chelipeds, and they have three pairs of maxillipeds. The last five pairs of thoracic legs are uniramous pereiopods.

GENERAL FEATURES OF STOMATOPODS

Stomatopods resemble preying mantids and are sometimes calling mantis shrimps. The less than 200 species include some interesting organisms from the structural and behavioral point of view. They are about 4 to 34 cm. long, with a number of relatively large species. They are especially characteristic of tropical seas, but extend into temperate zones, where they may be abundant locally. They live in littoral regions or in relatively shallow waters, and are very rarely found below 500 m.

Stomatopods like to lie in wait in crev-

the first two thoracic somites. The first thoracic legs are maxillipeds, and the second are chelate raptorial legs. The crowded abdominal somites are sometimes without appendages. *Gammarus*, shown at C, is a peracarid belonging to the order Amphipoda. Amphipods have the first (rarely the second) thoracic somite joined to the head, but have no carapace. They are usually bilaterally compressed. The first thoracic appendages are maxillipeds, and the next two are usually gnathopods. Gills occur on some of the thoracic legs. *Asellus*, shown at D, is a fresh-water peracarid belonging to the order Isopoda. Most isopods are dorsoventrally flattened. They have one or two thoracic somites joined to the head and one pair of maxillipeds. The remaining thoracic somites bear variously specialized appendages. Isopods are unusual in having gill-bearing pleopods. *Diastylis*, shown at E, is a peracarid belonging to the order Cumacea. These tiny mud-dwellers are characterized by the inflated carapace, three pairs of maxillipeds, reduced fifth thoracic legs, and modified appendages for burrowing on the next three somites. The arrows show the combined feeding and respiratory currents. (A, after Pennak. C, after Kunkel. D, after Hay, from Pennak. B, after Sara, from Smith and Weldon. E, composite.) 1, carapace; 2, pseudorostrum; 3, telson united with the last abdominal somite; 4, abdomen; 5, antennule; 6, antenna; 7, uropod.

ices or burrows until a likely-looking bit of food swims by, when the huge raptorial legs are shot out to drag the prey in. They accept any food of appropriate size, including fish. Some species leave the burrow to hunt, swimming about with the aid of the pleopods and with the huge scales on the antennae serving as rudders. The chopping movement of the raptorial leg is fast and effective, and large species can inflict a serious wound. They are often brightly colored, with greens and browns predominating, but reds and blues are occasionally seen.

The two movable pieces of the head anterior to the carapace are unique. Each piece represents a part of the protocephalon. The stalked eyes are on the front piece, and the antennules on the second. The remaining head somites and the first two thoracic somites are covered by the carapace. Although the thoracic somites are structurally joined to the head by the carapace, the first two thoracic appendages are not converted into mouth parts and have no endites for use in food handling. In contrast, some of the other Crustacea have free thoracic somites with maxillipeds. Evidently the selective forces favoring the union of somites to the head and the conversion of anterior thoracic legs to

maxillipeds are independent, although they may enforce one another when operating together. The third and fourth thoracic somites are reduced and lie under the rear margin of the carapace. The remaining four thoracic and six abdominal somites are free.

Stomatopod appendages have some unusual features. The antennules have three flagella in place of the usual two. The antennae have an unusually large scale on the exopodite. The first maxillae are unusual in having only a vestigial palp. The second maxillae (Fig. 18.19A) are unique, with little resemblance to other crustacean maxillae. They have four indistinct segments, and the antennal glands open near the bases of the maxillae. The first thoracic appendages have no endites for food handling, and the second pair is huge, serving as raptorial legs. An outstanding feature of the thoracic appendages is that all of them have subchelate tips, and, of course, the raptorial legs have very powerful subchelate weapons. The abdominal appendages are pleopods with one unusual feature, the presence of filamentous gills which branch from an axial stem, actually a process from the exopodite (Fig. 18.19B). Abdominal gills are found in relatively few crustaceans, and so are

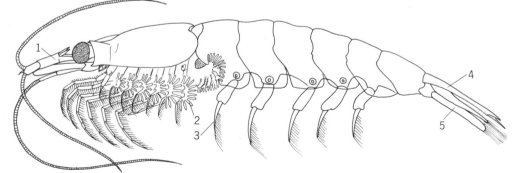

Fig. 18.18. *Meganyctiphanes*, a peracarid belonging to the order Euphausiacea. These pelagic crustaceans are important whale food. They have no maxillipeds, and the carapace does not cover the branchial processes on the thoracic legs. The pleopods are large. (After Holt and Tattersall, from Zimmer, in Kükenthal and Krumbach.) 1, antennal scale; 2, branchial epipodite of thoracic leg; 3, pleopod; 4, telson; 5, uropod.

quite distinctive. The broad, conspicuous tail fan has an unusual feature also. The uropod has a spiny, median plate on the protopodite (Fig. 18.19C).

The male reproductive organs are remarkable. The testes are delicate tubes, located in the abdomen and extending back to a median part in the telson. The sperm ductules pass to paired sperm ducts which open in the last thoracic segment. Up to this point the male system is not particularly different, but each gonoduct is equipped with a long, jointed, chitinous penis. This is most unusual, as most Crustacea form spermatophores and rarely have a penis.

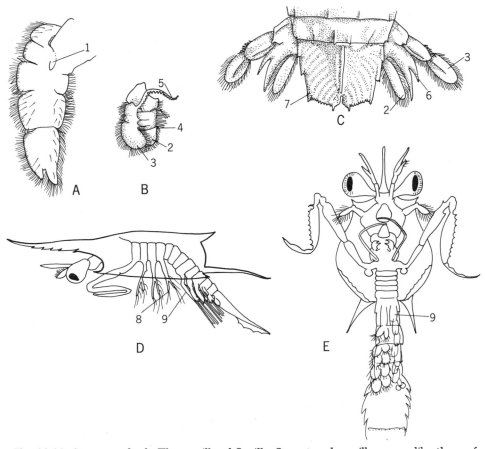

Fig. 18.19. Stomatopods. A. The maxilla of *Squilla*. Stomatopod maxillae are unlike those of any other crustaceans. B. A pleopod of *Squilla*, with the gill filaments removed from the axis. The abdominal gills of stomatopods are characteristic, and serve to distinguish them from most other Malacostraca. C. The tail fan of *Squilla*. The process extending from the protopodite of the uropod is unique. D. One kind of Erichthus larva, seen from the side. E. A second type of Erichthus larva, from ventral view. Note the suppression of the posterior thoracic appendages, also observed in zoaea larvae of the decapods. (A-C, after Calman, in Lankester. D and E, after Claus, from Korsheldt and Heider.) 1, papilla containing the opening of the maxillary gland; 2, endopodite; 3, exopodite; 4, internal appendage; 5, branchial appendage; 6, process from protopodite of uropod; 7, telson; 8, fifth thoracic appendage; 9, first abdominal appendage.

The large ovaries lie close to the midline, and join in the telson. The oviducts pass to gonopores on the sixth pair of thoracic legs. A small, epidermal seminal receptacle lies between them. Glands in the last three thoracic somites are used to cement the eggs together into a mass, which may be kept in the burrow or attached to the thoracic legs.

Adult stomatopods are benthonic organisms that are rarely taken on ordinary collecting trips, but the larvae sometimes occur in large numbers in tropical plankton, and are seen more often than the adults. They are large, transparent creatures with a characteristic form (Fig. 18.19D,E). Not all of the larvae have been matched with the adult stomatopods into which they develop. Two larval types have been recognized, an Erichthus and an Alima. An interesting feature of stomatopod larvae is that they pass through a long period when the last three thoracic somites have no appendages, although somites in front and behind have appendages. This is surprising because arthropods generally develop appendages in regular sequence, with the front ones appearing first. A number of Malacostraca pass through a zoaea stage in which these three somites and their appendages are suppressed. It may be that the stomatopod larvae reveal one step in the evolutionary development of the zoaea larva.

GENERAL FEATURES OF MYSIDACEA

Mysidacea is made up of about 450 species of almost exclusively marine Crustacea. The few fresh-water species appear to have left the sea relatively recently. Some creep about on the bottom or live among littoral vegetation, and others are pelagic. They prefer cold water, and some live at great depths. *Mysis oculata* lives only in deep lakes and undergoes a remarkable diurnal movement. During the daylight hours they stay within a meter of the bottom, but during the night they rise to the surface.

Most of the mysids are about 2 to 3 cm. long, but some reach 15 cm. and some are no more than 3 mm. long. In favorable habitats they can become very abundant and are important food organisms for economically important fish. Mysids sometimes account for 80 per cent of the diet of lake trout in the Great Lakes, and marine species are important food organisms for flounders.

Most of the thoracic somites are covered by the carapace, but only the first three somites have united with it. A conspicuous cervical sulcus usually crosses the carapace. It may be homologous with the division between the separate protocephalon of *Anaspides* and the back part of the head. An unusual feature of the body is the elongated posterior somite, sometimes divided by a transverse groove. Fossil mysids have a similar groove, and it may indicate that the mysid ancestors had eight abdominal somites, like the Leptostraca.

Deep sea mysids have curious eyestalks, which extend beyond the eye or are otherwise modified. The appendages have several peculiarities. Both the antennules and antennae have very long flagella, and the male antennules have a conical process with sensory filaments on it in addition to the usual two flagella. Antennae are equipped with a conspicuous antennal scale. The first thoracic appendages are maxillipeds and the rest are pereiopods, with a slender setose flagellum on the exopodite, used in swimming or to circulate water over the gills. Many of the mysids have branched gills on the pereiopods. Oöstegites on from two to all of the thoracic legs form a marsupium, or brood pouch, justifying the name "opossum shrimp." Sexual dimorphism is common in the pleopods, which are always present in males but may be missing in females. When the pleopods are reduced, the animals swim with the pereiopods or creep over the bottom mud or vegetation.

Most of the mysids are filter feeders, although some deep-sea forms are scavengers.

The appendages of *Gnathophausia* generate three distinct currents, a feeding current generated by an exite on the second maxillae, a respiratory current produced by the exopodites of the thoracic appendages, and a swimming current caused by the pleopods.

The reproductive system is simple in both sexes, and the gonopores are found on the usual appendages. Eggs are brooded in the marsupium, and development is direct, without larval stages. At the time of hatching the juveniles have all of their appendages.

GENERAL FEATURES OF ISOPODA

The three principal groups of Malacostraca are Isopoda, Amphipoda, and Decapoda. Together, they account for about two-thirds of all known species. The 4000 species of isopods are arranged in eight suborders, each representing a major adaptational line. The suborders are characterized by differences in body shape; amount of fusion of abdominal somites; mouthparts; and nature of the thoracic coxae. To a considerable extent, these differences are associated with diverse habits and approaches to some of the problems of survival.

Recognition of the various suborders is not particularly difficult. Most of them have one or two outstanding traits which make them distinctive. The members of suborder *Oniscoidea* are distinguished by being amphibious or terrestrial. The ventral surface of the body is partially consolidated by expansions of the thoracic coxae which form ventral coxal plates fused with the body. They also have vestigial antennae (example: *Ligidium*, Fig. 18.20A). Most of the isopods have a thorax and abdomen of about the same breadth, but suborder *Gnathiidea* is characterized by having an abdomen much narrower than the thorax. The first and seventh thoracic somites are reduced, and the seventh thoracic legs have been lost. Larval gnathiids are also distinctive, living as ectoparasites on marine

fishes. *Gnathia* (Fig. 18.20B) is an example. Two of the suborders of isopods are characterized by elongated, cylindrical bodies, contrasting sharply with the flattened bodies of most isopods. Of these, the *Anthuroidea* are characterized by elongated, cylindrical bodies and their marine habit. They are also unusual in having the first pleopods modified to form a protective operculum that folds over the gill-bearing pleopods behind (example: *Cyathura*, Fig. 18.20C). The other elongated isopods, the *Phreatoicidea*, are fresh-water forms found in the southern hemisphere. They are characterized by a bilaterally compressed body with styliform uropods (example: *Phreatoicus*, Fig. 18.20G). As a general rule, isopods have a full complement of mouthparts, but members of the parasitic suborder, *Epicaridea*, have suctorial mouths with both of the maxillae reduced or missing. The epicarids are parasites of other Crustacea and show some of the same tendencies seen in other crustacean parasites. The females are greatly modified, often bizarrely shaped, and sometimes lose all traces of segmentation and appendages (example: *Probopyrus*, Fig. 18.20D). The remaining suborders of isopods are all aquatic, and all have some evidence of fusion of the abdominal somites. They can be distinguished by the form of the uropod and telson. The predominantly marine *Flabellifera* have a tail fan formed by the uropods and telson and also have ventral coxal plates formed by the widened thoracic coxae. *Cirolana* (Fig. 18.20E) is an example. The *Valvifera* have highly modified uropods. The exopodite has been lost, and the endopodites fold over the pleopods to form a protective operculum (example: *Idothea*, Fig. 18.20F). The *Asellota* are found in marine and fresh-water habitats, and are characterized by styliform uropods which do not form a tail fan. The telson is fused with the abdominal plates to form a single, continuous, dorsal plate (example: *Asellus*, Fig. 18.17D).

Most isopods can be recognized at once

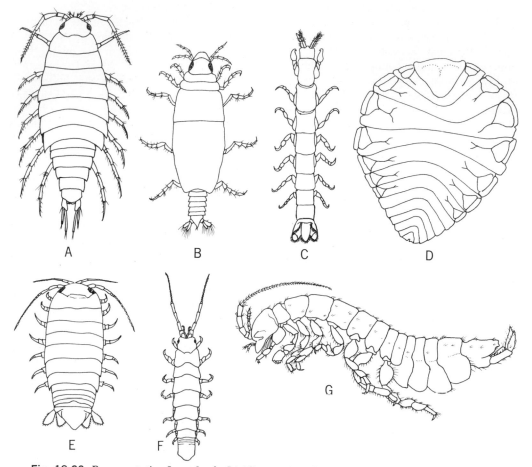

Fig. 18.20. Representative Isopods. **A.** *Ligidium,* a member of the suborder *Oniscoidea.* The oniscoids are terrestrial and have vestigial antennae. The ventral exoskeleton is consolidated by ventral coxal plates which fuse with the body. **B.** *Gnathia,* a member of the suborder *Gnathiidea.* These isopods are ectoparasitic on fishes, as larvae, and are unusual in having a broad thorax and narrow abdomen. **C.** *Cyathura,* a member of the suborder Anthuroidea. The body of anthuroids is cylindrical rather than dorsoventrally flattened. The first pleopod forms an operculum that covers the more posterior pleopods. Anthuroids are predominantly marine. **D.** *Probopyrus,* a member of the suborder Epicaridea. These isopods have suctorial mouths, and the females are greatly modified for life as parasites. **E.** *Cirolana,* a member of the predominantly marine Flabellifera, characterized by a tail fan and ventral coxal plates. **F.** *Idothea,* a member of the Valvifera. The endopodites of the uropod form an operculum that fits over the pleopods. **G.** *Phreatoicus,* a member of the suborder Phreatoicidea. These isopods are fresh-water, southern-hemisphere forms with bilaterally compressed bodies. (**A,** after Walker. **D,** after Van Name, from Van Name. **B,** after Sars from Calman, in Lankester. **C,** after Harger, from Pratt. **E** and **F,** after Johnson and Snook.)

794

by their flattened bodies and lack of a carapace, but nevertheless it is difficult to generalize about how isopods differ from other peracarid Crustacea. Some can roll up, armadillo-like, when disturbed. Land isopods, often called pill bugs, sow bugs, or wood lice, are frequently found under logs in wooded areas. Where the body form is unusual, it is necessary to depend on a combination of characteristics seen in no other peracarid group. Abdominal gills are an important characteristic, for very few Crustacea have gills on the pleopods. If identification is still unceratin, one must ascertain whether the first thoracic somite is joined to the head and look for a pair of maxillipeds. Some other important points are the absence of thoracic exopodites, the sessile or immovable eyes, the uniramous antennules, and the tendency of abdominal somites to fuse together, especially with the telson.

Isopods have uniramous walking legs without exopodites. They creep like insects, and many can run rapidly when out of water. This has undoubtedly been a factor in favoring the spread of isopods into amphibious and terrestrial habitats. Some of the aquatic isopods can also swim. They have flattened pereiopods or, more often, swimming pleopods. In some cases the anterior three pairs of pleopods are modified for swimming, and have natatory setae, while the last three pairs are modified for respiration.

Isopods are not filter feeders, another trait that may have favored the invasion of land. The mouthparts are somewhat consolidated, with a superficial resemblance to those of insects. The labrum hangs over the mouth, covering the strong mandibles. The first maxillae have no palp, and the second maxillae have overlapping endites. The maxillipeds can be coupled temporarily through the use of special coupling spines. Land isopods, with uniramous antennules and no antennae, are particularly insect-like at first glance (Fig. 18.21A). The parasitic isopods have profoundly

modified mouthparts. Larval *Gnathia* have long, piercing mandibles enclosed in a suctorial oral cone, formed by the mouthparts (Fig. 18.21B), and epicarids have a similar oral cone.

The different methods used to protect the abdominal gills provide an interesting example of convergent evolutionary forces arising from common problems. The first pair of pleopods is sometimes modified to form an operculum that fits over the branchial appendages, somewhat like the operculum of *Xiphosura*. Not all isopods, however, have found this solution to the problem. In some cases the exopodites of the pleopods have been modified to serve as protective covers, and are folded over the respiratory endopodites. This is the system used by land isopods. In the Valvifera, still another solution has appeared; the uropod has been modified as an operculum. The development of protective coverings for respiratory appendages was undoubtedly an important preparatory step for the invasion of terrestrial habitats. The same theme is seen in the chelicerates, where protective covers for the book gills appear to have preceded the development of book lungs in terrestrial organisms. Protection of the abdominal gills reduces the loss of water at the respiratory surface, but isopods have never fully adjusted to land life and are restricted to humid surroundings. They live in protected places and are often nocturnal animals.

The reproductive system is simple, and the gonoducts open on the sixth or eighth thoracic somites, as in other Malacostraca. In most species, the first one or two pleopods are specialized for sperm transfer. As a general rule, oöstegites on at least some of the thoracic legs form a marsupium in which the ova develop, but in a few species the sternal plates of the thorax are modified to form a brood pouch. The eggs are carried until they hatch, when the young usually leave the female. They are in a late stage of development, but with the last pair of thoracic legs still incomplete.

The epicarids have a remarkable life history, indicating a long history of parasitism and intensive adaptation for it. They hatch as epicarid larvae, looking like respectable young isopods (Fig. 18.21C). Each larva seeks a copepod and, if successful, attaches to its surface, here molting several times, becoming a microniscus and eventually a cryptoniscus larva. It is now ready to leave the copepod host and spends a period of time wandering about on the bottom until it chances upon an appropriate host, usually a crab. It enters the gill chamber or brood chamber to continue its development. At least some epicarids are sexually undetermined. If they attach to a host by themselves, they become females, but if a female is nearby, they attach to her instead and become dwarf males, retaining many of their juvenile characteristics (Fig. 18.21D).

GENERAL FEATURES OF AMPHIPODA

Amphipods are somewhat less diversified than the isopods, but about 3600 species of amphipods have been described, and they make up an interesting and important group of Crustacea. Although they are predominantly marine, there are many fresh-water species of amphipods. A few are semiterrestrial, living above the high-tide lines of temperature shores and sometimes extending inland in humid, tropical areas. Although some amphipods are pelagic, most of them creep about on the bottom or among algae or other aquatic plants. They are more common in shallow waters, but an extensive deep-water fauna is also known.

Most amphipods are bent and have a convex dorsal surface. They look a little

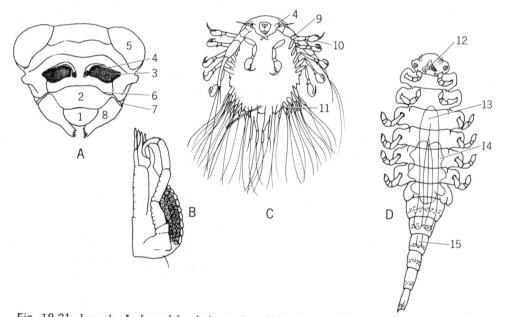

Fig. 18.21. Isopods. **A.** Isopod head, front view. Note its resemblance, probably convergent, to an insect head. **B.** Head of late larva of *Gnathia*. Mouthparts are modified to form a suctorial proboscis. **C.** An epicarid larva. **D.** A male epicarid. The dwarf males are in the entoniscus stage, permanently. (**A**, after Snodgrass. **B**, after Smith. **D**, after Giard, from Calman, in Lankester. **C**, after Giard and Bonnier, from Korscheldt.) 1, labrum; 2, clypeus; 3, antennae; 4, antennule; 5, eye; 6, frontal lamina; 7, gena; 8, mandible; 9, maxilla; 10, pereiopod; 11, pleopod; 12, oral cone; 13, hepatic caecum; 14, testis; 15, heart.

like laterally compressed isopods and have a number of isopod-like traits. The first, and sometimes the second, thoracic somite is united with the head, and there is no true carapace. The thoracic legs are uniramous, and have no exopodite. The eyes are sessile, and some of the abdominal somites are fused together. They differ most markedly from isopods in having thoracic gills.

The main suborders are the Gammaridea, Hyperiidea, and Caprellidea. The *Gammaridea* includes the many essentially ordinary amphipods, without unusually large heads or short abdomens. Most of them are laterally compressed, but some are dorsoventrally flattened and can be mistaken for isopods if one does not look at the position of the gills. Gammarids are characterized by having only the first thoracic somite united with the head; an abdomen, usually of separate somites, with a full complement of appendages; a thorax with a full set of legs having coxal plates; and maxillipeds with palps. A number of important fresh-water, marine, and semi-terrestrial gammarids are known. *Gammarus* (Fig. 18.17C) is a common aquatic gammarid, and *Orchestoidea* (Fig. 18.22D) is a semiterrestrial one. *Hyperiidea* includes amphipods with unusually large heads and eyes. The body is sometimes elongated or oddly shaped in other ways. The head is united with the first thoracic somite, the mandibles have no palps, the abdominal somites are distinct and have well-developed appendages, and the thoracic region has a full set of legs with small coxal segments. Hyperiids are transparent, pelagic forms, and many live in jellyfish or transparent tunicates (example: *Phronima*, Fig. 18.22B). There are two major types of *Caprellidea*, both greatly modified insofar as body shape is concerned. Caprellids have several unique features. The second as well as the first thoracic somite is joined to the head. The fourth and fifth thoracic legs are usually vestigial or missing. The small abdomen is made of fused somites

and bears vestigial appendages. The Caprellidae, one of the adaptive lines, are known as skeleton shrimps because they are narrow and elongated. They creep about among plants and are equipped with large, conspicuous raptorial legs (example: *Caprella*, Fig. 18.22A). The other line is the Cyamidae, known as whale-lice. They live on the body surface or external orifices of whales, and are modified for clinging to the host. The body is strongly flattened and the appendages are converted into anchoring devices (example: *Paracyamus*, Fig. 18.22C).

Amphipod appendages have some interesting features. The antennules are usually biramous, thus differing from isopod antennules, but the inner branch is sometimes small and occasionally wholly missing. The antennae never have a scale, and the female Hyperiidea have both pairs of antennae greatly reduced. The first maxillae are usually larger than the second, reversing the general trend in most Crustacea. The maxillipeds are fused at the base to form a median, ventral plate, but are otherwise quite variable. They are well developed in the gammarids, but far less so in the other amphipods. The first two pairs of thoracic legs tend to be modified as gnathopods with chelate or subchelate tips, and in caprellids are sometimes very large. Gills may be found on the last six pairs of thoracic legs, but in many cases some of the legs are without gills. Caprellids have gills on the fourth and fifth pairs of thoracic legs only. The pereiopods behind the gnathopods are essentially alike and have a variety of terminal specializations fitting them for burrowing, clinging to plants, clinging to a host, and the like. Two to four pairs of oöstegites form a marsupium under the thorax. The three anterior pairs of abdominal appendages are usually directed forward and are used in swimming, while the three posterior pairs, usually termed uropods, are directed posteriorly.

Amphipods usually use the pereiopods to scramble over plants or objects on the bottom, but sometimes fall back on the pleopods. The body is normally curved, but powerful muscles can straighten it suddenly, giving a sudden shove. In aquatic species this results in sudden, darting movements and enables beach fleas to hop vigorously. Amphipods that live on the bottom often have cement glands on the fourth or fifth thoracic legs, used to construct tubes of slime or to cement particles

together to form a tube. Others do not build tubes of their own but usurp the tubes or shells of other animals.

A number of amphipods are filter-feeders. The pleopods or thoracic appendages are used to generate feeding currents, and setose portions of the gnathopods, maxillipeds, or maxillae filter out particles. Detailed differences between groups provide no new principles and need not be dis-

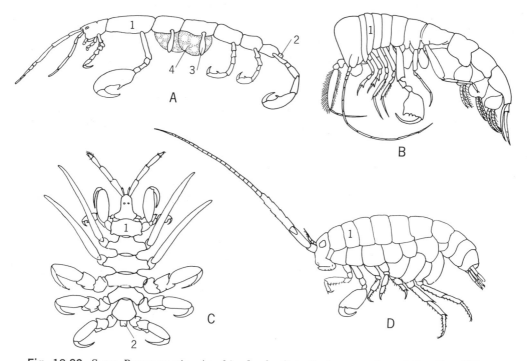

Fig. 18.22. Some Representative Amphipods. **A.** *Caprella* is a member of the Caprellidea, representing the line of skeleton shrimps belonging to the family Caprellidae. The small, fused abdomen, and elongated thorax, with a large raptorial leg makes caprellids easy to recognize. **B.** *Phronima*, a member of the Hyperiidea. Many of these are parasites of jellyfish or tunicates. The extremely large heads and eyes are characteristic. **C.** *Paracyamus*, is also one of the Caprellidea, but belongs to the line of whale lice classified in the family Cyamidae. These ectoparasites have fused abdominal somites forming a diminutive abdomen, and the large thorax is dorsoventrally flattened. Appendages are modified for clinging. **D.** *Orchestoidea*, a member of the suborder Gammaridea. Gammarids have a full set of appendages, thoracic legs with coxal plates, and the first thoracic somite fused with the head. They have no outstanding peculiarities to set them off from the generalized amphipod type. They occur in fresh and salt water, and some, like *Orchestoidea*, live as semiterrestrial animals on beaches. (A, after Ricketts and Calvin. B, after Claus. C, after Sars, from Calman, in Lankester. D, after Johnson and Snook.) 1, thoracic somite three; 2, abdomen; 3, reduced thoracic appendages; 4, marsupium, containing eggs.

cussed here. Other amphipods live on the surface of algae or colonial animals and feed on them, or capture other animals that visit the plants for food with the gnathopods. Some amphipods burrow in tunicates or sponges, living in a shadow-land between predaceous and parasitic life. Most of them feed on masses of plant or animal material as it is available, handling food with the gnathopods and fragmenting it with the strong mandibles.

The male and female reproductive systems are simple, with paired gonads on the sterna of the usual genital somites. The male pleopods are not specialized for copulation. In some cases the sperm are liberated in the respiratory current of the female, and so are carried past the eggs in the marsupium. The ova develop in the brood pouch and hatch after all of the appendages have been developed. The young generally remain in the marsupium until it is cast off by the female at the next molt.

GENERAL FEATURES OF DECAPODA

The eucarid Malacostraca are characterized by an intimate union of the carapace with the thoracic somites. The Euphausiacea (p. 789) have the gills outside of the carapace, while the decapods have the carapace extended laterally to form a branchial cavity. Decapods get their name because only five pairs of the thoracic appendages are leg-like pereiopods. The remaining three pairs are maxillipeds. Decapoda is the largest and most successful order of Crustacea, with about 8500 species. They have invaded nearly every kind of aquatic habitat, and some are semiterrestrial to nearly terrestrial. They are predominantly marine, but some of the species have invaded freshwater habitats. A detailed description of decapod classification cannot be undertaken here. Descriptions of the varied families and superfamilies will be found in specialist literature and in local faunistic guides.

Two suborders are recognized, the *Natantia*, or swimming decapods, and the *Reptantia*, or crawling decapods. The division is imperfect, for some Natantia can and do crawl about, and some Reptantia are good swimmers. However, it separates the true shrimps, predominantly pelagic, from the lobsters, crayfish, and crabs, which are predominantly benthonic.

Natants are characterized by:
1. a laterally compressed body with a prominent, often compressed and sawtoothed, rostrum;
2. a large, plate-like antennal scale, used as a rudder in swimming;
3. slender thoracic legs without a cheliped, or with a cheliped on one of the first three pairs of thoracic legs;
4. first abdominal somite essentially full-sized;
5. a full set of well-developed, swimming pleopods.

Reptants are characterized by:
1. bodies that are never laterally compressed, although they may be depressed dorsally, and in some cases with the rostrum missing;
2. antennae with a vestigial scale or without a scale;
3. strong thoracic legs, and almost universally with the first pereiopod modified into a strong cheliped;
4. a reduced first abdominal somite;
5. pleopods often reduced and not used for swimming.

It is evident that most of the natant characteristics are directly or indirectly related to their pelagic habits. The natants can be divided into two major lines, the *Penaeidea* and the *Caridea*. They are easily distinguished, for the penaeids generally have chelate third pereiopods and the side plates of the second abdominal somite do not overlap the side plates of the adjacent abdominal somite. Penaeids include the commercially important *Peneus* from the southern coastal waters of the United States. *Parapenaeopsis* is shown as an example of a penaeid (Fig. 18.23A).

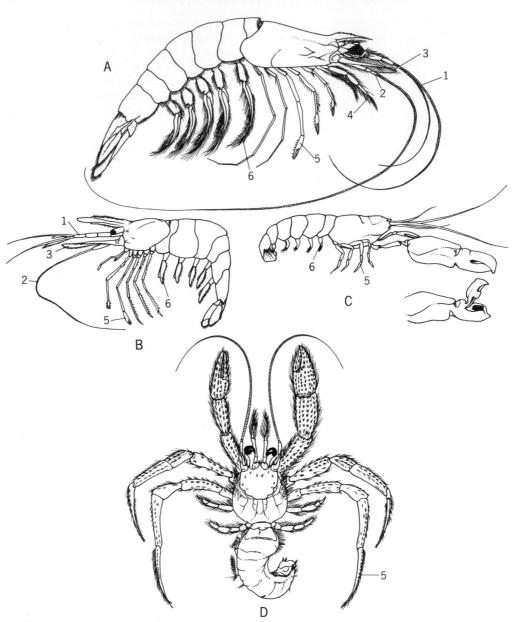

Fig. 18.23. Some Representative Malacostraca. A. *Parapenaeopsis*, a natant decapod belonging to the Penaeidea. The pelagic habits of the natant decapods is reflected in the well-developed natatory appendages and the large antennal scale. Most of the penaeids have a chela on the third pereiopod, and the pleura of the second abdominal somite do not overlap the adjacent abdominal pleura. B. *Palaemonetes*, a fresh-water shrimp. *Palaemonetes* is a natant decapod belonging to the Caridea, which have no chelae on the third pereiopods and have second abdominal pleura that overlap the adjacent plates. C. *Crangon*, a pistol shrimp. The modified chela can be snapped shut with enough force to kill or stun nearby prey. D. *Catapagurus*, a hermit crab removed from its shell. Hermit crabs belong to the Anomura,

Carid shrimps never have chelate third pereiopods, and the second abdominal pleura overlap the sides of the adjacent abdominal somites. They are a less homogeneous group than the penaeids. The fresh-water shrimp, *Palaemonetes*, is a carid shrimp that shows generalized carid structure (Fig. 18.23B). *Crangon* (Fig. 18.23C), the pistol shrimp, is a tube dweller. It has one large chela with a movable finger. It lies in wait at the burrow entrance with the chela cocked and ready. When a fish or other prey swims past, the chela is snapped shut, making a sharp, penetrating sound and stunning the prey. If the "shot" has been successful, the shrimp pulls its prey into the burrow for a leisurely meal.

Reptants are considerably more diversified than natants. Three major sections can be distinguished, the Macrura, Anomura, and Brachyura. As their names suggest, they differ primarily in the development of the abdomen and uropods.

Macrura have a large, posteriorly extended abdomen with conspicuous uropods. The uropods and telson compose a strong tail fan. The lobsters, crayfish (Fig. 18.24), and spiny lobsters belong to this section.

Anomura have a considerably smaller abdomen, modified in one way or another. Some are known as hermit crabs, and have soft, asymmetrical abdomens, which are protected by being thrust into the shells of snails or other animals. Other Anomura have the abdomen secondarily hardened and bent forward under the thorax. They all have a relatively small abdomen, and although there is no tail fan, small uropods are still present. The fifth pereiopod is bent upwards sharply. This is a large and varied section of the reptants, and includes such common forms as the hermit crabs (Fig. 18.23D), the sand crabs, and the porcelain crabs.

Brachyura includes the "true" crabs. They have an abdomen that is greatly reduced and bent forward sharply, so that it lies against the ventral side of the thorax. Uropods are almost always missing. The form and habits of crabs vary greatly, and only a few can be mentioned here. Spider crabs have long slender chelipeds and are narrowed anteriorly. *Macrocheira kaempferi*, a Japanese spider crab, is the largest living arthropod, sometimes measuring over 3 m. from the tip of one cheliped to another. Other crabs are broad at the anterior margin, and include such diverse forms as the common fiddler crabs that burrow along the margin of estuaries; the tiny, commensal pea crabs that live in oysters, snails, clams, sea cucumbers, and polychaete tubes; the swimming crabs; the grapsid land crabs; and many others (Fig. 18.25).

Decapods are among the most interesting invertebrates as well as the most important, and a great deal of fascinating information is available about them. Only a few general points can be made about their form; other sources must be consulted for details.

They have the characteristic set of crustacean head appendages. The long, appendage-like eye-stalks sometimes have movable joints. Natants have better developed antennules than reptants, with long flagella and a characteristic lobe or spine, the stylocerite, attached to the basal segment. The outer flagellum is often split in the carid shrimps, so the antennules appear to be trifid. Reptant antennules have no stylocerite, and the flagella are often greatly reduced, especially in brachyuran

characterized by the asymmetrical abdomen, usually without a tail fan. Like other reptant decapods, they never have a large antennal scale, are not laterally compressed, and have reduced pleopods. (A and D, after Balss, in Kükenthal and Krumbach. B, after Creaser, from Pennak. C, after the MacGinities.) 1, antennule; 2, antenna; 3, antennal scale; 4, third maxilliped; 5, third pereiopod; 6, first pleopod.

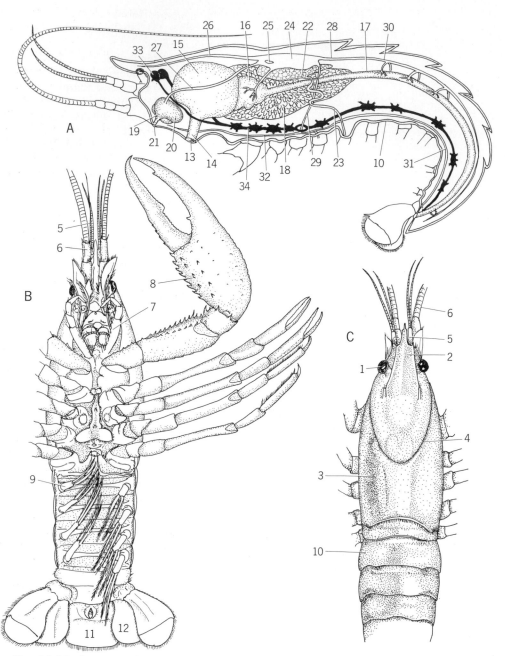

Fig. 18.24. Anatomy of a Crayfish. Crayfish are typical of the macruran reptants, with a large abdomen extending back from the thorax. Lobsters and spiny lobsters have essentially the same structure. A, Scheme of internal organization; B, ventral view; C, dorsal view. *External features:* 1, compound eye; 2, rostrum; 3, carapace of cephalothorax; 4, cervical groove; 5, antennule; 6, antenna; 7, third maxilliped; 8, first pereiopod (cheliped); 9, pleopod; 10, first abdominal somite; 11, telson; 12, uropod. *Digestive system:* 13, mouth; 14, esoph-

crabs. The natant antennae have a large scale (Fig. 18.27A), missing or greatly reduced in reptants. The base of the antenna contains five podites and clearly shows the exopodite and endopodite in more primitive forms, although the segments are reduced or fused in the more highly specialized forms. The antennal filament is very long in natants, but is much reduced in crabs and is sometimes lost entirely. The strong mandibles usually have a definite palp. The maxillae also have palps, and the most important development is the enlargement of the exopodite, possibly joined with the epipodite, to form a plate, the gill-bailer, or scaphognathite, whose rhythmic beating generates respiratory currents (Fig. 18.27B).

The eight thoracic somites bear three pairs of maxillipeds and five pairs of pereipods. Maxillipeds vary considerably in different kinds of decapods, but the anterior is the most highly modified, and the posterior the most leg-like. The last maxilliped of some of the natants is very leg-like indeed. The last maxilliped of the brachyuran crabs, however, is very highly modified, forming an operculum that covers the buccal region and bears no resemblance to a pereiopod. The pereiopods are walking legs, but one or more may be prehensile chelipeds. Chelipeds may be paired, as in crayfish and swimming crabs, or one may be large and one small, as in pistol shrimps and fiddler crabs. Where the chelae are of unequal size, the loss of the larger one is usually compensated for by the development of the chela on the other side at the next molt. The legs are made suitable for a variety of specialized functions by modifications of their tips. The adaptive radiation of the decapods, as that of other groups, has favored their retirement from close competition with each other. This tendency has depended greatly on specialization of the appendages as tools for specific tasks. Chelae may fit a powerful appendage for use as an offensive or defensive weapon, and also fit a small one for clinging to surfaces, climbing, or the manipulation of small objects, and subchelate legs can be used in much the same manner. Bristles and setae can make walking legs suitable for walking over soft mud or for clambering over smooth rocks. Coconut crabs climb trees in search of food, and ghost crabs run rapidly over the loose sand at the base of the coastal dunes. Flattened legs can be used for digging and for swimming. The flat paddles of the swimming crabs are good examples of pereiopods secondarily modified for swimming. The reduction or loss of some of the pereiopods has accompanied the development of peculiar habits. Hermit crabs, which thrust the body into a snail shell, have smaller pereiopods behind and larger ones in front, for example. Hermit crabs do not use the chelipeds for crawling, and the next two pairs of legs do the bulk of the work involved in hauling them and their shells about.

Many of the decapods are bulky animals, and respiratory surfaces have been amplified. Respiratory surface can be increased by adding to the number of gills and by increasing the surface area of individual gills. The gills are attached to the thoracic appendages and lie in a cavity formed by lateral extensions of the carapace, the branchiostegites. As many as four gills may occur on each side of a somite: one pleurobranchia, attached to the body wall above the base of the appendage; two arthrobranchiae, attached to the articular membrane of the coxopodite; and one podo-

agus; 15, cardiac stomach; 16, pyloric stomach; 17, intestine; 18, digestive gland. *Excretory system:* 19, green gland; 20, bladder; 21, excretory pore. *Reproductive system:* 22, testis; 23, sperm duct. *Circulatory system:* 24, heart; 25, ostium; 26, ophthalmic artery anterior aorta; 27, antennary artery; 28, dorsal abdominal artery; 29, sternal artery; 30, segmental artery; 31, ventral abdominal artery; 32, ventral thoracic artery. *Nervous system:* 33, brain; 34, ventral nerve cord.

A – B

C

Fig. 18.25. Some Representative Decapods. **A** and **B.** Female and male fiddler crabs, *Uca thayeri.* The single large cheliped of the male is characteristic of fiddler crabs. Few decapods have such marked sexual dimorphism. **C, D,** and **G.** Three different species of swimming crabs, *Callinectes sapidus* (**C**), *Portunus sanguinolentis* (**D**), and *P. sayi* (**G**). The modification of the last pereiopods as a flattened swimming appendage is characteristic of the swimming crabs. As in other groups of animals, the family groups are usually rather easily recognized because of similarities in specialized parts. **F.** A shrimp, *Penaeus marginatus.* The shrimps are natant decapods, adapted for a pelagic life. Notice the large swimmerets and the highly developed sense organs. (**C**, courtesy of the General Biological Supply Co. The rest, courtesy of the Smithsonian Institution.)

D

E

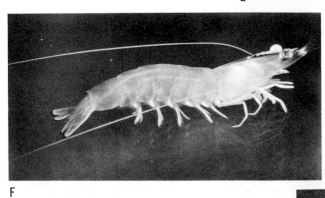

F

G

A

B

C

Fig. 18.26. Some More Decapods. **A.** A hermit crab, *Dardanus venosus*. The hermit crabs are anomurans, with highly modified, asymmetrical abdomens, adapted for being thrust into snail shells for protection. **B.** A land crab, *Grapsus grapsus*. The grapsid crabs have reduced gills and can live for considerable periods away from water. **C.** A spider crab, *Stenorhynchus seticornis*. The body is narrowed anteriorly. (Courtesy of the Smithsonian Institution.)

branchia, derived from the epipodite. Each gill consists of a central axis containing the afferent and efferent vessels and variously arranged filaments. Gills made up of branched filaments are dendrobranchiate gills; those composed of unbranched filaments are trichobranchiate gills; and those made up of flat plates are phyllobranchiate gills (Fig. 18.27C-E). The position and form of decapod gills are valuable in classification and taxonomy. As decapods adapt to a semiterrestrial life the respiratory surface is reduced, and the same principle applies to those which live in the intertidal zone and are exposed to air for short

periods of time. Crabs living above hightide line have less gill surface and fewer gills than crabs living in the intertidal zone, and crabs living in the intertidal zone have fewer gills and less gill surface than those living below low-water line.

Pleopods are usually biramous, but may vary considerably. In most natants they are long and setose, capable of providing propulsion during swimming. In reptants, however, they are usually small, and are often modified or reduced. The pleopods of macrurans are small, unless they have been secondarily modified for burrowing. Anomurans have pleopods that are unira-

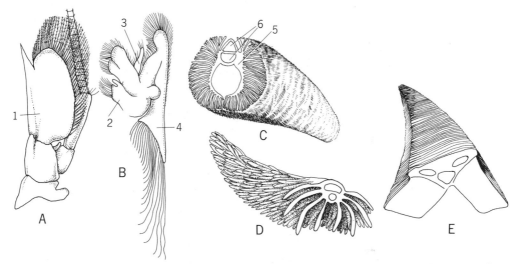

Fig. 18.27. A. Base of the antenna of a snapping shrimp, *Athanas*, showing the antennal scale characteristic of natants. The scale is a modified exopodite. B. The second maxilla of a carid shrimp, *Pandalus*, showing the scaphognathite or gill-bailer. Movements of the scaphognathite draw water over the gills in the gill chamber. C-E. Types of gills seen in decapods. The simple gill plates which suffice for most of the smaller types of Crustacea are inadequate in decapods, and various methods of increasing respiratory surface have appeared. One method is proliferation of gills, which may be attached to the wall of the somite immediately above the base of the appendage (pleurobranchia), to the articular membrane between the body wall and the coxopodite (arthrobranchiae), or to the coxopodite of the appendage (podobranchiae). In any case, the shaft or axis of the gill contains the system of afferent and efferent blood vessels, and filaments of one or another type extend from the axis in various patterns. Dendrobranchiate gills (C) have two series of primary filaments, and each primary filament is complexly branched to form a gill of many tiny filaments. Trichobranchiate gills (D) have a series of unbranched filaments arranged in various patterns around the axis. Phyllobranchiate gills (E) are composed of plate-like filaments, usually arranged in two series. (A and B, after Sars, from Calman, in Lankester.) 1, scale (exopodite); 2, endite of maxilla; 3, palp; 4, scaphognathite; 5, axis of gill; 6, blood vessels.

mous and somewhat reduced; in some cases they are wholly lost. Anomurans with asymmetrical abdomens may have well-developed pleopods on one side of the body and none on the other. Branchyuran males retain only the pleopods used in mating, and females have pleopods used for carrying the eggs. As a general rule, the first two pairs of pleopods are modified in males for copulation. The gonopods are often oddly shaped and have peculiarities that are useful in taxonomy. As a rule, female reptants have the first pair of pleopods greatly reduced. Uropods are well developed in natants and in macrurans, but reduced in anomurans and usually wholly missing in brachyurans.

The plasticity of crustacean appendages is truly remarkable. Each begins as a biramous primordium which undergoes differential growth to become the characteristic part of the adult. The development of appendages, however, is not a simple, continuous growth process. Each instar is a period of stability, and each molt is a time when great changes can occur. Appendages often change during development, sometimes undergoing remarkable changes in function. The nauplius larva swims with the aid of its third set of appendages, which are the mandibles in the adult. With each successive molt the appendages change and become diversified. As the primordia of all appendages are similar, the appendages are serially homologous. Crustaceans provide the best material for a study of serial homology, the homology of metamerically arranged parts of one animal. The developmental changes are similar in kind if not in detail to the changes wrought by selective pressure on the form of adult parts during evolutionary development. For that reason they are of considerable biological interest.

Decapod males have a pair of tubular testes, usually composed of tubular follicles. Each testis opens into a sperm duct leading to the gonoducts on or near the last thoracic coxae. A part of the sperm duct is glandular, secreting a cement used to mould spermatophores or consolidate the sperm into a cord. The last part of the sperm duct is the ejaculatory duct, which very rarely has a penis, although the brachyuran crabs have a pair of penes and some asymmetrical anomurans have a penis on one side. The ovaries are paired but are joined by a median lobe. They empty into simple oviducts that end in gonopores on the coxae of the third pereiopods. Many decapods have external seminal receptacles, usually on one of the last two thoracic sterna. The decapods with penes, however, have oviducts which contain a terminal vagina and a seminal receptacle.

Although most females carry the eggs on the pleopods, some penaeid shrimps liberate them immediately. Adhesive secretions from epidermal glands on the pleopods or the ventral abdominal surface are used to attach eggs to the pleopods, although crabs may use cement from the walls of the seminal receptacle for this purpose.

Decapod development is extremely interesting, for during their metamorphosis they pass through stages reminiscent of the adults of more primitive groups. Although they are larvae in the sense that they are independent juveniles that do not resemble the adults, they are not comparable to trochophore larvae but are at a much later stage of development. Even a nauplius has three pairs of appendages and therefore is composed of several segments. Crustacean larvae are more comparable to the post-trochophore stages of annelids, and as in annelids, somites are added at the posterior end, in front of the telson. Shrimps pass through protozoaea, zoaea, and mysis stages after hatching as nauplius larvae (Fig. 18.28). With each molt they undergo a transformation, adding somites and appendages. As they develop, they lose the more primitive traits and come to show more advanced ones, often passing through stages that are comparable, sometimes in considerable detail, to more primitive species. The mysis stage, for example, shares many traits with adult mysids. In Crustacea as in other groups, development tends to become more direct when eggs are brooded. Lobsters hatch in a stage that more or less corresponds to the mysis stage of shrimps, while marine crabs hatch in an earlier stage and pass through zoaea and mysis stages before developing into a megalops larva, somewhat resembling a macruran decapod. The succession of larval stages seems undoubtedly to reflect the recapitulation principle, the history of an individual as it passes through larval stages roughly corresponding to stages in its evolutionary history. The correspondence is never perfect and is made more sketchy by the strong tendency for development to become more direct, with more stages occurring within the egg membranes and a reduced number of free-living larval stages.

Internal Anatomy and Physiology

The details of external anatomy are especially important in Crustacea, for much of the classification depends primarily upon them. There can be no doubt that internal anatomy, in the detailed sense, is as diverse as external form, but the details are not so well known. Adaptation to particular habitats and diversification of ways of life depended strongly on the conversion of appendages and other external parts into specialized tools suitable for specific functions under specific kinds of conditions. The internal parts were certainly affected, but much less dramatically, by adaptation along the many lines that were followed. A strong tendency for the major organs systems to continue operating in basically the same manner is seen in all crustacean groups that did not become parasitic.

Simplicity of the organs in a system cannot be considered as evidence of a primitive organization in Crustacea, for many are very small and for this reason have more simple systems. Unfortunately, most of our information about crustacean physiology is based on the study of Malacostraca, and especially of decapods, so a full comparative treatment is not possible at the present time. Nevertheless, a great deal of information is available, much of which is summarized in the two volumes of Waterman's *The Physiology of Crustacea*. The student who intends to pursue the study of comparative physiology should familiarize himself with this fine discussion of crustacean functions.

DIGESTION

The crustacean digestive tract, like that of other arthropods, consists of a foregut, lined with cuticle and derived from the stomodaeum; a midgut lined with endoderm; and a hindgut, derived from the proctodaeum and lined with cuticle. The foregut develops into the buccal cavity, esophagus, and various kinds of chitinized grinding or triturating chambers. The midgut varies greatly in length and may be tubular or somewhat dilated. The midgut surface is almost invariably amplified by one or more diverticula, which may serve as digestive glands or as sites for absorption. The hindgut may be long or short and is generally responsible for feces formation, although some absorption may also occur in the hindgut. The exact limits of the stomodaeal and proctodael regions are not known in all Crustacea. The most uncertain point is often the junction of the foregut and midgut, for the foregut is often dilated to form triturating chambers and probably sometimes participates in stomach formation.

All animals face about the same kind of problems in digesting and absorbing food, but it is difficult, at times, to retain perspective when comparing very small and large species. A microcrustacean that has just caught a fairly sizable algal cell

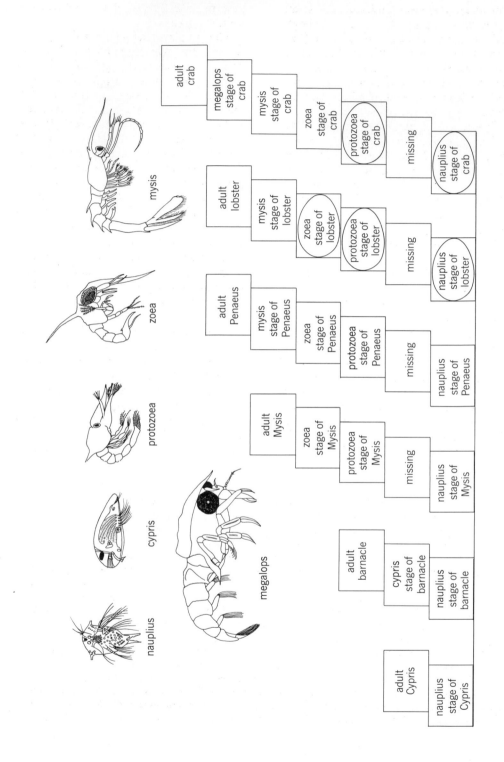

is in about the same position as a small boy with an apple. Its catch, although diminutive, requires mechanical as well as chemical trituration. Along the main protostome stem, the foregut is especially important for the reception of food, for breaking food into small particles, and for conducting it to the midgut, where most of digestion and absorption occurs. The hindgut and intestine may not be the same, for the hindgut is derived from the proctodaeum and is lined with chitin. It is generally not an important site of absorption, but is more directly concerned with the formation and expulsion of feces.

Foregut. The crustacean foregut is quite variable, as might be expected considering the differences in size and dietary habits found among Crustacea. On its way into the foregut, food passes the mandibles, which vary greatly in form and effectiveness. As a general rule, the mandibles fragment food for swallowing but do not adequately reduce it to particles that can be effectively digested. This is especially true of the larger Crustacea which feed on larger plants or animals. Here special triturating chambers are an almost constant feature of the foregut. Devices of this kind cannot be interpreted as providing evidence of relationship, for they ap-

pear to have developed independently in different groups.

The simplest kind of foregut is seen in entomostraca that feed on tiny food particles. Copepods, for example, have a short, tubular foregut, equipped only with extrinsic dilator muscles used for swallowing (Fig. 18.7B). Branchiopods, also, have a short foregut, and a stomach, probably derived from the midgut, is located in the head (Fig. 18.3D). Filtering setae in the foregut are used to strain out larger particles, preventing their entry into the stomach. It is probable that the triturating chambers found in the foregut are elaborations of the straining devices. In podocopan ostracods the narrow, muscular esophagus has toothed, chitinous ridges that serve as a straining device, while in some other ostracods a specialized triturating chamber occurs at the same point.

Crustacean triturating chambers are usually called gastric mills or masticatory stomachs, although they are essentially equivalent to the gizzards of annelids. The form and position of the gastric mill vary in different groups, indicating that they have evolved independently several times. Generally they consist of from one to several plates, equipped with bristles or teeth, which are manipulated by the

Fig. 18.28. Crustacean Larvae. Although a bewildering variety of crustacean larvae may be collected from fresh-water or marine habitats, several meaningful generalizations can be made. The nauplius larva appears to be the basic type, and occurs in a large number of crustacean groups. At molt, the nauplius may be transformed into some more complex larva. The later larval types often appear to reflect evolutionary relationships. Thus the cypris larva of barnacles appears to resemble an adult ostracod, suggesting that barnacles arose from ostracod-like ancestral stocks. A similar recapitulation may be seen in Malacostraca. Protozoea and zoea larval stages occur in *Mysis* and in the peneid shrimps. The peneid shrimps, however, pass through a mysis larval stage which has a number of organizational features that resemble an adult *Mysis*. Presumably, the mysis larva reflects the occurrence of a *Mysis*-like ancestor for the shrimps. The macruran decapods also pass through a mysis stage. Brachyuran decapods, however, pass through a megalops larval stage, which somewhat resembles the adult macrurans, suggesting that these highly specialized decapods arose from macruran ancestral stocks. Larval development is sometimes shortened by prolonged development within the egg. Thus in lobsters, stages which are comparable to the protozoea and zoea occur before hatching. This shortening of larval development by extending the pre-hatching phase of development is common in other kinds of animals. (After the MacGinities.)

intrinsic musculature of the gut wall and by extrinsic muscles attached to the body wall. They occur sporadically in some groups, where some species have them and others are without. Boring barnacles, for example, have a well-developed gastric mill, while most other barnacles do not.

Malacostraca may have one or two dilated regions in the gut. Where two are present, the first is called the cardiac and the second the pyloric stomach. Whatever other functions the stomachs may have, they are almost universally equipped with some kind of a gastric mill. The simplest system is found in *Anaspides*, consisting of a single stomach with longitudinal ridges bearing setae. Some amphipods and isopods have a gastric mill that is scarcely more highly developed, while others have complex gastric mills. The tendency is toward specializing a part of the mill for grinding and another part for straining. The front part of a complex amphipod gastric mill contains two spiny lateral ridges. These are attached to powerful extrinsic muscles and serve as the primary grinders. The posterior part of the gastric mill has transverse ridges equipped with straining setae, which permit only the pulverized material to pass. On the ventral midline is a longitudinal ridge bearing four rows of iridescent setae. A very similar ventral ridge is seen in the gastric mills of isopods and mysids.

The gastric mills of decapods have cardiac and pyloric regions. Penaeid shrimps (Fig. 18.29A) have the simplest equipment. A constriction separates the cardiac and plyoric stomachs. A large tooth is on the dorsal wall at the point of constriction. The ventral part of the cardiac region contains a median ventral ridge and a pair of lateral longitudinal ridges. Teeth on the lateral walls appear to correspond to the lateral denticles of the more complex types of gastric mills seen in macrurans. Food is ground in the cardiac region and passes to the pyloric region, which serves primarily as a strainer.

It narrows sharply near the junction with the midgut, where it is heavily setose. A groove in the floor delivers particles to a wedge-shaped straining chamber on the ventral side, which projects into the midgut as a valvular apparatus.

With increasing specialization of hard parts and musculature, gastric mills of considerable complexity appear. Sclerotized plates which serve as a platform for grinding or chewing teeth are a common development. Extrinsic muscles attach to the plates, making for more powerful movements. Plates or teeth are usually set to converge, improving the grinding action. Crayfish, for example, have three large gastric teeth which meet medially and are manipulated by a complex set of muscles. The sorting apparatus also becomes more complex. As a rule, the sorting device consists of grooves equipped with setae, which divert larger or smaller particles along appropriate channels. Smaller particles are conveyed to the pyloric stomach and larges ones are held in the cardiac stomach for further treatment. Intermediate particles follow a more dorsal course, and enter a setose muscular press in the pyloric stomach, where they are further reduced in size. A ventral groove carries the smallest particles to the openings of the digestive glands, where they must pass through special filters to gain entrance.

Midgut. Most of the Crustacea have a short midgut, but in forms with a simple, tubular esophagus, the midgut is usually long, as in Cladocera. It is often a simple, tubular intestine. but may be dilated. In at least some of the Malacostraca, the midgut forms the posterior end of the pyloric stomach. The last part of the intestine is derived from the hindgut, and in some cases there is no external mark of the division of midgut and hindgut. Digestion and absorption of food are time-consuming processes, and food must be kept in the midgut region long enough to complete them. Where there are no valves or other devices at the end of the midgut, some other system of delaying food passage is needed. Diverticula and caeca are most effective for the strategic delay of food particles, and are often the most important regions of the midgut from a functional point of view. A number

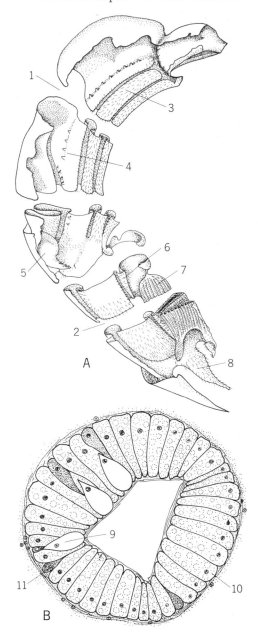

A

B

of different kinds of caeca and digestive glands have been described in Crustacea, and it is not yet possible to discuss the specific roles that they play in the digestion and absorption of food. It is known that in some of the larger species enzymes are secreted and food is absorbed in the diverticula. A variety of names has been applied to the branches of the midgut. A blind pouch that arises from the intestine is usually termed an intestinal caecum if it is not extensively branched. Where the diverticula are extensively branched, they are usually termed digestive glands or sometimes the term hepatopancreas is used. It cannot be too

Fig. 18.29. **A.** The stomach of a penaeid shrimp, *Cerataspis*. This is a primitive type of stomach, closely resembling the stomach of many of the more primitive types of Malacostraca. There are no grinding plates, as are found in many decapods, but the stomach is a complex organ which breaks down and strains food particles. The median and longitudinal ridges at the floor of the cardiac stomach are the areas which develop hard, grinding plates in some forms, and the denticles along the lateral wall of the stomach correspond to the lateral teeth in the stomach wall of many decapods. The much-folded walls of the pyloric stomach provide a sorting system of some delicacy, and terminate in lappets which project into the midgut. **B.** A cross section through a branch of the digestive gland of a crab, *Callinectes*. Large, branched digestive glands are an almost constant feature of arthropod digestive systems. They are important in secretion of enzymes, but, in at least many cases, are also responsible for absorption and for storage of glycogen and perhaps other food reserves. Small basal cells appear to replace the secretory and "hepatic" or absorptive cells, as they are exhausted. (A, after Bonnier, from Calman, in Lankester. B, after Regan, from Andrew.) **1,** cardiac stomach; **2,** pyloric stomach; **3,** median ventral ridge; **4,** lateral ridge; **5,** median tooth; **6,** ridge separating dorsal and ventral parts of the pyloric chamber; **7,** wedge-shaped straining ridge; **8,** lappets; **9,** secretory cells; **10,** "hepatic" cells; **11,** basal replacing cell.

strongly emphasized that these names are in no way dependable if any functional implications are drawn from them. Little information about the sites of enzyme formation and food absorption is available. In decapods, the histological structure of the midgut diverticula does not justify the term digestive gland, for the walls are like those of the intestine, and the diverticula appear to be merely branches of the intestine. Tall cells serve for the absorption and storage of food, and pyriform enzyme-secreting cells are scattered among them (Fig. 18.29B). At the base of the mucosal epithelium are small, basal cells that are thought to replace the absorptive and secretory cells as they deteriorate. While particles enter the digestive glands, as well as the caeca, digestion appears to be wholly extracellular in most Crustacea.

Adaptations for surface amplification of the midgut vary with groups and with the size of the animal. Branchiopods have a long intestine, sometimes coiled in Cladocera, derived largely from the midgut. The branches from the intestine tend to vary with the size of the organisms. Cladocera are very small and have a pair of simple caeca. The Anostraca are larger, and have lobated caeca. Notostracans and conchostracans have extensively ramified midgut diverticula. Copepods often have no caeca, and at the most they have a pair of small, lateral caeca bifurcated at the tip. Ostracods have a large, stomach-like digestive cavity, formed in part from the foregut and in part from the midgut. In the Podocopa the foregut part is divided off as a sclerotized chamber. The ostracods sometimes have no midgut caeca; sometimes have a pair of large, branched diverticula that extend into the mantle; and in other cases have a large number of tiny caeca. The barnacle midgut is expanded to form a stomach, studded with caeca. The caeca on the anterior part of the stomach are larger and less numerous, and the posterior caeca are much smaller and have tiny pores. Presumably the two kinds of caeca have different functions, but the details are unknown. Parasitic barnacles have a highly modified midgut, with extensive branches extending into the mantle. In these forms the mantle assumes an absorptive function, and the caecal cells serve, in part at least, for food storage.

The midgut of Malacostraca is usually a tubular intestine, although it sometimes forms a part of the pyloric stomach. The intestine is coiled in some cumaceans, and here there are no caeca. Generally, however, the intestine is straight and all surface amplification depends on diverticula. As a general rule there are from one to four pairs of diverticula, although each diverticulum may be very extensively ramified. As a general rule, the larger decapods have a single pore to the diverticula on each side of the midgut, leading to a very extensively branched duct system extending to tubular tips. An enormous amount of surface is provided by the diverticula.

Most of the midgut diverticula are laterally placed, but in some Crustaceans median caeca are found. Some amphipods have a single or a pair of dorsal caeca which extend forward, and it is common for decapods to have one or a pair of dorsal caeca arising from the midgut. It is not uncommon for these caeca to occur at the junction of the midgut with the foregut or hindgut. The median dorsal diverticulum of mysids arises at the junction of the foregut and midgut, and amphipods have paired or unpaired caeca at the junction of midgut and hindgut. Some of the dorsal diverticula of decapods also arise at this point. It is possible that such caeca may represent the precursors of Malpighian tubules found in terrestrial mandibulates.

Hindgut. Even when the hindgut is long it remains relatively simple in form. A narrow tube with a chitinous lining, it is typically equipped with intrinsic muscles used in defecation. In some instances the hindgut has extrinsic, dilator muscles used for anal pumping, undoubtedly a respiratory adaptation. Crustacean feces are somewhat compacted, and often mixed with mucus. Presumably at least the terrestrial and amphibious Crustacea absorb considerable quantities of water from the hindgut contents.

Parasitic Adaptation. About the same kinds of adaptations of the gut accompany parasitism as those seen in other groups of animals. Where food is taken in from the host through the body surface of the parasite, the gut tends to deteriorate. In some of these the stomodaeum fails to make contact with the midgut during development. The gut of parasitic barnacles is reduced or wholly lost. Some parasitic Crustacea feed on host tissues and others have suctorial mouth parts and take blood meals. In the latter case, large storage chambers, like those of leeches, tend to appear. Branchiura, the fish lice, have large caeca that are gorged with host tissue fluids. Some of the suctorial isopods have a very extensively modified gut. The entoniscids have three chambers in the gut after the esophagus. The anterior chamber is thin-walled and has many villi, and the posterior chamber is heavily muscled. The middle compartment is equipped with a typhlosole-like, setose strainer. The anterior and posterior chambers contract rhythmically, evidently pulling the ingested fluid over the straining apparatus. The details of digestion, however, are not known.

RESPIRATION

Crustacea respire at the body surface and at gills attached to the appendages or near their bases. The gills of the various crustacean groups have been described as a part of their external form. It remains only to consider the general features of respiration and the nature of adaptive trends in the group as a whole.

No new respiratory principles are seen in Crustacea, but they provide an excellent review of the basic lines followed in other phyla. Some of the adaptations are external. These involve: (a) the appearance and amplification of specialized respiratory surfaces; (b) the development of special mechanisms for ventilating the respiratory surfaces; and (c) the tendency for respiratory surfaces to move to a more internal position or to be otherwise protected. Other methods of improving respiration involve internal changes. These include: (d) the development and improvement of mechanisms for the pick-up and delivery of respiratory gases at the respiratory surfaces, and (e) mechanisms that improve the internal transport of the respiratory gases.

Each species must be equipped for normal respiratory exchange, and also needs a safety margin suitable for the emergencies growing out of its habits and habitat. The importance of structural adaptations, especially those concerned with safety margins, depends in part on internal, functional factors. Biochemical or excretory peculiarities that permit an animal to tolerate temporary anaerobiosis may take the place of other respiratory adaptations, and the ability of an animal to adjust the rate of respiratory transport or gill ventilation under conditions of stress is also an important factor. It is always the total respiratory situation that counts in determining the strength and direction of selective forces that lead to respiratory modifications, and the interplay of compensating factors has permitted a variety of responses to relatively similar respiratory needs. Selective pressures favoring the development of respiratory structures are minimized by small size, on the one hand, and inability to develop new means of improving respiration may produce selective pressures favoring small size, on the other. Where large organisms become smaller, the loss of structural or physiological respiratory adaptations is favored. Other factors operate in a similar manner. Changes in metabolic rate may favor either the amplification or reduction of respiratory adaptations, or may compensate for increased size where no new respiratory arrangements have appeared. The choice of a habitat is important, for animals may compensate for a relatively low respiratory competency by occupying a habitat rich in oxygen, while a group of organisms may exploit new habitats where new respiratory developments, changed metabolic rates, or smaller size permit. There are many avenues open to evolving organisms, and it is along these many avenues that adaptive radiation of a group of animals occur.

Entomostraca are small animals, and most of them have a delicate, transparent exoskeleton. Undoubtedly a considerable part of respiratory exchange occurs at the body surface. Nevertheless, most of them have gills formed from the epipodites of some or most of the appendages. The gills are flat plates, through which blood circulates. Where the gills are a part of the appendages, normal swimming movements tend to ventilate them, but especially in the larger species or in species with heavier exoskeletons the gills tend to be ventilated by definite respiratory currents, produced by the appendages which bear the gills or adjacent appendages. In filter-feeders, the feeding currents may be identical with the respiratory current or may be independent. It is probable that the strong tendency of gills to be placed on the thoracic appendages is related to the advantages of being able to combine feeding and respiratory currents.

Development of the respiratory capacity of the body wall may be associated with gill reduction. Ostracods, for example, have a relatively heavy shell and in some cases it contains a network of blood vessels that convert it into a respiratory surface. In general, ostracods have poorly developed gills, more important for current production than for respiration. It

is not clear whether the respiratory competency of the body surface has been increased because of the sharp reduction in the number of appendages, or whether development of surface respiration has favored gill reduction, but it is clear that the two are related. In the same manner, the development of the mantle of barnacles as a respiratory surface has been accompanied by loss of branchiae associated with the appendages. Some of the Malacostraca have followed the same line. Tanaids, for example, have a branchial chamber formed by the carapace and supplied with a rich plexus of blood vessels.

The Malacostraca, as a group, are appreciably larger than entomostraca and have more extensively amplified gill surfaces. Plate-like gills are found in the smaller and the more primitive groups of Malacostraca, as in *Nebalia*, for example. Smaller isopods and amphipods have relatively simple gill plates, but systems of surface amplification are seen in both groups. Transverse ridges on the gill plates increase the surface somewhat in both groups. As amphipod gills are on thoracic and isopod gills on abdominal appendages, it is evident that this is an independent, but parallel development in the two groups. Larger amphipods may have accessory gills attached to the thoracic legs, and in some cases, tufts of gill filaments are attached to the gill plates. Larger and more highly specialized Malacostraca have added respiratory surface by the development of filamentous gills in place of gill plates (p. 803). Gills formed by filamentous extensions from a central axis occur on the abdominal appendages of stomatopods and the thoracic appendages of decapods, indicating that here, too, parallel and independent adaptations have occurred. The development of accessory gills is also an important method of increasing respiratory surface, and has been employed in amphipods and in decapods. The accessory gills are borne on the joints

or at the bases of the respiratory appendages.

Amphibious or terrestrial habits have
appeared in several malacostracan groups.
Isopods have been most successful, but
amphipods and decapods have also spread
to amphibious or semiterrestrial habitats
with considerable success. Gills are not
usually suitable for land respiration, and
it is interesting to observe how terrestrial
crustaceans manage their respiration.

Amphibious amphipods and decapods
tend to reduce the importance of gills
and to develop a vascularized branchial
cavity, in this case paralleling the changes
seen in the mantle cavity of terrestrial
snails. The reduction of gill surface is
important because the gill surface is a
potent site of water loss. Amphipods are
restricted to humid surroundings, for their
small size makes water loss an important
matter. The much larger crabs have a
heavier exoskeleton and are more resistant to water loss. Nevertheless, the amphibious crabs generally do not circulate
air through the branchial cavity. Many
fill the branchial cavity with water, using
an opercular flap on the maxilliped to
retain the water while on land. The water
is circulated in the gill chamber by the
scaphognathite, and in some species circulates through special canals on the
carapace surface for aeration. The grapsid
land crabs, however, have the gills reduced
to such an extent that air can be circulated through the branchial cavity.
Movements of the carapace and fanning
movements of the scaphognathite circulate the air, and most of the respiratory
exchange occurs in the vascularized lining
of the branchial cavity.

Isopods have followed a different tack.
The plate-like pleopods are divided into
a respiratory endopodite and a protective
exopodite, which can be folded over the
endopodite. The arrangement cuts down
water loss and favors easy ventilation by
appendage movements. Immediately below the endopodite cuticle there is a system of thin, branching tubules, which
are filled with air and participate in
respiratory exchange. This arrangement
bears some relationship to the tracheal
systems of mandibulates adapted to land
life, and may reveal something about how
the tracheal systems first developed.

The respiratory efficiency of Crustacea
varies markedly. Some crustaceans can
withstand a considerable reduction of oxygen tension before oxygen consumption
falls, while others are oxygen conformers,
whose oxygen consumption falls with reduced oxygen tensions in the ranges normally encountered in their habitats.
Closely related species may fall into different categories, and a great deal more
information is needed before generalizations are justified. For example, lobsters
are oxygen conformers, while the closely
related crayfish are independent of oxygen tensions to about 40 mm. Hg.

Some Crustacea have no respiratory pigment, while others have haemoglobin or
haemocyanin. As a rule, crustacean blood
has only moderate oxygen-carrying capacities. Crab blood and lobster blood hold
about 1.2-2.3 ml. O_2/ 100 ml. This compares unfavorably with the blood of larger
molluscs (*Sepia*, 7 ml.; *Octopus*, 3.9-5.0
ml.) or with that of the lower vertebrates
(skate, 4.2-5.7 ml. and carp, 12.5 ml.).
Under normal physiological conditions,
the haemocyanin is not saturated with
oxygen. However, it has been shown that
haemocyanin picks up oxygen at the gills
of some Crustacea and loses oxygen before returning. Although only a small part
of its potential is utilized, it contributes
about 90 per cent of oxygen transport in
Panuliris.

The ability to adjust ventilation movements when under respiratory stress varies
markedly and may be one of the more
important factors in determining whether
organisms are oxygen conformers or oxygen regulators. A crayfish, for example, increases its ventilation rate in response to
reduced oxygen or increased carbon di-

oxide, and is an oxygen regulator. A lobster reduces the ventilation rate with reduced oxygen or increased carbon dioxide, and is an oxygen conformer, adjusting its metabolism rather than its respiration. Crustacea are generally more sensitive to a fall in oxygen than to an increase in carbon dioxide. However, the Malacostraca that are able to regulate the ventilation of the gills usually respond to changes in either oxygen or carbon dioxide tensions. Nevertheless, aquatic isopods and some amphipods increase gill ventilation only with a reduction in oxygen tension. No conclusions are as yet justified, except the obvious ones that some Crustacea have developed a feedback system that makes it possible to compensate for respiratory stress by increased respiratory movements, while others live very well as oxygen conformers, without the ability to regulate respiratory movements.

EXCRETION AND OSMOREGULATION

Crustacea, like other arthropods, have a reduced coelom. As in other kinds of animals in which the coelom is reduced, the metanephridia are highly modified. Only the head metanephridia persist, and of these only those found in the antennal or maxillary somites occur in adults. These are the antennal glands and the maxillary glands. Although both may be found in larvae, one or the other predominates in adults, and well-developed antennal glands and maxillary glands are never found in the same adult animal. Both kinds of glands have the same basic structure. An end sac appears to be a vestige of the coelomic compartment of the somite in which the gland occurs. A tubule arises from the end sac, and regardless of the kind of specialized regions it may contain, ends in an excretory pore in the base of the appendage with which it is associated. Branchiura are exceptional, for the maxillary gland opens in an excretory pore at the base of the first thoracic somite. A second type of excretory organ also occurs in Crustacea. Clusters of athrocytic cells appear at various points in the body of various types of Crustacea. In some cases these form definite masses with a special blood supply, located at the base of the thoracic legs or, more rarely, the abdominal appendages. Where the athrocytic organs are best developed, they appear to form a definitely organized excretory system. Where neither antennal glands nor maxillary glands are well developed, the athrocytic organs are most highly developed.

Adaptive trends follow about the same patterns as those seen in the excretory systems of other kinds of animals. As the number of nephridial organs is not increased with increased size or activity, improvements are brought about by the amplification of the excretory surfaces in the nephridia that are present, and by a more intimate association of the circulatory and nephridial organs. Small Crustacea have small antennal or maxillary glands with little tendency toward surface amplification, while the larger Malacostraca have glands with greatly folded walls, providing a large excretory surface.

In most of the cntomostraca, the antennal or maxillary glands are relatively simple. The end sac is exposed to the haemocoel and is followed by a short or long tubule, which is often dilated near the excretory pore to form a bladder. In forms with a carapace, the excretory tubule may extend into the shell, as in copepods and the shelled branchiopods. Barnacles, considerably larger than most of the entomostraca, have complex maxillary glands with long, slender, convoluted tubules, and with large end sacs which are often divided into compartments.

The Malacostraca have more complex excretory organs, and as they differ greatly in habitat and way of life it is not surprising to find that the excretory organs are quite diverse. Crayfish live in fresh water and may excrete a considerable quantity of hypotonic urine. They may be taken as characteristic of one adaptive line. The end sac is greatly folded and lies at the anterior and dorsal end of the large antennal (or green) gland. (Fig. 18.30A). It opens into the upper part of the excretory tubule, which is essentially a large sac with greatly folded walls dividing the lumen into many channels and providing a very large excretory surface. This portion of the tubule is the labyrinth and is greenish in color. In crayfish, the labyrinth opens into a long, white, elaborately convoluted tubule. When the antennal gland is in place in the animal, the labyrinth makes up the outer, cortical part of the antennal gland, and the convoluted tubule fills the central, medullary part of the gland. The two together make up the glandular part of the excretory organ. The convoluted tubule opens into the bladder, the expanded end of the tubule in simpler kinds of antennal glands. It is a large, membranous region which extends over the intestinal caeca and in some decapods is extensively ramified throughout the thoracic region. The bladder opens to the exterior through the excretory pore. As is typical of the more complex excretory organs, the green gland is intimately associated with the circulatory system. Arterial branches from the antennal and ventral thoracic arteries twig out through the substance of the glandular part of the green gland, ending in microscopic haemocoelic sinuses.

The physiology of green-gland excretion is not very well understood. Fluid certainly enters the green gland, and there is some reason to think that the end sac and labyrinth take up fluid from the blood by filtration, as in the glomerulus of the vertebrate kidney tubule. Filtration pressure would be very low, however, and it is not certain that this is an important factor. It appears that the fluid at the upper end of the tubule is rather more like the blood than the urine itself,

and that the changes in the composition of the urine as it passes along the tubule involve the reabsorption of some materials. Glucose is present in considerable quantities in the blood. It is normally absent from the urine, but if a substance which antagonizes the reabsorption of glucose is administered, glucose appears in the urine. It is also clear that chlorides are reabsorbed from the lumen of the green gland, especially in the region of the convoluted tubule, and, perhaps, the bladder (Fig. 18.30B). Droplets can be seen forming in the epithelial lining of the tubules in the glandular part of the green gland, indicating that some substances are secreted into the tubules by the lining cells.

Some of the differences in the form of the excretory organs in Decapoda appear to be related to the kind of urine formed. Lobsters produce a relatively small amount of isotonic urine. In lobsters the whole of the glandular part of the antennal gland is made up of the labyrinth, and the convoluted tubule is missing. Brachyuran crabs that live in estuaries and are exposed to both brackish and salt water excrete a relatively large amount of isotonic urine. They also lack a convoluted tubule, but are equipped with a greatly expanded bladder. It is tempting to conclude that the convoluted tubule is primarily responsible for osmotic control of the urine, on purely morphological grounds, but until a good deal more experimental evidence is available no firm generalizations are warranted. It is clear that osmotic control of the body fluids is by no means entirely dependent on the function of the antennal glands. Stoppage of the excretory pores has but a limited effect on the excretion of ammonia or urea. Apparently much of the soluble nitrogen wastes are or can be eliminated at the gill surfaces, and the digestive tube is also important in the excretion of some nitrogenous compounds, especially of uric acid. The gill surfaces are also important in eliminating salt when the regulation of the osmotic pressure of the body fluids is achieved by salt excretion.

Crustacea are predominantly ammonotelic, with most of the marine species excreting about 70 to 90 per cent of their nitrogenous wastes in the form of ammonia. Urea and uric acid make up but a small part of the nitrogen excreted. In some cases amino acids and other nitrogen compounds make up a significant part of the excreted nitrogen. The successful terrestrial invertebrates have developed methods of reducing ammonia excretion, and something of the same kind is sometimes seen in fresh-water forms. The Crustacea have never achieved this solution to the excretory problem. Freshwater Crustacea do excrete somewhat more urea, and terrestrial Crustacea excrete somewhat more uric acid, but the differ-

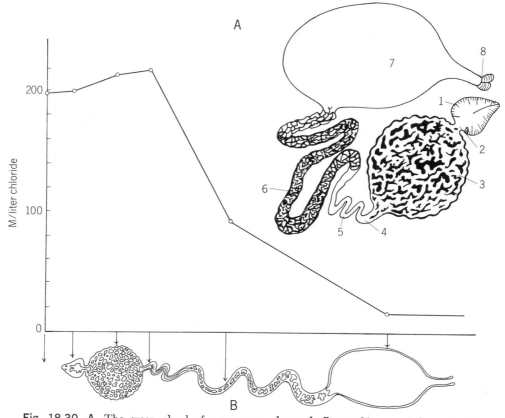

Fig. 18.30. A. The green gland of a macruran decapod, *Potamobius*, semischematic. The gland ends in a small coelomic remnant, the coelomic or end sac, which is open by a vestige of the nephrostome to a much coiled labyrinth. The nephridial canal leading from the labyrinth has a short intermediate part, a short transparent part, and a longer, convoluted white part, and ends in a dilated bladder region. B. Diagram to show correspondence of chloride content with the regions of the green gland of *Astacus*. The chloride content remains high until the convoluted part of the nephridial canal is reached. In this region it falls rapidly, and is at its minimum in the bladder. Probably water is reabsorbed with the chloride ion. (A, after Marchal, from Balss, in Kükenthal and Krumbach. B, after Parry, in Waterman.) 1, end sac; 2, nephrostome; 3, labyrinth or green canal; 4, intermediate part of nephridial canal; 5, transparent part of nephridial canal; 6, white part of nephridial canal; 7, bladder; 8, excretory pore.

ences are small at the best, and in no case does a significant shift in excretion patterns occur. The failure of the land isopods to develop an excretory pattern suitable for land animals may have been one of the factors that has prevented them from competing favorably with chilopods, diplopods, arachnids, and insects.

Crustacea occur in a wide range of aquatic habitats and differ markedly in the details of water and salt regulatory mechanisms. Some of the marine Crustacea have very little control over water intake, absorbing water and swelling when placed in a hypotonic medium. They soon excrete enough salt to make the blood isotonic and bring body volume back to normal. The spread of such forms into brackish water depends on the tolerance of the tissues to lower osmotic tensions in the body fluids. Some can tolerate a wide range of salinities, while others can live only in very nearly full-strength sea water. As a general rule, crustaceans lose water when placed in a hypertonic medium but absorb salt until the blood can be isotonic with the medium and normal volume of the tissues restored. Most of the marine crabs, lobsters, and barnacles work in this way. They are osmotic conformers (poikilosmotic) and secrete isotonic urine in larger or smaller quantities, as the situation demands. Curious osmotic relationships sometimes develop in osmotic conformers. *Lernaeocera*, a parasitic copepod, remains hypoosmotic while feeding on the hypoosmotic blood of its host, but quickly becomes isotonic with the medium when detached from the host.

Shore crabs and crabs that live in estuaries are usually osmoconformers in more saline habitats and become hypertonic in brackish water. The body surface and gills are less permeable to water, and the animals swell less when placed in hypotonic media and adjust more quickly. Under these conditions, urine production rises. The urine may not be hypotonic, but it accounts for enough water discharge to regulate volume while enough salt regulation occurs at the gills and intestinal lining to keep the animal close to its normal salinity. Some of the Crustacea can absorb salt in very dilute salt concentrations. *Erechior*, the wool-handed crab, normally lives in fresh-water streams and returns to the sea to breed. It thus tolerates both extremes. The body surface is very impermeable, permitting no change of volume in differing osmotic environments. It forms very little urine, but absorbs salts actively at the gill surfaces when in fresh-water environments.

Artemia, the brine shrimp, lives in very strongly saline habitats, and can be hypoosmotic. This is arranged by absorbing water and sodium chloride as water passes through the gut, while other salts are eliminated at the anus, and by the active elimination of salt at the gills.

CIRCULATION

The demands placed on the circulatory system in a small crustacean like a cladoceran are quite different from those occurring in a large crustacean like a lobster. It is not surprising to find that the circulatory system varies markedly in different groups of Crustacea. Some of the smaller Crustacea have no heart, and body movements suffice to drive blood through a system of haemocoelic lacunae. Many of the ostracods and copepods have no heart, for example. In these forms, valves preventing backflow in the lacunae are sometimes found. Barnacles are considerably larger, but also have no heart, and depend on a variable and rather informal system of haemocoelic lacunae. Considering the ostracod-like larval stages of barnacles, it is not impossible that they developed from an ancestral stock that had no heart, and have had to make do with a circulatory system better suited to smaller animals.

Wherever a typical circulatory system is found, it is patterned after the typical arthropod design. A dorsal heart lies in a pericardial sinus, into which blood returns from the gills. Blood enters the heart through paired ostia, and leaves the heart through an anterior aorta; usually a posterior aorta is also found. As a rule, other arterial channels are also present. These usually include some lateral arteries which arise from the heart or aortae, a descending artery which passes ventrally from the heart or the base of the posterior aorta, and a system of median ventral arteries to the viscera. However the arteries are arranged, the blood eventually reaches haemocoel lacunae where exchange of substances with the tissues occurs. Blood from the lacunae collects in a system of ventral venous sinuses. These converge on a median ventral sinus, from which blood flows into the gills. Efferent branchial vessels lead to branchiopericardial vessels, which deliver the aerated blood to the pericardial sinus. Crustacea thus have an arterial heart, pumping freshly aerated blood to the body tissues. In some cases accessory booster hearts are found, but as a general rule the movements of the appendages, the body musculature, and peristalsis in the gut keep blood flowing in the venous channels. Valves are often found at key points, such as the entrance and exit of the gill vessels, and play an important part in maintaining blood flow.

The heart has developed from a dorsal blood vessel, and in its primitive form is a long, slender tube with many pairs of ostia. Anostracans have a heart that runs the full length of the body, with ostia in all but the first and last somites, and the more primitive Malacostraca also have a long heart with many ostia. *Nebalia*, for example, have seven pairs of ostia. As the body regions become more distinct and the tendency for the body to shorten is expressed, the heart becomes shorter and has fewer ostia. For obvious reasons, it tends to lie above the appendages which bear the gills, and so is more posterior in isopods with abdominal gills but is in the thoracic region of most Crustacea. A short heart with few ostia indicates greater specialization, but may also be associated with small size. Cladocera, for example, have a very short heart with a single pair of ostia, although the closely related Anostraca have a very long heart. Copepods also have a very short heart when a heart is present (Fig. 18.31C).

Entomostraca are generally quite small and have poorly developed arterial systems. Branchiopods have no aortae, the heart discharging blood directly into the haemocoelic lacunae. Usually, however, there are short anterior and posterior aortae, and in some copepods the anterior aorta reaches the head and divides into two lateral arteries. In any event, the blood reaches the lacunae quickly, and circulates around the organs and among the tissues, draining into the ventral median sinus, from which it goes to the gills on its way to the pericardial sinus.

Malacostraca, on the other hand, sometimes have a minutely ramified arterial system. As a general rule the arterial systems of the more primitive forms are less definite. Leptostraca and Syncarida have relatively long hearts with many ostia and with poorly developed arterial systems. As most of the larger Crustacea are also less primitive, it is not always possible to separate simplicity associated with smallness from simplicity associated with primitiveness.

Pairs of lateral arteries arise from the heart or aortae of some malacostracans. Isopods, for example, have seven pairs of lateral thoracic arteries (Fig. 18.31D). The metameric arrangement of these arteries and their general position and relationships are reminiscent of the lateral arteries seen in some chelicerates and insects. It is probable that a series of lateral arteries were present in primitive ancestral stocks that have given rise to all of the modern forms. There is a tendency for two vascular rings to develop, one encircling the esophagus in the frontal plane, and the other encircling the brain in the medial plane. This arrangement is best seen in some isopods and amphipods. It bears some resemblance to the vascular ring seen in *Xiphosura*, and probably reveals a primitive tendency in arthropods.

The most complex arterial systems are found in the larger decapods. The polygonal heart gives rise to a posterior aorta, also known as the abdominal aorta, and to an ophthalmic artery that runs forward to the head (Fig. 18.24A). In many decapods the ophthalmic artery widens to form the cor frontale near the eyes. The cor frontale is not a pulsating chamber, but adjacent muscles press on it, so it nevertheless serves as a booster heart. Beyond the cor frontale the ophthalmic artery gives rise to branches that go to the brain, eyes, antennules, and adjacent parts. Just behind the ophthalmic artery a pair of arteries arise from the heart. These are the antennal arteries, which deliver blood to the head appendages, the body wall, and branchiostegites, and to the anterior part of the digestive tract. A pair of hepatic arteries issues from the heart behind the antennal arteries. These arteries bring blood to the digestive caeca and adjacent viscera. An unpaired, median descending artery arises from the floor of the heart just behind the bases of the hepatic arteries. The descending artery gives off branches to the gonads and continues to the intestine, where it gives rise to a dorsal intestinal artery that runs toward the head on top of the gut. The descending artery continues as the sternal artery, passing between the paired nerve cords to divide into a ventral thoracic artery that runs forward into the thoracic region, and a ventral abdominal artery that passes back into the abdomen. The ventral vessels supply blood to the body musculature, the nerve cord, and the appendages. The abdominal aorta supplies the dorsal part of the abdomen with blood and sends branches to the branchiostegites in terrestrial crabs. A vascular ring at the anus sometimes connects the abdominal aorta with the ventral abdominal artery. Connections between branches of the antennal arteries and the ventral thoracic arteries form a vascular ring around the anterior end of the gut, resembling the circumesophageal vascular ring seen in a number of other types of arthropods. In the larger decapods the arteries branch and rebranch before they open into the lacunae.

After passing through the lacunae, the blood collects in a median ventral sinus. Afferent branchial vessels bring blood to the gills from the ventral sinus, and efferent branchial vessels return the blood to a series of pairs of branchiopericardial sinuses running just below the body wall. These sinuses deliver the blood to the pericardial sinus.

An open circulatory system is less dependent on heartbeat and shows greater fluctuation in pressure than a closed system. Movements of internal organs and other body parts move blood in open lacunae more effectively than in capillary beds, and it is not impossible for small arthropods to get along very well without a heart. Pressure rises and falls dramatically with each heartbeat, for there are few elastic blood-vessel walls to absorb part of the pressure. Blood pressure in a resting lobster is 13 cm. H_2O at systole and only 1 cm. at diastole. Blood pressures rise markedly with body activity. Systolic pressure is doubled in an active lobster and diastolic pressure is brought to about the level of systolic pressures in resting animals. Pressure varies considerably in different parts of the animal and may differ in adjacent appendages, depending on their activity.

The most primitive crustaceans seem to have myogenic hearts, the stimulus for the beat originating in the heart muscle itself. Most crustacean hearts, however, have a pacemaker ganglion made up of relatively few neurons. The heart ganglion of a lobster contains five large and four small neurons. The small neurons are pacemakers and fire spontaneously. The large neurons are motor neurons, which

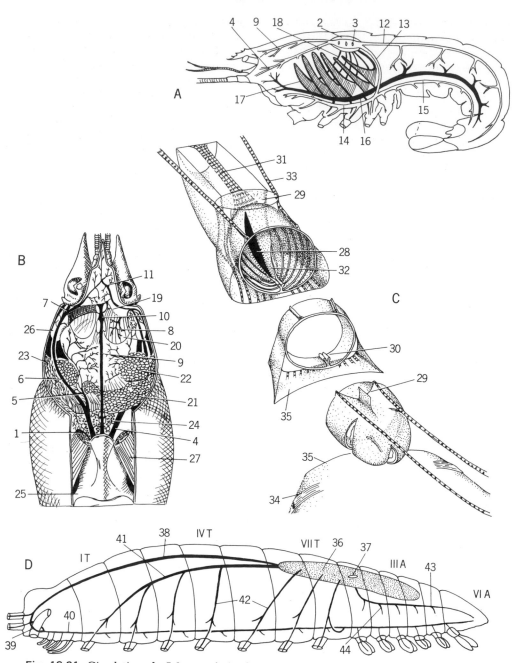

Fig. 18.31. Circulation. **A.** Scheme of circulatory system of a lobster, with venous channels shown in black. **B.** Anterior end of a macruran, *Potamobius*, showing the anterior arteries. **C.** The heart of a copepod, cut into three sections. **D.** Circulatory system of an isopod, schematic. (A, after Gegenbauer. B, after Baumann. D, after Delage, from Balss, in Kükenthal and Krumbach. C, after Marshall and Orr.) *Decapod: Circulatory system:* 1, pericardial septum; 2, heart; 3, ostium; 4, lateral cephalic artery; 5, internal ramus; 6, external ramus;

follow the pacemakers and do not fire spontaneously unless they are separated from the small neurons. Apparently the pacemaker and follower neurons interact, but the details are not yet clear. Accelerator and inhibitor fibers come to the heart ganglion from the central nervous system. They do not necessarily have an equal effect on the pacemaker and follower neurons. It is probable that the heart was originally myogenic, without innervation, and the direction of adaptation has been toward heart innervation and the development of a neurogenic beat. With the appearance of inhibitory and accelerator fibers, the machinery needed to effectively regulate heartbeat by feedback controls is achieved.

NEUROSENSORY APPARATUS

The same kinds of adaptive trends have appeared in the nervous system of chelicerates and crustaceans. The primitive system consists of a dorsal brain, a circumenteric ring, and a double nerve cord, with segmental ganglia connected by commissures. The nervous system tends to become more highly centralized by the fusion of ganglia and, to a lesser extent, by the suppression of ganglia. It never becomes as concentrated as in chelicerates, however, and definitely discrete ganglia are always present.

The most primitive arrangement is seen in Branchiopoda. Fairy shrimps have a simple, segmental nervous system, with ganglia and commissures in all thoracic somites (Fig. 18.32C). In abdominal somites which have no appendages, the ganglia and commissures are missing. The antennules are innervated from in front of the esophagus, and are evidently preoral. Nerves to the antennae arise from the connectives, although the nerve fibers pass to the brain. All other appendages are evidently postoral, as indicated by their innervation.

The nervous system of other entomostraca is far more highly centralized. As a general rule there is a ventral ganglionic mass, in which some of the component ganglia can sometimes be distinguished. Some ostracods have two or three such ganglionic masses, and the ganglia are partly separated in some of the copepods (Fig. 18.32B). It is not easy to determine how other adaptive trends influence the centralization of the nervous system in entomostraca. The tendency for the body to become shorter appears to have some influence, but this is not sufficient to account for all centralization. Ostracods, which have a very short body and are highly specialized in other ways, have a nervous system somewhat less centralized than some other forms which are longer and appear more primitive in other ways.

As a general rule, the nervous systems of Malacostraca are less centralized than those of entomostraca (Fig. 18.32E-G). At least some of the abdominal ganglia are

7, antennary artery; 8, anterior gastric artery; 9, anterior aorta; 10, cor frontale; 11, rostral artery; 12, posterior aorta; 13, descending artery (sternal artery); 14, thoracic artery; 15, abdominal artery; 16, ventral sinus; 17, afferent branchial vessel; 18, efferent branchial vessel. *Other parts:* 19, rostral process; 20, anterior gastric gland; 21, posterior gastric muscle; 22, posterior adductor muscle; 23, digestive gland; 24, gonad; 25, lateroposterior ligament; 26, bladder of green gland; 27, lateral thoracicoabdominal muscle. *Copepod:* 28, aortic valve; 29, attachment to dorsal endoskeleton; 30, ventral fold of heart; 31, anterior pericardial muscle; 35, floor of pericardial sinus. *Isopod* (IT, IVT, VIIT, first, fourth and seventh thoracic segments; IIIA, VIA, third and sixth abdominal segments): 36, heart; 37, ostium; 38, median cephalic artery; 39, periesophageal ring vessel; 40, sternal artery (not homologous with sternal artery of decapods); 41, anterior lateral vessel; 42, segmental thoracic artery; 43, posterior lateral vessel; 44, segmental abdominal artery.

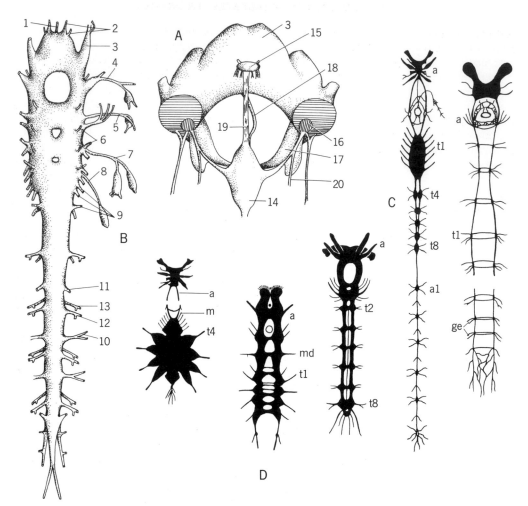

Fig. 18.32. Nervous System. **A.** Brain of copepod in posterior view, showing relations of the sympathetic (stomatogastric) system. **B.** Dorsal view of copepod brain and nerve cord. **C.** Scheme of an anostracan nervous system. This type of system is primitive in the sense that the nerve cord is double, the thoracic ganglia distinct, and the commissures relatively long. **D.** Scheme of nervous system of a cladoceran. The nerve cord is double and the ganglia discrete in the thoracic region. **E.** Scheme of nervous system of an isopod. The thoracic ganglia are distinct, although there is evidence of concentration of ganglia at the anterior end. **F.** Scheme of nervous system of a macruran decapod. Several of the anterior thoracic ganglia are united with the subesophageal ganglion, but the remaining thoracic and abdominal ganglia are distinct. **G.** Scheme of the nervous system of a brachyuran decapod. In the crabs, the thoracic ganglia are all concentrated in a large, compound thoracic ganglion. (A and B, after Marshall and Orr. C-G, after Giesbracht, from Hanström.) *Copepod:* 1, nerve to nauplius eye; 2, nerves to frontal organ; 3, nerve to antennule; 4, ganglion and nerve to antenna; 5, ganglion and nerve to mandible; 6, motor nerves to muscles from endosternite to head appendages; 7, ganglia and nerve to first maxilla; 8, ganglion and nerve to second maxilla; 9, nerves to the three maxillipeds; 10, nerve (giant fiber) to dorsal longitudinal muscle; 11, nerve to ventral longitudinal muscle; 12, nerve to flexor muscle of pereiopod; 13, nerve to extensor muscle of pereiopod; 14, gastric ganglion; 15, labral ganglion; 16, sympathetic nucleus; 17, labral loop

distinct, although there may be fewer ganglia than somites, as in amphipods. The presence of abdominal appendages may have played a part in the maintenance of abdominal ganglia. The thoracic ganglia are often crowded together and in many cases are partly or wholly united to form a compound thoracic ganglion. With the reduction of the abdomen, the nervous system becomes more highly centralized. Brachyuran crabs, for example, have a single thoracic ganglion from which nerves pass to the various parts of the body. Ganglia for the head appendages are distinct in Leptostraca and in the tanaids, but are otherwise closely crowded or have united. In isopods, amphipods, and decapods they have united with ganglia of the thoracic region. Giant fiber systems are common in Crustacea. Although their physiological properties are somewhat different from those of other invertebrates, their basic function is the same. They conduct impulses rapidly and evoke escape movements, prepackaged responses that are sometimes of considerable complexity.

Crustacea have a sympathetic (stomatogastric) nervous system associated with the gut (Fig. 18.32A). Details differ considerably in different groups, but as a general rule the nervous system centers in swellings located on the connectives, a postesophageal commissure, and a system of ganglia associated with the anterior end of the gut. In copepods, a small gastric ganglion is tucked into the junction of the esophagus and midgut, and a larger labral ganglion lies below the cerebral lobes. Nerves to the midgut, and eventually to the heart, arise from this system. The system has obvious similarities to the sympathetic nervous system of molluscs and annelids.

Neurosecretions play an important role in controlling some physiological processes, like molting (p. 680), and also control some immediate aspects of behavior. Color changes are more fully analyzed than most kinds of behavior associated with such secretions. The mechanism differs in detail in different crustaceans, but centers in the sinus glands of the eye-stalks and the postesophageal commissures. Substances which evoke the expansion or contraction of the pigment cells in the cuticle of prawns and crabs have been extracted, and there is evidence of a complex of secretions that operates in the fiddler crab color-control system.

Crustacea have a varied set of sense organs, similar in many respects to those found in other arthropods. Many of the sense organs are mechanoreceptors, associated with movable bristles or pits with thinner cuticle than that covering the body as a whole. Eyes are varied in structure and function, as well as in origin. The most outstanding development in eye structure is the appearance of a compound eye, which to a considerable extent parallels the development of the compound eye found in terrestrial mandibulates. Chemoreceptors are not as well understood, but are important for the recognition of food and mates, as well as general orientation to the environment.

Mechanoreception depends on the sensitivity of cells that initiate a stimulus when deformed by physical forces. The nerve stimuli that are evoked by different mechanoreceptors are much alike. Information about the environment or internal conditions is made more specific by the kind of instrumentation associated with the receptor endings. Through varying the nature of the mechanisms which deform mechanoreceptor cells, a rich variety of information about the environment can be obtained.

of ganglion cells; 18, connective between labral ganglion and brain; 19, connective between gastric ganglion and labral ganglion; 20, nerve to labrum. *Other crustacea* (nerves are identified to letter and number): a, nerve to antenna; md, nerve to mandible; t1, nerve to first thoracic appendage; a1, nerve to first abdominal appendage, etc.

Stretch receptors are mechanoreceptors which are primarily concerned with internal conditions. They consist of small muscles surrounded by many sensory endings. The sensory endings are stimulated by passive stretch and by contraction of the muscles. Fast and slow receptors occur in each abdominal somite. The fast receptors respond to stimuli of short duration, while slow receptors fire repeatedly for several hours when continuously stretched. The presence of both types of receptors enables the animal to distinguish between temporary, short changes resulting from movements and long-lasting, postural stimuli. Rather similar proprioceptors are found in muscles, tendons, or the articular membranes of joints in the body or appendages. They are stimulated by the stretching of tissues accompanying movements and by vibrations of the substrate. The stretch receptors and general proprioceptors are important in establishing postural reflexes, and in reflexes associated with body control during movement. More information about them is badly needed.

Many of the bristles and hairs at the body surface contain sensory neurons and are mechanoreceptors of one kind or another. Like the stretch receptors, they are stimulated by deformation of the sensory endings, and the information they yield depends on the nature of the neuron, the mechanical properties of the bristle or hair, and, in some cases, the position of the sense organ. Sensory bristles located at a joint may provide information about the bending of the joint, while similar bristles at the tip of a leg may be stimulated by contact with the substrate. Some of the mechanoreceptors adapt rapidly, and respond less to stimuli that are repeated. Others continue to discharge for long periods when the stimulus is sustained. Endings that adapt rapidly are especially suitable for tactile sensations. The sensory bristles at the margins of a crayfish uropod, for example, discharge once when the bristle is bent. The rigidity of the bristle determines the ease with which a stimulus is evoked, and thus determines the kind of event to which it is sensitive. When rapid-fire stimulation of a hair results in a matching pattern of rapid-fire neuronal discharge, the sense organ is suitable for vibration reception. Delicate hairs of this kind are useful in detecting water currents and, in land forms, air currents. No full analysis of the many kinds of sensory bristles and hairs is available, but even a casual examination with a microscope gives an impression of considerable diversity, and there can be no doubt that these mechanoreceptors, working together, provide the animal with a good deal of information about itself, its body attitudes, and a number of factors affecting it from without. Certainly Crustacea have complex behavior patterns, indicating a rather well-developed ability to discriminate between different kinds of mechanical stimulation of the body surface.

Statocysts are specialized mechanoreceptors found in the base of the antennules or, in some cases, in the abdomen (Fig. 18.33F). Structurally and functionally they resemble the georeceptors of other animals. Each is a cavity lined with sensory epithelium and containing one or more heavy bodies. Some secrete statoliths, while others use sand or other particles present in the immediate surroundings. The sensory epithelium contains several kinds of fibers. In a lobster, some nerve fibers discharge with respect to position, others to direction of movement, and still others with respect to acceleration or vibration. The frequency of nerve impulses varies with the strength and nature of the stimulation of the sensory hairs on the epithelium. Removal of one of the statocysts causes the animal to circle toward the defective side, indicating that the signal evoking behavioral responses depends on a summing of the stimuli from both statocysts.

A median eye is found in crustacean larvae. It is composed of several ocelli, united as a single structure (Fig. 18.33A).

This kind of eye persists in some adults, but in the majority of Crustacea a pair of compound eyes is found. Each compound eye is composed of a number of discrete optical units, the ommatidia. Compound eyes vary greatly in side and structure. Some contain only a few dozen ommatidia, while others have well over 10,000. Each ommatidium sends a single stimulus to the central nervous system, and the precision of the image depends on the number of ommatidia present. Some compound eyes are sessile, while others are on short or long stalks. The large stalked eyes of decapods have a considerable advantage over sessile eyes, for they have a very wide visual field, reaching up to 200°.

Each ommatidium (Fig. 18.33B) is

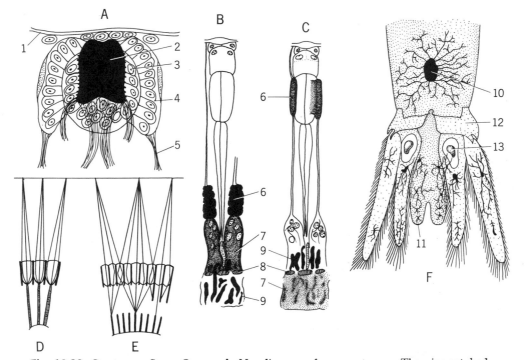

Fig. 18.33. Crustacean Sense Organs. **A.** Nauplius eye of an anostracan. The pigment body provides a complex pattern of shading. Bilaterally arranged nerve fibers carry symmetrical or asymmetrical stimuli, depending on the direction from which the light comes. **B.** A light-adapted ommatidium of a shrimp. *Palaemonetes.* The distal dark pigment and the proximal dark pigment cluster about the light-sensitive elements, while the white, reflecting pigment lies below the basement membrane. Under these conditions, the eye functions as an apposition eye (**D**), with each ommatidium functioning independently. **C.** A dark-adapted ommatidium of *Palaemonetes.* The distal pigment has migrated up to surround the crystalline cone, and the proximal dark pigment has migrated below the basement membrane. The white, reflecting pigment surrounds the rhabdome. The eye now functions as a superposition eye (**E**), with light from several ommatidia reaching the light-sensitive elements. **F.** The posterior end of a mysid, *Macromysis,* showing the statocysts in the uropods. (A, after Claus, from Broch, in Kükenthal and Krumbach. B and C after Kleinholz. D and E, after Kühn, from Wigglesworth.) 1, cornea; 2, pigment body; 3, sensory cell; 4, nerve cell; 5, nerve fiber; 6, distal dark pigment; 7, proximal dark pigment; 8, basement membrane; 9, white, reflecting pigment; 10, chromatophore; 11, telson; 12, base of uropod; 13, statocyst.

covered by a cornea, produced by the corneagenous cells that lie immediately below it. Below the cornea a crystalline cone is found. This serves as a lens apparatus. Below the crystalline cone is a circlet of retinula cells. Each retinula cell contains a differentiated border, directed toward the center of the cluster. This is the rhabdomere. The rhabdomeres of all of the cells in the cluster are joined to form the rhabdome. In simpler types of crustacean eyes the retinula cells contain pigment, but in more complex eyes the pigment around the crystalline cone is held in special pigment cells. Processes from the neurosensory retinula cells extend through the basement membrane at the base of the eye.

The ommatidia contain three pigments, a black distal pigment, and two proximal pigments, one black and the other white. The black pigments are melanin or ommochrome, and the white, reflecting pigments are purines or pteridines. The pigments migrate in response to changes in illumination, under the influence of secretions from the eye-stalk sinus glands and probably also under the influence of nervous stimuli. In a light-adapted eye the distal and proximal black pigments are clustered about the retinula cells and the white, reflecting pigment is below the basement membrane (Fig. 18.33B). Under these conditions, only light passing down directly from above can reach the rhabdome. In a dark-adapted eye, the distal pigment migrates around the crystalline cone, while the proximal black pigment moves below the basement membrane. Meanwhile, the white proximal pigment moves up around the rhabdome forming a reflecting layer, the tapetum. Light from several crystalline cones can now strike a rhabdome. Injections of eye-stalk extract causes the distal pigment and the white proximal pigment to assume the position normally held in light-adapted eyes, but leaves the proximal black pigment below the basement membrane (Fig. 18.33C).

Evidently the eye-stalk secretions are an important, but not the only, factor in charge of pigment migration.

Eye function changes with pigment migration. When each ommatidium responds only to light from its own crystalline cone, as in a light-adapted eye, an apposition image is formed (Fig. 18.33D). When each ommatidium responds to light from several crystalline cones, a superposition image is formed (Fig. 18.33E). The superposition image is better suited to the analysis of a rapidly changing visual field, and, of course, makes better use of the light available for vision. The apposition image is better adapted to a clear, mosaic image. The details of pigment movement vary in different species of Crustacea, and intermediate conditions provide considerably more variation than the discussion above suggests. As a general rule, Crustacea have eyes that function predominantly as apposition eyes or as superposition eyes, with the latter occurring in animals from deep-water or turbid habitats.

Chemoreception is somewhat better known in terrestrial than in aquatic mandibulates, and will be discussed elsewhere. As a general rule, the gnathobases and mouth parts are responsive to food substances, and sensory bristles or pads located on the antennae and antennules are also chemoreceptive. No very full description of chemical sensitivity is available, but work so far clearly shows that Crustacea can receive chemical stimuli from a distance as well as on contact. Contact chemoreception, however, appears to predominate. A few special chemoreceptors are known, such as organs sensitive to salinity in some of the brackish water species.

Crustacean behavior reflects the diversity of end organs and the complexity of the nervous system. Crustaceans respond in definite ways to a variety of environmental factors. Many species undergo cycles of diurnal activity, seeking deeper water during the day and surfacing at night, or otherwise modifying behavior during day and night hours. Terrestrial species are usually nocturnal, as is suitable in animals that live in constant danger of desiccation. Shore species often have cyclical behavior patterns, associated with the tides, and continuing when placed under constant laboratory conditions. Even when kept in constant darkness, the eye pigments of crabs and crayfish maintain the diurnal rhythm of light and dark adaptation. The stimuli responsible for the maintenance of rhythms which are sensible in the natural habitat but are continued under constant conditions in the laboratory are among the real biological mysteries at the present time. Do crustaceans have some time sense? Or are they sensitive to kinds of stimuli that we cannot receive and so have not thought of? Answers are very slow to come in, but it is increasingly clear that a crusteacean is a delicately adjusted and very complex living system, with deep-seated behavioral adaptations to its environment.

Summary Table 18.2. Crustacean subclasses [1]

	HEAD	THORAX	ABDOMEN	TELSON
Cephalocarida	Typical appendages with second maxillae leg-like	Nine somites, with similar triramous appendages	Ten segments, without appendages	With furca
Branchiopoda	Antennae modified for swimming, reproduction or reduced	Long, with many similar phyllopodia, or four to six somites with differentiated appendages	Long or short, with or without phyllopodia	Usually with furca or claw
Mystacocarida	Antennae and mandibles used for swimming	Five segments, one pair of maxillipeds, and four similar appendages	Ten somites, first four with appendages	With furca
Copepoda	Antennae modified for swimming	Six somites; one pair of maxillipeds and fifth and sixth pairs modified	Four segments, without appendages	With furca
Cirripedia	Much modified for attachment to substrate; antennae reduced or missing	Six somites, all with highly modified but similar appendages	Reduced, without appendages	With furca
Malacostraca	Typical appendages, but second maxillae leg-like in primitive forms	Eight somites, typically with specialized appendages; female gonopore on sixth and male on eighth segment	Six somites, first five with pleopods and last with uropods	With or without furca

[1] Based on free-living forms.

Summary Table 18.3. Superorders of Malacostraca

	PHYLLOCARIDA	SYNCARIDA	HOPLOCARIDA	PERACARIDA	EUCARIDA
Carapace	Bivalved, with adductor muscle; over head, thorax, and first abdominal somites	Anterior plate over protocephalon; compound plate over rest of head	Separate pieces for eyes and first antennae, then plate over head and first thoracic somites	Variable, but never over more than four thoracic somites	Over whole thorax and head
First antennae	With scale	Biramous	With three flagella and large scale	Variable	Variable
			HEAD APPENDAGES		
Second antennae	Long flagellum	Long flagellum and scale	Large scale	Variable	Variable
Mandibles	Large palps	Large palps	Vestigial palps	Variable	Variable
First maxillae	Long, slender palp	Setose, flat	Reduced palp	Variable	Variable
Second maxillae	Leg-like	Setose, flat	Flat, uniquely formed	Variable	Variable
Thorax	Eight somites, all with phyllopodia generating feeding and respiratory currents	Eight somites; first with maxilliped and rest pereiopods with gills and exopodites generating currents	Eight somites; first with slender subchelate leg; second with strong raptorial leg; rest with subchelate pereiopods	Eight somites; first with maxilliped, others variable pereiopods, some of which bear oöstegites	Eight somites, with variable appendages but typically with maxillipeds, the first pereiopod chelate, and with gills
Abdomen	Seven somites, the first five with pleopods and the last two with reduced appendages	Six somites, the first five with pleopods used for swimming and the last with uropods	Six somites, the first five with pleopods bearing gills, and the last with uropods with a spiny medial plate	Six somites, the first five bearing pleopods of variable form and the last a uropod	Six somites, typically with pleopods on the first five and uropods on the last
Telson	With furca	In tail fan	In tail fan	In tail fan as a rule	Typically in tail fan

Summary Table 18.4. Orders of Peracarida

	MYSIDACEA	CUMACEA	TANAIDACEA	ISOPODA	AMPHIPODA
Carapace	Over most thoracic somites	Inflated, with gill cavity; over three to four thoracic somites	With vascular gill cavity; over two thoracic somites	None	None
Thorax	Not united with head	First somites fused to carapace	First two somites fused to carapace	One to two somites fused to head	One to two somites fused to head
Thoracic appendages	One to two pairs of maxillipeds; remaining pereiopods with exopodite flagellum and some with gills and oöstegites	Three pairs of maxillipeds and pereiopods on sixth to eighth thoracic somites modified for digging; four periopods with oöstegites	One pair of maxillipeds, followed by cheliped and three to four pairs of pereiopods; some with oöstegites	One pair of maxillipeds and remaining pereiopods uniramous; some with oöstegites	One pair of maxillipeds and next two pairs of legs often chelate; some pereiopods with oöstegites and gills
Abdomen	Last somite long, with ring; pleopods may be absent in females; last somites with flat uropods	Pleopods typically absent in females; last somite with filiform uropods	Short, with crowded somites; five pairs of pleopods, but may be reduced in females; uropods filiform	Partly fused; pleopods biramous, with gills	Somites not fused; first three pairs of appendages swimming pleopods and last three uropods
Telson	In tail fan	No tail fan	No tail fan; fused to last abdominal somite	Usually fused to last abdominal somite; usually no tail fan	No tail fan

References

Anderson, B. G., *et al.* 1937. Growth and variability in *Daphnia pulex*. *Biol. Bull.* 73: 444.

Armstrong, J. C. 1949. The systematic position of the crustacean genus *Deirocheilocaris* and the status of the subclass *Mystacocarida*. *Amer. Mus. Novit.* 1413.

Banta, A. M. 1939. Studies on the physiology, genetics, and evolution of some Cladocera. *Publ. Carnegie Inst. Wash.* 513: 1.

Bigelow, H. B. 1926. Plankton of the offshore waters of the Gulf of Maine. *Bull. Bur. Fish.* 40, Pt. II.

Borradaile, L. A. 1926. On the primitive phyllopodium. *Ann. Mag. Nat. Hist.* 18: 16.

Brooks, J. L. 1946. Cyclomorphosis in *Daphnia*. *Ecol. Monogr.* 16: 409.

Brown, F. A. 1944. Hormones in the Crustacea. *Quart. Rev. Biol.* 19: 32, 118. (G)

Bursell, E. 1955. Cutaneous respiration in woodlice. *Jour. Exp. Biol.* 32: 256.

Cannon, H. G. 1928. On the feeding mechanisms of the copepods *Calanus finmarchicus* and *Diaptomus gracilis*. *Jour. Exp. Biol.* 6: 131.

——. 1933. On the feeding mechanism of the Branchiopoda. *Phil. Trans. Roy. Soc. London* 222: 267.

Carlisle, D. B., and F. Knowles. 1959. *Endocrine Control in Crustaceans*. Cambridge Univ. Press, Cambridge, Eng. (G)

Chappuis, P.-A., and C. D. Debouteville. 1954. Morphologie des Mystacocarides. *Arch. Zool. exp. gen.* 91: 7.

Clarke, G. L. 1934. The role of copepods in the economy of the sea. *Fifth Pacific Sci. Cong.* 2017.

Coker, R. E. 1939. The problem of cyclomorphosis in *Daphnia*. *Quart. Rev. Biol.* 14: 137.

Costlow, J. D., Jr. 1956. Shell development in *Balanus improvisus*. *Jour. Morph.* 99: 359.

Creaser, E. P. 1931. The Michigan decapod crustaceans. *Pap. Mich. Acad. Sci. Arts and Lett.* 13: 257. (F)

——, and A. I. Ortenburger. 1933. The decapod crustaceans of Oklahoma. *Publ. Univ. Okla. Biol. Surv.* 5: 14.

Cushing, D. J. 1951. The vertical migration of planktonic Crustacea. *Biol. Rev.* 26: 158. (E)

Davis, C. C. 1955. *The Marine and Fresh-Water Plankton*. Mich. State Univ., East Lansing, Mich. (F)

Darwin, C. 1851–54. *A Monograph on the Subclass Cirripedia*. London.

Day, J. 1953. The life history of *Sacculina*. *Quart. Jour. Micr. Sci.* 77: 549.

Dennell, R. 1947. The occurrence and significance of phenolic hardening in the newly formed cuticle of decapod crustaceans. *Proc. Roy. Soc.* 134: 485.

Dexter, R. W., and M. S. Ferguson. 1943. Life history and distributional studies on *Eubranchipus serratus* Forbes. *Amer. Midl. Nat.* 29: 210.

Digby, P. S. B. 1954. The biology of the marine planktonic copepods of Scoresby Sound, East Greenland. *Jour. An. Ecol.* 23: 298.

Dobbin, C. N. 1941. Fresh-water Ostracoda from Washington and other western localities. *Univ. Wash. Publ. Biol.* 4: 175. (F)

Durand, J. B. 1960. Limb regeneration and endocrine activity in the crayfish. *Biol. Bull.* 118: 250.

Eddy, S. 1934. A study of the fresh-water plankton communities. *Ill. Biol. Monogr.* 12: 1.

Fox, H. M. 1948. The haemoglobin of *Daphnia*. *Proc. Roy. Soc.* 135: 195.

Fryer, G. 1957. The feeding mechanism of some freshwater cyclopoid copepods. *Proc. Zool. Soc.* 129: 1.

——. 1957a. The food of some freshwater cyclopoid copepods and its ecological significance. *Jour. An. Ecol.* 26: 263.

Furtos, N. C. 1933. The Ostracoda of Ohio. *Bull. Ohio Biol. Surv.* 29: 413.

Gauld, D. T. 1959. Swimming and feeding in crustacean larvae; the *Nauplius larva*. *Proc. Zool. Soc.* 132: 31.

Giesbrecht, W. 1910. Stomatopoden. *Fauna u. Flora Golfes Neapel, Monogr.* 33.

Giesler, Sister F. S. 1944. Studies on the postembryonic development of *Hyalella azteca*. *Biol. Bull.* 86: 6.

Glaessner, M. F. 1957. Evolutionary trends in the Crustacea. *Evol.* 11: 178.

Green, J. 1961. *A Biology of Crustacea*. Witherby, London. (G)

Gurney, R. 1942. *Larvae of Decapod Crustacea*. Wheldon, London.

Hansen, H. J. 1925. *On the Comparative Morphology of the Appendages in the Arthropoda. A. Crustacea*. Gyldendal, Copenhagen.

Hatchett, S. P. 1947. Biology of the Isopoda of Michigan. *Ecol. Monogr.* 17: 47.

Heath, H. 1924. The external development of certain phyllopods. *Jour. Morph.* 38: 453.

Hoff, C. C. 1942. The ostracods of Illinois. *Ill. Biol. Monogr.* 19: 1. (F)

Holmes, S. J. 1900. Synopsis of California stalk-eyed Crustacea. *Occ. Pap. Calif. Acad. Sci.* 7: 1. (F)

Holmes, W. 1942. The giant myelinated nerve fibers of the prawn. *Phil. Trans.* 231: 293.

Hult, J. 1941. On the soft-bottom isopods of the Skagerrak. *Zool. Bidrag Uppsala.* 17: 1.

Huxley, J. S., and O. W. Richards. 1931. Relative growth rates of the abdomen and carapace of the shore crab *Carcinus maenas*. *Jour. Mar. Biol. Ass.* 17: 1001.

Hynes, H. B. N. 1954. The ecology of *Gammarus duebeni* Lilljeborg and its occurrence in fresh water in western Britain. *Jour. An. Ecol.* 23: 38.

Jennings, R. H., and D. M. Whitaker. 1941. The effect of salinity upon excystment of *Artemia*. *Biol. Bull.* 80: 194.

Katz, B. 1949. Neuromuscular transmission in invertebrates. *Biol. Rev.* 24: 1.

Keim, W. 1915. Das Nervensystem von *Astacus fluviatilis*. *Ztschr. wiss. Zool.* 113: 485.

Kessling, R. V. 1951. The morphology of ostracod molt stages. *Ill. Biol. Monogr.* 21: 1.

Kiser, R. W. 1950. *A Revision of the North American Species of the Cladoceran Genus Daphnia*. Seattle.

Klugh, A. B. 1927. The ecology, food relations, and culture of fresh-water entomostraca. *Trans. Roy. Canad. Inst. Toronto* 16: 15.

Linder, F. 1952. Contributions to the morphology and taxonomy of the Branchiopoda Notostraca, with special reference to the North American species. *Proc. U.S. Nat. Mus.* 102: 1.

———. 1959. Studies on the fresh water fairy shrimp, *Chirocephalopsis* bundyi. *Jour. Morph.* 104: 1.

Lochhead, J. H., and M. S. Lochhead. 1941. Studies on the blood and related tissues in *Artemia* (Crustacea, Anostraca). *Jour. Morph.* 68: 593.

Lockwood, A. P. M. 1960. Some effect of temperature and concentration of the medium on ionic regulation of the isopod *Asellus aquatica*. *Jour. Exp. Biol.* 37: 614.

Lowndes, A. G. 1933. The feeding mechanism of *Chirocephalus diaphanus* Prevost, the fairy shrimp. *Proc. Zool. Soc. London* 1933: 1093.

———. 1935. The sperms of fresh-water ostracods. *Proc. Zool. Soc. London* 1935: 35.

Maluf, N. S. R. 1939. On the anatomy of the kidney of the crayfish and on the absorption of chloride from freshwater by this animal. *Zool. Jahrb. Abt. Allg. Zool.* 59: 515.

Manton, S. M. 1930. Notes on the habits and feeding mechanisms of *Anaspides* and *Paranaspides* (Crustacea, Syncarida). *Proc. Zool. Soc. London* 1930: 791.

Marshall, S. M., and A. P. Orr. 1955. *The Biology of Calanus finmarchicus*. Oliver & Boyd, London. (G)

Moore, H. B. The biology of *Balanus balanoides*. *Jour. Mar. Biol. Ass.* 20: 263.

Packard, A. 1883. A monograph of the phyllopod Crustacea of North America, with remarks on the Order Phyllocarida. *12th Ann. Rep. U.S. Geol. Geog. Surv. Terr.* 1878. I: 295.

Parker, G. H. 1902. The reactions of copepods to various stimuli and the bearing of this on daily depth-migrations. *Bull. U.S. Fish. Comm.* 21: 103.

Passano, L. M. 1961. The regulation of crustacean metamorphosis. *Am. Zool.* 1: 89.

Pennak, R. W., and D. J. Zinn. 1943. Mystacocarida, a new order of Crustacea from intertidal beaches in Massachusetts and Connecticut. *Smithson. Misc. Coll.* 103: 1.

Prentiss, C. W. 1901. The otocyst of decapod Crustacea: its structure, development, and functions. *Bull. Mus. Comp. Zool.* 36: 165.

Reddy, A. R. 1935. The structure, mechanism, and development of the gastric armature in Stomatopoda with a discussion as to its evolution in Decapoda. *Proc. Ind. Acad. Sci. Biol.* 1: 650.

Richardson, H. 1905. A monograph of the isopods of North America. *Bull. U.S. Nat. Mus.* 54: 1.

Richman, S. 1958. The transformation of energy by *Daphnia pulex*. *Ecol. Monogr.* 28: 273.

Rylov, W. M. 1935. Die Cladoceren. *Die Binnengewasser* 15: 97.

Sanders, H. L. 1958. The Cephalocarida and crustacean phylogeny. *15th Int. Congr. Zool. London* 1958: 337.

Schmidt, W. 1915. Die Muskalatur von *Astacus fluviatilis. Ztschr. wiss. Zool.* 113: 165.

Scudamore, H. H. 1948. Factors influencing molting and the sexual cycles in the crayfish. *Biol. Bull.* 95: 229.

Snodgrass, R. E. 1956. Crustacean metamorphoses. *Smithson. Misc. Coll.* 131, No. 10.

Tattersall, W. M. 1951. A review of the Mysidacea of the United States National Museum. *Bull. U.S. Nat. Mus.* 201: 1.

Teal, J. M. 1959. Respiration of crabs in Georgia salt marshes and its relation to their ecology. *Physiol. Zool.* 32: 1.

Tressler, W. L. 1947. A check list of the known species of North American freshwater Ostracoda. *Amer. Midl. Nat.* 38: 698.

Van Name, W. G. 1936. The American land and fresh-water isopod Crustacea. *Bull. Amer. Mus. Nat. Hist.* 71: 1. (F)

Waterman, T. H. (ed.). 1960–61. *The Physiology of Crustacea.* Academic Press, New York. (!)

Weckel, A. L. 1907. The fresh-water Amphipoda of North America. *Proc. U.S. Nat. Mus.* 32: 25.

Wiersma, C. A. G. 1952. Neurons of arthropods. *Cold Spring Harbor Symp.* 17: 155.

Wilder, J. 1940. The effects of population density upon growth, reproduction and survival of *Hyalella azteca. Physiol. Zool.* 13: 439.

Woltereck, R. 1932. Races, associations and stratification of pelagic daphnids in some lakes of Wisconsin and other regions of the United States and Canada. *Trans. Wis. Acad. Sci. Arts and Lett.* 27: 487.

19
Insects and Myriapods—
The Terrestrial Mandibulates

The most remarkable success story in the animal kingdom has been the one lived by the terrestrial mandibulates. It has taken place on land, which has been so inhospitable, as a general rule, to invertebrates. A number of phyla have made tentative invasions of land, and a few have firmly established themselves in the soil or surface litter. Nematodes, earthworms, and Protozoa abound in the special environment of the soil, where moisture is generally available and the problems of water-loss by surface evaporation are minimal. Snails, a few leeches, tardigrades, Onychophora and Crustacea have made a place for themselves in special, humid situations. Parasites have been carried everywhere in the special habitats that their hosts provide. However, despite the great diversity of organizational plans found among the invertebrate phyla, only the arachnids and terrestrial mandibulates can be said to have become truly successful land animals, adapting to arid as well as to humid habitats.

The outstanding success of the terrestrial mandibulates rests squarely on the insects. A remarkable series of adaptive radiations have taken insects to all kinds of terrestrial habitats where temperatures are high enough to permit activity by cold-blooded animals, and have returned some as juveniles or adults to fresh-water habitats, where they have often become influential members of their communities. Only the ocean, the natural habitat of nearly all of the phyla, has been inhospitable to them. By and large, the tremendous success of insects has been associated with the development of wings. The wingless insects and myriapods, restricted largely to the soil and surface litter, like most of their arachnid competitors, may be locally abundant but are not more important than other invertebrates living in the same habitats. The development of wings brought the air age to the invertebrate world. A river that is a formidable barrier to a small, creeping animal is no problem to an air-borne one, and though it is a long walk to the top of a tree for a small spider, it is but a short flight for an insect.

Certainly the insects have undergone a series of amazing adaptations, fitting them into the web of community life at nearly every level, as herbivore, scavenger, carnivore, and parasite. The magnitude of their success is shown by the fact that somewhere between a third and a half of all animal species are insects, as well as by the vast economic costs involved in keeping the destructive species in check to protect our crops.

Terrestrial mandibulates have followed two main evolutionary pathways. One line is characterized by the division of the body into two tagmata, the head and trunk, and is generally termed the myriapod stem. The other is characterized by a body of three tagmata, head, thorax, and abdomen, and includes only the insects. Contrasting views of the relationships of these two stems have been presented, but it is generally agreed that the insects arose from early myriapod stocks. They may have arisen from an early protomyriapod stem that was leading off toward the Symphyla, a small group of centipede-like animals.

The head of a terrestrial mandibulate somewhat resembles the head of a crustacean, but is much more consolidated and has no antennules. The appendages are quite unlike the appendages of Crustacea. They are uniramous, the leg corresponding to the endopodite of a crustacean appendage. At no time during development are the legs biramous. This is one of the weak points in the view that the mandibulates are more closely related to each other than to other arthropod stems, and one of the strong points in the view that arthropods have arisen from several different protoarthropod stems. Myriapods have appendages on nearly all of the somites, while, except for the highly modified appendages associated with the reproductive organs. insects have appendages only on the head and thorax. Respiratory exchange occurs at the body surface and, generally, by way of a tracheal system. While juvenile insects may have secondary gills if they live in an aquatic habitat, their gills are never homologous to the gills of Crustacea. Malpighian tubules, attached to the gut, are the characteristic excretory organs.

Four classes of myriapods are recognized Two of these are small groups, but the others are relatively large and include a number of smaller groups. Note that the only discussion of the groups marked with an asterisk is given in the classification section.

Myriapod Classification

Class Pauropoda. Pauropoda includes about 60 species of small (0.5 to 2.0 mm.), soft-bodied, blind myriapods living under objects, in moist surface litter, or in the upper soil in temperate to tropical regions. A small, conical head bears large, branched antennae; solid, deep-set mandibles with a comb of delicate blades at the tip; and a pair of maxillae that are united with the sternum of the maxillary somite to form a floor for the mouth cavity. Eyes are missing, but characteristic head sense organs, the pseudoculi, are present near the position ordinarily occupied by eyes. The last head segment has no appendages, and is separated from the remaining head segments, forming the collum, a separate ring. The trunk is made up of 11 segments, counting the pygidium, with six-segmented legs on the first nine somites (ten in one species). Each tergal plate covers two somites, as in millipedes. They have no heart, no arteries, and no respiratory organs. Blood circulates in a system of haemocoelic lacunae, and respiratory exchange occurs at the body surface. The gonads are primitively ventral, but the testes become dorsal secondarily. The epidermal gonoducts open through paired gonopores located between the coxae of the second legs. Male gonoducts end in ejaculatory ducts containing penes. Female gonopores and a seminal receptacle open into a genital depression. Development is anamorphic, as the juvenile hatches with three pairs of legs. Example: *Pauropous* (Fig. 19.1A,B).

Class Diplopoda. Millipedes. Predominantly herbivorous myriapods with the trunk composed of double somites (diplosomites), of which all but the first three bear two pairs of legs; the first three trunk somites modified, with one pair of legs and with the gonopores on the second somite; hear with antennae, mandibles, and typically with a chilognatharium formed of sternal elements, first maxillae, and the vestiges of the appendages of the last head somite; the last head somite typically appearing legless as the result of chilognatharium formation and forming a separate ring, the collum; body typically circular in cross section.

Subclass Pselaphognatha. A small group of minute, broad, soft-bodied millipedes with a trunk of 10 to 12 somites and dorsal and lateral tufts of hairy bristles; maxillae on the head and collum leg-like; not fused to form a gnathochilarium; with eyes; without repugnatorial glands or legs modified for copulation (gonopods); anus in the next to last trunk segment. Example: *Polyxenus* (Fig. 19.1C).

Subclass Opisthandria. Millipedes with a gnathochilarium and without appendages on the collum; the last one or two pairs of legs modified as gonopods.

Order Oniscomorpha. Pill millipedes. Mostly tropical millipedes with 11 to 13 trunk somites, flattened on the ventral surface; with the last two pairs of legs modified in males, and the last pair used for sperm transfer; body can be rolled into a ball. Example: *Glomeris* (Fig. 19.1D).

Order Limacomorpha. Blind millipedes. Small, tropical millipedes with 19 to 20 trunk somites and the last pair of legs modified as gonopods in males; without repugnatorial glands.

Subclass Proterandria. Millipedes with a gnathochilarium and a collum without appendages; male gonopods typically on the sixth diplosomite.

Order Colobognatha. Suctorial millipedes. Largely tropical, elongated millipedes with 30 or more diplosomites; exoskeleton hardened, but sternal plates not fused with the rest of the exoskeleton; small head with mouthparts usually altered to form a suctorial proboscis; a row of repugnatorial glands on each side of the body; both pairs of legs on the sixth diplosomite modified as gonopods in the male. Example: *Polyzonium* (Fig. 19.1E).

Order Polydesmoidea. Flat-backed millipedes. Relatively short millipedes with 18 to 19 trunk diplosomites, each covered by two skeletal rings, an anterior prozonite and a posterior metazonite; flattened lateral carinae on the exoskeleton give the back a flat shape; repugnatorial glands on some trunk somites; no eyes; first pair of legs on the sixth diplosomite modified as gonopods in males. Example: *Polydesmus* (Fig. 19.1F).

Order Ascospermomorpha. Millipedes resembling the Polydesmoidea, but with 25 to 31 diplosomites; usually with a cluster of small ocelli on each side of the head; without repugnatorial glands; silk glands open on papillae in last tergal plate. Example: *Chordeuma* (Fig. 19.1G).

Order Juliformia. Millipedes with many diplosomites; second genital somite usually without legs; both pairs of legs on the sixth diplosomite modified as male gonopods; repugnatorial glands on each trunk diplosomite. Examples: *Julus, Spirobolus* (Fig. 19.2).

Class Chilopoda. Centipedes. Carnivorous myriapods with relatively long, flattened bodies; head with long antennae of 12 or more segments; mandibles, and two pairs of maxillae; trunk with one pair of seven-segmented legs on each somite; first pair of legs modified as maxillipeds, with poison glands; bases of maxillipeds fused to form a lower lip; a tracheal respiratory system; last two somites in front of the pygidium

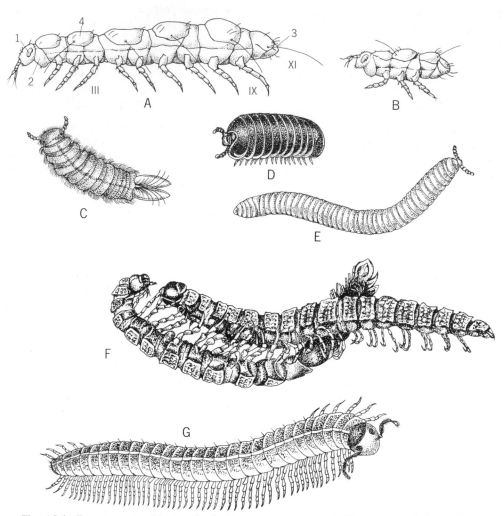

Fig. 19.1. Representative Myriapods. **A.** *Pauropus*, a pauropod. The pauropods have eleven trunk segments (Roman numerals) but only six dorsal plates or terga, thus somewhat resembling millipedes. The last head segment bears no maxillae and is a separate, appendageless somite, known as the collum. Characteristic sense organs known as pseudoculi are found on the head. **B.** First instar of *Pauropus*. Pauropod development is anamorphic, as they hatch with only three pairs of legs and gain somites and appendages as molts occur. **C.** *Polyxenus*, a diplopod belonging to the subclass Pselaphognatha. These tiny, blind millipedes have no gonopods or repugnatorial glands and the maxillae do not form a gnathochilarium. The short trunk of 10 to 12 segments and tufts of bristles are characteristic. **D.** *Glomeris*, a pill millipede. They belong to the subclass Opisthandria, which have a gnathochilarium, and to the order Oniscomorpha. They have only 11 to 13 trunk somites and are ventrally flattened. The last two pairs of appendages are modified in males. **E.** *Polyzonium*, a colobognath millipede. The colobognaths have an elongated body, gonopods on the sixth diplosomite of the males, and suctorial mouth parts. **F.** Copulation in *Polydesmus*, a flat-backed millipede. The order Polydesmoidea is characterized by the dorsolateral flares of the exoskeleton, and the double skeletal rings for each diplosomite. **G.** *Chordeuma*, a millipede belonging to the Asco-

840

are the pregenital and genital somites and are legless; gonads dorsal.

Order Scolopendromorpha. Predominantly tropical and subtropical centipedes with 21 or 23 pairs of legs and antennae with 17 to 31 segments; with 9 to 11 pairs of spiracles; eyes absent or composed of four ocelli; tergal plates correspond to the sternal plates and are equally large; development epimorphic, with all somites present at hatching. Example: *Scolopendra* (Fig. 19.3C).

Order Lithobiomorpha. Predominantly temperate and subtropical centipedes, with 15 pairs of legs and antennae of about 19 to 70 segments; nine large and six small somites; coxal glands associated with the last four pairs of legs; eyes usually with many ocelli; development anamorphic, with seven pairs of legs present at hatching. Example: *Lithobius* (Fig. 19.3A).

Order Scutigeromorpha. Widespread centipedes with 15 pairs of long, slender legs and 15 sternal plates, but with only eight tergal plates; long slender antennae; large faceted eyes; seven middorsal spiracles; development anamorphic, with seven pairs of legs present at hatching. Example: *Scutigera* (Fig. 19.3B).

Order Geophilomorpha. Widespread, elongated, blind centipedes with 31 to over 180 pairs of legs; each trunk somite with a dorsal tergite and intertergite and a ventral sternite and intersternite; antennae with 14 segments; a pair of spiracles in all but the first and last somites; development epimorphic. Example: *Geophilus* (Fig. 19.4A).

Class Symphyla. A widespread but small group of centipede-like myriapods with 12 pairs of legs and a pair of spinnerets on the next to last somite; head with long antennae, mandibles, maxillae, and a lower lip formed by the union of the second maxillae; gonopores on the fourth trunk segment; development anamorphic, with juveniles hatching with six to seven pairs of legs. Example: *Scutigerella* (Fig. 19.4B).

External Form of Myriapods

The composition of the head, the nature of the trunk somites, and the disposition and form of the appendages differ markedly in the various myriapod groups. While classification is based largely on external differences, these are correlated with important internal differences.

THE HEAD

The mandibulate head may be divided into a procephalon (also known as the protocephalon), and a gnathocephalon. The procephalon is the sensory part of the head, and corresponds to the prostomium of the polychaetes or the acron of the trilobites, together with the two somites which, in Crustacea, bear the first and second antennae. The second antennae are absent, however, in all terrestrial mandibulates. The gnathocephalon is the part of the head associated with the mouthparts, and includes the mandibular and two maxillary somites. Important differences between the various kinds of myriapods are seen in both parts of the head.

The surface of the head is made up of a cranium and a part extending forward or down toward the mouth, the epistome (Fig. 19.5A-C). A partially free upper lip, the labrum, is attached to the epistome and hangs down over the top of the mouth. Although inconspicuous in myriapods, the labrum is equipped with setose sense organs thought to be chemoreceptive. The external form of the head of myriapods is

spermomorpha. These millipedes resemble the polydesmoids, but have more diplosomites, silk glands, and lack repugnatorial glands. (A and B, after Tiegs. C-E and G, after Koch. F, after Seifert, from Cloudsley-Thompson.) 1, pseudoculi; 2, last head segment (collum); 3, pygidium; 4, tergal plate.

Fig. 19.2. A. A millipede, *Spirobolus*. Millipedes are predominantly herbivorous, and have the body divided into diplosomites, each with two pairs of legs except for the most anterior somites. **B.** A centipede, *Lithobius*. The centipedes are predominantly carnivorous, and have the body divided into somites with a single pair of legs. They have, as a rule, fewer somites and fewer legs than millipedes. The legs are proportionately longer, and they generally run much faster. (Courtesy of the General Biological Supply Co.)

842

simpler than in insects, where conspicuous head sutures associated with endoskeletal apodemes are important features. Although the parts have changed position somewhat during the evolution of the head, the procephalon is the preoral part of the primitive head. The cranium corresponds to the roof of the ancestral head and the epistome to its anterior face. The floor of the primitive preoral head is concealed by the mouth parts, which extend forward from the gnathocephalon. It has been modified to form a preoral cavity which leads back to the mouth. The upper surface of the preoral cavity is lined by the epipharynx (Fig. 19.5C) and its lower surface by a ventral fold, the hypopharynx, both derived from the floor of the head anterior to the mouth. The lateral walls of the preoral cavity vary markedly in different groups. They sometimes contain several sclerites and are sometimes partially composed of the bases of the mandibles. The hypopharynx is concealed by the lower lip, the labium in insects and the gnathochilarium in myriapods. In each case, the lower lip is formed by the union of maxillary elements and the sterna of the postoral head somites.

The special sense organs associated with the procephalon are located on the cranium. The sensory equipment differs somewhat in each group of myriapods. Some are blind, or have ocelli located in small clusters or in other patterns. Some chilopods have large faceted eyes that superficially resemble the compound eyes of insects but are differently constructed. The antennae vary in length, in the number of segments, and in other structural features. Pauropods have unique branched antennae. Some of the chilopods have extremely long antennae to which segments are added at each molt throughout adult life, while others have a constant number of segments. Symphylans, most diplopods, and some chilopods have sensory pits, known as organs of Tömösvary, at the bases of the antennae. Pauropods have a

pair of unique sense organs, the pseudoculi, situated at the site of the eyes of other myriapods. They are probably used for vibration reception. A pair of spiracles located at the base of the antennae are unique features of the symphylans.

The structure of the gnathocephalon is extremely variable in myriapods. A good deal of the variability is associated with the extent to which the elements of the gnathocephalon have been united to form a complex lower lip. The nature and development of the second maxillae is related to the formation of the lower lip. Most diplopods and all pauropods have a legless somite, the collum, about which there has been considerable difference of opinion. Pflugfelder has described the incorporation of reduced appendages from the collum into the lower lip of some diplopods, leaving little room for doubt that it is the second maxillary somite. Presumably the head of pauropods is similarly built.

The terrestrial mandibulates are characterized as having three pairs of appendages modified as mouth parts, a pair of mandibles, and two pairs of maxillae. Not all of them, however, live up to this characterization. As a general rule, the arthropod head developed by the addition of somites to it from behind, and mouthparts have been added in the same way. It appears that the second maxillary somite, the most recent addition to the gnathocephalon, has not been fully incorporated into the head structure in many myriapods, and just as in some Crustacea, where the second maxilla may be scarcely distinguishable from the thoracic appendages, the second maxilla of some myriapods is leg-like. In other cases the second maxillae have been reduced and form a part of the lower lip.

Pauropods and millipedes, as a rule, have greatly reduced second maxillae. The pselaphognathid diplopods are exceptions, for they have leg-like second maxillae on the collum. In the other millipedes and pauropods any vestiges of the appendages on the

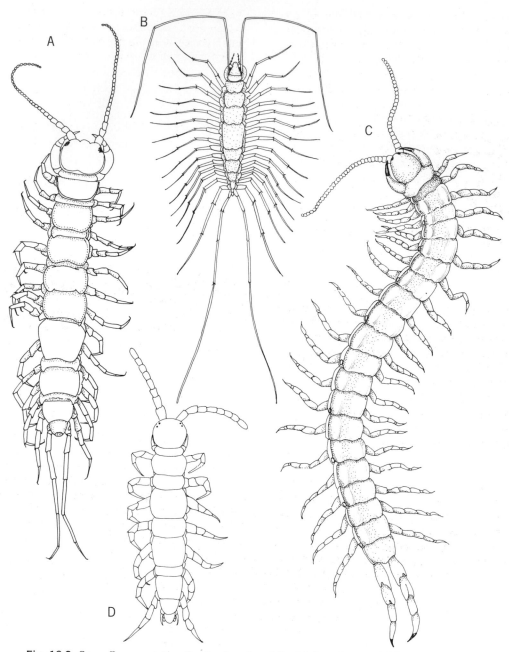

Fig. 19.3. Some Representative Centipedes. **A** and **D.** Adult and young *Lithobius*, a centipede belonging to the order Lithobiomorpha. These centipedes have long antennae and 15 pairs of legs. Alternating short and long somites are thought to serve as a stabilizing adaptation to rapid running. They hatch with only seven pairs of legs. **B.** *Scutigera*, the house centipede, a member of the order Scutigeromorpha. They have 15 pairs of very long legs, the last pair serving as anal feelers. The large, faceted eyes and dorsal spiracles, opening into tracheal lungs,

second maxillary somite, or collum, are incorporated in the lower lip or gnathochilarium. The main differences center about the intimacy of the union of the elements of which the gnathochilarium is built. In pauropods the parts of the gnathochilarium are not fully fused, and in pselaphognaths, also, the parts are partially separate. In the majority of diplopods the gnathochilarium (Fig. 19.5D) is composed of the united gnathal lobes of the mandibles, the first maxillae, the sternum of the first maxillary somite, and the vestiges of the second maxillae, and is hinged on the sternum of the second maxillary somite or collum. The two first maxillae are attached at the base, but are free distally and retain some freedom of movement.

Symphylans and chilopods, as a rule, have more conspicuous second maxillae. The second maxillae are leg-like in the scutigeromorph centipedes, but in the other groups are incorporated into the gnathochilarium to a greater or lesser extent. Details of the structure of the gnathochilarium differ with the order in chilopods, and need not be discussed here. As a rule the first thoracic legs, which are modified to form maxillipeds, have very large bases that extend forward over the maxillae, while the two maxillary appendages and the sterna of their somites project forward toward the labrum (Fig. 19.5 E,F). The symphylan head is considerably more like the head of insects. The first maxillae are more laterally placed, and the second maxillae are partially united to form a labium-like ventral plate (Fig. 19.5G,H). The mandibles, however, have movable gnathal lobes and so are myriapod-like. The parts of the two maxillae appear

to correspond to the parts of the maxillae which are seen in the labium of insects in some detail, and are given similar names. The first maxillae are long, and are formed

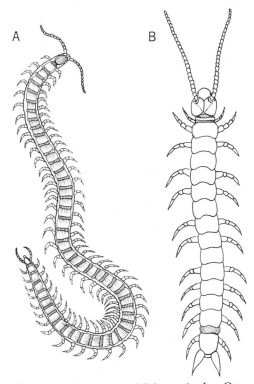

Fig. 19.4. A. A geophilid centipede. Geophilids are burrowers, with short legs and antennae. Their many somites have two dorsal and two ventral plates. All but the first and last somites have spiracles. B. *Scutigerella*, a member of the class Symphyla. Symphylans have maxillae that resemble insect maxillae and in other ways resemble primitive insects. For that reason they are of interest to entomologists. They have 12 pairs of legs and a pair of spinnerets on the thirteen trunk somite. (After Snodgrass.)

are unique among centipedes. They are very fast runners, and have a number of interesting specializations that fit them for speed. C. *Scolopendra*, a centipede belonging to the order Scolopendromorpha. Although they never have more than 23 pairs of legs some of the scolopendromorph centipedes become quite large; one species is nearly a foot long. The bite of some of the larger species is painful and may be dangerous. Scolopendromorphs have 9 to 11 pairs of spiracles and are unusual in having all of the somites present at hatching. (A and D after Eason. C after Koch.)

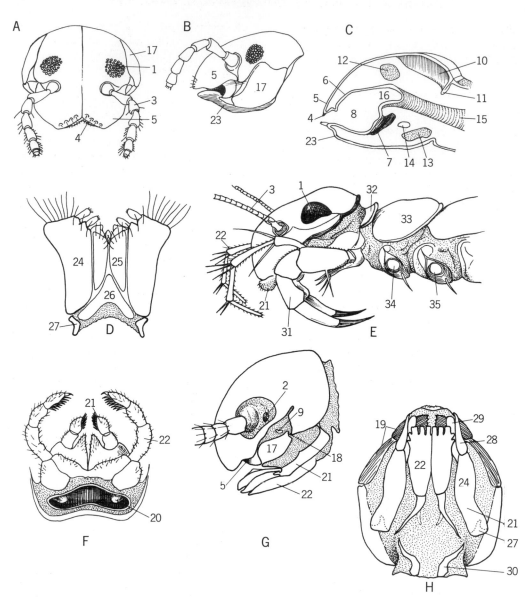

Fig. 19.5. Myriapod Head Structure. A and B, front and side views of the head of a millipede, *Arctobolus*. C. Schematic section through the head of a millipede, showing the preoral cavity and the surrounding mouth parts. D. A millipede gnathochilarium. E. Lateral view of head of a centipede, *Scutigera*. F. Maxillae of a centipede, *Lithobius*. They are close together and extend forward to serve as a lower lip. G and H. Lateral and ventral view of the head of a symphylan. Note the insect-like maxillae with the second maxillae united to form an underlip that can be partially homologized with the insect labium. (After Snodgrass.) *Head sense organs:* 1, eye; 2, organ of Tömösvary; 3, antenna. *Regions and skeletal plates:* 4, labrum; 5, epistome; 6, epipharynx; 7, hypopharynx; 8, preoral cavity; 9, spiracle; 10, midcranial ridge; 11, postoccipital ridge. *Internal parts:* 12, brain; 13, subesophageal ganglion; 14, inter-gnathal ligament; 15, stomodaeum. *Mouthparts:* 16, mouth; 17, base of mandible; 18, cranial

of a basal stipes and two apical segments, a more ventrally placed galea, and more dorsal lacinia.

TRUNK SOMITES AND APPENDAGES

The exoskeleton of the trunk varies a great deal in different kinds of myriapods. As a rule the dorsal surface is more heavily armored than the ventral surface, and smaller forms have softer bodies, especially on the ventral side. The simplest exoskeletons are found in the minute pauropods (Fig. 19.1A). All of the cuticle is membranous except for a series of dorsal plates, the terga. Symphyla are somewhat larger, and have a slightly more solid exoskeleton. The dorsal surface is covered by terga, and paired skeletal plates or sclerites are found at the bases of the legs (Fig. 19.6A). Chilopods have a strong sternum on each somite, and the dorsal surface is covered by strong tergal plates. The sides of the body are largely membranous in the majority of centipedes, although several subcoxal sclerites, located at the bases of the legs, provide points for muscle attachment. The geophilids, however, are burrowing forms and drive the head forward as a battering-ram in some cases. The exoskeleton is strengthened by distinct pleura, or lateral sclerites (Fig. 19.6B,C). The millipedes have the most thoroughly consolidated and strongest exoskeleton. Each of the diplosomites is enclosed in a continuous skeletal ring, with no articular membranes between the tergal, pleural, and sternal elements. The polydesmoid millipedes have two complete skeletal rings for each diplosomite, an anterior prozonite and a posterior metazonite. The single or double rings overlap on the dorsal side, so none of the more membranous articular membranes are exposed. The rings slide past each other at the point of the dorsal overlap, permitting the body to be curled without any loss of protection (Fig. 19.6D,E).

Specializations of the dorsal sclerites are common. The pauropods have terga that are not metameric, with fewer terga than somites, and the scutigeromorph centipedes also have some tergal plates that cover two or several somites. The lithobiomorph centipedes have alternating broad and narrow terga, and geophilids have intertergal and intersternal plates between the main tergites and sternites. The polydesmoid millipedes have a different kind of dorsal specialization. Lateral alae on the metazonites give the dorsal surface a flattened appearance. The functional significance of some of these specializations is not very well understood. In some cases they appear to increase the protective qualities of the dorsal exoskeleton, while in others, particularly in cases where two or more segments are covered by a single tergum, they may help to prevent the sinuous bending of the body during rapid movement.

The legs of myriapods are typical uniramous legs, not unlike those seen in insects or spiders. Gonopods may vary considerably from the typical legs in basic form, but the walking legs show considerable stability of form within groups. Pauropods and symphylans have legs with six segments or podites (Fig. 19.7A,B). They are quite similar, but the longer legs of the pauropods have an extra tarsal piece. Diplopods and chilopods have legs with seven segments, with a double trochanter in place of the single trochanter of the pauropods and symphylans. Diplopod legs are short and resemble the legs of geophilid centipedes (Fig. 19.7C,D). Long legs go with fast running; the herbivorous millipedes are slower than the carnivorous

articulation of mandible; 19, mandible; 20, mandibular pouch; 21, first maxilla; 22, second maxilla; 23, gnathochilarium; 24, stipes; 25, lamina lingualis; 26, mentum; 27, cardo; 28, galea; 29, lacinia; 30, cervical plate. *Trunk:* 31, maxilliped; 32, tergum 1; 33, tergum 2; 34, leg 1; 35, leg 2.

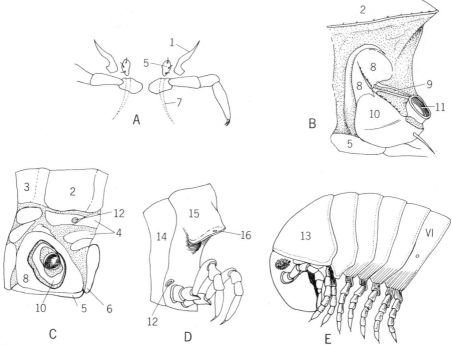

Fig. 19.6. **A.** Ventral sclerites associated with the first pair of legs of a symphylan
B and **C.** Comparison of the skeletal plates of the somites of a scutigerid and a geophilid
centipede. Scutigerids are essentially like most other centipedes in having a single tergum over
the dorsal surface, a sternum below, and a soft pleural region, strengthened by a few sclerites
associated with the appendage base. Geophilids, however, have two dorsal plates, a tergum
and an intertergite, and two ventral plates, a sternum and intersternite. Some pleural plates, in
addition to the sclerites associated with the bases of the appendages, strengthen the lateral
wall of the somite. **D.** Somite of a polydesmoid millipede. Each millipede diplosomite is usually
covered by a continuous skeletal ring, in which tergum, pleura, and sternum cannot be distinguished, around each diplosomite. Polydesmoids have two such rings for each diplosomite,
an anterior prozonite, and posterior metazonite. The lateral flares which give the polydesmoids
their flattened appearance are located on the metazonite. This kind of skeletal strengthening
results in some loss of flexibility. **E.** The head and anterior part of the trunk of a juliform
millipede, *Arctobolus*. In these millipedes, each diplosomite is covered by a single skeletal
ring. The rings overlap, permitting the animal to roll up in a spiral. The collum does not belong
to the somite on which the first pair of legs insert. A small sternum, without a corresponding
tergum, lies immediately behind the sternal plate below the collum. The first pair of legs
insert on this intercalated sternum. Each of the first five pairs of legs is a single pair, attached
to different somites. Somite VI, however, carries the sixth and seventh legs, and the succeeding diplosomites have two pairs of legs. (After Snodgrass.) **1,** cervical plate; **2,** tergum;
3, intertergite; **4,** pleura; **5,** sternum; **6,** intersternite; **7,** apodeme; **8,** subcoxal sclerite; **9,** post-
coxal sclerite; **10,** coxa; **11,** first trochanter; **12,** spiracle; **13,** collum; **14,** prozonite; **15,** metazonite; **16,** pore of repugnatorial gland.

848

centipedes, on the whole. Geophilids, however, live in the soil and surface litter. Many of them are burrowers, and none are fast runners. Legs are elongated by subdivision of the tarsus. Most of the chilopods have at least two tarsal pieces, and the very fast scutigeromorphs have a large number of tarsal pieces (Fig. 19.7E,F). In all of these cases, however, the long tendon of the pretarsus flexor muscle passes through the tarsal pieces without inserting on them, as is typical of the terrestrial mandibulates generally.

Extensive specialization of the legs is

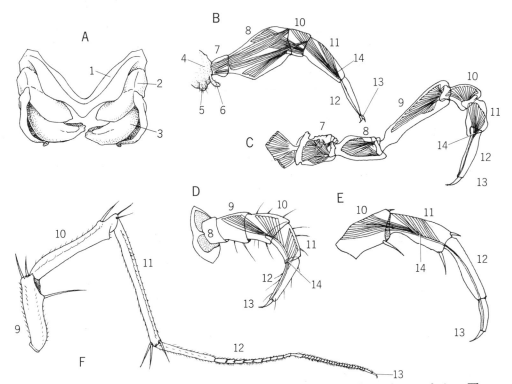

Fig. 19.7. A. Male millipedes generally have some modified appendages for copulation. The figure shows the sternum and gonopods found on the seventh somite of a juliform millipede, *Arctobolus*. B-F. Comparison of some myriapod legs. B. A symphlan leg (*Scutigerella*). It arises from a more or less conical lobe of the body wall, from which an eversible vesicle and stylus extend. The styli resemble similar processes found in some primitive insects. C. The leg of *Euryurus*, a millipede. Millipedes have two trochanters, while symphylans have one. Millipedes feed predominantly on decaying vegetation, and are relatively slow-moving, with short legs. D. The leg of a geophilid centipede. Geophilids burrow in soil and litter, and are slow-moving, with short, powerful legs. Although short, the legs have the two trochanters characteristic of chilopods. They have a single tarsus. E. The end of the leg of a lithobiomorph centipede. These carnivorous centipedes are fast runners, and have legs lengthened by the addition of a second tarsal piece. F. The end of the leg of a scutigerid centipede. Scutigerids run even faster than the lithobiomorphs, and have remarkably long legs. The individual podites are prolonged, and there are many tarsal pieces. (After Snodgrass.) 1, sternum; 2, first gonopod; 3, second gonopod; 4, lobe of body at base of leg; 5, eversible vesicle; 6, stylus; 7, coxa; 8, trochanter; 9, second trochanter (prefemur); 10, femur; 11, tibia; 12, tarsus; 13, pretarsus; 14, pretarsal flexor.

not typical of myriapods. Specialized legs are found on the genital somite, and males often have specialized gonopods, used as claspers or for sperm transfer. In centipedes the first pair of legs are modified as maxillipeds. They contain poison glands and end in a sharp fang, through which the poison is injected. Otherwise the legs are all much alike, but close examination shows some small differences in the proportions of the leg segments, and in some cases the first and last legs have one less segment. The back legs of *Scutigera* are held extended and pointing to the rear, serving as posterior antennae, and are somewhat modified. Among chilopods, the outstanding leg specializations are seen in interruptions of the general rule of two pairs of legs for each diplosomite. Some of the diplosomites are legless or have a single pair of legs. Nearly all millipedes have a single pair of legs on the first three trunk diplosomites, counting the legless collum as the last head somite. This pattern is broken in the pselaphognaths, which have a pair of leg-like maxillae on the collum. It is also broken in the juliform millipedes, which have no appendages on the collum, but have a single pair of legs on the fourth and fifth trunk diplosomites. Legs are never found on the pygidium, and in many myriapods the somite immediately in front of the pygidium is also legless.

A number of structures are characteristic of the trunk somites or legs, and occupy distinctive positions in groups or species. Sensory setae and hairs are found on the trunk somites and also on the legs. The tracheal system opens through spiracles with characteristic positions in centipedes and millipedes. Millipedes usually have two spiracular openings on each diplosomite, while centipedes have one on each somite. In nearly all centipedes and millipedes the spiracles are openings in the membranous pleura near the leg bases, but the scutigeromorph centipedes are unique in having a series of middorsal spiracles in the middle of the terga. Symphylans have a stylus and eversible vesicle located near the leg bases. The vesicle arises from an embryonic rudiment known as the ventral organ. Its function is unknown. The styli resemble styli found in the abdominal somites of some insects. Symphylans also have a pair of spinnerets on the preanal somite. The spinnerets resemble the cerci of insects, but are probably not homologous to them.

LOCOMOTION

Millipedes feed on plant material, as a rule, and have no particular need for speed. They move slowly, burrowing in the leaf mold or forcing themselves into crevices under bark or in rotting wood. When disturbed many roll up, presenting the heavily protected dorsal surface, and eject toxic or nauseating substances from the repugnatorial glands. They have short, stout legs, suitable for thrusting the body forward against a resistance and particularly useful in burrowing. Each leg makes a step consisting of a quick recovery movement and a slow, powerful effective movement. An animal with as many legs as a millipede cannot afford disorganization in its stepping. It is important that the many legs work together, each stepping in advance of the leg behind. As in polychaetes with a large number of similar parapodia, harmonious co-operation of the appendages is achieved by the passage of activation waves along the body. When a millipede is making its fastest time, wave follows wave rapidly, and each wave involves only a few pairs of legs. During slow, burrowing movements, on the other hand, the waves are very slow and involve a large number of legs. In a long millipede, fifty or more legs may step together in a single, powerful shove. It is probable that the double somites, the consolidated exoskeleton, and the many legs with their slow activation waves are adaptations for burrowing or forcing the body into tight places. Body rigidity probably helps considerably in forcing the body forward. The exoskeleton is very firm, consisting of a cuticle hardened by phenolic tanning and strengthened by calcium deposits. The overlapping of the dorsal borders of the diplosomites may also aid in holding the body rigid when burrowing.

Centipedes are predominantly predaceous animals. Many live in the surface litter or under objects, but these can often run very rapidly in pursuit of prey. They present an interesting contrast to the slower millipedes. The longer legs are important for high speed, but create problems as well. As many as four pairs of legs may have overlapping strides, and if the steps were not very precisely co-ordinated, centipedes would be too tangle-footed to run. In millipedes, faster movement is achieved by the more rapid movement of activation waves along the body, and by the reduction in the number of legs involved in a wave. The same principles apply in centipede movement, but the application is a good deal more complex. Centipedes have far fewer legs than millipedes, on the whole, and as running speed increases and the waves pass along the body more rapidly, a single metachronal wave does not suffice. Alternating waves pass along the bodies of the speediest forms. The step as well as the pattern of activation waves is different in centipedes. The longer legs make very quick backward, effective movements, and somewhat slower forward, recovery movements. The fast centipedes make some of the fastest effective leg thrusts to be found among arthropods. As a result of the quick thrust and the fast activation waves, only two or three pairs of legs may touch the ground together, and in fast species the rigidity of the body is as important as in the burrowing millipedes, although for a different reason. The extremely long-legged and fast scutigeromorphs have terga covering two or three somites, increasing the rigidity of the body. The somewhat slower, but nevertheless fast, lithobiomorphs have alternating long and short terga, which also appear to be an anti-undulatory adaptation. Millipedes may move the legs slowly enough to feel for good footing, but centipedes step far too rapidly for such niceties. Gripping hairs and other compensatory structures are found at the tips of the legs.

The geophilids, however, have followed an entirely different adaptational line. They live in cramped quarters beneath objects and can burrow like millipedes. They achieve their power in a different manner from millipedes, however. The very short legs do not provide the propulsive power. The body elongates and contracts during burrowing in much the same manner as in earthworms, and the short legs play about the same role as the setae of earthworms. When the geophilids walk, the legs move relatively slowly and feel about for a foothold. Each leg is on its own, in a sense, for metachronal stepping waves are not characteristic of the group. It is likely that the very short legs, with little overlap in step, have de-emphasized the importance of the close co-ordination of the legs during walking.

OFFENSE AND DEFENSE

Centipedes, as carnivores without appendages appropriate for handling the food, are greatly benefited by a mechanism that will quickly stun or immobilize their prey. The maxillipeds, with their sharp fangs and poison glands, are formidable weapons. They will cause very rapid immobilization of animals that are fair prey, and many centipedes have maxillipeds powerful enough to penetrate the skin of large animals, like man. Centipede bites cause severe local pain, swelling, and in at least one authenticated case, human death. Most of the smallest species cannot bite man, but species as small as *Scutigera* can give a painful bite. The maxillipeds may have been developed primarily as offensive weapons, but they are no less effective for defense. With their rapid movements and fangs, centipedes are very well protected.

A predator, however, may injure its prey even though forced to drop it because of a painful bite. It is well for an animal if its enemy can recognize it as one that is well protected. The brilliantly colored tropical centipedes are probably protected by their color, for a predator large enough to survive the bite of a centipede may be trained not to attack another member of the same species. In coloration as in so many other facets of evolutionary adaptation, there may be several paths leading to the same goal. An otherwise defenseless animal may be protected by resembling its background and becoming inconspicuous, while a powerfully defended one may be protected by vivid color and visibility.

The slow-moving millipedes have no offensive weapons, as is often the case in herbivorous animals. As a general rule the herbivore prefers a quiet, undisturbed life of munching, but as this is rarely possible in a world filled with carnivores, herbivores develop a variety of protective devices. A good example is the millipede, of all of the myriapods the most heavily armored. When disturbed, many millipedes roll the body up into a ball or coil, presenting an unbroken expanse of tough exoskeleton to the unfriendly world. This habit has another advantage, for since many predators are better at sensing movement than perceiving form, in some cases they may lose sight of the motionless prey. Still another advantage comes from coiling. It reduces water-loss at the surface and is helpful when the surroundings become less humid. However, a large number of millipedes have another defensive adaptation in the form of repugnatorial glands, opening through pores on the body surface. The duct from the repugnatorial glands and the soft tissues around the pore are equipped with muscles, and small quantities of the secretion are liberated when the duct and pore is opened. Once such a device appears, it tends to be improved by further adaptation, and a few species have evolved powerful weapons from the repugnatorial

gland system. Where the secretion is copious and the pores and ducts are held open, contractions of the body-wall muscles can spray the vicinity with the forbidding material. A few species have developed this habit, and in some it is extremely effective. A Haitian *Rhinocrisis* is said to achieve distances of almost a meter with its spray. The nature of the secretions produced by the repugnatorial glands undoubtedly varies greatly with species, but in general these secretions are found to contain such substances as hydrocyanic acid, iodine, quinine, and small amounts of chlorine. The fluid can be extremely irritating, even to man, and causes blindness in chickens and other small animals that are unwary enough to attack millipedes with strong repugnatorial glands. Here again is a weapon powerful enough to provide protection without use, and it is probable that the more brightly colored tropical millipedes are protected by their bright color.

Internal Anatomy and Physiology

Myriapods have not been studied as intensively as insects, and a number of points about their physiology are undescribed. Many of their organs are very like the organs of insects, and at present one is limited to supposing that they work in much the same manner. In general, these will be discussed more fully later. No attempt will be made to undertake a discussion of detailed differences in the organization of different kinds of myriapods. On the whole, all of the myriapods have relatively similar internal parts.

THE DIGESTIVE SYSTEM

Except for the colobognaths, which have suctorial mouth parts and are adapted to pierce plants and suck the sap, millipedes and symphylans generally feed on dead plant tissues. Some will attack living

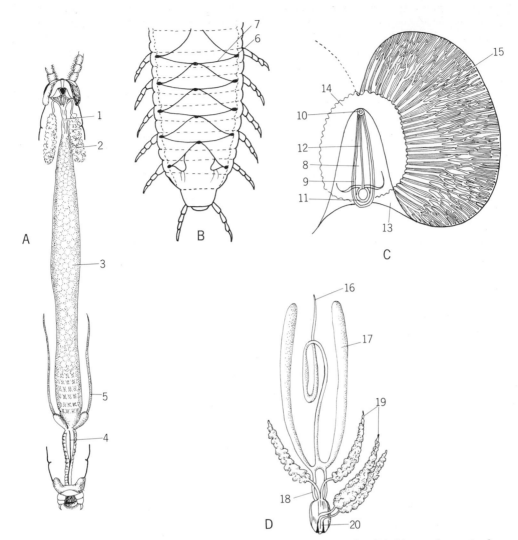

Fig. 19.8. Centipede Anatomy. **A.** The internal organization of a lithobiomorph centipede. **B.** Spiracles and main tracheae of a geophilid centipede. Geophilids have a pair of spiracles on all but the first and last body somites, and while there are some connections between the tracheae of adjacent somites, there are no really effective longitudinal trunks. **C.** The tracheal lung of a scutigerid centipede. Scutigerids have a unique respiratory system, with middorsal spiracles opening into tracheal lungs which hang down into blood in the haemocoel. The blood is, therefore, used for respiratory transport. **D.** The reproductive organs of a male lithobiomorph. (**A**, after Plateau, from Attems, in Kükenthal and Krumbach. **B**, after Kaufmann. **C**, after Hasse. **D**, after Schaufler, from Snodgrass.) *Digestive system:* 1, esophagus; 2, salivary glands; 3, midgut; 4, hindgut; 5, Malpighian tubule. *Respiratory system:* 6, spiracle; 7, commissural trachea; 8, external pore; 9, internal opening of spiracle; 10, anterior pore; 11, posterior pore; 12, chitinous wall; 13, tergal thickening around spiracle; 14, atrium; 15, tuft of tracheal tubes. *Reproductive system:* 16, testis; 17, seminal vesicle; 18, sperm duct; 19, glands; 20, penis.

plants, and where they become abundant can be quite destructive. Pauropod food habits are not very well described. Some feed on fungi, while others are thought to feed on dead animal or plant tissues. Centipedes are carnivores, feeding on annelids and arthropods of suitable size. While diversity in dietary habits is reflected in modifications of the mouth parts and the development of maxillipeds in centipedes, the kind of food eaten seems to have little relationship to the general form of the digestive tract, and all myriapods have rather similar digestive systems.

A slender esophagus opens into a wide midgut, separated by a valvular constriction from the short, muscular rectum (Fig. 19.8A). Although the intestine or midgut is usually straight, it is coiled in oniscomorphs. The esophagus arises from the stomodaeum and is lined with thin cuticle. The rectum arises from the proctodaeum and is also lined with cuticle. A delicate cuticular lining, the peritrophic membrane, lines the midgut of some species. It is derived from special secretory cells in the stomodaeum, and closely resembles the similar membrane found in many insects. From one to three pairs of salivary glands open into the esophagus, but myriapods lack the extensive system of diverticula so often found in arthropods. Not much is known about digestive physiology. Presumably it is similar to that of insects.

THE RESPIRATORY SYSTEM

Myriapods are all air-breathers. Respiratory transfer occurs at the body surface of pauropods. Their minute size and soft exoskeleton evidently makes this method adequate. With increased size and increased armoring of the body, a tracheal system becomes an essential part of the body organization. It is probable that at least a simple tracheal system appeared early in the evolutionary development of the terrestrial mandibulate stocks. One cannot safely conclude that since pauropods have no tracheae and show a number of primitive characteristics in other ways, the myriapod groups developed tracheae independently. Minute insects, also, are sometimes without a tracheal system. Apparently the tracheal system can be reduced and lost in minute organisms. Nevertheless, the tracheal systems of different types of myriapods differ markedly. Some have quite primitive types of tracheae, and differences in the placement of the tracheae would suggest that the tracheal system, if present in the very early ancestral stocks, must have been so primitive that there was room for a great deal of independent experimentation in each of the myriapod groups.

Several generalizations about the adaptive trends in tracheal systems appear to be justified. The tracheal system tends to be more highly developed in larger, and in more active, animals. As in the arachnids, the tracheal system may be adapted along two lines, with the tracheae serving to aerate the blood along one line, and the tracheae distributing oxygen directly to the tissues along the other line. Tracheae adapted to the aeration of the blood form a tracheal lung. They are characteristic of scutigeromorph centipedes. The main line of improvement involves adaptations which bring the short tracheal tubes into close contact with the blood.

Tracheae adapted to transport oxygen and carbon dioxide directly to the tissues have undergone rather similar modifications in arachnids, insects, and myriapods. In primitive tracheal systems the tracheal tubes from each spiracle form an independent system, and each tracheal tube in the tuft arising at a spiracle passes directly to the tissues without branching. Improvements of this primitive arrangement follow several lines. (1) An important line of improvement is ramification of the tracheae. Individual tracheal tubes may branch on their way to the tissues, and later main trunks appear, from which branching tributaries arise. This increases the capacity of the tracheal system for holding air and increases the potential number of tracheae, permitting more nearly equal distribution to the tissues. (2) Another important line of development is the integration of the tracheae from the various spiracles into a continuous system. This is brought about by commissural tracheae which connect the tracheae within the same somite, and by the anastomosis of tracheae from adjacent somites, with the subsequent development of longitudinal tracheal trunks. As a result, the plugging of a spiracle or local injury does not necessarily lead to respiratory failure in any of the body tissues. An even more important advantage is the fact that body movements may partially compress the longitudinal trunks, resulting in movement of air in the tracheal tubes, and in more rapid delivery of oxygen to the tissues. This advantage may be capitalized upon by the coupling of dilated air sacs with the longitudinal trunks. Pressure on the air sacs may result in an appreciable flow of air in the outer part of the tracheal system throughout the body. (3) A certain amount of water loss is inevitable, but this can be reduced by control of the spiracles. The development of spiracle valves that can close the tracheae off when respiratory needs are low and open when the animal is under respiratory stress is an important factor in reducing water loss. Control of the spiracles, when accompanied by the development of longitudinal trunks and especially when air sacs are present, can result in the passage of air along a definite course, with some spiracles serving as inhalant and other spiracles as exhalant openings. None of the myriapods have all of the kinds of improvements that might be made, and for some of the final types of tracheal improvement, insects must provide the examples. However, a considerable development of the tracheal system can be seen in various kinds of myriapods.

The Symphyla have a tracheal system that differs markedly from that of millipedes and centipedes. They have a single pair of spiracles, located on the head. The branching tracheae extend to the tissues of the head and the first three trunk somites. All other parts of the body must receive oxygen from the blood, and probably a considerable part of respiratory exchange occurs at the body surface.

Millipedes have many spiracles and a simple tracheal system with a number of primitive characteristics. No spiracles are found on the first three trunk somites, whose tissues receive tracheae from the fourth somite. From the fourth somite on, each diplosomite is equipped with two pairs of spiracles, located near the coxae of the legs. Air enters the spiracles and passes to air reservoirs in the transverse apodemes to which the leg muscles attach. Tufts of tracheae, differing in nature in different millipede orders, arise from the air reservoirs. The majority of millipedes have long, slender tracheae that pass without branching to the tissues they serve. In some cases, however, the tracheae branch on their way to the tissues. Anastomosis of the tracheae does not occur, however, and the tracheal system consists of a series of small systems within each somite, except at the front of the body, where the fourth somite takes in air for the more anterior part of the animal.

Centipedes have a considerably more highly developed tracheal system, characterized by branching and anastomosing of the tubes. Geophilids have spiracles in each somite except the first and last, and a relatively simple tracheal system (Fig. 19.8B), without conspicuous longitudinal trunks. The tracheae of other centipedes anastomose more freely, resulting in an integrated system with longitudinal trunks like those of insects. Many of the somites have no spiracles, the pattern differing in different groups. In lithobiomorphs, for example, there are usually no spiracles in the somites with narrow tergal plates. Little is known of the ways in which the tracheal system is ventilated. Presumably they use the same techniques as wingless insects.

The respiratory system of the scutigeromorphs is so different that it is probably an independent development. Each of the terga except the last contains a middorsal spiracle (Fig. 19.8C). The spiracle opens into an air sac, from which innumerable short tracheae arise. These are immersed in the blood of the pericardial sinus, aerating the blood before it is circulated to the tissues. This tracheal lung, similar in function though so different in structure to the tracheal lung of some spiders, is a unique development. Aeration of blood by tracheae occurs in some other mandibulates, but in no case is the lung structure similar to that of scutigeromorphs.

THE EXCRETORY SYSTEM

Myriapods have Malpighian tubules attached at the junction of the midgut and hindgut (Fig. 19.8A). Two or four Malpighian tubules are present. Amplification of the tubule surface is achieved by the elongation of the tubules. They often extend forward to the esophagus and turn back, ending near the posterior end of the body. In large-bodied forms, like *Spirobolus*, they are greatly coiled. Each tubule ends blindly and is composed of a single layer of tall, columnar cells. The tubules probably function like the Malpighian tubules of insects.

THE CIRCULATORY SYSTEM

Myriapods have a circulatory system like that of other arthropods, but the very long heart is more like a modified dorsal blood vessel than is generally true. It lies in a long pericardial sinus that extends the whole length of the trunk. Segmental alary muscles attach the heart to the dorsal wall of the sinus and contract to dilate the heart. Blood flows into the heart through paired ostia, with one pair in each chilopod somite and two pairs in each diplopod segment. Between the ostia lateral blood vessels arise. These pass through the adjacent fat bodies and open into the haemocoelic lacunae. As a rule the centipedes have a stronger heart than the less active millipedes.

THE NEUROSENSORY APPARATUS

There is very little specific information on the function of the mechanoreceptors and chemoreceptors of myriapods. They are equipped with sensory setae, bristles, and pits which are essentially like those of other arthropods, and presumably function in much the same way. The structure of some of the special sense organs is of interest, however.

A pair of peculiar sense organs known as pseudoculi occur on the head of pauropods, about in the position ordinarily occupied by eyes. At first they were thought to be unusual photoreceptors, but their structure seems to preclude any possibility of their being light-sensitive. Each pseudoculus consists of a convex field of cuticle which roofs a large, fluid-filled space. Beneath the fluid there is a sensory epithelium made up of large cells, which are innervated from the protocerebrum. No definite function has been ascribed to them, but it has been suggested that they might be sensitive to vibrations.

Symphylans, most millipedes, and some centipedes have a pair of sensory pits on the head, immediately behind the antennae. These are the organs of Tömösvary. They vary considerably in form in different species. They are sometimes open pits or grooves and in some cases are lined with cuticle. At the bottom of the depression there are sensory cells that are innervated from the optic lobe of the brain. Their function is uncertain.

Many of the myriapods are blind, but others have eyes of one kind or another. Their eyes are ocelli, but they are lateral eyes nevertheless, innervated like the lateral compound eyes found in other arthropods.

Details of ocellar structure are quite variable, but the general scheme of the ocellus remains about the same. A corneal lens covers the optic cup. The cup is lined with peripheral and central sensory cells equipped with striated sensory borders, somewhat like the rhabdomeres found in the retinula cells of the ommatidia in compound eyes. Ocelli are sometimes isolated, but are usually clustered in smaller or larger groups. In many cases the members of a cluster are closely packed, and in this case the corneal lenses unite to form a single lens structure. The ocelli beneath, however, do not unite, and each retains its individuality. The scutigeromorph centipedes are exceptions. They have large compound eyes, with each element rather like the ommatidia of insects and crustaceans. Although the eye of *Scutigera* has a far more advanced structure than the eyes of other centipedes, it does not approach the complexity of most insect or decapod eyes. At the most only a couple of hundred ommatidia are present. It is more like the eyes of some larval insects than the eyes of the adults.

Strong tactic responses are common among myriapods. They are usually negatively phototactic, as is suitable for organisms not well protected against desiccation. Even the eyeless species are usually photonegative, indicating a considerable dermoptic sensitivity.

The central nervous system follows the typical arthropod plan. A dorsal brain is connected to a double nerve cord by a circumenteric ring. Segmental ganglia occur on the nerve cord. They are actually double, though in many cases they appear single to the naked eye. Commissures connect the ganglionic pairs, and segmentally arranged lateral nerves issue from each ganglion to the sense organs and muscles of the somite.

As in other arthropods, union of ganglia on the ventral nerve cord leads to further centralization of the nervous system. This has not progressed very far in any kind of myriapod, however. The ganglia of the first three trunk somites of millipedes are close together, and sometimes have partly fused. Although the brain is rather highly differentiated, the nerve cord and metameric ganglia are relatively primitive.

A close relationship between sense-organ development and brain structure can be seen in myriapods. In eyeless species the optic centers in the corpora pedunculata are dwarfed and olfactory centers are correspondingly increased. As a general rule the olfactory centers constitute a large part of the brain of myriapods. In the scutigerid centipedes, however, well-developed optic centers are found, and chiasmatic tracts cross from right to left optic relay centers in the brain.

REPRODUCTION

Myriapods have a relatively simple reproductive system. The gonads are dorsal and unpaired, and open into a paired system of gonoducts which pass to the genital somite. In some cases the males form spermatophores, and in others the sperm is stored in large seminal vesicles associated with the sperm ducts. One or two pairs of accessory glands are present. The female system is essentially similar in its construction, and includes seminal receptacles in which the sperm obtained during mating is stored.

Males have specialized legs, differently located in different myriapod groups. They are used as claspers during mating or for sperm transfer. Some of the millipedes have penes associated with the sperm ducts at the gonopore. Mating habits are quite different in different kinds of myriapods. Gonopores may be apposed, penes may inject sperm into the seminal receptacles, gonopods may be charged with sperm and brought in contact with the female gonopores, or spermatophores may be transferred with the gonopods. In any case, the seminal receptacles are charged with sperm, in some cases long before the eggs are mature.

The females produce shelled ova, and exhibit a wide range of maternal-care instincts. In some cases the eggs are produced more or less continuously and left in the soil or surface litter. Many millipedes construct nests for their eggs, using secretions from the anus to consolidate particles of soil or other materials. They tend the nests for a few days before leaving the young to develop on their own. Centipedes may produce nests of one kind or another, or leave the eggs in small clusters in the soil or litter. It is not uncommon for centipedes to guard the young as well as the eggs for a time. Apparently the nests and guard duty are important to prevent the growth of fungi, which is one of the principal hazards of early development.

Eggs may hatch before all of the legs and somites are present. In this case development is said to be anamorphic. Most myriapods are anamorphic. Pauropods hatch with three pair of legs, and symphylans with six or seven pairs of legs. All of the millipedes are anamorphic, and the scutigeromorph and lithobiomorph centipedes are also anamorphic, hatching with four or seven pairs of legs. Anamorphic development involves the addition of somites and legs with each of the succeeding molts. Although there is considerable variation in the way that somites are added in different species or groups, each species adds somites in a constant fashion, with each stadium having a definite number of pairs of legs. Only a small number of exceptions to this rule are known. In most cases, more than one somite is added at a molt. Millipedes, for example, generally add four somites at a time. Somites are added in the traditional arthropod manner, at the back end of the body in front of the pygidial somite. Most of the centipedes have a full complement of legs when they hatch, and development is said to be epimorphic. In this case the body and somites become larger during the develop-mental molts, and it is much more difficult to recognize the juveniles as belonging to a particular stadium. Some of the anamorphic myriapods have acquired a full set of somites and legs before the last developmental molts have occurred. In this case the last of the developmental molts are epimorphic, and development is sometimes termed hemianamorphic. One of the more common lines of evolutionary adaptation involves lengthening the period of development before hatching, and in this sense anamorphic development is more primitive than epimorphic development. It should be noted, however, that it is not rare to find a species which is otherwise highly specialized that continues to show the more primitive type of development.

Class Insecta

It is not unlikely that the class Insecta includes more pests than all of the other invertebrate phyla combined. Insects bite man, irritate him, and sometimes make him ill. Insect vectors transmit such scourges as bubonic plague, malaria, typhus, and African sleeping sickness. Lice, fleas, and sometimes other types of insects are themselves parasites. Insects bite, irritate, and parasitize our domestic animals as they do man. They suck from, chew on, bore in, parasitize, and bring diseases to the food plants growing in fields and, unless controlled, ruin crops after they are harvested. It is tempting to think of insects as biological villains, from man's point of view, to put all of them in the same category, and to consider the indiscriminate destruction of any kind of insect an act that promotes human welfare. Nothing could be farther from the truth, however. For all of the damage that some insects do, the total destruction of all insects would do as much, and perhaps more, harm as good to the biological communities of which man is a part. Thousands of plant species depend primarily upon insects for the pollenization of the flowers, and these species would disappear. With them would go some of man's most valuable crops. A few insects are important for their own products. For many centuries, bees were the only dependable source of sugar in many parts of the world, and natural silk is produced only by silkworms. All of them are integral parts of the ecological communities of which they form a small but active portion, and without them the food chains would be seriously disturbed, and some of our nicest birds would disappear. They play many roles in their communities. Predaceous insects are important allies for man, as important as birds in controlling some kinds of insect pests. Many of the insects found in the forest floor are important in reducing the dead plant material to small particles that can be incorporated in the soil. It is difficult, sometimes, for the layman to understand the vital role, on the beneficial side, that insects play in his world, and with the growing practice of spraying the landscape with highly effective insecticides, the beneficial as well as the destructive insects are eliminated. One of the more important problems that faces us is the need for developing more discriminate methods of insect control, methods that will control the destructive species without eliminating the beneficial ones.

It is quite impossible to discuss insects in detail in a book that deals with all types of invertebrates, and a more detailed account of their form and activities must be sought in books on entomology. It will suffice to view the insects as the culmination of the terrestrial mandibulate line, to seek to explain some of the factors that have made them so successful, and to reflect something of the diversity of insects as a group. Their success can be dealt with only in superlatives, for they constitute the largest class of animals, one that contains more species than occurs in any phylum other than the one to which they belong. Insect classification is necessarily complex,

for it must reflect the tremendous adaptability and the series of adaptive radiations that have occurred in this successful class.

CLASSIFICATION

Subclass Myrientomata. Long-bodied, wingless insects that hatch before the full complement of abdominal somites is present.

Order Protura. Proturans. Minute, soft, wingless insects, living in surface litter and in humid situations, with no antennae and with forelegs used as tactile appendages; without compound eyes or ocelli; pseudoculi, perhaps vestigial antennae, on the sides of the head; chewing mouthparts of a primitive type; Malpighian tubules reduced to papillae; a non-pulsating pericardial cord in place of a heart; a simple or no tracheal system; a 12-segmented abdoment without cerci. Example: *Eosentomon* (Fig. 19.9A).

Subclass Oligoentoma. Insects with only six abdominal somites and without genitalia or Malpighian tubules.

Order Collembola. Springtails. Minute, soft, primitive insects with short antennae; compound eyes very simple or missing; simple, chewing mouthparts with sharp mandibles; usually with a springing mechanism composed of a spring (furcula) on the fifth abdominal somite and a clasp (tenaculum) on the third abdominal somite, used to hold the spring until it is released suddenly; a ventral tube (colophore) of unknown function on the first abdominal somite; without abdominal cerci; cleavage holoblastic but young with all somites present at hatching and maturing by epimorphic molts. Example: *Entomobrya.*

Subclass Euentoma. Insects with definite genitalia and with Malpighian tubules; typically with an abdomen of nine or ten segments; eggs developing by meroblastic cleavage and hatching with all somites present; juvenile molts following several different patterns, but never anamorphic.

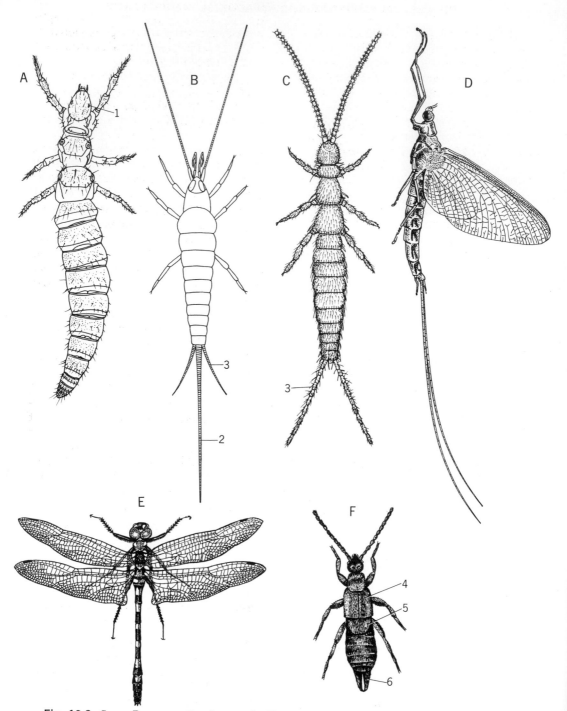

Fig. 19.9. Some Representative Insects. A. *Eosentomon*, a representative of order Protura. Proturans belong to the subclass Myrientomata, which are anamorphic, adding three somites to the body after hatching. They are wingless, with primitive chewing mouthparts and

Division Apterygota. Primitive, wingless insects with segmentally arranged gonads, simple thoracic terga, and rudimentary appendages known as styli on the abdomen. Juveniles resemble adults at hatching and undergo epimorphic molts.

Order Thysanura. Silverfish. Small insects with long, often scaly bodies; long antennae; compound eyes and ocelli present or absent; short cursorial legs, sometimes with exopodites on the middle or hind coxi; ten abdominal segments, some with styli; eleventh abdominal somite drawn out as a caudal filament; long abdominal cerci; Malpighian tubules and tracheae well developed. Example: *Machilis* (Fig. 19.9B).

Order Diplura. Campodeids and japygids. Small, soft, wingless insects with, slender, flattened bodies, seeking dark and humid environments; long antennae; without eyes; primitive chewing mouthparts; 11-segmented abdomen with styli and with conspicuous cerci; papilliform or no Malpighian tubules. Example: *Campodea* (Fig. 19.9C).

Division Pterygota. Insects with wings or secondarily wingless; usually with a complete set of organ systems, including tracheae and Malpighian tubules.

Series Hemimetabola. Winged insects which hatch as nymphs, typically with wing buds, and which undergo a series of molts accompanied by gradual metamorphosis.

Order Ephemeroptera. Mayflies. Small to medium, soft, slender insects with short hair-like antennae; large compound eyes and three ocelli; chewing mouthparts in the aquatic nymphs and vestigial mouthparts in adults; forewings larger than hindwings and both pairs held vertically over the back when at rest; two very long abdominal cerci and a caudal filament; ten abdominal somites and a vestigial eleventh somite; tracheal gills in aquatic nymphs. Example: *Hexagenia* (Fig. 19.9D).

Order Odonata. Dragonflies and damselflies. Medium to large, slender, predaceous insects with strong chewing mouthparts; small, hair-like antennae; huge compound eyes and three ocelli; stout legs; two pairs of similar, narrow, net-veined wings held straight out from body

pseudoculi on the head. **B.** *Machilis*, a thysanuran. The thysanurans are primitively wingless and have the last abdominal somite prolonged as a caudal filament, flanked by the long cerci. Some of the abdominal somites have styli. Some are common in houses, while others live in decaying logs or forest litter. **C.** *Campodea*, a member of the order Diplura. Also primitively wingless, the diplurans have prominent abdominal cerci, but no caudal filament. Japygids have forceps formed by the cerci, while campodeids have filamentous cerci. Some of the abdominal sternites bear styli. Diplurans are retiring animals, living in soil and litter predominantly. **D.** *Hexagenia*, a mayfly (Ephemeroptera). Mayflies are primitive pterygote insects of the series Hemimetabola, characterized by gradual metamorphosis. The aquatic nymphs have chewing mouthparts, but the adults have vestigial mouthparts, and die soon after emerging from the water. The delicate, net-veined wings are dissimilar, the forewing being larger. The two long abdominal cerci and a caudal filament are characteristic of mayflies. **E.** *Macromia*, a dragonfly (Odonata). The huge compound eyes; the narrow, net-veined wings of approximately equal size; long, slender abdomen with inconspicuous cerci, and strong biting mouthparts are characteristic of dragonflies and damselflies. **F.** *Labia*, an earwig (Dermaptera). The conspicuous characteristic features of the earwigs are the abdominal forceps formed of the cerci, and the short, leathery forewings (egmina), which cover only a part of the membranous hindwings. Although predominately tropical, some earwigs cause economically important damage to gardens in warm temperate areas. (**A**, after Berlase. **B**, after Lubbock. **C**, after Essig, from Essig. **D**, after *Ill. Nat. Hist. Survey.* **E**, after Kennedy, from Ross. **F**, after Bebard.) 1, pseudoculus; 2, caudal filament; 3, cercus; 4, tegmina (forewings); 5, hindwings; 6, caudal forceps.

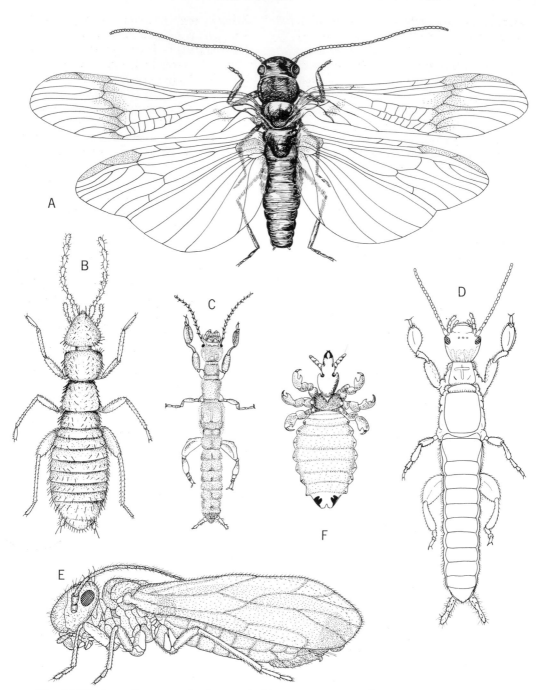

Fig. 19.10. Some Representative Insects. **A.** *Taeniopteryx,* a stonefly (Plecoptera). The long membranous wings of stoneflies are folded over the back when at rest. The forewings are generally smaller. Most stoneflies have prominent abdominal cerci. **B.** *Zorotypus,* a zorapteran. Both winged and wingless forms of these tiny insects occur. A fracture point at the base of

when at rest (dragonflies) or held vertically (damselflies); long abdomen with ten distinct somites and two rudimentary anal somites; very short, inconspicuous cerci; nymphs aquatic and with or without caudal gills. Example: *Macromia* (Fig. 19.9E).

Order Orthoptera. Grasshoppers, locusts, katydids, cockroaches, mantids, walking sticks, and leaf insects. Generally medium to large insects, with compound eyes and variable ocelli; usually strong chewing mouthparts; legs modified for running (cursorial), jumping (saltatorial), capture of prey (raptorial), or digging (fossorial); usually with two pairs of wings, the fore-wings tough, leathery tegmina that cover the larger, folded, membranous hindwings when at rest; abdomen with short cerci. Example: *Melanoplus* (Fig. 19.18).

Order Dermaptera. Earwigs. Small to medium-sized, elongated insects with a tough exoskeleton; long antennae; usually without ocelli but with compound eyes; wingless or with short forewings forming truncate tegmina that cover all but the tip of the much-folded, membranous, radially veined hindwings; abdomen ending in prominent cerci modified to form forceps. Example: *Labia* (Fig. 19.9F).

Order Plecoptera. Stoneflies. Moderate to large, long, soft insects with long antennae; modest compound eyes and variable ocelli; chewing mouthparts; two pairs of membranous wings folded over the back

when at rest; forewings usually smaller; abdomen with 11 segments, the last segment reduced; long abdominal cerci; nymphs aquatic, with or without gills. Example: *Taeniopteryx* (Fig. 19.10A).

Order Isoptera. Termites. Small to medium, social insects with soft exoskeleton; members of the society differentiated as reproductive members, workers, and soldiers; with biting mouthparts, modified in soldiers; eyes and ocelli variable; antennae slender; short, stout legs; wings, when present, similar, with basal fractures at the point where they break when shed. Example: *Reticulitermes.*

Order Zoraptera. Zorapterans. Minute insects, forming small social aggregations without division of labor but with winged and wingless members; winged members with compound eyes and ocelli and wingless members without eyes; all with slender antennae; biting mouthparts; short, stout legs; wings, long, slender, with few veins and with basal fractures; wings are shed after mating; abdomen with ten segments and with short cerci. Example: *Zorotypus* (Fig. 19.10B).

Order Embioptera. Webspinners. Small, slender, elongated insects, forming large social aggregations without division of labor; without ocelli but with compound eyes; slender antennae; biting mouthparts; short, stout legs; foreleg tarsus enlarged and containing silk glands and spinnerets used to spin a common web for the colony;

the wing permits their being shed. Zorapterans live in small casteless colonies in rotting wood or litter. C. *Embia*, a webspinner. The embiids have silk glands and spinnerets in the foreleg tarsi. Rather large, casteless societies live in communal webs, spun in rotting wood or surface litter. Both winged and wingless forms occur. D. *Oligotoma*, another webspinner (Embioptera). E. *Ectopsocus*, a booklouse (Corrodentia). Corrodentia, also known as psocids, are important pests, living in houses and warehouses, and attacking packaged goods, books, and other household goods. They also live in rotting wood and surface litter in natural habitats. Some are wingless, but two pairs of wings that fold over the back may be present. Labial spinnerets and silk glands are used to form webs for brooding the young, or, in some cases, living webs. F. *Haematopinus*, a sucking louse (Anoplura). The anoplura live as ectoparasites on mammals, and have piercing and sucking mouthparts and appendages modified for clinging to the host hair. The cootie, *Pediculus humanus*, an important carrier of typhus, and other anoplurans cause livestock losses. (A, after Newcomer. C, after Essig, in Essig. B, after Caudell. E, after Sommerman. F, after *Ill. Nat. Hist. Survey.*)

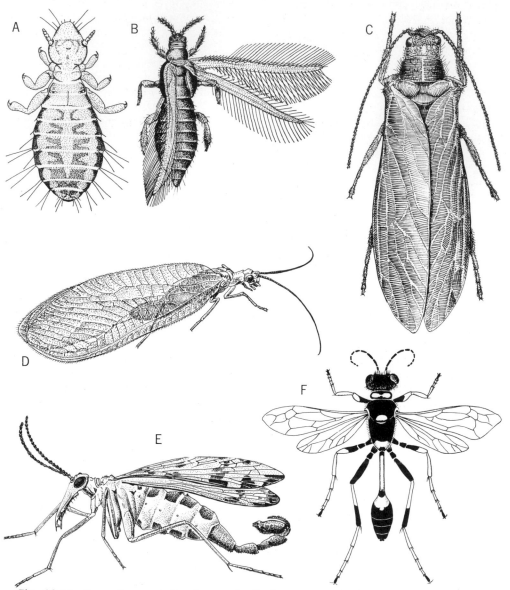

Fig. 19.11. Some Representative Insects. **A.** *Cuclotogaster*, a chicken louse. The bird lice (Mallophaga) live on birds and mammals and have chewing mouthparts. They feed on bits of feather and skin, and some cause considerable irritation to domestic animals. The wingless, flattened body and modifications of the appendages are suitable for their parasitic life. **B.** *Taeniothrips inconsequens*, the pear thrips, a typical thysanopteran. The fringed wings are characteristic features of the thrips. Many species cause serious damage to garden or field plants with their piercing and sucking mouths. **C.** *Sialis*, an alderfly (Megaloptera). The alderflies, or dobsonflies, have two pairs of large, many-veined wings, folded over the back at rest. Strong biting mouthparts and long antennae are characteristic features. The aquatic larvae, known as hellgrammites, have unusual abdominal gills. **D.** *Chrysopa*, a lacewing (Neuroptera).

males sometimes with two similar, membranous wings, held flat over the body when at rest; abdomen with ten segments and short ceri. Example: *Oligotoma* (Fig. 19.10D).

Order Corrodentia. Booklice. Small insects with chewing mouthparts; usually long antennae; large compound eyes and variable ocelli; slender legs; sometimes with two pairs of wings, folded roof-like over the back when at rest; forewings larger; spinnerets on the labial palps used to produce living webs or webs for the protection of eggs; abdomen with ten segments and without cerci. Example: *Ectopsocus* (Fig. 19.10E).

Order Mallophaga. Chewing lice. Small to medium, flattened insects, living as ectoparasites on warm-blooded vertebrates; chewing mouthparts; short antennae; reduced compound eyes and no ocelli; small, fused thorax; short, stout legs, sometimes with grasping claws; without wings; abdomen with eight to ten segments and without cerci. Example: *Cuclotogaster* (Fig. 19.11A).

Order Anoplura. Sucking lice. Minute to small, usually flattened insects, living as ectoparasites on mammals; with piercing and sucking mouthparts, short antennae; eyes reduced or missing; small, fused thorax; short, stout legs modified for grasping hairs; without wings; nine-segmented abdomen, but not all of the somites visible externally; without cerci. Example: *Haematopinus* (Fig. 19.10F).

Order Thysanoptera. Thrips. Small, long-bodied insects with piercing, sucking mouthparts; short antennae; conspicuous compound eyes and three ocelli in winged species; wings sometimes missing; forewings larger and both pairs narrow, nearly veinless, and with a fringe of fine hairs on the posterior margin; short, stout legs; abdomen with 10 to 11 segments and without cerci. Example: *Taeniothrips* (Fig. 9.11B).

Order Hemiptera. Bugs. Minute to large insects with diversified habits and structure; piercing and sucking mouthparts; large compound eyes and variable ocelli; legs absent or adapted for running, jumping, digging, grasping prey, or swimming; wings absent in some; typically with similar, membranous wings in suborder *Homoptera* (cicadas, scale insects, and leafhoppers) and forewings modified as hemielytrae, with a membranous apex and leathery base, used to cover the membranous hindwings, in *Heteroptera* (true bugs); abdomen with few to ten segments and without cerci. Example: *Anas* (Fig. 19.31).

Series Holometabola. Insects that hatch as larvae, without wingbuds, and which undergo a special metamorphic molt associated with an inactive, pupal stage in the life cycle.

Order Neuroptera. Lacewings. Minute to moderately sized, carnivorous insects with chewing mouthparts; antennae usually long and slender; large compound eyes and variable ocelli; forelegs sometimes modified as raptorial legs; two pairs of similar, net-veined wings held roof-like over the back when at rest; abdomen with ten segments and without cerci. Example: *Chrysopa* (Fig. 19.11D).

The predaceous neuropterans have two pairs of similar, net-veined wings held over the back at rest. Large eyes and slender legs, sometimes with one raptorial pair, are typical of the lacewings. E. *Panorpa*, a scorpionfly (Mecoptera). These unusual insects have biting mouths, borne on a snout. The swollen tip of the male abdomen resembles a scorpion sting. F. A mud dauber, *Sceliphron* (Hymenoptera). Ants, bees, and wasps make up the order Hymenoptera. The slender pedicel at the front of the abdomen is characteristic of the group, but their habits are so diverse that most body parts are quite varied. Many Hymenoptera form large social aggregations, with special worker castes. (A and E, *Ill. Nat. Hist. Survey*. B, after Moulton. C, after Ross. F, after Essig).

Order Megaloptera. Dobsonflies. Medium to large insects with chewing mouthparts; long antennae; large compound eyes and three or no ocelli; long legs; two pairs of large wings held flat or roof-like over the back when at rest; wings with many veins; abdomen with ten segments and without cerci; aquatic larvae with lateral abdominal gills. Example: *Sialis* (Fig. 19.11C).

Order Rhaphidoidea. Snakeflies. Long, fragile insects with a slender, neck-like prothorax; biting mouthparts; conspicuous compound eyes; three or no ocelli; long, slender antennae; short legs; two pairs of similar, net-veined wings; abdomen with ten segments and without cerci. Example: *Rhaphidia.*

Order Mecoptera. Scorpionflies. Small to medium-sized, carnivorous insects with chewing mouthparts borne on a snout; long, slender antennae; large compound eyes; three or no ocelli; long, slender legs; wings absent, reduced, or two similar pairs held flat or roof-like over the head when at rest; abdomen with ten segments and with cerci; the male with the tip of the abdomen swollen by a bulbous genital capsule, superficially resembling a scorpion's sting. Example: *Panorpa* (Fig. 19.11E).

Order Hymenoptera. Ants, bees, wasps, and sawflies. Minute to large insects of diverse structure and habits; with a strong exoskeleton; chewing, lapping, or sucking mouthparts; slender antennae; large compound eyes and usually three ocelli; slender legs; wings absent, reduced, or two pairs of stiff membranous wings, coupled by hooks on the hind pair; forewings larger; abdomen with a slender pedicel; often living in nests in large societies with division of labor among several specialized castes. Example: *Sceliphron* (Fig. 19.11F).

Order Coleoptera. Beetles. Minute to large insects, with tough or hard exoskeleton, chewing mouthparts, antennae of variable form; large compound eyes and usually no ocelli; forewings modified as elytra, hardened like the body and meeting in a straight line at the middle of the back; hindwings membranous and usually completely hidden by the elytra when at rest; usually a ten-segmented abdomen without cerci. This is the largest and most varied order of insects. Example: *Hippodamia* (Fig. 19.12A).

Order Trichoptera. Caddisflies. Minute to medium-sized insects with weak, chewing mouthparts; long, slender antennae; large compound eyes and three or no ocelli; long slender legs; two pairs of large, hairy, sometimes scaled wings folded over the back when at rest; hindwings somewhat larger than forewings; abdomen with nine to ten segments and with short cerci; aquatic larvae, usually living in cases. Example: *Rhyacophila* (Fig. 19.12B).

Order Lepidoptera. Moths and butterflies. Medium to large insects, with mouthparts reduced to form a coiled tube for sucking liquid food; antennae long and often feathery; large compound eyes and two or no ocelli; two pairs of wings, often large and showy; forewings often larger than hindwings; wings with overlapping scales and often hairy; abdomen with ten segments and without cerci. Example: *Papilio* (Fig. 19.12C).

Order Diptera. Flies. Minute to medium-sized insects with lapping, sucking, piercing, or vestigial mouthparts; large compound eyes and usually three ocelli; antennae short or long; legs short or long; forewings membranous and used for flying and hindwings reduced to balancers (halteres); abdomen with four to ten visible somites and without cerci. Example: *Drosophila* (Fig. 19.12D).

Order Siphonaptera. Fleas. Minute to small insects, ectoparasitic on birds and mammals; with piercing and sucking mouthparts; short antennae; simple compound eyes and no ocelli; legs long, stout, adapted for jumping; wingless; abdomen probably with ten segments and without cerci. Example: *Pulex* (Fig. 19.12E).

EXTERNAL FORM

The insect body is composed of three tagmata, the head, thorax, and abdomen. All are distinct. The head is strongly consolidated. It bears a pair of large compound eyes in most cases, and, in addition, two to three small, simple eyes or ocelli are commonly found near the center of the head. A pair of antennae, a pair of mandibles, and two pairs of maxillae are the characteristic head appendages. The thorax is made up of three segments, a prothorax bearing the forelegs, a mesothorax to which the middle pair of legs are attached, and a metathorax bearing the hindlegs. In the majority of insects the dorsolateral surface of the mesothorax and metathorax has been drawn out at the sides to form movable flaps, the wings. A few insect groups had diverged from the mainstream of insect evolution before the wings appeared and are primitively wingless. Wings are extremely useful tools, but are in the way in some of the more specialized habitats that insects occupy. In a number of the orders of insects, some members, especially parasitic forms, have become secondarily wingless, and several of the orders are characterized by the loss of wings. The abdomen is usually made up of 10 or 11 somites, without appendages except at the posterior tip. The tenth somite often has a pair of tactile appendages known as cerci. The eighth and ninth somites usually have highly modified appendages used for copulation or egg-laying.

The Head. The insect head is composed of a procephalon, corresponding to the prostomium of annelids, and a gnathocephalon bearing the mouthparts and consisting of at least four somites. The antennae attach to the procephalon. They are sensory appendages, important as tactile organs and for chemoreception. On the basis of their innervation, they appear to be homologous to the sensory appendages of the polychaete prostomium. The compound eyes and ocelli, when present, are also found on the procephalon. The first somite of the gnathocephalon bears no appendages in the adult, but in some cases develops a pair of embryonic appendages, the postantennae. The postantennae are thought to be homologous to the second antennae of Crustacea. The remaining three somites of the gnathocephalon bear the mandibles and the two pairs of maxillae (Fig. 19.13A).

The front part of the head corresponds to the anterior face of the polychaete prostomium and is divided into regions by sutures (Fig. 19.13B,C). The anterior face of the head is the frons. An immovable suture divides it from the clypeus below. The labrum is the upper lip, attached to the clypeus by a membranous, movable articulation. The covering of the head is the vertex, formed by the fusion of the dorsal plates of the somites of the gnathocephalon and the dorsal surface of the procephalon. At the posterior end of the vertex a groove, the occipital suture, separates it from the posterior head plate or occiput. The sides of the head are covered by the cheek plates, known as genae. A genal suture, often missing, separates the gena from the front head plates. A posterior cheek plate, the postgena, joins the occiput. The occiput and postgena are bounded posteriorly by the postoccipital suture, behind which a skeletal ring, the postocciput, is found. Occipital condyles on the postocciput meet the neck sclerites in a movable articulation permitting independent movements of the head (Fig. 19.13D).

The mouthparts articulate with the membranous lower part of the head surface. The mandibles are so reduced that they have lost all resemblance to ordinary appendages. Only the basal segment and the endite or gnathobase attached to it are retained. The first maxillae are more limb-like, unless the mouthparts are highly specialized. In a generalized species, each

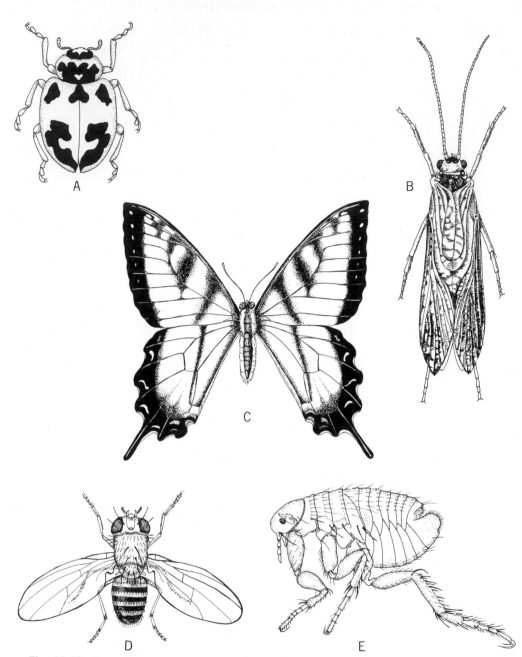

Fig. 19.12. Some Representative Insects. **A.** A ladybug, *Hippodamia* (Coleoptera). Beetles are easily recognized by the heavy forewings (tegmina), which cover the larger, membranous hindwings. The tegmina meet in a straight line. Coleoptera is an enormous order, including **an** extremely diversified group of insects insofar as habits and habitats are concerned. **B.** *Rhya-cophila*, a caddisfly (Trichoptera). Caddisflies have large hairy or scaly wings that fold over the back. The hindwings are larger than the forewings. Adults have large eyes and weak, chewing mouth parts. The aquatic larvae are well known because of their interesting cases,

868

first maxilla is made up of a basal segment, the cardo, by which it is hinged; a main piece, the stipes, to which the other pieces attach; a lateral and usually sensory lobe, the galea; a medial lobe which is often equipped with spines or teeth along its border, the lacinia; and a sensory palp usually composed of several segments (Fig. 19.13F). The second maxillae are fused medially, forming the lower lip, or labium, and have parts corresponding to those of the first maxillae. The mentum and sub-mentum are medial plates, formed by the union of the two pieces of the two second maxillae that correspond to the cardo of the first maxillae. The prementum cor-responds to the stipes of the first maxillae. The median glossa and lateral paraglossa correspond to the medial lacinia and the lateral galea of the first maxillae. The labial palps are usually shorter than the maxillary palps, but are corresponding parts. Insects have an epipharynx and hypopharynx forming the roof and floor of a preoral cavity, similar in general form and relationships to the corresponding parts of myriapods (p. 843).

As a general rule insects are hypogna-thous, with the jaws projecting below the head, but some are prognathous, and have the head tilted upward to bring the jaws in front. In a group with such widely diver-sified habits and utilizing such different kinds of food, it is inevitable that the mouthparts are subject to a great deal of evolutionary adaptation. Several major types of mouths can be distinguished, and there are a number of modifications of each type. The mouthparts that have been de-scribed are those found in the primitive, chewing type of mouth. Blood-eating flies have a cutting-sponging mouth. The man-dibles are modified to form sharp blades and the maxillae to form styles. The labium is spongy, and is used to mop up blood from the wound made by the mandibles. Blood is sucked in through a tube formed by the modified epipharynx and hypo-pharynx. Many other flies have a sponging mouth. The mandibles and maxillae are reduced, and a large spongy labellum is found on the tip of the labium. Bees have a chewing-lapping mouth. The mandibles are not much modified and are of the biting type. The maxillae and labium are modified to form a proboscis, which can be thrust into flowers to gather nectar. Bugs, fleas, sucking lice, and mosquitoes have a piercing-sucking mouth. Details of con-struction vary, but the general principle is that the labrum, maxillae, and mandibles are united to form a beak containing an inner, sclerotized, sharp tube, formed of the epipharynx and hypopharynx. When the plant or animal surface has been pierced, juices are sucked in through the tube.

The Neck. The insect neck is covered by membranous cuticle, providing for free movement of the head. The postocciput projects back from the head, providing protection to the soft neck region. Two small sclerites are found in the neck. They are fused to or articulate with the lateral skeleton of the thorax (Fig. 19.13D), and they meet the occipital condyles, forming

formed of sand grains, or bits of debris. C. *Papilio*, a swallowtail butterfly (Lepidoptera). Lepidoptera includes moths, butterflies and skippers. These familiar insects are characterized by the overlapping scales, often beautifully colored, which cover the wings, and the sucking proboscis. Many of the caterpillars are important pests of garden and field plants. D. *Dro-sophila*, a fruit fly (Diptera). The true flies are easily recognized because they have but one pair of wings; the hindwings are reduced to small balancers known as halteres. Diptera is a large order, including insects with diverse habits. Some, like the mosquitoes, are bloodsuckers that transmit important diseases of man and his domestic animals. E. A flea, *Pulex* (Siphonaptera). The fleas are wingless and have greatly developed hind legs. Ectoparasitic on birds and mammals, some are responsible for disease transmission. (A, after Essig. B, after Ross. D, from Ross.)

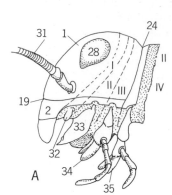

A

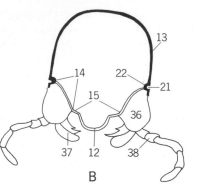

B

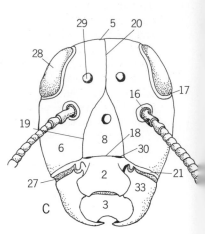

C

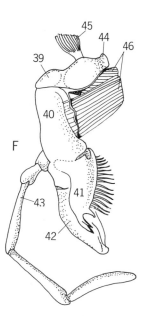

D

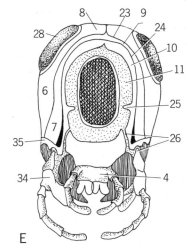

E

F

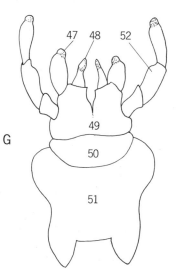

G

a pivot on which the head can swing. The neck region is not a separate somite, but is formed by the margins of the last head and first thoracic somites.

The Thorax. The primitive somite structure is as in the Chilopoda. The dorsal surface of a somite is covered by a skeletal sclerite, the tergum. The ventral surface is covered by a ventral sclerite, the sternum. The membranous sidewalls are the pleural regions in which subcoxal sclerites associated with the leg bases are placed, and which is further strengthened in many species with additional pleural plates. Abdominal somites have no articulations for legs, and the thoracic somites are greatly modified by the formation of wings and provisions for their attachment to the body.

The term notum is applied to the dorsal thoracic plates, but otherwise the general terminology is used for the thoracic somites. The least modified thoracic somite is the prothorax, although it is somewhat more strongly consolidated in winged than in wingless species. The wing-bearing somites are considerably modified. The notum is divided into a more anterior sclerite, the alinotum, and a more posterior

somite, the postnotum (Fig. 19.15). The postnotum is fused to the lateral skeleton to form a solid bridge behind the wings. At each end of the somite a deep, plate-like apodeme, the phragma, provides a surface for the attachment of the flight muscles. The pleural region is strengthened by the pleuron, which is divided into an anterior episternum and a posterior epimeron by the pleural suture. An apodeme, the pleurodema, extends in from the pleural suture. Before and behind the coxal cavity the pleuron unites with the sternum. The main sternal sclerite is the eusternum, associated with a deeply invaginated apodeme, the furca. The rest of the sternal plate is a small spinasternum, which usually unites with the sternum of the segment behind.

The wings are attached at a membranous region of the pleural wall. Two free sclerites, the basalare and the subalare, are found in the pleural wall near the wing bases, and small axillary sclerites in the base of the wings articulate with the edges of the notal plates.

The wings are lateral flaps of the body wall, and so are double, consisting of upper and lower membranes, tightly adherent to

Fig. 19.13. The Anatomy of the Head. **A.** Scheme of head, showing the postoral head somites. At least four postoral somites are incorporated into the head, the first corresponding to a pair of postantennal appendages which are rudimentary or missing, and are probably homologous with the second antennae of Crustacea and the chelicera of chelicerates. **B.** Scheme of cross section through the head, showing the tergal, pleural, and sternal regions of the head, and the basic relationship of the appendages to the head. **C-E.** Front, side, and back views of a generalized insect head, showing the basic regions and sutures, and the position of the mouth parts. **F.** An insect maxilla, showing the parts of the base and palp. **G.** A generalized type of insect second maxillae, which unite to form the labium. (A-F, after Snodgrass. G, after Imms, from Ross.) *Head regions:* 1, cranium; 2, clypeus; 3, labrum; 4, labium; 5, vertex; 6, gena; 7, postgena; 8, frons; 9, occiput; 10, postocciput; 11, cervix; 12, hypopharynx; 13, tergal region of head; 14, pleural region of head; 15, venter (sternal region) of head. *Sutures:* 16, antennal suture; 17, ocular suture; 18, epistomal suture; 19, frontal suture; 20, coronal suture; 21, subgenal suture; 22, subgenal ridge; 23, occipital suture; 24, postoccipital suture. *Condyles and articulations:* 25, occipital condyle; 26, primary articulation of the mouth parts; 27, secondary anterior articulation of mandible. *Specialized head parts:* 28, eye; 29, ocellus; 30, anterior tentorial pit. *Appendages:* 31, antenna; 32, postantennal appendage; 33, mandible; 34, first maxilla; 35, second maxilla; 36, coxa; 37, endite; 38, telopodite. *Maxillae:* 39, cardo; 40, stipes; 41, lacinia; 42, galea; 43, palp; 44, basal condyle of cardo; 45, anterior dorsal muscle; 46, ventral adductor muscles. *Labium:* 47, paraglossa; 48, glossa; 49, prementum; 50, mentum; 51, submentum; 52, palp.

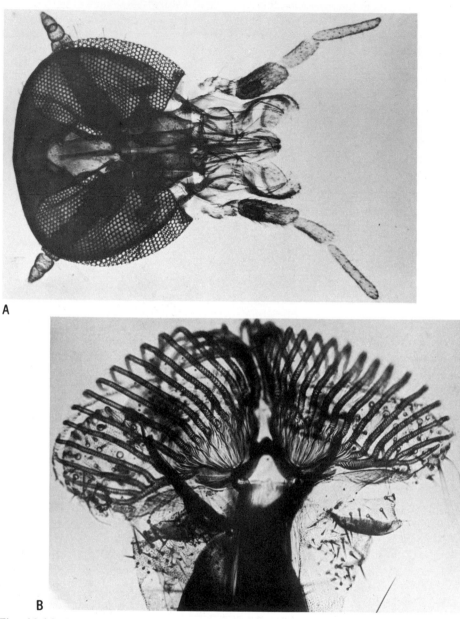

A

B

Fig. 19.14. Insect Mouthparts. **A.** Head of *Simulium*, a dipteran. The mandibulary and maxillary palps are well developed. The mandibles are sharp, and capable of wounding the skin. The labium and labrum, with the modified hypopharynx and epipharynx, form a sucking proboscis. This type of mouth is characteristic of blood-sucking dipterans. **B.** Labella of a house fly. The joined labrum and epipharynx fit into the labium, forming a food channel. At the tip of the proboscis the labella is found (shown in the figure). It is thrust into liquid food, which is carried to the food channel by way of capillary channels over the surface. (Courtesy of General Biological Supply Co.)

each other, and supported by veins. The main veins run obliquely from the wing base to the wing margin, and are connected by small veins known as crossveins. The system of veins has developed from tracheae, which have broken away from the main tracheal system and hardened to form a system of supporting struts. Wing venation is remarkably varied, and is important in insect identification. The basic pattern of wing venation is shown schematically in Fig. 19.16, with the major vein systems labeled. The letter designations are conventional ones used in taxonomic literature.

The major vein systems are:

Costa (C). Unbranched, heavy vein forming the anterior margin of the wing.

Subcosta (Sc). Unbranched or two-branched vein in the trough between the costa and the radius, and ending on the costal margin.

Radius (R). A stout vein immediately behind the subcosta, connecting with the axillary sclerite at the base of the wing. It is typically five-branched, with the branches defining the radial sector of the wing. The anterior branches reach the costal margin of the wing, and the posterior branches extend to the wing apex.

Media (M). A four-branched vein behind the radius, in the middle part of the wing, and articulating with median axillary sclerites.

Cubitus (Cu). A two-branched vein, articulating with the median axillary sclerites and extending to the wing margin. The second branch lies in a depression, the cubital furrow.

Anals (A). A system of from one to four veins behind the cubital furrow and supporting the anal region of the wing. These veins articulate with the third axillary sclerite. The anal region extends from the cubital furrow to the jugal furrow.

Jugals (J). The jugal region is a small area behind the jugal fold, supported by several short, jugal veins.

An examination of the figures or repre-

sentative species of insects will show something of the diversity of wing structure in insects. In more primitive insect wings, many delicate crossveins connect the main veins, and the main veins are often extensively branched near the wing margin. Wings of this kind tend to be rather delicate. The general course of wing evolution has tended to 1) reduce the number of crossveins, 2) strengthen the main wing veins, and 3) simplify the strut system by the union of the main veins. The result is a mechanically stronger wing. During the simplification of the vein sys-

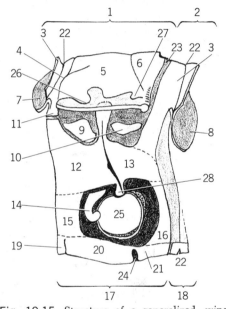

Fig. 19.15. Structure of a generalized, wing-bearing thoracic segment, showing the skeletal plates and sutures. (After Snodgrass.) 1, alinotum; 2, postnotum; 3, acrotergite; 4, prescutum; 5, scutum; 6, scutellum; 7, anterior phragma; 8, posterior phragma; 9, basalare; 10, subalare; 11, prealare; 12, episternite; 13, epimeron; 14, trochanter; 15, procoxale; 16, postcoxale; 17, eusternum; 18, spinisternum; 19, presternum; 20, basisternum; 21, sternellum; 22, antecostal suture; 23, conjunctiva of secondary intersegmental membrane; 24, sternacostal suture; 25, coxal cavity; 26, anterior notal wing process; 27, posterior notal wing process; 28, pleural coxal process.

tem, some insect wings have become so highly modified that the main wing veins are difficult to homologize with the primitive vein system. Identification of insects often involves the identification of crossveins as well as the main veins. The crossveins are named for the main veins they connect. Costal crossveins connect the costa and the subcosta or radius. Crossveins between the branches of the radius are radial crossveins, and crossveins between branches of the radius and media are radio-medial crossveins. The same system is used in designating the remaining crossveins. It is conventional to use capital letters to designate the main veins and lower case letters to designate the crossveins.

While the main line of wing evolution may have been directed toward improving the mechanical qualities of the wing and making it a more efficient flight organ, this is only one of the many lines of wing evolution that have occurred. The reduction and

loss of wings is an important part of adaptation to a life of parasitism or burrowing. In some groups this has been counterbalanced by the advantages of wings for distribution of the species, and the wings are shed after use. Termites and ants, for example, have the reproductive members of the colony equipped with temporary wings used during mating and the establishment of new nests. In this case the wings have a basal fracture, a predetermined point where the wings will break when they are shed. In several groups of insects only one pair of wings is used for flying. Flies have followed a unique evolutionary line, developing the membranous forewings for flight, and reducing the hindwings to halteres. The halteres are responsible for equilibrium during flight; many flies cannot balance well enough to fly if deprived of their halteres. In a number of insect groups, the hindwings are used for flight, while the forewings have become modified into protective

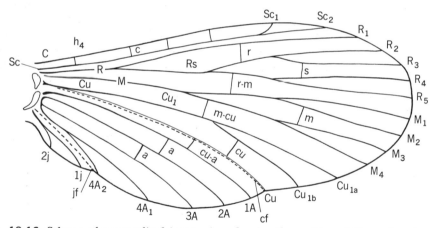

Fig. 19.16. Scheme of a generalized insect wing, showing the position of the main veins and crossveins. The letter designations are those of the widely used Comstock-Needham system of terminology. (After Ross.) Veins are shown in capital letters, and crossveins in lower case letters. Numbered branches of veins are sequentially numbered, from front to back of wing. *Veins:* Costa (C); Subcosta (Sc); Radius (R); Media (M); Cubitus (Cu); Anal (A); Jugal (J). The posterior main branch of the radius is the radial sector (Rs). *Crossveins:* humeral (h), between costa and subcosta near their base; costal (c); radial (r); sectoral (s), between branches of the radial sector; radiomedial (r-m); medial (m); mediocubital (m-cu); cubital (cu); cubitoanal (cu-a); anal (a).

covers for the hindwings. Three kinds of protective forewings are found. In Orthoptera and Dermaptera the forewings are leathery tegmina. In beetles they are hardened elytra. In Hemiptera the forewings are leathery at the base and membranous at the tip, and are known as hemielytra.

Wing development follows a different line in minute insects than in larger ones. A tiny insect has an enormous surface in proportion to its weight, and so encounters a very high air resistance. They do not fall rapidly through the air, and can scarcely be said to fly; they very nearly swim through the air. The wings are not so extensively veined, and in some cases the wings are nearly devoid of veins. The minute thrips have very slender wings, equipped with a fringe of hairs, not unlike the natatory fringes on the swimming appendages of crustaceans.

Insects have legs designed like myriapod legs. In the great majority of insects there are six segments in the leg, but a few have a second trochanter. The tarsal podite is divided into several pieces, lengthening the leg and providing a pedal surface. Leg form is variable, for insects live in diverse habitats and use legs in a number of different ways. Legs specialized for running are said to be cursorial. They may be short and stout or long and slender. The cursorial leg is the primitive and most common type. A number of insects are excellent jumpers and have saltatorial legs. The hindleg is modified, usually being much elongated and having a very powerful and muscular femur (Fig. 19.12E; 19.18). Some carnivorous insects have raptorial legs, used to grasp and kill prey. They have elongated, powerful forelegs, often armed with claws or spines. The preying mantis is probably the best-known insect with raptorial legs. Some insects have fossorial legs, specialized for digging. Fossorial legs are short and stout and are often flattened. Still other insects have natatorial legs, specialized for swimming. They are often elongated, and somewhat flattened,

and are equipped with natatory bristles.

Many kinds of minor modifications are found in insect legs, fitting them for use under the special conditions which the species encounters. The pretarsus may be modified with terminal claws or spines that aid in clinging to various kinds of surfaces. Diptera have paired, pad-like pulvilli containing adhesive glands, which attach to surfaces and make it possible to creep up a window pane or across a ceiling. Diptera and some other insects have a median empodium between the tarsal claws. Ectoparasitic insects often have specially modified legs, especially suited to clinging to the hair or feathers of the host. An examination of a number of representative insects will usually reveal a variety of interesting leg modifications.

The Abdomen. Abdominal somites are relatively simple. The exoskeleton consists of a dorsal tergum and a ventral sternum, connected by a membranous pleural region. In some cases pleural sclerites are present. These are probably vestiges of the subcoxal sclerites of the lost abdominal appendages. In some of the primitive insects, however, remnants of the coxae of abdominal somites persist and bear rudimentary appendages, known as styli. A pair of cerci extend back from the posterior end of the abdomen in a number of insects. These are posterior tactile organs derived by the specialization of a pair of appendages (Fig. 19.17). Highly specialized appendages on the last few somites are used for copulation and egg-laying. These parts are not found in the primitively wingless insects, and are extremely diverse in the pterygote insects. They are often equipped with detailed adaptations that are useful in taxonomy.

In a generalized insect, the female gonopore is found on the eighth somite, partially covered by a projection of the sternum, the subgenital plate. Highly modified appendages (Fig. 19.17A) are attached to the ventral side of the eighth somite, composed of a basal valvifer, derived from the coxa, and a valvula, derived from the main branch of the leg. The ninth somite also bears a plate, the valvifer, and two valvulae, a dorsal one behind and a ventral one in front. The valvulae form the ovipositor, which is variously modified in different insect groups. The sting of a bee is the most remarkable modification of the ovipositor. In some insects the abdomen itself serves as an ovipositor and the highly modified genital appendages are missing. The eleventh somite contains the anus and is covered by an often triangular tergum, the epiproct, and a pair of ventrolateral lobes, the paraprocts. The paraprocts meet

medially in a membranous region that sometimes contains a small, median hypoproct.

The male genital appendages are found on the ninth somite, but are often partly fused with the tenth somite (Fig. 19.17D,E). A midventral penis is located on the ventral articular membrane between the ninth and tenth somites. Penal structure varies greatly in different insect groups and is sometimes important in the identification of species. During mating, the penis serves for sperm transfer and the genital appendages act as claspers.

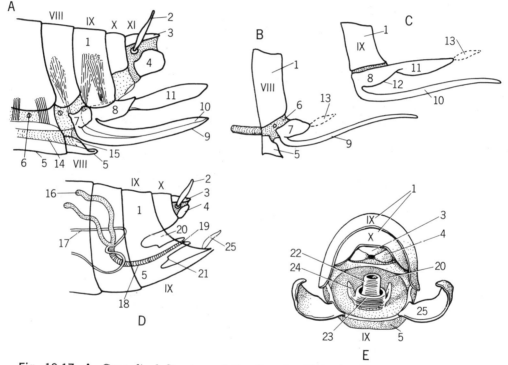

Fig. 19.17. A. Generalized Structure of the Posterior End of a Female Winged Insect. B and C. Lateral view of detached eighth and ninth abdominal segments, showing the parts of the ovipositor associated with each. D. Generalized structure of the genitalia of a male winged insect (lateral view). E. End view of the same, with claspers developed from the styli. (After Snodgrass.) *Abdominal parts:* 1, tergum; 2, cercus; 3, epiproct; 4, paraproct; 5, sternum; 6, spiracle. *Female parts:* 7, first valvifer; 8, second valvifer; 9, first valvula; 10, second valvula; 11, third valvula; 12, coxopodite; 13, stylus; 14, common oviduct; 15, female gonopore. *Male parts:* 16, accessory gland; 17, sperm duct; 18, ejaculatory duct; 19, male gonopore; 20, genital chamber; 21, phallus; 22, aedeagus; 23, phallobase; 24, paramere; 25, stylus (harpago).

INTERNAL ANATOMY AND PHYSIOLOGY

Digestive System. The basic design of the insect digestive system is the same as that of other arthropods. The foregut is derived from the stomodaeum and is lined with cuticle. The hindgut is derived from the proctodaeum and is also lined with cuticle. The midgut is lined with a mucosa

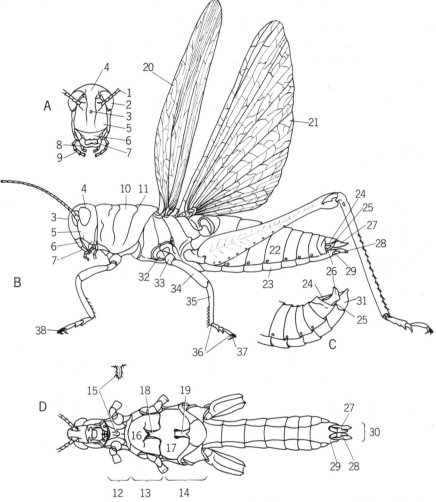

Fig. 19.18. External Anatomy of a Locust, *Melanoplus*. Locusts are especially good examples of a relatively generalized insect, insofar as mouth structure and external anatomy is concerned. (After Essig.) *Head:* 1, antenna; 2, eye; 3, ocellus; 4, vertex; 5, gena; 6, clypeus; 7, labrum; 8, labial palp; 9, maxillary palp. *Thorax:* 10, pronotum; 11, sulcus; 12, prothorax; 13, mesothorax; 14, metathorax; 15, prosternal spine; 16, mesosternum; 17, metasternum; 18, intermesosternal space; 19, intermetasternal space; 20, tegmen (forewing); 21, hindwing. *Abdomen:* 22, tergum; 23, sternum; 24, epiproct (supra-anal plate); 25, paraproct; 26, cercus; 27, dorsal valvula; 28, ventral valvula; 29, basivalvula; 30, ovipositor; 31, subgenital plate. *Appendages:* 32, coxa; 33, trochanter; 34, femur; 35, tibia; 36, tarsus; 37, pretarsus; 38, arolium.

derived from the endoderm. Stomodaeal and proctodaeal valves usually guard the two ends of the midgut. Some of the primitive insects have a very simple, tubular gut, with no obvious dilations. As a general rule, however, the gut is divided into a number of specialized regions, each with a special part to play in the whole digestive process. Insects differ so greatly in size, feeding habits, and diet that the digestive tract is necessarily quite variable.

Locusts are good examples of a generalized insect and have a typical insect digestive system (Fig. 19.19). The mouth appendages, the epipharynx, and the hypopharynx surround a preoral cavity, which opens into the stomodaeal region. The stomodaeum consists of a buccal cavity, pharynx, esophagus, crop, and proventriculus. A constriction marks the position of the stomodaeal valve, which guards the entrance into the midgut. The midgut is short, and consists of the stomach and gastric caeca associated with it. At the junction of the midgut and hindgut there is a deep constriction, containing the

proctodeal valve. Malpighian tubules are attached to the gut at this point. The hindgut is relatively long, and is divided into an anterior intestine made up of a somewhat dilated pylorus, a more slender ileum, and a slightly dilated colon, and a posterior intestine composed of a short rectum, dilated anteriorly as a rectal sac.

The foregut is the center for food reception, storage, and preliminary processing. The cuticular lining is thickened at points of maximal wear and in order to produce grinding surfaces, and a variety of glands open into it, providing lubrication, some enzymes, and other useful factors.

The buccal cavity is generally small, and it merges with the pharynx indistinctly, with the only external differentiation indicated by the musculature. Large salivary glands open into the buccal cavity. Salivary secretions are extremely diverse. They lubricate the mouth parts and moisten the food in preparation for swallowing. In blood-sucking insects, the saliva contains an anticoagulant that keeps blood flowing while the blood meal is taken. Some insects live

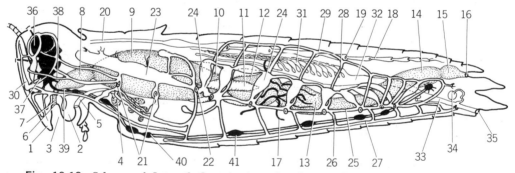

Fig. 19.19. Scheme of Internal Organization of a Locust. *Digestive system:* 1, labrum; 2, labium; 3, preoral cavity; 4, salivary gland; 5, salivary duct; 6, mouth; 7, pharynx; 8, esophagus; 9, crop; 10, proventriculus; 11, gastric caeca; 12, ventriculus; 13, pylorus; 14, colon; 15, rectum; 16, anus. *Excretory system:* 17, Malpighian tubules. *Circulatory system:* 18, heart; 19, ostium; 20, aorta. *Respiratory system:* 21, thoracic spiracle; 22, abdominal spiracle; 23, thoracic air sac; 24, abdominal air sac; 25, lateral tracheal trunk; 26, ventral tracheal branch; 27, ventral tracheal trunk; 28, dorsal tracheal branch; 29, dorsal tracheal trunk; 30, cephalic trachea. *Reproductive system:* 31, ovary; 32, calyx; 33, oviduct; 34, seminal receptacle; 35, female gonopore. *Nervous system:* 36, protocerebrum; 37, deutocerebrum; 38, tritocerebrum; 39, circumenteric connective; 40, last thoracic ganglion; 41, first abdominal ganglion.

within the food mass, like the larvae so often seen in apples and other fruits. In these the saliva often contains enzymes that are ejected on the food, partially digesting it before it is eaten. Occasionally salivary glands are modified for purposes not connected with digestion. In the Lepidoptera the salivary glands are modified to form silk glands, and the mouthparts and buccal cavity contain specialized parts used in spinning the cocoon.

The pharynx is usually short, ending at a constriction where the foregut passes through the nerve ring, and emptying at this point into the esophagus. In some insects, however, a posterior pharynx lies behind the nerve ring. In any case, the primary function of the pharynx is to convey the food to the esophagus.

The muscular coat of the foregut changes at the junction of the pharynx and esophagus. The esophagus, however, is essentially a continuation of the pharynx, and serves to convey the food to the midgut. It very commonly also serves as a site for the temporary storage of food and the mechanical or chemical trituration of the food. The insect crop is a part of the esophagus, and may be a dilation of the esophagus itself or a diverticulum from it. When empty, the crop wall is folded, and as it is highly distensible the crop can store a considerable quantity of food. In many species the crop is a place for preliminary digestion, depending on enzymes added to the food from the salivary glands or the midgut. In rare cases, food is also absorbed from the crop. Cockroaches, for example, absorb fats in the crop. Food passes from the crop to the proventriculus. The proventriculus is extremely varied in structure. In insects that take fluid food it is little more than a valve, sometimes equipped with straining bristles. Where solid foods are eaten, the proventriculus is a gastric mill, with chitinous plates and spines that increase its effectiveness. Where food has been softened by some preliminary digestion in the crop, the proventriculus is very

effective in reducing the food to tiny particles. Large particles are held back by the stomodaeal valve for further treatment in the proventriculus.

The midgut may be expanded or it may be a rather narrow tube, but it is generally equipped with prominent gastric caeca. In a large number of insects the midgut is lined with a chitinous tube, the peritrophic membrane (Fig. 19.20A). The peritrophic membrane is not a product of the midgut cells, but is secreted by a ring of cells, apparently derived from the stomodaeum, located near the stomodaeal valve. In some species the peritrophic membrane is secreted continuously. It forms at the rate of 6 mm./hr. in *Eristalis* larvae, and the nymphs of *Aeschna* discard two peritrophic membranes per day when unfed. The disposition of the peritrophic membrane varies in different insects. As a general rule it is destroyed in the hindgut. In some cases special spines used for this purpose are found, and the musculature of the proctodaeal valve sometimes helps to break the peritrophic membrane into small pieces. In other cases, however, it passes through the hindgut unharmed and encloses the fecal pellets. The part that the peritrophic membrane plays in digestion and absorption is uncertain. Many of the insects that feed on fluid foods have no peritrophic membrane, while insects that eat solid food usually have good peritrophic membranes, although exceptions occur on both sides. It is generally agreed that it tends to protect the midgut cells from mechanical injury by hard food particles. The membrane is known to be permeable to enzymes as well as to the end products of digestion, and it may be an ultra-filter, whose mesh size, varying from species to species, determines the maximal size of the particles that pass through it.

The epithelial lining of the midgut is always a simple epithelium. The lining cells are generally tall and columnar, and sometimes can be divided into goblet cells and ordinary columnar cells. The appearance of the epithelium changes markedly during digestion, especially in beetles and flies. Resting cells appear to become enzyme-secreting cells when food is present. Apparently the secretion of enzymes is exhausting, for new cells are produced at a remarkably rapid rate. The differentiated epithelial cells do not themselves divide to replace the exhausted cells, however. Small basal cells, sometimes termed regenerative cells, are responsible for the production of new epithelial cells. The distribution of the regenerative cells varies markedly in different kinds of insects. They may be scattered about as individual cells, appear in small clusters, or form large clusters which may be visible from the outside of the midgut as small plaques. In *Blatella*, a cockroach, division rates are high enough for the regenerative cells to completely renew the epithelium in about two days to a week.

The high cost of enzyme production, as measured by cell regeneration, would make it advantageous to secrete enzymes only during active digestion. Controls of this kind, however, appear to be only moderately developed. Undoubtedly this is, in part, a normal result of the feeding habits of some insects. Many of them live within or upon food plants and feed more or less continuously. It may also be in part a reflection of the techniques used to estimate enzyme production, which are usually dependent on the histological condition of the midgut cells and may not be wholly dependable. However that may be, it seems fairly certain that in some carnivorous insects enzyme secretion does change markedly when food is present in the gut. As all of the nerves reaching the intestine appear to be motor nerves to the intestinal musculature, the mechanism used for the control of secretion remains a mystery. Regulation by means of hormones has been suggested, but as yet there is no clear evidence of a mechanism of this kind.

As might be expected, a variety of enzymes have been recovered from the intestine of various kinds of insects. Lipases, carbohydrases, and proteases have been reported. A few produce cellulase, and it seems certain that special enzymes must be present in wool-eating and silk-eating insects and in others that take very specialized diets. Most insects are so small, however, that knowledge of specific enzymes has been accumulating rather slowly. It is known that at least some enzymes are formed by microorganisms present in the insect gut. The most famous examples are the flagellates found in the intestine of wood-eating roaches and termites, some of which produce cellulase. Without their protozoan fauna these insects starve to death, even though they have a full digestive tract. In recent years, considerably more interest has been expressed in the contributions that microorganisms make to digestion in insects, as well as in other kinds of invertebrates. The results of studies along these lines indicate that microorganisms may rather often enter into some kind of mutualistic relationship with invertebrates, and that these relationships may extend to the digestion of relatively common as well as uncommon types of foods. It appears that the haemolysis of blood in the stomach of mosquitoes may depend on enzymes from bacteria, and the carbohydrases found in the blowfly larvae appear to be formed entirely by the action of bacteria. If this system of digestion is very widespread, it may also be a factor in reducing the control of enzyme formation in insects.

The gastric caeca increase the surface of the midgut and provide a place where food may be retained for a time. Undoubtedly they play different parts in digestion in insects of different kinds. In at least some cases they provide sites for particular kinds of food processing. In some cockroaches and in mosquitoes, the gastric caeca are important in fat digestion. Considerably more work is needed before the gastric caeca can be discussed very meaningfully.

After food has been reduced to end

products by intrinsic enzymes or enzymes produced by microorganisms, it must be absorbed if it is to be utilized. As a general rule, most absorption occurs in the midgut and the middle part of the hindgut. In terms of specific materials and the site of their absorption, far too little is known to make a general discussion very profitable at this time. It is clear, however, that the sites of the absorption of substances may be very sharply defined in some species. In some insects, for example, a very short section of the midgut absorbs the greater part of copper and iron salts present in the gut (Fig. 19.20B). There is every reason to suppose that this principle of relatively specific sites of absorption of materials, correlated with the site of digestion and the place where the best pH and other conditions for absorption occur, has a wide application. From information now available, fat absorption seems to center in the anterior part of the midgut. Carbohydrates are absorbed in diverse regions in different kinds of insects, but as a rule the stomodaeum appears to be impermeable to carbohydrates. In some cases the deposition of glycogen during the absorption of food indicates that the posterior half of the midgut is the primary site of carbohydrate absorption. Where sugars are not fully absorbed in the midgut they may be absorbed in the hindgut. The site of protein absorption is largely unknown, but it appears that some proteins are absorbed in the midgut, and in some insects protein absorption occurs in the hindgut.

Although the hindgut participates in digestion and absorption, it is especially important in feces formation and water conservation. As in other very small land animals, water conservation is of prime importance. No small part of the success of insects can be credited to the remarkable ability of insects to conserve water passing through the hindgut. Cushions of tall epithelial cells located in the rectal lining, the rectal pads, are the most active sites of water absorption. They can be ex-

tremely efficient. Insects that live in dry places and feed on dry foods, for example, produce dry, powdery feces containing a very small amount of water.

Desiccation is not a problem for some insects, however. Aquatic insects often produce relatively liquid feces, although some form rather firm fecal pellets. Some insects face the problem of too much fluid. Aphids and other Homoptera take in plant juices containing very little protein and must process a very large amount of material to obtain an adequate protein supply. They have a unique filter chamber (Fig. 19.20C,D), the details of which differ markedly in different species. As a rule, water and some carbohydrates pass from the filter chamber into a tube leading to the hindgut or pass directly into the hindgut. The rest of the fluid food passes through the long midgut, where it is processed, and where protein is absorbed. The feces are rich in sugar, and are voided as a sweetish liquid known as honeydew. The relationship between ants and aphids is relatively well known. Some species of ants regularly tend aphids, placing them in position on plants and visiting them for the honeydew they produce. There is evidence that the rate of passage of fluids through aphids is a factor in growth rates, for aphids attended by ants pass more honeydew and reproduce at a higher rate than unattended aphids.

Respiration. Insect respiration is predominantly aerobic, although anaerobic energy release occurs in muscles and other tissues as a normal part of metabolism. Oxygen and carbon dioxide are exchanged with the environment at the body surface, at gills in some aquatic insect larvae and nymphs, and by way of the tracheal system.

Surface respiratory exchange is most important in small insects with a large surface area, and in species with a thinner, more permeable cuticle. It is especially important in primitive, wingless insects that are both soft and small. Collembola, for example, have no tracheae and depend en-

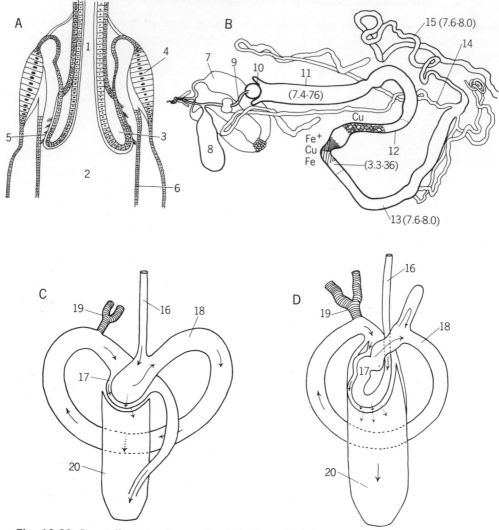

Fig. 19.20. Insect Digestive System Specializations. **A.** Scheme of lower end of esophagus and upper end of midgut, showing the site of peritrophic membrane secretion in a Simuliid larva. **B.** Diagram of the gut of the larval *Lucilia*. The *p*H of the gut contents in several regions as well as the site of absorption of copper and iron, is shown. There is evidence that in a number of other kinds of insects, absorption of particular substances occurs in a small area of the gut. **C** and **D.** The filter chamber of two homopterans. The filter chambers are used to permit large quantities of water and carbohydrates to bypass the midgut. The exact function of the bypassing mechanism is not well understood, but it may permit the processing of more fluid food to obtain sufficient quantities of substances present in low concentrations in the food. The details of filter chamber construction vary considerably in different species. (**A,** after Strickland. **B,** after Waterhouse, from Waterhouse and Day, in Roeder. **C** and **D,** after Weber.) *Simuliid larva:* 1, esophagus; 2, midgut; 3, blood sinus; 4, secretory cells that form the peritrophic membrane; 5, spines; 6, peritrophic membrane. *Lucilia larva:* 7, salivary gland; 8, crop; 9, foregut; 10, caeca; 11, anterior midgut; 12, middle midgut; 13, posterior midgut; 14, Malpighian tubule; 15, hindgut. *Filter chambers:* 16, foregut; 17, filter chamber; 18, midgut; 19, Malpighian tubule; 20, hindgut.

tirely on surface exchange. The first instar larvae of many other insects respire only at the body surface. Where respiratory exchange occurs at the body surface, it is evident that blood is responsible for distributing the oxygen to the tissues. What is known of the oxygen capacity of insect blood indicates that except for *Chironomus* larvae, which have haemoglobin dissolved in the blood plasma, the blood has a low capacity for dissolving oxygen. Respiratory pigments are missing, and the blood carries about the amount of oxygen that the blood plasma of vertebrates can handle. Insects are small, however, and this is adequate to transport enough oxygen to make an appreciable contribution to respiration in even some of the relatively large insects. About 25 to 50 per cent of the respiratory exchange of various kinds of insect larvae occurs at the body surface, and even adult roaches and grasshoppers carry on 10 per cent or more of their exchange at the body surface. Under conditions of stress, however, surface respiration increases in importance, and may reach as high as 50 per cent in adult insects with blocked tracheal systems.

Juvenile insects that live beneath the surface of the water do not normally come in contact with air, and are necessarily restricted to respiratory exchange at the surface of the body. Two courses are open to such insects. They may depend upon the blood for respiratory transport, or they may make an exchange between the water and a tracheal system. Both systems are used. Little need be said of insect nymphs or larvae that depend on the blood for respiratory transport. They tend to develop a rich distribution of blood to the body surface, and may also develop special amplified surfaces which serve as gills for respiratory exchange, as do other aquatic organisms. A number of aquatic insect larvae or nymphs have well-developed tracheal systems which are completely closed but nevertheless are responsible for delivering oxygen to the tissues. As this is a mechanism that has not

appeared in other invertebrates, it is particularly interesting. The general lines of improvement observed in these systems are what might be predicted by the nature of the process, and to a considerable extent parallel the adaptive changes of an ordinary circulatory system in respiratory organs. Trachea extending to the surface are finely branched, and the tracheal capillaries function in much the same manner as blood capillary beds in other animals (Fig. 19.21A). The tracheal capillary beds may be found over the general body surface, as in midge larvae, or may be concentrated in specialized gills. Many of the larger aquatic insect larvae have filamentous, plumose, or lamellate extensions of the body surface that serves as gills and contain repetitively branched tracheal trunks (Fig. 19.21B). Gills may be found on any part of the body, but are most common on the abdomen.

While structural modifications may implify the respiratory surface and provide for more efficient drain-off of oxygen, the ventilation of the respiratory surface is a very important factor in determining the rate of respiratory exchange. Gill ventilation is relatively unimportant for insect larvae living in habitats with high oxygen content or with rapid currents, but is more consequential in still waters with considerable bacterial activity, where oxygen tensions may be relatively low. A number of insect larvae have gills which move rhythmically, or make body movements that ventilate the gills at times of respiratory stress. Dragonfly nymphs fall back on a system that is used in a number of other invertebrates. Water is pumped in and out of the anus, and rectal folds contain a rich bed of tracheal capillaries, used for respiratory exchange.

It would be easy to overevaluate the importance of gills in aquatic insect nymphs and larvae. Where more or less equally active forms live side by side and are of about the same size, the survival of some which have no specialized gill surfaces

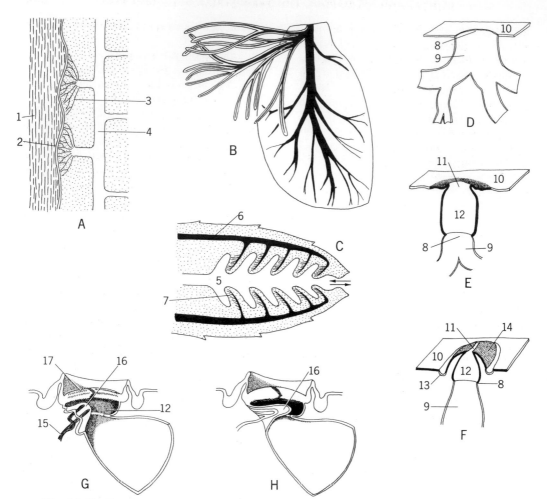

Fig. 19.21. Respiratory Adaptations. **A.** Scheme of surface trachea in aquatic insects with closed tracheal systems. Tracheal capillaries immediately below the epidermis are the site of respiratory exchange. Oxygen absorbed here moves into the main tracheal trunks which branch through the body tissues. **B.** A tracheal gill from a mayfly nymph. Surface amplification may be seen in broad, flat surfaces or in filamentous tufts. In either case, tracheal branching produces a bed of capillary tracheae more or less resembling the blood capillary beds in animals with respiratory organs served by blood vessels. **C.** Rectal gills of a dragonfly nymph (schematic). Anal pumping, a relatively common method of ventilating a respiratory surface in aquatic animals, occurs in dragonfly nymphs. The folded rectal wall provides ample surface for respiratory exchange, and a tracheal capillary system extends into the gills. **D-H.** Some adaptations of spiracles. The small size, and relatively large surface area of insects makes water conservation important if they live in places with low relative humidity. The exoskeleton provides some protection against evaporation, but each spiracle represents a site of rapid evaporation. Some protection is afforded by the chitinized lining of the tracheal system, especially heavy near the spiracles. However, important changes in spiracular form are also found. At **D**, a simple, open spiracle is shown. This type of spiracle provides the least protection against water loss. At **E**, a chitinized antechamber, the atrium, is present, providing somewhat more protection against evaporation in the immediate vicinity of the spiracle.

should raise the question of how important gills are to those who have them. In some cases the gills can be removed without appreciably changing the rate of oxygen consumption. Presumably the gills are important only at times of respiratory stress in these forms. On the other hand, the removal of the gills of some mayfly nymphs reduces oxygen consumption to about one-fourth of the normal rate. Evidently the gills are extremely important in some species. As in other kinds of animals, where respiratory pigments may appear although used only in emergencies, the ability to cope with unusual conditions or to survive unusual exertions is sufficiently advantageous to produce selective pressures that direct the course of evolution.

The great majority of insect larvae and adults depend on an open tracheal system for respiratory transport. Tracheae are deep invaginations of the body surface that form at the future spiracles. As a result, the tracheal system is lined with epidermis continuous with the epidermis of the body wall, which secretes a cuticular lining for the tracheal system that is continuous with the cuticle that covers the body surface. This is important, for air-filled tubes would tend to collapse unless their walls were strengthened by some firm material. The cuticular lining of the tracheae contains spiral or beaded thickenings known as taenidia. Taenidia become less conspicuous in the smallest branches of the tracheal system, but electron photomicrographs indicate that they extend to the most delicate branches.

The first insects probably had a completely independent tracheal system from each spiracle, as in some arachnids and myriapods. The tracheal tubes were branching tracheae and hence somewhat more advanced than the tracheae of some other terrestrial arthropods. Judging by the distribution of tracheae in modern forms, the tracheal system must have, very early in its development, established a pattern of branching that is the basis for the modern systems. A short main trunk led from the spiracle, the spiracular trachea. This gave rise to three main branches, from which smaller branches to the tissues arose. One branch, the dorsal trachea, extended to the dorsal blood vessel and body wall; another, the ventral trachea, extended to the ventral nerve cord and body wall; and a third, the visceral trachea, extended to the viscera. Modern insects, however, have an integrated tracheal system as a result of the development of longitudinal and commissural connections between the tracheal systems associated with each spiracle (Fig. 19.22A). The pattern of longitudinal trunks varies greatly in different insects and in the same species at different periods of development. Anastomoses between the main tracheae of adjacent somites have been responsible for the formation of longitudinal trunks. These anastomoses may occur between the spiracular tracheae below the spiracle to form lateral longitudinal trunks,

At F, a spiracle with an atrium and lip is shown. The lips, separated from the exoskeletal plates by an articular membrane, can be closed by muscular contraction, thus guarding against evaporation except when the spiracle is necessarily opened for ventilation. Atria of this type, when combined with large tracheal trunks or air sacs, can be used exclusively for intake or exhaust, permitting a more organized flow of air through the tracheal system. At G and H, a spiracle with an atrial valve is shown, with the valve open and closed. A skeletal lever, operated by muscles, forces the flexible valve wall in and closes the atrial chamber. These are examples, only, for spiracular control is effected by a variety of special adaptations in different kinds of insects. (A, after Ross. C, after Wigglesworth, from Ross. B, after McDunnough. G and H, after Snodgrass.) *Tracheal capillaries:* 1, cuticle; 2, epidermis; 3, tracheal capillaries; 4, trachea. *Rectal gills:* 5, rectum; 6, trachea; 7, tracheal gills. *Spiracles:* 8, tracheal pore; 9, trachea; 10, body surface; 11, atrial pore; 12, spiracle; 13, peritreme; 14, lips of atrial pore; 15, lever; 16, valve; 17, filter formed by brush of cuticular hairs.

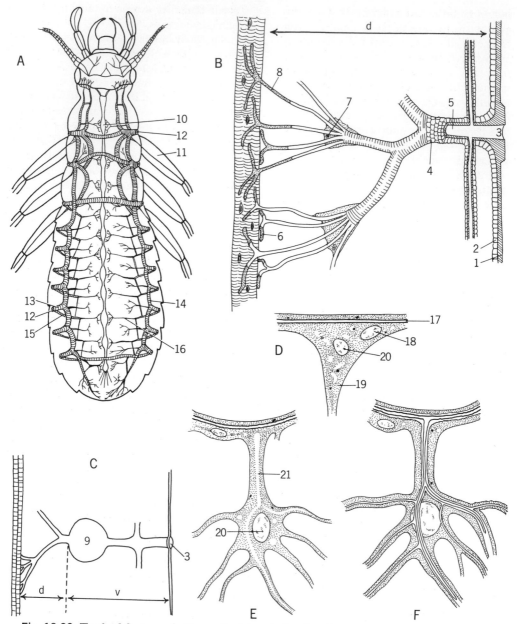

Fig. 19.22. Tracheal Systems. **A.** Generalized insect, showing the arrangement of the tracheae. **B.** Scheme of tracheal systems operating by simple diffusion. The internal branches are, of course, greatly simplified. The tracheae are continuations of the body wall, and the body wall cuticle is continuous with the tracheal lining. In fine branches, the cuticle is in the form of circular or spiral thickenings. The finest branches develop within the tracheole cells, and are without cuticular supports. In many insects, the tips of the end tracheoles are filled with a tracheolar fluid. In relaxed muscles the fluid is high in the tracheoles, as shown in the upper tracheoles. In fatigued muscle, the fluid is low, as shown in the lower tracheoles. It is thought

between the dorsal tracheae to form dorsal longitudinal trunks, between the ventral tracheae to form ventral longitudinal trunks, and between the visceral tracheae to form visceral longitudinal trunks. Commissural tracheae develop by anastomoses of corresponding branches on the right and left sides of the body. These are most commonly seen between the dorsal and ventral tracheae, but may occur in the visceral system also.

Calculations show that the diffusion of gases in a tracheal system is adequate to account for the delivery of oxygen and pick-up of carbon dioxide in most insects. The system of branching tubes provides a continuous column of air that extends to the smallest tracheae. Gaseous diffusion is quite rapid, and the tracheal system is surprisingly efficient. The least-understood aspect of tracheal respiration by diffusion is the way that the tracheole end cells function. The final branches of the tracheal system are tracheoles, which are formed in special end cells (Fig. 19.22D-F). The end cells persist after the tracheoles have formed. A fluid extends part way up the tracheoles. In fresh tissue the fluid extends further than in exhausted tissue. Presumably osmotic changes in the tissue cells and blood cause different levels of tracheolar filling. In any case, the mechanism tends to increase the delivery of oxygen at times of maximal needs. In fireflies, however, it appears that the tracheolar end cell may pump this fluid during flashing, thus actively increasing the rate of oxygen delivery. Further information is needed in this area.

While diffusion of gases may be adequate to deliver oxygen to the tissues in most insects, the margin of safety is increased and higher levels of activity can be maintained if the tracheal system is actively ventilated. Tracheal ventilation is made possible by the development of tracheal air sacs. Small, somewhat isolated air sacs may be found in legs or other parts of the body, where muscular movements will fill and empty them. In a number of insects, however, a system of large air sacs that ventilate the whole outer part of the tracheal system has developed. The details differ markedly in different orders and in different species within an order, but the basic form of a complex tracheal system is well illustrated in a locust (Fig. 19.19). Even in insects with a complex tracheal system, however, the smaller, internal tracheae work as a diffusion system (Fig. 19.22C).

As a general rule, complex ventilation mechanisms tend to appear in insects with

that the change in level of tracheolar fluid is associated with delivery of oxygen to muscle at times of greatest need. In tracheal systems of this kind, diffusion suffices for respiratory exchange. C. Scheme of tracheal systems in which active ventilation augments the movement of gases in the tracheae. The intervention of air sacs or other very spacious tracheal trunks, which can be collapsed or expanded as a result of body activity or special musculature, makes the outer part of the tracheal system a ventilating region. However, in the part of the tracheal system internal to the air sacs, gases move by diffusion, as indicated by the letters d and v on the arrows at the bottom of the diagram. D-F. Three stages in the development of a tracheole cell and its tracheoles. The tracheole cell develops from the tracheal epithelium, as seen at D. Within the young tracheoblast, a system of fine canals develops, which eventually make contact with the lumen of the tracheal trunk, as seen at E and F. (A, after Kolbe. C, after Ross, from Ross. B, composite. D-F, after Keister.) *Schemes of tracheal systems:* 1, cuticle of body wall; 2, epidermis; 3, spiracle; 4, main trachea; 5, intima of trachea; 6, tracheole; 7, tracheole cell; 8, tissue fluid in tracheole; 9, air sac. *Main tracheal tubes:* (landmark parts—10, nerve cord; 11, leg; 12, spiracle); 13, spiracular branch; 14, main longitudinal tracheal trunk; 15, ventral tracheal branch; 16, visceral tracheal branch. *Tracheole development:* 17, dorsal tracheal trunk; 18, nucleus of tracheal epithelium; 19, developing tracheoblast; 20, nucleus of tracheoblast; 21, developing tracheole.

a complex tracheal system. Grasshoppers, for example, relax the abdominal muscles for about 0.25 sec. During the last 0.2 sec. of this period, the anterior four spiracles are opened and air enters through them. These spiracles close just before the abdominal muscles contract, thus retaining the air that has entered. With all ports closed, the abdominal muscles are contracted. This compresses the air sacs and air is driven into the smaller, deeper air sacs, beyond which diffusion is the main mechanism for delivery of oxygen. The contraction of the abdominal muscles is maintained for about 0.4 to 1.5 sec. During the last half to third of this period the spiracles that were not used for inspiration are opened, and air escapes.

The spiracles are usually small and hidden. Each spiracle opens into an atrium, from which the spiracular trachea arises. Several kinds of improvements have been made in spiracular form (Fig. 19.21D-H), leading to the reduction of water loss by evaporation at the spiracle and the escape of water vapor from the tracheae. This involves the partial or complete closing of the spiracle by valves or lips. With the development of valves for closing the spiracles, control of air-flow in the tracheal system with specialization of inhalant and exhalant spiracles becomes possible. Special muscles close the spiracles and work rhythmically in complex tracheal systems. The rhythmic contractions are under the control of the ventral nerve cord, and appear to be to some degree segmental, with each ganglion in control of a specific pair of spiracles. Changing oxygen levels and changing carbon dioxide tensions change the rhythm of spiracular opening and closing and of breathing movements. The details of the feedback system that operates in respiratory control have not yet been described.

Some of the most remarkable respiratory adaptations are seen in adult aquatic insects, which have an open tracheal system but remain submerged most of the time. By using waxy secretions and fine hydrophobic hairs, an air bubble is formed and taken down with the insect. The simplest arrangements permit the formation of a bubble that will support several minutes of submerged activity. Improvements of the system, however, have had spectacular results. In some insects, a very fine, hairy region has evolved. The hairs are most remarkably fine and densely set. As many as 2,500,000 hairs may be present in a square millimeter of surface. Once charged, they hold a thin layer of gases known as the plastron. The plastron never needs to be renewed, for an adequate exchange between the gases dissolved in the water and the plastron is maintained to convert the tracheal-breathing insect into an animal that can be permanently submerged.

Excretion. Aquatic animals are almost universally ammonotelic, excreting most of their nitrogen in the form of ammonia. They can dispose of ammonia successfully at the body surface or dump it into a dilute urine. As water is all around them, the urine can be kept dilute enough to prevent any toxic effects of the ammonia. Land animals cannot easily afford the water expenditure required for ammonia excretion, and tend to develop alternative excretory patterns. To a very considerable extent, a group of organisms adapting to land become more or less successful depending on a single factor —how effectively they can conserve water. The kind of excretory system they develop is an important factor in water conservation. In this respect, insects have adapted very well, and a good part of the credit for their success must be given to the Malpighian tubules as effective excretory organs. Insects are predominantly uricotelic. While uric acid is the most important waste, small amounts of ammonia, urea, and allantoin are also excreted, and some wastes are stored as non-toxic compounds in the cuticle. Some wastes are used for the synthesis of pigments. Nitrogenous wastes are sometimes excreted by the salivary glands or the intestine, and athrocytic cells known as nephrocytes are often found around the gut wall and the Malpighian tubules. The Malpighian tubules, however, are the principal excretory organs, and the other methods of excretion are minor factors.

Malpighian tubules are attached to the gut at the junction of the midgut and hindgut. The amount of excretory surface is increased by increasing the number of Malpighian tubules, in some insects, or by the elongation of the tubules in others. Where a small number of very long Malpighian tubules are present, they are often greatly coiled. Wastes formed in the Malpighian tubules are discharged through the rectum. This arrangement permits a maximum reabsorption of water.

Two kinds of Malpighian tubules can be distinguished. One picks up water and waste materials throughout its length, and pours fluid urine into the gut. In tubules that work in this way, all of the reabsorption of water occurs in the rectum (Fig. 19.23). Other insects have Malpighian tubules that are divided into a proximal tubule filled with fluid urine, and a distal tubule where water is reabsorbed and crystals of uric acid appear. The crystals, suspended in water, pass to the rectum, where further water reabsorption completes the drying of the wastes. Water reabsorbed in the rectum is returned to the blood and can re-enter the proximal tubules with a new load of wastes. This cycling of water makes the most of the modest water resources of the insect body. Both types of Malpighian tubules are sometimes free at the tip and in other cases are bound by connective tissue to the rectal wall.

The Malpighian tubules have muscular walls and move about in the haemocoel vigorously. As insects have no cilia, these movements are important to agitate the contents of the tubules and help to keep the diffusion gradients as favorable as possible at the cell surfaces. The muscular movements also convey the contents of the Malpighian tubules to the hindgut. Tubule movements appear to be uncoordinated and independent of nerve stimuli.

Circulation. The circulatory system of insects closely resembles that of other arthropods. The body cavity is a haemocoel, divided into several sinuses by diaphragms. An incomplete plate of muscles, the dorsal diaphragm, cuts off the most dorsal part of the haemocoel as the pericardial sinus. The viscera lie below the dorsal diaphragm in a large perivisceral sinus (Fig. 19.24A). A ventral diaphragm below the perivisceral sinus usually cuts off the ventral sinus, containing the ventral nerve cord. A dorsal blood vessel lies in the pericardial sinus. It is differentiated into a heart in the abdominal region, and an aorta in the thoracic region.

Blood flows forward in the aorta and is discharged into the tissue spaces of the head region (Fig. 19.24B). It flows back in the perivisceral and ventral sinuses, entering the legs from the ventral sinus, and returning into the perivisceral sinus. In the abdominal region the blood flows upward, entering the pericardial sinus, and passing through the ostia into the heart. Booster hearts in the mesothorax and metathorax maintain circulation in the wing veins.

The tubular heart is usually dilated in each somite (Fig. 19.24C). Blood enters the heart through the paired ostia, and ostial valves prevent backflow during systole. A few insects have chambered hearts, with valves to prevent backflow, but the heart is usually a continuous tube, closed at the posterior end. In a few insects, especially the orthopterids, a series of paired lateral arteries arise from the heart, passing to the fat body. In the majority of insects, however, the aorta is the only blood vessel found in adult stages.

Booster hearts are found at various points

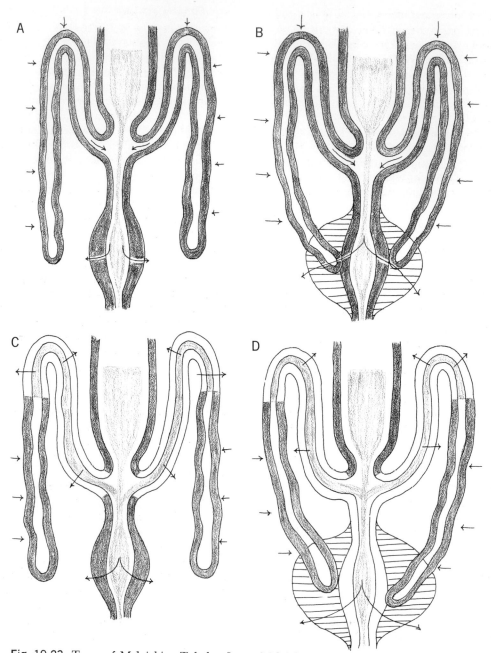

Fig. 19.23. Types of Malpighian Tubules. Insect Malpighian tubules arise from the junction of the midgut and hindgut. They may lie free in the haemocoel, as in **A** and **C**, or may be bound at the tips to the rectum, as in **B** and **D**. In some insects, the urine is fluid when it emerges from the Malpighian tubules, and is concentrated as it passes through the hindgut, as in **A** and **B**. In others, water reabsorption in the basal part of the Malpighian tubules occurs, and the urine is crystalline as it passes into the hindgut, as in **C** and **D**. In any case, as

in the body and are quite variable in different insect species. They are usually pulsating membranes, sometimes perforated with marginal openings that play the same part as the ostia of the heart. Booster hearts are especially important in insects with an extensive circulation through the wing veins. Wing circulation is important, for if it is impeded, the wing tracheae collapse and the wing becomes dry and brittle. It is also important during the spreading of the wings when the young insect emerges from the pupa. Other specializations to improve the flow of blood are sometimes found. Membranes across the leg may divide it into definite incurrent and excurrent channels, and many insects with large legs have booster hearts to maintain leg circulation.

Heartbeat physiology is imperfectly understood, and the data so far available suggest considerable diversity. Triangular alary muscles are arranged segmentally along the heart wall. When they contract they dilate the heart, helping to fill it. In some insects the rhythmic contraction of the alary muscles has been shown to alternate with the heart contractions, and there is no doubt that they normally help in filling the heart during diastole. In some insects, however, transsection of the alary muscles does not interfere with heartbeat. Some insects have myogenic hearts, with the beat originating in the striated cardiac muscle itself. Others have neurogenic hearts, with definite ganglion cells in the wall. Some tendency for insect hearts to change from myogenic to neurogenic during development has been noted, and there are other indications that myogenic hearts are more primitive and have tended to be improved by the addition of neurogenic mechanisms.

Although the insect circulatory system is open, the large haemocoelic spaces are enclosed by the body wall, and appreciable pressures may be present. From 18 to 87 mm. H_2O pressure has been reported in dragonfly nymphs, for example. There is surprisingly little information about the blood pressure of insects, however. In many instances no hemorrhage occurs at a wound, suggesting that the pressure is very low. It is probable that the pressure gradients involved in blood flow are quite low. Certainly the flow of the blood is not dependent only on heartbeat. Contraction of the abdominal muscles during respiration and of the thoracic muscles during flight play an important part in propelling the blood. However it may be effected, some regulation of blood flow is achieved. Blood flow increases with temperature, and is affected by activity, carbon dioxide content, and oxygen availability. Much more work is needed to analyze the factors involved. Apparently there are many species differences, and these may have so far made it difficult to draw any general conclusions about circulatory physiology in insects.

Insect blood transports foods, wastes, and hormones. It undoubtedly aids somewhat in respiratory transport, especially of carbon dioxide, but this is a less important function than in organisms without a tracheal system. The blood is also an important hydraulic fluid, in this way contributing to respiratory movements of the air sacs and tracheae, to stretching the new cuticle after a molt, and to inflating the wings before they harden as the insect emerges from the pupal stage.

Insect blood cells present a challenging field of study. A number of morphological types of blood cells can be distinguished. So far attempts to homologize blood cells have met with only moderate success, although some idea of the relationship of

shown by the arrows which indicate the movement of water and dissolved substances, water circulates through the Malpighian tubules, entering with wastes into the tubule, and departing from the tubule, rectal wall, or both, thus conserving the water supply in the body. A, orthopteran type; B, coleopteran type; C, hemipteran type; D, lepidopteran type. (Based on Wigglesworth.)

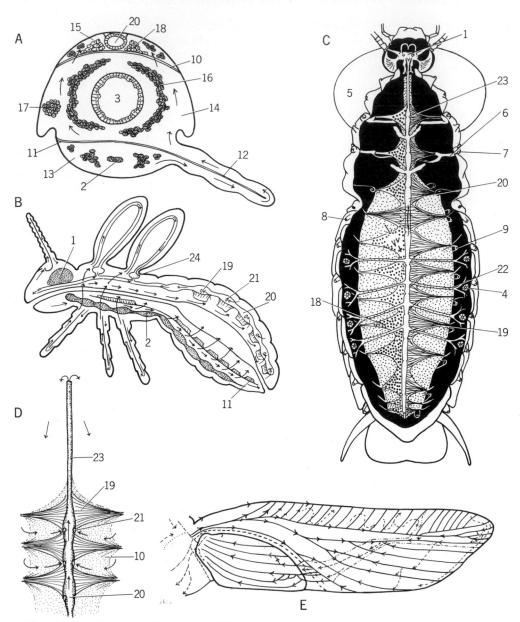

Fig. 19.24. Circulatory System. **A.** Schematic cross section of insect body, showing the divisions of the body cavity and the course of circulation. The dorsal diaphragm is formed by the dorsal transverse muscles and connective tissue, and is not a solid partition, permitting blood to pass through into the pericardial sinus above. The ventral diaphragm, when present, is formed of the ventral transverse muscles and is also incomplete, permitting blood to enter the perivisceral sinus. Septa in the legs divide the internal space into afferent and efferent channels. Oenocytes and fat cells in the body cavity and pericardial cells in the pericardial sinus provide for food storage, enter into excretory activities, and probably secrete substances. **B.** Scheme of circulation in insect. Arrows show direction of flow. **C.** Ventral dissection of a

some of the kinds of cells is beginning to emerge (Fig. 19.25). Some haemocytes contain fats or carbohydrates, and probably function in food storage and transport. Marked fluctuations of some of the blood cells are noted in premolt and postmolt stages, and in prepupation and postpupation stages, and some of these probably reflect changes in phagocytic cells as well as cells utilized for food storage. Some of the phagocytic cells have the usual functions of protecting the body from bacterial invasion and removing foreign particles, but others appear to be extremely active during metamorphosis. Haemocytes also migrate into injured areas and appear to be important in wound-healing. They can also agglutinate to prevent the loss of blood at an injured surface.

THE FAT BODY AND OENOCYTES

Trophocytes are characteristic insect cells. They are large cells, filled with reserves of saturated and unsaturated fats, varying greatly in chemical nature in different species. They sometimes float freely in the blood, where they are difficult to distinguish from some of the haemocytes. Generally, however, the trophocytes aggregate to form fat bodies, especially on each side of the digestive tract in the abdominal region. The arrangement and discreteness of the fat bodies vary with the order, and, to a lesser extent, within the orders. Trophocytes also store glycogen and proteins, particularly as metamorphosis approaches. During metamorphosis, the fat bodies tend to disperse, and the released cells break down in the blood, releasing food for the actively metabolizing tissues. Toward the end of pupation, however, the fat bodies regenerate.

Interspersed among the trophocytes of the fat bodies are urate cells, filled with crystals of nitrogenous waste. The urates appear to be derived primarily from purine metabolism. Although they are important points for storage excretion, it is not clear whether this is their primary function. They may process the wastes formed by the trophocytes; they may accumulate wastes when the Malpighian tubules are ineffective, as at a molt or during pupation or hibernation; or they may serve as points where the intermediate processing of wastes occur, preparing compounds that can be handled by the Malpighian tubules.

Loose clusters or bands of a different kind of cell are also found associated with the fat bodies or in separate masses. These are large cells, derived from the ectoderm, and known as oenocytes. They appear to be especially active during molting and cuticle production. Their precise function is un-

cockroach, showing the heart and associated structures. In some insects, contraction of the alary muscle dilates the heart, causing it to fill. Valves close the ostia when the heart wall contracts. In some insects, segmental vessels arise from the heart. These contain valves at the junction with the heart, preventing backflow into the heart. D. Schematic view of anterior end of generalized insect heart, showing several ostia. E. Course of circulation in the forewing of a cockroach. The flow of blood through the wing veins, important during metamorphosis in expanding the wing, is also important in maintaining the adult wing. Disturbances of circulation in the wing increase its brittleness, which result in collapse of the wing tracheae. (A, composite. B, after Wigglesworth. C, after Nutting. D, after Snodgrass. E, after Clare and Tauber.) *Landmark organs:* 1, brain; 2, nerve cord; 3, gut; 4, tergosternal muscle; 5, pronotum; 6, third anterior notal ridge; 7, third thoracic spiracle; 8, first abdominal spiracle; 9, trachea. *Diaphragms and divisions of haemocoel:* 10, dorsal diaphragm; 11, ventral diaphragm; 12, septum in leg; 13, ventral sinus; 14, perivisceral sinus; 15, pericardial cavity (dorsal sinus); 16, fat cells; 17, oenocytes; 18, pericardial cells (nephrocytes); 19, alary muscle. *Circulatory system:* 20, heart; 21, ostium; 22, abdominal segmental vessels; 23, aorta; 24, booster heart at wing base.

known, but it is thought that they may be centers of intermediary metabolism.

THE SENSE ORGANS

All arthropods have had about the same problems in developing sense organs. All are covered by a firm cuticle that makes the reception of even a touch stimulus a challenge. But the cuticle that seems at first to make sense reception difficult has proved adaptable to constructing sense organs of great variety and sensitivity. Movable bristles and hairs can be used to obtain a great deal of information about the environment, and pits with thin cuticular floors can also be utilized in a variety of ways. Probably because of the problems presented by the cuticle and the potentialities it brought with it, the sense organs of all arthropods tend to be superficially similar. It is important to remember that sense organs that are similar in appearance and structure can be used for very different purposes, however. A great deal more is known about the sense organs of insects than of other groups of arthropods. Probably the general principles noted in insect sensory reception apply to other arthro-

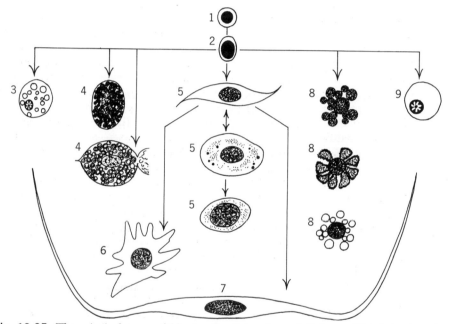

Fig. 19.25. The principal types of blood cells of insects, and their possible derivation. At 1 is a prohemocytoid, considered the stem cell from which the whole group of haemocytes arise. At 2 is a chromophil cell, which may differentiate into a number of cell types. At 3 is a spheroidocyte, a round vaculated cell that becomes eosinophilic during metamorphosis. At 4 are two types of cystocytes, which contain cystlike inclusions. At 5, several types of plasmatocytes are shown. At 6, is a polypodocyte. The pseudopodia are apparently not functional for movement. At 7 is a vermiform cell, apparently an extremely elongated form of plasmatocyte. At 8 are eruptive cells, which contain a variety of vesicles and granules. At 9 is an oenocyte-like cell. In some cases these rather rare cells increase in abundance just before pupation; they have been suspected of serving as a source of tyrosinase, used to harden the pupa wall. Knowledge of the morphology and functions of the cells found free in the blood is very incomplete at present. (After Jones, from Munson, in Roeder.)

pods, although the specific details may vary widely.

Other than the eyes, the principal sense organs may be classified as 1) hair organs, consisting of long or short sensory hairs or bristles; 2) campaniform organs, dome-shaped sense organs with a sensory ending; 3) plate organs, covered by a flat plate beneath which the sensory elements lie; and 4) compound scolopophorous organs, usually consisting of a bundle or cluster of associated sensillae.

Mechanoreceptors discharge when the sensory ending is mechanically deformed. They are used primarily for touch, orientation in space, and vibration reception. Sensory hairs and bristles are characteristic mechanocreceptors in arthropods generally. A hair sensillum (Fig. 19.26A) is set in a socket which is covered by membranous, flexible cuticle. It is formed by the co-operation of two cells, a tormogen cell and a trichogen cell. The tormogen cell is a modified epidermal cell that secretes the delicate membrane on which the hair rests. The trichogen cell projects through the tormogen cell, and secretes the cuticle of the hollow hair. A sensory cell is associated with the tormogen and trichogen cells, typically extending through them and ending in a sensory projection that extends into the hair. In some cases, however, the sensory tip ends at the base of the hair. Any movement of the hair excites the sensory ending, evoking a nerve impulse in the nerve process of the sensory cell.

The nerve endings may discharge only when moved or may discharge continuously while under pressure, depending on whether they adapt rapidly or slowly. Rapidly adapting endings are ready to discharge in small fractions of a second and are especially valuable for vibration reception, while the slow-adapting endings are better suited for tactile reception. Vibration reception is important in providing information about the movements of the air or water in which the animal lives. Vibra-

tion receptors are especially well developed in swimming and flying insects.

Hair sensilla are sometimes used to form compound sense organs. Hair plates, for example, are associated with the joints of cockroaches. They are deformed by movements of the joints and adapt slowly. Their characteristics would make them especially useful in providing information about the position of the body and the attitude of its parts, and are thought to be important in proprioreception.

The campaniform sensilla are also used for proprioreception. Each sensillum is formed by a thin dome of two-layered cuticle. The tip of a sensory cell extends to the inner layer of the dome (Fig. 19.26B). A single epidermal cell is associated with the campaniform organ, presumably laying down the modified cuticle in the dome. The campaniform organs are sensitive to cuticular stress and are important proprioreceptors. Most of the proprioreceptors are stretch receptors, providing information about the tension of a particular muscle. The campaniform organ, however, is responsive to the stress affecting the cuticle at a given point, and so provides information based on the resultant of all of the forces being applied to the exoskeleton. Proprioreception has replaced gravity reception insofar as righting reflexes are concerned. Righting reflexes are initiated when no stimuli are received from the leg proprioreceptors. The same mechanism is used in take-off and landing in flying insects where the tensions recorded by the leg proprioreceptors initiate predetermined movements of the body and wings.

Scolopophorous organs are groups of sensilla, each consisting of a cap cell which touches the cuticle, and an enveloping cell that encloses the sensitive tip of a sensory cell (Fig. 19.26C). The sensory ending is characterized by a scolops, or sensory peg, which contains a central axial filament that passes up to the cuticle, to which it is usually attached. The scolopophorous organs are widely distributed in insects and are found in various positions in the body. Some of them are definitely used for vibration reception, but these are found in connection with other parts that are suitable for sound reception. Very little is known of the function of the other scolopophorous organs. They may be sensitive to inner pressures placed on them by the surrounding tissues, for the scolops is often tethered to the cuticle and would remain in place even though the tissues around were to be pushed to one side. If this idea proves to be correct, the scolopophorous organs would be ideal for the reception of stimuli associated with acceleration. There is evidence to show that an acceleration sense may be of importance in the flight of dragonflies. These organs would also be useful in orientation to gravitational pull, which deforms the soft tissues around them. Even in flight, however, orientation to gravity appears to be relatively unimportant. A dragonfly flies with its dorsal surface toward the light, and if illuminated from below flies upside down, and light has a very strong influence on the flight behavior of all insects.

Scolopophorous sensilla are used for sound reception. In this case the cuticle associated with the scolopophorous organs forms a tympanic membrane, as in the phonoreceptors in the legs of some grasshoppers (Fig. 19.26D,E). Phonoreceptors are found on the thorax, abdomen, legs, and antennae of various kinds of insects.

Chemoreception is especially associated with modified sensory hairs and plate organs. They are concentrated in the antennae and mouthparts, and in the vicinity of the ovipositor. One form of chemoreceptor is a peg-like sensory hair with a thin cuticle. Cap and enveloping cells like those of mechanoreceptors may or may not be present. The sense organ contains a vacuolar fluid in which the sensory endings of several cells are bathed. It is thought that the chemical evoking a response penetrates the thin cuticle, dissolves in the vacuolar fluid, and so comes to stimulate the sensory end-

ings. Technical difficulties of recording impulses from the delicate endings have made information about how stimuli are evoked difficult to obtain. There is evidence to indicate that the several different endings in chemoreceptors produce different firing patterns, and that mechanoreceptors accompany the chemoreceptive cells.

Insects are capable of receiving chemical stimuli from distant sources as well as from those in contact with the receptor. Presumably the principal difference between these receptors is the threshold at which impulses are initiated. The most delicate chemoreceptors are known to be located on the antennae in some cases, and this is probably generally true. Another point of high sensitivity is the maxillary palp. In the larvae of cabbage butterflies and in blowflies, removal of the antennae raises the concentration of substances required to cause response by the animal. Removal of the palps when the antennae are intact does not alter the threshold for response, but removal of the palps when the antennae have been destroyed causes a second increase in the threshold.

Although not very much is known of the mechanism by which stimuli are initiated, a very extensive literature deals with the kinds of compounds to which insects will respond at a distance or by contact, and the relative sensitivity to related compounds. While this information may give some hints about the way that the sensory endings are stimulated, it is based on the behavior of the organism, and so is always complicated by the fact that the central nervous system is involved. Furthermore, as concentrations are increased the behavior changes, so that it is quite possible that other sense organs become involved. Very few generalizations can be made as yet, but the chain length of organic compounds, the molecular weight, and the boiling point, as well as the solubility in water, appear to be related to the effectiveness of compounds to evoke responses.

Humidity reception is a special case of

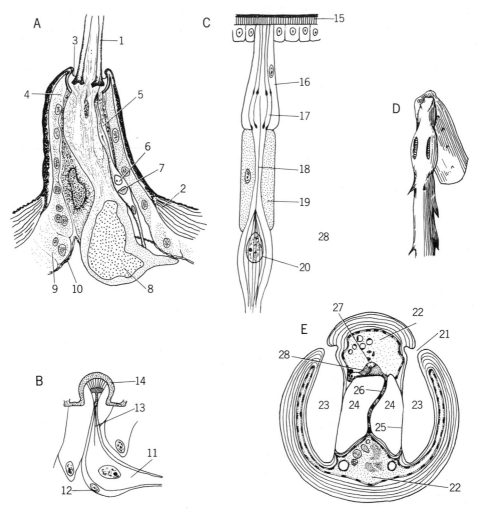

Fig. 19.26. Sense Organs. **A.** Section through the base of a hair sensillum. **B.** A campaniform organ. **C.** A scolopophorous or chordotonal organ. **D.** Tibia of a grasshopper, showing openings of the tympanal organ. **E.** Section through the tibia, showing structure of the tympanal organ. (**A**, after Hsü. **B**, after Pflugstaedt. **C**, after Snodgrass. **D**, after Weber. **E**, after Schwabe, from Wigglesworth.) *Hair sensillum:* 1, base of hair; 2, cuticle; 3, articular membrane; 4, epidermis; 5, scolopoid body; 6, sensory cell; 7, neurilemma cell; 8, trichogen cell; 9, tormogen cell; 10, basement membrane. *Campaniform organ:* 11, sensory cell; 12, neurilemma; 13, terminal filament to scolopale; 14, longitudinal thickening in dome roof. *Scolopophorous organ:* 15, cuticle; 16, distal (cap) cell; 17, scolopale (sensory rod); 18, terminal filament; 19, sheath cell; 20, sensory cell. *Tympanal organ:* 21, cleft in tibia; 22, blood channel; 23, tympanal cavity; 24, enlarged trachea; 25, tympanum; 26, rigid wall around trachea; 27, trachea; 28, crista acoustica, containing chordotonal organs.

chemoreception and appears to involve special chemoreceptors, built on similar lines but separated from the distance chemoreceptors. Humidity reception does not involve simple acceptance or rejection. As a rule, some humidity level is preferred, and negative reactions are evoked by drier or moister surroundings. Insects often distribute themselves in an area in patterns that indicate a strong sensitivity to microclimatic factors resulting from the effects of the surrounding vegetation. Undoubtedly the humidity receptors play an important role in facilitating the choice of many insects for a home area, for sites for egg deposition, and the like. Well-fed and starved insects of the same species may differ in their humidity choices, as may different stages in the life cycle. It is likely that humidity reception is an important factor in some of the characteristic movements that many insect species make, passing from one part of the habitat to another as they mature, or after feeding, resting, or carrying out other activities. In some insects all humidity reception occurs in antennal organs, and removal of the antennae completely destroys the ability to orient to water vapor. In others the humidity receptors are more widely distributed. More work on humidity reception would be useful in evaluating its importance in insect behavior.

Photoreception centers in the compound eyes and ocelli, although some insects also have dermoptic sense organs. The compound eyes are remarkably like the eyes of the higher Crustacea, and their structure need not be discussed here. As in the Crustacea, pigment migrates distally and proximally about the ommatidia, converting the eye from an apposition to a superposition eye and back again, and diurnal rhythms of pigment movement follow patterns essentially like those of Crustacea. It appears, however, that nerve stimuli are responsible for pigment migration in insect eyes instead of hormones.

A great deal of work has gone into studies of the sensitivity of insects to light waves of differing amplitudes and frequencies, and of the ability of insects to distinguish between colors and shapes of objects. In many respects the compound eye compares very unfavorably to the human eye. Even large compound eyes compare unfavorably in the sense that they contain far fewer ommatidia than the number of rods and cones in a human retina. Experiments have shown that bees can be taught to distinguish some shapes by providing food at sites marked by symbols of a specific shape. Similar experiments have been used to determine the ability to distinguish colors. It is evident that bees can distinguish between different colors from these experiments, and that they have a very limited ability to distinguish shapes. Only the simplest kinds of shapes are effective for training, and the kinds of errors that they make when faced by what we consider very simple shapes are remarkable. The physical analysis of the eye indicates that it can form a far better image than experiments with bees would indicate. It is not clear whether bees cannot distinguish between shapes very well, do not respond adequately to the system of rewards that is used, cannot use information of this kind in relation to the search for food, have a central nervous system that is unable to record patterns of the kind we naturally think of, or have eyes with receptors that do not record images. Some of the same difficulties are inherent in any attempt to analyze sensory reception in non-human subjects, although results based on reflex movements resulting from light stimuli or on patterns of discharge in the optic nerve are probably more dependable. It is quite one thing to observe that two areas are differently illuminated and another to make a reflex movement in response, and we have no idea what the different firing patterns in the optic nerve may mean in the life of an insect. On the basis of the available information, it would appear that the

the various components of the brain. The ganglia associated with the remainder of the head appendages have coalesced to form a compound subesophageal ganglion that innervates the mandibles and two maxillary somites. Two commissures form an inner ring around the stomodaeum, one associated with the frontal ganglion, which innervates the stomodaeal region, and one connecting the right and left tritocerebra, as seen in the grasshopper brain (Fig. 19.27A).

The protocerebrum is composed of the large protocerebral lobes, an intercerebral region, and sometimes of accessory lobes. It contains a number of important centers (Fig. 19.27B). The pons cerebralis is an anterior, medial center that appears to have an associational function. The corpus centrale (central body) lies immediately behind. This center is rather simple in Crustacea, but is divided into several definite masses in insects. It is also an associational center, receiving fibers from all other parts of the brain. The pedunculate bodies, also found in other arthropods, are the most important associative centers. The pedunculate bodies are first seen in polychaetes, and have been further developed in the various arthropod groups. In insects they contain a number of discrete groups of neurons forming definite divisions in the stalked part of the pedun-

culate bodies. The size and complexity of the pedunculate bodies correlate well with the complexity of the behavior patterns of different species, and tend to vary with the size and development of the compound eyes. Another associational center is found in a pair of ventral bodies, connected by a commissure. These have been thought a part of the deutocerebrum, but lie in the protocerebrum and are generally considered with the forebrain. They are especially well developed in Lepidoptera, where they form a pair of accessory lobes. As a general rule, insects with larger ventral bodies tend to have smaller pedunculate bodies, suggesting that they have somewhat similar general functions. The most complex nerve centers are associated with the compound eyes. Three centers can be recognized: an outer periopticon, a middle epiopticon, and an inner opticon. The details of their functions are not yet understood.

The deutocerebrum contains the antennal relay centers, connected by a commissural tract. The tritocerebrum is small in insects, as there is no appendage in the somite to which it belongs. A commissural tract connects the two sides of the tritocerebrum. It is sometimes embedded in the circumesophageal connectives and sometimes free. It is most closely associated with the labral nerves and the frontal con-

nervous system by union of ganglia and predominance of more anterior centers is the common evolutionary trend in arthropods. (A, after Snodgrass. B, after Hanström. C, after Zawarzin, from Wigglesworth. D-G, after Brandt, from Folson and Wardle.) *Brain and head nervous system:* 1, aorta; 2, pharynx; 3, crop; 4, protocerebrum; 5, ocellar pedicel; 6, optic lobe; 7, nerve to occipital ganglion; 8, deutocerebrum; 9, antennal nerve; 10, tritocerebrum; 11, dorsal tegumentary nerve; 12, labrofrontal nerve; 13, labral nerve; 14, frontal ganglion connective; 15, frontal ganglion; 16, recurrent nerve; 17, occipital ganglion; 18, corpus allatum; 19, nerve to corpus allatum; 20, nerve to anterior crop; 21, nerve to lateral crop; 22, tritocerebral commissure; 23, nerve to neurilemma of circumenteric connective; 24, circumenteric connective; 25, subesophageal ganglion; 26, mandibular nerve; 27, hypopharyngeal nerve; 28, maxillary nerve; 29, labial nerve; 30, nerves to salivary duct; 31, cervical nerve to neck muscle. *Section through brain:* 32, central body; 33, mushroom body (corpus pedunculatum); 34, optic centers; 35, antennal glomerulus; 36, sensory nerve to antenna; 37, motor nerve to antenna. *Section through ganglion:* 38, sensory fibers; 39, sensory neuropile; 40, ventral fiber tracts of longitudinal commissures; 41, associational neuron; 42, central neuropile; 43, motor neuron; 44, motor fiber tract of longitudinal commissure; 45, motor fibers.

nectives, which are important parts in the stomodaeal nervous system.

The subesophageal ganglion is a compound ganglion and innervates all three of the somites associated with the mouth parts, the salivary glands, and some of the neck muscles. It is generally composed of a cortex containing the nerve cells and an inner neuropile. It is more than a center for the gnathocephalon, however, and exercises an important influence on motor activities in the body somites.

The body ganglia are complex. At the surface there are dorsal and ventral tracts that are continuous with the ventral nerve trunks. Motor fibers are placed on the dorsal side, and sensory fibers on the ventral side of the ganglion. Clusters of motor neurons and associational neurons occur laterally, and the central neuropile can be divided into several regions (Fig. 19.27C). Peripheral nerves from the ganglion twig out to the musculature and the sense organs of the somite. As in other arthropods, the ganglia on the ventral nerve trunks tend to aggregate by moving forward and coalescing (Fig. 19.27D-G). As the thoracic ganglia aggregate, the abdominal ganglia tend to diminish in the Diptera, and something of the same tendency is seen in other orders.

The stomodaeal nervous system corresponds functionally to the autonomic nervous system of vertebrates. It centers in the frontal ganglion and recurrent nerve, which passes along the floor of the brain and twigs out over the stomodaeal region. Subsidiary ganglia and nerves are associated with some of the mouth parts, the salivary glands, the upper part of the digestive tract, and the aorta. It functions as a pathway for feedback mechanisms that affect the physiological functioning of the viscera.

The complex nervous system of insects is the structural basis for interesting and diversified behavior patterns. No group of animals is more interesting from a behavioral point of view. Some of the most striking developments in behavior are seen among the social insects, where some integration of the activities of the members of the organization is an essential element of the success of the group as a whole. This calls for something akin to communication in human social organizations, although the degree and type of symbolization upon which insect communication depends is far simpler and more limited.

LOCOMOTION

Walking. Walking movements are different in adult insects and in caterpillars, where peristaltic movements of the body accompany leg movements, and also differ in different kinds of insects. Jumping, digging, and running all present somewhat different problems and require somewhat different kinds of movements. However, the problems associated with walking are the same in principle if not in detail as those involved in jumping, digging, or other kinds of locomotor activity. As all cannot be discussed, walking has been chosen for discussion as the most basic type of leg locomotion.

Walking involves three kinds of problems. Each leg must make the movements of a step, the two members of a pair of legs must be suitably co-ordinated, and the three pairs of legs must work in co-operation. When a leg makes a step, the tarsal segments must be alternately flexed and extended, to grip the substrate and free the the foot, and the leg must be alternately flexed and extended to provide propulsion. If the insect is not to fall flat on its face, it must maintain a tripod at all times, and the legs tend to move in a tripod fashion. The first and third left legs and middle right leg work together as one tripod, and the other three legs act as the other tripod. Co-ordination for walking thus involves the control of individual legs to alternate properly the leg and tarsal movements in a step and the co-ordination of the six legs to produce organized forward movements, as well as an appropriate adjustment of the walking movements to the information about the environment available at the time.

The legs of isolated thoracic segments will make stepping movements. These are controlled by the thoracic ganglion and are triggered by impulses received through the proprioreceptors of the somite when the somite is isolated. In the intact animal, however, stepping can be evoked by impulses moving through the nerve cord from other somites. Co-ordination of the several legs is achieved by intersegmental reflexes in the nerve cord. It is by no means a simple mechanical co-ordinating system, however, for an insect can compensate for the loss of a leg by modifying its method of stepping. In establishing a stepping rhythm the prothoracic ganglion acts as the pacemaker, and several different pathways may be used for the movement of the stimulus to the more posterior thoracic somites. A second, and important, factor is the proprioreceptive situation resulting from the stepping movements in the somite immediately in front of the middle and hind legs. The co-ordinating system is thus double, and the double set of controls gives a degree of plasticity to the system not seen in the co-ordinating system of annelids, for example.

Flight. Flying vertebrates have an entirely different kind of flight equipment and face different kinds of problems than insects. Insect flight is unique and especially interesting for this reason.

An insect wing may be thought of as a lever, pivoting on the pleural process of the lateral exoskeleton (Fig. 19.28). The wing base projects inward from the pivot, and is moved as the notum of its thoracic segment moves, but in the opposite direction. The notum is depressed when the dorsoventral flight muscles contract, and the wings are lifted. The notum is bowed upward by the longitudinal muscles that extend from the anterior and posterior phragma at the ends of the notum; this depresses the wings.

It is evident that a simple flailing of the wings up and down would never result in flight. Forward thrust must be generated. Three factors enter into the forward drive. In the first place the costal vein is the most rigid vein in the majority of insect wings, and the wing does not remain flat as it moves up and down. Air is spilled from the buckled back margin, providing some forward impulse. The great variations in wing venation have been mentioned. It is very probable that these variations in veining and the minor modifications in the relative rigidity of parts of the wing are a far more important factor in flight than some of the factors that are more carefully analyzed. Certainly the wing movements of different kinds of insects are different, and they are very probably associated with differences in the qualities of the wings as airfoils as well as with differences in the center of gravity and wing placement. In the second place, the wings are tilted or feathered as they move up and down. Tilting the wing aids in spilling air at the trailing edge, and helps markedly in providing forward thrust. In the third place, wings do not move straight up and down, but make a figure-of-eight movement (Fig. 19.28F,G), intensifying the tendency of air to spill from the trailing edges of the wings. These three factors combine differently in insects of different kinds, but can be seen clearly through the use of experimental and comparative techniques. Narrow, fast-moving wings with a strong tilt and a strong figure-of-eight component are found in the fastest flyers. Insects with flat wings with little give and with wings that tilt little during flight and move more or less up and down with a minor tendency toward a figure-of-eight motion are slow and hesitant flyers. Dragonflies are good examples of strong flyers, and most butterflies are relatively poor flyers. Where all of the factors are favorable, insects can achieve quite good speeds, although there has been a tendency to overestimate them. Sphinx moths and horseflies are the best that have been tested, achieving speeds of up to 30 miles per hour. Dragonflies reach speeds of about 25 miles per hour. It should be noted that the good flyers are heavy insects. The air resistance becomes greater in proportion to the muscle weight in smaller insects. In much the same way as the smaller crustaceans are planktonic or-

ganisms, unable to cope with the water currents even though able to swim about, the smaller insects are "air plankton," carried about by air currents even when wind velocities are not unusually high. The specifics of insect aerodynamics rapidly become challenging from a mathematical point of view. Those who are interested in

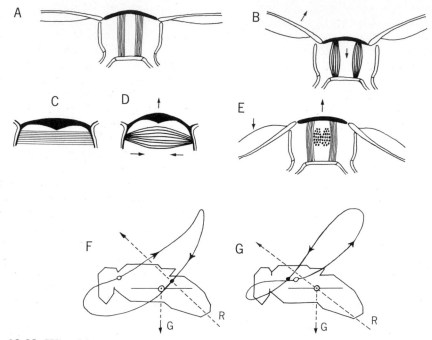

Fig. 19.28. Wing Movements. The wing bases articulate with the tergal plates and pass over the pleural plates. As a result, the wings are raised when dorsoventral muscles are contracted, as in B, and at rest when the muscles are relaxed, as at A. A further downward stroke requires a more marked upward movement of the tergal plate. This is made possible by longitudinal muscles when pass from the anterior to posterior phragma in the somite, as shown at C. Contraction of these muscles bows the tergum, lifting it in the middle, as at D. The resulting movement permits the depression of the wings, as seen at E. Actually, wing movement is not directly up and down, but includes forward and backward components, which add to the speed and stability of flight. Suspended in still air, a fly moves its wings in the path shown in F. The resultant force passes along the dotted line, marked R, inclined at an angle of 48 degrees and sufficient to hold the fly up. This line passes behind the center of gravity (G), and if the fly is suddenly released, it dives downward to the ground. A light air current, however, stimulates mechanoreceptors, and the wing beat changes, assuming a figure-of-eight shape, as shown at G. Under these conditions, the resultant of the wing movements is not changed in direction, but is shifted forward, passing through or in front of the center of gravity. When released, the fly moves forward. Such a simple experiment demonstrates the flexibility of the actual movements performed by the wings, the importance of sense reception in co-ordinating these movements with air currents, and something of what is required of an insect to achieve stability in flight. (A-E, after Ross. F and G, after Hollicks, from Wigglesworth.)

this phase of insect behavior might consult the excellent review by Chadwick, in *Insect Physiology*, edited by K. D. Roeder, who cites a good bibliography of the most important studies.

However the wings may move, and whatever their aerodynamic qualities, they must be manipulated by muscles. The problems of insect flight muscles are evident when one considers the nature of muscle tissue. When repetitive stimuli are delivered to muscles at ever-increasing frequencies, a point is reached where the individual contractions cannot be maintained, and sustained contraction or tetany results. The frequencies with which wings move vary greatly in different kinds of animals, and as a general rule the larger the animal, the slower its wings move, although there are many exceptions related to differences in the ability of creatures to fly. The wings of an albatross or an eagle move slowly. The wings of a hummingbird move very rapidly. What of the wings of insects? How fast do they move, and how can muscles be arranged to manipulate them so fast?

The frequency of wingbeat varies with age, sex, species, and the composition, density, and temperature of the air, as well as the speed of air currents and the physiolgical condition of an insect. The wingbeat of very light-bodied insects with large wings is very slow. Butterflies, for example, may move the wings as slowly as 4 times per second. Where the body is heavier and the wings are smaller the frequency of beat rises. Bees and flies vibrate the wings far more rapidly, at speeds of 100 times per second or more. The frequency of wingbeat becomes audible in insects of this kind, and serves as a very reliable guide. The heavy drone of a bumblebee corresponds to measured wingbeat frequencies of 130 to 240 beats per second, while the high-pitched whine of the mosquito indicates wingbeats of nearly 1000 per second. It is clear that the demands placed on the flight muscles vary enormously with the species as well as the conditions under which it flies.

Dragonflies, moths, butterflies, and orthopterans, among others, have direct flight muscles. These contract with each wing movement and are not much faster than the leg muscles. The movements of the wing fall into the range of about 20 to 40 per second. In these insects the muscles are not arranged in the system shown in Fig. 19.28, but are attached directly to the bases of the wings. In most of the more highly specialized and "higher" insect orders, however, the flight muscles are attached to the exoskeleton of the somite rather than to the wing bases, and the muscles are differently constructed. Muscles attached to the wing bases are said to be direct flight muscles, while those attached to the phragma, terga, and sternum are said to be indirect.

Indirect flight muscles are constructed of very large muscle fibers, composed of very large myofibrils which, in turn, are made up of very large myofibrils. It is clear that they cannot receive a distinct nerve stimulus for each wingbeat, for they undergo tetany when receiving stimuli at frequencies of about 40 per second, and they contract at far greater frequencies. The maximum recorded frequency is in a midge with clipped wings, which achieved rates of 2218 beats per second. Evidently, if the muscle cannot receive a separate stimulus for each contraction, it must contract several times for each stimulus. How can this be arranged? One of the peculiarities of muscle tissue is that when relaxed and suddenly stretched, it tends to contract. This property is utilized in the flight muscles. The longitudinal flight muscles pull on the phragma. Beyond a certain point it springs in and releases the muscle tension. Immediately afterwards, the dorsoventral flight muscles contract and stretch the muscle once again, and in response to the new stretch, it contracts again. The muscle is thus stimulated mechanically over and over again, and responds as long as it is in an active or responsive state. Only enough nerve impulses to maintain the responsiveness of the muscle to mechanical stimulation are needed for continued flight.

Flight and walking may serve as examples of insect behavior at the level of individual body parts. Behind every movement of insects lurk similar complex and holistic mechanisms. Insects are tiny creatures, with a finite and relatively small number of neurons responsible for delivering sensory impulses to the central nervous system, for delivering motor impulses to the muscles, and for carrying out whatever kinds of associational activities they are capable of. As a painter may be admired for achieving an effect with a minimum of detail, insects may be admired for achieving a tremendously complex behavior with an "economy of means." This mechanism which insects use depends upon their ability to utilize a single muscle fiber for varied kinds of activities by means of multiple innervation, on the one hand, and through the basic properties of their muscle tissue, on the other. Insects have utilized the very simple properties of bristles, hairs, and other minor modifications of the cuticular covering to develop a remarkably diversified set of sense organs. They have also built into the nervous system itself mechanisms which can provide prepackaged, but nevertheless variable, unitary fragments of behavior that are suitable for the conditions under which they live.

THE REPRODUCTION SYSTEM

Insects are almost universally dioecious. Details of the reproductive system vary greatly from group to group, although the format remains remarkably stable.

The Male System. The elements of the male system are the testes, sperm ducts, ejaculatory duct, and intromittent organ. The testes are composed of groups of tubular follicles bound together by a sheath of epithelial tissue (Fig. 19.29C). Each follicle contains an apical cell at the tip,

thought to be a specialized spermatogonium that has assumed a nutritive function. A series of clusters of cells fill the follicle. The cells of each cluster are in the same stage of development. The youngest stages are found at the apical end of the follicle, and in a testis actively producing sperm, spermatogonial clusters are found at the apex of the follicle, followed by clusters of primary spermatocytes, secondary spermatocytes, spermatids, and mature sperm in regular sequence. Each follicle ends in a sperm ductule that unites with the sperm ductules from other follicles to form a sperm duct on each side of the body. The two sperm ducts pass posteriorly and join the ejaculatory duct. In a sense the ejaculatory duct is the first part of the external genitalia, for it arises from an invagination of the body surface and is lined with epidermis and cuticle. The ejaculatory duct has muscular walls, and receives the secretions of a pair of tubular accessory glands. The accessory gland secretion serves as a vehicle for suspending the sperm or else hardens to mold the sperm into a spermatophore. The ejaculatory duct typically ends on the ninth abdominal somite or in the articular membrane between the ninth and tenth somites. An evagination of the body wall forms a phallus around the opening of the ejaculatory duct. Various kinds of periphallic organs are found lateral to the phallus. These consist of modified appendages of the ninth somite (p. 876) and various movable or immovable parts derived from the ninth or adjacent somites. Details of phallic and periphallic structure cannot be covered here; those interested should examine a text on entomology. It may suffice to say that the external genitalia differ in groups and in species and are often important in taxonomy.

The Female Organs. The female system closely parallels the male system in its basic organization. Each ovary consists of a group of ovarian tubules known as ovarioles, bound together by an epithelial sheath. The ovarioles open into oviduct-ules, which unite to form an oviduct on each side of the body. A typical ovariole consists of a terminal filament, often used to suspend the ovary from the body wall, a germarium in which the oögonia form, and a follicle or egg chamber where the ova mature (Fig. 19.29A,B). The paired oviducts unite to form a common oviduct, which opens into the genital chamber. The genital chamber corresponds to the ejaculatory duct. It is formed by an invag-ination of the body surface on the eighth somite. It functions as a copulatory bursa, receiving the sperm at the time of mating. Its external orifice is the vulva, located on the eighth somite at the point of the evag-ination from which the genital chamber was formed. In some insects the genital chamber is drawn out into a tubular part and is then called the vagina. In more gen-eralized insects, a diverticulum arises from the genital chamber. This is the seminal receptacle, used to store the sperm received during mating.

Typically a second invagination occurs on the ninth somite. This gives rise to the accessory glands and their external pore. In many insects the accessory glands have been joined to the genital chamber. The accessory glands secrete a variety of sub-stances, used for a variety of purposes. They most commonly produce an adhesive used to glue the eggs to a surface or a sub-stance that hardens to form an egg case, but unusual secretions are formed in a number of insects. It is the accessory glands that secrete the toxic materials that transform the ovipositor of a bee into an effective weapon.

The generalized form of the external genitalia have been described (p. 875). As

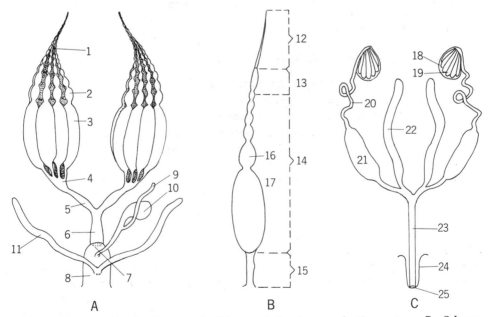

A   B   C

Fig. 19.29. Reproductive System. A. Scheme of female reproductive system. B. Scheme of a single ovariole. C. Scheme of a male reproductive system. (After Snodgrass.) *Female system:* 1, ovarial ligament; 2, ovary; 3, ovariole; 4, calyx; 5, lateral oviduct; 6, common ovi-duct; 7, gonopore; 8, genital chamber; 9, spermathecal gland; 10, seminal receptacle; 11, ac-cessory gland. *Ovariole:* 12, terminal filament; 13, germarium; 14, egg tube; 15, ovariole pedicel; 16, follicle; 17, vitellarium. *Male system:* 18, testis; 19, seminal tubule; 20, sperm duct; 21, seminal vesicle; 22, accessory gland; 23, ejaculatory duct; 24, penis; 25, gonopore.

in males, the details of the genitalia differ greatly in different species and groups and are important taxonomic characteristics. For further details a text on entomology should be consulted.

Insect Reproduction

The female insect has arrangements for storing sperm, and usually mates once or a few times in her lifetime, even though an

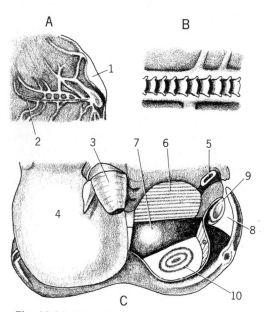

Fig. 19.30. Musical Organs. A variety of organs for the production of sound are found in insects. Crickets produce their chirp by rubbing a file-like rasp (B) on the wing over a special wing surface, the scraper (A), which vibrates to create a sound. Cicadas have one of the most complex stridulating organs (C). A muscle is attached to the dome-shaped membrane. It contracts and relaxes in quick succession, causing the membrane to vibrate. The cavity in which it is placed serves as a sounding board, and sound is reflected by other membranes to reach the outside. (After Comstock.) 1, scraper; 2, file; 3, base of leg; 4, operculum, removed on right side; 5, spiracle; 6, folded membrane; 7, ventral cavity; 8, lateral cavity; 9, timbal; 10, mirror.

extensive period of egg-laying follows. The stimuli which initiate mating vary widely, ranging from odor signals, sound signals in insects with sound-producing or stridulating organs (Fig. 19.30), color signals, and various kinds of courtship behavior. Mating occurs very quickly in some insects, and in others may take several hours or several days. As a general rule the phallus is inserted into the bursa or seminal receptacle and sperm are either injected as a suspension in a fluid vehicle or conveyed in a sac-like spermatophore. In any case, the sperm find their way to the seminal receptacle, where they are stored.

The course of early development has been described (p. 684). At the end of embryonic development, the young insect faces its first crisis. If it is to continue its development it must escape from the chorion. In some insects the way has been prepared. The chorion contains an opening, covered by a cap-like operculum. As the operculum is easily detached, escape is not difficult. Otherwise the embryo inflates itself with fluid, beats its head against the front face of the chorion, or splits the chorion by pulling at it. In spite of its efforts, the chorion of the egg sometimes becomes a shroud for the young insect. Some insects have reduced the dangers of hatching by the development of an egg-buster, a special chitinized exoskeletal part, used during their escape from the egg.

Once out, the young insect faces a long period of growth and development before it reaches maturity. Covered by a firm cuticle, it can only grow and change form at molt. Development consists of a series of molts and instars. As a general rule, the number of molts is predetermined, and the form of the young insect at each instar follows a precise pattern characteristic of the species. For this reason the period between molts is called a stadium, and development can be pictured as a regular sequence of stadia that have an inherent form in each species.

When eggs are large and well protected, there is a tendency for embryonic development to be longer, with a corresponding reduction in the developmental period of the juvenile. This tendency has been very marked in arthropods generally, which do not hatch in an early larval stage like polychaetes, but in more advanced stages. Among the terrestrial mandibulates the same tendency continues to operate. A number of the myriapods, and some of the most primitive insects, hatch before all of the body somites have formed. In these species, new somites are added during molts, and development is said to be anamorphic. In all but a few insects, however, the period of development in the egg is prolonged, so that all of the somites are present when it hatches.

Insects that hatch with all of the somites characteristic of the adult do not ordinarily resemble the parent, however, as is the case with centipedes. No insect hatches with its wings fully developed, and even the wingless insects may have early stadia that are not very much like the adults. Exceptions to this general rule are seen in insects that are primitively wingless. Insects belonging to the division Apterygota, the Thysanura and Diplura, rather closely resemble the adult, although they are diminutive. Their development is essentially like the epimorphic development of some centipedes. As insects generally must undergo some metamorphosis to become adults, these orders are unusual. They are ametabolous, or undergo inconspicuous metamorphosis.

All of the winged or secondarily wingless insects undergo marked changes in appearance during the post-hatching period of development. A large number of the insect orders are placed in the series Hemimetabola. All of these change gradually as they molt, and the body slowly assumes adult shape as well as size. In this large group of insects, the wings are present as wing buds at the time of hatching unless the adult is wingless. A juvenile insect that

undergoes this gradual metamorphosis is called a nymph. Each developmental molt is accompanied by some change in form, and no one molt can be considered more metamorphic than another (Fig. 19.31). Development involving gradual metamorphosis is said to be paurometabolous. Some of the orders of insects belonging to the Hemimetabola have adapted to undergoing their early development in ponds and streams. The term naiad is used to designate the nymphal stages of these insects. Dragonflies, stoneflies, and mayflies are common examples of insects with this type of development. In these insects the juvenile lives in and is adapted to an aquatic habitat. It usually has external gills or other specialized respiratory adaptations, and may be adapted for swimming or other activities that are suitable for its aquatic home. Wings would be a nuisance in the water, and the wing buds of these young insects do not grow as rapidly as in land insects that undergo gradual metamorphosis. Although each molt is accompanied by some metamorphic changes, the last aquatic stadium is by no means very like the adult. When the time for the last molt comes, the naiad creeps up on emergent vegetation, deserting its watery home for the air, and the last molt strips the body of its aquatic adaptations and provides the animal with terrestrial adaptations, including a fully grown set of wings. This molt is not far removed from the metamorphic molt that occurs in insects passing through a pupal stage. This type of development is sometimes termed hemimetabolous, in contrast to paurometabolous development. Some entomologists, however, use the term hemimetabolous for all cases of gradual metamorphosis, and when reading about insect development it is necessary to determine how an author uses the term hemimetabolous.

Insects belonging to the series Holometabola undergo a different kind of development. They bear no real resemblance to the adult when they hatch, and are called

larvae. Insect larvae are worm-like creatures, with no traces of the wings that will
appear later. Most insect larvae eat like
mad, growing rapidly and achieving a
weight and volume considerably greater
than that of the adult. They are building
up food reserves that will be required later.
Eventually they enter a quiescent, non-
feeding, and metamorphic stage known as
the pupa (Fig. 19.32). During pupation
the insect is helpless, and most species have
developed burrowing or cocoon-spinning
habits that protect them during this critical period of development. Pupation usually requires a considerable period of time,
and many insects overwinter in the pupal
stage. Eventually the fully formed adult
emerges from the pupa, having undergone
a complete metamorphosis. Development
of this kind is termed holometabolus.
Pupation is in actuality a metamorphic
molt. It is a complex event, involving the

wholesale destruction of some tissues, and
the formation of new organs. These profound changes are partly under the control
of hormones (p. 683).

Insects live a long time as juveniles. In
many, and probably in most, species the
insect lives longer as a juvenile than as an
adult. There are exceptions, of course, but
it is far more usual for crop destruction
to be caused by juveniles than by adults.
In some insects, this has been carried to
extremes. A mayfly naiad may live for a
long time in a pond, sometimes for as long
as three years, gradually changing with its
naiadal molts. It emerges for a few hours
of winged life as an adult. The adult stage
is no more than a migratory set of reproductive organs, useful for distributing eggs
but for little else. It cannot feed, for it
lacks mouth parts, and is suitably adapted
to its ephemeral reproductive life.

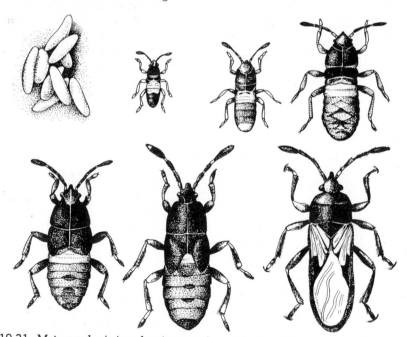

Fig. 19.31. Metamorphosis in a hemipteran, *Anas*. The hemipterans, or true bugs, are characterized by wings that have leathery bases and membranous tips. They fold over the back,
with the membranous part of one wing lying over the membranous part of the other wing.
They undergo a gradual metamorphosis. Wing buds, which can be seen in the youngest
nymphs, increase in size as the insect grows with each molt. (From Ross.)

Insect Behavior

Considered as individual animals or as species populations, insects, and their behavior, are of great biological interest. They are so abundant, so varied, and so influential in so many kinds of environments that they have remarkably diversified habits, and many lifetimes could be spent in the study of their behavior.

Insect behavior is well integrated and is usually suited in a detailed manner for the habitat and way of life characteristic of the species. Removed from its normal habitat, an insect may seem stupid and inadaptable, but in its own home its responses are surprisingly suitable to the kinds of situations that normally arise during its life.

The insect brain is a complex, if small, bit of controlling gear. It has two primary functions. It serves as a relay center for incoming sensory stimuli from the head organs, mediating behavior suitably related to the information received. If the brain of a praying mantis is removed, it walks straight forward until it is exhausted, or until it is so entangled that it can no longer walk. It cannot step backward or avoid objects. It cannot disentangle itself from obstacles. It is clear, from experiments of this kind, that movements of body parts are initiated outside of the brain, but that the brain is responsible for policy decisions that give point and purpose to the movements made by the body parts. It is also apparent from experiments of this kind that removal of the brain makes an insect hyperactive. This provides a clue as to the way that the brain imposes its policy decisions on the subsidiary nerve centers. It is primarily an inhibitory influence, and mediates behavior by inhibiting one set of movements and permitting some alternative set of movements.

When specific body movements are under the control of local reflexes and may be related in definite ways to environmental factors, definite behavior patterns of considerable complexity can result. Many of the acts of insects are highly stereotyped, as if built into the form and physiology of the nervous system, the sense organs, and the locomotor parts. This

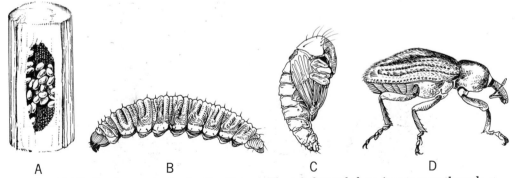

A   B   C   D

Fig. 19.32. Development of a beetle, *Hypera*. These holometabolous insects pass through a series of larval stages, growing with each molt, but have no external wing buds, as is seen in the hemimetabolous insects. After the last larval instar, a pupa is formed. The pupa is not a feeding stage, but a metamorphic instar. The wings and other structures typical of the adult develop within the pupal covering, and a fully formed adult emerges. All types of insects which undergo pupation undergo no molts after emerging from the pupa. They do not, therefore, increase in size. A. Eggs. B. Larva. C. Pupa. D. Adult or imago. (After Michelbacher, from Essig.)

is especially true of reproductive behavior, where standard and apparently forced reactions appear to predominate. Many of the studies in this area make fascinating reading. A male *Aedes* mosquito will approach a tuning fork vibrating at the proper frequency and will seize and clasp the female genitalia if these are presented. Male silkworm moths aggregate on a piece of blotting paper containing juices from the body of a female and attempt to copulate with it. These bits of stereotyped behavior lead to nothing under the abnormal conditions of experimentation, but in nature evoke equally stereotyped responses in the mate, which in turn evoke further pieces of stereotyped behavior. Stereotyped behavior is also evoked by other kinds of stimuli. Positively phototactic insects will kill themselves in approaching an artificial light, for example. Much of an insect's life consists of exchanging one kind of predetermined response for another as his physiological state changes and as the environmental factors around him run through their characteristic diurnal and seasonal cycles. Forced and stereotyped behavior patterns have their disadvantages in a changing world, and responses that were adaptive in the natural forest may bring a creature to harm in a world dominated by man. Special traps can be designed that are remarkably effective because they depend on known, forced responses of insect species.

Some of the most interesting bits of insect behavior are seen in the choice of sites and conditions for the deposition of eggs. Some wasps, for example, dig a burrow, leave it to find a caterpillar or spider, sting the unfortunate prey into a paralyzed state, bring it to the burrow, pull it into the bottom of the burrow, attach an egg, fill in the burrow entrance, and fly away. This is an exceedingly complicated set of affairs, and it is not easy to discuss it without getting into conceptual difficulties. It is unpopular today to speak of the female wasp as doing all of these things

"to provide food for the young" and yet ridiculous to suppose that the habits of the wasp have any other function. To imply a purposiveness to the acts of the individual wasp is unwarranted, since there is no indication that they involve a foreknowledge or awareness of the future. On the other hand, to deny the purposiveness of the behavior pattern in the web of activities is nonsense, since it does have a role or purpose in relation to wasp survival. A remarkable feature of animal behavior in general is that the very complex anatomical and physiological factors on which behavior partly depends, and the equally complex environmental factors, on which it is also partially dependent, are suitably adjusted so that life can go on successfully. The suitability of form for function and of both for the environment in which the organism lives is not accidental or random but depends on the selection, in the past, of successful ancestral stocks. Biological "purpose," the role of a part or of an act in the life of an organism, must always be seen in relationship to the perpetuation of a living system, the organism, the species, or the community of which it is a part, and specifically, its perpetuation in the complex of environmental factors natural for it. In this sense, every adaptive aspect of body structure and function reflects a kind of purposiveness, although a limited one, and it is this purposiveness that makes the science of biology meaningful, on the one hand, and possible on the other.

What of the complex activities of a wasp during its egg-laying? How is the animal programmed for all of these activities? On the basis of what is known, it is probable that the completion of one part of the ritual is the stimulus which initiates the next. The whole complex of acts is built of smaller ones, which follow each other in a certain sequence. This does not mean that every part of the whole is completely and inevitably forced. Only rarely is an act completely forced by a single stimulus. Even in simple behavior, like stepping, the loss of a leg leads to a change in the pattern of activity, and a complex of environmental and internal factors converge to cause a given step at a given moment. A sizable body of myth has grown up about the reproducibility and predictability of some of the more complex insect activities. The female wasp does not always sting a caterpillar in the same place, nor even the same number of times. She does modify the way in which the burrow is dug, making adjustments for the nature of the soil and specific obstacles that are encountered. She may find that her burrow cannot be completed and eventually "give up" when internal factors such as hunger and fatigue initiate a different set of activities. She is also capable of adjusting other specific acts in ways that are eminently suitable to the situation. She exercises "judgment," but this does not mean that her behavior is not, to a very considerable extent, "built into" her neurosensory architecture. The simple stepping reflexes are the result of a number of factors, adjustment to stimuli from higher centers, prothoracic pacemaker stimuli, and proprioreceptive stimuli from each somite. The legs do not exercise judgment, but the machinery of control is adequate to provide considerable flexibility and compensation, and in the long run it comes to the same thing. Even the most complex behavior patterns may prove to be analyzable into adjustable, but nonetheless innate, mechanisms.

Much more analysis of insect behavior is needed before very definite conclusions about its nature are justified. One of the factors that needs more careful study is the size of the prepackaged responses. It may be taken as probable that any complex operation, such as the building of a cocoon or the moulding of a mud nest, is not a single piece of behavior but is rather a sequence of many small responses, each individually modified by the nature of the stimuli received at the moment. That this is actually the case is fairly well indicated by the ability of insects to repair a damaged object on which they are working.

There can be no doubt that insects are able to modify their reactions on the basis of past experience. They can be conditioned by reward and punishment. As with other animals, it is far easier to reinforce normal responses than to inhibit them. Unlike most invertebrates, however, insects can be trained to inhibit normal behavior. For example, a cockroach can learn not to enter a darkened box if it is shocked in the box, even though it seeks such darkened enclosures in nature. It shows signs of its disturbance at the light-dark border and becomes very "excited," but does not enter. The training is slow, however, and is soon forgotten. On the other hand, if no deep-seated tactic response is violated, more substantial results can be obtained. Bees can easily be trained to seek food at sites marked by color and odor signals, and to a certain extent, at sites marked by specific shapes, although the ability to discriminate between shapes is limited. Bees cannot distinguish between discs and squares in experiments of this kind, but can tell either from crosses or Y shapes. Insects have also been trained to go through a maze. Members of a single species, as well as members of different species, differ in their ability to learn a maze—in this resembling mammals. They do not learn as quickly as mammals, however.

There is some evidence that complex behavior involving a sequence of acts is lived as a series of small or single-event sequences, and that these are not equally important in their impact upon the organism. Bees that visit a feeding dish marked by one color at arrival, another color during feeding, and a third color at departure, return only to dishes marked with the arrival color. This is not conclusive, of course, for it is possible that the bee mind might "interpret" the conditions as implying that the way to get food was to start at this color and go through the original sequence.

A large number of factors probably enter into the ability of insects to learn or to co-operate with the experimenter. Many flying insects center their behavior about the region where they first become adults, and visual or other clues gained at this time may be more or less predominant in their behavior. This may confer upon them a semblance of fixity of response that is not justified. Ants respond to the same maze differently when they are leaving the nest and returning, and learn to cope with it at different rates. It is clear that many more kinds of experiments are needed before it will be possible to describe the capacities of insects to learn and to explain their abilities to cope with the factors that the environment exposes them to. Their behavior is certainly very complex, and while insects are inferior to mammals in individual learning they appear to be superior to mammals in learning to cope with a social situation. It may be that the two tend to be mutually incompatible.

The study of insect social behavior is a fascinating field. Some species are no more than aggregative, with no organized common activities. Others spin a common web, for example, tentworms, and occupy it without any major adjustment of individual behavior. Still others, like ants, dig or build a common nest, and are extensively modified by their adjustment to a social life. Intensive social life culminates, as in termites and some ants, in the specialization of members into different castes. Each caste has its role to play in the life of the whole society and is structurally as well as behaviorally specialized for its part. A most interesting parallelism is seen in social insects and the colonial members of other invertebrate groups. The first separation of function among the members of a society divides the members into reproducers and non-reproducers, resembling the gonozooids and gastrozooids of coelenterate colonies, for example. In the more highly organized insect societies, several morphologically different kinds of workers appear (Fig. 19.33). In coelenterates, similar division of labor among non-reproducing members of a colony are found in siphonophores, for example.

Social life has a number of advantages for insects as it does for mammals. Ant and termite nests often provide considerable control over the environment. The more complex termite nests contain special devices that give a measure of control over the temperature, humidity, and air of the nest. Just as human farms and dwellings have special flora and fauna, the ants' and termites' nests are special worlds containing special inhabitants. Some of the social insects cultivate species of fungi as we cultivate wheat or rice. About 3000 species of insects, arachnids, isopods, and myriapods live only in the highly specialized environments of ant and termite nests, living as predators, parasites, hangers-on, or guests of the social insects.

Much remains to be learned about the cohesiveness of an insect society. Our information suggests that a good insect citizen, like a good human citizen, results from the conditioning it received from members of the society when it was young. Workers "pet" young ants and feed them with regurgitated food. While group cohesiveness may be built up through such simple devices, it is more difficult to explain how returning workers inform their fellows how to find remote food supplies, and how other kinds of information pass through the members of a society. Odor trails are laid by ants to lead the workers to food sources. Bees cannot depend on odor trails, however, as they fly to the feeding place. A returning worker performs a round dance (Fig. 19.34) to indicate the presence of food nearby and a waggle dance when food is more distant. The straight run of the waggle dance in connection with the position of the sun indicates the direction of the food supply. The frequency of the waggle runs decreases with the distance away from the hive. A dance is executed with great vigor when the food stocks are large or at times of food scarcity, and with less vigor when the find of food has been small or when food is plentiful. There is evidence that other bees observe and respond to the round and

waggle dances, but the factors that underlie their effectiveness are not yet analyzed. No schools for learning how to execute the dances or how to interpret them appear to be necessary. Whatever factors may prove to be involved in insect social life, it is evident that the social insects have de-

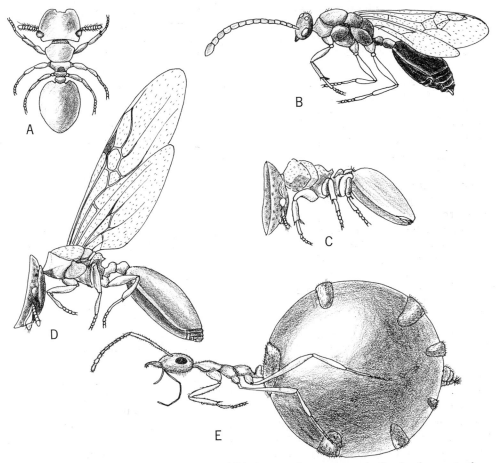

Fig. 19.33. A remarkable feature of social life in some insect groups is the development of a series of castes. The members of the society include specialized reproductive members, and several types of workers, each with a characteristic body form and with different behavior patterns. An ordinary worker of *Cryptocerus varians* is shown at **A**, and a winged male at **B**. The queen is shown at **C**, with the wings developed as before the mating flight, and a soldier at **D**. Modifications of the proportionate growth rates of the parts result in the changed appearance of the various members of the society. A most unusual type of ant found in the honey-ant societies are the repletes, whose function it is to fill themselves with honey and hang from the roof of chambers in the nests, regurgitating food to workers on demand. A replete of *Myrmecocystus* is shown at **E**. (After Wheeler.)

veloped surprisingly complex and effective social organizations, which present tantalizing physiological and behavioral problems.

Insect Affinities

It is beyond the scope of this volume to discuss the affinities of the various orders of insects. For this, a text on entomology should be consulted. It is clear enough that the primitively wingless insect orders are the most primitive of the living insects, and myriapod-like traits are seen among them, particularly among the Protura. Orders of insects that undergo complete metamorphosis are less generalized than those undergoing gradual metamorphosis, on the whole, and may be taken as having fewer primitive and more advanced characterics. Some of the more important evolutionary trends have been mentioned in connection with various parts of insects.

All of the available evidence supports the idea that insects are considerably more

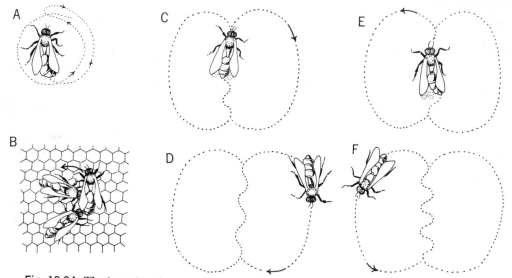

Fig. 19.34. The integrity of insect society, like that of any society, depends on the centripetal influences involving identification of the individual member with the group as a whole and a reasonable flow of communication throughout the membership. Feeding of the young by adult members of the society and odor signals, unique for each social unit, aid in orienting the young to the community to which they belong. Communication is most commonly achieved simply, by odor or other signals, but in some cases more complex symbolization is involved. Some of the more remarkable examples of behavior of this kind are seen in bees. A bee returning to the hive after a find of food performs a round dance (A) if the food source is near the hive (up to about 100 m.). This arouses other bees (B), who are stimulated to go out to the food. When food is farther from the hive, a waggle dance is used (C-F). The speed with which the waggle dance is executed is related to the distance from the hive to the food. Food about 200 m. from the hive, for example, is associated with waggle dances at about 30/min., while food 2000 m. from the hive evokes waggle dances at about 13/min. The straight middle run, during which the waggles are made, is related to the location of the food. Food toward the sun evokes a waggle dance upward on the comb, and food away from the sun evokes a waggle dance downward. The angle of the food source from the direction of the sun is indicated by slanting runs, where the angle from the sun roughly corresponds to the angle between the waggle run and a vertical line.

closely related to myriapods than to any other arthropod group. The detailed correspondence of head parts, and the tendency of the mouth parts of symphylans to converge with those of insects, would point to Symphyla as the line of myriapods that are closest to the insects. Beyond this point, however, general agreement is lacking. Many feel that the biramous appendages of the crustaceans indicate that they are a wholly discrete stem of arthropods, which have arisen from stocks different from the myriapod-insect line. Others are more impressed by the rather detailed correspondences of innervation and brain centers in Crustacea and insects and by other points of similarity, and believe that all of the mandibulates arose from a single stem which differentiated very early in Crustacea and a myriapod line that eventually formed the ancestral line for insects. At the present time, no firm conclusions can be drawn.

References

Auerbach, S. I. 1951. The centipedes of the Chicago area with special reference to their ecology. *Ecol. Monogr.* 21: 97.

Birch, L. C. Experimental background to the study of the distribution and abundance of insects. III. *Evol.* 7: 136.

Bodenhemier, F. S. 1937. Population problems of social insects. *Biol. Rev.* 12: 393. (E)

Borror, D. J., and D. M. Delong. 1954. *An Introduction to the Study of Insects*. Holt, Rinehart & Winston, New York. (G)

Brian, M. V. 1952. The structure of a dense natural ant population. *Jour. An. Ecol.* 21: 12.

Brown, C. R., and M. H. Hatch. 1929. Orientation and "fright" reactions of whirligig beetles (Gyrinidae). *Jour. Comp. Psych.* 9: 159.

Burtt, E. 1947. Exudate from millipedes, with particular reference to its injurious effects. *Trop. Dis. Bull.* 44: 7.

Caspari, E. 1951. On the biological basis of adaptedness. *Amer. Sci.* 39: 441. (G)

Causey, N. B. 1943. Studies on the life history and the ecology of the hothouse millipede, *Orthromorpha gracilis* (C. L. Koch, 1847). *Amer. Midl. Nat.* 29: 670.

Chamberlain, W. J. 1952. *Entomological Nomenclature and Literature*. Brown, Dubuque, Ia.

Chamberlin, R. V. 1943. On Mexican millipedes. *Bull. Univ. Utah* 34: 1.

Cloudsley-Thompson, J. L. 1950. The water relations and cuticle of *Paradesmus gracilis* (Diplopoda: Strongylosomidae). *Quart. Jour. Micr. Sci.* 91: 453.

———. 1951. On the responses to environmental stimuli and the sensory physiology of millipedes (Diplopoda). *Proc. Zool. Soc. London* 121: 253.

———. 1952. The behaviour of centipedes and millipedes. 1. *Ann. Mag. Nat. Hist.* 5: 417.

———. 1954. The ecological significance of diurnal rhythms in terrestrial Arthropoda. *Sci. Prog.* 42: 46.

Comstock, J. H. 1918. *The Wings of Insects*. Comstock Co., New York.

Crampton, G. C. 1925. The external anatomy of the head and abdomen of the roach, *Periplaneta americana*. *Psychd.* 32: 197.

Dennell, R. 1958. The hardening of the insect cuticle. *Biol. Rev.* 33: 178.

Essig, E. O. 1942. *College Entomology*. Macmillan, New York (G)

———. 1958. *Insects and Mites of Western North America*. Macmillan, New York.

Fahlander, K. 1938. Beiträge zur Anatomie und systematische Einteilung der Chilopoden. *Zool. Bidrag. Uppsala* 17: 1.

Folsom, J. W., and R. A. Wardle. 1934. *Entomology with Special Reference to its Ecological Aspects*. Blakiston, Philadelphia.

Ford, N. 1923. A comparative study of the abdominal musculature of orthopteroid insects. *Trans. Roy. Canad. Inst.* 14: 207.

Fox, H. M., et al. 1935. Metabolic rates of ephemerid nymphs from swiftly moving and from still water. *Jour. Exp. Biol.* 12: 179.

Fraenkel, G. 1932. Die Wanderungen der Insekten. *Erg. Biol.* 9: 1.

Gersch, M. 1961. Insect metamorphosis and the activation hormone. *Amer. Zool.* 1: 53.

Gilbert, L. I., and H. A. Scheiderman. 1961. Some biochemical aspects of insect metamorphosis. *Amer. Zool.* 1: 11.

Gilmour, D. 1960. *Biochemistry of Insects.* Academic Press, New York.

Goetsch, W. 1957. *The Ants.* Univ. of Mich., Ann Arbor, Mich.

Graham, S. A. 1952. *Forest Entomology.* McGraw-Hill, New York. (G)

Gupta, P. D. 1948. On the structure, development and homology of the female reproductive organs of orthopteroid insects. *Ind. Jour. Ent.* 10: 75.

Hansen, H. J. 1902. On the genera and species of the order Pauropoda. *Vidensk. Medd. naturh. Foren. Copenhagen* 53: 323.

————. 1903. The genera and species of the order Symphyla. *Quart. Jour. Micr. Sci.* 47: 1.

————. 1930. *Studies on Arthropoda III. On the comparative morphology of the appendages of Arthropoda. B. Crustacea (supplement), Insecta Myriapoda, and Arachnida.* Glydendal, Copenhagen.

Imms, A. D. 1936. The ancestry of insects. *Trans. Soc. Brit. Ent.* 3: 1. (G)

————, O. W. Richards, and R. G. Davies. 1957. *A General Textbook of Entomology,* rev. ed. Methuen, London. (G)

Jacobs, M. E. 1955. Studies on territorialism and sexual selection in dragonflies. *Ecol.* 36: 566.

Jacques, H. E. 1947. *How To Know the Insects.* Brown, Dubuque, Ia.

Johannsen, O. A., and F. H. Butt. 1941. *Embryology of the Insects and Myriapods.* McGraw-Hill, New York.

Krug, H. 1907. Beiträge zur Anatomie der Gattung *Iulus. Jena. Ztschr. Naturwiss.* 42: 485.

Lindsay, E. 1940. The biology of the silverfish, *Ctenolepisma longicaudata* Esch., with particular reference to its feeding habits. *Proc. Roy. Soc. Victoria.* 52: 35.

Lutz, F. E. 1935. *Field Book of Insects.* Putnam, New York.

Manton, S. M. 1952. The locomotion of the Chilopoda and Pauropoda. *Jour. Linn. Soc., Zool.* 42: 118.

————. 1954. The structure, habits and evolution of the Diplopoda. *Jour. Linn. Soc., Zool.* 42: 299.

Miall, L. C. 1934. *The Natural History of Aquatic Insects.* New York. (G)

Michelbacher, A. E. 1938. The biology of the garden centipede *Scutigerella immaculata. Hilgardia* 11: 55.

Milne, A. 1957. Theories of natural control of insect populations. *Cold Spring Harb. Symp. Quant. Biol.* 22: 253. (E)

Needham, J. G., et al. 1935. *The Biology of Mayflies.* Cornell Univ., Ithaca, N.Y. (G)

————, and M. J. Westfall, Jr. 1955. *A Manual of the Dragonflies of North America (Anisoptera).* Univ. of Calif., Berkeley, Calif.

Pierce, G. W. 1949. *The Songs of Insects.* Harvard Univ., Cambridge, Mass.

Portier, P. 1911. Recherches physiologiques sur les insects aquatiques. *Arch. Zool. Exp. Gen.* 8: 89.

Pringle, J. W. S. 1957. *Insect Flight.* Cambridge Univ. Press, Cambridge, Eng.

Richards, O. W. 1953. *The Social Insects.* MacDonald, London.

Roeder, K., ed. 1953. *Insect Physiology.* Wiley, New York. (!)

Rogers, J. S. 1933. The ecological distribution of the craneflies of northern Florida. *Ecol. Mono.* 3: 1.

Ross, H. H. 1944. The caddis flies, or Trichoptera, of Illinois. *Bull. Ill. Nat. Hist. Surv.* 23: 1.

Sargent, W. D. 1951. The flight of the dragonfly. *Biol. Rev. C. C. N.Y.* 13: 8.

Seifert, B. 1932. Anatomie und Biologie des Diplopoden *Strongylosoma pallipes* Oliv. *Ztschr. Morph. Ökol. Tiere* 25: 362.

Shelford, V. E. 1913. The reactions of certain animals to gradients of evaporating power of air. *Biol. Bull.* 25: 79.

————, and W. P. Flint. 1943. Populations of the chinch bug in the upper Mississippi Valley from 1823 to 1940. *Ecol.* 24: 435.

Snodgrass, R. E. 1935. *The Principles of Insect Morphology.* McGraw-Hill, New York. (!)

Starling, J. H. 1944. Ecological studies of the Pauropoda of the Duke Forest. *Ecol. Mono.* 14: 291.

Swain, R. B. 1948. *The Insect Guide.* Doubleday, New York.

Thorpe, W. H. 1950. Plastron respiration in aquatic insects. *Biol. Rev.* 25: 344.

————. 1956. *Learning and Instinct in Animals.* Methuen, London.

Tiegs, O. W. 1940. The embryology and affinities of the Symphyla, based on a study
of *Hanseniella agilis*. *Quart. Jour. Micr.
Sci.* 82: 1.
———. 1947. The development and affinities
of the Pauropoda, based on a study of
Pauropus silvaticus. *Quart. Jour. Micr.
Sci.* 88: 165.
Van der Kloot, W. G. 1961. Insect metamorphosis and its endocrine control. *Amer.
Zool.* 1: 3.
von Frisch, K. 1950. *Bees, Their Vision, Chemical Senses and Language.* Cornell Univ.,
Ithaca, N.Y.

Wesenberg-Lund., C. 1943. *Biologie der Süss-
wasserinsekten.* Copenhagen.
Wigglesworth, V. B. 1953. *The Principles of
Insect Physiology.* Methuen, London (!)
Williams, C. B. 1958. *Insect Migration.* Collins, New York.
Wingfield, C. A. 1939. The function of the
gills of mayfly nymphs from different
habitats. *Jour. Exp. Biol.* 16: 363.
Yeager, J. F., and G. O. Hendrickson. 1934.
Circulation of blood in wings and wing
pads of the cockroach, *Periplaneta americana* Linn. *Ann. Ent. Soc. Amer.* 27: 257.

Use of the Library

The literature on invertebrates is far too extensive to permit the inclusion of an exhaustive bibliography in any one book. The references included in the book are merely representative of the thousands of research articles, monographs, review articles, and books that have been written about invertebrates. They may serve to introduce some of the specific topics and interests that have developed in the study of invertebrates, and some typical monographs and articles. A student who is developing a high interest in a particular group of animals or in some specific physiological or ecological topic will do well to search for a review article or monograph dealing with the group or topic first. From such a source a substantial start toward a bibliography can be assembled. The search for review articles and extensive accounts of specific groups of animals can best be made with the aid of one of the bibliographic journals that deal specifically with biological material.

Of the bibliographic sources, two stand out as being especially useful, *Biological Abstracts* and *Zoological Record*. *Biological Abstracts* has provided a listing of papers, books, and monographs dealing with biological topics since 1926. It is more time-consuming to use than the *Zoological Record*, which has provided the same service since 1864, but has the advantage of including a brief summary of the papers and other materials cited. Where abstracts are not needed, the *Zoological Record* is to be preferred because of its compactness.

Monographic accounts of invertebrate groups found in advanced treatises are also excellent for the development of a bibliography. Textbooks or books that deal with one or a few phyla or classes are also good sources of bibliographic material for the areas they cover, and are recommended as first port of call to the student who wishes to become more highly informed about specific groups.

To make the listing of articles and other literature given below as efficient as possible, the works cited in the general section are not repeated in the sections for the individual phyla. In a search for material, check the general section first, and then refer to the separate phylum headings.

Certain symbols are used in parentheses following the citations, where the title of the article does not seem to adequately describe its nature. B is used .where the work cited is an especially good source of bibliographic material in the field suggested by its title, whether broad or narrow. G is used for works that seem particularly useful from the general point of view, and may be particularly useful to students wishing to develop a general comprehension of biological theory. F indicates that the work cited is especially useful in faunistic or taxonomic work. E is used for works thought to be of especial interest to those with an ecological bent. A few works have been marked with an ex-clamation point. These are of such general interest or of such high quality that they may be considered truly essential references on invertebrate zoology and will be found especially rich in bibliographic material as well as other kinds of information. In some cases, a parenthetical remark is substituted for symbols, to make more specific comments about the nature of the cited work.

Works of General Interest

Allee, W. C., A. E. Emerson, O. Park, and K. P. Schmidt. 1949. *Principles of Animal Ecology*. Saunders, Philadelphia. (!)

Andrew, W. 1959. *Textbook of Comparative Histology*. Oxford Univ. Press, New York. (G)

Barnes, R. D. 1963. *Invertebrate Zoology*. Saunders, Philadelphia. (An excellent general text on invertebrates, with good illustrations and good accounts of invertebrate life.)

Berrill, N. J. 1961. *Growth, Development, and Pattern*. Freeman, San Francisco.

Borradaile, L. A., F. A. Potts, L. E. S. Eastham, J. T. Saunders, and G. A. Kerkut. 1961. *The Invertebrata*. Cambridge Univ. Press, Cambridge, Eng. (A good general account of invertebrates.)

Brachet, J. 1960. *The Biochemistry of Development*. Pergamon, London.

v. Brand, T. 1946. *Anaerobiosis in Invertebrates*. (Biodynamica) Normandy, Mo.

Bronn, H. 1873—. *Klassen und Ordnung des Thier-Reichs*. Friedlander & Sohn, Leipzig. (A remarkable series of monographs on various classes and orders of animals, originated by Bronn. No single source summarizes more of the classical work on the various animal groups.)

Brown, F. A., Jr., ed. 1950. *Selected Invertebrate Types*. Wiley, New York. (An ex-cellent account of a number of important invertebrate animals, with information about their habits and physiology.)

Buchsbaum, R. 1948. *Animals without Backbones*. Univ. of Chicago Press, Chicago.

v. Buddenbrock, W. 1953. *Vergleichende Physiologie*. Birkhauser, Basel, Switzerland. (A major, six-volume effort to summarize the important principles of comparative physiology up to its time.)

Bullough, W. S. 1959. *Practical Invertebrate Anatomy*. Macmillan, London.

Cameron, T. W. M. 1956. *Parasites and Parasitism*. Methuen, London. (G)

Carter, G. S. 1951. *General Zoology of the Invertebrates*. Sidgewick and Jackson, London. (G)

Carthy, J. D. 1958. *An Introduction to the Behaviour of Invertebrates*. Allen and Unwin, London.

Cloudsley-Thompson, J. L. 1954. *Biology of Deserts*. Hafner, New York. (E)

——. 1960. *Animal Behaviour*. Oliver and Boyd, London.

Coker, R. W. 1947. *This Great and Wide Sea*. Univ. of North Carolina Press, Chapel Hill, N. C. (E)

Crowder, W. 1931. *Between the Tides*. Dodd, Mead, and Co., New York. (G)

Dawydoff, C. 1928. *Traité d'embryologie comparée des invertebrés*. Masson et Cie, Paris.

Eales, N. B. 1950. *Littoral Fauna of Great Britain*. Cambridge Univ. Press, Cambridge, Eng. (F)

Edmondson, W. T., ed. 1959. *Ward and Whipple's Fresh Water Biology*. Wiley, New York. (F, !)

Elton, C. 1927. *Animal Biology*. Macmillan, London.

Fraenkel, G. S., and D. L. Gunn. 1940. *The Orientation of Animals*. Oxford University Press, London.

Gadow, H. F. 1913. *The Wanderings of Animals*. Cambridge Univ. Press, Cambridge, Eng.

Galtsoff, P., ed. 1937. *Culture Methods for Invertebrate Animals*. Cornell Univ. Press, Ithaca. (!)

Grassé, P-P., ed. 1948–   . *Traité de Zoologie*. Masson et Cie, Paris. (!)

Hardy, A. C. 1956. *The Open Sea*. Houghton Mifflin, Boston. (E)

Harmer, S. F., and A. E. Shipley, eds. 1895–1909. *The Cambridge Natural History*. Cambridge Univ. Press, Cambridge, Eng. (One of the two classical advanced treatises in English.)

Hedgepeth, J. W. 1957. Treatise on marine ecology and palaeoecology. *Geo. Soc. Amer., Mem.* 67: 1–1296. (!)

Hesse, R., W. C. Allee, and K. P. Schmidt. 1951. *Ecological Animal Geography*. Wiley, New York.

Hewatt, W. G. 1937. Ecological studies on selected marine intertidal communities of Monterey Bay, California. *Am. Midl. Nat.* 18: 161.

Holme, N. A. 1953. The biomass of the bottom fauna in the English Channel off Plymouth. *J. Mar. Biol. Assoc. U. K.* 37: 1.

Hyman, L. H. 1940–   . *The Invertebrates*. McGraw-Hill, New York. (A remarkable work on the invertebrates, with some volumes still unfinished. It has the great advantage of bringing a single point of view to bear on a large number of invertebrate groups and is the most modern advanced treatise in English.)

Jacot, A. P. 1940. The fauna of the soil. *Quart. Rev. Biol.* 15: 28. (E)

Jenkins, P. L. 1961. *Animal Hormones*. Pergamon, London.

Jennings, H. S. 1915. *The Behavior of Lower Organisms*. Columbia Univ. Press, New York. (A classical discussion of this important topic.)

Johnson, M. E., and H. J. Snook. 1927. *Seashore Animals of the Pacific Coast*. Macmillan, New York. (G,F)

Jones, N. S. 1950. Marine Bottom Communities. *Biol. Rev.* 25: 283. (B,E)

Kendeigh, S. C. 1961. *Animal Ecology.* Prentice-Hall, Inc., Englewood Cliffs, N.J.

Kevan, D. K. M., ed. 1955. *Soil Zoology.* Academic Press, New York.

v. d. Klaauw, C. J. 1948. Ecological morphology. *Bibl. Bioth.* 4: 27.

Korscheldt, E., 1936. *Lehrbuch der vergleichenden Entwicklungsgeschichte der wirbellosen Tiere.* Fischer, Jena, Germany. (!)

Krogh, A. 1939. *Osmotic Regulation in Aquatic Animals.* Cambridge Univ. Press, Cambridge, Eng.

———. 1941. *The Comparative Physiology of Respiratory Movements.* Univ. of Penn. Press, Philadelphia.

Lankester, R., ed. 1900–   . *A Treatise on Zoology.* Adam and Charles Black, London. (A classical series of volumes covering the invertebrate groups.)

Lawrence, R. F. 1953. *The Biology of the Cryptic Fauna of Forests.* Balkema, Amsterdam. (G,E)

Lowenstein, O., ed. 1962. *Recent Advances in Comparative Physiology and Biochemistry.* Academic Press, New York.

Macan, T. T., and E. B. Worthington. 1951. *Life in Lakes and Rivers.* Collins, London.

MacGinitie, G. E. 1935. Ecological aspects of a California marine estuary. *Amer. Midl. Nat.* 16: 629.

———, and N. MacGinitie. 1949. *Natural History of Marine Animals.* McGraw-Hill, New York. (G)

Morgan, A. H. 1930. *Field Book of Ponds and Streams.* Putnam, New York. (G,F)

Needham, J. G., and G. R. Needham. 1938. *A Guide to the Study of Fresh-water Biology.* Cornell Univ. Press, Ithaca. (F)

Nicol, J. A. C. 1960. *The Biology of Marine Animals.* Pitman, New York. (!)

Odum, E. P. 1959. *Fundamentals of Ecology.* Saunders, Philadelphia.

Pearse, A. S. 1939. *Animal Ecology.* McGraw-Hill, New York.

———. 1950. *The Emigrations of Animals from the Sea.* Sherwood, Dryden, N. Y.

Pennak, R. W. 1953. *Fresh-Water Invertebrates of the United States.* Ronald Press, New York. (!)

Pratt, H. S. 1935. *Manual of the Common Invertebrate Animals.* Blakiston, Philadelphia. (F)

Prosser, C. L., and F. A. Brown, Jr. 1961. *Comparative Animal Physiology.* Saunders, Philadelphia. (!)

Ramsay, J. A. 1952. *Physiological Approach to Lower Animals.* Cambridge Univ. Press, Cambridge, Eng. (G)

Ricketts, E. F., and J. Calvin. 1947. *Between Pacific Tides.* Stanford Univ. Press, Palo Alto, Calif. (F)

Scheer, B. T. 1948. *Comparative Physiology.* Wiley, New York. (G)

———. 1957. *Recent Advances in Invertebrate Physiology.* Univ. of Oregon Press, Eugene, Ore.

Shrock, R. R., and W. H. Twenhofel, 1953. *Principles of Invertebrate Paleontology.* McGraw-Hill, New York. (!)

Stephenson, T. A., and A. Stephenson. 1949. The universal features of zonation between tide-marks on rocky coasts. *Jour. Ecol.* 37: 289.

Sverdrup, H. U., M. W. Johnson, and R. H. Fleming. 1942. *The Oceans*. Prentice-Hall, Inc., New York.

Thorpe, W. H. 1956. *Learning and Instinct in Animals*. Methuen, London. (G)

Welch, P. S. 1952. *Limnology*. McGraw-Hill, New York.

Wesenberg-Lund, C. 1939. *Biologie de Süsswassertiere*. Vienna. (G)

Yonge, C. M. 1949. *The Sea Shore*, Collins, London. (G)

I

Summary of Geological History

It cannot be too strongly emphasized that the time estimates given here are no more than rough approximations, and become increasingly accurate as more recent eras and periods are reached. Our knowledge of invertebrate fossils is at the very best fragmentary. Evidently only the first known examples can be quoted, and one must suppose that origins of groups occurred at an earlier time than the records show. Nevertheless, a fairly good picture of the development of some groups has been put together, and as more data are gathered, one may hope that some kinds of invertebrates may be traced to their origins.

ARCHEOZOIC ERA

BEGAN: About 3600 million years ago, at least, and probably earlier.

LASTED: About 2000 million years, including a discontinuity which separates it from the following Proterozoic era. This discontinuity, which may represent as much as 200 million years, involved a major loss in fossil history.

NATURE: Little is known with definiteness. It appears to have been an era of great volcanic activity and probably a time of violent storms and extensive erosion of the exposed land surfaces. Topographic features retained water, and some sedimentary deposition occurred.

LIFE: It is probable that during this period organic compounds appeared during a period when a reducing atmosphere covered the earth's surface and that a primeval period of heterotrophic development utilized the materials laid down before organisms were present. The early heterotrophs presumably diverged into streams which included one that became autotrophic, and, as autotrophism established itself, the atmosphere came to be an oxidizing atmosphere. Presumably the main stems from which the producer, consumer, and decomposers have developed arose during this time. All of this, however, must be deduced from indirect evidence. Evidences of organic life are restricted to organic carbon deposits found in some rocks, to iron formations which resemble those laid down by iron bacteria, and similar more or less questionable bits of data.

PROTEROZOIC ERA

BEGAN: About 1600 million years ago.

LASTED: About 1000 million years, including a period of discontinuity of perhaps 100 million years between its end and the beginning of the Paleozoic.

NATURE: There is evidence of a series of glacial periods and a large amount of sedimentary rock formation. Intensive erosion was occurring, and toward the close of the Proterozoic, volcanic activity again became pronounced. With the glaciation periods, sea levels rose and fell repeatedly, and climatic conditions varied markedly in specific regions.

LIFE: One must assume that during this period, all of the forms that appear in the early Cambrian periods must have taken shape. This, however, must be deduced, as no well-preserved and unquestionable fossils from this time have been preserved. Some of the findings suggest that organisms were present which may have been annelid worms; at least tubes and tracks somewhat like those formed by annelids have been described. The impression of a jellyfish has also been described, and a brachiopod may have been present in pre-Cambrian rocks. The most distinctive evidence is for the presence of certain kinds of algae and the spicules of sponges. On the basis of available material, no clear picture of evolutionary processes during this very important period can be assembled.

PALEOZOIC ERA

BEGAN: About 600 million years ago.

LASTED: About 370 million years. It is separated from the Mesozoic era by a discontinuity associated with the formation of the Appalachian ranges, and which involved some loss of fossil material.

NATURE: A varied period, divided into a series of geologic periods. On the whole, a period of rising land with warmer conditions early, and a time of increasing aridity and coldness, leading to glaciations, as it progressed.

Cambrian Period

BEGAN: About 600 million years ago.

LASTED: About 100 million years.

NATURE: A period of mild climates and high sea levels, with low-lying land masses.

LIFE: Fossils are abundant in the earliest Cambrian rocks, indicating that there had been a considerable diversification during pre-Cambrian times, for which no definite fossil evidence is available. It is clear that marine algae had become highly diversified during the Cambrian times.

Protozoa. A few radiolarians and some probable foraminiferans at the beginning of the Cambrian. These groups continue to the present, with modifications. Foraminiferans largely with chitinous tests.

Porifera. The wholly extinct Pleospongia appears to have been well established at the beginning of Cambrian, and had differentiated into several types. The lyssacine hexactinellids and the calcareous sponges also appear during the Cambrian. Tetractinellid and Monaxonid Demospongia are also found in the Cambrian.

Cnidaria. They undoubtedly arose in pre-Cambrian seas. In the lower Cambrian rocks hydroids are found, and porpitid siphonophores appear in the middle Cambrian. Fossil Scyphozoa are more questionable, although there is reason to think they extend to the lower Cambrian and perhaps into the pre-Cambrian. A fortunate impression indicates that the sea anemones were present in the middle Cambrian, although no further findings appear until relatively recent times.

Lophophorates. Ctenostomate ectoprocts appear for the first time in the upper Cambrian. Extinct Cryptostomate ectoprocts also appeared at about this time. Some upright tubes have been ascribed to phoronids, but these are questionable. Both atremate and neotremate inarticulate and articulate brachiopods are found throughout the Cambrian. As they are all found in the lower Cambrian period, it seems probable that they differentiated during the pre-Cambrian.

Echinoderms. A few echinoderms during the Cambrian; Edrioasteroidea from lower Cambrian and Eocrinoids, of uncertain affinities, also present in lower Cambrian. Presumably they arose in pre-Cambrian times.

Other Deuterostomes. A chaetognath is probably represented in the middle Cambrian rocks. If graptolites are protochordates, they appeared in the middle Cambrian also.

Molluscs. Cup-shaped and simple spiral shells of the Protogastropoda are found in the lower Cambrian, with a few evidences of chitons. Nautiloids appear in the upper Cambrian.

Annelids. Many findings throughout the Cambrian indicate worm tubes, impressions, castings, and the like. Chitinous tubes appear in the middle Cambrian.

Onychophora. A fortunate finding indicates that Onychophora were probably present in the Cambrian.

Trilobita. Rich findings from early Cambrian throughout the period. Trilobites were the dominant form during much of the Cambrian and were extremely abundant by the end of the period.

Chelicerata. The first chelicerates—wholly extinct aglaspids—appeared in the middle Cambrian.

Mandibulata. Ostrocods appear in the upper Cambrian.

SUMMARY. It is clear that there must have been a number of animal types alive at the beginning of the Cambrian, as the lower Cambrian includes a number of distinct phyla. Little is known about soft-bodied forms, but it is evident that there was a diversified population of worms, and it is probable that most of the major lines leading to the phyla of modern animals were established during pre-Cambrian or very early Cambrian times. Rather highly organized lophophorates were present, and echinoderms were beginning to appear. The protostome stem had differentiated into what appear to be annelid and arthropod lines, and if graptolites are protochordates or closely related to them, this stem had begun to take form.

Ordovician Period

BEGAN: About 500 million years ago.
LASTED: About 75 million years.
NATURE: A very warm period, with high sea levels. Many land masses were submerged.
LIFE: The first land plants probably appeared during this period. Warmth and high humidity meant that biotic pressures growing out of intra- and inter-specific competition and cooperation were especially important in natural selection.

Protozoa: Silicious flagellates fairly common; foraminifera with simple arenaceous tests appear in the lower Ordovician and reach their peak during the Ordovician. *Porifera.* The Pleospongia are gone.

Cnidaria: The extinct tetracoralline and tabulate corals appeared in the lower Ordovician, and coral reefs were formed for the first time.

Lophophorates: The trepostome and ctenostome ectoprocts appear for the first time. Brachiopods continue abundant as new forms appear and some Cambrian stocks disappear.

Echinoderms: Cystoids and coronate blastoids appear; crinoids are found for the first time in the lower Ordovician; the first echinoids, asteroids, and holothuroids appear during the last half of the Ordovician.

Other Deuterostomes: Graptolites reach their peak. The first Cephalodiscoids appear among them. The first fishes appear as the chordates begin to establish themselves.

Molluscs: The Cochliostraca disappear; Archeogastropoda begin to differentiate, and Mesogastropods appear. The first scaphopods and pelecypods are found in the Ordovician, and the nautiloid cephalopods reach their peak. Ammonoid cephalopods appear during the upper Ordovician.

Annelids: Continued evidence of a rich and varied worm population, among which are calcareous tubes resembling those of some modern Sedentaria.

Trilobites: Continue at a high level.

Chelicerata: Xiphosurids and Eurypterids appear.

Mandibulata: Ostracods become abundant.

SUMMARY: While some of the most primitive Cambrian forms were disappearing, they were being replaced by other and apparently more diversified forms in several phyla. Protozoan tests and worm tubes were becoming more complex, and originally chitinous structures were tending to become calcareous. Corals arose and reef formation began. The main echinoderm groups are established, and the molluscans were becoming diverse. Nautiloid cephalopods and brachiopods were at or near their peak. Trilobites were still near their peak, and chelicerate and mandibulate arthropods were present.

Mandibulata: Anaspid Crustacea first appeared. The first centipede fossils also date from this period. The outstanding development, however, was the differentiation of insects. The first cockroaches appeared, with primitive insect stocks which appear to have been ancestral to dragonflies, mayflies, orthopertans, and hemipterans.

SUMMARY: As in the Mississippian, the sessile marine forms appear to have gradually declined, while the more progressive terrestrial stocks, especially the arachnids and insects, were beginning to differentiate. There is some evidence of the increasing importance of fresh-water habitats, as well.

Permian Period

BEGAN: About 280 million years ago.

LASTED: About 50 million years.

NATURE: A period of great activity, during which the Appalachian range was formed and continental land masses rose, while many low-lying areas sank beneath the sea. The changing altitudes brought dry, cold conditions to regions previously wet and warm, but changes in the other direction also occurred. At the end of the Permian activity, the Appalachian discontinuity brought the Paleozoic era to an end and ushered in the Mesozoic.

LIFE: The great changes in conditions put new stresses on the ancient flora and fauna, and a large number of the ancient stocks died out. The horsetails and lycopods declined markedly, with corresponding development of the gymnosperms. The reptiles were undergoing an adaptive radiation which established the ancient reptile stocks.

Protozoa: Many fusulinid Foraminifera early, but this stock died out by the end of the Permian.

Porifera: No dramatic changes.

Cnidaria: The Paleozoic tetracoralline and tabulate corals declined and became extinct. Reef formation ceased.

Lophophorates. The Paleozoic ectoprocts, the Trepostomata and Cryptostomata, declined abruptly and became extinct. Cyclostome ectoprocts continued on, undergoing some moderate development. Brachiopods declined markedly. All but a few lines of neotremates disappeared, and many of the articulate stocks declined and disappeared in the upper Permian. The brachiopods were never again to be highly influential.

Echinoderms: Early in the Permian, a new, moderate peak of crinoids developed in some areas, but by the end of the period the crinoids declined abruptly and dramatically, with nearly all of the Paleozoic stocks becoming wholly extinct. Blastoids became extinct.

Molluscs: Pelecypods were not very actively progressive, but the major groups present at the beginning of the Permian survived its changes. No drastic changes occurred in the gastropods. Nautiloids continued to decline, and the ammonoid cephalopods were becoming more highly differentiated.

Trilobites: Became extinct.

Chelicerates: Eurypterids became extinct and Xiphosura declined. The remaining ancient arachnids apparently disappeared, and while the group may have been differentiating, no new groups are reported for the first time.

Mandibulates: Notostracans appeared for the first time, although they may have been present earlier; presumably the Crustacea were expanding, but scanty records leave many gaps. The Paleozoic lines of insects disappeared, and in their place a number of modern orders appeared for the first time, including the dragonflies, mayflies, plecopterans, psocids, thrips, hemipterans, beetles, neuropterans, and mecopterans.

SUMMARY: A further decline in the ancient types of stalked aquatic forms brought the end of the abundant Paleozoic fauna. Few of the modern sessile forms, however, had established themselves. There are great changes in the terrestrial arthropod fauna, with the establishment of many modern insect orders. Notostracans appear, and probably fresh-water crustacean stocks were active.

MESOZOIC ERA

Triassic Period

BEGAN: About 230 million years ago.

LASTED: About 50 million years.

NATURE: Dry, often arid conditions were common over the now-exposed continents, favoring further adaptation to land conditions.

LIFE: The Paleozoic plant life had dropped out of the picture or declined rapidly during the Triassic. Seed ferns had become extinct, and the gymnosperms became predominant. The newer dicotyledonous plants were beginning to differentiate somewhat. The primitive amphibian stocks became extinct, while the reptiles continued to spread and become more diverse. The first (oviparous) mammals appeared, and the first, small dinosaurs were spreading into different kinds of habitats.

Protozoa: With the disappearance of the fusulinids, foraminiferans were at a low ebb.

Porifera: The first dioctynine hexactinellids appeared.

Cnidaria: The last few stragglers of the Paleozoic coral groups were dying out, and the early Triassic is almost without coral remains. During the middle of the Triassic the new hexacoralline corals had appeared, and by the end of the period reef-building had begun anew. Several cnidarian groups have been found for the first time in Triassic formations. Millepores appear for the first time in Triassic rocks, and the sea pens also occur in the Triassic.

Lophophorates: Ectoprocts were not abundant, as the Paleozoic stocks had died out and only the Cyclostomata are found to any extent. The great brachiopod period was over, and while several families of articulates were expanding somewhat, the group as a whole was not particularly abundant.

Echinoderms: The last few vestiges of the Paleozoic crinoid stocks became extinct in the Triassic, while the new articulate crinoids appeared during the early part of the period, and have survived to the present.

Molluscs: In molluscs as in other groups, there is a great deal of evidence of a

Molluscs: The ammonoids underwent an abrupt decline and became extinct. The belemnoids also became extinct, and the coeloids, at least from the standpoint of fossil remains, began to decline markedly. Other molluscs remained abundant and progressive. Scaphopod remains, for the first time, appeared in abundance, and the pulmonate snails also became reasonably abundant for the first time.
Chelicerates: No outstanding developments.
Mandibulates: No outstanding developments.

SUMMARY: The great events of invertebrate evolution came to a close with the Mesozoic. The last great population explosion of the cephalopods had occurred, and the creatures participating in it had died out. From this point on, the various phyla gradually assume a more modern appearance without spectacular developments. For the sake of completeness, some of the first records seen in the Coenozoic are listed, but the Coenozoic is a great deal more interesting to the vertebrate than the invertebrate paleontologist, except for detailed changes in specific groups of animals.

Coenozoic Era

BEGAN: About 65 million years ago.
PERIODS: Tertiary (65 million to about 1 million years ago), and Quarternary.
TERTIARY: Composed of several epochs:

Paleocene—65–60 million years ago
Eocene—60–40 million years ago
Oligocene—40–25 million years ago
Miocene—25–13 million years ago
Pliocene—13–1 million years ago

The continents rose and fell several times, bringing warmer, dryer, and colder, more moist conditions. The last of the western North American mountains were laid down during the Miocene and Pliocene, and after this a series of ice ages alternating with warmer periods began. The mountains eroded, and streams built deltas at their mouths. The forest spread early, but, as the monocotyledonous plants developed, the forests declined during the Pliocene, with the formation of extensive grasslands. Meanwhile, the ancient mammals became extinct, and the placental mammals established the familiar modern groups.

DEVELOPMENTS:

Protozoa: Testacea first noted in Eocene.
Chelicerates: Pseudoscorpions first seen in lower Oligocene.
Uropygi first seen in Miocene.
Mandibulates: Isopterans first seen in Eocene.
Embropterans first seen in Oligocene.
Lepidoptera first seen in Eocene.
Siphonaptera first seen in Oligocene.
Strepsiptera first seen in Oligocene.
Anostraca first seen in Eocene.

APPENDIX II

Stratification of Ocean Habitats

Pelagic (living above bottom)

Littoral
   Between the highest high and the lowest low tide lines.

Neritic
   Living over the sublittoral region.

Oceanic
   Living over bathyal or abyssal regions. Divided into strata:

   Epipelagic:
   To a depth of about 100 m., where effective light penetration ceases.

   Mesopelagic:
   To a depth of about 1000 m.

   Bathypelagic:
   To a depth of about 4000 m.

   Abyssopelagic:
   Below about 4000 m.

Benthic (living on the bottom)

Littoral
   Between the highest high and the lowest low tide lines.

Sublittoral
   To a depth of about 200 m., below which the strongest storms do not stir the water.

Bathyal
   To a depth of about 4000 m.

Abyssal
   Below about 4000 m.

III

Some Useful Techniques

One of the problems of observing small, transparent invertebrates is that they move too rapidly to be seen well when alive and are distorted by most preserving fluids. As a rule, most of these organisms are best studied alive, at least for a part of the period of study. They may be slowed down or anesthetized sufficiently to permit careful study by some of the following solutions, or by some of the narcotizing agents more commonly used before preserving animals.

For study of small, fast-moving animals in life, the following solutions are especially valuable:

Methyl cellulose. Highly viscous in solution, slowing swimming animals down mechanically.

1% Nickel sulfate. Inactivates cilia and flagella.

0.1% KCl. Interferes with ciliary and muscular movements, may distort some species.

Before preserving both small and large invertebrates, a narcotizing agent is often used. In some instances, these substances are also useful to prepare an organism for study in life. No one agent is good for all kinds of organisms, and it is well to have several solutions on hand to try with the species actually used.

Carbon dioxide. Charged water added to the culture fluid is effective for a number of animals. Try it with some of the annelids and ectoprocts.

Ether or chloroform. Prepare a moist chamber, with a pad of cotton charged with ether or chloroform. The vapor dissolves in the water containing the specimen and anesthetizes it. Useful for many kinds of animals. Turbellaria; some aquatic annelids.

Menthol crystals. A few small crystals dropped on the water containing the organ-

943

isms prove very effective in many cases. Very good for ectoprocts and cnidarians, but useful for many others as well.

1% Potassium iodide. Added to the water containing the specimens, it is often very effective. Some protozoa and rotifers respond very well to it.

Chloral hydrate. Solutions of from 2 to 10% are used. Add drop by drop until the organism is quieted.

1% Neosynephrin. Also effective, added by the drop to small amounts of water containing organisms. Rotifers and gastrotrichs often respond well to this.

Methanol. Diluted to 5 to 10%, it is effective for many invertebrates when added to the fluid containing the specimen drop by drop.

Magnesium sulfate. A saturated solution is added to the fluid containing the specimen. It works very well with many annelids.

For larger organisms, ether and chloroform are, by and large, about as effective as any other reagent. If other reagents are used, it is well to remember that if narcotization is carried on too rapidly, a distorted specimen often results.

When specimens are relaxed, they may be killed with a fixative appropriate for the material. The most universally useful fixative is a mixture of formalin, alcohol, and acetic acid. Various combinations are preferred. A common mixture is 95% alcohol 20 parts; formalin 5 parts, and acetic acid 1 part. If this hardens material too rapidly, 70% alcohol may be substituted for 95%. Most material can be left safely overnight, and larger organisms can be left for several days without serious harm. Decant the fixative, and preserve in formalin or 70% alcohol, to which 5% glycerol has been added.

As a general stain for preserved invertebrates of small size, it is very difficult to improve on alum carmine. It may be made by bringing a 4% solution of ammonia alum to the boil and adding 1 gram of carmine per 100 ml. of alum solution. Boil for 15 minutes. Cool, filter, and store as a stock solution. I prefer to dilute the stock solution by half, which tends to prevent precipitation.

Staining with alum carmine is very easy. Use it in dilute solutions, so the small specimens can be seen easily in the container. As a rule, staining slowly in a dilute solution over several days, adding more stain as needed, gives a better result than a rapid staining procedure in strong dye. The material can be dehydrated in an alcohol series, cleared with xylene, and small amounts of balsam added to the xylene. The dilute balsam is concentrated by evaporation, and the specimen mounted on the slide when the balsam has reached a suitable consistency.

The best source of information about preparing reagents and slides is Peter Gray's *The Microtomist's Formulary and Guide* (Blakiston), an exhaustive account of the materials and methods for the preparation of material of all kinds.

Index

The index has been designed especially to permit the location of (1) material dealing with groups of animals and major topic areas, (2) definitions or descriptions of unfamiliar terms, and (3) information concerning the nature of unfamiliar genera encountered in the literature. Pages on which figures occur are identified by **bold-face** numbers.

945